STRATEGIES FOR ENERGY EFFICIENT PLANTS AND INTELLIGENT BUILDINGS

STRATEGIES
FOR
ENERGY EFFICIENT PLANTS
AND
INTELLIGENT BUILDINGS

STRATEGIES FOR ENERGY EFFICIENT PLANTS AND INTELLIGENT BUILDINGS

Library of Congress Catalog Card No: 86-82315

Published by
THE FAIRMONT PRESS, INC.
700 Indian Trail
Lilburn, Georgia 30247

ISBN 0-88173-020-3 FP

ISBN 0-13-850686-8 PH

Printed in the United States of America.

Distributed by Prentice-Hall, Inc.
A division of Simon & Schuster
Englewood Cliffs, NJ 07632

Prentice-Hall International (UK) Limited, *London*
Prentice-Hall of Australia Pty. Limited, *Sydney*
Editora Prentice-Hall do Brasil, Ltda., *Rio de Janeiro*
Prentice-Hall Canada Inc., *Toronto*
Prentice-Hall Hispanoamericana, S.A., *Mexico*
Prentice-Hall of India Private Limited, *New Delhi*
Prentice-Hall of Japan, Inc., *Tokyo*
Prentice-Hall of Southeast Asia Pte. Ltd., *Singapore*

CONTENTS

PREFACE—CONFERENCE SPONSOR'S STATEMENT

The papers which are compiled herein are based upon presentations made at the 9th World Energy Engineering Congress, October 21-24, 1986. The Congress is sponsored by the Association of Energy Engineers.

The sharing of information is essential to the continued growth of the energy profession. AEE is proud to have played a major role in sponsoring this important conference.

Albert Thumann, P.E., CEM
Executive Director
Association of Energy Engineers

CONTRIBUTORS

Amberger, Ronald F., P.E., *RIT Research Corporation*
Armwood, Levin G., P.E., *Consulting Engineer*
Bailey, Carrol, *Pinellas County School Board, Florida*
Balon, Ronald Joseph, *The City of Phoenix*
Bechard, Bruce D., P.E., CEM, *E M C Engineers, Inc.*
Bellenger, Lynn G., P.E., CEM, *Donald McGeddy Consulting Engineers*
Benagh, Christine P., Esq., *Nixon, Hargrave, Devans & Doyle*
Boutni, Lahcen M., *IBM Systems Product Division*
Bruns, Gregory A., P.E., *Honeywell Commercial Division*
Burch, Robert F., P.E., *The George Washington University*
Burger, Robert, *Burger Associates, Inc.*
Burks, Paul, *Georgia Office of Energy Resources*
Capehart, Barney, Ph.D., *University of Florida*
Casselman, J. Kirk, *Wells Fargo Leasing Corporation*
Chang, Li-Yang, Ph.D., *Veritay Technology, Inc.*
Chappell, Harold, Jr., *IllumElex Corporation*
Clarkson, James, P.E., CEM, *Southwire Company*
Cowden, N.E., *Georgia Institute of Technology*
Daugherty, Kenneth E., Ph.D., *North Texas State University*
Davidson, Keith G., *Gas Research Institute*
DeFrees, John A., *RIT Research Corporation*
Desmond, Robert M., Ph.D., P.E., *RIT Research Corporation*
Dickman, Frank, *Engineering Resources, Inc.*
Dugan, David D., *Spirax/Sarco*
Dymek, A. A., *Georgia Institute of Technology*
Egan, Joseph W., P.E., CEM, *Verle A. Williams & Associates, Inc.*
Evans, Evan A., *E M C Engineers, Inc.*
Fadel, G.M., *Georgia Institute of Technology*
Feldman, Roger D., P.C., *Nixon, Hargrave, Devans & Doyle*
Fetters, John L., CEM, *AT&T Network Systems*
Fiorino, Donald P., *Texas Instruments*
Fisher, David M., *American Auto-Matrix, Inc.*
Flynn, Jack, CEM, *Verle A. Williams & Associates*
Gelburd, Laurence E., *American Auto-Matrix, Inc.*
Gidwani, B.N., P.E., *Roy F. Weston, Inc.*
Giovanetto, Kevin, CEM, *Entec Services, Inc.*
Graves, Kristin, *E.H. Pechan & Associates, Inc.*
Greenwade, Jack D., *Houston Lighting & Power Company*
Griffiths, William C., *Kathabar Systems*
Güven, M. Halil, Ph.D., *San Diego State University*
Hamp, Albert G., *Weber State College-Ogden, Utah*
Hansen, Jaque, *Montana State University*
Hansen, Shirley, Ph.D., *Hansen Associates, Inc.*
Heis, Mel, P.E., CEM, *John W. Galbreath & Co.*
Hellemans, Govert, *Krachtwerktuigen*
Herro, Michael J., *The Trane Company*
Heselton, Kenneth E., P.E., CEM, *Power and Combustion, Inc.*
Hobbs, Roy E., *Energy Watch International*
Hoffman, Scott L., Attorney, *Nixon, Hargrave, Devans & Doyle*
Jeter, S.M., Ph.D., P.E., *Georgia Institute of Technology*
Keck, Dee, *Governor's Energy Office, Florida*
Kennedy, Robert A., P.E., *Natkin Energy Management*
Knight, Nick R., *Montana State University*
Kopfle, John, P.E., CEM, *Southwire Company*
Koplow, Michael D., *Tecogen, Inc.*
Krause, Siegfried, Ph.D., *DFVLR, Institute for Technical Thermodynamics, Stuttgart*
La Fontaine, Harry, Ph.D., *Biomass Energy Foundation, Inc.*
Lark, Donald H., CEM, *Energetics Systems*
Lehman, G. Ronald, *Energy Efficiency Consultants, Inc.*
Lindsay, Bruce B., *Gas Research Institute*
Lints, Michael C., P.E., *RIT Research Corporation*
Lobnitz, Margaret, *Jacobs Engineering Group, Inc.*
Lother, James D., Ph.D., P.E., *Louisiana Tech University*
Lowthian, Walter E., P.E., *Kinetics Consulting Group, Ltd.*
Lundstrom Carl E., *E M C Engineers, Inc.*
McCauley, James F., P.E., *Naval Facilities Engineering Command, Northern Division, Energy Programs Branch*
McGeddy, Donald, P.E., CEM, *Donald McGeddy Consulting Engineers*
McGowan, John J., CEM, *Automation Management Systems, Inc.*
Mehta, D. Paul, Ph.D., *Bradley University*
Mirchandani, M.G., P.E., *Roy F. Weston, Inc.*
Morris, Rik, CEM, *Young & Pratt*
Mozzo, Martin A., Jr., P.E., *American Standard, Inc.*
Mulligan, Patrick J., *Baker Consultants, Inc.*
Napp, Edmund, *RIT Research Corporation*
Nelson, Robert L., *Westinghouse Electric Corporation*
Neyer, John R., *American Auto-Matrix, Inc.*
Niess, Richard C., *Dames & Moore*
Nieuwlaar, Evert, *State University of Utrecht, Netherlands*
Norland, Douglas L., Ph.D., *Alliance to Save Energy*
O'Farrell, Peter M., *Technical Marketing Associates*
Ohlsson, Oscar, P.E., *Argonne National Laboratory*
Oliver, Wayne J., *R.J. Rudden Associates, Inc.*
Paquette, Randy G., *Energy Records Management Co.*
Pearson, Richard J., P.E., *Pearson Engineering*
Pestle, John W., *Varnum, Riddering, Schmidt & Howlett*
Peterson, Kent W., *Sosoka & Associates*
Pollock, James A., *Baker Consultants, Inc.*
Pope, David L., P.E., *Heery Energy Consultants, Inc.*
Priest, John W., Ph.D., P.E., *The University of Texas at Arlington*
Pudell, Dennis, P.E., *Sheller-Globe Corporation*
Redpath, Richard J., P.E., *Ralston Purina Company*
Richardson, Brian P., P.E., *Kinetics Consulting Group, Ltd.*
Roach, Robert, *The Trane Company*
Rocke, David J., *Bradley University*
Ross, Charles C., *Georgia Tech Research Institute*
Rowe, Bob, *U.S. Postal Service-San Diego County*
Rudden, Richard J., *R.J. Rudden Associates, Inc.*
Saul, Chuck, *L.J. Sheridan & Company*
Schneidewind, Eric J., *Varnum, Riddering, Schmidt & Howlett*
Seboda, Earl F., P.E., *Maryland Dept. of General Services*
Shear, Charles K., *City of College Station, Texas*
Sher, Bruce A., CEM, *Kiddie & Sher Engineering*
Shirley, James M., *Webb & Shirley Management Consultants*
Sosoka, John R., P.E., *Sosoka & Associates*
Stebbins, Wayne L., *Celanese Textile Fibers*
Steinhardt, Emil, Ph.D., P.E., *West Virginia University*
Teji, Darshan Singh, P.E., CEM, *The City of Phoenix*
Thorn, William F., *Rocket Research Company*
Turner, Donna L., *E.H. Pechan & Associates, Inc.*
Turner, Wayne C., Ph.D., P.E., CEM, *Montana State University*
van Gool, W., Ph.D., *State University of Utrecht, Netherlands*
Venables, Barry J., Ph.D., *TRAC Laboratories*
Villa, Richard P., CEM, *Abonmarche Consultants, Inc.*
Walsh, James L., P.E., *Georgia Tech Research Institute*
Warden, Alan R., P.E., *University of Missouri-Columbia*
Watson, Richard D., *Solid State Heating Corp.*
Watt, John R., Ph.D., *Consultant*
Webb, Richard E., *Webb & Shirley Management Consultants*
Weesner, John D., P.E., *Decker Energy International, Inc.*
Weisman, Jeannie, *Georgia Office of Energy Resources*
Wepfer, W.J., Ph.D., *Georgia Institute of Technology*
Whiting, Macauley, Jr., *Decker Energy International, Inc.*
Williams, Verle A., P.E., CEM, *Verle A. Williams & Associates, Inc.*
Woehrle, Robert C., Jr., P.E., CEM, *Bell Atlantic*
Wortman, Amy D., *Baltimore Aircoil Company*
Zietlow, David C., *CILCO*

ACKNOWLEDGEMENTS

Appreciation is expressed to all those who have contributed their expertise to this volume, to the conference chairmen for their outstanding contribution to the 9th World Energy Engineering Congress, and to the officers of the Association of Energy Engineers for their help in bringing about this important conference.

INTRODUCTION

Strategic planning is more important than ever to today's energy manager. *Strategies for Energy Efficient Plants and Intelligent Buildings* brings the latest technical knowledge and management techniques to conconcerned professionals. This up-to-the-minute volume will help you improve the efficiency of your operations and reduce utility costs.

The growing importance of HVAC and thermal storage as a means of improving load management is a major feature of this reference. HVAC design techniques including the latest advances in equipment and controls are thoroughly covered.

Several chapters are devoted to new trends in building automation and energy management systems, as they relate to the "intelligent building".

A series of chapters on the growing field of cogeneration and small power production will help the engineer and manager keep abreast of this important technology.

More than twenty chapters delineate technical advances in such key areas as lighting, biomass, resource recovery, waste heat recovery, steam systems, heat pumps, combustion processes, hazardous waste disposal and controls.

Strategies for Energy Efficient Plants and Intelligent Buildings is a comprehensive book on strategies and new technologies, and can be used to reduce operating costs and improve overall efficiency of any facility, large or small. More than 90 chapters bring to the professional a complete perspective of the latest state-of-the-art advances in the energy field.

SECTION 1
HVAC

Chapter 1

SELECTING THE OPTIMAL SEQUENCE OF REFRIGERATION EQUIPMENT

D. P. Fiorino, J. W. Priest

INTRODUCTION

A dynamic programming model was developed to find a viable solution to the problem of selecting the optimal sequence of refrigeration equipment (chillers, cooling towers, pumps) to operate in the Central Utility Plant of the Texas Instruments facility on Forest Lane in Dallas, Texas. The optimal equipment sequence is that sequence which has the lowest energy cost to operate at a given plant cooling load and outside air wet bulb temperature and satisfies all the constraints associated with the refrigeration system. Selection of the optimal equipment sequence is very important given the high energy costs to operate large refrigeration equipment. However, selection of the optimal equipment sequence is very difficult given the size and complexity of the refrigeration system and the dynamic nature of the plant cooling load and outside air wet bulb temperature.

Highlights of the project include a dynamic programming model of the plant's refrigeration system. A computer program solves the model and generates optimal equipment sequences to operate for combinations of a wide range of plant cooling loads and outside air wet bulb temperatures. Validation testing based upon utility plant operating data and refrigeration equipment performance data confirms that the model reasonably represents the plant's refrigeration system. A sensitivity analysis identifies sensitive ranges of the plant cooling load and outside air wet bulb temperature and a Pareto analysis identifies "vital" constraints causing infeasible solutions. A retrofit project to remove the "vital" constraints and improve the refrigeration system's performance resulted from the study and the solution to the problem was incorporated in the operating procedure for the plant's refrigeration system.

BACKGROUND

The Texas Instruments plant on Forest Lane in Dallas, Texas, is an ultramodern, mixed-use facility of approximately 1.3 million square feet. The plant was constructed in four phases between 1979 and 1985. Administration, engineering, support, and manufacturing activities are conducted at the plant. Approximately 4400 personnel worked at the plant as of May 1985 with an additional 1200 personnel expected by December 1986. The plant was designed and constructed in distributed manner with centralized support areas, i.e. utility plant, warehouse, cafeteria, etc., and modular work areas, i.e. modules, linked by major corridors.

The Forest Lane plant experiences a very large and dynamic cooling load composed of comfort cooling, i.e. 75°F and 50% RH in areas of the plant occupied by personnel, and process cooling, i.e. removal of heat generated by manufacturing processes and equipment. The plant cooling load fluctuates according to a variety of factors including work shifts, production levels, and outside air conditions.

To satisfy its cooling load, the Forest Lane plant is equipped with a variety of large capacity refrigeration equipment in its Central Utility Plant. The primary cooling medium used throughout the plant is 42°F chilled water. It is produced by four chillers totaling 4200 tons of refrigeration. The chilled water is pumped through the chillers and then through the plant's chilled water supply and return lines by five chilled water primary pumps totaling 625 horsepower and two chilled water booster pumps totaling 200 horsepower. Heat liberated by the chiller's vapor-compression cycles is rejected to the atmosphere by five cooling towers totaling 4325 tons of refrigeration. Condenser water is pumped between the chillers and the cooling towers by four condenser water pumps totaling 400 horsepower.

PROBLEM

It is the Central Utility Plant Operator's responsibility to select and operate sequences or combinations of refrigeration equipment to satisfy any particular cooling load experienced during his shift. The operator's selection was based upon his bi-hourly calculation of the plant'instantaneous cooling load and measurement of the outside air wet bulb temperature. Also, the operator considered the limitations, i.e. maximum and minimum flow rates, temperatures, pressures, etc., of the plant's refrigeration system and equipment. He utilized the above data as well as his knowledge, experience, and judgment to select the optimal sequence of refrigeration equipment to operate in order to satisfy the plant's cooling load with the lowest possible energy cost and without violating any of the limitations of the plant's refrigeration system.

Given the size and complexity of the plant's refrigeration system, the dynamic nature of the plant cooling load and outside air wet bulb temperature, and the variability of knowledge, experience, and judgment among the operators, the possibility of selecting a sub-optimal sequence of refrigeration equipment existed. This problem was considered serious as a less than optimal sequence of refrigeration equipment for a particular plant cooling load and outside air temperature could cost several hundred dollars per day more to operate than an optimal sequence. This situation presented an opportunity to reduce the high energy costs associated with operating the plant's large refrigeration equipment by establishing an improved procedure to be used by the operators when selecting the optimal sequence of refrigeration equipment to operate.

OPTIMIZATION MODEL

The objective of the project was to find a viable solution to the problem of selecting the optimal sequence of refrigeration equipment to operate in order to satisfy any particular plant cooling load and outside air wet bulb temperature experienced. The optimal equipment sequence is defined as that sequence of refrigeration equipment which satisfies the plant cooling load with the lowest possible energy cost and without violating any constraints associated with the refrigeration system. The project was approached as an optimization problem to be solved by constructing a mathematical model of the refrigeration system and deriving the solution to the problem there-from. The model was intended to incorporate those features of the refrigeration system which have a significant effect on the system's performance and ignore those features which have only negligible effect. The optimal equipment sequence must be selected from a set of approximately 10,000 alternative sequences of refrigeration equipment.

The first element of our approach was to determine the relevant parameters to be included in the model. An input/output diagram identifies the plant cooling load and outside air wet bulb temperature as the input variables for the model. The output variables for the model are the number and size of chillers to operate, the number and type of chilled water pumps to operate, the number and size of cooling towers to operate, and the number of condenser water pumps to operate. It should be noted that although the output variables are discrete, partial loading conditions may exist. Partial loading is an important concept because some types of refrigeration equipment, particularly chillers, operate most economically when partially loaded. The objective function expresses the hourly energy cost to operate the refrigeration system and consists of the sum of several single variable objective functions that express the hourly energy cost to operate the various items of equipment comprising the refrigeration system. The constraints included in the model consist of particular limitations, i.e. maximum and minimum flow rates, temperatures, pressures, etc., associated with the refrigeration system.

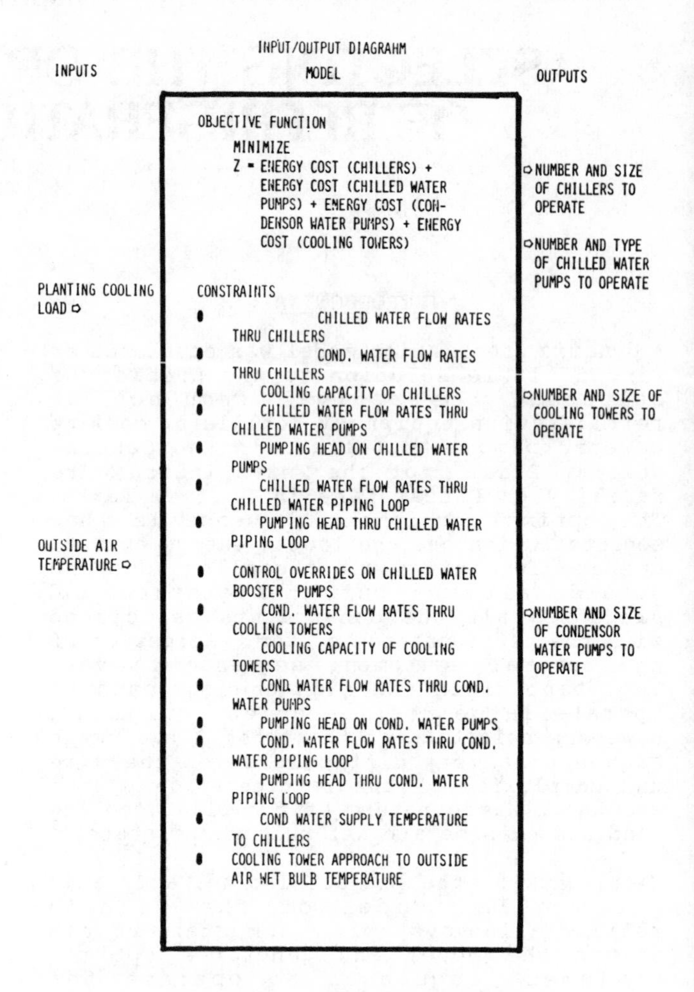

DYNAMIC PROGRAMMING TECHNIQUE

The second element of our approach was to select an optimization technique capable of solving the model. Given the Markovian nature of the refrigeration system, i.e. the sequence of interrelated decision stages and a finite number of states associated with each decision stage, a dynamic programming technique was selected. Dynamic programming provides a systematic approach for determining the combination of decisions that maximizes overall system effectiveness. In effect, dynamic programming translates this one problem with seven decision variables into seven problems each with one decision variable. These sub-problems can then be solved one at a time.

The key elements of dynamic programming are stages, states, decisions, policies, and sub-policies. The concept of a stage allows a sequence of interrelated decisions to be ordered. An index variable n is associated with each stage of the refrigeration system.

The state variables describe the various possible conditions in which the system might be at a given stage of the problem. An index variable s is associated with each state of the refrigeration system. A decision $x_n(s_n)$ is a choice made in state s at stage n that transforms the system to another state s' in stage n + 1.

STAGES

n	Description
1	100 HP CW Booster Pumps
2	125 HP CW Primary Pumps
3	900 Ton Chillers
4	1200 Ton Chillers
5	100 HP Cond W Pumps
6	750 Ton Cooling Towers
7	945 Ton Cooling Towers

STATES

s	n	Description
1	1	0x100 HP C W Booster Pumps
2	1	1x100 HP C W Booster Pumps
3	1	2x100 HP C W Booster Pumps
4	2	0x125 HP C W Primary Pumps
5	2	1x125 HP C W Primary Pumps
6	2	2x125 HP C W Primary Pumps
7	2	3x125 HP C W Primary Pumps
8	2	4x125 HP C W Primary Pumps
9	2	5x125 HP C W Primary Pumps
10	3	0x900 Ton Chillers
11	3	1x900 Ton Chillers
12	3	2x900 Ton Chillers
13	4	0x1200 Ton Chillers
14	4	1x1200 Ton Chillers
15	4	2x1200 Ton Chillers
16	5	0x100 HP Cond W Pumps
17	5	1x100 HP Cond W Pumps
18	5	2x100 HP Cond W Pumps
19	5	3x100 HP Cond W Pumps
20	5	4x100 HP Cond W Pumps
21	6	0x750 Ton Cooling Towers
22	6	1x750 Ton Cooling Towers
23	6	2x750 Ton Cooling Towers
24	7	0x945 Ton Cooling Towers
25	7	1x945 Ton Cooling Towers
26	7	2x945 Ton Cooling Towers
27	7	3x945 Ton Cooling Towers

Multiple choices are available to proceed from any given state at any given stage in the refrigeration system. A policy is an ordered set of decisions,

$$X = (x_1, x_2, x_3 \ldots x_7)$$

there being one decision for each state as the system progresses from stage to stage.

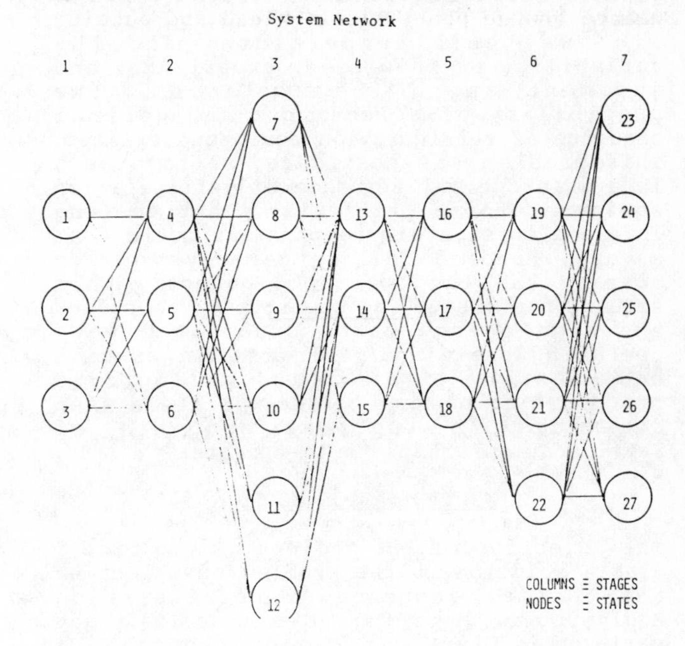

The optimal policy is that policy which minimizes or maximizes the objective function $f_n(s_n, x_n)$ while satisfying all constraints. The principle of optimality is central to dynamic programming and requires that a optimal policy consist only of optimal sub-policies.

The basis of the solution procedure for a dynamic programming problem is that, given the current state, the optimal policy for the remaining stages of the system is independent of the policy adopted in the previous stages. The solution procedure begins by finding the optimal sub-policy for each state of the last stage. The solution procedure then moves backward stage by stage n = (N,N-1,...1) each time determining the optimal sub-policy for each state of each stage until it finds the optimal policy when starting at the initial stage of the system. This is accomplished by utilizing a recursive relationship to identify the optimal sub-policy for each state at stage n given the optimal sub-policy for each state at stage n + 1.

COMPUTER PROGRAM

The computer program iterates the input variables over their prescribed ranges; calculates the optimal equipment sequence for each iteration of the input variables according to the recursive relationship and dynamic programming algorithm; calculates the operating parameters, i.e. flow rates, pressures, temperatures, of the refrigeration system and verifies that the constraints are satisfied for each equipment sub-sequence at each iteration of the input variables; and generates output data for each iteration of the input variables. The central feature of the computer program is the close correspondence between its architecture, i.e. sub-routines, and the structure of the refrigeration system as represented by the dynamic programming model, i.e. stages and states.

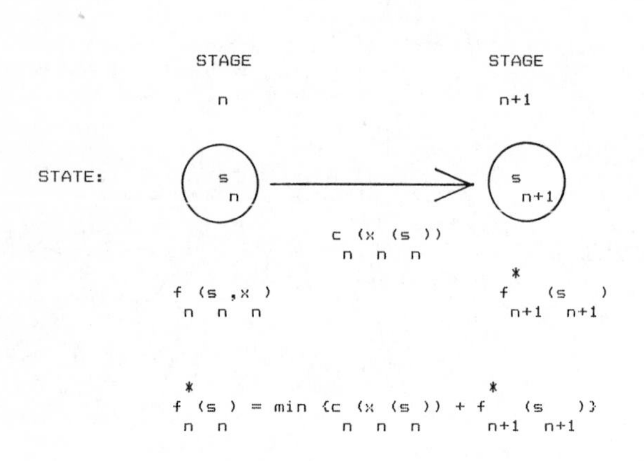

VALIDATION TESTING

Validation of the model and solution consisted of determining that the model reasonably represented the refrigeration system. Validation testing was accomplished by comparing refrigeration system performance as represented by the model to actual system performance as represented by system operating data and equipment performance data.

This task was simplified by the close correspondence between the model's architecture and the refrigeration system's structure. Comparisons were performed in three levels, i.e. input parameters, equipment performance and costs, and output parameters. The ranges of inputed plant cooling load and inputed outside air wet bulb temperature compared closely to actual ranges recorded throughout the year. The model's representation of the performance and operating costs of the cooling towers, chillers, and pumps compared reasonably to actual performance and operating costs recorded during routine system operation. Also, the model's representation of system operating parameters, i.e. condensor water flow rate, condensor water head, condensor water supply temperature, chilled water flow rate, chilled water head, and chilled water supply temperature, compared resonably to actual system operating parameters recorded during routine system operation. Finally, the model was able to generate optimal equipment sequences and operating costs which were superior to actual equipment sequences and operating costs realized during routine system operation.

SENSITIVITY ANALYSIS

Sensitivity analysis was employed to investigate the effect on the optimal solution if the parameters changed values. Those parameters which cause a substantial change in the value of the objective function when their values change are sensitive parameters. Sensitive parameters are particularly serious when a change in their value causes an inferior or infeasible value of the objective function to result.

Data of optimal operating cost versus plant cooling load with outside air wet bulb temperature fixed was organized in graphical form. Optimal operating cost varied moderately with changes in plant cooling load in the range of 700 to 2700 tons. Optimal operating cost became infeasible when the plant cooling load ranged below 700 tons or above 2700 tons. In these ranges, plant cooling load is a sensitive parameter. Validation testing revealed that plant cooling loads below 700 tons and above 3600 tons are rarely experienced. However, the sensitivity of optimal operating cost to plant cooling load in the range of 2800 to 3600 tons was of significance to the system and solution and warranted further investigation.

Data of optimal operating cost versus outside air wet bulb temperature with plant cooling load fixed was organized in graphical form. Optimal operating cost varied moderately with changes in outside air wet bulb temperature in the range of 20°F to 75°F. Optimal operating cost became infeasible when the outside air wet bulb temperature reached 80°F. Fortunately, validation testing revealed that outside air temperatures of 80°F are rarely experienced.

PARETO ANALYSIS

The sensitivity analysis was helpful in determining that the optimal operating cost became infeasible at the upper range of plant cooling loads and that further investigation was necessary. However, the sensitivity analysis did not provide the detail needed to identify which specific system constraints or sub-systems were causing the above problem. Once identified, a retrofit project can be undertaken to reduce or remove the constraint at fault by modifying the sub-system at fault, thereby improving the refrigeration system's and solution's performance in the sensitive region. The tool employed to accomplish this was Pareto analysis. Pareto analysis compares the relative and cumulative frequencies and/or magnitudes of defects by category in order to distinguish between the "vital few" categories of defects and the "trivial many" according to their impact on total quality losses.

The model simulated system performance for 36 iterations of the plant cooling load with 13 iterations of the outside air wet bulb temperature nested inside each iteration of the plant cooling load. Thus, the model simulated system performance for 36 x 13 = 468 unique combinations of the input variables. The model assigned an arbitrary operating cost of $1,000,000.00 per hour to any equipment state which violated a system constraint. An analysis of the output data revealed that an optimal operating cost of $1,000,000.00 per hour or greater, i.e. an infeasible solution, resulted for 212 combinations of the input variables. This means that in (212/468) x 100 = 45.3% of the simulations the model was unable to select an optimal equipment sequence that did not violate at least one system constraint. A further analysis of the output data revealed 326 separate constraint violations. This means that an average of 1.54 constraint violations with a standard deviation of 0.79 constraint violations caused each infeasible solution.

Each of the simulations in which an infeasible solution resulted was analyzed to determine the system constraint(s) which was violated and the associated sub-system(s), i.e. stage(s), of the dynamic programming network at which the violation occurred. The results of the analysis revealed that violations were concentrated among only 8 of 22 constraints and among 3 of 4 sub-systems.

A Pareto analysis of the relative and cumulative frequency of violations by constraint was prepared in a graphical plot. This Pareto analysis revealed that nearly 50% of the violations were attributable to only 2 "vital few" constraints, i.e. maximum chilled water flow rate to Phases III/IV and minimum unsatisfied chilled water head to operate a chilled water booster pump. A scan of the output data showed the violations of these two constraints to have occurred largely within the range of plant cooling load that was identified by sensitivity analysis as being of significance to the system and solution. This Pareto analysis also revealed that the remaining 50% of the violations were attributable to 20 "trivial many" constraints.

A Pareto analysis of the relative and cumulative frequency of violations by sub-systems was prepared in a graphical plot. This Pareto analysis revealed that nearly 70% of the violations occurred at one "vital" sub-system, i.e. chilled water pumps and piping. A scan of the output data showed the violations which occurred at the chilled water pumps and piping fell largely within the range of plant cooling load that was identified by sensitivity analysis as being of significance to the system and solution. This Pareto analysis also revealed that the remaining 30% of the violations occurred at 3 "trivial many" sub-systems.

RETROFIT PROJECT

The results of the Pareto analysis by constraints corresponded very closely to those from the Pareto analysis by sub-systems. They identified two "vital" constraints, i.e. maximum chilled water flow rate to Phases III/IV and minimum unsatisfied chilled water head to operate a chilled water booster pump, in one sub-system, i.e. the chilled water pumps and piping sub-system, as the most significant causes of infeasible solutions. The infeasible solutions caused by the above constraints and sub-system were concentrated in the range of plant cooling load, i.e. 2800-3600 tons, which was identified by sensitivity analysis as a sensitive range of that parameter and which was identified by validation testing as a reasonable range of that parameter.

All of the above was corroborated by chilled water flow/pressure problems actually experienced at the Forest Lane Plant. A retrofit project to reduce or remove the two "vital" constraints in the chilled water pumps and piping sub-system became evident as a means of improving the refrigeration system's performance.

Increasing the chilled water piping capacity between the Central Utility Plant and Phases III/IV was defined first and chilled water booster pump modifications were defined thereafter based on the final definition of chilled water piping capacity.

A field survey was performed to estimate the peak building and process chilled water demands in Phases III/IV. The peak chilled water demand in Phase III was 3650 gallons per minute and the peak chilled water demand in Phase IV was 1194 gallons per minute, yielding a combined peak chilled water demand of 4844 gallons per minute. Additionally, a future peak chilled water demand of 400 gallons per minute for a planned HVAC (heating, ventilation, air conditioning) upgrade in the Warehouse attached to Phase III was considered. An overlay of combined peak chilled water demand for Phases III/IV on existing chilled water piping capacity showed that the 4844 gallons per minute peak demand exceeded the 2500 gallons per minute pipe capacity between the Central Utility Plant and Phases III/IV by 2344 gallons per minute or 93.8%. Alternatives proposed to remove this piping capacity shortfall consisted of a four pipe system, i.e. installing a second set of twelve inch diameter chilled water supply and return lines in parallel with the existing set of twelve inch diameter chilled water supply and return lines between the Central Utility Plant and Phases III/IV, and a three pipe system, i.e. installing an eighteen inch diameter chilled water supply line between the Central Utility Plant and Phases III/IV and converting the existing twelve inch diameter chilled water supply line between the Central Utility Plant and Phases III/IV into a second return line. Both alternatives would supply 5000 gallons per minute to Phases III/IV at a reasonable velocity of 7.17 feet per second and a moderate pressure loss of 0.515 pounds per square inch per 100 feet, thereby satisfying Phase III/IV peak chilled water demand.

The advantages and disadvantages of each piping system were determined and compared, as were those for two pipe routing alternatives and two pipe anchoring alternatives. The combination of alternatives selected for installation were the three pipe system with the eighteen inch diameter chilled water supply line routed through the Module A corridor and buried.

The constraint of minimum unsatisfied chilled water head to operate a chilled water booster pump related to both the chilled water primary and booster pumps as the chilled water booster pumps are piped in parallel in the chilled water supply line to Phases III/IV and are in series with the chilled water primary pumps in the chilled water primary piping loop. Hence, the chilled water flow rate delivered by the booster pumps is common to that delivered by the primary pumps and the chilled water head delivered by the booster pumps is in addition to that delivered by the primary pumps. Thus, if system chilled water head is 170 feet, a likely value of that parameter as established by validation testing, and the primary pumps are delivering their design head of 135 feet, then the unsatisfied head to be delivered by the booster pumps would be 170 - 135 = 35 feet. Yet, the minimum head which a booster pumps can deliver at 1150 revolutions per minute is 44 feet as shown by the booster pump performance curve and a booster pump cannot be energized. The result is an infeasible model solution and poor system performance. Yet, the performance curve of the same booster pump operating at 860 revolutions per minute rather than 1150 revolutions per minute was noted. At 860 revolutions per minute, the booster pump can deliver the 35 feet of head unsatisfied by the primary pumps. In this instance, a feasible model solution and satisfactory system performance would result. Alternatives proposed to modify the booster pumps consisted of replacing the two existing booster pumps with multi-speed pumps, i.e. identical pumps each coupled to both an 1150 revolution per minute motor and an 860 revolution per minute motor, and installing adjustable frequency speed controllers, i.e. very advanced electronic devices which vary input power frequency to adjust motor speed, on the two existing booster pumps. Results of adjustable frequency speed controller testing conducted earlier were reviewed and the advantages and disadvantages of each alternative were determined and compared. Installation of adjustable frequency speed controllers was selected.

In order to estimate the degree of improvement in the refrigeration system's performance as a result of the retrofit project, the original model representing the existing refrigeration system was updated to represent the retrofitted refrigeration system. Updating the original model was simplified by the fact that all of the additions and modifications are concentrated in the chilled water piping and pumps sub-system of the refrigeration system. An updated input/output diagram highlights five system constraints and one component of the objective function which had to be updated. A solution was derived from the updated model, validated, and analyzed. The performance of the retrofitted refrigeration system was then compared to that of the existing refrigeration system by comparing the solutions from their respective models.

Updating the solution was simplified by the fact that all of the additions and modifications were concentrated in stages 1 and 2 of the dynamic programming network. Therefore, the solution was updated by updating only those subroutines corresponding to stages and states affected by the additions and modifications. Testing the updated model and solution had to be deferred until the retrofit additions and modifications were installed and started up.

The updated data of optimal operating cost versus plant cooling load with outside air wet bulb temperature fixed was organized in graphical form. Optimal operating cost varied moderately with changes in plant cooling load in the range of 700 to 3600 tons. Optimal operating cost become infeasible when the plant cooling load ranged below 700 tons or above 3600 tons. Validation testing revealed, fortunately, that plant cooling loads in those ranges are rarely experienced.

The updated data of optimal operating cost versus outside air wet bulb temperature with plant cooling load fixed was organized in graphical form. Optimal operating cost varied moderately with changes in outside air wet bulb temperature in the range of 20°F to 75°F. Optimal operating cost become infeasible when the outside air wet bulb temperature reached 80°F. Validation testing revealed, fortunately, that outside air wet bulb temperatures of 80°F are rarely experienced.

The updated model simulated system performance for 468 unique combinations of the input variables just as the original model did. An analysis of the updated output data revealed that an infeasible solution resulted for 104 combinations of the input variables. This means that in (104/468) * 100 = 24.4% of the simulations the updated model was unable to select an optimal equipment sequence which did not violate at least one system constraint. A further analysis of the updated output data revealed 118 separate constraint violations. This means that an average of 1.13 constraint violations with a standard deviation of 0.34 constraint violations caused each infeasible solution.

Each of the updated simulations in which an infeasible solution resulted was analyzed to determine the system constraint(s) which was violated and the associated stage(s), i.e. sub-system of the dynamic programming network, at which the violation(s) occurred. The results of the analysis revealed that violations were concentrated among only 4 of 21 constraints and 3 of 4 sub-systems.

An updated Pareto analysis of the relative and cumulative frequency of violations by constraint was prepared in a graphical plot. This Pareto analysis revealed that nearly 45% of the violations were attributable to one "vital" constraint, i.e. maximum system condensor water flow rate. A scan of the updated output data showed the violations of this constraint occurred within the range of plant cooling load that was identified by validation testing as rarely occurring. This Pareto analysis also revealed that the remaining 55% of the violations were attributable to 20 "trivial many" constraints.

An updated Pareto analysis of the relative and cumulative frequency of violations by sub-systems was prepared in graphical plot. This Pareto analysis revealed that 67% of the violations occurred at one "vital" sub-system, i.e. condensor water pumps and piping. A scan of the updated output data showed that the violations which occurred at the condensor water pumps and piping sub-system occurred within the range of plant cooling load identified by validation testing as rarely occurring. This Pareto analysis also revealed that the remaining 33% of the violations occurred at 3 "trivial many" sub-systems.

Performance statistics resulting from establishing control over the original model representing the existing refrigeration system and the updated model representing the retrofitted refrigeration system were compared. The percentage by which refrigeration system performance improved as a result of the retrofit project was calculated for key statistics measuring system performance. The updated model represented that the retrofitted refrigeration system's performance was greatly improved over that of the existing refrigeration system as represented by the original model. Of greatest significance, the updated model simulated 51% fewer infeasible solutions than the original model and reduced the sensitivity of optimal operating cost to changes in plant cooling load by 69%.

COMPARISON OF EXISTING AND RETROFITTED REFRIGERATION SYSTEM PERFORMANCE

Category	Original Model	Updated Model	Improvement Over Original
Simulations	468	468	---
Infeasible Solutions	212	104	51%
% of Simulations	45.3	24.4	46%
Constant Violations	326	118	64%
Constant Violations/ Infeasible Solution	---	---	---
Average	1.54	1.13	27%
Std Dev	0.79	0.34	57%
Sensitive Range of Y	2800-4000 Tons	3700-4000 Tons	69%
Sensitive Range of Z	80°F	80°F	0%
Worst Constant	SCWFR(1,2,X)>2500	KWFR(Y,Z)>11000	---
Worst Sub-System	1/2	5	---

IMPLEMENTING THE SOLUTION

The first step in implementing the solution was undertaking and completing the chilled water piping and pumps retrofit project. Mr. Fiorino performed as project manager and engineer.

A support solicitation effort was conducted to gather support from key personnel in the organization. Integral to the success of this effort was an information briefing presented to the architect and key facilities managers as well as an important decision to ally the chilled water piping and pumps retrofit project with the heating, ventilating, and air conditioning upgrade planned in the Warehouse attached to Phase III. A preliminary design and preliminary schedule were prepared to add detail to the information briefing and to guide the extensive engineering and construction efforts to follow.

A formal project proposal, i.e. capital request, was submitted through a series of capital approval committees to secure funding for the project. During this phase, facilities cost analysis personnel performed formal return on investment analysis and risk assessment analysis of the project. Integral to the success of this phase was support secured during the support solicitation phase as well as the approach of submitting an initial capital request for design funds only followed by a final capital request, based upon detailed engineering and solicited bids, for construction funds.

Detailed engineering of the chilled water piping/warehouse HVAC project was initiated immediately upon approval of the capital request for design funds. Given the major scope of the project and the inherent complexity and difficulty of retrofit/upgrade projects, an intensive engineering effort was anticipated and a two-stage design process was employed. Drawings and specifications were prepared for installation of the measures included in the preliminary design. These were forwarded to the architect's office to be reviewed and modified and/or supplemented as necessary. In particular, the architect issued appendix items for structure interface matters, i.e. pipe supports and anchors, wall/floor/roof penetrations, thrust blocks and expansion measures, etc., and reviewed equipment submittal data. The two-stage design process identified protection of the buried eighteen inch diameter black iron pipe against corrosion as a latent, yet critical, aspect of the design. Corrosion protection involves coating, electrically isolating, and cathodically protecting structures to minimize corrosion and maximize service life. A corrosion protection consultant was retained to write an amendment to the drawings and specifications addressing corrosion protection for the buried eighteen inch diameter black iron pipe.

Installation and start-up of the chilled water piping/warehouse HVAC project was initiated immediately upon approval of the capital request for construction funds. The construction contract was awarded to the winning bidder - a large piping/mechanical contractor with an extensive record of similar projects completed satisfactorily at the Forest Lane plant and other Texas Instruments facilities.

Critical project elements such as assuring quality workmanship, equipment/material delivery and staging, installation sequencing and scheduling, system start-up and testing, shutdown of chilled water service, safety/environmental and security measures, avoiding interference with plant operations, related work by crews other than the contractor, contingency measures, and cost control measures required careful coordination. A "critical path method" network and schedule was developed to monitor equipment/material delivery, installation sequencing and scheduling, system start-up, related work by crews other than the contractor, and contingency planning. Daily worksite inspections were performed to monitor the above as well as assure quality workmanship, safety/ environmental and security measures, and avoidance of interference with plant operations. Weekly project review meetings were conducted to review progress to date and coordinate critical project elements for the following week. The "critical path" network and schedule was updated following each project review meeting to reflect actual progress and changes/contingencies. A system start-up team consisting of the project manager and members of building preventative maintenance and operations was organized to work alongside the contractor in order to startup, test, troubleshoot, and de-bugg the system. Lastly, an automated project cost model was utilized to monitor project costs by resource on a real-time basis versus monthly forecasts and the approved budget. Monthly project cost review meetings were conducted with key facilities managers.

Start-up of the retrofitted refrigeration system was accomplished by the start-up team and the contractor during the scheduled shutdown of plant chilled water service. Minor mechanical and electrical problems which surfaced during start-up and testing were quickly corrected by troubleshooting and debugging. Extending beyond start-up and testing, the retrofitted refrigeration system's operation was monitored closely for a period of six months during which a wide range of plant cooling loads and outside air wet bulb temperatures were experienced. During this period of extended operation, mechanical reliability of the retrofitted refrigeration was proven, its performance capabilities were demonstrated, and operator training was strengthened.

Documentation of the chilled water piping/warehouse HVAC project consisted of the drawings, specifications, and amendments to the drawings and specifications. The "as-built" drawings submitted by the contractor upon completion of the construction contract supplemented the above documentation. Additional documentation of the chilled water piping/warehouse HVAC project consisted of the project's cost history recorded in its project cost model and its actual schedule recorded in its "critical path" network and schedule. Based on the above, Mr. Fiorino prepared a capitalization package containing an itemized list of assets, each asset's cost, each asset's ready-for-use date, and each asset's estimated service life. The capitalization package was submitted to capital accounts personnel who prepared depreciation schedules and formally capitalized the project.

The second step in implementing the solution was testing and proving the updated solution during actual operation of the retrofitted refrigeration system. This was accomplished during the period of operation of the retrofitted refrigeration system extending beyond start-up. The improved procedure for selecting the optimal sequence of refrigeration equipment to operate in the Central Utility Plant now consists of the Central Utility Plant Operator calculating the plant's instantaneous cooling load and measuring the outside air wet bulb temperature as before, but now referring to the solution, i.e. the updated computer output listing optimal equipment sequences for combinations of plant cooling load ranging from 500-4000 tons and outside air wet bulb temperature ranging from 20-80°F, to select the optimal equipment sequence to operate. This improved procedure is standard operating procedure and documentation of the solution, i.e. the written study, is incorporated in the written operating instructions for the Central Utility Plant. Should a control system be installed in the future to automatically operate the retrofitted refrigeration system, the solution will be the basis of the control algorithm.

Chapter 2

SPREADSHEET MODELS TO DETERMINE HVAC SYSTEM SAVINGS

D. L. Pope

ABSTRACT

Energy savings calculations which use only one or two load points at average or full load conditions can give misleading results, especially if more than one conservation measure is being evaluated. A more accurate method is presented using a computerized spreadsheet model of building part load conditions as a function of standard hourly bin weather data. The full range of building operation from heating through cooling conditions are examined. Individual loads, equipment and their operating characteristics are tabulated against changing load conditions and can be adjusted individually to reflect changes caused by energy conservation measures. In addition, the tabulated load components may be adjusted to reflect the interactive effects of system changes. The full range of building heating and cooling loads, and equipment part load operations are then considered for a more accurate calculation of savings. This technique is based on ASHRAE's "Simplified Energy Analysis Using The Modified Bin Method".

Degree Day Method

The traditional method for estimating energy use has been the Degree Day Method. In 1932, the American Gas Association and National District Heating Association developed the Degree Day Method based on 65 degrees for estimating annual fuel bills on residential buildings. This is referred to as a "Single Measure" method since only one calculation is made. The temperature where the addition of heat is required in residential buildings, known as the balance point, was determined to be close to a constant 65°F. This reflected building techniques of the day which included poor insulation, relatively low internal heat generation, loose fit windows, and construction with high infiltration rates. Fuel consumption was estimated by taking the difference between 65° and the 24-hour average of the day's temperature and accumulating these degree days into a one year total. This total was multiplied by the peak building load/hour, 24 hours and various correction factors, then divided by the design temperature difference, fuel efficiency, and BTU/fuel unit. The resulting answer was claimed to be within 20% of actual fuel bills.

A similar method uses Cooling Degree Days to estimate annual required cooling energy in residential buildings. A cooling degree day is an average daily temperature one degree above 65 degrees. Figure 1 illustrates the basic relationship between outside temperature and degree day calculated load. Note that the load line is a wide line covering a typical daily range of plus or minus 10 degrees with balance points as low as 45 degrees.

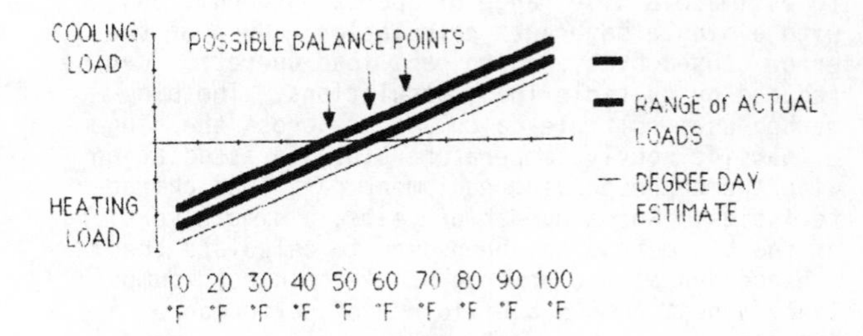

FIGURE 1 - COMPARISON of the DEGREE DAY MODEL vs RANGE of ACTUAL LOADS

A number of inaccuracies can occur, due primarily to assumed "average" values. First, the Degree Day method was intended for use in residential buildings with internal loads typical of 1930. Today's residential internal electric loads are typically 15 times the level of the 1930's. Second, this method will not address internal loads and occupancy characteristics of larger commercial buildings. A modern building's balance point can vary considerably depending on internal load and the amount of outside air introduced. It is possible for this balance point to be in the range of 35 to 65 degrees Fahrenheit. Since only the average daily temperature is used, substantial error can result on days when the daily average is 65 or above, but a nighttime low temperature swing can require heating. The farther below 3,000 degree days for a given region, the more error will occur due to partial heating days. It is easily possible to over-estimate fuel consumption by 100% or under-estimate by 50%. Fuel burning equipment efficiencies decrease considerably at partial load. An 80 percent efficient furnace typically has an overall average efficiency of 55%, but this can vary from 33% to 77% for a 65% confidence range (one standard deviation)[1]. Attempts have been made to develop correction factors, but the wide range of error possible in these factors limit their usefulness[2]. Occupancy patterns for commercial buildings also contribute significantly to fuel estimation error. The Degree Day Method assumes 24-hour occupancy. Offices are not occupied during colder night hours and will not use as much energy as a residential occupancy would. The Heating Degree Day Method is totally unsatisfactory as an energy estimation method for large commercial buildings.

Using the Colling Degree Day Method as an energy estimation tool has all of the above problems plus some. In the Cooling Degree Day Method, the cooling load is assumed to be dependent only on average daily outside temperature. Daily extremes are not considered. Neither are solar gains through walls and windows, nor latent cooling loads from outside side air and people. Latent load alone can exceed sensible loading in a 100% outside air system. Cooling Degree Days is an even less satisfactory energy estimation method than Heating Degree Days and again is totally unsatisfactory as an estimation Method for a large commercial building.

Bin Method

Most of the problems with Degree Day energy estimation methods have been the results of trying to estimate a wide range of operating conditions with a single "average" calculation. Much of the error caused by averaging part load operation can be reduced by multiple load calculations. The bin method uses multiple calculations across the range of outside hourly temperature bins, in association with the corresponding equipment part load characteristics. For a number of years, a simple version of the bin method has been used to calculate the average annual performance of electric heat pumps. Since a heat pump's coefficient of performance changes dramatically with outside air temperature, this method was necessary to get a realistic estimate of power consumption over a year.

Standard hourly bin data, for many locations, is available from Air Force "Manual 88-29, Engineering Weather Data". Copies can be obtained from the Government Printing Office. This weather data is normally grouped into total number of hours per bin temperature range by month with an annual total. Each day is divided into 3 time groups: Midnight to 8 A.M.; 8 A.M to 4 P.M.; and 4 P.M. to Midnight. The second group and a fraction of the third group may be taken as weather data for the occupied period of an office. Figure 2 below is a histogram of weather data showing total hours and office occupancy hours from 8 A.M. to 6 P.M. in the Atlanta area.

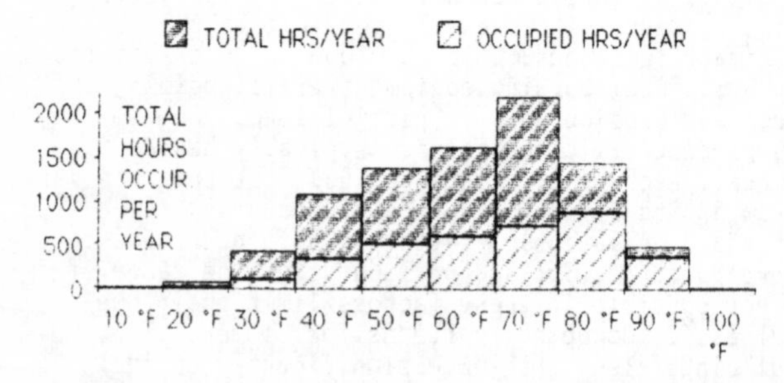

FIGURE 2 - HISTOGRAM OF AVERAGE WEATHER DATA for ATLANTA, GA.

Modified Bin Method

In 1983 ASHRAE published "Simplified Energy Analysis Using the Modified Bin Method" which presents a detailed methodology of estimating energy use relative to weather data. A building's heating and cooling load is broken into its component loads that are calculated for their average diversified values rather than peak load conditions. Generally two sets of calculations are performed, one for occupied and one for unoccupied periods. When completed, this load profile will resemble that of Figure 3. These loads are then taken as a percentage of full load boiler or chiller capacity. Figure 4 and Figure 5 show the relationships between part load operation and energy consumption for efficient boilers and chillers respectively.

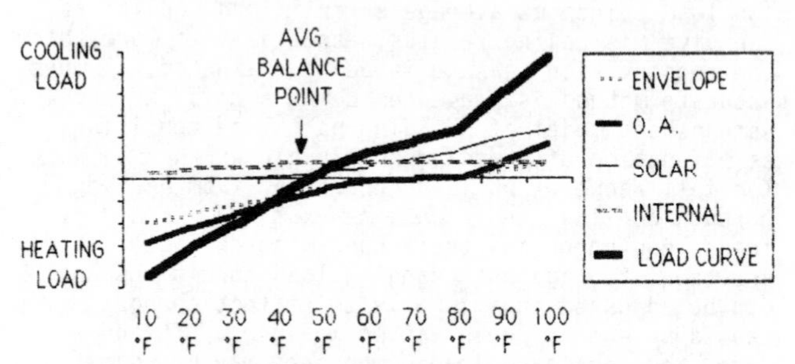

FIGURE 3 - MODIFIED BIN MODEL SHOWING INDIVIDUAL LOAD COMPONENTS and the COMBINED LOAD CURVE

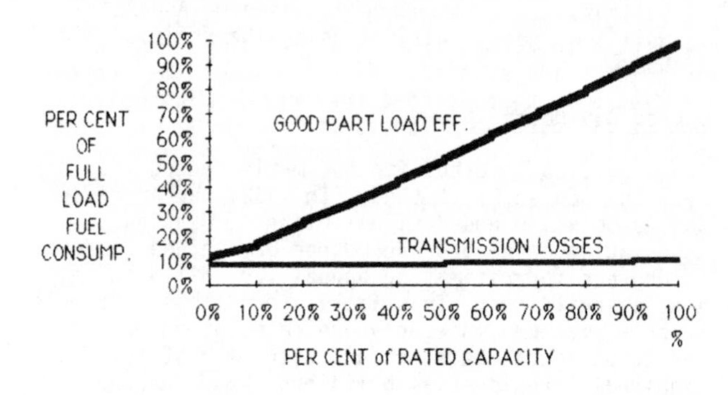

FIGURE 4 - BOILER PART LOAD FUEL CONSUMPTION

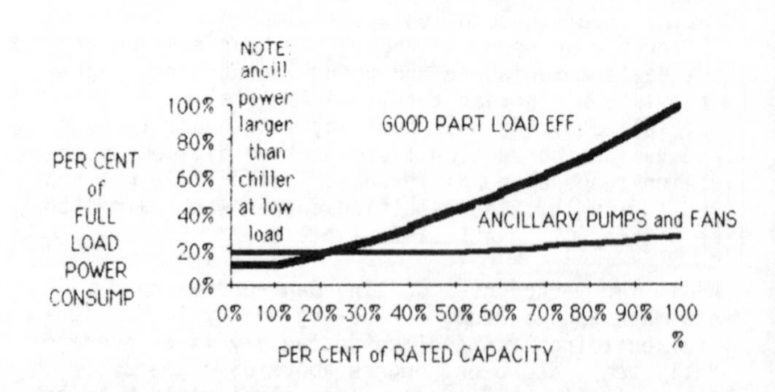

FIGURE 5 - CHILLER PART LOAD POWER CONSUMPTION

A separate calculation is performed at each bin temperature. The total load is determined for each bin, its percentage of full load capacity of cooling or heating and its resulting electric or fuel consumption. The hourly fuel consumption multiplied by the hours per year yields the annual consumption in each bin. Totaling all bin calculations determines total annual consumption. If a significant load exists during unoccupied hours a second set of calculations must be performed for the unoccupied period. Both the occupied and the unoccupied calculations are totaled to determine annual consumption. If monthly bills are to be calculated to determine actual cost on a seasonal utility rate, the calculations must be repeated twelve times using monthly bin data.

Spread Sheets

Personal computers offer a powerful tool for solving such tedious calculations as discussed above: spread sheet programs. ASHRAE's "Simplified Energy Analysis Using the Modified Bin Method" proposes that the engineer write a specific computer program for each building model. Few practicing engineers have the time, budget, experience or desire to write and de-bug such programs. Most, however are capable of entering values and formulae on a spread sheet.

Load curves represented in Figure-3 are defined as a function of the bin temperature midpoints. These functions are linear or polynomial equations. These equations may be generated with a curve fitting program from actual calculated data. Likewise, the hourly fuel consumption of boilers or chillers are functions of the percent of full load capacity. Again these functions are defined by equations for the curves shown in Figures 4 and 5. These curves are fitted to actual test data from the specific equipment being studied. Once the equations for one bin line have been defined they are simply copied down to all other bin lines. The totals are obtained by defining the cell at the bottom as the sum of the column of numbers above it. Once this has been done you have "template" models of the building being analyzed. They will appear as follows in Table-1A and Table-1B.

	B	C	D	E	F	G	H	I
1	TABLE 1.A							
2	MODIFIED BIN SPREADSHEET ANALYSIS OF A BUILDING IN ATLANTA, GA. - SUMMER							
3	BIN	MEAN	FREQ.	AVG TONS	% TOTAL	ANCILL.	CHILLER	TOTAL
4	TEMP	COINC.	OCCUR.	DIVERS.	COOLING	COOLING	KW PER	COOLING
5	RANGE	W. B.	HRS/YR	COOLING	CAPACITY	LOAD	BIN	KWH PER
6	(degrees F)		occupied	LOAD	(300tons)	KW		BIN
7	55 - 60	52	773	20	7%	50	39	68,797
8	60 - 65	57	845	40	13%	50	50	84,500
9	65 - 70	62	986	76	25%	51	77	126,208
10	70 - 75	67	1,201	111	37%	51	104	186,155
11	75 - 80	69	839	147	49%	71	151	186,258
12	80 - 85	70	612	183	61%	72	179	153,612
13	85 - 90	72	367	219	73%	72	207	102,393
14	90 - 95	74	135	254	85%	72	233	41,175
15	95-100	74	20	290	97%	74	262	6,720
16	TOTALS		5,778		TOTAL ANNUAL KWH			955,818

	B	C	D	E	F	G	H	I
1	TABLE 1.B							
2	MODIFIED BIN SPREADSHEET ANALYSIS OF A BUILDING IN ATLANTA, GA. - WINTER							
3	BIN	MEAN	FREQ.	AVG mbh	% TOTAL	HEATING	TOTAL	TOTAL
4	TEMP	COINC.	OCCUR.	DIVERS.	HEATING	TRANSM.	HEATING	HEATING
5	RANGE	W. B.	HRS/YR	HEATING	CAPACITY	LOSS	mbh load	MCF GAS
6	(degrees F)		occupied	LOAD	(2,000mbh)	(mbh)	per BIN	per BIN
7	5 - 10	6	1	1,800	90%	120	1,920	2
8	10 - 15	11	9	1,636	82%	118	1,754	20
9	15 - 20	15	23	1,473	74%	116	1,589	50
10	20 - 25	20	51	1,342	67%	115	1,457	106
11	25 - 30	24	134	1,145	57%	113	1,258	260
12	30 - 35	29	303	982	49%	111	1,093	540
13	35 - 40	34	471	818	41%	109	927	749
14	40 - 45	38	608	655	33%	107	762	830
15	45 - 50	42	665	491	25%	105	596	736
16	50 - 55	47	709	327	16%	104	431	582
17	55 - 60	52	773	164	8%	102	265	397
18	60 - 65	57	845	0	0%	100	100	164
19	ANNUAL TOTAL		4,592		ANNUAL TOTAL GAS CONSUMP.			4,436
20					AVG. ANNUAL SYSTEM EFFICIENCY			45%

These templates may be copied, renamed, and modified to calculate energy use in other similar buildings, or to look at the same building with different equipment or a modified system. The beauty of a spreadsheet is that once the template structure has been created it may be modified with relative ease to play "what-if" for as many alternatives as you wish. Furthermore, intermediate answers may be checked by calculating in stages, as in column "F" in Table-1A & 1B show how loaded the boiler and chiller are at a given Bin range. When your calculations are complete the spreadsheets depicting various alternatives may be printed out for a neat detailed record of your calculations. Many spreadsheets allow you to print the cell formulas as well.

Methodology

Depending on whether you are modeling a building under design or an existing building you will take one of two approaches to setting up the spreadsheet load curve. If the building is under design or very new the average diversified load model must be calculated. This is done in the manner described above, by developing separate equations for each load component and totaling, or by manually calculating average component loads at three or more points along the Bin range. A more detailed description of this process is given in the ASHRAE book "Simplified Energy Analysis Using The Modified Bin Method."[3] However, if the building is existing, has been operating for two or more years, and has good records on energy demand and consumption, a simpler technique should be used. Gas meter consumption data is coordinated with recorded weather data from the National Oceanic and Atmospheric Administration to develop a "Scatter Plot" of consumption versus average outside temperature. An average gas trend line is constructed from this data and used as a load profile. The same method should be used with electrical demand data to produce an electrical trend line. Figure 6 on the next page illustrates such a plot for gas consumption. This method of using actual meter history to derive average load curves is preferred when possible since a large amount of guess-work is eliminated.

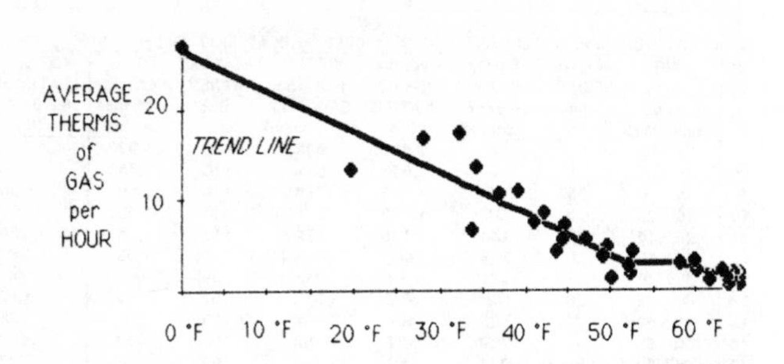

FIGURE 6 - SCATTER PLOT of GAS CONSUMPTION vs AVERAGE DAILY WEATHER DATA

The curves representing equipment part load performance are best obtained from the equipment manufacturer. A reasonably accurate curve can be constructed from four or five points of part load operation. Some curves may prove difficult to fit to an equation, or you may not want to go through this step for a simple analysis. In such a case, the data points of the spreadsheets are mannually determined by interpolation from a manufacturer's chart. The manually derived points are then entered into the spreadsheet without generating equations from the performance curves. By example, in Table-1A above, the cooling KW consumption column could be manually calculated using the manufacturer's performance charts, at the percent load shown instead of fitting an equation to the manufacturer's chart. This is one of the chief advantages of a spreadsheet: you can observe the calculations in stages and manually perform part of them. This is also of great advantage when a system modification has interactive effects. For example, if you are simulating a water side economizer, the chiller KW savings should be offset to some degree by the extra KWH consumption of the cooling tower fan and the condenser water pumps, especially if higher pumping head results from heat exchangers or filters. Each of these pieces of equipment should be listed in a separate column, for clarity.

When examining energy conservation alternatives, a base case of the building must be used for comparison so that a net energy and cost savings may be determined. When utility data is available, it should be used to check the accuracy of the spreadsheet model. The actual fuel consumption should be within 10 to 15% of the total value calculated by the spreadsheet. If several years data is available, the average should be within 5% to 10%, since weather effects have been reduced.

Applications

When applying this technique, it is implicit that the more itemized and detailed the spreadsheet, the more accurate the results and conclusions. For example, if the building load curve were broken into its individual components as represented in Figure 3, the solar load component may be reduced by the amount reflected by window film. The spreadsheet bin model would show not only the cooling energy saved but also the extra heating energy required due to less winter solar gain. If the solar component were broken down even further into north, east, west and south walls and windows, more specific solar energy conservation opportunities may be examined. For example, solar film on a south wall may not be practical. The internal load component should be adjusted to reflect the effects of daily occupancy as well as low occupancy on weekends.

Some of the most significant savings have been found by modifying the primary boiler and chiller systems and their secondary distribution systems. This calculation method reveals how significant part load operating efficiences are with respect to total annual energy consumption. Most of the time during the year, heating and cooling equipment is operating at a low part load range. Figure 7 shows the total energy consumed per year by bin range. Note that most energy is consumed in the moderate temperature ranges where boilers and chillers are loaded at less than 50% capacity. This is more a result of the higher number of hours in these bin ranges than load or equipment efficiencies.

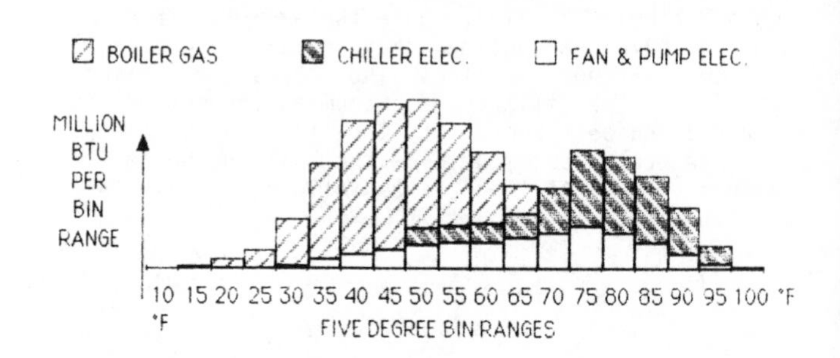

FIGURE 7 - EXAMPLE of BTU 's CONSUMED PER BIN RANGE in an ATLANTA, GA. BUILDING

Primary boilers and chillers with good efficiency at part load conditions and a good turndown ratio can provide significant savings and payback. Multiple boilers and chillers improve this further by allowing even better turndown ratios. Water and air distribution systems that utilize variable volume operation at part load provide some of the best savings in these temperature bins. Figures 8 and 9 on the next page graphically demonstrate these relationships.

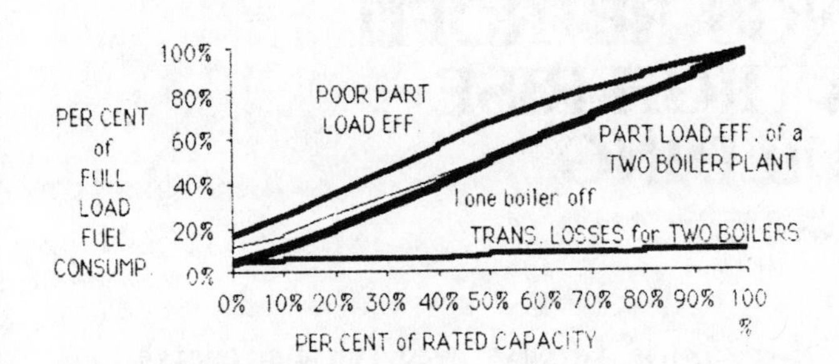

FIGURE 8 - PART LOAD FUEL CONSUMP. for DIFFERENT BOILERS and CONFIGURATIONS

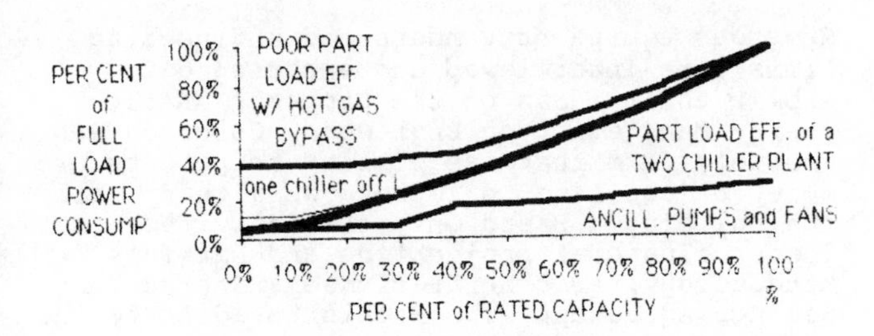

FIGURE 9 - PART LOAD POWER CONSUMP. for DIFFERENT CHILLERS and CONFIGURATIONS

Somewhat more involved are the techniques used for modeling various control concepts of air distribution systems and chilled water/hot water reset. The referenced book "Simplified Energy Analysis Using The Modified Bin Method"[3] goes into these techniques with great detail.

Summary

Using computerized spreadsheets to perform a Modified Bin Analysis on a building is an effective and accurate tool for estimating energy consumption of commercial and institutional buildings. It is not limited to small residential buildings, as is the Degree Day Method. Instead, it is as flexible and complex as the analysis requires. If properly set up it can produce answers approaching the accuracy of large main frame computer programs that calculate hourly values for the full year. As with any analysis the complexity must be kept to reasonable limits given the expected accuracy of estimated energy consumption. Unpredictable parameters, such as changing occupancy patterns and weather variations, can cause even the most complex main frame program analysis to vary from actual recorded usage. It must be understood that the value of a building model is not necessarily its accuracy in predicting utility bills. Its greatest value is in predicting energy savings from various proposed alternatives. Modified Bin analysis using computerized spreadsheets is an excellent tool for this use.

References

1 ASHRAE, "1985 Fundamentals", Pg. 28.9

2 ASHRAE, "1976 Systems", Pg. 43.8

3 ASHRAE, Prepared by David E. Knebel, "Simplified Energy Analysis Using The Modified BIN Method", 1983

Chapter 3

A SHARED SAVINGS RETROFIT PROJECT AT A HIGH-RISE OFFICE BUILDING

R. A. Kennedy, C. Saul

The Goal: Reduce operating expenses, improve comfort and control, spend no capital funds and avoid risk.

The Best Solution: Develop a Shared Savings program with an Energy Service Company willing to meet these goals as a condition of payment.

INITIAL SITUATION: NEW BUILDING, OLD DESIGN

The 30 North LaSalle office building contains one million square feet and is located in the heart of Chicago's central business district. It is owned as an investment property by the Prudential Insurance Company of America and managed by L.J. Sheridan & Company. Tenants include law firms, banks and major corporations.

Completed in 1974, the building contains mechanical systems typical of the pre-energy crisis era. For example, constant air volume induction systems were used; while these systems provided excellent comfort to the tenants, they often produced more cooling than needed. The heating or cooling output of the existing mechanical system was controlled by the building operators without the benefit of instantaneous monitoring possible today. Since the building operators had already performed the vast majority of low cost modifications, reductions from the 1985 energy consumption levels would require advanced technology and major capital investment. 1985 energy consumption levels were $1.06 per square foot per year, and 85,000 BTU per square foot per year. These figures do not include electric costs billed directly to tenants.

COMPETITIVE PRESSURES MANDATE ACTION

Today's building owner and manager has to confront increased competition in the leasing market. The appearance of newer, more attractive and more efficient buildings has increased market pressure considerably. Increasing vacancy rates have increased the need for effective competitive measures. With a large number of tenant leases expiring, Prudential and L.J. Sheridan were fearful that they would lose many tenants unless the 30 North LaSalle Building was competitively priced. Energy costs were clearly a large area. While the building was only 11 years old, it appeared that additional investment would make it more competitive.

In response to this need, an aggressive program to reposition the building began. Prudential and L.J. Sheridan wished to examine each potential area of improvement; this included the HVAC systems, the main lobby, elevators, public spaces, restrooms, and fire life and safety systems. A successful program would be measured by lower operating expenses, increased resale value of the building, and improved ability to lease due to lower costs, better comfort control and a more attractive place to work.

WHY PRUDENTIAL CHOSE SHARED SAVINGS

Numerous equipment vendors and engineering firms were interviewed and encouraged to submit their ideas on the project. Natkin Energy Management of Englewood, Colorado was the only firm that was willing to put its own money on the line to improve an already well-run building. Based on preliminary technical ideas, financial projections and Natkin's methodology, Prudential signed a Shared Savings Agreement with Natkin to identify the necessary upgrades.

As one of the country's largest commercial real estate investors, Prudential certainly had access to the funds required for the entire upgrade program. However, Prudential learned of the possibility of using Natkin to finance and perform all of the energy-related modifications. After comparing the details of Natkin's Shared Savings program against other forms of funding, Prudential chose Shared Savings financing.

Why? As financial experts, Prudential saw that the Shared Savings program would provide the greatest benefit to Prudential and its tenants. Under the performance-based contract, the potential reward was great. The annual savings which the measures were projected to generate were substantial. This factor interested Prudential highly, but was only the beginning of Prudential's financial analysis.

Prudential's decision making was based predominantly on the amount of risk involved and the financial return available.One of Prudential's options was to fund the modifications itself. However, after analysis, Prudential chose the Shared Savings method.

Prudential liked the fact that under Shared Savings, substantial benefits could be derived without taking risks. These risks included cost overruns, change orders, delivery problems, subcontractor failures, poor engineering, and failure to achieve predicted savings. With Shared Savings, Natkin agreed to be responsible for all these risks; in fact, Natkin banked on its ability to successfully manage the project. In order to be paid, Natkin had to install at its cost the capital improvements it recommended, and those improvements had to save Prudential and their tenants money. If it performed, Natkin would be paid a portion of the savings achieved; the building's tenants would keep the rest. The net impact to Prudential would be that its cash flow would be increased immediately upon achieving savings, without having to pay for the improvements first. These benefits would be achieved without risk because if the measures Natkin recommended did not work, Prudential would not have to pay for them. Prudential contrasted this with what would result if a Prudential-funded upgrade did not work. In that case, Prudential would still have to pay for the cost of the modifications, although no savings were achieved.

Prudential also observed that minimizing its risk did not mean that it minimized its return. Under the Shared Savings program, Natkin had agreed to fund the new equipment and its installation, as well as engineering, construction management, operations training, and ongoing management costs during the seven year contract. In order to recoup its costs and make a fair profit, Natkin had every incentive to maximize the savings upon which it would be paid. Further, although L.J. Sheridan was doing a good job of managing the property, Prudential recognized that by combining the experience of L.J. Sheridan and Natkin, the projected savings were more likely to be achieved. Prudential saw that by using the Shared Savings method of funding, a very acceptable level of reward could be achieved without taking risks. In addition, funds which might have been used to fund the improvements could be invested elsewhere to improve the reward.

SHARED SAVINGS: FAIR COMPENSATION

Natkin is paid based on the amount of money it saves its customer. The amount of money saved is calculated by comparing consumption from the time before modifications were made to the consumption after making the modifications. However, because changes in weather, occupancy and billing cycles affect the amount consumed in a given period, fair comparison of before- and after-retrofit consumption requires adjustment for these factors.

Natkin developed software which ensures that the amount of savings it bills for has been actually achieved. Using multiple regressions analysis on each utility, Natkin developed mathematical models which showed how energy consumption changed in the past against variations in weather and occupancy. The accuracy of these models can be measured by how well they "project" what consumption levels occurred in a previous year. By using current conditions in the models, a projection of the consumption which would have occurred had the upgrades not been performed can be obtained with this technique. Determination of savings is fair because it is based on periods with similar consumption conditions.

Prudential was already well acquainted with this technique, having selected Natkin's PACE (Periodic Audit for the Conservation of Energy) program as their corporate energy tracking system in 1980. Over 200 of Prudential's wholly owned and joint venture investment buildings are monitored monthly with PACE to determine savings and track energy efficiency. As a smart investor with a strong commitment to energy conservation, Prudential knows the importance of documenting the results of its investments in energy improvements.

Under the Shared Savings program, the method of determining savings is agreed upon before Natkin begins construction of the modifications. After construction is completed, the level of savings is tracked monthly. Prudential receives a copy of all calculations used to determine the savings and thus can ensure that the amount paid Natkin is fair.

THE STEPS IN SHARED SAVINGS PROJECTS

When the Shared Savings agreement was signed, Natkin began the detailed engineering required to identify cost-effective improvements. Working in conjunction with the operations department of L.J. Sheridan & Company, Natkin engineers investigated many possible modifications to hardware and operating procedures. Those with the best potential were analyzed in detail using Natkin's proprietary software to accurately determine potential savings taking weather fluctuations into account.

Concurrently, design and bid documents were prepared so that firm prices could be obtained from equipment vendors and installing contractors. Great care was used in selecting only well qualified subcontractors who could demonstrate financial stability and previous success in similar projects. As more of the project details became available, review sessions occurred involving the owner, manager and Natkin.

After final selection, the "Schedules" to the Energy Service Agreement were completed. The Schedules defined all the technical details such as equipment to be installed, service and maintenance responsibilities, required comfort conditions, savings calculation formulas plus the financial issues like termination or buyout provisions and the percentage of savings to be paid to Natkin.

THE MODIFICATIONS MADE

The engineering analysis showed that several retrofits offered good savings potential. Natkin installed four major modifications at its cost:

1. Fan Speed Reduction/Air Balance

   All of the major air distribution systems were rebalanced so that air flows were properly matched to the current needs of the building. Due to the rebalancing it was found that a permanent reduction in fan speeds was permissible. This saves motor horsepower at all times of the year. In addition, there was increased flexibility in setting supply air temperatures.

2. Variable Speed Induction Fans

   Because induction systems are designed for peak heating and cooling conditions most of the year, these units were oversized. Based on manufacturer's data and experience with other buildings, Natkin knew that the primary air fan could be run at reduced speeds for many hours of the year without affecting tenant comfort. This is because in most induction systems the load capacity is determined mostly by the volume of the secondary (induced) air and the characteristics of the hydronic coil and circulating water.

   To run the fans at the correct speed during both peak and nonpeak times, a variable frequency drive manufactured by Robicon Corporation was installed on each of the four 125 HP primary air fans. Selecting the necessary speed can be difficult in such applications and a unique strategy was devised. Using the help of a new building automation system and various sensors, the solar heat gain and temperatures of interior spaces as well as exterior walls are constantly monitored. This system predicts the cooling or heating requirements and automatically adjusts the fan speeds so that comfort is maintained in all areas using the lowest possible energy.

3. Direct Injection Tower Cooling

   During the feasibility study, it was found that expensive chillers had to be run at times when the exterior conditions would allow for a far less expensive alternative. This situation is common for buildings with high internal loads and limited outside air capacity. Certain measures, such as using outside air for cooling, have limited effectiveness in this situation.

   Natkin designed a cooling tower system which would save 300-500 hours of chiller operation annually. This system takes advantage of the difference between wet bulb and dry bulb temperatures to produce low cost cooling. With proper filtration and chemical treatment, this water can be used directly in the chilled water circuit to provide cooling for the building. This technique is particularly effective for the secondary water of induction systems. In addition to the energy savings, the system will reduce wear and tear on the chillers and lower service requirements.

4. Building Automation System

   While recognizing that the operations personnel of L.J. Sheridan were doing an excellent job, Natkin determined during the feasibility study that a building automation system could increase savings. Natkin installed an Andover system which can monitor over 100 variables and automatically make adjustments to major components of the HVAC system every few seconds. This includes complete control of the 1500 ton chillers, tower cooling, and variable speed perimeter fans.

   The building automation system also allows Natkin to monitor operations from its headquarters. Thus, Natkin can assure that the HVAC system is functioning most economically. If desirable, Natkin can assist L.J. Sheridan operators to reprogram the system's software or try new control strategies to optimize operations.

NATKIN'S COMMITMENT

Numerous other minor modifications were performed which contribute to energy savings and operating flexibility. From time to time during the term of the contract, Natkin will pay for other upgrades to achieve more savings.

To assure that the most is received from the program, extensive training is being performed for all operators on the optimal use of all equipment. As part of Natkin's involvement, operations and maintenance manuals as well as video taped training sessions are provided to the customer to assist efficient operation of the system.

With the Shared Savings program, Natkin has a strong incentive to assure that things continue to run smoothly. Natkin banks on its ability to make sure that the system installed continues to perform as promised.

THE BOTTOM LINE

The goals of the project have been met. Operating expenses have been reduced by Natkin. The modifications have increased comfort and control and are performing well. Over $500,000 in upgrades were funded by Natkin. The performance contract insulated Prudential from risk. But, as satisfying as this was to those involved, the project has enabled the parties to realize other substantial rewards.

The Shared Savings program was based on one central philosophy: promoting a win-win situation. The program was structured such that meeting its goals was beneficial to all involved. Prudential, L.J. Sheridan and Natkin worked together as a team, sharing the expertise that each had developed. This not only enabled the goals of the project to be met, but also caused each party to feel the essential satisfaction of knowing that they contributed to a job well done.

Since construction began, the savings have been growing month by month. Current savings are meeting projections and Prudential, L.J. Sheridan and Natkin are continuing the fine-tuning process. The end result will be a reduction in operating expenses of $.20 per square foot and savings of 13,000 BTU per square foot per year.

The savings to Prudential and its tenants will average $66,500 per year over a 10 year period. This comes without risk or capital investment.

Chapter 4

NEW DEVELOPMENTS IN ICE STORAGE SYSTEMS

A. D. Wortman

The use of ice storage in air conditioning systems is now a widely accepted and proven concept. Ice storage is becoming the basic system of design for office buildings in many areas such as Baltimore, Washington, Florida, and Chicago. Why are so many air conditioning projects now using ice storage systems? The main reason why ice storage is so popular is the financial incentives available and the new developments in ice storage.

Major ice storage projects include the Merchandise Mart in Chicago, the Alabama Power Power Company Headquarters in Birmingham, Pacific Telephone & Telegraph Headquarters in San Ramon, California, the Christian Broadcasting Network in Virginia Beach, Virginia, the Dallas Power & Light Headquarters in Dallas, the Industrial Commission of Ohio Building in Columbus, the Industrial Research & Technology Building in San Diego, and the Kellogg Company World Headquarters in Battle Creek, Michigan. Small ice storage projects include the Arnold Elementary School, in Anne Arundel County, Maryland, the Washington Junior High in Sanger, California, St. Mary Magdaline Church in Rossford, Ohio, and the Victory Memorial Hospital in Waukegan, Illinois. Over two hundred ice storage installations exist in the U.S. and Canada alone.

As electrical usage increases and approaches the limit of generating capacity, utilities have imposed rate schedules that discourage the use of electricity during peak demand hours. These rate schedules may include a demand charge based on the maximum power recorded during peak hours in a given month, high time of day rates during peak hours, and/or up-front cash incentives to shift load to off-peak hours.

Traditionally these utility charges were used to offset the higher first cost of installing an ice storage system vs. a conventional system. But now the days of additional first cost for ice storage systems are over. New developments in ice storage systems allow air conditioning systems with ice storage to be installed at the same or a lower first cost than conventional systems. Lower first costs are obtained by taking full advantage of the 34°F water supplied by the ice storage system. The 34°F water can be used to reduce the cost of air handling units, ductwork, piping, pumps, and electrical equipment. The financial incentives provided by the utilities are now a bonus for installing an ice storage system.

To illustrate how a ice storage system can be lower in first cost than a conventional system, let us compare the size of the equipment needed in a typical 20-story office building using both a conventional system and an ice storage system. In this example we will use differences in power requirements to indicate differences in cost.

The building in this example has 20,000 sq. ft. per floor, a 1000 ton air conditioning load, and a 10 hour hour building occupancy.

Compressor Size Analysis:

A conventional system requires .7 kW/ton for a 1000 ton instantaneous load and would therefore require 700 kW or 845 BHP. An ice storage system operates 24 hours per day. Assume that the average load on a design day is 80% of design load. Required capacity = (1000 tons x 10 hours x .8)/24 hours = 333 tons. Assuming a 95° condensing temperature and a 25° average suction temperature, the compressor will require 1.12 BHP/ton. A 373 BHP compressor will be needed. Below is a comparison of the compressor and evaporative condenser HP required for each system.

	Conventional	Ice Storage
Capacity, Tons	**1,000**	**333**
Compressor HP	845	373
Evaporative condenser:	**1,000**	**333**
Fan HP	--	30
Pump HP	--	5
Total equipment HP	**965**	**408**

The ice storage system requires 44% of the connected horsepower of a conventional system.

Pumping and Piping Comparison

A conventional system chilled water loop with a range of 44° to 56° requires 2000 gpm. An ice storage system with a 36° to 56° range requires only 1200 gpm. The condenser circuit of a conventional system requires 3000 gpm vs. 2400 gpm for the ice water circuit (the ice water circuit gpm is usually twice the chilled water circuit gpm). The chart on the next page shows a comparison of pipe and pump sizes.

Conventional Chilled water	
Chilled water supply temp., °F	44
Chilled water return temp., °F	56
∠T, °F	12
Flow rate, GPM	**2,000**
Pipe size, in.	10
Head, ft.	75
Pump efficiency, %	80
Pump HP	**50**
Condenser water	
Return condenser water temp., °F	95
Supply condenser water temp., °F	85
∠T, °F	10
Heat rejection, Btu/hr	14,150,000
Flow rate, GPM	2,830
Pipe size, in.	12
Head, ft.	60
Pump efficiency, %	80
Pump HP	**60**
Total pump HP--Conventional	**110**

Ice Storage Chilled water	
Chilled water supply temp., °F	36
Chilled water return temp., °F	56
∠T, °F	20
Flow rate, GPM	**1,200**
Pipe size, in.	8
Head, ft.	75
Pump efficiency, %	80
Pump HP	**30**
Ice water	
Return ice water temp., °F	46
Supply ice water temp., °F	36
∠T, °F	10
Heat transferred, Btu/hr	12,000,000
Flow rate, GPM	2,400
Pipe size, in.	10
Head, ft.	40
Pump Efficiency, %	80
Pump HP	**30**
Total pump HP--ice storage	**60**

The ice storage system requires 40% less GPM and saves on piping costs by requiring smaller pipes and less total insulation due to the smaller pipes. Savings are also found in pumping costs due to smaller pumps and smaller electrical equipment. Pumping horsepower is reduced by 41% with an ice storage system.

Air System Analysis

Air quantity is usually determined on the basis of room sensible load. For example, we will assume that the total room sensible load is 8,000,000 Btu/hr or two-thirds of the total load. For the conventional system, the supply discharge air temperature is 55°, and we will assume a design room temperature of 75°. Based on a 20° temperature difference between room air and supply air, 370,370 CFM will be required. The ice storage system will have 42° discharge air temperature from the air handling units. The 33° temperature difference between room air and supply air means just 224,470 CFM is required. Below is a comparison of the two systems.

	Conventional	Ice Storage
Total load, Btu/hr	12,000,000	12,000,000
Sensible load, Btu/hr	8,000,000	8,000,000
Return air temp., °F	75	75
Supply air temp., °F	55	42
ΔT, °F	20	33
Total CFM	**370,370**	**224,470**
CFM/floor	18,519	11,224
Fan HP/floor	20	10
Total fan HP	400	200
Terminal fans total HP	--	100
Total airside HP	**400**	**300**

The air handling and ductwork system in the ice storage system result in a first cost savings because smaller ductwork, less total insulation due to smaller ductwork, smaller air handling units and smaller electrical equipment and wiring is used. In addition, if the main supply duct size is a determining factor in establishing ceiling height, then smaller ducts can result in lower ceiling heights. Some of the savings on the airside equipment is offset because fan-powered mixing boxes are required to insure proper air mixing and distribution of the low temperature air in lieu of VAV boxes and other air distribution outlets. In this case these mixing boxes would add 100 HP. The ice storage system has a total of 25% less connected horsepower.

Total System Comparison

If we summarize all of the energy uses in each system, we have the following result.

Connected Horsepower Summary

	Conventional	Ice Storage
Refrigeration equipment	965	408
Airside system	400	300
Pumping Systems	110	60
Total connected horsepower	**1,475**	**768**

This example has shown how an ice storage system can have a lower first cost and lower operating cost than a conventional system. Colder supply water temperatures permit the design of a system with 40% less airflow and 40% less water flow. The 24 hour refrigeration system is about one-third the size of conventional systems. The result is first cost savings in compressors, pumps, air handling units, ductwork, insulation, piping, and electrical equipment. These savings are somewhat lessened by the need for ice storage units, a heat exchanger, and a mixing terminal system.

As seen in the preceding example, the connected load for the ice storage system is about one-half that of a conventional system. This results in a 50% decrease in demand billing, which has a substantial impact on the cost of power.

Even without time-of-day rates, energy costs for ice storage systems are usually lower than for conventional systems because total energy usage is slightly less. When time-of-day rates are present, the energy cost savings available from ice storage systems are even greater because much of their operation is during off-peak periods.

One of the leaders in this design concept is H.C. Yu, consulting engineer in Richmond, Virginia. H.C. Yu has designed over 100 projects, and all of his recent designs have used ice storage with low temperature air and water supply, which he calls "Super Cooled Air" designs. His experience indicates that the first cost savings in piping, pumping, air handlers, ductwork, and associated electrical apparatus offsets the added cost of the ice storage apparatus.

The new CBN (Christian Broadcasting Network) World Outreach Support Center in Virginia Beach is one of the "Super Cooled Air" ice storage systems designed by H.C. Yu. The CBN project is a 320,000 sq. ft. building which houses the television programming staff for the CBN programs. The air conditioning system started operation in August 1985. Ice storage was selected for this application because it was competitive in first cost and operating cost. The first cost was actually $40,000 less than a conventional system. Operating costs were also less even though the local utility, Virginia Electric Company does not have any financial incentives for using ice storage, except for demand charges.

The CBN ice storage system consists of four ice banks with two screw compressors. The total ice storage is 2640 ton hours. The water off the ice banks is 34° with an average suction temperature of 27° according to Tom Brady of Brady Mechanical Company of Chicago, Illinois, who is the contractor on this project. The 34°F water is circulated to high performance heat exchangers which results in 36°F water being furnished to the system. During the September of 1985 and the summer of 1986, outdoor temperatures and humidity levels reached design conditions quite often, but the system operated with no major difficulty.

The use of an ice storage system will not only provide benefits for new buildings, but also for retrofit applications. Currently, in the midst of a HVAC system overhaul, is Chicago's Merchandise Mart. The Merchandise Mart was built in 1930 and encompasses 4.5 million sq. ft. Since its construction, greater people density--over 15,000 either work or visit there daily--computer systems and other heat generating electronic equipment, higher lighting loads, etc., has substantially increased the usual air conditioning load. Many tenants in various parts of the building were requesting more cooling which taxed the existing AC system to the limit. Mart management was faced with the expense of the inevitable replacement of the old AC system.

The first solution considered was replacement of the existing system with a larger capacity system which would accommodate the increased load. In addition to the high cost of the new equipment, larger pipes and larger ducts throughout the building would have been needed to deliver the increased cooling volume. Predictably, a larger system would mean prohibitive first costs and an unacceptable disruption to business activities during distribution system renovation.

The alternative suggested and adopted was an ice thermal storage system. The world's largest ice storage system, capable of producing 2,213,860 pounds of ice per day has been installed. The ice storage system will reduce the system water temperature by approximately 8 degrees so that the existing ductwork and piping is capable of transferring 40 percent more cooling throughout the system. By avoiding the need to replace or upgrade the distribution system, considerable first cost dollars were saved, and system installation can proceed without disruption of business at the Mart. In addition, over $2,000,000 in yearly energy savings are expected.

While most engineers accept the fact that the first cost of a "Super Cooled Air" ice storage system is competitive (since it is documented by bids received), some still question whether the use of colder water and colder main supply air really works in a practical sense. They cite the possibility of drafty air distribution and condensation on ductwork and piping as potential sources for trouble.

H.C. Yu said his system low temperature air from the main supply is mixed with return air in fan powered mixing-boxes. The air distribution discharge temperature in the occupied space is identical to that of a conventional system and, therefore, occupants are not aware that there is a change in the system.

He also indicates that the problem of sweating can be eliminated by applying reasonable care to the installation of the insulation.

On the other hand, the "Super Cooled Air" system provides many significant advantages that are not available in a conventional system. This would include such considerations as improved comfort levels at higher space temperatures and lower overall energy levels.

Lower temperature air in the main air supply provides drier air to the space. If a lower relative humidity is maintained in the space, then the room temperature can be maintained at a higher level with the same degree of comfort. This could help eliminate complaints of the air being too cold while at the same time supporting a higher room temperature than would be normal with a conventional system.

In addition, the "Super Cooled Air" system requires 50-60% of the installed electrical capacity for air conditioning that a conventional system requires. This means that the system is basically a lower energy level system. Although the components of the system will operate for a longer time and the units of electrical operation will not necessarily be substanially less, it is still a system that reduces installed energy levels. This is important because more and more engineers today are designing systems with an objective to use the lowest base energy requirements. If they do this job well, it will make optimum use of existing electrical generation equipment and avoid the necessity of providing costly new generating equipment.

Another issue that worries consulting engineers is the understanding of how a system like ice that basically has a higher kW/ton cost in the compression equipment really can save operating cost, particularly if the local utility does not have a substantially lower nighttime electrical rate. The answer to this is a consideration of the electrical requirements of the entire system on an hour-by-hour basis 12 months a year and not just focusing primarily on what happens on a design day. Some of the major operating savings result from the following factors:

1. Lower Demand Charges - Too many people focus on on the base electrical rate cost of cent/kWH without giving adequate attention to the impact of demand charges. Demand charges are pretty universal and can account for 30-50% of the total monthly electrical bill. If ice is made at night, the daytime demand portion of the bill is minimized.

2. Ice is made at night - Ice is made during the middle of the night when the condensing wet bulb temperature is usually 10° below the daytime wet bulb temperature. This produces operating cost savings of roughly 7-10% in compression equipment.

3. Smaller fans and pumps use lower horsepower - Since 40% less air and water are being circulated in the system with a 36° basic chilled water temperature, this requires a substantially lower horsepower to operate this equipment.

Other new developments in ice storage design which makes ice storage more popular are the development of higher efficiency systems, the availability of large systems for use with glycol instead of refrigerant, and the use of custom designed units to meet project requirements.

Higher efficiency ice storage systems reduce the kW/ton requirement of the system. A reduction in energy usage and chiller or compressor size is the result.

The availability of large glycol systems allows the installation of equipment that is more familiar to both designers and end users. A glycol system will use a packaged glycol chiller instead of a refrigeration system to store ice. Although not as efficiency as a refrigeration system, its simplicity in design and use is a major benefit.

Custom designed ice storage units allow designers and end users to match equipment to their needs. Units can be designed to fit special space requirements, kW/ton limitations, and to match exact ice storage needs.

With all the innovations in ice storage design and all of the practical experience gained from installations across the U.S. and Canada, ice storage continues to increase in popularity. While it is now becoming the basic system of design for office buildings in many areas, it will soon be the basic system of design across the country as engineers and building owners become more familiar with the advantages of ice storage.

Chapter 5

COOLING TOWERS, THE NEGLECTED ENERGY RESOURCE

R. Burger

ABSTRACT: Loving care is paid to the compressors, condensers, and computer programs of refrigeration systems. When problems arise, operators run around in circles with expensive "fixes", but historically ignore the poor orphan, the cooling tower perched on the roof or located somewhere in the backyard. When the cooling water is too hot, high temperature cut-outs occur and more energy must be provided to the motors to maintain the refrigeration cycle.

Cooling Towers:

1) ... are just as important a link in the chain as the other equipment,
2) ... are an important source of energy conservation,
3) ... can be big money makers, and
4) ... operators should be aware of the potential of maximizing cold water.

Most towers designed over 20 years ago were inefficiently engineered due to cheap power and the "low bidder" syndrome. Operating energy costs were ignored and purchasing criteria was to award the contract to the lowest bidder.

This paper investigates internal elements of typical towers, delineates their functions and shows how to upgrade them in the real world for energy savings and profitability of operation.

HISTORICAL NEGLECT

From the very beginning, cooling towers were ignored. Figure 1 is an illustration from the ASHRAE Basic Fundamentals Refrigeration Manual (1) that delineates the refrigeration cycle consisting of compression, evaporation, expansion, and condensing. The discussion continues on and explains that heat is not generated or destroyed, it is just moved from one location to another. What is ignored though, is "How is that waste heat dissipated?" As we know, it is picked up by the circulating water and brought to the cooling tower where it is discharged into the atmosphere.

While the cooling tower seems like a simple mechanism, it is just as important to the refrigeration cycle as any of the other units. If the cooling tower does not function properly, high head temperatures require that additional electricity be pumped into the system to make it operate and at a critical point, the equipment will shut the system down if the cooling tower cannot produce sufficient cold water for the equipment.

REFRIGERATION ECONOMICS

A cost-effective approach to the solution of conserving energy (and therefore, money) would be to reduce the power input to your system while maintaining maximum efficiency. The power is either purchased from a public utility in the form of electricity or steam, or is generated by the facility by purchasing fuel oil for a diesel engine to power the system.

The following basic principles explain how colder water from the cooling tower conserves energy to create a cost-effective rapid dollar return for cooling tower upgrading expenditures.

Whether it be heat rejection from compressors, electric motor, or chemical process equipment, the cost of "hotter" cooling water is expensive in requiring additional energy to run the equipment at efficient levels to reduce head pressures and temperatures. Excessive heat will create maintenance problems, deteriorate the equipment, and cause shut downs of the process.

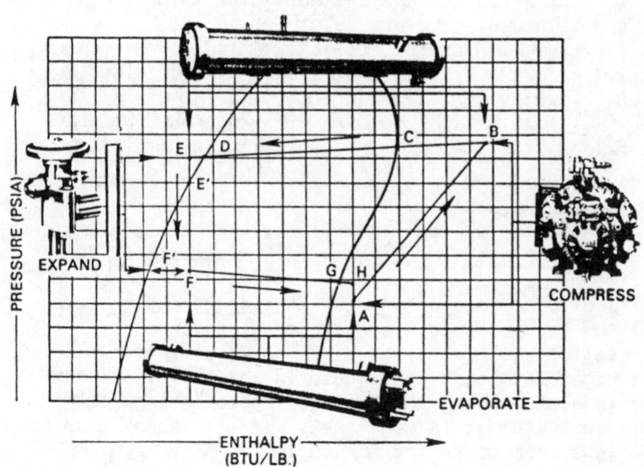

Figure 1: Equipment diagram for basic vapor compression cycle.

A typical example of this is where a refrigerant is cooled (condensed) in the condenser and in turn cools "chilled" water to reduce the temperature of the circulating air throughout the facility to maintain comfortable conditions. Input (electricity or steam) and output (tons of refrigeration) depend upon the speed (rpm) of the compressors and refrigerant temperature (condenser temperature). At any particular speed, both the power requirements and capacities of the refrigeration machine will vary significantly with the refrigerant pressure and temperature. These refrigerant conditions are determined by the cooling in the refrigerant condenser. The quantity and temperature of the condenser water (tower water) determines the available cooling. When operating at full condenser water flow a reduction in condenser water temperature will reduce refrigerant temperatures and pressures. This will permit producing similar refrigeration capacities at lower machine speeds (rpm) and lower power (steam and electricity requirements.)

It can be seen that for various types of refrigeration machinery, colder condensing water off the cooling tower increases the coefficient of performance. For example, a 5°F reduction to a reciprocating compressor can result in a 7% increase in coefficient of performance. Translating this to dollars and cents, if it cost $250,000.00 to operate the system a year, this 5°F colder water can result in a savings of almost $44,000.00 a year in compressor operating costs since the head temperatures are considerably lowered.

Enthalpy charts for refrigerants indicate that for every degree of colder water to the equipment, a 3½% reduction in energy input can be attained. (3)

If, for example, the refrigeration system utilizes $400,000.00 of electricity per year (typical for a 2,000 ton installation) and a 4°F reduction of cooling tower water is obtained, this will lower the utility bill by $56,000.00 ($400,000.00)(4)(.035). With utility costs soaring, this savings will increase each year.

The facts are readily available in most Operating and Maintenance Departments to determine the cost of energy used, and the reduction in water temperature that can be obtained, indicating the cost savings involved. By comparing the cost savings as against the retrofit cost, a payback will usually occur within 6 months to a year and a half depending upon the conditions of the cooling tower before retrofit.

Many authorities point out that lower temperature cooling tower water can produce significant savings for refrigeration equipment. The cooling tower plays one of the key roles in the efficiency of your air conditioning machines.

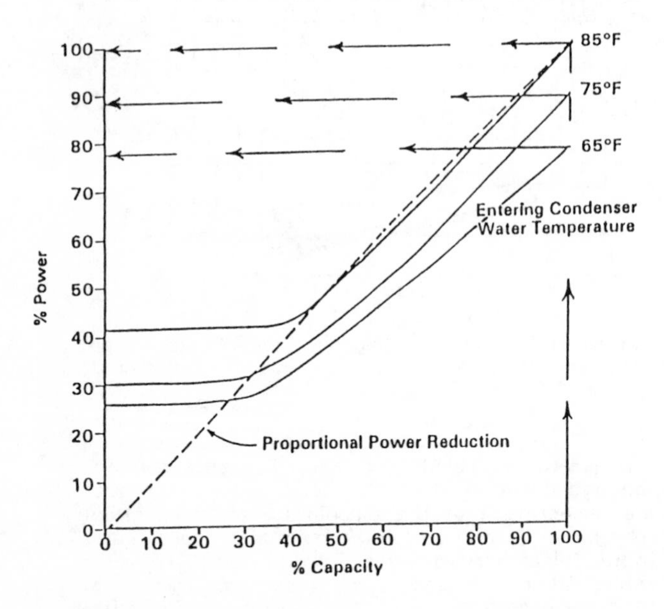

Figure 2 - The relationship of colder water and electric power in the above diagram, (energy) conservation for a 2,000 ton centrifugal system /5/.

Energy consumption is measured in kilowatt hour usage and this reflects efficiency. If your tower does not create the proper heat transfer, your machine will work harder to compensate for the loss and inefficiency (4). Figure 2 clearly indicates that colder condensing temperatures will improve the performance of a compressor significantly. This can result in a substantial energy and dollar savings.

The role of the cooling tower is to remove waste heat in the refrigeration or chemical reaction. The degree of elevation of the discharge temperature above ambient conditions is the sum of the tower's approach of the cold water to the Wet Bulb temperature, i.e., the difference between cold water and Wet Bulb, the cooling range (which equals the temperature rise in the heat exchanger), and the terminal difference in the exchanger. A reduction in operating temperature, always desirable for economic reasons, may be obtained by increasing the capability of the cooling tower's performance (5).

REAL WORLD PRACTICALITIES

Due to the inaccessible location of the cooling tower (usually installed to conserve real estate on the top of a building, or in the backyard) maintenance personnel are many times hard pressed to adequately service the equipment.

Training and misplaced priorities tend to keep the operating engineers more closely attuned to the requirements of the compressors, condensers, and evaporators rather than to the quality of cold water being discharged from the cooling tower.

Since the cooling tower is open to the atmosphere, it can quite readily deteriorate due to corrosion of the ferrous parts, and bacteriological and chemical attack of the wood. Many maintenance people feel that if it is ignored, it will go away. But, of course, being familiar with Murphy's Laws - this does not happen.

COOLING TOWER MODERNIZATION

A great majority of cooling towers operating today, even though some are newly installed, have been engineered with techniques over 20 years old. Today's technology can be utilized to retrofit practically all towers and upgrade their capability of producing colder water or cooling greater volumes of circulating water (6).

Listed below in ascending order of cost are some of the major components that can be upgraded. It is axiomatic that the greater the dollar input, the more rapid and profitable the return that can be obtained.

a) Air Handling - More air volume results in better thermal transfer and colder discharge water. By pitching the fan blades up to a higher angle, which is determined by the plate amperage, additional air can be generated for the same horse power. Velocity regain (VR) Venturi Stacks should be investigated for increasing air flow through the tower while reducing fan motor horse power.

b) Drift Eliminators - Conventional two-pass wood slat herringbone or steel "zig-zag" configurations usually have a higher pressure drop than the new PVC cellular units, Figure 3. By eliminating the solid droplets of water to a higher degree and at a lower pressure loss, the cellular drift eliminator provides additional cooling air through the tower for colder temperatures.

c) Water Distribution Systems - By installing metered orifice target nozzles in older crossflow towers, a more uniform water pattern is obtained and the resulting uniformity will improve the tower's performance. Counterflow towers with spray systems can be greatly improved by installing the new

Figure 3 - Left, old-fashioned herringbone heavy wood slat drift eliminators with high static pressure loss which are prone to deterioration, permitting solid droplets of water to escape. Right, modern high efficiency low pressure drop, self-extinguishing PVC cellular eliminator replacements on typical cross-flow tower.

square spray ABS practically non-clogging nozzles. An added advantage of this newer type nozzle is that maintenance and cleaning are greatly simplified due to upwards of 75% fewer nozzles required than the conventional small orifice conical pattern spray units.

d) The greatest improvement in performance modernization is obtained by changing out the old wood splash bars, Figure 6, and installing self-extinguishing PVC cellular film fill, Figure 5, together with the new efficient nozzles, Figure 4.

EXAMPLES OF UPGRADING:

Blow Through Squirrel Cage Tower

The subject three cell metal tower had a water distribution system of 960 small orifice nozzles on 1½" pipe, Figure 5, and was operating at high head temperatures. The clogged and corroded water distribution system was removed from the tower and the rusted clogged steel plate corrugated wet decking fill was also disposed of. After sandblasting and coating with moisture cured urethane, the new spray system consisting of 36 nozzles on 3" diameter PVC pipes was installed together with new PVC cellular fill.

Figure 4 - A startling improvement in performance by producing colder water or cooling greater volumes of circulating water can be obtained by installing cellular fill and square spray non-clogging nozzles.

Figure 5 - By changing 1,152 small orifice nozzles on 1½" pipe to 36 square spray non-clogging (1¼") on 3" diameter pipe, a 5°F colder water discharge was obtained and nozzle cleaning time was reduced 90%.

BLOW THRU

WATER IN @ 100°F OUT @ 90° @ 78 F°WBT

960 NOZZLES ON 1 1/2" PIPE

OPERATING WITH HIGH HEADS

---

36 NOZZLES + CELLULAR FILL

PRODUCES DESIGN OF 95°– 85°– 78

---

5 APPR x 3 1/2% SAVES 17% ENERGY

17% x $250,000 = $43,750 /YEAR

10 YEARS = $437,500 EARNED

This chart illustrates the rapid payback for converting the tower, illustrated in Figure 5. Enthalpy charts for Freon indicate that 3½% of the electrical energy to the compressors and condensers can be saved for every 1°F colder water (3). The subject cooling tower was tested in accordance with the Cooling Tower Institute Acceptance Test Code 105 which indicated that 5°F colder water was obtained after retrofit. Since the rebuilding for colder water cost $38,500.00, the return on the investment was realized in approximately 9 months with a projected ten year savings of close to $500,000.00. This payback estimate wa generated on the basis of 100% air conditioning utilization per year. If it is realistically cut back 50%, the savings still are well worth the rebuilding and upgrading investment.

Crossflow Air-Conditioner Tower

The conventional deteriorating wood splash bar slats together with the leaking two-pass herringbone drift eliminators were taken out o the tower and disposed of, Figure 6.

Cellular drift eliminators and PVC splash bars were installed to obtain higher levels of heat transfer, Figure 7.

A new basin lining was also installed, consisting of exterior plywood, urethane caulking and 25 to 30 mil. urethane coating sprayed to provided monolithic rubber waterproof membrane, Figure 8.

Before retrofit, operating records indicated that the 1,250 gallons per minute of circulating water was entering the tower at an average of 100°F, leaving at 90°F, during a 78°F Wet Bulb. After retrofit and certified testing, /7/ the same 1,250 gallons of circulating water was now entering the cooling tower at 95°F, be discharges at 85°F, during a 78°F Wet Bulb. Besides reducing the approach to the Wet Bulb by 5°F, the entire system temperature was reduced by 5°F. This saved the Company approximately $45,000 in electrical costs per year.

Inefficient wood fill and leaking drift eliminators were retrofitted with new state of the art self-extinguishing PVC high heat transfer cellular fill and drift eliminators, which reduced the discharge water temperatures by 5°F, representing an approximate 600,000 kilowatt hour and $45,000 energy savings 7½¢ KwH utility charge.

Figure 6 - Inefficient wood fill and leaking drift eliminators were retrofitted with new state of the art self-extinguishing PVC high heat transfer cellular fill and drift eliminators, which reduced the discharge water temperatures by 5°F, representing an approximate 600,000 kilowatt hour and $45,000 energy savings at 7½¢ KwH utility charge.

Figure 6 - Innefficient wood fill and leaking wood drift eliminators were retrofitted with state-of-the-art self extinguishing PVC heat transfer cellular fill and drift eliminators (see Fig.3) which reduced cold water discharge temperature by 5°F, representing an approximate 600,000 KWh and $45,000 energy savings at 7½KWh utility charge. Rubberizing basin saved demolition of the cooling tower.

CONCLUSION

If a refrigeration/air-conditioning system is operating marginally due to high head temperatures, it behooves the owner and operator to investigate the possibility of upgrading the existing cooling tower rather than installing another O.E.M. unit which may or may not the necessary colder water. It should be well understood that colder water can save energy and create an operating profit. Cooling towers are hidden bonanzas for energy conservation and dollar savings when properly engineered and maintained. In many cases, the limiting factor is the quality and quantity of cold water coming off the cooling tower (8).

The thermal upgrading and structural retrofitting technology of all types of cooling towers is the same, only the size is different, as illustrated in Figure 7.

It would be prudent for the engineer with responsibility for the efficient operation of the refrigeration/air conditioning system to have a professional inspection of the cooling tower done by a consultant who can analyze the energy savings potential of his installation. In these days of high energy costs, the savings accrued from a well engineered and retrofitted cooling tower bringing it into the 1980's can make a significant impact on a company's profit and loss statement.

REFERENCES

1. ASHRAE Handbook "Fundamentals" Chapter 1, Page 1.6.
2. Michael N. Hart, P.E., Energy Engineering Associates, Austin, Texas.
3. Allied Chemical Corp., "The Pressure Enthalpy Diagram, Its Construction, Use, and Value".
4. Charles Weiss, Technical Engineering Instructor, "Cooling Tower Inspection and Economies", National Engineer, (April, 1985).
5. ASHRAE Equipment Handbook, Chapter 21, Page 11, (1975)
6. Robert Burger, "Cooling Tower Technology", Chapter 8, (1979)
7. Dallas Texas College, test report upon request.
8. Jim Willa, "Cooling Tower Operations", Cooling Tower Institute Proceedings, (1980).

Figure 7 - The techniques, thermal, mechanical, engineering, and structural retrofit for all sizes of cooling towers are practically the same. The difference being the size and cost which is indicated on Figure 6.

Chapter 6

SURVEY OF THE INDIRECT EVAPORATIVE COOLING FIELD

J. R. Watt

ABSTRACT

Rising power costs since 1973 are creating interest in evaporative air cooling types useful outside the arid Southwest. Many companies now offer indirect evaporative cooling equipment acceptable in all but a handful of mostly coastal U.S. counties.

These cool air in heat exchangers separate from the evaporating water, so deliver dry supply air which can be further cooled by direct evaporative or refrigerative second stages. Power savings of 50% over all-refrigerative systems are common, plus first, maintenance, and winter heat-recovery economies.

THE OTHER EVAPORATIVE COOLING

Direct evaporative coolers like drip and other wet-pad coolers and some air washers, cool air adiabatically in wet porous pads which evaporate water into it. This removes no heat; instead, at constant wet-bulb temperature it converts the air's sensible heat into latent heat in the absorbed water vapor. This lowers the air's dry-bulb temperature perhaps 70-90% of original wet-bulb depression (dry-bulb minus wet-bulb temperature), so creates a damp cooling medium usually called washed air.

Its humidity prevents its recirculation indoors like refrigerated supply air, so it must be exhausted outside after one pass through the cooled premises. Much of its cooling effect depends upon contacting human skin at velocities above 100 fpm (30.5 m/min), so large volumes and high room-entering velocities are needed. Power savings over refrigeration around 70% result, but with those handicaps, direct evaporative cooling has little use outside arid regions except where massive ventilation is needed.

INDIRECT EVAPORATIVE COOLING

Indirect evaporative cooling is more like refrigerative air conditioning; it occurs at constant dew-point temperature, and removes sensible heat without adding humidity. The air being dry-cooled, termed primary air, is processed in finned-coil, tubular, plate-type, rotary, or other heat exchangers which separate it from the secondary air into which the water evaporates and which carries away the unwanted humidity.

The primary air is usually cooled 40-70% of outside wet-bulb depression, so is cool enough for good comfort-cooling supply air only in the driest weather. Further, the air flow resistance of most heat exchangers precludes using the volumes and circulating velocities of direct cooling. Thus, almost all indirect coolers have second stages of either direct cooling or small-scale refrigeration to lower the cooled-air temperatures further for better comfort effect.

In the former case, washed air is created, subject to discharge outdoors after brief use; this wastes perhaps 50% of its cooling potential, but the overall process still saves at least half the power of refrigerated cooling. In the second case, the cool air remains dry and becomes supply air comparable to that from all refrigerated systems. It can be recirculated as return air as in refrigerated cooling, and also used regeneratively (see below).

Because both types of second stage effectively extend the wet-bulb depression, staged indirect cooling operates far outside its original Southwest, the former type in all but a few, mostly sea coast areas of Alabama, Arkansas, Florida, Georgia, Louisiana, Mississippi, South Carolina, and Texas.

Systems with refrigerated second stages, of course, operate anywhere. Because the latter is relieved of most sensible cooling, power savings over total refrigeration remain significant, ranging around 25%.

Regenerative gains are commonly sought, especially in buildings with large ventilating needs. To remove indoor pollutants, these must exhaust large volumes of used cooling air. If this is still essentially dry, adding it to entering secondary air lowers the latter's wet-bulb temperature, creating cooler primary air and improving the economy.

Naturally, washed air from indirect-direct two-stage systems cannot be so used. However, such air routed into the air-cooled condensers of refrigerated air conditioning or refrigerated second stages of other systems accomplishes a like result.

Most indirect systems also save winter energy for such buildings by pre-heating the new make-up air they draw in for ventilation. Here, warm used, indoor air being discharged becomes dry secondary air and conducts heat to fresh cold air entering the primary-air system. In cooler climates this heat-recovery saving may exceed that in summer.

AVAILABLE INDIRECT COOLING SYSTEMS

At least six indirect systems employ types of cooling towers and finned coils or equivalent dry surfaces. Three use plastic-tube heat exchangers, two with absorbent wick-like coatings. At least four firms make plate-type indirect coolers, two with thin plastic plates, two with absorbent coatings. Two other manufacturers use heat-transfer wheels, and one uses a desiccant-enhanced indirect system employing solar heat. All will be discussed in order.

Tower-and-Coil (Dry Surface) Systems.

These originated in Arizona before 1930, using natural-draft spray or deck towers and indoor auto radiators and fans. Oversized towers cooled water near 3 deg F (1.7 deg C) of wet-bulb,and the thick multi-pass finned water coils which replaced the radiators often cooled primary air equally near tower water temperature. In the hottest weather, supply air was often 30 deg F (16.7 deg C) below outdoor dry-bulb.

Unhappily, with scant tower bleed-off and water treatment, circulating hard water augmented by trapped dust lined the coil tubes with performance-destroying scale. Yearly acid removal deteriorated the coils and WW II copper shortages prevented replacement. The development around 1935 of plate-type indirect coolers and drip coolers delivering larger volumes of cooler air at a fraction of the cost also helped scrap tower-and-coil systems.

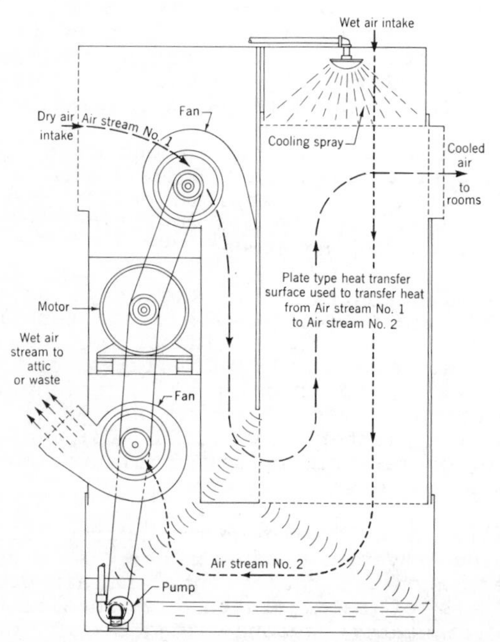

FIG. 1. AN EARLY PLATE-TYPE INDIRECT COOLER. Spreading from California, these cooled scores of Southwestern chain stores in the 1930s and 1940s.

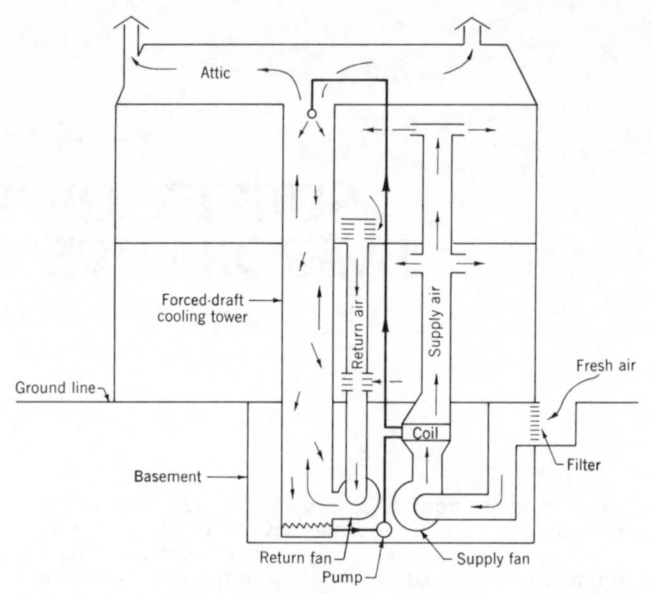

FIG. 2. THE UNIVERSITY OF ARIZONA ADMINISTRATION BUILDING COOLING SYSTEM, 1936-1952. This demonstrated the best tower-and-coil cooling, regenerative use of return air, and attic removal of solar heat load.

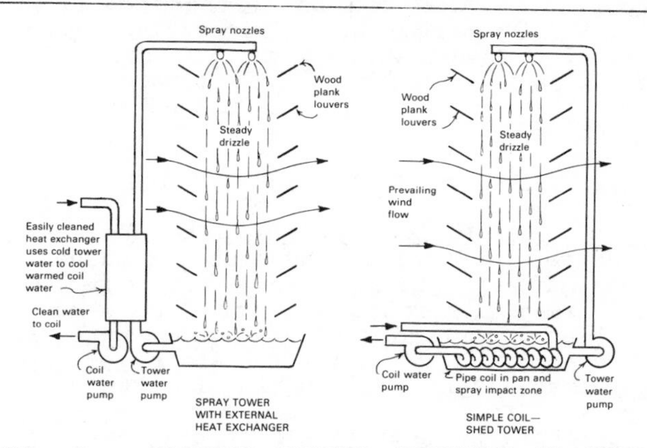

FIG. 3. COOLING TOWERS ARRANGED TO KEEP SCALE OUT OF COOLING COILS. Unfortunately, they require extra pumps and cut performance slightly.

With better bleed-off and water treatment they are reviving today, mostly in soft water areas:

First: Norsaire Systems, of Englewood, CO, which also makes large plate-type and rotary heat-exchanger wheel systems, uses powered, counterflow vertical towers and multi-pass coils followed by direct evaporative second stages for loads over 90 tons (1,139 mJ/hr).

Unknown engineers and contractors are following suit, best using "coil-shed" towers or heat-exchangers to separate tower and circulating water.

Second: "open loop" use of cooling towers in large chilled water systems is growing each winter. Here, buildings with large indoor human, lighting, and process heat gains all year stop their compressors when outdoor dry-bulbs approach 40 F (4.4 C), and circulate carefully filtered, bled-off and treated tower water through their chilled water coils and air handlers.

Cooled by atmospheric contact as well as by evaporation, such water deposits little scale, but some systems use heat exchangers or coil-shed towers for further protection. Reduced water flows in colder weather prevent tower icing. Power savings vary with weather and usage. Around New York, installation payback is reportedly two years.

Third: in some areas with large diurnal temperature swings between day and night, cooling towers are operated nightly at off-peak power rates to store cold water for next day use. In Colorado a college and a public school keep respectively 60,000 and 100,000 gal (227 and 379 kl) tanks below 58 F (14.4 C) for water-coil use.

As noted, such cool-air use of towers minimizes scaling tendencies. However, the large insulated tanks push first costs above those for refrigeration, but power savings suggest four-year paybacks.

Fourth: Aztech International, Ltd., Albuquerque, NM, manufactures very compact four-stage indirect-direct coolers containing two identifiable tower-and-coil sets plus multiple regeneration.

Stage 1: filtered outside primary air is cooled dry in metal tubes chilled by washed air from thick, high cooling-efficiency rigid-media saturation pads that serve as both direct coolers and towers. Stage 2: the primary air is next cooled in finned coils carrying water cooled in these pads. Stage 3: the same air is dry-cooled again in similar finned coils cooled by water from the fourth stage pads. Because three indirect stages have lowered primary-air wet-bulb temperatures, this water is regeneratively cold. Stage 4: the thrice dry-cooled air is adiabatically converted in a final high-efficiency wet pad to cold washed air, well below original wet-bulb temperature.

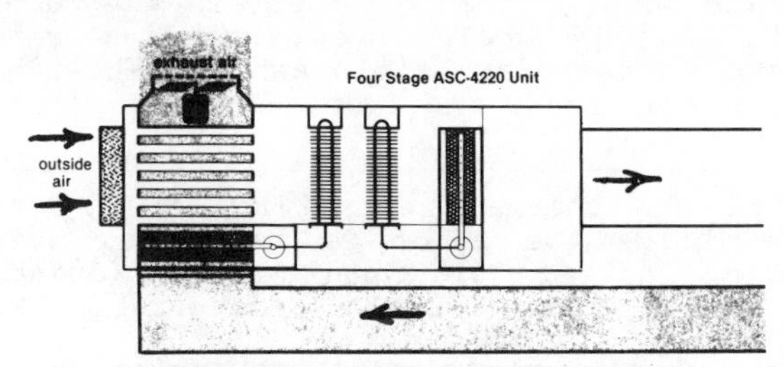

FIG. 4. AN AZTEC FOUR-STAGE INDIRECT-DIRECT COOLER. Shown in winter heat-recovery use, it has two tower-and-coil pairs. Here, with pads and coils dry, used ventilating air in bottom duct warms fresh make-up air, left, in the Stage 1 tubular heat-exchanger, left center, and discharges, top.

Made in several sizes to 8,000 cfm (3.8 m^3/s), these units should operate in almost any climate. However, water quality and ample bleed-off seem essential.

Fifth: an historic system seems worth improving. In the 1940s, the late Professor B.N. Gafford of Electrical Engineering, University of Texas at Austin, built a compact regenerative rooftop single-stage cooler. It consisted of two large vertical truck radiators connected so a 1/6 hp pump circulated sealed-in water between them.

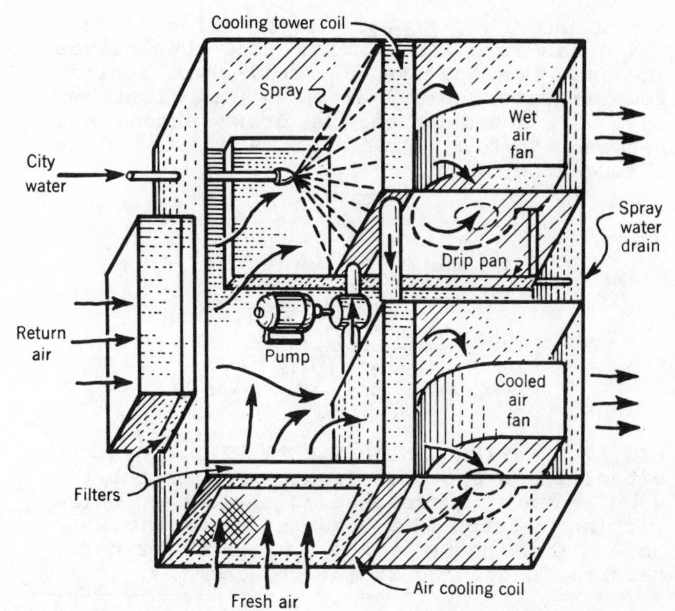

FIG. 5. THE 1940s GAFFORD REGENERATIVE SINGLE-STAGE COOLER. The cooling-tower coil, rear, sprayed with city water, and the closed-circuit water circulation prevented internal scaling. The used water flooded a flat roof against solar heat.

One, serving as coil-shed tower, had city water mist sprayed on its fins and discarded while mixed outdoor and return house-air was drawn through it. Water cooled inside it circulated through the other radiator and cooled primary air.

When the author tested it in 1953, it still cooled 3,711 cfm (1.75 m^3/s) of air within 10 deg F (5.6 deg C) of outside wet-bulb for about 5/6 hp. Maintenance costs and deterioration seemed nil. Use seems recommended where the waste water can be profitably used.

Fig. 6.

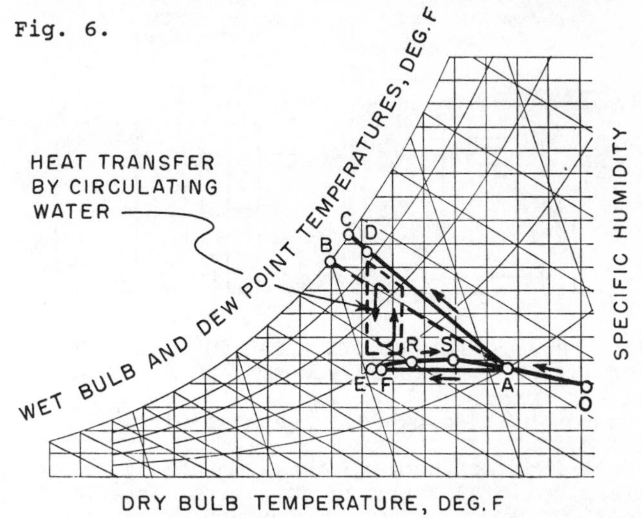

Psychrometric Process in Regenerative Dry-Surface and Gafford Indirect Evaporative Coolers. Outside air O and return air S mix, forming air A of wet-bulb temperature B. Nonadiabatic process AD cools water to DE, which cools dry air from A to E. It enters room at F and absorbs heat to S past room average R. Heat loss AE equals heat gain AD. (Not to scale.)

Finally: Howden Heat Pipe Division, Bloomfield, CT, offers a very new but similar system composed of one or more vertical grids of closely spaced horizontal, sealed and finned heat pipes. A partition divides the grids into two panels. The tube halves in one panel serve as coil-shed cooling towers; water sprays above and in front wet them as secondary air is drawn around and between them. Fresh primary air blows through the other panel.

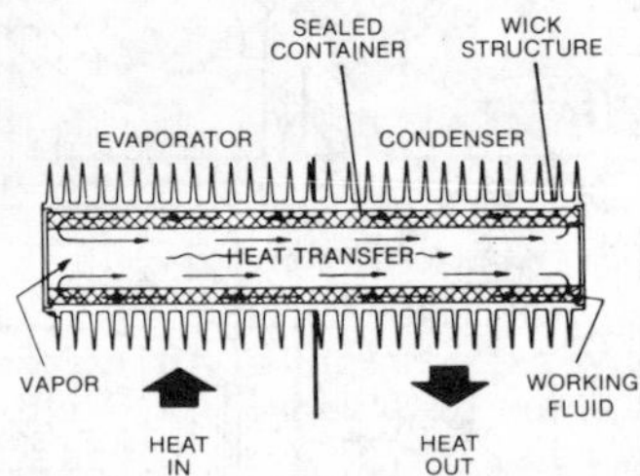

FIG. 7. INSIDE A HOWDEN HEAT PIPE. Heat at either end evaporates liquid refrigerant and sends vapors to condense at the other, while wicking returns the condensate to the warm end. Continuous end-to-end heat transfer results in even 20 ft (6.1 m) lengths.

The tubes are lined with wick-like absorbent and contain measured amounts of appropriate refrigerant gas. The wet cooling-tower ends condense it to liquid which moves by capillary action to the air-cooling ends, where it absorbs primary-air sensible heat through the metal walls. Vaporized, it returns as gas to the cool end, where it condenses again and delivers the absorbed heat to evaporating water.

Thus, the heat pipes continuously transfer heat from primary to secondary air. They form seemingly foolproof heat exchangers only inches thick and with purely external and removable scale, if any. They serve as well for winter heat-recovery.

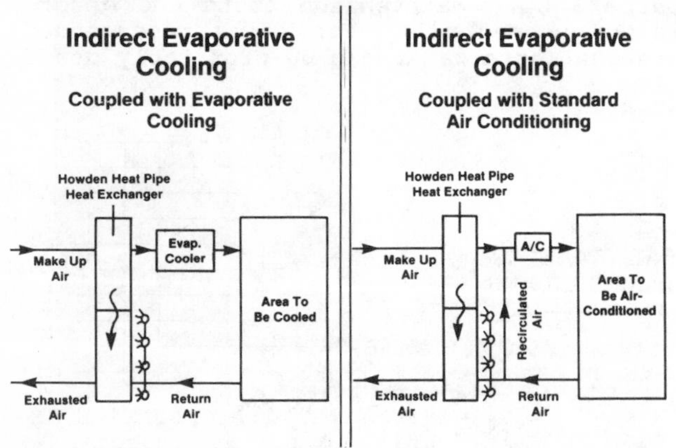

FIG. 8. STAGED HOWDEN HEAT-PIPE COOLING. Left: with a direct second stage. Right, with a refrigerative one. The heat pipes conduct heat downward in each drawing.

These indirect coolers are available in many sizes up to 28 tubes 20 ft (6.1 m) long by 8 rows thick. Including fan and pump power they reportedly achieve Energy Efficiency Ratios (Btus removed per watt) as follows:

Single stage indirect cooler	119 EER
Two-stage indirect-direct cooler adjusted for 50% washed air losses	46 EER
Indirect cooler with refrigerative second stage	20.2 EER

For comparison, most air cooled refrigerated air conditioning averages about 6-10 EER; cooling-tower versions possibly reaching 15.

Tubular Heat-Exchanger Systems

The Vari-Cool Division of H & C Industries, Santa Rosa, CA, makes heat exchanger cores about 5 ft long, 3 ft wide,and about 2 ft high (1.5 x 0.9 x 0.6 m), containing 165 longitudinal 1 in. (2.4 cm) diameter polystyrene tubes covered with wick-like synthetic fabric sleeves to distribute impinging water and create 100% wetting.

FIG. 9. A VARI-COOL TUBULAR HEAT-EXCHANGER. It has five cores stacked over a water-sump base and pump. Primary air enters the tubes, right, and is cooled by descending water exposed to secondary air drawn left-to-right between and around the fabric-covered plastic tubes.

Because the thermal resistivity of dry air films inside the tubes is so great, using plastic instead of metal tubes creates negligible loss, while preventing all corrosion.

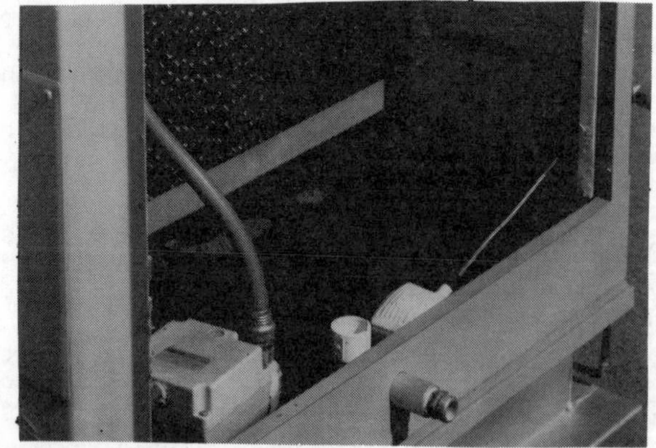

FIG. 10. THE OUTLET OF A VARI-COOL DIRECT SECOND STAGE. Shown are the pump, left; float valve, right; and thick rigid-media cellulose saturating pad, rear.

Filtered primary air enters the tubes at one end. Secondary air is drawn horizontally around and between the wet-sleeved tubes, in crossflow to the primary air, by propeller fans, and discharged. Small pumps are the only moving parts. Induction primary-air fans attach to the cabinet ends.

The cores are designed to cool 1,000-2,000 cfm (22.7 to 45.4 m^3/min) each of fresh primary air. Up to eight cores can be stacked in cabinets upon standard bases and with standard water distribution pans and covers on top. Two such cabinets side-by-side thus can cool 32,000 cfm (906.1 m^3/min).

These units are usually staged with direct cooling units after the fans. As indirect-direct systems these deliver washed air at about 25% of refrigerating power costs. To gain colder and drier air, three-stage indirect-direct systems with one indirect cooler cooling the secondary air for a separate indirect-direct unit correspondingly costs 30%, and three-stage ones with one indirect cooler pre-cooling half of both primary and secondary air for an indirect-direct unit costs 24.8%.

Because washed air sacrifices perhaps half its cooling potential in discharge, these percentages should be doubled for realistic comparisons. However, it is clear that 50% power savings are easily attained, not counting maintenance and possible winter heat savings.

The Diperi Manufacturing Corp. of Northridge, CA, also uses fabric-covered polystyrene tubes in horizontal-flow indirect coolers. These have over 200 3/4 in. (1.9 cm) diameter, 3 ft (0.91 m) long tubes in almost cubical cabinets which mount and connect very flexibly in various installations. Each cools up to 4,000 cfm (1.9 m^3/s) of primary air while half as much secondary air is drawn crossflow between the tubes by a propeller fan.

Performance varies with weather, but reportedly averages 2 to 3 tons (24-36,000 Btuh or 25.3-38 kJ/h) of sensible cooling from less than 1 hp fan and pumping costs. Primary air is cooled about 40% of wet-bulb depression; two units in series raise this to 60%.

FIG. 11. A BASIC DIPERI INDIRECT COOLING INSTALLATION. Primary air enters the tubes as secondary air enters between the wet fabric-covered plastic tubes, center, propelled by the primary-air fan, far left, and secondary-air fan, far right. Such units reportedly cool up to 4,000 cfm (1.9 m^3/s) of primary air, 3 tons of sensible cooling for less than 1 hp.

FIG. 12. FOUR DIPERI INDIRECT COOLERS IN SERIES-PARALLEL. Two pairs in series are mounted side-by-side with a joint secondary-air exhaust plenum between them, exhausted by four rain-hooded propeller fans blowing upward. Primary air enters far right; is cooled, right and center; enters a rotary wheel direct cooler, left center, and is delivered by a fan, left.

Energy Labs, Ltd., of Santa Fe Springs, CA, makes compact single-stage, vertical-tube indirect coolers with enclosed primary air induction blowers. They have banks of closely spaced plastic tubes, about 1 in. (2.5 cm) square, in which sprayed water films slide downward, counterflow to rising secondary air drawn by propeller fans above. Simultaneously, filtered primary air enters between the tubes, which are arranged for maximum turbulent air contact, and the built-in fans deliver it.

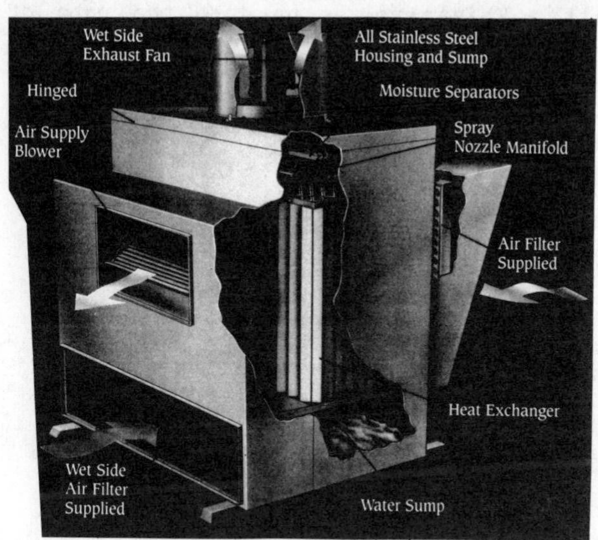

FIG. 13. A COMPACT ENERGY LABS VERTICAL-TUBE INDIRECT COOLER. With built-in induction-type primary-air fan, it cools primary air 60% of wet-bulb depression; with two tube-banks in series, 92%. With two in parallel, output is 10,000 cfm (4.8 m^3/s).

The basic model cools either 4,000 or 5,000 cfm (1.9 or 2.4 m^3/s) of primary air, depending on fan sizes; with two tube banks in parallel, outputs are doubled. Primary air cooled 92% by two banks in series often gives excellent comfort single-stage.

These coolers often pre-cool make-up air for large refrigerated cooling systems. Computer simulations of 500-ton (6,330 kJ/hr) combined equipment in 12 widely scattered U.S. cities, including Boston, New York and Chicago, showed average savings that paid for the indirect equipment in only 2.1 years. Naturally, these coolers can be staged with direct coolers as well.

Rotary Heat-Exchanger Coolers.

These were invented in about 1950 by Neal Pennington of Tucson, who used a thick porous wheel of wire screening and aluminum shavings. Cold washed air was blown directly through one half as it revolved slowly. The cooled metal fill revolved into the path of warm primary air which it cooled before revolving back into the washed air.

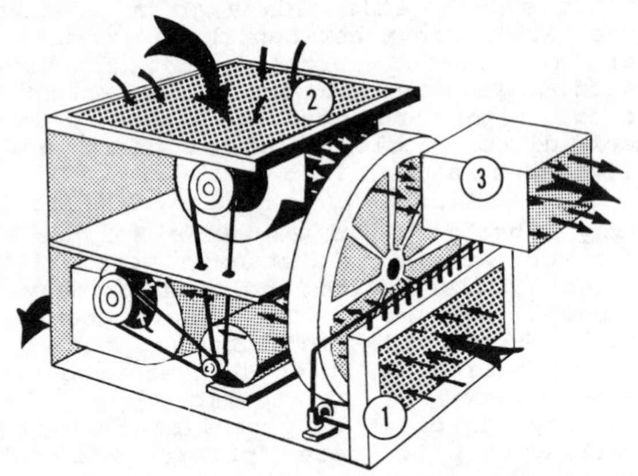

FIG. 14. AN INDIRECT COOLER WITH ROTARY HEAT TRANSFER WHEEL. Washed air from wet pad 1, cools half the turning wheel's porous metal fill. This revolves up into the path of primary air from filter 2 and cools it. Duct 3 delivers it.

FIG. 15.

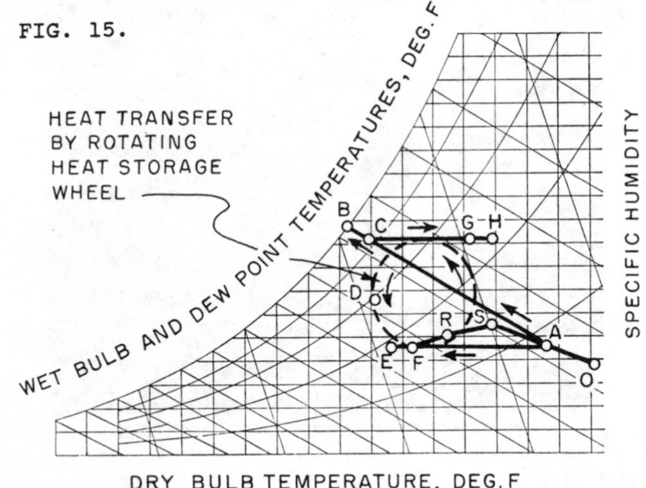

Psychrometric Process in Pennington Indirect Evaporative Coolers. Outside air O and return air S mix, forming air A which is cooled adiabatically to C. It cools wheel filler to D and is warmed to G and exhausted to H. Filler cools dry air from A to E, which enters room at F and absorbs heat to S past room average R. Heat loss AE equals heat gain CG. (Not to scale.)

Today, Norsaire Systems, also maker of cooling-tower and plate-type systems, makes similar large-size systems. Wheels are now spirally wound of alternate flat and corrugated metal ribbons sometimes 10 in. (2.5 cm) wide. Wheels can be 14 ft(4.3 m) diameter if needed.

Highly efficient direct cooler pads blow washed air through half the face while primary air is drawn counterflow through the other; the coldest metal fill thus meets the coolest primary air, maximizing performance.

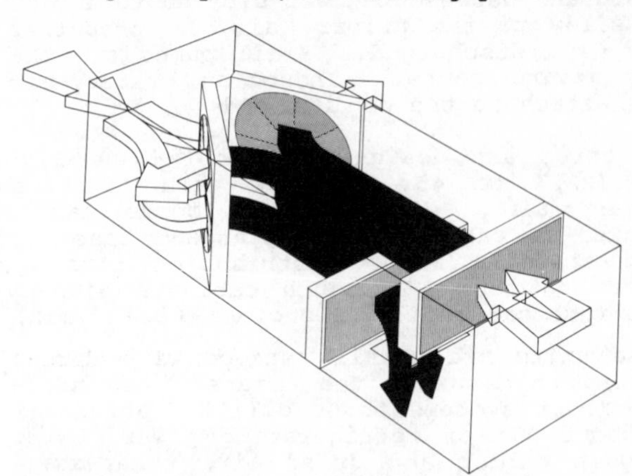

FIG. 16. A LARGE NORSAIRE INDIRECT-DIRECT COOLER WITH ROTARY HEAT EXCHANGER WHEELS. Secondary air enters right front, is cooled in a wet pad, then exhausts through and cools two rotary heat exchangers, left center. Primary air enters left rear, is cooled dry by these wheels, then passes through a direct cooling pad, and delivers downward for cooling service, near right.

The cooling efficiencies range between 60 and 90%, averaging about 76%, very good for indirect coolers. However, the wheels have considerable air flow resistance, requiring either extra fan power or the use of very large wheels or several in parallel. Further, considerable air leakage occurs at rim edges and at the dividers between the two air streams.

This manufacturer makes both single stage and indirect-direct models, mostly for 25 to 50 ton (317 to 633 kJ/m) loads. Because of ready wheel availability, some engineers and contractors may build systems. Rotary heat exchangers also serve desiccant type coolers noted later.

Plate-Type Indirect Coolers

These typically cool primary air in thin flat tubes called "plates," often of sheet aluminum, exposed on either side to moving secondary air, water films and spray. They were developed by Californians in 1930s.

The first were failures: huge air-to-air plate-type heat exchangers installed to cool a Walt Disney studio and a medical building received dry washed secondary air from commercial air washers. Stagnant air films insulated both sides of each plate wall and minimized heat transfer, so the equipment was scrapped.

The lesson was clear: primary air must be turbulent enough to prevent stagnant films, and secondary air must contact water films or impinging spray on heat transfer surfaces.

Later designs used tall vertical hollow plates, in which primary air moved counterflow to descending secondary air and water outside them. Many units opened above so that scale could be brushed from the plates without interrupting operation.

One which cooled the Tucson J.C. Penney store from 1935 to 1955 had 20,000 sq ft (1,858 m^2) of plate surface and delivered about 60 tons (760 kJ/hr) of sensible cooling from about 19-1/2 hp. This is equivalent to a 49.5 EER today. When the author examined it in 1952, it operated well, also discharging its secondary air to cool the Penney attic. (See Fig. 1.)

In 1952-54 for the Navy, the author built and tested three similar plate-type units, including a two-stage one, at the University of Texas at Austin. With the late Professor R.A. Bacon, he derived early design equations published in the author's 1963 book, Evaporative Air Conditioning.

A fourth cooler was built by a local engineer for the author's completion. Wetting between its deep, long, closely-spaced plates proved difficult, but its 402 sq ft (37.3 m^2) of smooth metal cooled primary air 72% of wet-bulb depression, with an equivalent 17.9 EER single-stage economy. It remains an inexpensive design for cooling make-up air. Modern dimpled and absorbent-coated plates might treble its performance.

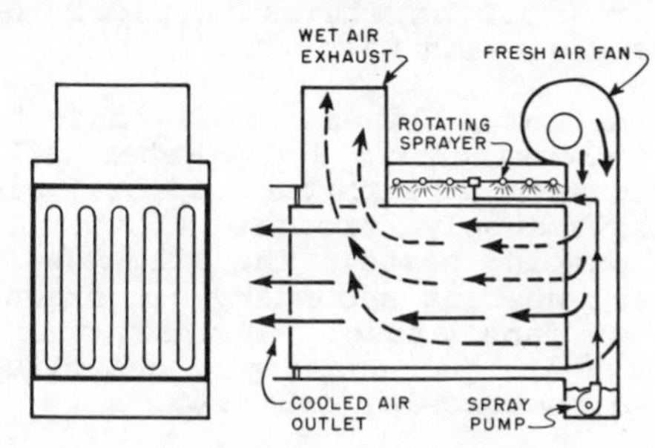

FIG. 17. AN ECONOMICAL DESIGN FOR COOLING MAKE-UP AIR. Tested by the author in 1953, it achieved an equivalent of 17.9 EER. Dimpled and absorbent-covered plates might treble performance today.

Today, Des Champs Laboratories, Inc., East Hanover, NJ, makes a wide range of indirect coolers with hollow plates of dimpled aluminum, outputs ranging from 1,700 to 17,000 cfm (48-481 m^3/min). Cooling effectiveness approximates 80% of wet-bulb depression, 81% in larger units.

A typical model with a direct second stage achieved an EER of 76. When reduced 50% for anticipated washed-air losses on discharge, this becomes 38 EER, almost 5 times that of most refrigerated cooling. Power savings of 79% and payback within three years were anticipated, not counting reduced compressor wear and possible winter fuel savings.

The larger units are available as complete rooftop modular packages containing, as needed, special filters, heating coils, cooling coils, etc. Various stagings are possible.

Norsaire, noted earlier, also makes large plate-type coolers. In the 5 to 20 ton (63 to 253 kJ/hr) range, these have thin, deep vertical plates with corrugated aluminum surfaces coated with a wick-like absorbent that ensures 100% wetting. Primary air moves horizontally within, cross-flow to rising secondary air and falling drizzles of water.

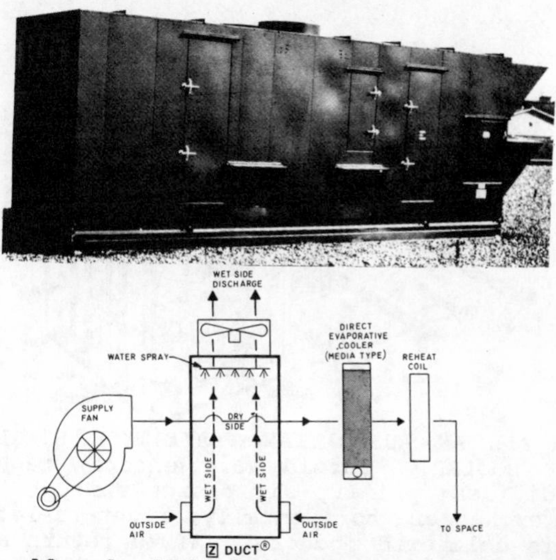

FIG. 18. A BIG DES CHAMPS LABORATORIES INDIRECT-DIRECT COOLER WITH FLOW DIAGRAM. Primary air enters, left, is dry-cooled, center, direct-cooled in a thick wet pad, passes through a winter-use reheat coil, and is delivered, right. Secondary air enters below and discharges above.

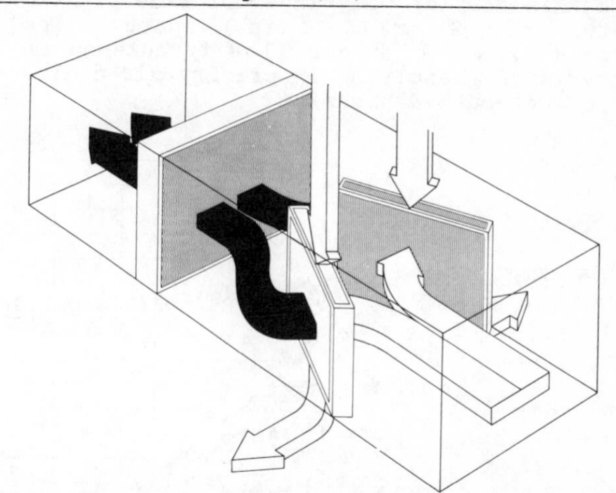

FIG. 20. A LARGE NORSAIRE PLATE-TYPE INDIRECT-DIRECT COOLER. Primary air enters, right; is cooled in two plate-type heat exchangers, center right; is cooled further in a direct saturating pad, center left, and is delivered, far left. Secondary air enters above and discharges below.

Reported power savings are 1.4 kw/ton for buildings using 15% make-up air, and 2.2 kw/ton for those using 100% new air.

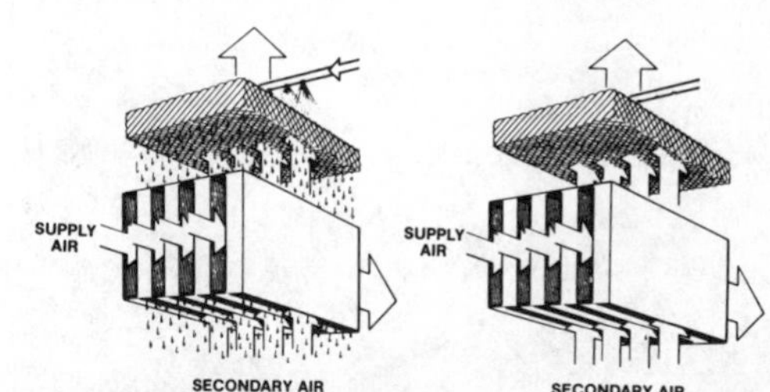

FIG. 19. SCHEMATIC VIEWS OF NORSAIRE PLATE USE IN SUMMER AND WINTER. This illustrates how easily most indirect coolers transfer waste heat from discharged ventilating air to incoming fresh make-up air.

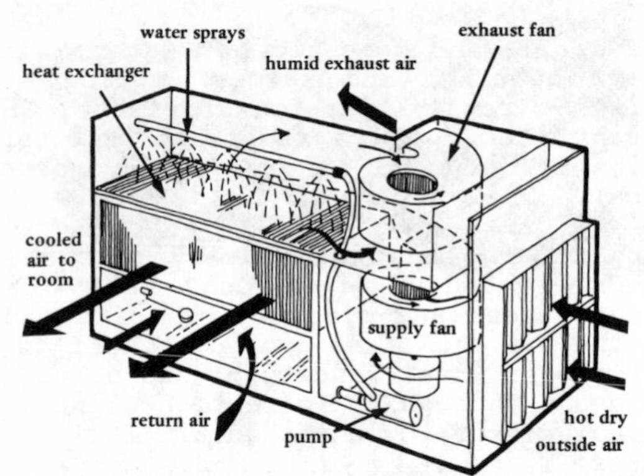

FIG. 21. AN AUSTRALIAN PLATE-TYPE SINGLE-STAGE COOLER. Outside air enters, right, and divides; primary air passes through the heat exchanger horizontally, right-to-left, and is delivered indoors. Mixed return and outdoor secondary air are drawn up the heat exchanger vertical passages, counterflow to water films, and discharge, top center.

Commonwealth Scientific and Industrial Research Organization, Melbourne, Australia, developed highly engineered indirect coolers with thin dimpled polyvinyl chloride plastic plates only 2 mm (0.08 in.) apart. The dimples create high air flow turbulence on either side, resulting in primary air cooled 85% of wet-bulb depression.

FIG. 22.

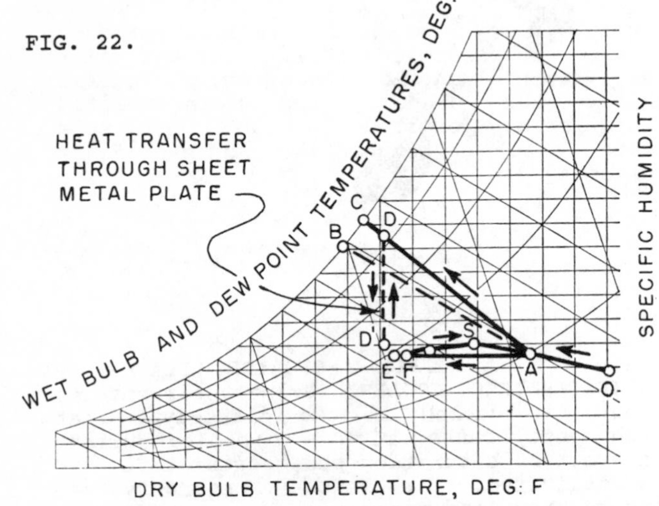

Psychrometric Process in Plate-Type Indirect Evaporative Coolers. Outside air O and return air S mix, forming air A of wet-bulb temperature B. Air A cools sprayed plates nonadiabatically to DD[1], cooling dry air inside from A to E. This enters rooms at F and absorbs heat to S past unmarked room average. Heat loss AE equals heat gain AD. (Not to scale.)

FIG. 23. AUSTRALIAN SINGLE-STAGE PLATE-TYPE INDIRECT COOLERS MOUNTED OUTSIDE TELEPHONE SWITCH-GEAR BUILDING. Supply-air ducts enter through windows; return air, through grilles below them.

These coolers are manufactured single-stage to cool hot Australian telephone switch-gear rooms, where washed air might be damaging and refrigeration uneconomic. All return air from the cooled spaces becomes secondary air, so regenerative gains are great. In other usage, staging is possible.

P.H.E. Pty., Ltd., Marleston, South Australia, makes two sizes: 0.5 and 1.5 m^3/s (1,059 and 3,180 cfm). Others may be developed. A unit in Phoenix, AZ, achieves 4.8 tons and an EER of 31.8. Use for winter heat recovery seems rare.

Arvin Air Division of Arvin Industries, Phoenix, AZ, a large drip cooler manufacturer, also makes moderate-size direct coolers whose single thick rigid-media saturation pads offer much better performance and life. Arvin has developed a compact indirect cooler to pair with these direct units in an indirect-direct package.

The heat exchangers are of thin polystyrene sheets embossed and cemented together to form horizontal primary air passages and about 1/8 in. (3.2 mm) thick vertical tubes for secondary air and water.

These tubes are lined with absorbent synthetic "flocking" to hold water films. Water is fed each tube through special wicks from shallow supply troughs above, thus minimizing pumping costs. The films descend in the tubes, meeting secondary air drawn up by propeller fans above. Primary air is drawn through its passages by a centrifugal fan in the direct cooler cabinet.

The two-stage packages are available in four sizes from 2,270 to 3,320 cfm (1.1-1.6 m^3/s), the first stages cooling primary air about 43%. When colder and drier washed air is desired, as in semi-humid areas, two indirect units can feed one direct unit, to achieve 3,900 cfm (1.8 m^3/s) output and dry-cooling of 53%. Either way, washed air is delivered at or below original wet-bulb.

FIG. 24. AN ARVIN TWO-STAGE INDIRECT-DIRECT PLATE-TYPE COOLER. Air enters the front louvers and divides; primary air successively advances through the heat exchanger, the direct stage saturation pad and its centrifugal fan, rear, and delivers horizontally or downward. The secondary air is drawn up through the heat exchanger, and is discharged by the propeller fan above.

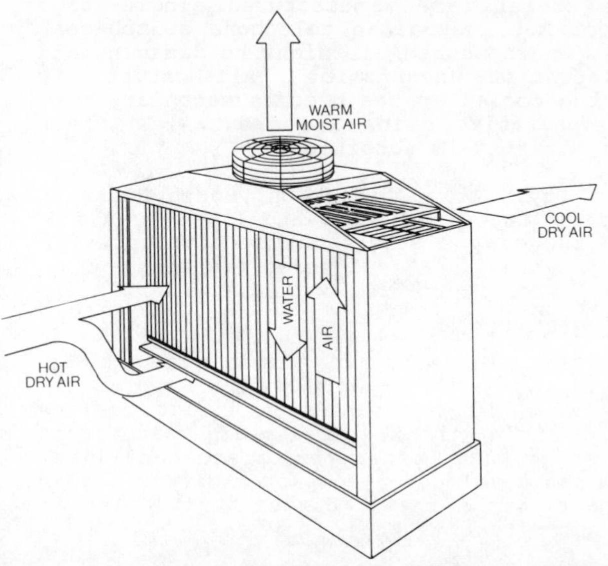

FIG. 25. INSIDE AN ARVIN PLATE-TYPE INDIRECT STAGE. Primary air enters the heat-exchanger, left-to-right, as secondary air enters below and is exhausted by the fan above. Water films in the secondary air tubes are supplied by wicks from small supply troughs. The films descend counterflow to rising secondary air.

A computer projection of these standard two-stage units averaged over nine southwestern cities' summer weather showed outputs equivalent to 5.4 tons, and EER's of 22, adjusted for washed air loss. Anticipated yearly power savings over 8.9 EER refrigeration averaged $372.; over 6.9 EER refrigeration, $496. These savings do not include others in compressor wear and overall maintenance. Use for warming winter make-up air is unreported.

6500 MasterCool 2-Stage Performance And Savings

CITY	1% ASHRAE DESIGN CONDITIONS		PERFORMANCE AT DESIGN CONDITIONS*				ANNUAL COOLING COST SAVINGS*** RELATIVE TO A/C WITH EFFICIENCY OF:	
			DISCHARGE TEMP					
	DRY BULB	WET BULB	MASTER 2-STAGE	CONVENTIONAL COOLER	EQUIVALENT A/C TONS**	MASTERCOOL 2-STAGE S EER	8.9 EER	6.9 EER
PHOENIX	109	71	69.8	78.7	3.1	33	$331	$520
TUCSON	104	66	64.2	73.8	5.2	40	533	687
DENVER	93	59	56.8	66.1	7.9	54	240	327
LAS VEGAS	108	66	64.0	74.6	5.2	47	603	758
SALT LAKE CITY	97	62	60.1	69.3	6.7	51	329	437
ALBUQUERQUE	96	61	58.9	68.2	7.1	50	338	447
EL PASO	100	64	62.2	71.4	5.9	44	507	661
LUBBOCK	98	69	68.1	75.0	3.8	33	233	315
FRESNO SAN BERNARDINO	102	70	69.0	76.6	3.4	39	237	311

*0.3 INCHES EXTERNAL STATIC
**SENSIBLE HEAT RATIO 0.83
***KWH COST OF $.07, THERMOSTAT SET AT 80°

FIG. 26. ARVIN INDIRECT-DIRECT COOLER PERFORMANCE IN SOUTHWEST CITIES. Output averages 5.4 tons of sensible cooling, with washed air 9 deg F (5 deg C) below direct coolers. Average EER, adjusted for washed-air losses, approximates 22. Yearly savings over good and ordinary refrigeration average 60% and 69% respectively.

The William Lamb Co., of North Hollywood, CA, sells these Arvin indirect-direct packages with photo-voltaic solar panels and accessories to operate them with solar electricity.

A Desiccant-Type Indirect Cooler

The American Solar King Co., of Waco, TX markets a clever solar heating system, which provides all-year domestic hot water; winter warm-air heating; and summer cooling which uses both a rotary heat-transfer wheel and a desiccant wheel, which resembles the former but is filled with a porous hygroscopic chemical.

Cooling occurs thusly: primary outside air is drawn in and blown through half of the desiccant wheel and gives up humidity. This heats the air, so it is cooled in half of the heat transfer wheel. Now cool and ultra-dry, it passes through a direct cooling pad, emerging as extra-cold washed air for cooling purposes.

After cooling its assigned rooms, it returns as cool secondary air. It passes through the heat exchange wheel, cooling it and warming itself. Then it passes through a solar heated coil connected to solar rooftop collectors. This heats it enough to regenerate (dry) the desiccant. It passes also through the latter, absorbing its active moisture, and discharges outdoors.

This ingenious system reportedly provides enough 58 F (14.4 C) washed air to cool 1,800 sq ft (167 m^2) of building, 75,000 Btuh (1,319 kJ/min) of winter heat, plus 90% of hot water needs.

Without energy storage for sunless periods, backup heaters are suggested. However, all-year savings should be great. Federal income tax credits for solar-related installations expired in 1985, but some state ones continue, discounting first costs.

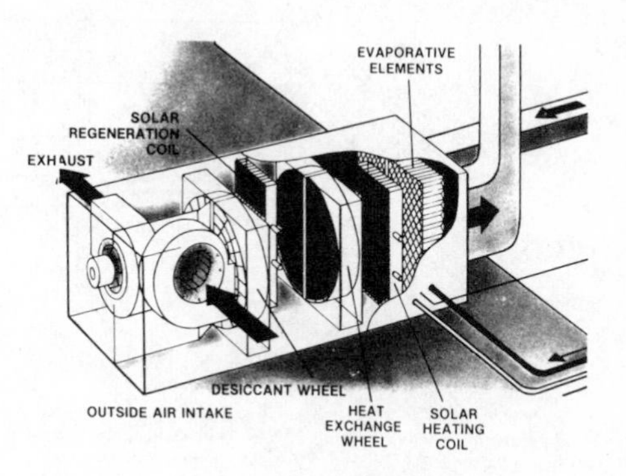

FIG. 27. AMERICAN SOLAR KING UNIT SUPPLIES HEATING, HOT WATER, AND INDIRECT-DIRECT COOLING. In cooling, a solar-regenerated desiccant wheel, like a rotary heat-exchanger wheel but carrying moisture-absorbing chemicals, dries the air; a rotary heat exchanger dry-cools it, and a saturation pad makes it extra-cold washed air. Heat from roof-top solar collectors keeps the desiccant wheel absorbent.

COMFORT AND CLIMATIC ASPECTS

Although human comfort involves more factors, the ASHRAE official Comfort Zone is a standard. However, even when extended for 350 fpm (1.8 m/s) room air velocities, it is less appropriate for evaporative cooling than an older one the author revives in EVAPORATIVE AIR CONDITIONING HANDBOOK, 1986.

Nevertheless, most indirect coolers of 60% cooling efficiency with direct second stages can attain ASHRAE comfort when outside wet bulbs are 72 F (22.2 C) or below, provided that related dry bulbs are under 115 F (46.1 C).

The revived evaporative cooling Comfort Zone reaches higher on psychometric charts. Most indirect-direct coolers can correspondingly achieve it when wet bulbs are 78 F (25.6 C), a great geographic advantage. Thus, such coolers can achieve comfort almost everywhere; if not, excellent relief cooling.

Of course, refrigerative second stages open all climates to indirect coolers.

Direct coolers would require wet bulbs below 67 F (19.4 C) and 72 F (22.2 C), respectively, to achieve these zones, limiting regional expansion.

CONCLUSIONS

A wide variety of successful indirect coolers is available, most with second stages. Almost all will operate successfully on, say, 95% of U.S. soil. Almost all save 50% or more of refrigerative system power, plus possible winter fuel.

Chapter 7

RADIANT HEAT FOR AFFORDABLE COMFORT

R. D. Watson

INTRODUCTION

Radiant, or infrared, heating is not new; however, there is a renewed respect for radiant advantages both as primary and backup heating as architects, engineers and builders increasingly incorporate extensive solar design, skylights and glass in their residential, commercial and institutional building.

Unlike conventional, convective systems, radiant heat satisfies the three main factors controlling heat loss from the human body - radiation (electromagnectic waves, or warmth, radiating from the body), convection and evaporation. The major loss, and physiologically the most important, is due to radiation. In spite of this, it rarely receives consideration in any type of air conditioning system and is entirely ignored in all types of convected heat systems.

According to the ASHRAE Systems Handbook, 1976, "We must conclude, therefore, that the usual methods of heating and cooling are basically inadequate, since no system can produce conditions compatible with the physiological demands of the human body, unless radiation losses are satisfied in some way.

"It is sometimes claimed that a radiant heat system is desirable for only certain buildings and in some climates, but not desirable otherwise. This is undoubtedly due to lack of understanding.."

BACKGROUND

The invigorating effect of exposure to the sun's rays on a cool, but sunny, day is familiar to everyone. Radiant heat produces a comfortable feeling in much the same way by heating people and objects first, which reradiate that warmth, gradually warming the surrounding air. ASHRAE studies indicate that comfort can be achieved at a 6°-8°F lower ambient air temperature setting than convective systems. There are no chilling drafts with radiant, and ceiling to floor temperature varies only 2°-4°.

Just like the sun, radiant heat is clean, noiseless, odorless, requires no useable space, and is almost allergy free, as no foreign particles introduced into the environment or stirred up by the system.

Radiant heat systems generate operating cost savings of 20%-50% annually compared with convective systems. This is accomplished through room by room temperature control and permanent setback due to equivalent comfort at lower thermostat settings. Savings are also due to the superior, cost effective design inherent in direct source to object radiant heating products.

The Department of Energy concurs with generally accepted studies that 3%-4% is saved for each degree the thermostat is lowered (See Figure 1). Users of surface mounted radiant panels take advantage of this fact in two ways. First, they are able to achieve comfort at a lower ambient air temperature, normally 60°-64°F as compared with convection heating air temperatures of 68°-72°F. Second, they are able to practice comfortable day and night temperature setback - usually 58°F in areas used frequently, 55°F in areas occasionally used, and 50°F in those seldom used.

FIGURE 1 PERCENTAGE REDUCTION IN ANNUAL HEATING LOAD RESULTING FROM LOWER SETTING OF THERMOSTAT*

Original Thermostat Setting °F	Degree Decrease in Original Thermostat Setting									
°F	1°	2°	3°	4°	5°	6°	7°	8°	9°	10°
70	3.74	7.41	11.02	14.56	18.03	21.42	24.74	27.99	31.16	34.26
69	3.81	7.56	11.24	14.84	18.37	21.81	25.19	28.49	31.70	34.85
68	3.90	7.72	11.46	15.13	18.71	22.23	25.65	29.00	32.27	35.46
67	3.97	7.87	11.69	15.42	19.07	22.64	26.12	29.52	32.84	26.10
66	4.06	8.04	11.92	15.72	19.44	23.06	26.60	30.07	33.46	36.76
65	4.14	8.19	12.15	16.03	19.80	23.49	27.10	30.64	34.09	37.44
64	4.22	8.36	12.40	16.34	20.19	23.95	27.64	31.24	34.74	38.13
63	4.32	8.54	12.65	16.67	20.60	24.45	28.21	31.86	35.41	38.86
62	4.41	8.71	12.91	17.02	21.04	24.97	28.87	32.49	36.09	39.61
61	4.50	8.90	13.19	17.40	21.51	25.50	29.38	33.15	36.83	40.40
60	4.60	9.11	13.51	17.81	21.99	26.05	30.00	33.85	37.59	41.20
59	4.72	9.34	13.85	18.23	22.48	26.62	30.66	34.58	38.36	
58	4.85	9.58	14.18	18.65	22.99	27.23	31.34	35.30		
57	4.97	9.80	14.50	19.06	23.52	27.84	32.01			
56	5.09	10.03	14.83	19.52	24.06	28.45				
55	5.21	10.27	15.21	19.99	24.62					

*Results assume no internal or external heat gains. This chart is applicable to residences and commercial buildings where these gains are minimal.

Example: Setback from 70°F to 60°F would result in an annual heat load reduction of 34.26%, as snown in the circled numbers.

COMPARATIVE ANALYSIS

Convective systems are designed to heat the room or entire building. Any heating system which primarily uses the air as the heat transfer medium is a convective heating system. Normally the heat transfer source or outlets are positioned at the perimeter on the outside walls of the room to be heated. Forced air systems usually involve placement of hot air ducts on the outside floor or wall and return cold air ducts on the opposite wall. With this system, cold air is sucked out of a given area and replaced by warm air which rises to the ceiling, warming the wall and the ceiling in the process and gradually losing heat and falling down to the cold air return.

Fin tube central hot water "radiant" systems, are largely convective heaters warming the air which rises along the exterior walls in much the same way as a forced air system. They lose considerable heat to the adjacent exterior wall which may well be exposed to below 0°F temperatures only 6"-8" away. An interesting way to view this conventional heating approach is to consider how much lighting power would be needed if we tried to light rooms by placing all lighting along the outside walls at floor level behind or under furniture and draperies.

Another costly characteristic of hot water or force air systems is considerable heat transmission loss through ducts or pipes used to convey heat to the area to be warmed. In addition, the heater or boiler must initially be warmed resulting in significant heatloss. For gas systems, efficiency averages 60%-80% and oil systems average 55%-65%, depending upon burner age, adjustment and condition. The newer gas hydro-pulse furnaces have a high combustion efficiency, but this must be offset by the considerable increase in power consumption resulting from the electric arcing process essential to system performance. Maintenance, which is normally low for a gas burner, increases significantly for the high efficiency furnace. In general, the recovery response time of these systems is relatively long and results in use of the entire furnace no matter how small the heating area requirement might be. Therefore, temperature setback is not very meaningful or practical.

Heat pumps, in addition to the normal convective disadvantages, are drafty because the heated air they produce is about 80°-95°F; therefore, a larger volume of air must be circulated to satisfy the heat load. Efficiency declines markedly as the temperature drops below 35°F. Maintenance is a major annual cost factor. The argument that you have both heating and air conditioning is not compelling, as historically, heat pumps have been approximately 15% more expensive in terms of lifecycle costs than stand-alone central air conditioners. For a variety of reasons room by room temperature control is neither practical or cost effective.

PRODUCT ARRAY

Radiant systems vary from oil or gas hot water piping in the floor or ceiling, to electric coils, wiring, gypsum panels with Ni-chrome wire, flexible elements in the ceiling - either on or above the gypsum board, metal panels generally mounted by means of a bracket about an inch below the ceiling surface and fiberglass heat modules mounted directly to the ceiling surface, several models may be dropped directly into a T-Bar grid. The radiant heating industry has been expanding in recent years. Consumers now have a broad range of products available to choose from.

Each radiant system affords the economics of individual zone control, no maintenance, and 100% efficient use of electricity. For comfort you have to feel to believe and cost you can afford, zoned electric radiant heat deserves a close examination.

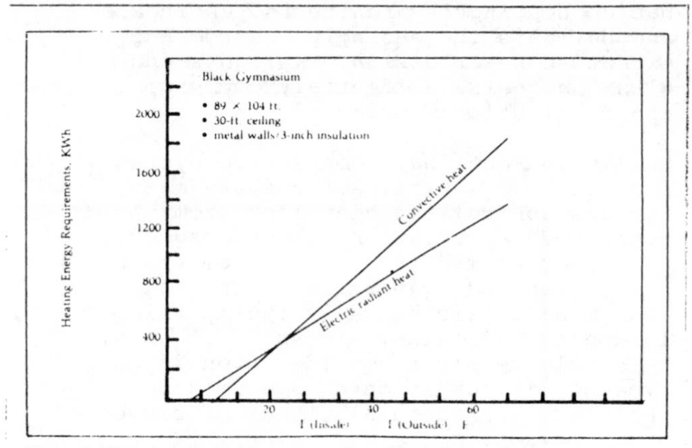

Figure 2 Electric Infrared System vs Convective Heat System

COMMERCIAL PERIMETER ENERJOY^{tm} RADIANT HEATING MAKES SENSE

In the review of commercial building heating and cooling requirements, focus centers on determining design heat loss and occupied cooling load. By briefly walking through a typical case analysis, it is easy to see why Enerjoy^{tm} Solid State Radiant Heating Modules should be the obvious heating choice.

The first figure traditionally examined is the design heat loss, which is the heat loss under conditions of an empty building with absolutely no contributory heat gains under design (worst case) conditions. Normally, in one way or another, this heat loss must be demonstrated to be met for local building code purposes.

In the real world, heat from people, lighting, computers, etc. routinely supply 50% or more of the heat needed during the most severe weather. When the outdoor temperature is above 30°F (virtually 70% of the time even in northern climates), heating from people, lights, and power, supplies too much heat. As the following analysis illustrates, cooling a commercial building is the problem. Commercial buildings heat themselves. Supplementary heating is all that is required. The unfortunate fact is that most commercial buildings have grossly oversized heating plants that waste enormous amounts of energy and money.

Description Of Assumptions

The case analysis we are examining is the top floor of a commercial office building. The floor area is 10,000FT². The top floor zone was chosen because for this particular building it has the highest heat loss rate per square foot of occupied floor space. In the winter we are maintaining 70°F indoor temperature at 0°F outdoor temperature, 15mph wind. In the summer we are maintaining 78°F indoor temperature at 95°F dry bulb, 77°F wet bulb, 7½ mph wind. The building is located in Westport, Connecticut, which has approximately 5,800 annual degree days. We are assuming 100 people will be occupying the space and that lighting and power heat gains will be about 3 watts per square foot. Fresh air is being introduced mechanically at approximately 7½ CFM per person.

Basic Analysis

We constructed a heating/cooling load profile (Figure 1) for the 10,000 FT² space, which relates graphically the various heating and cooling demands for every temperature between 0°F and 95°F for both occupied and unoccupied cycles. Line S-R is the Occupied Heating Line, Line P-G is the Unoccupied Heating Line, Line T-L-E is the Cooling Line. Heating BTUH's are read on the vertical axis below temperature scale.

The load profile can be used to analyze many things. However, for this discussion we are focusing on heating the building at 0°F. The broken line B-C represents the heating load requirement considering the skin losses and fresh air requirements, but no credits are taken for people or lighting. It intersects the heating BTUH axis at point B (164,000 BTUH). This value will be the number that is typically used to size the heating equipment for building permit purposes. It is the number most heat loss calculation procedures will produce. It works out to be 16.9 BTUH FT²

Figure 1

TOP FLOOR—COOLING/HEATING LOAD PROFILE

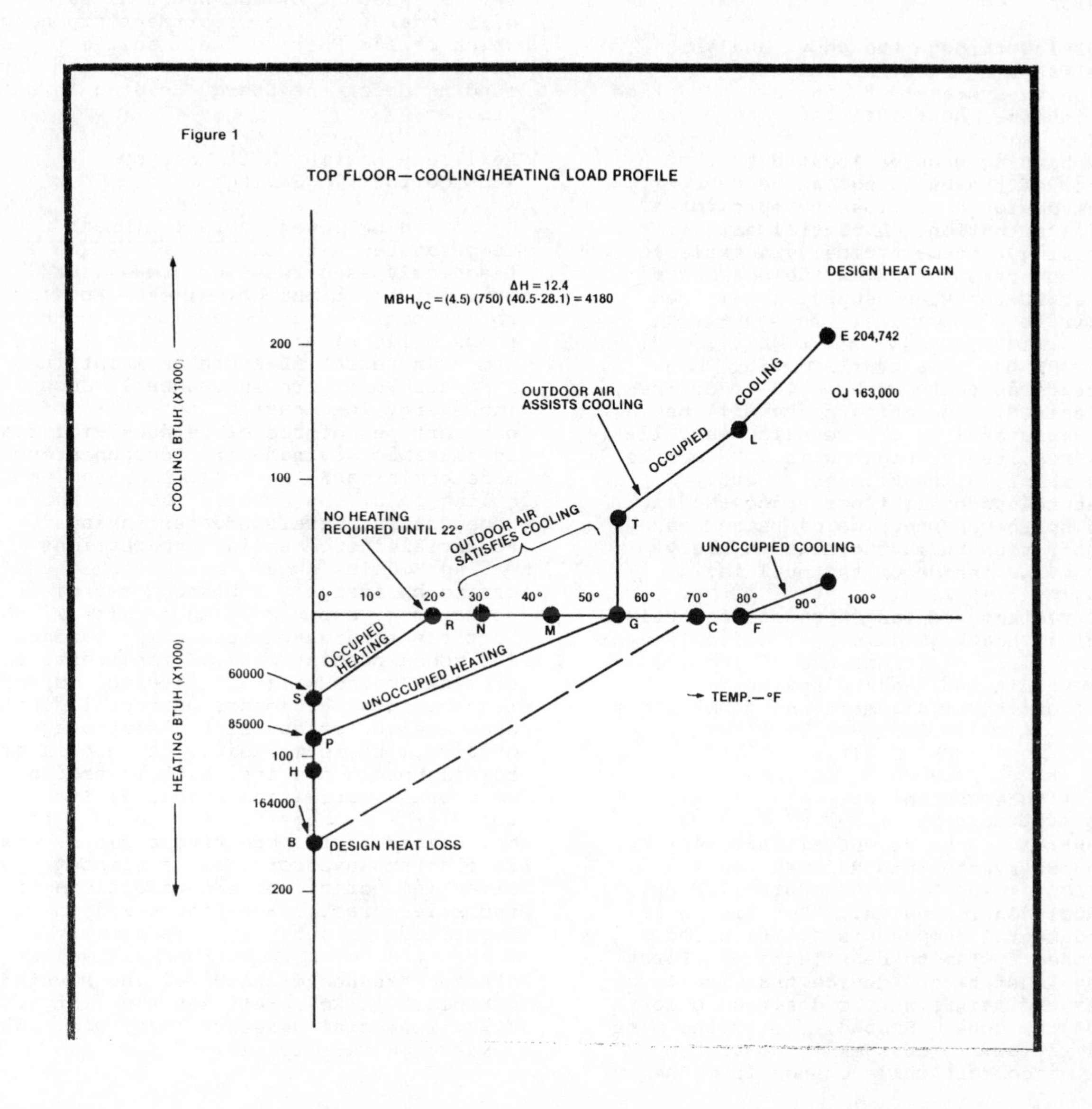

or Watts FT², typical for today's well insulated building. Moving up the heating axis, the next important value we come to is point P, the unoccupied heating requirement of 85,000 BTUH on a 0°F day. Here we are allowing the building temperature to float down to 55°F (point G); the mechanical fresh air systems are assumed to be turned off. This load is slightly less than 50% of the calculated design heat loss value.

Finally, moving further up the heating axis, we come to point S the occupied heating requirement at 0°F, including the fresh air load, but also allowing for heating contributions from people, lights, and power. It's value of 60,000 BTUH, a little more than 1/3 the value usually used to size heating equipment. Surprised? Follow along the Occupied Heating Line until you come to Point R. Read 22°F on the Temperature Scale. Point R represents the temperature where this building no longer needs air conditioning, but begins (emphasis on begins) to need heating. This building actually requires air conditioning down to 22°F, when it is fully occupied!

Conclusion

When working through the above analysis one must assume a heating and air conditioning system that can take advantage of the internal heat loads.

Enerjoy heating modules located on the perimeter of the building can be part of a system designed to closely approximate the ideal situation. A central air conditioning system, typically a variable air volume system, handles the cooling for the interior zones and supplies tempered fresh air to the perimeter at all times. The radiant modules supply heat only where it is needed, and when it is needed. There can be as many thermostats as there are people or offices, if so desired. Operating costs will be low, because as Figure 1 reveals, very little heat is required to begin with. No monster boilers maintaining steam or water temperature occupying floor space sending dollars up the chimney; no oversized gas fired roof tops radiating heat to everything but the inside of the building.

Enerjoy radiant modules represent an optimum approach to heating commercial office space: low first cost, efficient use of energy, flexible zoning and easy adaption to changing office arrangement and floor plans.

ZONE CONTROL

Effective Zone Control

Zone control is the decentralization of the comfort system into defined areas, independently supplied and controlled by individual control units. (See Figure 1). Two fundamental components are required for a zoned system to be effective. First each zone must have a device that monitors, controls and maintains the desired comfort level of the zone. Second, the system must respond rapidly to changes in demand to prevent discomfort while change from one level to another takes place.

The Enerjoy^{R} solid-state heating system effectively meets these requirements. First, it is decentralized, with each zone having its own thermostat which controls and monitors a module or group of modules to maintain the desired comfort level within the zone. Second the desired comfort level is reached within minutes because each module responds as soon as it is energized. The occupant is immediately warmed, independent of the surrounding air temperature.

Detailed testing provided that the same temperature level is reached three times faster with Enerjoy than electric baseboard heaters.[1]

When mounted to the ceiling, the Enerjoy module is thermally insulated from the ceiling mass to give the desired quick radiant response with minimal back and side losses when compared to other radiant systems. These factors combine to provide a rapid sense of comfort from the Enerjoy module within 4-5 minutes from the time it is energized. This is supported in the 1979 report by the National Bureau of Standards to the Department of Energy which called Enerjoy "well suited to zone heating" and recommended the system for funding under the Energy Related Inventions Program.

Auxillary Heating With Enerjoy Adds Comfort To Savings

By combining lower overall ambient temperatures with Enerjoy placed in frequently used rooms or areas (for example, the bathroom, kitchen and family room), comfort can be achieved in those rooms while significantly reduced temperature settings can be maintained in areas which are infrequently occupied. The energy load savings potential of 3 per cent per degree of setback will result in sizeable savings with occupants much more comfortable as well.

Zone Control Offers Greates Savings Potential in Commercial Applications

Office buildings and other commercial structures, especially those with mixed tenancies and usages are prime candidates for zoned heating. Total zone control provides maximum flexibility to respond to varying solar loads, wind chill factors and wide variations of building usage on a room by room basis. Commercial or retail spaces combined with warehouse or storage facilities should always be zoned, for storage areas need only be maintained at temperature levels necessary to prevent inventory damage without affecting normal comfort conditions of the sales area. (See Figure 1)

[1] "Baseboard Heaters and Ceiling Mounted Panels: A Comparative Evaluation, Environmental Research Institute, Kansas State University, 1979."

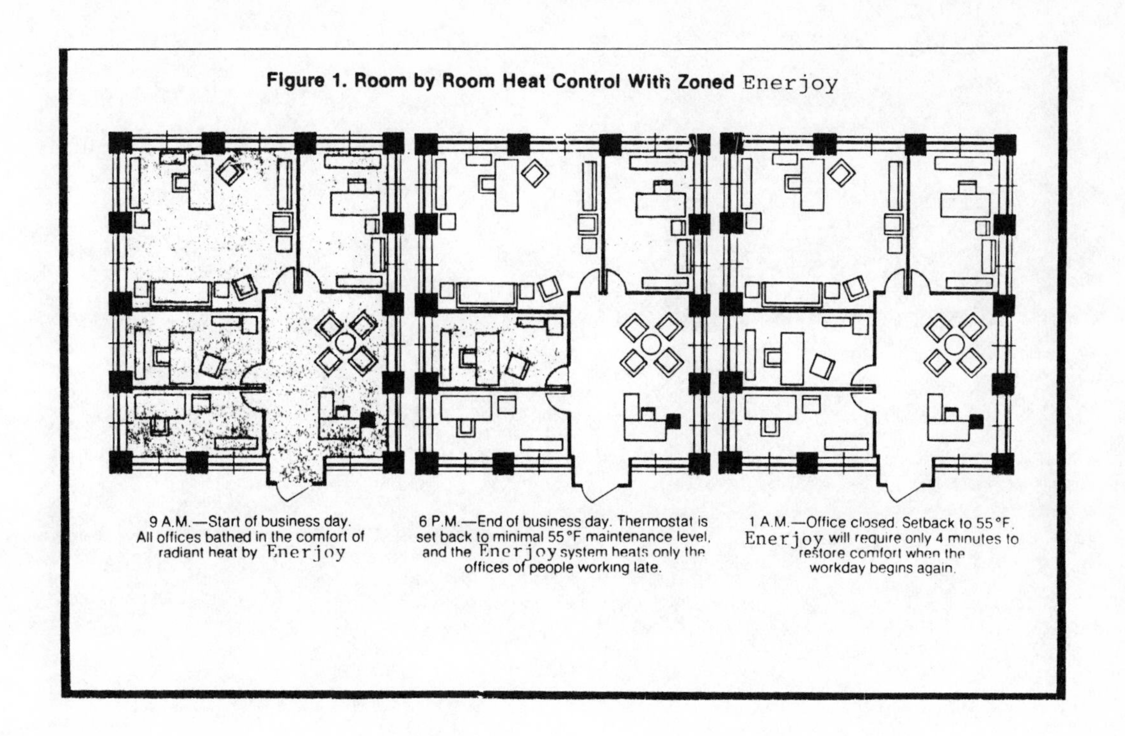

Figure 1. Room by Room Heat Control With Zoned Enerjoy

9 A.M.—Start of business day. All offices bathed in the comfort of radiant heat by Enerjoy

6 P.M.—End of business day. Thermostat is set back to minimal 55°F maintenance level, and the Enerjoy system heats only the offices of people working late.

1 A.M.—Office closed. Setback to 55°F. Enerjoy will require only 4 minutes to restore comfort when the workday begins again.

Multi-room facilities such as hotels, motels and schools face the problems of intermittent use and varying degrees of solar loading as the sun changes position throughout the day. With a zoned system, each room is provided with the capacity to maintain the highest level of comfort at the lowest cost as these changes take place.

Multi-family dwelling units also greatly benefit from fully zoned systems. Each tenant-owner retains control of his energy usage and decides for himself how his energy dollars should be spent to best suit his customary life style. Rental units can be separately metered to equitably distribute utility costs to each tenant, thereby limiting the energy cost liability of the owner.

Well Designed Control System Assures Zone Control Efficiency

The properly designed and installed control system plays an important role in any zoned comfort system. In addition to the availability of good line and low voltage thermostats, new technology now makes it possible for comfort zones to be automatically advanced to warm-up before use, or set back to lower levels after use with solid-state "smart" thermostats which can be programmed according to need. School classrooms and office buildings are particularly good applications because of predictable routines. Also available are individual room thermostats which can be controlled from a central monitor.

Proper Design Of System And Sizing Layout Assures Efficient Zone Control

Designing the Enerjoy solid-state heating system for efficient zone control begins with a heat loss analysis calculated room by room and includes degree days for the particular geographical location, number and location of doors and windows, how much and what type of insulation and other factors. Each room must be sized and treated as an individual unit for correct design.

Compared to a central system, where all interior walls are kept at the same temperature, some heat transfer may take place from room to room in a zoned system where an occupied warm room is adjacent to an unoccupied colder one. Also a chilled room surrounded by other cold rooms will require a slightly greater capacity to recover and maintain a desired comfort level than will a room adjacent to other heated ares. This heat transfer, depending on room location and the combination of factors involved, can vary as much as 10-15 per cent and should be considered when sizing a room to meet minimum comfort levels under 'worst case' conditions. When it is properly sized, optimum performance and most desirable comfort at greatest operating economy may be achieved with Enerjoy.

In conclusion, the quick four minute comfort response of Enerjoy radiant heat modules offers the design engineer the opportunity to provide exactly the heat required so that occupants pay only for comfort heat when, where, and as needed in commercial, institutional, and residential buildings.

Chapter 8

COMPARISON OF COST AND PERFORMANCE OF HVAC CONTROLS

C. E. Lundstrom

During the past decade, sizable challenges have been faced by design engineers, building owners, and facility operations personnel in choosing the right HVAC controls and Energy Monitoring and Control System (EMCS) for their applications. Recent advancements in HVAC controls and EMCS are going to make those decisions even more complex. Decision makers will need to keep abreast of the ever-changing controls market. The recent introduction of microprocessor-based control systems which are smaller, modular, and less expensive will require engineers, owners, and operators to compare the performance to the cost of HVAC controls when the installation of new controls becomes necessary.

The information provided in this paper will identify some of the most recent advances in controls, compare the performance of the control options, and compare initial costs and life cycle costs for various alternatives.

RECENT ADVANCES IN HVAC CONTROLS

Direct digital controls (DDC) have been used in HVAC for a number of years and generally would not be considered a recent advancement. However, the size and form of the DDC which are presently appearing in the HVAC market could be termed "state of the art." The current trend in DDC is toward smaller, modular, microprocessor-based controllers. Moreover, manufacturers in increasing number and types are supplying DDC--and especially the HVAC equipment suppliers themselves.

Chiller Controls

Within the last year, manufacturers of large chillers have begun to install sophisticated microprocessor-based controllers on their chillers as standard factory equipment. Essential control and status monitoring points from the entire chiller system are being fed into a single DDC panel. The panels have a data display line which allows the building operator to read out any parameters in English descriptions.

Typical operating parameters which are provided on the controller include:

- o Chilled- and condensor-liquid temperatures.
- o Evaporator- and condensor-refrigerant pressures.
- o Percentage of motor current.
- o Oil pressure.

As with other types of DDC, temperature controls on the chiller packages can be either proportional or proportional-plus-derivative. A built-in clock gives automatic start/stop control over both chiller functions, as well as over all the associated auxiliary equipment, including the water pumps and cooling tower. Built into some systems is the ability to interface directly with building automation systems. The RS-232 connections allow remote control or monitoring of the panels. These types of connections may have limitations, depending upon the ability of the chiller control panel to "interface" with other EMCS/DDC building controllers. The execution of some of the more sophisticated chiller optimization programs (such as those for chiller sequencing, water temperature resetting, and demand limiting) will require a separate processor and the ability to override or change parameters at each chiller. This may mean using a different manufacturer of building automation systems, thus raising the question of interface.

Boiler Controls

Not to be outdone by the chiller industry, the boiler manufacturers have come out with their own version of DDC for hot water boilers. Because the control strategies for boilers are fairly straightforward, their controls do not require the sophistication of a complex chiller package. Examples of the types of controls developed for boilers include:

- o Sequencing of boilers to maintain water temperatures.
- o Outdoor, indoor, and water temperature monitoring for hot-water temperature reset.
- o Lead-lag capability for increased efficiency and longer boiler life.

A built-in clock provides automatic start/stop control of the boiler system. Like the chiller DDC controllers, boiler controller interface may or may not be possible, depending on who manufactured the control system. This may not be as critical a problem with the boiler system as it is with a chiller system.

HVAC Controls

Trying to describe the most recent advances in HVAC controls would require a whole technical paper in itself. However, the types and trends in control systems for and from the HVAC industry is very interesting. First of all, from the control industry, second- and third-generation DDC panels are becoming more powerful in both software and hardware. Many manufacturers are offering lines of DDC panels with fewer control and monitoring points. This is probably in response to the general criticism of DDC reliability, which includes counting on one processor to handle many control loops. One manufacturer has a DDC panel with an on-board diagnostic processor, which they claim can diagnose failures down to the chip level. This means a repair may be as simple as replacing a very inexpensive chip instead of replacing a very expensive motherboard.

Another criticism made of the first generation of DDC systems was that the systems were too hard to program. Trying to compromise on a software programming language which is both "easy to program" and "provides good performance" may be mutually exclusive. Languages designed for ease of programming normally run too slow and can be cumbersome. Software designed to speed up the process requires a more experienced programmer. With the current generation of DDC, manufacturers are trying to come up with their versions of compromise languages. Most of these are based on a common language such as Basic or Pascal, but the controls people have undertaken the necessary modifications to make them operate at reasonable speeds.

While the controls industry was pouring manpower into third generation DDC systems, the HVAC industry was looking at ways to install microprocessor-based controls as standard equipment from the factory. Many large manufacturers of HVAC systems either have signed agreements with control manufacturers to supply controls or have developed their own control systems and begun shipping equipment with DDC-mounted controls from the factory. The types of functions available for the HVAC controls basically run the same gamut as the pneumatic and electronic controls they will be replacing (coil, damper, and fan controls), but with the added capability to tie them back into a building automation system.

Zone Controls

Probably the newest development in DDC controls within the past year is the increase in the number of companies offering microprocessor-based, zone terminal controls. This concept is not totally new to the industry. But, with the recent introduction of many different and powerful controllers on the market within just the past few months, market analysis is revealing a trend toward this type of design. For many years, the best argument against DDC was the need for having too many control loops maintained on one processor board. If the processor board crashed, many environmental zones could be affected. With the new individual DDC terminal loop controllers, this problem has been alleviated. The overall sophistication designed into the new controllers presents some new design and energy management capabilities not previously available.

Each manufacturer's controller has different capabilities, but the key features handled by the zone controller include:

- o Space temperature monitoring.
- o Temperature setpoint adjustments.
- o VAV damper control.
- o Airflow monitoring.
- o Airflow minimum/maximum adjustments.
- o Fan-assisted control sequencing.
- o Electric reheat sequencing.
- o Hot water valve control.
- o Duct temperature sensing.
- o Warmup control sequencing.

The principal building automation control system programs the zone controllers through the data communications network. All monitoring points (such as space temperature) can be used for alarm and interactive controls applications. The basic programming of the terminal controller differs according to the manufacturer. Generally speaking, if the units are tied back into a data communications network, they all offer some type of control interface through a microcomputer such as an IBM PC.

Figure 1 shows a block diagram of a representative DDC/VAV terminal controller.

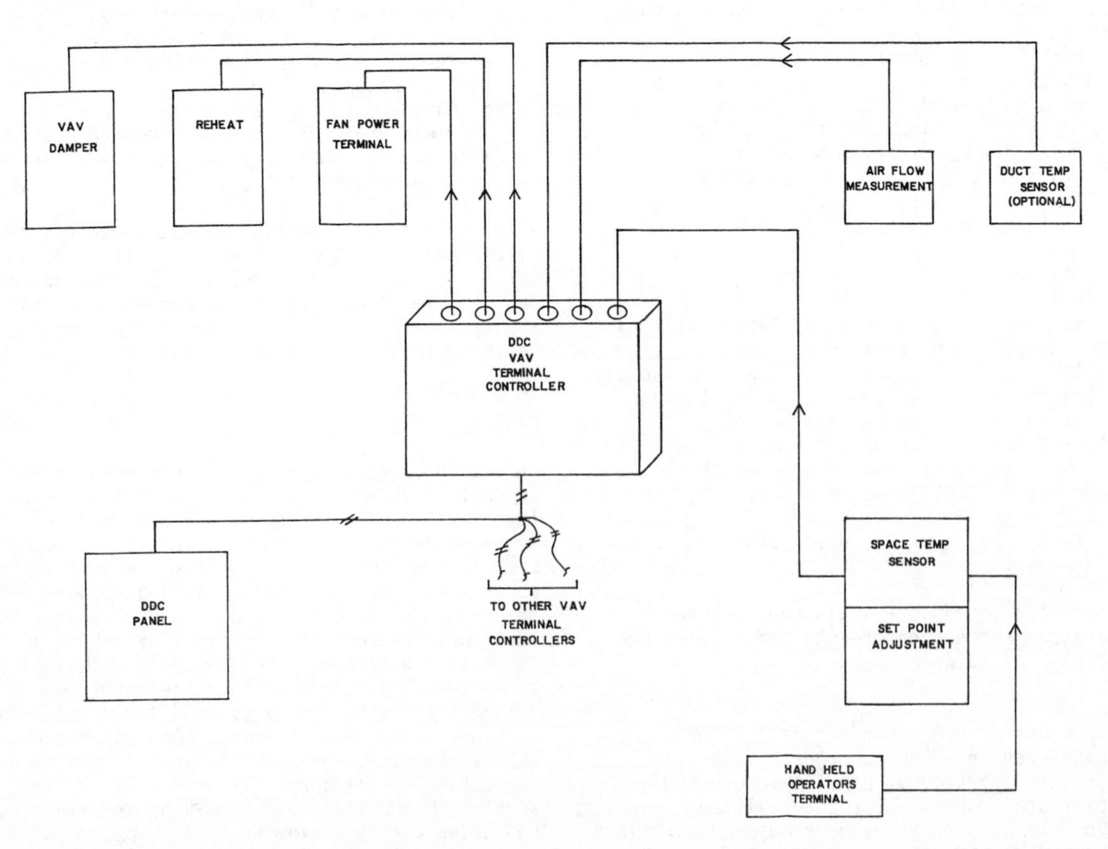

FIGURE 1. DDC/VAV TERMINAL CONTROLLER

Interface Controls

Two of the important advantages of pneumatic controls (as opposed to electric, electronic, and DDC controls) are high reliability and low cost. However, the low accuracy of pneumatic controls has thrown doubt on their use in areas demanding more precise control. For other types of controls to utilize the advantages of pneumatic controls but retain the sophistication of DDC logic, electronic/pneumatic (E/P) transducers are required. Although E/P transducers are not new to the controls arena, some of the functions available on the new units will lend themselves well to retrofitting the DDC of existing pneumatic control systems.

The new line of combination controller boards with E/P transducers will accept pulse-width modulated (PWM) output or 4-20mA output from any source and convert that signal to a 0-18 psi output (in steps of less than 0.1 psi, in the case of PWM). In addition, the output pressure is monitored by the controller and is converted back to a voltage feedback signal. This signal then goes back to the EMCS or DDC panel to read the actual output pressure being sent to the actuator. Failsafe features allow the transducer to transfer control to a standard pneumatic controller if the transducer stops receiving signals from the computer control system. A manual override switch also forces the controller to operate from the standard pneumatic controller. In retrofit jobs, using this type of output controller permits existing pneumatic control loops to be left in place as backups for the new DDC. A more detailed cost comparison is included in later sections of this paper. But, for this single E/P transducer controller, the contractor price range is just over $300 each (uninstalled).

Figure 2 shows an example of a retrofit of DDC controls to a hot water converter system which is pneumatically controlled. In this case, the existing receiver controller would remain and become an input to the pneumatic port marked "original controls" on the controller card. The other two pneumatic inputs on the controller are the "Main" and "Branch" lines. Terminal inputs to the controller cards include the DDC electronic signal, pressure status feedback loop, and low voltage power supply. In this design, the temperature and pressure data are fed back to the DDC panel, whose software then calculates the proper control output to maintain the hot water discharge temperature. The electronic output of the DDC is converted to a pneumatic signal at the E/P transducer controller, and a pneumatic signal is sent to the steam valve actuators. The feedback loop from the E/P controller card monitors the output pressure, and sends a signal back to the DDC panel to be used in tuning its PI control algorithm. If a failure condition is sensed by the controller, the controller automatically switches the signal output from the original receiver controller.

PERFORMANCE COMPARISONS OF HVAC CONTROLS, 1986

Each site has its own unique requirements which should be identified in order to determine what performance is expected from HVAC controls. While evaluating these requirements, decision makers should keep in mind the pros and cons discussed in the following paragraphs.

Pneumatic Controls

For years, pneumatic controls have won the favor of engineers and technicians because they are simple to understand. In addition, pneumatic actuators are both inexpensive and reliable. This makes them very popular, for a wide range of applications, to control dampers and valves.

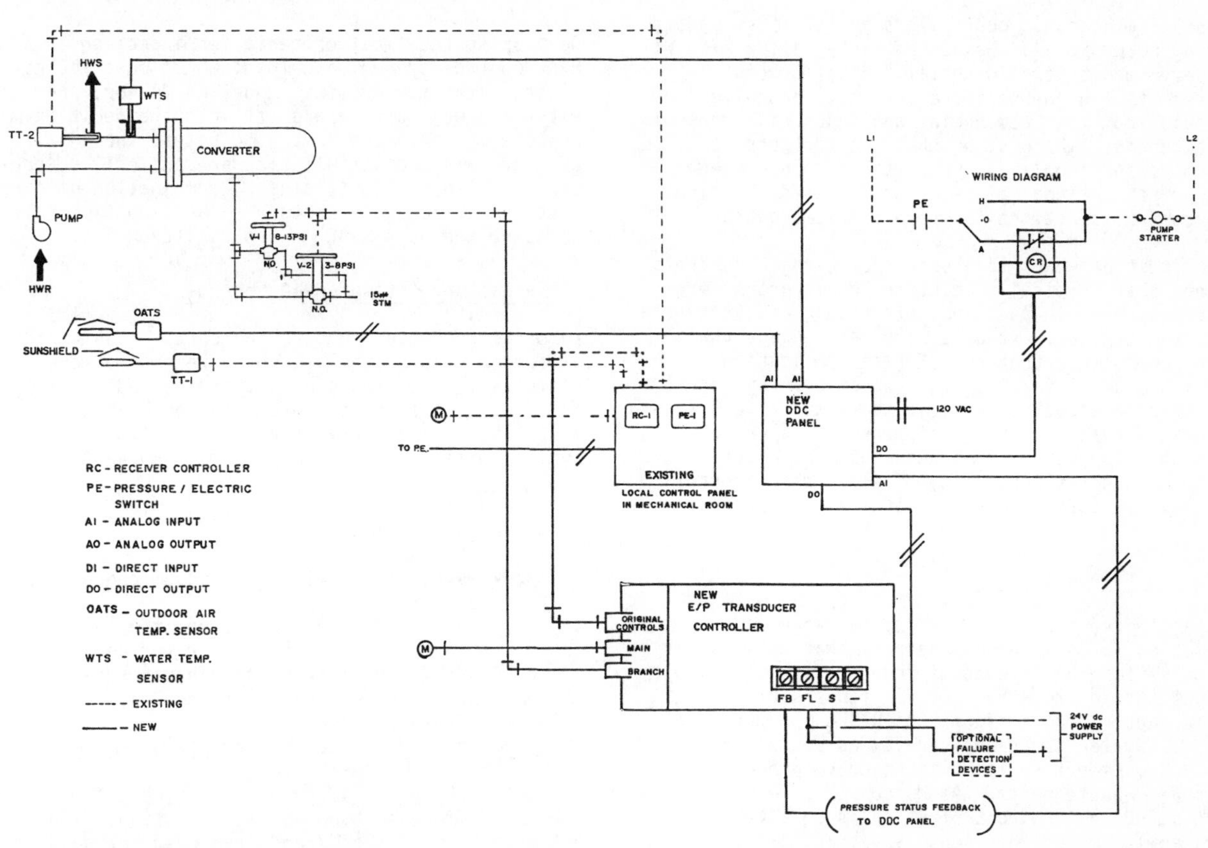

FIGURE 2. INTERFACE CONTROLLER

The disadvantages of pneumatics are threefold:

1. The instruments use very small orifices to modulate the air pressures. Unless the air source for the system is very clean, the controls will start to break down. The infiltration of oil or water into a pneumatic control system should be of great concern.

2. Pneumatic instruments are, generally speaking, the least accurate of all control systems. In recent published test results, accuracies of temperature transducers were ±4°F. The basic receiver control had an accuracy of ±2°F. The combination of a receiver controller with temperature transmitter had an accuracy of ±4°F [1].

3. Pneumatic controls have the largest number of moving parts in their controllers, which increases their tendency to go out of calibration quickly. The need to keep pneumatic instruments calibrated is an on-going process during the life of the controls.

Electric/Electronic Controls

In the HVAC market, basic electric/electronic controls for fan and terminal units are not as common as pneumatic controls. However, their use is sometimes advocated because of the advantages they offer. This category of controls provides an increase in accuracy over pneumatic controls. For example, the platinum resistance temperature detectors (RTD), which are used almost exclusively in electronic controls applications, can be built to provide tolerances of 0.5°F. They also never require site calibration, do have linear resistance to temperature profiles, are almost drift-free, and, most importantly, are inexpensive [1].

The use of electronic controllers built with standard bridging networks and the use of high-quality RTDs will give very good control with limited calibration requirements. High-quality electronic controllers are available from both commercial and industrial control manufacturers. The best of these controllers can perform proportional (P), proportional-plus-integral (PI), or proportional-plus-integral-plus-derivative (PID) control functions for more precise control.

The greatest drawback to electric/electronic controls has been that, typically, electronic actuators were more expensive. In addition, electronic actuators are slower and typically require more maintenance than normal pneumatic actuators. For an application requiring a smaller actuator, such as a VAV terminal, an electronic actuator may cost the same or less than a pneumatic actuator. Some designers have approached this problem by using E/P transducers and pneumatic actuators to get the accuracy of electronic controls and still use cost-effective pneumatic actuators.

Direct Digital Controls

The use of direct digital control can take many application forms in HVAC controls. Not only can it be used to perform basic control sequences to maintain a constant static pressure on a VAV fan system, for example, but it can perform the full complement of energy management programs equally as well. This is where DDC will out-perform its standard pneumatic or electronic counterparts. As discussed under electronic controls, DDC offers control which is equally as accurate with electronic sensors such as RTDs. However, DDC falls into the same pitfall of using similar electronic actuators for standard interface. Many DDC manufacturers are now producing panels with direct E/P transducer output in the expectation that designers will want to use pneumatic actuators. Some DDC manufacturers even offer pneumatic inputs if a designer wishes to use a pneumatic temperature or pressure sensor.

The basic disadvantages of DDC against which skeptics have protested in the past are:

- Hardware reliability has not yet been proven.
- Programming DDC is too difficult.
- Too many functions are controlled by one processor.
- The cost of DDC is prohibitive.
- The increased control potential does not warrant the increased cost.

As mentioned previously, DDC manufacturers are starting to build third-generation DDC panels. Reliability problems are being designed out of the earlier versions of DDC systems.

The arguments used against DDC regarding high-point density control panels are also diminishing. With the further introduction of small DDC panels and DDC/VAV terminal controllers, the problem of mass control failure is greatly reduced. The cost of DDC is still a major concern for many purchasers of controls. However, with the new DDC/VAV terminal controllers, and with more factory-installed DDC equipment, labor and material costs should continue to drop.

The need for powerful control strategies may or may not be warranted for every application. Again, this gets back to the decision-making process: "How much control do I need?"

COST COMPARISON OF HVAC CONTROLS, 1986

Developing the final criteria for investing in a new HVAC control system, a comparison of cost for different alternatives is the most important factor. For each site, the way costs are enter into the decision-making process is different. At some sites, the initial costs of materials and installation are the only criteria used. For other facilities, a combination of first costs and life-cycle costs play an important role in choosing the best HVAC controls alternative.

Installation Costs of HVAC Controls

In order to better compare the costs of some of the different HVAC control methods, we estimated the cost of installing controls on a typical, medium-rise office building. This process was done for both a new installation and for a retrofit installation. This typical office building had the following features:

- Total square footage = 105,000.
- Eight stories high.
- HVAC type
  - VAV systems, with individual central fans on each floor.
  - Hot water reheat coils on exterior zones.
  - Minimum fixed outside air for ventilation.
- Central ventilation and exhaust fans.
- Central centrifugal chiller plant, with cooling tower strainer cycle.
- Central hot-water boiler plant.

The cost estimates included all the necessary hardware for the different types of installations. Cost estimates were adjusted and developed for six different geographic areas by applying local area labor rates, material cost factors, and local taxes. This was done to show the fluctuations in costs, as well as the need for individual analysis in selecting HVAC controls at each site.

Installed Costs, New Installation

For comparison, we developed three types of cost estimates for a new installation:

1. Basic pneumatic controls.

2. DDC system, using pneumatic actuators.

3. DDC system, using all electric/electronic actuators with new DDC/VAV terminal controllers.

The basic pneumatic control system used a standard thermostat and VAV boxes with hot-water reheat coils for zone controls. The central fan required discharge-air and fan-speed controls using single input receiver controllers. Miscellaneous hardware such as firestats, thermometers, and gauges were also included for the fan systems. Pneumatic controls and interlocks were included for the chiller, cooling tower, strainer system, boiler, building ventilation system, and associated auxiliaries. The necessary material and installation costs were also included for air compressors, air drying and filtering devices, and for pneumatic tubing.

We assumed that the DDC system with pneumatic actuators would use a completely electronic input and output control system, with pneumatic outputs for devices with actuators such as VAV dampers and valves. Overall, the DDC system was designed to provide all the basic temperature control functions as did the pneumatic controls previously described, but also using software to provide optimization and sequencing of control outputs. The cost estimate for this option was developed once with, and once without, a front-end personal computer (PC) for operator interface. This was done to illustrate the cost penalty for adding a PC for operator interface. The basic DDC temperature control system might not need the PC for normal control operation.

For the last DDC option, we developed cost estimates using all electronic sensing and actuator equipment. Included in this estimate were the DDC/VAV terminal controllers. Again, this DDC cost estimate is broken down into inclusion and exclusion of the PC front end to better compare the basic cost of this option with a strictly pneumatic control system.

Table 1 shows a breakdown of the three control options based on the descriptions above. These estimates are also broken down into six geographic areas of the United States to show the range of costs by area.

City	Pneumatic Controls	DDC with Pneumatic Actuators		DDC with Electronic Actuators	
		Without PC	With PC	Without PC	With PC
Dallas	$105,000	$185,000	$211,000	$109,000	$135,000
Chicago	106,000	187,000	212,000	111,000	137,000
Denver	108,000	190,000	217,000	113,000	140,000
Los Angeles	109,000	194,000	219,584	118,000	144,000
Atlanta	103,000	181,000	206,000	106,000	131,000
New York	115,000	203,000	231,000	123,000	150,000

TABLE 1. INSTALLED COST OF NEW HVAC CONTROLS

The results reveal a significant cost difference between a basic pneumatic control and a DDC system based around pneumatic actuators. The added control capability of DDC would have added almost 80 cents per square foot to the total construction costs. However, for the DDC system with electronic actuators using the DDC/VAV terminal controller for basic temperature control, the costs are close to being competitive with those of basic pneumatic controls. To add a PC with software and graphic capability for operator interface, there is a $25,000 premium.

We generated separate cost estimates to examine the feasibility of retrofitting DDC controls in locations where there are existing controls. Table 2 shows the costs for replacing both a pneumatic and electronic control system with a DDC. The approximate $70,000 difference in cost between a new and a retrofit DDC with pneumatic actuator installation is due to the assumption that there are existing actuators available for valves and dampers. For DDC systems with a PC interface, the cost ranged from $900 per point for a pneumatic retrofit in New York, to $800 per point in Atlanta. The lowest cost overall was $550 per point for an electronic retrofit in Atlanta.

City	Pneumatic Controls	DDC with Pneumatic Actuators		DDC with Electronic Actuators	
		Without PC	With PC	Without PC	With PC
Dallas	Base	$116,000	$141,000	$70,000	$96,000
Chicago	Case	117,000	143,000	72,000	97,000
Denver		119,000	145,000	73,000	99,000
Los Angeles		122,000	148,000	76,000	102,000
Atlanta		113,000	138,000	67,000	93,000
New York		128,000	155,000	79,000	107,000

TABLE 2. INSTALLED COST OF RETROFIT HVAC CONTROLS

The costs for retrofitting DDC can be further reduced if the building has an existing supervisory EMCS system. Table 3 gives the estimated cost for using this type of retrofit DDC in the typical office building described. In this case, it was assumed not only that dampers and valves were available, but also that much of the wiring was already installed for interfacing to AHUs, chillers, boilers, and auxiliary equipment. This represents approximately $30,000 in savings between a retrofit DDC with a pneumatic actuator retrofit (see Table 2) and a retrofit DDC to an existing EMCS. The final cost per point for a DDC system with a PC interface would range from $500 to $700. On a square foot basis, the average cost for a DDC interface to an existing electronic control system with an EMCS was found to be approximately 90 cents per square foot.

City	Pneumatic Controls	DDC with Pneumatic Actuators		DDC with Electronic Actuators	
		Without PC	With PC	Without PC	With PC
Dallas	Base	$84,000	$110,000	$64,000	$90,000
Chicago	Case	85,000	111,000	65,000	91,000
Denver		87,000	113,000	67,000	93,000
Los Angeles		89,000	114,000	68,000	94,000
Atlanta		82,000	108,000	63,000	88,000
New York		93,000	121,000	72,000	99,000

TABLE 3. INSTALLED COST OF RETROFIT HVAC CONTROLS WITH EXISTING SUPERVISORY EMCS

Building Energy Costs for Various HVAC Controls

To properly evaluate the various control options which have been discussed in this paper, we performed an energy analysis. The purpose of this analysis was to estimate the building energy usage, based upon different control configurations.

The energy analysis involved the computer simulation of the same typical, medium-rise office building described in the cost estimate section. We assumed that the eight-story building was occupied only during a normal day shift, five days a week. Two basic simulations were carried out with the following control function modifications:

o Pneumatic Controls

- Systems operate from 0500 hours to 1800 hours, Monday through Friday.
- Heating setpoints: 71°F occupied, 55°F unoccupied.
- Cooling setpoints: 75°F occupied, 85°F unoccupied.
- Cooling-coil discharge temperature: 55°F.

o Direct Digital Controls (DDC)

- Systems operate from 0600 hours to 1700 hours, Monday through Friday.
- Heating setpoints: 68°F occupied, 55°F unoccupied.
- Cooling setpoints: 78°F occupied, 85°F unoccupied.
- Cooling-coil discharge temperature: 59°F.

The changes made in the two computer runs were to illustrate the difference in space temperature control, cooling-coil temperature control, and optimized start-stop timing. Because of the poor calibration in the pneumatic controls, cooling coils designed to be operating at 59°F may actually have operated at 55°F. This would have resulted in increased cooling and reheating. Likewise, the heating and cooling setpoints for the two simulations were used to represent the differences between local thermostats as opposed to temperatures maintained through remote control by DDC through software.

The simulations were performed on the DOE-2.B computer program, using TRY weather for six different geographical areas [2]. Monthly results were extracted from each run for electrical energy and demand, and for natural gas energy. This data, along with the actual utility rate structures for fuels in each geographical area, was used to determine the present energy cost per year. Table 4 lists the results of the energy simulations for both pneumatic control and DDC. The first two columns represent the annual electric and natural gas energy usage. Overall, for pneumatic and DDC controls, we found that the largest energy consumer by geographical region was Chicago, mainly because of its higher natural gas heating requirements. The minimum energy user in this analysis was the Los Angeles area. Figure 3 is a graphic representation of the comparison of the control types and cities.

Applying the local utility rates for energy and demand illustrated the significant differences, in annual dollar costs, between average city-to-city energy consumptions. These figures, listed in Table 4, range from a high in New York of $247,000 for pneumatic controls to only $52,000 for DDC used in Dallas. The bar chart in Figure 4 shows the annual energy costs in the six locations for both the pneumatic control and DDC simulation results. It is interesting to compare the results shown in Figures 3 and 4, where, for

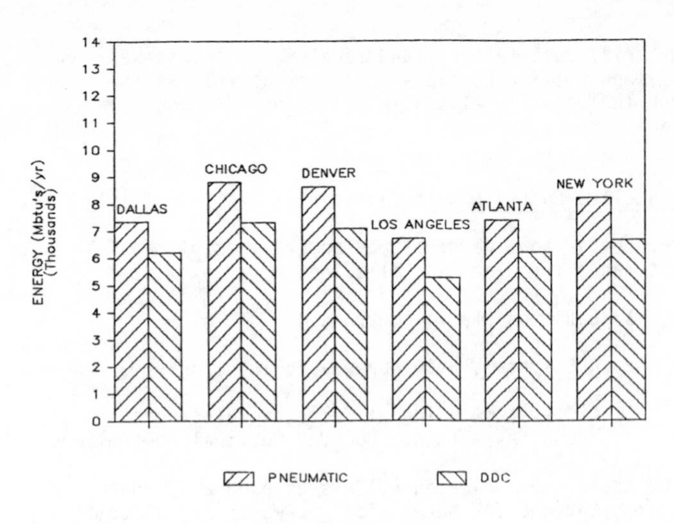

FIGURE 3. ANNUAL ENERGY COMPARISON

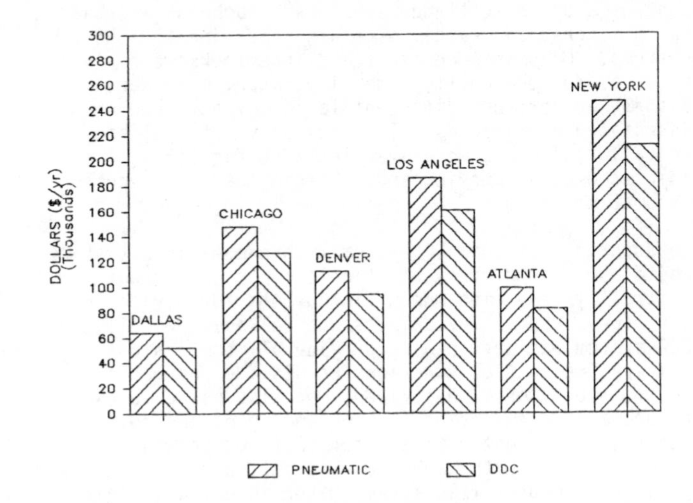

FIGURE 4. ANNUAL ENERGY COST COMPARISON

example, Los Angeles was found to have the lowest overall energy consumption but also the second-highest annual energy costs.

To complete the picture of the economic benefits for different control options, we performed a life-cycle cost analysis using the energy predictions from the computer simulations and the cost estimates developed in the previous sections. The life-cycle energy costs were determined by taking the annual energy costs and applying the Uniform Present Worth (UPW) factors for the different geographical regions over a 15-year lifetime at a 7% discount factor [3]. Again, New York had the highest overall, life-cycle energy cost ($2,000,000) for a typical office building with pneumatic controls. This contrasts with a minimum of only $500,000 for Dallas. Figure 5 shows the estimated, life-cycle energy costs for the six geographical locations.

We then calculated the cost premium for installing a DDC with electronic actuators and a PC interface (as opposed to using pneumatic controls in a new installation) along with the incremental energy savings to find the simple payback and savings-to-investment ratio (SIR). These calculations, presented in Table 4, showed that, for a new installation, the additional costs for DDC controls can be justified over a 15-year lifetime. In many cases, the economics indicated an SIR greater than six.

	Electric (MBtu/Yr)	N. Gas (MBtu/Yr)	Total (MBtu/Yr)	Energy Cost ($/Yr)	Life Cycle Cost ($/15 Yrs)	Installed Cost	Simple Payback	SIR
Dallas, Texas								
Pneumatic controls	5,550	1,794	7,344	64,369	665,080	105,000		
Direct digital controls	5,324	864	6,188	52,450	534,372	135,000		
Difference	226	930	1,156	11,919	130,708	30,000	3	4
Chicago, Illinois								
Pneumatic controls	4,949	3,861	8,810	147,822	1,371,013	106,000		
Direct digital controls	4,692	2,634	7,326	126,922	1,165,077	137,000		
Difference	257	1,227	1,484	20,900	205,936	31,000	1	7
Denver, Colorado								
Pneumatic controls	4,878	3,761	8,639	112,634	1,050,350	108,000		
Direct digital controls	4,627	2,468	7,095	94,136	868,646	140,000		
Difference	251	1,293	1,544	18,498	181,704	32,000	2	6
Los Angeles, California								
Pneumatic controls	5,033	1,684	6,717	186,291	1,862,320	109,000		
Direct digital controls	4,779	498	5,277	160,564	1,598,086	144,000		
Difference	254	1,186	1,440	25,727	264,234	35,000	1	8
Atlanta, Georgia								
Pneumatic controls	5,544	1,857	7,401	99,008	89,2910	103,000		
Direct digital controls	5,320	897	6,217	82,567	730,786	131,000		
Difference	224	960	1,184	16,441	162,124	28,000	2	6
New York, New York								
Pneumatic controls	5,047	3,166	8,213	246,775	2,306,432	115,000		
Direct digital controls	4,795	1,850	6,645	211,691	1,965,275	150,000		
Difference	252	1,316	1,568	35,084	341,157	35,000	1	10

TABLE 4. HVAC CONTROLS ECONOMIC SUMMARY

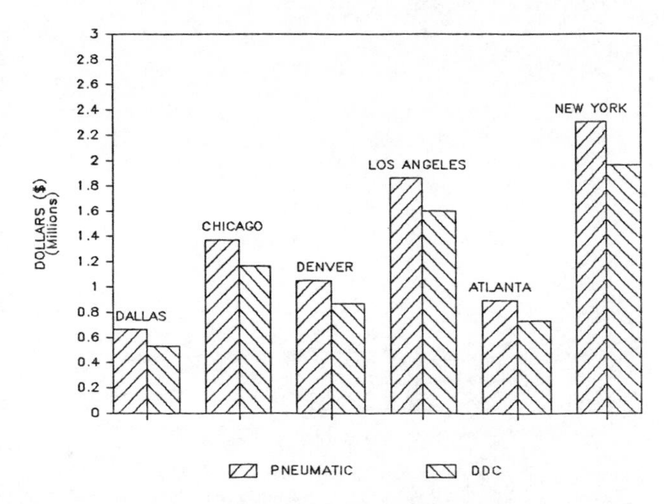

FIGURE 5. LIFE-CYCLE ENERGY COST COMPARISON

These numbers represent only hypothetical cases. However, we made conservative assumptions in simulating the typical office used for calculating the installed costs and energy costs for different control configurations. We concluded that the installation of a DDC would be favorable for similar type structures in most geographical areas of the United States.

SUMMARY

In the years to come, controls will be changing and developing at a pace equal to that of the microchip age. The current advances in microcomputer-based controls for chillers, boilers, HVAC, and terminal units will provide:

- o Sophisticated control capability.
- o Better reliability.
- o Easier maintenance.

In designing a control system to be installed either in a new building or as a retrofit in an existing building, one should determine which criteria are important for that installation. Pneumatic controls are easy to use, less expensive, and have a high reliability rating, but they fall short on accuracy and flexibility. Electronic controls have much better accuracy, but their larger actuators are more expensive and less reliable. For applications requiring smaller actuators, such as VAV terminals, the cost for electronic actuators may be the same or less than the cost for pneumatic actuators. DDC provide the highest degree of control power, accuracy, and flexibility, but are more expensive for basic temperature control.

The installed costs for pneumatic controls are still the most competitive for basic temperature control. The costs for DDC can vary widely, depending upon whether pneumatic or electronic actuators are used. The costs of DDC will also drop substantially for retrofit installations. Based on computer energy simulations, the savings available for DDC, as compared with those of basic pneumatic controls, should more than offset the premium costs for more powerful control features. The geographical differences in energy dollar costs vary widely and will greatly affect economic justification.

REFERENCES

1. Hittle, D.C. and D.L. Johnson. "Energy Efficiency Through Standard Air Conditioning Control Systems." Heating/Piping/Air Conditioning, April 1986.

2. U.S. Department of Energy. "DOE-2.1B." Building Energy Simulation Group, Energy and Environment Division, Lawrence Berkeley Laboratory, January 1983.

3. Lippiatt, Wever, and Ruegg. "Energy Prices and Discount Factors for Life-Cycle Cost Analysis." United States Department of Commerce, National Bureau of Standards, November 1985.

SECTION 2

HVAC ALTERNATIVES

Sponsored by the Gas Research Institute

Chapter 9

ENGINE-EERING LOWER COOLING COSTS WITH GAS

B. B. Lindsay, M. D. Koplow, P. M. O'Farrell

In the 1960s the natural gas industry was very effective in promoting an alternative to electric-driven cooling. Absorption cooling and engine chillers were successfully marketed on the basis of lower operating costs, better system performance, and unusual configurations. Unfortunately for the gas industry, innovations in compressors, motors, and controls increased the performance and decreased the cost of electric cooling systems. Additionally, and perhaps more importantly, the gas crunch of the Seventies curtailed gas cooling promotion and forced prospective buyers to remain with conventional electric systems.

The advent of the Eighties has seen a drastic change in traditional energy pricing and supply. Gas is no longer perceived as scarce. Gas is available now and far into the future. Better yet, gas is reasonably priced. Not all electric utilities can make that claim for their product. The events of the decade have had a major impact on the electric industry and its ability to compete in the commercial market place. Three Mile Island, high interest rates, and foreign competition in basic industries have driven the cost of electric generating plants through the roof while the demand for power has diminished. Some utilities are over-capacity, forced to pass 40% to 95% increases on to consumers as nuclear plants are rolled into rates. Other utilities, not so fortunate as to burden themselves with overcapacity, are capacity-limited and predict possible serious shortages in the near future.

The outlook for affordable commercial cooling is precarious. The increased electric costs will invariably be passed on to the commercial sector. The brunt of the increase will be disguised as "demand charges", which either recover fixed costs of nuclear plants or promote load management for a beleaguered utility. The demand charges usually apply at periods of peak use--commercial business hours during the summer--which is the exact time commercial cooling is most needed. Commercial customers will be paying more to cool their buildings.

The time for gas cooling to reemerge is now. The lower cost of gas has prompted many firms to reexamine the options for space cooling. In Japan, where gas cooling predominates, manufacturers have developed advanced absorption chillers, which reduce gas consumption by 50% over conventional absorption systems, and have recently initiated major campaigns in the U.S. to market the new technology. Building owners in several areas of the country are already moving quickly to install gas-fired chillers. These areas are experiencing nightmarish electric costs, and the high first cost of absorption systems can be easily justified.

While absorption cooling is gaining momentum, another gas cooling option is being resurrected: engine-driven chillers. The engine chiller capitalizes on the tremendous increases in performance and cost that electric vapor-compression systems have made over the past twenty years. The concept of replacing an electric motor with a gas-fueled engine can realize significant cost savings where the electric-to-gas price ratio is high.

ENGINE-DRIVEN CHILLER DEVELOPMENT

The Gas Research Institute (GRI) initiated a program in 1984 to develop commercial chillers using the engine-driven concept. GRI is a not-for-profit organization that manages R&D programs for the benefit of gas consumers and the natural gas industry. As part of the program, an extensive study was conducted to evaluate the problems of past systems, the potential impact of engine chillers on the HVAC market, and the design considerations which would lead to favorable economics and commercialization potential.

Engine-driven chillers were successfully marketed by the gas utilities and manufacturers in the Sixties. The gas companies used promotional rates and subsidy programs to entice buyers. The outstanding operating economics were sufficient to place nearly 2000 units in the field between 1962 and 1970. The majority of these were located in Texas, presumably due to the availability of cheap gas. There were several manufacturers and packagers of engine-driven chillers. Caterpillar and Waukesha actively promoted the use of their engines in cooling configurations with Carrier, York, Trane, Vilter, Bell & Gossett, Ingersoll Rand, Frick, and Dunham Bush compressor packages. Continental, Ready Power, Gascool, ICED, and Janitrol developed packaged engine chillers for commercial application.

Installations of engine chillers included a variety of building types: apartment buildings, hotels, hospitals, industrial plants, schools, and ice rinks, etc. The owners cited operating economics as the principal reason for purchase: Gas was cheaper than electricity. The added benefits of free hot water, emergency power capability, and improved part load performance were further attractive inducements. Owners did cite problems with engine chillers, however. Maintenance was the principal complaint. The expense of servicing engines was often a suitable plum for cost reduction. The building owner or engineer would choose not to renew the maintenance contract, which included a sinking fund for major overhauls. The ensuing repairs were often extensive. In some instances, repairs were accompanied by extended downtime. Parts were not readily available, and sinetunes specialized service was required. Several manufacturers of engine chillers did not establish an adequate distributor network capable of providing the level of service required.

The problems with maintaining engine systems often precipitated the removal of the system. Undoubtedly, the gas utilities' caveats for future gas curtailments accelerated the removal of engine systems that were due for major overhauls. It should be noted, however, that when service was available and complete, engine chillers exhibited extremely high reliability. Several units are still operating after 40,000 hours, and their owners are very pleased with their performance. This is particularly true for multiunit installations, such as hospitals or industrial plants, which had sufficient in-house expertise to maintain their investment.

The experience of the first-generation engine chillers has established the criteria for the successful commercialization of engine chillers for the Eighties:

- The economics must be acceptable to building owners. The annual fuel and maintenance costs must be significantly lower than corresponding electricity and maintenance costs of conventional chillers.
- Provision for maintenance of the engine chiller is essential. An infrastructure to perform adequate service and supply parts must be incorporated into any business planning to enter the market.
- The engine should require minimum maintenance. Service intervals should be seasonal. Major overhauls should be relatively inexpensive.
- The engine chiller should have the capability to recover waste heat and operate at part load.
- Noise, vibration, and emissions must be acceptable.

TODAY'S CHILLER MARKET

Air-conditioning systems for the commercial building market can be categorized into several system types. Some of the more prominent types are: chiller packages, built-up systems, penthouse units, rooftop units, and indoor units. Large commercial structures, such as multi-story apartment buildings, office buildings, and hospitals, often require a chiller package. The chiller produces cold water, which is piped to coils in the air distribution network, to dehumidify and cool a building zone. Chillers are typically very large, ranging from 100 to 2500 tons (12,000 Btu/hr) of cooling capacity. Buildings of a less complex nature may opt to install a direct expansion system, which cools the building zone directly. These units are typically rooftop mounted, are ideally suited to low-profile buildings, and rarely exceed 100 tons in capacity.

Commercial chillers are classified by compressor type:

- Centrifugal compressors are typically used on large-tonnage chillers. A multiple stage compressor can achieve efficiencies ranging from 0.6 to 0.8 kW/ton.
- Reciprocating compressors are rarely used on chillers exceeding 100 tons. An electric motor will drive several reciprocating compressors which can be individually unloaded to operate at part load. Efficiency ranges from 0.8 to 1.3 kW/ton.
- Screw compressors have a small portion of the chiller market. They achieve efficiencies of 0.8 to 1.1 kW/ton and can operate at part load.

Shipments of chillers within the U.S. for 1984 exhibit a large market for commercial cooling systems.

Centrifugal 500 Tons	1300 units
Centrifugal 500 Tons	2500 units
Reciprocating	13800 units
Screw	800 units
Total	18400 units

Chiller systems are purchased for two distinct market segments: new construction and replacement. The new construction segment has evolved into two subsegments: the speculative builder and the owner-builder. Each group exhibits different purchasing criteria that impact the chiller market.

The speculative builder is hoping to "flip" the building--lease or sell the structure to a third party in the shortest possible timeframe--then move on to his next project. Life-cycle costs are important to him only if they can move his project. The speculative builder endeavors to keep his first costs at the absolute minimum. This includes equipment, engineering, and construction costs. The speculative builder is increasingly utilizing rooftop or individual floor HVAC systems to minimize engineering through repetitive design, speed installation, and reduce equipment costs. Although the speculative builder may respond to market trends, first cost dictates equipment choice, and energy saving is a secondary concern.

The owner-builder market segment is more concerned with long-term operating costs. The owner will consider added costs if the payback is reasonable, typically two to three years. The owner has several options at his disposal to reduce his cooling costs: gas cooling, cogeneration, ice storage, reflective glazing, high efficiency electric chillers, and adjustable speed drives. Among these, the electric industry has promoted ice storage and offers considerable incentives to install these peak-leveling systems. Several utilities are currently offering $115 to $350 per kilowatt of peak-load shift. With the conventional systems so highly subsidized, the owner-builder is resistant to consider "unconventional" systems. Some gas utilities have responded by offering similar programs for gas cooling with $100/ton inducements.

The replacement market has been a small portion of the chiller industry's sales until recent years. Today, however, the replacement market is estimated to constitute nearly 35% of all chiller shipments. The 15 to 20 year life cycle of electric chillers has prompted a major initiative by manufacturers to sell replacements for old, inefficient, and troublesome units. Tenants and owners are willing to consider operating costs and investment paybacks. The replacements are usually planned, which allows the owner and his engineer to select the most efficient chiller package. The electric industry still offers considerable incentive to install ice storage, but the constraints on space and structural integrity in older buildings will severely hamper retrofitting. The planned replacement of electric chillers with gas-fired engine-driven chillers is a viable and attractive option in older buildings.

The opportunities in the replacement market become even more attractive as one considers the building stock in the United States. Older buildings are normally in the mature East Coast and North Central regions, which exhibit the highest electric rates in the nation. Older buildings are also typically multi-story, which improves the likelihood of a central chilled water system being in place. Finally, older buildings will typically have gas service. In short, the replacement market should have attractive economics and sales prospects are well defined and abundant.

The design of HVAC systems incorporates a healthy degree of redundancy. Most engineers specify two or three chillers, instead of a single larger one, to permit better part-load operation and to ensure that the building will still have partial service if one chiller fails. Replacing one electric chiller with an engine-driven chiller assures the owner that he will have partial service. The owner also has extended options to shave peak electric demand, the most expensive component of cooling costs. The building engineer can operate one electric chiller baseloaded--the most economical strategy--and use the engine chiller to meet peak demands. The engineer can also operate the electric chiller just for off-peak hours and use the engine chiller for all peak-hour cooling. The engineer's decision will be based solely on the specific rate designs and the building loads.

ENGINE-DRIVEN CHILLER ECONOMICS

The economics of air-conditioning systems vary as a function of electric and natural gas rates, maintenance costs, operating hours, load factor, parasitic power requirements, and equipment costs. The complexity of electric rates could constitute a paper by itself. Demand charges, peak and off-peak energy charges, ratchet, power factor, load factor, minimum and maximum billings, and special discounts must be considered in the total analysis of chiller system operating costs. The operating strategy will be greatly affected by the particular utility rate and structure. The use of so-called "average" electric rates is inappropriate and misleading.

The customary approach to analyzing chiller economics has been to employ "equivalent full-load hour" methodology. Part-load operation is modified to obtain the equivalent of running at full load. While this method does not reflect the efficiency of part load operation, it does simplify economic comparison. Because the engine chiller has superior part-load performance, it does not benefit from this approach and the results are consequently conservative. Equivalent full-load hours (EFLH) are normally a function of seasonal cooling loads and vary regionally. The specific structure type also influences the EFLH. Office buildings and shopping centers have high internal heat gains from lighting, equipment, and occupants, which greatly increase the cooling load. The American Society of Heating, Refrigerating, and Air Conditioning Engineers (ASHRAE) has established average EFLH for cities throughout the U.S. that are applicable to light commercial buildings:

TABLE 1

ESTIMATED EQUIVALENT FULL LOAD HOURS

Residential and Light Commercial Buildings

City	EFLH
Albuquerque, NM	800-2200
Atlantic City, NJ	500- 800
Birmingham, AL	1200-2200
Boston, MA	400-1200
Burlington, VT	200- 600
Charlotte, NC	700-1100
Chicago, IL	500-1000
Cleveland, OH	500-1000
Cincinnati, OH	1000-1500
Columbia, SC	1200-1400
Corpus Christi, TX	2000-2500
Dallas, TX	1200-1600
Denver, CO	400- 800
Des Moines, IA	600-1000
Detroit, MI	700-1000
Duluth, MN	300- 500
El Paso, TX	1000-1400
Honolulu, HI	1500-3500
Indianapolis, IN	600-1600
Little Rock, AR	1400-2400
Minneapolis, MN	400- 800
New Orleans, LA	1400-2800
New York, NY	500-1000
Newark, NJ	400- 900
Oklahoma City, OK	1100-2000
Pittsburgh, PA	900-1200
Rapid City, SD	800-1000
St.Joseph, MO	1000-1600
St.Petersburg, FL	1500-2700
San Diego, CA	800-1700
Savannah, GA	1200-1400
Seattle, WA	400-1200
Syracuse, NY	200-1000
Trenton, NJ	800-1000
Tulsa, OK	1500-2200
Washington, DC	700-1200

Source: ASHRAE 1985 Fundamentals Handbook, 28.7

To illustrate the economics of engine-driven chillers, an analysis is presented that uses data representative of a Chicago area office building.

In the analysis, the electric rates are simplified to $13.34/kW demand charge per month; a 4-month demand ratchet; 5.8c/kwh peak energy charge. The gas rate assumed is $5.00/million Btu. The office operates its chiller 2000 hours per year with 1200 equivalent full-load hours, which reflects the higher internal heat gains of large commercial structures.

The electric chiller would cost approximately $300/ton. It requires 0.15 kW/ton for auxiliary equipment, such as the chilled water pump, condenser water pump, the cooling tower fan, and controls. An HVAC maintenance contract of $1000/year is assumed. A high-efficiency centrifugal chiller is specified with a coefficent of performance (COP) of 5.5, or 0.64 kW/ton.

The engine chiller costs significantly more than the electric chiller. $360/ton is assumed. The engine chiller requires additional power for the radiator fan and oil pump, increasing the auxiliary load to 0.19 kW/ton. An additional maintenance contract for the engine chiller at 1c/ton-hr is assumed. The engine chiller achieves a COP of 1.7, neglecting electric requirements, or a heat rate of 7059 Btu/ton-hr.

TABLE 2
ANNUAL COST COMPARISON
Electric Centrifugal vs Gas Engine Chiller

	Electric	Gas
Compressor		
Demand	$5,117	$ 0
Energy	6,674	0
Gas	0	6,353
Auxiliaries		
Demand	1,201	1,521
Energy	2,610	3,306
Maintenance	1,000	2,800
TOTAL COST	16,601	13,980
Savings	--	2,621
Equipment Cost	45,000	54,000
Incremental	--	9,000
SIMPLE PAYBACK	--	3.4 years

*Assumptions: $13.34/kW; 4-month ratchet; 5.8c/kWh peak energy charge; $5.00/million Btu gas rate; $60/ton price premium for engine chiller; 1200 EFLH; 2000 hour/year.

The attractiveness of engine chillers is more pronounced in applications where the engine chiller is replacing one of two electric centrifugals. The engine chiller should be operated to maximize electric peak-shaving in areas with high demand charges or extended ratchets. Baseloading the gas chiller is an attractive option in regions with high energy component costs, such as San Francisco.

A typical building with two electric chillers would normally operate one unit in a baseload mode and bring the other unit on as needed to meet peak loads. The cost of the peaking chiller is very high due to the small number of hours over which to amortize the demand charges. The baseload chiller would operate approximately 2000 EFLH and the peaking chiller would operate only 400 EFLH to average 1200 EFLH for the system. In contrast, a gas-fueled engine-driven chiller can easily operate in the peaking mode, following load, and obtain significant savings. The engine chiller also has the unique capability to overspeed, increasing the capacity of the chiller by as much as 25% for short periods without harm to the engine or compressor. The efficiency of the engine chiller falls off at the higher speeds, but the effects are minimal for such short periods. The engine chiller's ability to increase output would permit the electric centrifugal to be partially idled during peak cooling loads and reduce compressor demand charges by up to 25%. The net impact of incorporating an engine chiller for peaking applications is a very attractive payback on the incremental investment.

TABLE 3
ANNUAL COST COMPARISON
Two Electric Centrifugals vs
Electric & Gas Chillers
(Chicago Area Office Building Application)

	Electric		Electric/Gas	
EFLH	2000	400	2000	400
Compressor				
Demand	$ 5,117	$ 5,117	$ 3,837	$ 0
Energy	11,123	2,225	11,123	0
Gas	0	0	0	2,329
Auxiliaries				
Demand	1,201	1,201	1,201	1,521
Energy	2,610	2,610	2,610	3,306
Maintenance	1,000	1,000	1,000	1,600
Subtotal	$21,051	$12,153	$19,771	$ 8,756
TOTAL		$33,204		$28,527
Savings		--		4,677
Equipment Cost		$45,000		$54,000
Incremental Payback		--		1.9 years

*Assumptions: $13.34/kW; 4-month ratchet; 5.8c/kWh peak energy charge; $5.00/million Btu gas rate; 1200 ELFH; 2000 hours/year; $60/ton price premium for engine chiller.

CONCLUSIONS

Natural-gas-fired engine chillers offer a unique and very attractive opportunity for commercial building owners to shave electric demand charges and reduce operating expenses. The development of engine chillers has been revitalized to capitalize on the window of opportunity for gas cooling, opened by the electric utilities' escalating plant costs. New engine chillers will incorporate advances in compressor technology and control systems that will increase performance, reduce costs, and improve reliability. The key to the successful commercialization of the engine chiller will be the development of a maintenance infrastructure to provide low-cost service and retain high availability.

The market for the engine chiller is extremely attractive in regions that suffer high electric demand charges. The chiller's capability to operate efficiently at part load, coupled with its ability to overspeed, makes it an ideal peaking unit. The economic advantages are very clear. Further, the gas chiller can replace centrifugal systems with only minor site modification, allowing the engine chiller to capitalize on the large replacement market and compete on a incremental first-cost basis. Engine chillers will also compete effectively as baseload units, as electric prices continue to escalate. The additional revenue from recovered engine heat will only improve the very attractive economics of this alternative cooling system.

Gas cooling is a viable option today. Engine chillers offer the potential to expand the market for natural gas and secure a significant share of the cooling business in the very near future. While gas utilities will enjoy increased sales at offpeak seasons, electric utilities also prosper by the reduction of peak demand and the avoidance of larger plant construction.

Chapter 10

DESICCANT-BASED ENVIRONMENTAL CONTROL SYSTEMS

W. C. Griffiths

ABSTRACT

For over 50 years, liquid desiccant humidity conditioning equipment has been used to provide air at controlled temperature and humidity for a wide variety of industrial and institutional process air-conditioning applications. Performance features of liquid desiccant equipment utilized in these applications include the following:

* Ability to simultaneously cool and dehumidify air.
* Ability to dry air to dewpoint humidities about 40°F below the conditioner coolant temperature.
* Ability to fully modulate coolant and heat use and fully control air cooling and dehumidification to match the process load requirements.
* Ability to deliver bacteriologically decontaminated air.

In the past, the relatively low cost of electric energy created little economic incentive to incorporate desiccant dehumidification equipment in comfort conditioning systems. More recently, increases in the cost of electricity and the increased impact of electrical demand charges make desiccant dehumidification considerably more attractive for these applications. Use of liquid desiccant dehumidification to handle building latent loads can reduce maximum refrigeration loads by 25 to 40%, and minimize refrigeration load variations.

The effectiveness of liquid desiccant dehumidification in reducing comfort-conditioning refrigeration loads has been demonstrated in a number of buildings. The cost-effectiveness of integrated liquid desiccant/refrigeration comfort conditioning systems can be further enhanced by improving the thermal efficiency of the regeneration process and by developing lower-cost liquid desiccant equipment designed for the commercial market. GRI-sponsored research currently planned will significantly advance toward these objectives and also provide valuable tools for modeling the performance of integrated systems in a variety of building types and climates.

INTRODUCTION TO LIQUID DESICCANT DEHUMIDIFICATION

Figure 1 is a schematic depiction of a liquid desiccant air conditioning system. The system is similar to an absorption refrigeration system in that it operates on the principle of chemical absorption of water vapor by a desiccant solution, typically a water solution of lithium chloride. In operation, air passes through the conditioner unit and is cooled and dehumidified by contact with the desiccant solution. The heat absorbed from the air by the desiccant solution is rejected to a coolant through a suitable heat transfer surface. Coolants typically used are cooling tower water, ground water, chilled water, refrigerants, or air. The conditioner unit is analogous to the absorber section of an absorption refrigeration system.

Water absorbed by the desiccant in the conditioner unit is stripped from the desiccant in the regenerator unit by heating the desiccant to elevate its water vapor pressure and contacting the heated desiccant with a scavenger airstream. The desiccant solution is heated through a suitable heat transfer surface by steam, hot water, gas or oil firing, or refrigeration condenser heat. The regenerator unit is analogous to the generator section of an absorption refrigeration system.

FIGURE 1

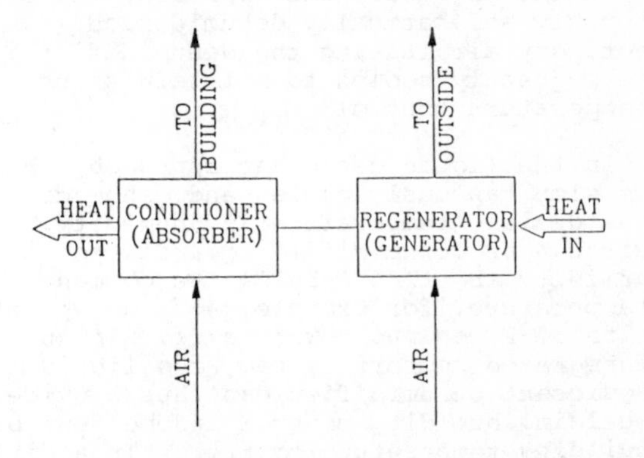

Figure 2 shows the vapor pressure charateristics of lithium chloride solution. At a given concentration of salt by weight, the solution is in equilibrium with air at a practically constant relative humidity, regardless of temperature. The air humidity leaving the conditioner unit can be adjusted by adjusting the concentration of the solution. At practical operating concentrations, the conditioner unit can dehumidify air to relative humidities as low as 18%, and can humidify air to relative humidities as high as 90%.

FIGURE 2

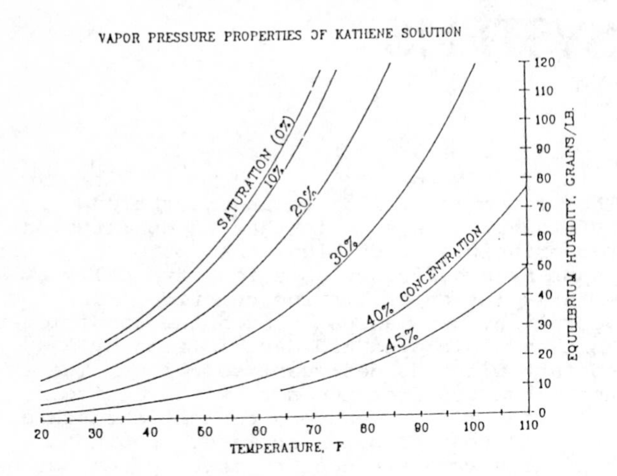

COMPARISON OF DEHUMIDIFICATION METHODS

Figure 3 illustrates the three common methods of dehumidifying air for process and comfort air-conditioning applications. In the refrigeration approach, the air is dehumidified by condensing the water on the surface of a cooling coil. The dew point humidity of the air leaving the coil is roughly equal to its dry-bulb temperatures so the coolant must be several degrees colder than the dew point humidity of the air. Substantial reheating of the air may be required to maintain temperature control in the conditioned space. In comfort conditioning applications, if the air cooling is limited to that required to maintain space temperature control, the dew point humidity of the delivered air will increase and high building humidities and discomfort may result.

In the dry desiccant approach, the air is roughly adiabatically dehumidified. The hot, dry air leaving the dehumidifier is subsequently cooled to maintain space temperature control.

In the liquid desiccant approach, the air is simultaneously cooled and dehumidified to the desired temperature and humidity. The air can be dehumidified to a dew point humidity about 40°F below the coolant temperature, for example, 45°F dew point with 85°F cooling tower water. In an integrated comfort system, the liquid desiccant dehumidifier can thus provide building humidity control independent of building temperature control. In addition, the building latent loads can be rejected to cooling tower water, reducing the refrigeration cooling load.

FIGURE 3

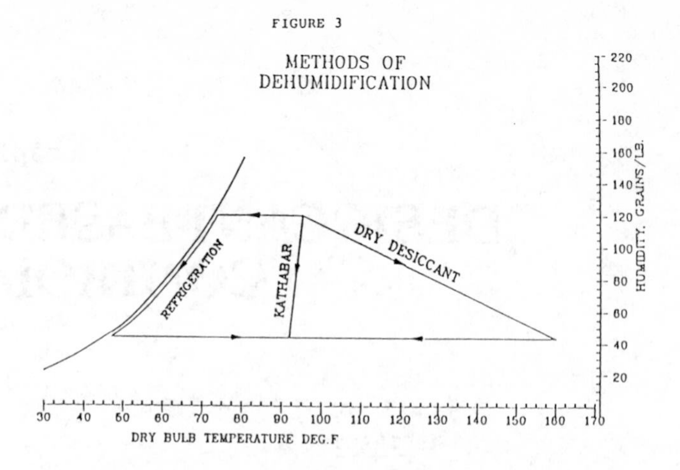

Figure 4 illustrates the desiccant regeneration processes. In the dry desiccant approach, the scavenger air is heated and subsequently heats and dries the desiccant. In the liquid desiccant approach, the desiccant solution is directly heated, and in turn is regenerated by heating and humidifying the scavenger air. The temperature level required for the regeneration process is basically a function of the relative humidity of the air leaving the dehumidifier. The high air temperature leaving the dry desiccant dehumidifier result in a lower relative humidity than the same dewpoint delivered from the liquid desiccant dehumidifier; hence, substantially higher heat source temperatures are required to drive the dry desiccant regeneration process.

FIGURE 4

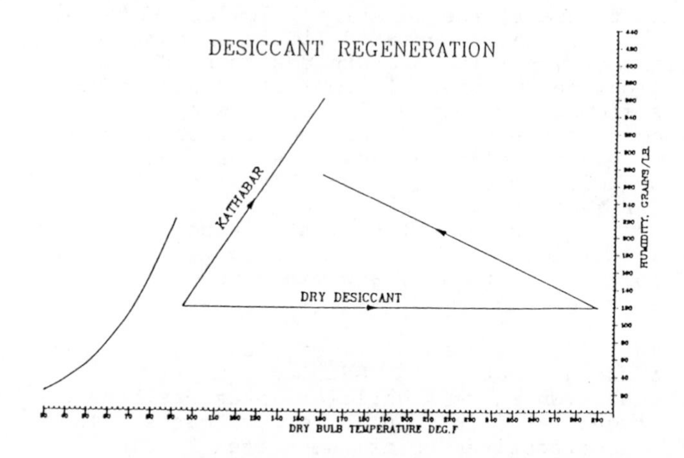

APPLICATION OF LIQUID DESICCANT DEHUMIDIFICATION TO COMFORT CONDITIONING SYSTEM

Figure 5 schematically represents a typical refrigeration air conditioning system. In operation, building return air and ventilation air are mixed. The mixed air is cooled and dehumidified by condensation by one or more cooling coils. All the heat extracted from the air is rejected to the refrigeration system.

FIGURE 5

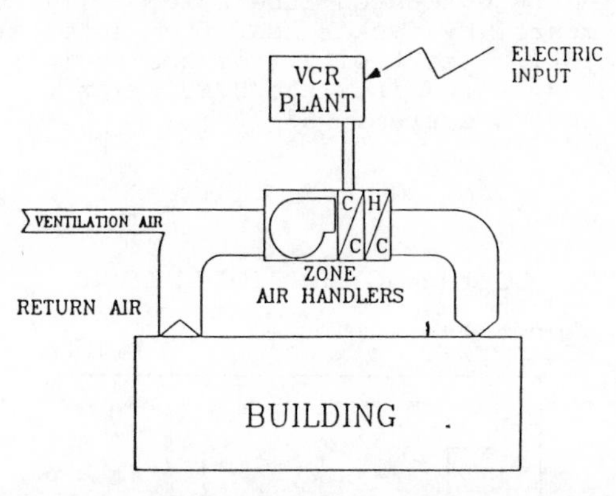

This process is psychrometrically depicted in Figure 8. It should be noted that the portion of the cooling load attributed to the ventilation air is typically 25 to 40% of the total cooling load at summer design conditions. As shown in Figure 8, if the ventilation air is pre-conditioned in a liquid desiccant dehumidifier, the ventilation air cooling load can be removed from the refrigeration system, and the dehumidifier can deliver the air dry enough to absorb the building latent load.

The removal of the ventilation air load from the refrigeration system not only reduces the size and design power requirements of the refrigeration plant, but also minimizes the change in refrigeration load with changing weather conditions. This can significantly reduce the impact of high demand charges by allowing the smaller refrigeration plant to operate closer to full load, since it handles only building sensible loads, which are relatively insensitive to weather conditions.

The reduction in refrigeration equipment size and operating cost via use of the liquid desiccant dehumidifier is at the expense of heat energy required to operate the regenerator. State of the art regenerators have thermal COP's in the range of 0.4 to 0.5 (BTU Latent Work per BTU Heat Input). At this efficiency level, the use of liquid desiccant dehumidification for comfort conditioning is economically attractive only in areas with very high combined electric demand and usage charges. Reductions in prime (fossil-fueled) heat input would make the use of liquid desiccant dehumidification for comfort conditioning economically attractive in a much broader range of applications and rate structures. The relatively low operating temperatures of the liquid desiccant regeneration process make it possible to effectively use waste heat from the refrigeration cycle to supply a portion of the heat required for regeneration. GRI-sponsored research currently planned will investigate two such integrated liquid desiccant-refrigeration systems.

FIGURE 8

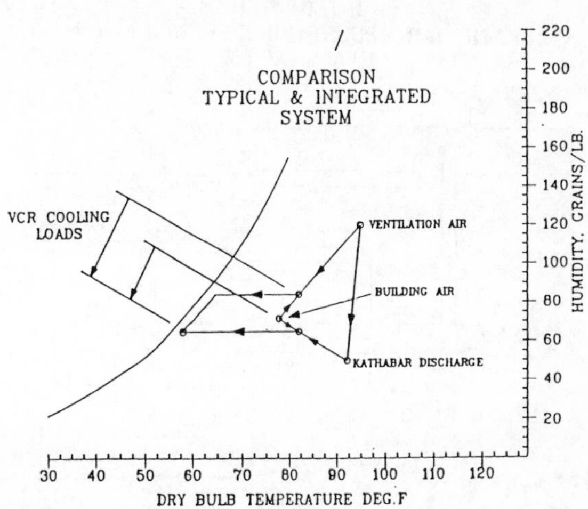

The first, schematically shown in Figure 6, will utilize condenser heat from the vapor compression refrigeration system to provide a portion of the regeneration heat by preheating the regenerator inlet air and/or preheating the desiccant solution. The remaining heat energy required will be supplied by a gas-fired solution heater. Targeted thermal efficiency for the regeneration process is 0.9 to 0.95 BTU of cooling per BTU of gas input, on a seasonal basis.

FIGURE 6

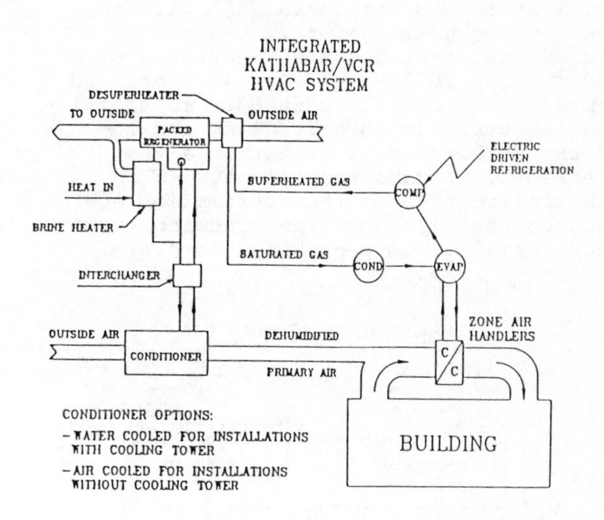

The second integrated system, schematically shown in Figure 7, will utilize condenser heat from a double-effect gas-fired absorption chiller as the sole source of heat for regeneration. This system basically adds an open-cycle third effect to the closed-cycle double effect chiller.

Using state-of-the-art technology, liquid desiccant dehumidification has been successfully applied in a number of comfort-conditioning systems, typified by the following examples.

FIGURE 7

INTEGRATED
KATHABAR/ABSORPTION REFRIGERATION
HVAC SYSTEM.

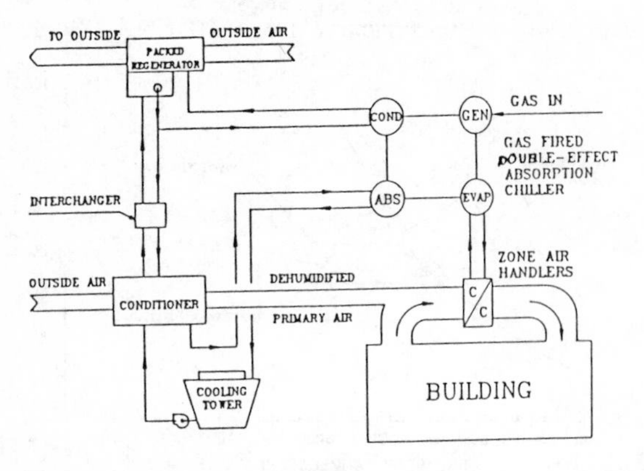

Figure 9 schematically represents the HVAC system installed at the Social Security Administration Metro West Complex in Baltimore, MD. In this system serving approximately 790,000 FT^2 of office space, 0.1 CFM/FT^2 of ventilation air is dehumidified to 31 GR/# moisture content in a two-stage liquid desiccant conditioner. The dehumidified air is distributed to fan coil terminal units utilizing air cells in the steel deck flooring. Each fan coil recirculates the air locally and provides only sensible cooling. Since the building latent load is handled by the dehumidified primary air, the building chiller water temperature was raised to 55°F with no loss in occupant comfort. Use of the liquid desiccant dehumidification system reduced the chiller size by 600 tons and improved its COP by about 8%. In addition, the low ventilation air volume and the use of the decking for ventilation air distribution (made possible by dehumidification of the ventilation air) reduced the floor-ceiling sandwich by 30%, substantially reducing building costs.

FIGURE 9

FEDERAL OFFICE BUILDING

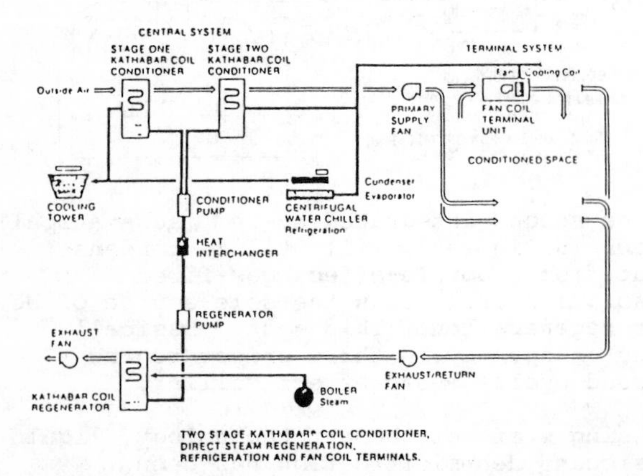

TWO STAGE KATHABAR® COIL CONDITIONER,
DIRECT STEAM REGENERATION,
REFRIGERATION AND FAN COIL TERMINALS.

Figure 10 schematically shows an integrated system installed at Monroe County Courthouse in Strousburg, PA. In this 75,000 FT^2 facility, 0.2 CFM/FT^2 of ventilation air is dehumidified to 45 GR/# by a liquid desiccant conditioner using cooling tower water as a coolant. The dehumidified ventilation air is distributed to unitary terminal heat pumps which perform sensible cooling only. Regeneration heat is supplied by evacuated-tube solar collectors supplemented by jacket heat from an engine-generator. Electricity from the engine-generator is fed into the HVAC power distribution system.

FIGURE 10

COUNTY GOVERNMENT BUILDING

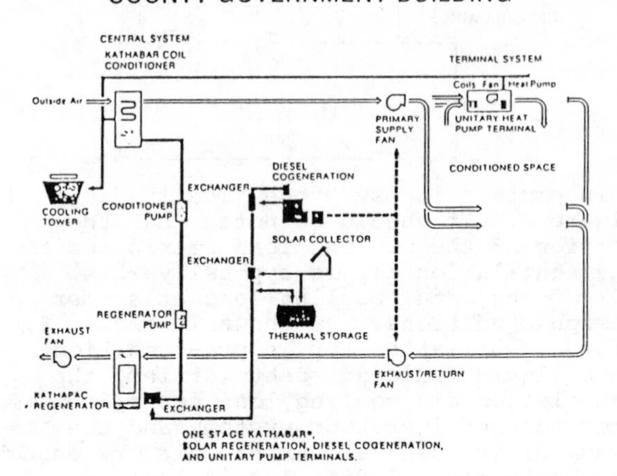

ONE STAGE KATHABAR®,
SOLAR REGENERATION, DIESEL COGENERATION,
AND UNITARY PUMP TERMINALS.

SECTION 3

BUILDING AUTOMATION – ENERGY MANAGEMENT SYSTEMS AND CONTROLS

Sponsored by the Energy Management and Controls Council

Chapter 11

DISTRIBUTED INTELLIGENCE AND COMMUNICATION IN BUILDING AUTOMATION SYSTEMS

G. A. Bruns

INTRODUCTION

The cost of energy and the advent of reasonably priced microprocessors has resulted in some major changes in building control and communication systems. This paper will address these changes and how they are affecting the way a building is operated.

Until recently, control of the heating and air conditioning systems in a commercial building has been by pneumatic control. From a control standpoint, pneumatic controls provide good, efficient and reliable control. The power provided by pneumatic actuators still makes pneumatic actuation the first choice.

The precipitous rise in the cost of energy has imposed some additional constraints on control systems, however, where pneumatic controls sometimes fall short. It is now necessary to monitor and coordinate all the control systems in a building to assure most efficient operation. In a large building with many HVAC systems, communication of information among the various control systems and to the manager of the facility becomes a significant factor. This is where the new microprocessor based systems provide significant advantages.

You have, no doubt, heard about digital control. The trade publications are full of stories and advertisements for it. Digital control simply means that control is being done by a processor or, if you will, a computer. HVAC functions are nearly all analog -- meaning they are continuously variable. Temperature, humidity and pressure are all analog values. Output devices such as valves and dampers are also almost always analog -- they can move to any position between full open and full closed. Pneumatic controls, some electric controls, and many electronic controls are inherently analog and, therefore, can directly monitor and control HVAC functions.

Microprocessors are strictly digital. That means they can only recognize a signal that is either full on or full off. They can count on-off pulses or take some sort of action in response to a signal going on or off, but they cannot deal with analog values such as temperature.

In early building management systems, there was just one processor, called the central processing unit or CPU. All the information from various sensors around the building was sent to this processor which

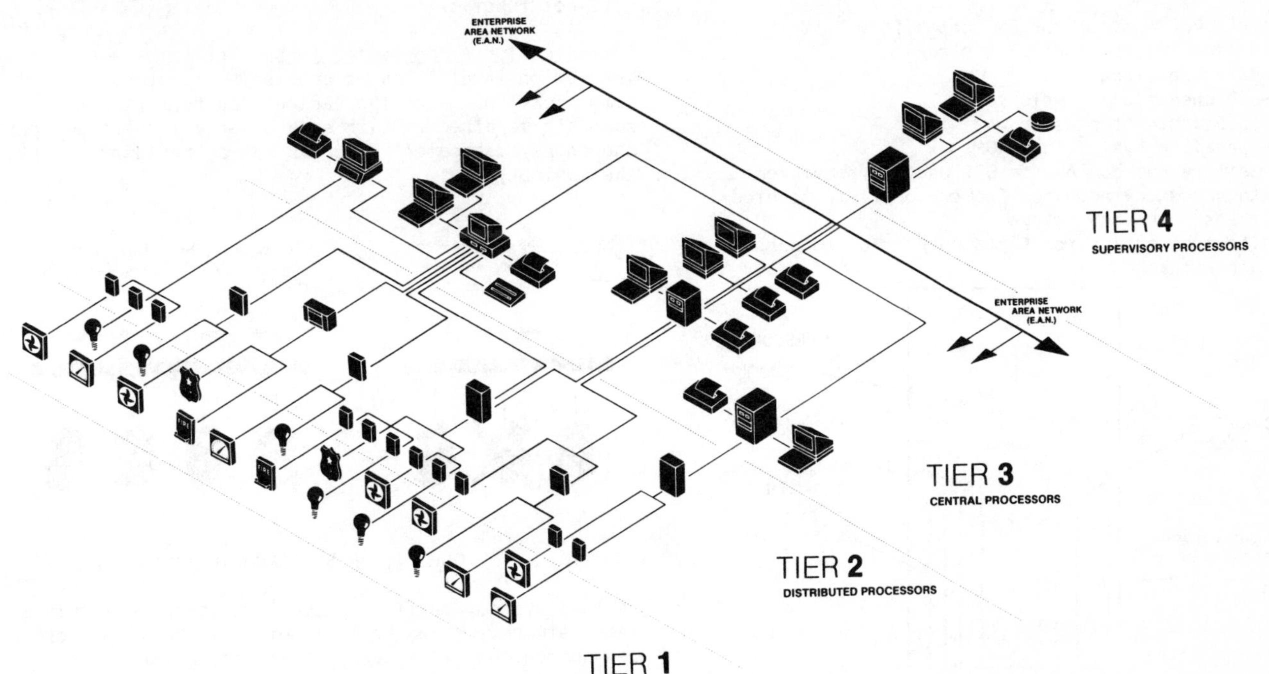

FIGURE 1. SYSTEMS ARCHITECTURE

monitored what was going on but usually did not perform any control functions other than to change the setpoint of a local control system or open or close a damper. It did not provide any direct control because of the possibility of significant delay in responding to changes in the controlled system and the serious problem that would result if the CPU failed -- the whole building could go out of control.

SYSTEMS ARCHITECTURE

As microprocessors became lower in cost, it became practical to use many processors and distribute this intelligence around the building. This greatly increases the reliability of the system and makes it practical to directly control the HVAC, lighting and other systems by these distributed controllers. It also changed the requirements for communication among the processors and to a central. The architecture of the system has evolved into a tier system. A representation is shown in Figure 1.

Tier 1 includes the sensing and actuating functions typically found in commercial buildings.

Distributed Processors

The distributed processors are located in Tier 2. The DDC processor does the following:

- o Receives information from sensors.
- o Processes information according to program.
- o Outputs signals to actuators.
- o Stores information for future use.
- o Provides control functions - can provide complicated functions more easily than pneumatic.
- o Adaptive control
- o Has capability of communicating with other processors to send and receive information and commands.

The distributed DDC processors can be a single circuit board packaged in a wall mounted panel (Figure 2) with features as follows:

--Full DDC control and EMS capability
--Battery backed real time clock
--Universal inputs
--LED operational indicators
--16 bit microprocessor
--Operating system in EPROM
--Battery backed RAM for DDC and EMS parameters
--An accessory area for factory or field mounted transducers and relays
--Terminal strips for field connection to sensors and actuators

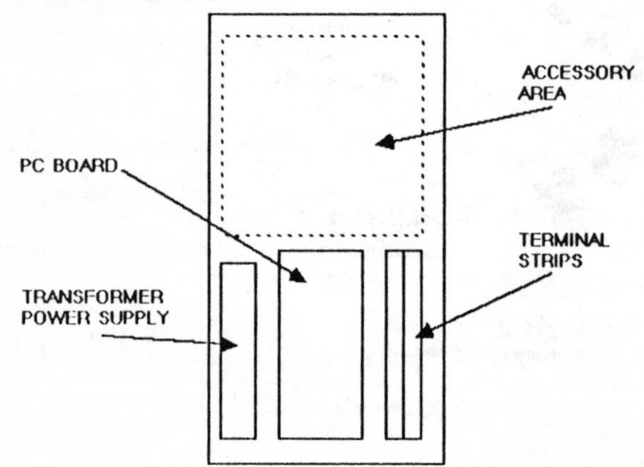

FIGURE 2. DISTRIBUTED PROCESSOR PANEL

Standalone Distributed Processor: The distributed DDC processor can be applied in a standalone application. (See Figure 3.)

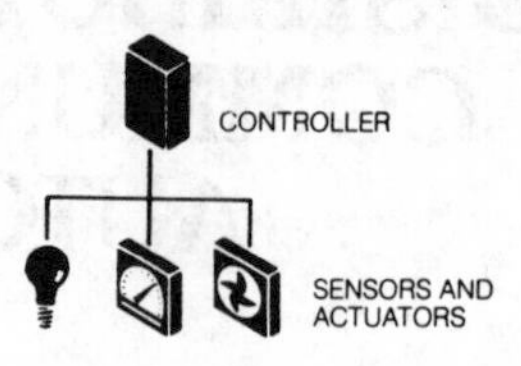

FIGURE 3. STANDALONE CONTROLLER

One processor typically serves one or two air handling units. This processor provides complete DDC control and EMS functions. A portable hand held operator's terminal is available for functions such as:

- o Display and change setpoint values
- o Display and set application program data
- o Enable/disable points, initiators and programs
- o Display point summary and alarm summary

Data is accessed through descriptive menus for ease of use.

In larger systems, there is often information which must be sent from one controller to another and it is usually desirable to provide central access to all the information in the system. Most systems have provided this via a central processor or computer which relays information from one controller to another to gather information from all the controllers for display and printout and for total system energy management. This has been a very effective and efficient system but it still suffers from the major shortcoming of the earlier centralized system in that, if the central processor fails, communication between controllers is lost and the energy management programs in the central will not function.

Communication Among Controllers: The latest innovation in distributed processing is peer communication. Here the various controllers can communicate directly with each other without a central and energy management programs can be resident in all the controllers.

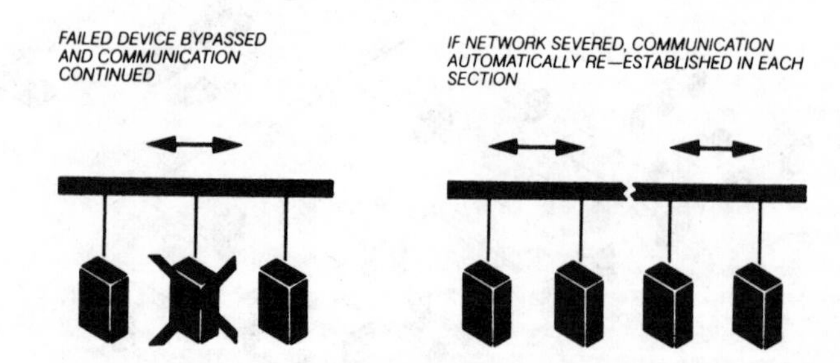

FIGURE 4. PEER COMMUNICATION

In this system, multiple processors communicate via a Peer Network. With the Peer Network, every controller can communicate with every other controller as an equal or peer, with or without a central. There are several ways to allow the controllers access to the communication bus. An important feature must be that failed devices are automatically bypassed and, if the bus is cut, the individual segments must automatically re-establish communication and control.

Even with a fully loaded peer network, reporting of alarms and response to commands must occur within a maximum of a few seconds. Proper peer network communication protocol makes it possible to have distributed electric demand control without a central.

Peer communication makes it practical to share sensor data; e.g., all controllers have access to outdoor temperature from a sensor connected to one controller.

It is also feasible to have global event programs, again without a central.

The peer network should also permit downline and upline load of information from the central without taking controllers offline or stopping the global transfer of information.

Central Processor

Central processors are located in Tier 3 of the systems architecture as shown in Figure 5. Video display terminals or personal computers provide a window to the system at this level.

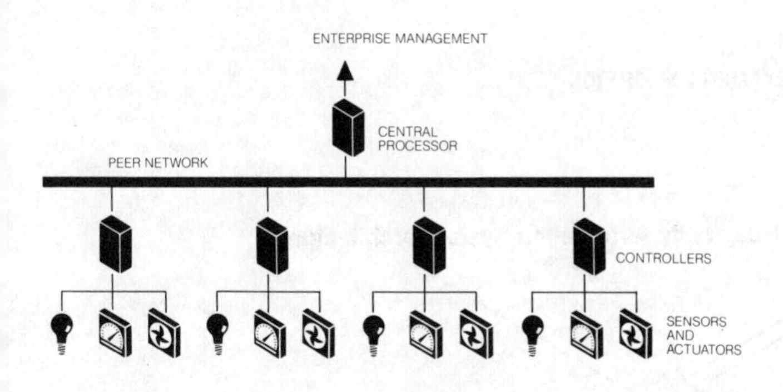

FIGURE 5. CENTRAL SYSTEM

Point data from multiple distributed control processors may be displayed in logical groups.

Alarms, operator responses, operator commands and returns to normal are automatically saved to disk. These can be retrieved later as a history log.

Critical operations can have temperatures or other analog values logged at regular intervals for later recall as an historical report.

Software Application Packages: Examples of software application packages include maintenance manager and energy auditor.

Maintenance manager automatically schedules and prints maintenance work orders and provides financial analysis of the costs associated with building maintenance. Maintenance schedules are generated based on calendar date, run time of equipment or an event. The system automatically prints work orders. A work order includes a description of the task, maintenance instructions, skill level, estimated time to complete and the necessary materials. Daily, monthly and yearly reports provide a summary of materials and skill costs and a summary of tasks that are completed or delinquent.

A simplified example of an energy auditor display is shown in Figure 6. Sensors for kilowatt hours (KW), kilowatt demand and fuel flow rates provide data. The building owner inputs unit cost information. Energy auditor software then processes data to provide month to date and year to date reports. The reports can be expanded to include heating degree days, BTU's per square foot and other building efficiency indicators.

Other central processors may co-exist with, and share information with, the central processor just described. These central processors would be part of an Enterprise Area Network. An example of this is the hospitality automation system shown in Figure 7. This system provides total integrated control for the hotel business. It integrates the following environmental and control subsystems:

- Energy management
- Life safety monitoring/control
- Telecommunications
- Rooms management
- Property management

We will continue to see significant technology and software advances which will provide you with more usable information, even greater efficiency, more distributed intelligence and better/more reliable communication. You can expect to see intelligent controllers for individual terminal units such as the VAV box controllers. There will be more sophisticated communications systems. Fiber optics and power line carrier options in some systems and communication via telephone circuits within a building will soon be a reality. Digital communication systems will soon be standard so that telephones, computers, video and many other functions can use common lines.

In buying a new system or expanding an existing system, it is important to be aware of two important features -- software and potential for expansion. Software is a very important feature because it is the determining factor in whether a system performs effectively or not. As the hardware becomes more generic -- as in the expanding use of standard personal computers -- the software makes the difference. A vendor's background in computers does not make him an expert in HVAC and energy management. Choose your software carefully.

It is also important that your system can be modified and/or expanded as your needs change and your building grows. Check your vendor to be sure that the vendor has accommodated older versions of a system in his new system. You do not want your system to become obsolete whenever a new system is announced.

CONCLUSION

In summary, the basis of control and energy management have not and will not change, just the way they are done. Communication systems will continue to become more sophisticated and versatile.

This is an exciting and challenging field to be in. You will continue to see interesting changes and innovations. It is important for you and your facility that you keep abreast of them.

PARKWAY BUILDING 320,000 SQ FT	BUILDING ENERGY AUDIT REPORT FOR MARCH 1986		
	THIS MONTH		
	1985	1986	% CHANGE
ELECTRICITY			
KWH	790,435	649,330	-18
KWH COST ($)	45,924	44,090	- 4
PEAK DEMAND (KW)	3525	3201	- 9
DEMAND COST ($)	14,276	16,645	17
NO. 2 OIL			
GALLONS	10,507	9141	-13
TOTAL COST ($)	11,663	8958	-23
MILLION BTU	1471	1280	-13
TOTAL ENERGY			
COST ($)	57,587	53,048	- 8
MILLION BTU	4168	3495	-16

FIGURE 6. ENERGY AUDITOR OPTION

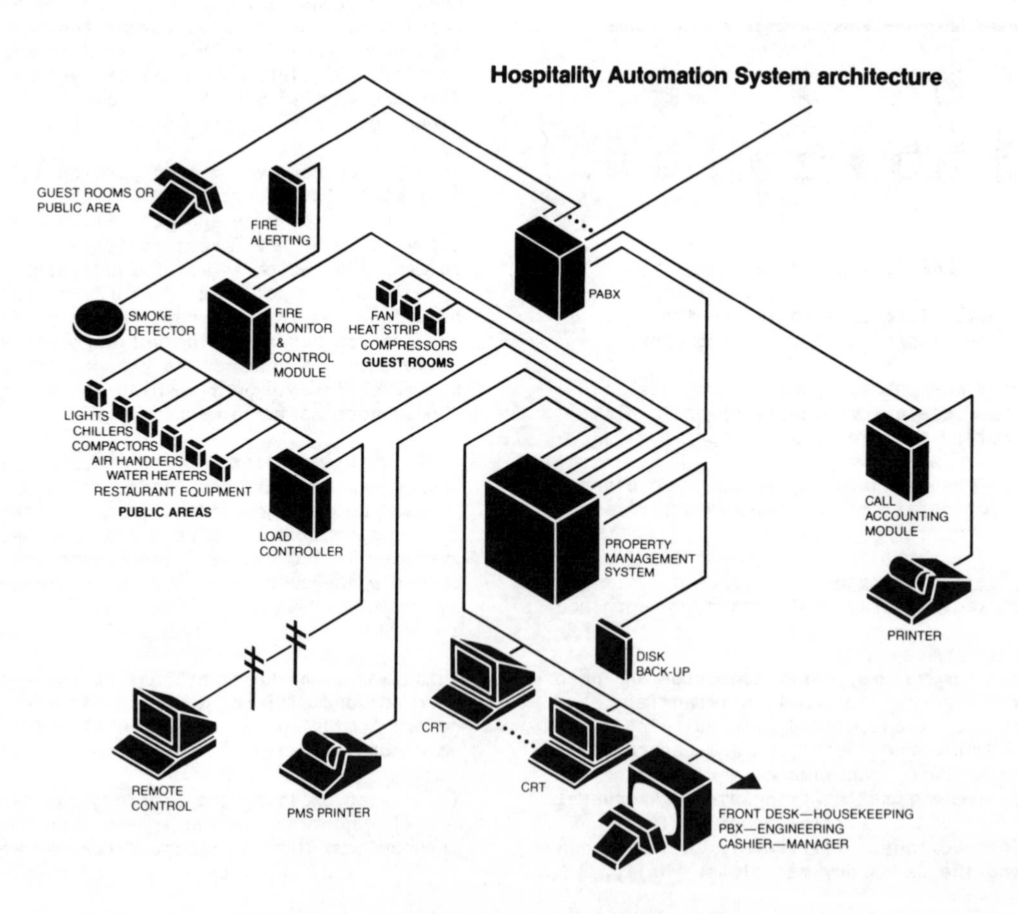

FIGURE 7. HOSPITALITY AUTOMATION SYSTEM

Chapter 12

THE INTELLIGENT BUILDING: FACT OR FICTION?

D. M. Fisher

INTELLIGENT BUILDINGS

The Intelligent Building is a concept which has received much attention and promotion recently. The phrase itself brings to mind many assumptions about potential capabilities. Thanks to skillful marketing and a great deal of expectation on the part of building owners, developers and architects, the perception is that the Intelligent Building is here today. But what does it mean to have an "Intelligent Building" and, perhaps more importantly, why do we need it?

Ironically, the promoters of Intelligent Buildings have a vision which is largely misunderstood because of the term "intelligent." These pioneers have the vision that buildings of the future will integrate all of the building's services together into multi-functional information networks. Such buildings would combine Temperature Control, Energy Management, Fire, Security, Telephone, Video, Word Processing and Computing services under a common backbone network which would be as integral to the building as its plumbing. This kind of integration could accommodate a wide variety of different tenant needs: tenants could lease central services from the building owner or manager, or utilize the existing facilities with tenant-owned equipment. This integration would also allow the cross-correlation of information from these various systems to be easily compiled for a wide variety of services and analyses.

The major benefit of this approach is that it provides the opportunity for Computer-Integrated Building Operations (CIBO).

The integration of services and building operations management has clear benefits; however, integration is not the same as intelligence. Integrating all of a building's systems together into a common backbone communications network is only one part of the Intelligent Building puzzle.

So how does CIBO make a building more "intelligent"? The first step toward more intelligence in buildings is more intelligence in the Building Automation System (BAS).

The trend in modern Building Automation Systems is to integrate the traditionally separate functions of Temperature Control, Energy Management, Fire and Security under one common operation and, in some cases, using a single network which is not dedicated to any one function. Today this can be achieved without sacrificing the benefits of distributed processing and control. Many vendors, driven by this trend, can now provide the kinds of centralized operation required by fire and security applications, in addition to the distributed processing features which are desirable in HVAC and Energy Management System (EMS) applications. So, today's BAS can provide many of the functions that the layman associates with the "intelligent" building.

DIRECT DIGITAL CONTROL: EASIER THAN EVER

Direct Digital Control (DDC) is gaining wide acceptance throughout the industry. Although there are many newcomers, there are a number of vendors offering mature and sophisticated DDC systems with a proven track record of successful installations. With the increasing demand for better performance and energy savings, DDC is rapidly becoming the technology of choice. Per loop costs of DDC systems continue to diminish as the technology matures. A number of recent innovations are helping to make DDC easier to implement, as well as pointing the way for future developments.

Most mature DDC systems provide either Proportional plus Integral (P+I) or Proportional, Integral and Derivative (PID) control strategies. These control algorithms provide significant benefits over traditional pneumatic proportioning controls. With proper use, these control strategies can eliminate cycling and offset problems which have long been associated with pneumatics. Many of these systems can accommodate a wide variety of actuators and sensor types.

Although pneumatic actuation was once considered a costly option for DDC systems, it is now offered by many vendors at a reasonable cost. The specifying engineer can now trade-off cost and performance requirements for loops requiring pneumatic actuation. Loops which require faster response can utilize analog outputs in the form of voltage or current along with an appropriate E/P or I/P transducer. Many control loops in HVAC applications can be effectively implemented using lower cost multiplexing transducers or stepping valves. In general, the lower cost methods are open loop transducers without position feedback; the higher cost transducers utilize position sensing or pressure feedback. In spite of these trade-offs, many systems can offer tight control capabilities which surpass traditional pneumatic methods.

In retrofit installations, DDC can be especially effective and produce real energy savings. It is important to match the DDC technology to the system which is being replaced. In particular, the flow and volume requirements of a pneumatic system should be considered when choosing a DDC system to replace and enhance existing receiver/controllers. Some DDC systems are not suited to driving pilot positioners and other low volume, constant bleed devices for example. On the other hand, some DDC systems do not provide sufficient flow for rapid actuation. These seemingly simple considerations can render an otherwise capable DDC system ineffective.

Of course, DDC systems can also drive electric actuators. These fall into three general categories: floating setpoint, position proportioning and pulse-width modulating. Floating setpoint actuators are driven by a varying voltage or current which varies the position of the motor in proportion to the amount of voltage or current. Position proportioning actuators are generally bi-directional motors (AC or DC) which are moved to a given position by a timed pulse which is proportional to the end-to-end travel time of the motor. Pulse-width modulating actuators are generally spring loaded on-off devices. When a pulse is applied to the actuator it begins turning in one direction. When the pulse is removed the spring returns the motor to its original position. By applying a continuous cycling to the actuator, an 'average' position can be achieved. The pulse-width determines the average position. In general, the floating setpoint actuators deliver the highest performance in terms of speed of response and accuracy. They are also the most expensive. The other two technologies deliver more modest performance and respectively lower accuracy. Needless to say they cost less.

DISTRIBUTED UNITARY CONTROL SYSTEMS

DDC is finding widespread use in Distributed Unitary Control applications, such as VAV control systems. DDC is well suited to two different aspects of VAV control systems: static pressure control and room control. Static pressure control applications utilize DDC's tight control capabilities to maintain duct static pressure setpoint regardless of changing zone requirements. In a typical system, the DDC loop monitors duct static pressure and modulates air volume to maintain a given static pressure setpoint. Air volume is typically modulated in one of two ways: varying fan speed or varying fan blade pitch. Although both of these techniques are in wide use, fan speed modulation is gaining favor because of its lower energy use and superior performance. The fan speed is varied by a motor speed controller, typically with a 4-20 milliamp input. Recent advances in Power Inverter technology are helping to lower the cost of fan speed modulation. This trend is encouraging many specifying engineers to consider using variable speed fan modulation in smaller VAV applications.

Historically, VAV Room Control has been a pneumatic controls stronghold, since no other technology could be applied cost-effectively. There is an on-going debate regarding the benefits of distributed room controls especially in terms of their potential contribution to an integrated building management system. Pneumatic room control strategies suffer from several key drawbacks. First, the basic control which they can deliver is, at best, strictly proportional. The rooms are thus subject to cycling and offset problems which compromise comfort and/or energy savings. The second problem is that the only way to integrate such distributed pneumatic controls into a typical EMS/DDC system is through the use of pneumatic overlay controls. In such a system, the DDC controllers produce a pneumatic output which is used to reset the pneumatic room controller. Since the room controller uses a pneumatic temperature sensor, it is usually necessary to add a redundant electronic temperature sensor for the DDC overlay system. Clearly this approach is costly and complicated; this fact has restricted its use only to facilities which absolutely had to have the EMS features.

Recently, several vendors have introduced new controllers which address many, and in some cases all, of these drawbacks. A new breed of distributed DDC controllers are now available for VAV room control. These controllers generally have the following key features:

- Standalone DDC control of room temperature, (P+I)
- Electronic Temperature Sensing (usually thermistor)
- Integral Electric Actuator, or compatibility with them
- Network connections to EMS system

The last feature is really the key to this technology. The BAS network can access all of the relevant parameters of the VAV controller, such as Room Temperature, Damper position and Room Temperature Setpoint. Since the BAS can also command the VAV controller, all of the capabilities of the overlay system can be accommodated with a relatively modest increase in cost over the traditional pneumatic system.

This type of distributed control system provides many useful capabilities for the integrated BAS. Life Safety and Fire Management systems can easily coordinate room damper closing and opening for effective smoke purge without the need for a redundant set of override relays and wiring or piping. The damper positions of each distributed controller can be averaged and used to reset the central VAV air handler for more even comfort control. The distributed room sensors can be trended for very accurate building thermal profiles. Some of these new VAV controllers can also measure energy use with airflow sensing. This feature can be valuable in multi-tenant facilities for BTU-submetering, since the distributed controllers could then meter the actual energy used for heating or cooling in each room.

MAINTENANCE MANAGEMENT: MOVING AWAY FROM GUESSWORK

Certainly one of the major benefits from all of these attempts at integrating BAS subsystems together is access to data about the dynamic state of building operations. If this data can be integrated into automated tools for management and scheduling, then the costs of building management can be greatly reduced. Traditionally, mechanical maintenance scheduling has been based on empirical data regarding average run time per month, rate of failure etc. At best, this technique is manpower intensive (walking around reading run time counters; performing maintenance that isn't really required). At worst, it can lead to more equipment failure because accurate run time information was not available. This all translates into higher costs.

Today, sophisticated Maintenance Management tools are available for use with personal computers, as well as proprietary BAS. These software programs can provide complete services for managing scheduled maintenance, parts inventories, work order generation and a variety of other desirable services for building operators. However, the ultimate effectiveness of these tools may be limited by dependence on empirical data. To eliminate this element of guesswork, it is necessary for the maintenance management system to have access to actual run time and supervisory data. For example, run time limit and clogged filter alarms should be available to the maintenance management system so that it can schedule maintenance dynamically. Fortunately, this feature is already part of some vendors systems. As the integration of more and more diverse subsystems into the overall BAS continues, the need for closely coupled maintenance tracking features will become more and more important.

SIMPLE IDEAS THAT MAKE LIGHTING SMART

Effective and flexible control of lighting systems is another critical factor in the realization of intelligent buildings. In larger buildings, lighting can represent a major portion of the energy cost. The traditional issues in lighting control have been: how to provide acceptable levels of illumination, reduce energy consumption during demand peaks and how to provide flexible scheduling and override capabilities to tenants without compromising energy savings.

Many of todays buildings are designed to aggressive standards for illumination levels. This has led many building managers and owners to seek alternative schemes for reducing lighting levels, such as group re-lamping. Many of these schemes are very costly, and the fact that they can be justified is a testament to the high operating costs caused by over-illumination. The trend is away from past levels of 100 foot-candles toward the new architectural standard of 76 foot-candles.

How can this standard be implemented cost-effectively in existing buildings? One technique that has emerged recently is the use of variable transformers to reduce the operating voltage, and thus the lighting level, of entire lighting areas. This technique can be applied to all types of lighting: incandescent, flourescent, low-pressure sodium etc. The variable transformer is controlled by its own distributed controller. A controller is required for certain types of lighting, such as flourescent, so that voltage levels can be increased to a level sufficient to start the lamps whenever additional loads are switched on. The controller uses a slow 'ramp-up' technique so that changes in lighting level will not be noticable. This type of lighting control can also be performed by specialized Direct Digital Lighting Controllers (DDLC). These techniques are equally effective in new buildings.

Another new technique is the use of dynamic area illumination. Flourescent fixtures are fitted with a solid-state electronic ballast which has reset capabilities. The electronic ballast improves energy efficiency and waste heat generated by conventional ballasts. In addition, the reset capability of many of these new ballasts can be utilized for dynamic control. A photocell is made integral to the flourescent fixture with a diffusing lense so that the photocell can measure the ambient lighting level in the area that the fixture is lighting. The photocell is used to reset the ballast, thus affecting the amount of light produced by the flourescent lamps. If the ambient lighting level is high, for example near a window, then the flourescent lamps will be reduced to a low lighting level. If the ambient light level drops, then the ballast will increase the flourescent lamp level. These types of ballasts are available from a number of vendors with different types of mounting options and features for photocell mounting and sensitivity.

REDUCING ELECTRICAL DEMAND

Many of today's EMS utilize a technique called Load Shedding to control electrical demand. These systems are designed to reduce or eliminate Demand Peaks. Since electricity typically carries a premium rate based on the maximum amount of electricity used during any given period, it is usually desirable to reduce the peak level during demand periods. Load Shedding accomplishes this by turning electrical loads off according to priorities established by the building owner or operator. Unfortunately, what frequently happens is that there are not sufficient numbers of loads which can be shed without causing major disruptions or discomfort to building occupants. The alternatives are both undesirable: suffer some inconvenience or pay more.

Resettable ballast systems and DDLC systems can be used separately and together with EMS to make the lighting systems of a building more intelligent about demand control. When the EMS senses an impending demand peak, DDLC systems can be commanded to reduce overall lighting levels in areas until the demand peak has passed. Since the DDLC changes the lighting levels fairly slowly, tenants will generally not even realize that the lighting levels have been temporarily reduced. A similar technique can be utilized with resettable ballasts. In fact, the technique of reducing demand by incremental reset of energy-consuming systems is gaining widespread acceptance in the specifying community. This technique works equally well with HVAC equipment such as chillers and boilers.

TENANT OVERRIDE FOR LIGHTING SCHEDULES

From a building tenant's perspective, flexibility is often the single most important aspect of intelligence. In most modern EMS, lighting is controlled according to scheduled periods of occupancy. Many times tenants have a need to use a portion of the building's facilities at unscheduled times. Many EMS provide the tenant with the ability to override the scheduled shutdown of lighting or HVAC systems. A flexible set of options for tenant override can make a big difference in energy savings as well.

For example, consider a multi-tenant building which has all lighting for a given floor controlled by a single contactor. The EMS controls the contactor according to a schedule of occupancy of the building. Now a tenant wants to use his group of offices on that floor after hours. Since the EMS has only the single contactor to control with, the entire floor must be turned on so that the tenant can use his portion. Many buildings are wired in this way so that simpler EMS can be utilized.

Clearly, more contactors can be installed, but this is often undesirable for the building owner as the partitioning of each floor may change from time to time.

There is a simple technique which can be utilized to overcome these problems while still using a simple EMS. Each office on the floor can be fitted with zero power resetting switches. These new devices function in a similar way to normal on-off wall switches in that they turn the lights on and off each time a button is pressed or a switch is switched. The difference is that, unlike normal wall switches, when power is removed from the switch, it is reset. So, the contactor which provides power to the floor is not turned on and off on a schedule, but is left on almost all of the time. At the end of scheduled building occupancy, the EMS commands the contactor to interrupt power for a few seconds. This resets all of the wall switches, thus turning off all of the lighting on the floor. When a particular tenant needs to use one or more offices, he can simply turn on his wall switch as normal. The EMS can be programmed to interrupt the contactor every so-often during unoccupied hours, to assure that the lights then get shut off if they have been 'overriden'. If the tenant is still using the office when such a 'sweep' occurs, a simple push of the wall switch button restores the lights. By making the time between sweeps two or four hours, the inconvenience will be minimal.

In many buildings the tenants require flexibility with more than just the lighting control. A number of vendors are now offering interfaces to telephone and paging equipment which can be used for additional override capabilities. One technique which is just starting to be used successfully is dial-in override. This is a feature of some EMS or BAS which allows them to connect to a standard telephone line. When someone dials-up the line that the EMS controls, it will answer the phone and wait for a sequence of digits to be entered by the caller on a touch-tone phone. The digits identify the caller and authorize a particular function such as "override zone 37". These features are available in various levels of security. The least secure systems use a particular phone number as a command. So if you call that number and let it ring once, that is sufficient to activate the override. This technique is generally used only with private PABX systems that can dedicate a block of sequential extension numbers to EMS use. Systems that connect directly to the public switched network generally use a single number. The least secure of these systems answers in-coming calls and waits for a few digits to be entered. The digits represent the zone to override or function to be performed. These systems have the obvious drawback that anyone can call them, thus inviting potential mischief. The most desirable systems require some kind of authorization code as well, but these systems also command a higher price.

PRE-INTEGRATION OF BUILDING SYSTEMS COMPONENTS

In the past, mechanical systems contractors purchased mechanical components (air handlers, chillers, compressors etc.) and installed the mechanical system; control systems contractors purchased controls components (actuators, sensors, controllers) and installed the control system; security systems contractors purchased security components (card access systems, detectors, alarms); electrical contractors purchased lighting control systems and wired the whole thing together. In those buildings which have fully integrated building automation systems, the BAS contractor usually had to be responsible for getting each piece of equipment integrated under one common system, often displacing one or more other contractors.

One of the side effects of this approach is a lot of back-end tailoring of equipment to customize it for an integrated system. For example, a packaged air handler has to be retrofitted with sensors and controls for basic HVAC operation, then fire system overrides have to be retrofitted to that, then (possibly different) EMS controls have to be overlaid on that. It would seem to make more sense to outfit the complete control system into the air handler when it is manufactured, and its internals are completely exposed. Such a unit would come ready to use, pre-integrated for one or more applications. The mechanical contractor could install it; the electrical contractor could wire it; the controls contractor could program and tune it. In the end, it would be much easier for all of these contractors. This approach also offers a unique feature to the building owner or specifying engineer: it's practically guaranteed to work every time.

The pre-integration concept is applicable to a very wide range of traditional controls and mechanical equipment. Rooftop units, heat pumps, VAV boxes, chillers and boilers are just a few examples of mechanical equipment which is available in pre-integrated form today, from a number of vendors. Most major mechanical systems vendors are either offering or thinking about offering this kind of capability to the contractor.

Pre-integration is also reaching down into traditionally mechanical sub-systems. The intelligent compressors in each rooftop unit are now pre-integrated to permit sophisticated coordination of protection, multi-loop temperature control, duty-cycling, adaptive loading, and real-runtime maintenance management.

There is one small problem though. These systems are still not simple to integrate into the overall BAS because there are no widely accepted standards for networking them all together. So today's intelligent building can only really be created by a few vendors who have integrated most of the desirable functions together under one system, or who have the networking sophistication to utilize the emerging range of pre-integrated products.

OPEN SYSTEMS PHILOSOPHY: THE CORE OF CIBO

The ultimate acceptance of pre-integration, and the integration of building systems in general, depends on open systems philosophy. This philosophy promotes standards by which building systems can be networked together. Thus, one manufacturer's automation system can "talk to" another manufacturer's pre-integrated mechanical equipment. The vendor is then free to make major changes to the implementation or features of a piece of equipment, without having to worry about compatibility with previous installations. This also gives the building owner security against obsolescence.

The situation that exists today with the development

of intelligent buildings, is very similar to the situation in Factory Automation and Computer Integrated Manufacturing (CIM). There are many capable subsystems which exist, but the problem is: how to get them to talk to each other and coordinate their operation? General Motors decided to lead the way by calling for compatibility between automation systems components. GM published the Manufacturing Automation Protocol (MAP) which is essentially a universal language for coordinating communications between computer-based subsystems in factories. GM is hoping that this will become the defacto standard for factory automation and CIM. It has been enthusiastically received by many vendors in that industry. MAP appears to be well on the way to becoming the standard that is so desparately needed for factory automation. Unfortunately, MAP is too expensive and complex for use in building operations and controls.

Some vendors of equipment are currently proposing standards which could prove to be the catalyst to achieving the widespread acceptance of open systems philosophy in building automation.

THE BENEFITS OF CIBO

CIBO amplifies the capbilities of building operators and management allowing them to extend their intelligence, information management and control throughout the building and its operation.

Communications networks within the intelligent building can provide access to all forms of information and control capabilities. This allows comprehensive analysis and building-wide optimization to be performed. Today, such analyses can be performed by human experts who collect and study building performance data. Clearly, an important benefit to CIBO is that it can provide a vehicle for integrating these diverse sources of information.

THE FUTURE: EXPERT BUILDING OPERATIONS SYSTEMS

By coupling such a network with the emerging technology of Expert Systems, all of these intelligent buildings can have the benefit of state-of-the-art expertise in building optimization, energy management and performance analysis.

The Expert System is a relatively new concept which has come out of extensive research in the field of Artificial Intelligence. The Expert System is a form of computer programming which is based on rules-of-thumb rather than fixed algorithms. The rules have a more or less equal influence on the behavior of the overall system. The rules are continually re-examined and compared with the current situation. Any applicable rules are then followed by the system, possibly causing control actions to be taken, or new sets of rules to be considered. This somewhat radical departure from conventional notions of control and programming turns out to be well suited to describing expertise in human terms.

With the ability to collect information from diverse sources throughout a facility, and the ability to influence a wide range of control activities, a suitable expert system could greatly extend the sophistication and quality of performance available from the intelligent building. At the same time, it would provide a very high level framework for the building owner, operator or manager to communicate with, and direct, the building's intelligent core.

So, is the intelligent building a fact or fiction? The tools and products exist today to make buildings very smart. Pre-integrated equipment with open systems philosophy is a fast growing trend. Manufacturers are talking about standards for control and automation equipment which would protect the owner from obsolescence. The elements are almost all available, and yet the intelligent building is elusively far from commonplace. With the cooperation of manufacturers and the help of specifying engineers, we can make the intelligent building the rule, rather than the exception.

GLOSSARY

Algorithm

A method or program for solving a particular problem.

Artificial Intelligence

A branch of Computer Science which is concerned with the nature of intelligence, and the creation of machines that exhibit behavior which, if humans behaved that way, we would call 'intelligent'.

Backbone Network

A communications network within a building or group of buildings which provides a common point for attaching all communicating devices.

Ballast

An electrical or electronic device which produces the starting current required by flourescent lamps.

Building Automation System (BAS)

A computer-based system which is used to monitor and control various aspects of building operation, such as Heating Ventilation and Air conditioning, Energy Management, Fire/Life Safety and Security.

Computer Integrated Manufacturing (CIM)

A factory-wide system which integrates all aspects of the manufacturing process into one system. From the initial design of equipment through to its shipment, the same system integrates all information about the overall manufacturing process.

Direct Digital Control (DDC)

A form of closed-loop feedback control system where the control decision is based on a mathematical calculation performed by computer, rather than depending on a purely mechanical or electrical effect.

Energy Management System (EMS)

A computer-based system for evaluating and controlling energy use.

E/P, I/P Transducer

E/P (voltage to pressure) and I/P (current to pressure). These devices are used to convert a varying voltage or current to a proportional air pressure (pneumatic).

Expert Systems

A form of computer programming which uses rules rather than algorithms. Particularly well suited to expressing human expertise about situations which cannot be easily described procedurally.

Factory Automation

Systems which are used to automate various aspects of factory operation, such as materials handling, assembly, inspection etc.

Heating Ventilation and Air Conditioning (HVAC)

Manufacuring Automation Protocol (MAP)

A technique proposed by General Motors for integrating communications among factory automation components to help coordinate overall factory control and management.

Multiplexing Transducer

A device which multiplexes (shares) an air pressure sensor between several air pressure outputs to save cost.

Private Access Branch Exchange (PABX)

A private telephone exchange system which is dedicated to one or more buildings.

Photocell

A device which converts light into an electrical signal.

Power Inverter

A device which is used to drive electric motors with a varying frequency electric signal which affects the motor's speed. Typically used as a transducer to convert a varying voltage or current into a proportional change in motor speed.

Proportional, Integral, Derivative Control (PID)

A technique for achieving stable closed-loop feedback control. Based on the mathematical relationships of difference, average and rate of change. A variable is measured and compared to a desired value. A corrective control action is calculated based on the difference between the measured and desired values (error). The technique can also take into account the average error and rate-of-change of error.

Reset

A technique of biasing the setpoint of a controller above or below a preset value, based on some control signal.

Stepping Valve

A pneumatic air valve which can be opened or closed in steps which correspond to fixed angular movements, based on on-off pulses.

Trending The periodic sampling and recording of any number of variables.

Variable Air Volume (VAV)

An air delivery system for buildings which is based on varying the volume of air supplied to each space, rather than the amount of heat or cooling applied, to control the temperature in the space.

Chapter 13

PC-BASED DDC ENERGY MANAGEMENT SYSTEM

L. M. Boutni

INTRODUCTION

The IBM facility at Rochester, Minnesota has implemented a direct digital control system which is the state of the art in energy management. The DDC system covers almost 2,500,000 square feet of space in 40 buildings with 2,000 points of monitor and control.

SITE STRATEGY

The IBM site is divided into six zones. Each zone has a PC as the command computer and operates independently. All six zones will eventually be linked to a host computer. The host computer will provide global strategies and management reports. To date, five zones have been installed (see Table A).

ZONES 3 AND 4 RETROFIT

The zones incorporate standalone microprocessors that provide a true distributed process. Existing HVAC systems with pneumatic sensors and pneumatic control schemes were retrofitted with DDC in Zones 3 and 4. Electronic sensors are installed for better accuracy and closer and tighter control. The pneumatic system is used as a back-up system in the event of a DDC failure. A computer pneumatic interface device allows for manual or automatic computer operation.

Each zone control system took 9 months to implement. Zone 3 installation was completed in December 1984; Zone 4 was completed June 1985. The total installation cost for both zones was $592,000 with calculated energy savings of $401,500 per year.

NEW CONSTRUCTION

Zones 5 and 6 represent new buildings. DDC without pneumatic control back-up has been implemented in the recently constructed buildings as an integral part of the project. Gradual switches are provided for manual control in the event of a DDC failure.

ENERGY SAVINGS

Each DDC installation has been justified on its own merits. In the case of Zones 3 and 4, the payback is less than two years with a favorable calculated IRR (internal rate of return).

The potential energy savings are based on engineering analysis. DDC uses proportional integral derivative (PID) control techniques which can save 8% to 12% of heating and cooling costs. Energy management strategies (such as demand limiting, enthalpy control, duty cycling, and time scheduling) are incorporated in the DDC system for further savings and convenience. The system is designed with adequate capacity for future expansion and enhancements.

Controlled experiments on DDC versus pneumatic controls confirmed a significant superiority of DDC over the conventional pneumatics.

MAINTENANCE/SERVICE/PERFORMANCE

The DDC system technology is vendor supplied in accordance with IBM DDC Instrumentation Subsystems Specification. The system has a remote access feature which allows the vendor to access the network via a telephone line to perform troubleshooting and diagnostics.

The DDC operators daily examine the system's performance by completing monitor and control functions through software at the PC level. Mechanical problems such as leaky dampers and air lines, malfunctioning valves and actuators are detected and analyzed at the PC. A printer records variables and trends.

DDC is a sophisticated system that required debugging and fine tuning. So far, it has performed satisfactorily. It is difficult to accurately measure the contribution of the DDC system, but it appears to contribute to energy conservation based on actual energy expenditures versus plan. Further, it is an effective troubleshooting tool for maintenance personnel as it increases their productivity.

TABLE A. IBM ROCHESTER DDC ZONES

Zone	Description	Installation Cost ($000)	Calculated Energy Savings/Yr ($000)	Remarks
1	Central Utilities Plant	35	100.0 potential savings on a demand penalty	Justification based on kVA demand limiting
2	High Technology Process Building	NA	NA	Under study
3	Manufacturing and Administration Building	324.6	235.5	Retrofit of HVAC equipment and lighting control
4	Laboratory Buildings	267.4	166	Retrofit of HVAC equipment
5	Building 114 New Administration and Manufacturing Building	NA	NA	New construction
6	Leased Buildings	NA	NA	New construction

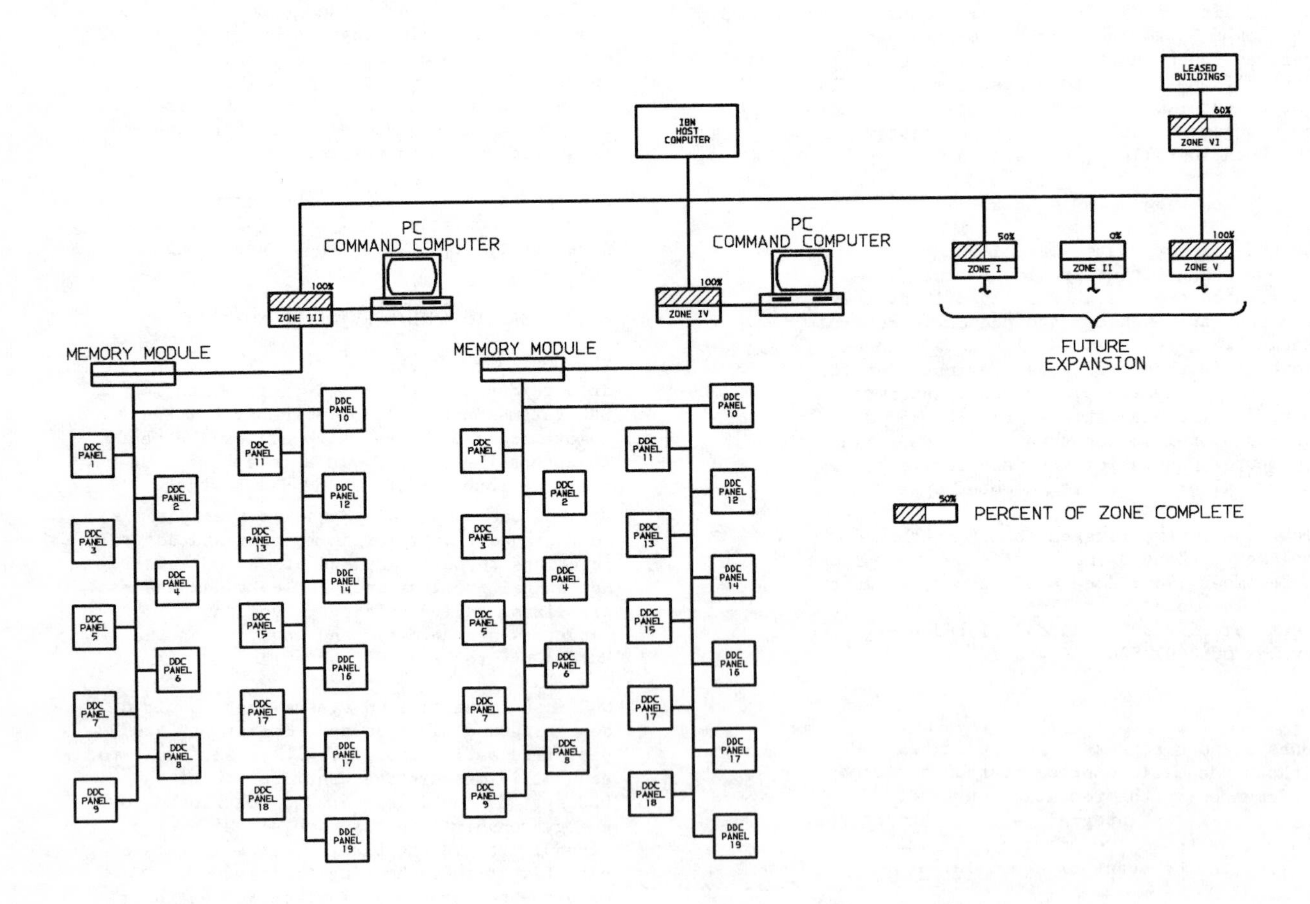

FIGURE 1. DIRECT DIGITAL CONTROL ENERGY MANAGEMENT SYSTEM

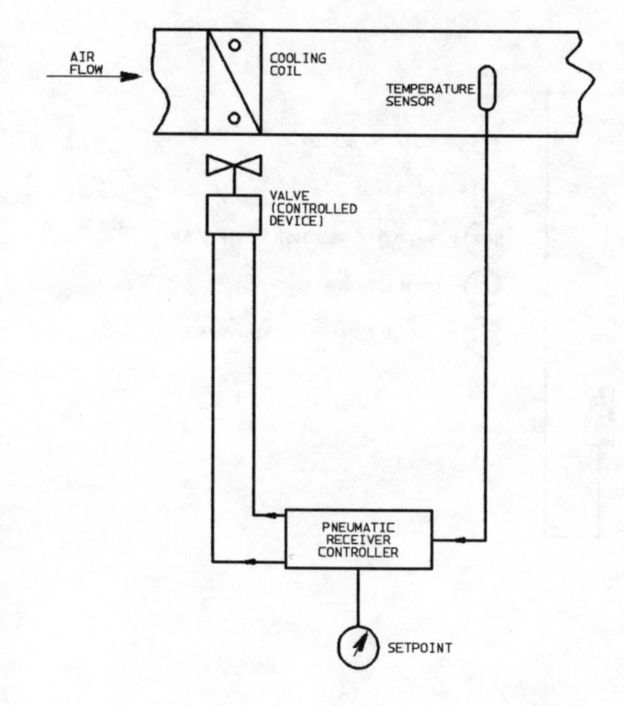

FIGURE 2. REAL TIME AUTOMATIC TEMPERATURE CONTROL CLOSED CONTROL LOOP

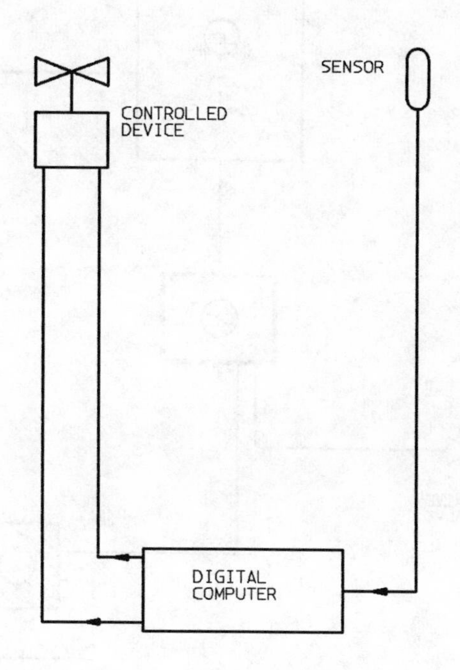

FIGURE 3. DIRECT DIGITAL CONTROL DDC LOOP

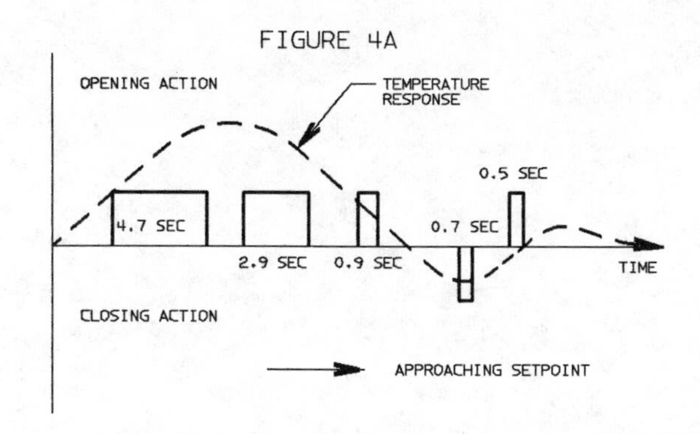

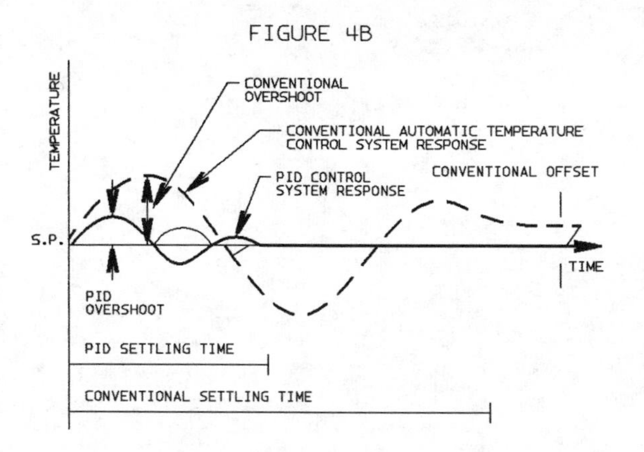

FIGURE 4. PROPORTIONAL-INTEGRAL-DERIVATIVE & PULSE-WIDTH MODULATION

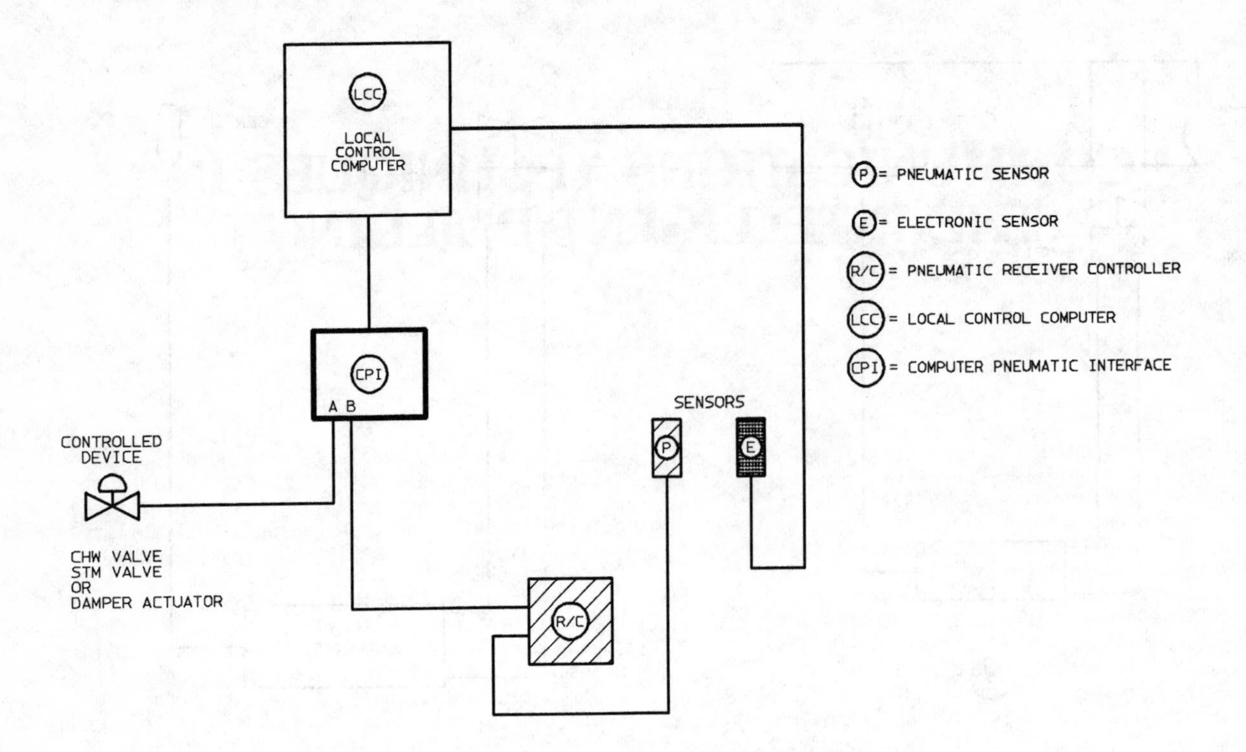

FIGURE 5. DDC-EMS: COMPUTER TO PNEUMATIC INTERFACE (CPI)

Chapter 14

COMMUNICATIONS TECHNIQUES IN THE INTELLIGENT BUILDING

L. E. Gelburd

In the intelligent building, many control and information systems will be operating simultaneously. These systems must be able to operate independently for reliability; however, they also need to share information with other systems in the building. Information is shared between and within these systems over a variety of communications media. To share information, two aspects of communications are critical - media and protocol. Simply stated, media refers to the various ways of moving information from one place to another, while protocol describes the format of that information.

Advances in both hardware and software technologies have made more choices available in the selection of media and protocol. More choices mean more complex decision-making. Media vary in key characteristics: cost of the media, installation cost, transmission bandwidth, available protocols, and the cost of adding new devices to the network. When selecting the communications techniques to be used in an intelligent building, all of these factors should be considered, since each may affect the cost, expandability, reliability and flexibility of the network.

The intelligent building is not desirable if it is not reliable in its operation. From an operational standpoint, it is unacceptable for all systems in an intelligent building to depend on the continuous availability of the entire communications network. Each node of each system must be able to function in a useful way even if the communications network is unavailable. On the other hand, it is essential that access to the communications network allows access to information from other systems using the network. These requirements make distributed control essential. Fortunately, many current systems take the distributed approach to control.

CENTRALIZED SYSTEMS VS. DISTRIBUTED SYSTEMS

Historically, there has been a tradeoff between distributed and centralized control systems. Centralized systems have the advantage of providing uniform access to the entire system for control and monitoring; they have the disadvantages of high cost, performance which degrades as point count increases, limited expansion capability, and presenting a single point of failure. Distributed systems have the advantages of lower cost, consistent performance with increasing point count, easy expansion and no single point of failure; in the past, however, distributed systems sometimes lacked a uniform access method for the entire system.

Today, systems are available which provide the best features of centralization AND distributed control without their associated drawbacks. Intelligent buidings require the combination of reliability and ease-of-use which these systems provide.

One advantage of distributed systems is that the amount of information they need to share is far less than a centralized system of the same size. This means that the communications network connecting distributed systems does not need to be as high speed (and high cost) as it would if it connected centralized systems. However, if high speed is needed for another part of the network, or if a high speed network is already installed, the distributed approach can use the network just as effectively.

In an intelligent building, the communications media and protocol should promote flexibility, expandability and maintainability. These features are important because initial installations of building systems are frequently expanded in function and size. The sheer scope and diversity of the systems in an intelligent building suggest that maintainabilty of the systems is a key issue.

More building owners are becoming aware that the flexibility, expandability and maintainability of the protocol is just as critical to the long-term success of the intelligent building as the communications media selected. A system which promotes flexibility, expandability and maintainability as well as independence from the system manufacturer can be referred to as having an "open architecture." The use of an open architecture protocol can make the difference between a system which is an information exchange bottleneck and one which is a powerful information management tool.

COMMUNICATIONS MEDIA

The media used for the transmission of information can be broadly categorized into two classes - direct connect and unbounded. Direct connect can be thought of as those media which physically connect the nodes on the communications network. Unbounded media encompass those media which do not require a direct physical connection for the transmission of information.

Direct connect media are widely used in communications networks. Available direct connect media include twisted pair, fiber optics and coaxial cable. Some advantages of direct connect media include data security and relatively high immunity to radio interference. Unbounded techniques, alternately, can reduce installation costs.

Twisted pair is a communications medium with a long history. By having the two wires twisted about a common axis, interference between adjacent pairs is minimized. Since telephone communications use multiple twisted pairs, this medium is very widespread. Simple, inexpensive copper wire is used, and installation is easily accomplished. Although higher transmission speeds are possible, most twisted pairs are used at transmission frequencies of 56K baud (56,000 bits/second) or below.

Fiber optics is a communications medium which has a tremendously high bandwidth capacity. Transmission frequency of 1G baud (1,000,000,000 bits/second) has been achieved. It is also unaffected by electrical and radio frequency interference. Data is completely secure. Unfortunately, fiber has other mitigating properties. It is expensive, and requires special tools to install and expand. It is not easily used for multidrop systems because the technology for fiber "taps" is expensive and not widespread. Future developments should make this technology more popular and less expensive.

Coaxial cable is a popular medium for many local area networks (LANs). It is a good compromise between twisted pair and fiber optics. It has a large bandwidth (hundreds of Mhz) so that many independent signals can be transmitted over a single cable using different frequency ranges. Coaxial cable is significantly more expensive than twisted pair and is more complex to tap, but is superior to fiber in these areas. Coaxial cable is often used in one of two ways: for carrying many modulated signals at separate frequencies (Broadband) and for carrying a single high speed unmodulated signal (Baseband).

Other communications media are direct connect and have the virtue of being in place in many buildings. These include Computerized Branch Exchanges (CBXs), Digital Branch Exchanges (DBXs) and, for lower level communications, installed power lines (the AC wiring throughout a building). Use of these media is limited, but convenience can make them worth consideration.

Unbounded media include infra-red and radio frequency (from very low to ultra-high). Since the transmission of information using these media occurs through air (and sometimes buildings), one advantage is the lower installation cost. Data is somewhat less secure than when direct connect media are used. Radio frequency transmission is becoming more popular for multi-building facilities spread over a fairly large area, while infra-red transmission is useful within a physically enclosed area (such as a room).

COMMUNICATIONS PROTOCOL

Communications networks require more than a transmission medium; they require the selection of a protocol. This is the prescribed format of information exchange on the network. Protocol encompasses both the determination of access to the network (which node can initiate communications at what time) as well as the structure of the information transmitted by the node accessing the network.

To illustrate the difference between the medium and the protocol, consider a person who wants to call another person on the phone. The caller dials the other person, and when the connection is established, the dial phone network is the transmission medium. However, if the person called speaks in french while the caller speaks in english, the people are not sharing a single protocol, and no useful information is exchanged. Being able to communicate in and of itself is not enough; nodes which need to share information must use a protocol agreed upon in advance.

OPEN ARCHITECTURE AND PUBLIC PROTOCOLS

When it comes to protocols, standards are a critical issue. Standards allow users of equipment manufactured by different sources to operate them in a uniform manner. Unfortunately, there has been a proliferation of custom (non-standard) protocols from manufacturers seeking to lock customers into their equipment. This creates an information bottleneck when systems using different protocols need to share information. Fortunately, there is a worldwide recognition of this problem, and there are signs of progress: the promotion of systems with open architectures and the promulgation of the ISO seven-layer model for open systems interconnection (OSI). The wide acceptance of General Motors' Manufacturing Automation Protocol (MAP) which conforms to the OSI model is a strong indication of the desire for standards (as well as the desire to be able to sell automation equipment to GM). The highest level of the OSI model is the application level. This level must be easily extensible and general enough to permit the transfer of many different types of information. In particular, a protocol which is made public and has an object-oriented structure (access to information using names of objects and attributes of those objects) becomes critical. In facilities automation, one manufacturer has published such a public host protocol. Hopefully, this methodology will become a standard, allowing user independence from any single manufacturer.

Intelligent buildings with sophisticated communications capabilities are great. Of course, many organizations own multiple facilities. What about communications among buildings? There are various methodologies used in inter-building communications networks; they include dial-up phone lines, dedicated leased lines, radio frequency networks including microwave and satellite transmission. For many applications, the low cost and ease-of-use presented by dial-up communications makes choosing dial-up simple. This is particularly true when the need for information is intermittent and the volume of information needed is moderate or low.

Automation systems which support dial in/out communications from any size installation are available today. These systems are capable of dialing out when alarm conditions occur and when historical data should be recorded. Some systems are capable of dialng to a remote printer, CRT or host computer system. When a host system is present, data is exchanged and processed once the connection has been established. In the future, as the price of modems continues to drop, more intelligent buildings will use 9600 baud modems for dial-up data transfer; currently, 300 and 1200 baud predominate, although 2400 baud modems are being used more frequently.

All in all, communications networks in the

intelligent building are becoming less expensive and more available. Choices of transmission media and protocols are expanding; open system architectures and public protocols are receiving much attention. Future trends will be toward more use of radio frequency networks as well as dial-up communications for multiple building facilities, higher speed and lower cost information transmission, and more manufacturers adopting open systems architectures.

Chapter 15

A TREATISE ON EMS PROGRAM MANAGEMENT AND LINK TECHNOLOGY

J. J. McGowan

Energy Management System users have been making a vital request of the energy and controls industry for serveral years which, until recently, has fallen on deaf ears. The single most important factor to ensure the success of an EMS project, beyond the quality of installation, is program management. Users have asked for assistance in developing well defined procedures for managing their programs, and documenting system operations. Traditionally, this function has not been viewed as within the manufacturers scope of responsibility. Although communications systems have typically been provided for the EMS, their capabilities were limited and the apparatus was proprietary, often requiring special hardware and software. As a result, user interface or "Front End" systems, conventionally offered with most systems, fall short of the average users needs for communications and data access capabilities. The advent and proliferation of the personal microcomputer "PC", in particular the International Business Machines (IBM) PC, has reoriented the controls industry, as all other sectors. The important development in the area of EMS is that users now are able to standardize on PC equipment, and utiltize these systems for numerous functions. This ability resulted in the request from users, particularly those with multiple systems, for PC compatible front ends. It is especially important for such systems to utilize "off the shelf" components, rather than special equipment. Recent developments in the industry indicate that this is a concept for which the time has come. This reception is a major shift in manufacturer philosophy, and significantly complicates EMS buying decisions.

This paper is intended to define the basic components of EMS program management and discuss them in relation to the new technological options in the area of front ends. It will delineate the features which have traditionally been provided for EMS interface, as well as optimum front end features. It is also important to discuss the issue of the EMS manufacturers responsibility, and the schools of thought on how best to address user interface functions. In relation to specific user needs, this paper will establish some guidelines for evaluation front end technology, and making purchasing decisions based upon this issue. Finally this paper considers some of the implications of this technology for future EMS program management.

PROGRAM MANAGEMENT COMPONENTS

To present a framework for discussion of this subject, it is important to examine EMS program management in greater detail. Energy Managers are currently faced with a myriad of technical and logistical program management concerns. This situation has been exacerbated by the current consumer opinion, that the consequence of energy issue has waned, which has carried over from the living room to the board room. As a result it is imperative for Energy Managers to resell the importance of their programs, and the best sales tool available is a successful track record. To accomplish such a track record with EMS equipment requires an effective program designed to: (1) verify system operation, and (2) to access raw data and make computations in the process of finetuning system performance. This paper does not global address the concerns of energy management, rather it is confined primarily to one aspect of this issue: efficient management of building automation programs. It is the authors contention that a primary focus of this function must involve the mobilization PC's. In many cases automation is a major component of the global energy program, and one which requires diligence and time intensive oversight, and front end automation is essential.

With respect to Front End Automation, the concept of EMS "Link Technology" has received a great deal of attention recently, and with good cause. There are many interpretations for this concept, in terms of how various sectors of the industry approach discussion and implementation. Though the term will be discussed in greater detail under Link Technology, in general the most viable definition is: an interface system which would allow communication with any manufacturers EMS: A PC Compatible, Universal Front End. In this context, some revolutionary changes have taken place over the past year that will certainly sustain a lasting impact on the industry.

Set aside for a moment, the issues of microcomputers and compatibility. Initially lets define, in this section, components to the management of an EMS program. Among those areas of concern which must be discussed are: (1) SYSTEM VERIFICATION via: Physical Maintenance, Security issues, Performance and Management Reporting, and (2) SYSTEM FINE TUNING. It is also of prime importance to consider maintenance of controlled loads in the evaluation of EMS programs. Each of these concerns will be discussed in relation to program management.

System Verification

Physical maintenance will be discussed first under this section. Maintenance requirements are typically quite limited with electronic equipment. As a result, in many cases long term programs are not developed for addressing these needs. It is important to consider that all components of the EMS installation are not electronic. Normally, at least a portion of the project is comprised of off the shelf electrical gear, such as low voltage relays and transformers of various sizes. This is particularly true where lighting and other ancillary equipment is to be controlled. Redundancy has also been introduced into EMS control, especially on the low end of the spectrum where systems employ less than 100 points. Therefore, it is also an issue where control interfaces including Direct Digital Control (DDC) have interfaced with pneumatic controls, or other local controls. It is crucial to maintain the EMS interface to ensure that a failure does not occur which goes unnoticed due to this control redundancy. The primary focus of physical maintenance is to ensure that EMS savings are not jeopardized by a minor equipment failure. The reputation that Electronic equipment has earned over the years for good reliable service is well deserved. However that does not mean that it can be neglected. Hence a regular physical maintenance and inspection program should be developed along with an operating budget for repairs which may be necessary.

This discussion of security issues is confined to system inefficiencies, translating to missed cost savings, which are introduced via unauthorized and uneducated interface with the equipment. Such problems are limited to those exchanges which occur at the local panel it self, and those which may occur via front end. With respect to local panel exchanges, Unauthorized refers to any type of system exchange that occurs through unsanctioned channels. It is commonly known that manufacturers generally provide for three "Password" levels of interface or access to their systems "Read Only", "Read and Program", "Read, Program and Change Password". For purposes of this discussion, it is assumed that the individuals conducting the interchange do not have terminal or site interface passwords. This category includes the classic EMS savings deterents such as, pulling the plug, fuse, etc., and could also include electrical recircuiting to bypass the EMS interface. Often, the severity of this problem is determined by the amount of direct local presence the energy manager has on site. It is assumed that most users will deal with uneducated exchanges from time to time, during training of new employees, etc. These are primary source of lost savings. These usually involve features which have been provided with the local system apparatus to allow site interface. Often these are overrides or bypasses which are abused. It is also possible to have an Uneducated interface with system software. This happens when site personnel are provided with a site terminal and a password, allowing them to make changes that effect system integrity. Further discussion related to this concept, will be addressed under performance and programing style.

The topic of PC compatible front ends and remote system communication introduces a number of interesting variables into the discussion of unauthorized exchanges. Normally front end systems are password protected, thus limiting unauthorized interface. In general unauthorized interface can be severely limited by careful maintenance of password integrity. Uneducated interface is likely a greater problem from remote communication. There are several considerations under this heading which will be discussed under system performance, as it is also necessary to consider programing access and style issues. The primary point is that interchanges should be monitored, and that individuals responsible for this activity should be trained supervised and follow an established procedure to minimize problems stemming from this cause.

Performance

System performance is a broad category, and is effected by many variables. To simplify the discussion, assume that the actions recommended thus far have been carried out, so that the discussion may be limited to software access and style. First consider that a segment of the equipment available on the market allows limited user interface. Mini computer based systems which employ proprietary programing languages, and provide read only passwords for user are an example. This paper is more germane for systems which allow direct user access to system programing. Which is not to be confused whith some codes, etc. that are discussed under link technology. Systems of interest here may be viewed in two general categories: flexible and structured. As a clarification, all languages are structured, but the EMS Firmware provides a language for user interface which will vary in format and style. Structured styles provide very specific formats which require a response to a prompt. Such systems are usually menu driven and employ error trapping which limits responses to a particular prompt to answers within a specific range. Flexible programing styles vary in degrees, for example some systems will provide a library of strategies for the programer to draw upon or link together, and incorporate into an individual control program. Others require programs or equations to accomplish each specific task. Each of the categories outlined under performance applies to both flexible and structured program style, however the extent of the effect will vary as noted.

As with global system issues, software performance factors will be examined in two general categories: Verification and Finetuning. Verification is a check on software integrity which involves: System Update Maintenance and software problems through Programing Errors and Software Inconsistencies. Finetuning is a process of improving efficiency through adaptive programing modifications based on the examination of historical data.

Software Verification

System Update Integrity refers to changes in

parameters that are stored permanently on disk and noted to all system users. This should be a part of general software maintenance, yet it becomes complicated when more than one front end is employed. This is even more difficult when more than one front end is employed. This is even more difficult when geographic distance is applied, and individuals who make changes to system parameters and strategies are not diligent about communicating those changes to other users. A further complication occurs if for some reason the program residing in the EMS is lost, due to extended power failure, etc., and a new program must be downloaded. This situation can result in the need to retrace every step taken in the process of fine tuning and modifying the original program, a time intensive process. Equally important to the Energy Manager, is the fact that such occurances often erode the facility users faith in the EMS system.

Program Integrity is a problem which is caused by software inconsistencies of several types. Basically this problem occurs when there are errors made in programing, the intital program is modified incorrectly or a parameter input to the program is inconsistent with related control strategies. These concerns can be acute where flexible program styles are employed, and if there are no internal error trapping routines to guide the programer. Often such problems are the result of programing that is not proof read adequately. However, depending upon the data checking features employed, this can also happen when programs are transmitted via modem. Interference or noise introduced to the line during transmission can result in a minor transposition of characters which is not picked up by the front end, and renders the control strategy ineffective.

Reporting is an essential function to program management. It is necessary to produce reports on the fast track while maintaining a high level of quality. There are two general categories of reports: Operating Reports and Management Reports. Operating reports are normally of significance to the energy management staff only. These typically provide hard data for use in making day to day decisions, evaluating program performance and justifying new projects. Management Reports summarily review major milestones and provide bottom line results. These reports will often employ charts, tables and other graphic displays of the information. Their primary function is to present program results to upper management in a concise manner.

Software Fine Tuning

System Fine tuning differs from the activities discussed thus far in that it addresses modifications to software. The performance issues duscussed above are oriented towards maintaining the EMS in an optimum working environment, and ensuring integrity of the original programing. The issue of Finetuning, as the term implies, is a process of evaluating the existing program instruction to determine whether control may be implemented more efficiently. This requires that specific processes be pinpointed for examination, and the following steps are carried out:

1. Interrogate the system to determine current operating characteristics.

2. Trend logs of historical data are developed and monitored.

3. Opportunities for control enhancements are targeted.

4. Make calculations or assumptions based upon the above and modify program instructions.

5. Implement on a test basis in a system without controlled loads.

6. Field Implementation.

7. Evaluate results.

This process should be conducted periodically on all controlled loads.

PROGRAM MANAGEMENT FUNCTIONS

Under the previous section tasks were discussed rather than the functions or tools necessary to complete the tasks. There are in fact tools for accomplishing these tasks, and purpose of this paper is to provide a framework for evaluating those tools. Before discussing specifics, however it is necessary to describe the functions which are necessary to complete program management tasks. There are four primary functions necessary, and currently the author is unaware of a fully automated link or system which incorporates all of them. As a result these functions are carried out through a hybrid combination of manual and automated steps. The issue of Energy Manager efficiency or productivity is primary determinant of the success of a program, and therefore hybrid management techniques detract from the prime objective.

The basic program management functions to be completed are: Communications, Database management, Analysis and Reporting. It is important to discuss these functions in relation to the program management components outlined above, as well as the hardware and software necessary to conduct each function. Each of these functions will be discussed in detail under this section, however a cursory definition of each will provided initially.

Communications is defined as the process of human interface with the EMS firmware. It is the elementary requirement to execute both System Verification and Performance tasks, because interface with the EMS is basic to program management.

Database management is the process whereby data is prepared for management review. This may entail sorting data by category, etc., placing it in arrays, summarizing and preparing data for analysis. It is essential to the performance aspects of program management.

Analysis is the process of conducting engineering or other operations on the above information. This function is the primary building block for System performance enhancements, and in particular fine tuning.

The byproduct of these processes is to provide management with "Decision Data".

Reporting, as previously discussed, is designed to take decision data and present it for both in house reporting and Management summary of program status. Though this function is not directly utilized in program management, it is the corner stone of a successful track record.

In considering each of the functions defined above, it is important to address these functions in relation to the real world. To describe every variation on System interface available in the market today, is beyond the scope of this paper. Rather it is important, in definition of each of the functions, to touch upon the topic of market availability. Functions will be treating in the context of Conventional and optimum user interface packages. A final point of clarification, this discussion may appear to address EMS capabilities rather than front ends. This is because front ends have traditionally been designed to mirror system capabilities, and therefore act as an extension of the manufacturers terminal interface.

The primary importance of this section is rooted in the general misunderstanding of Link Technology. At this point there are unlimited variations on: the definition of the term, the segment of the industry that is responsible to provide the technology, and the form that the technology should take. Prior to discussing link technology at great length this section will attempt to define the environment within which it must operate. Further it will define the tasks which must be accomplished and their importance to overall program success.

Conventional User Interface

To set the stage for discussion of Link technology, the topic of conventional user communications bears discussion first. There have been many variations on the user interface provided with EMS systems. As discussed before, some systems, often those which are at the high end of the cost continuum, provide very limited "Read Only" interface to the user. In essence this paper is directed towards users that have full access to their systems, and are using manufacturer provided front ends. At the risk of dedicating undue space to the discussion of individual manufacturer approaches, this outline of conventional front end will be limited to three basic functions. Manufacturers have traditionally taken the posture that their responsibility was to provide for: System Programing, System Interrogation, Logging.

Conventional system programing and interrogation functions include some type of communications feature. Communications is typically handled by: Site Terminal or Remote Communication. Site terminals often consist of hard wire interface via an RS232 port or local dial up via a modem. The device utilized is often a terminal with limited intelligence capability, and in general, rarely used for other functions such as office automation, etc. Remote communications, if provided, is via proprietary front end terminals. These are often specially configured personal computers or terminals manufactured solely for front end purposes. In essence communications are provided, though limited, and the user is able to program. Users are provided with access to system instructions, and have the capability to conduct a portion of the tasks outlined under program management.

System Interrogation pertains to daily polling operations for purposes of monitoring facility operations. Among the tasks which may be conducted are: tracking space conditions and point status, as well as, diagnosis of problems with system or controlled equipment and review of logs. All of these functions are read only, and provisions are made in conventional front ends for such tasks to be carried out by various members of the energy management staff.

Logging features are typically provided so that historical data may be developed on various control and monitoring points. The data may be arrayed by point address, and logged based upon user defined time intervals. This issue is crucial to the energy manager, because access to this data is vital to program management. The deficiency in most conventional front ends is that data is provided in specific formats, ie: hard copy to printer, and this requires that users re-handle that data for massage. This generally involves time intensive manual work with voluminous print outs, rekeying of data into applications programs or hand analysis and ultimately reporting. The bottom line here is that the time frame for completing these tasks is so prohibitive, that managers either never have time to complete the work, or end up making decisions based upon old data.

Optimum User Interface

This section will outline each of the primary program management function addressed above along with a definition of that function. It will build upon the conventional front end outline by addressing needs and features which are not met by those systems.

Communications: Communications may be the most crucial function available to an energy manager. A majority of the requirements mentioned in the discussion of program management rely greatly on communications for their success. This discussion will primarily be oriented to the user interface via remote communications. The important elements in this process are a standard Micro computer and software. It is imperative for users to have the ability to monitor, interrograte and program their systems from a remote location, a single building within a complex, etc. This issue becomes vastly complicated when users are supporting more than one manufactures equipment. At the simplest level the functions mentioned under conventional systems must be provided, however there are numerous other communications features which can substantially improve user productivity. Among these are functions such as: unattended terminal features, dumb terminal capability, communicator files, program mass update functions and others which will be defined herein.

The conventional communications functions are designed for utilization in an attended mode, where the user is a direct participant in the process. They may be conducted in cumb terminal or via a software defined set of communications instructions and menu prompts. Optimum features on the other hand, rely on more complex communications capabilities. The steps in this process are based on the need for both attended and unattended communications among the essential features are: Communicator File Capability, Communication Sequencing or Auto-Call and an Executive or execution program. It is first necessary to set up a communicator file consisting of a program instruction set written in the language of the equipment to be interfaced. This communicator would contain the sign on, user password, each of the commands necessary to access desired data and the sign off. Communicator sequencing is the process of identifying the systems to be accessed, so that the user can poll groups of systems in succession. The final step of this process is an executive function which allow the user to define the time for this sequenced process to begin. This allows a user to target a group of systems for polling in the afternoon, have the system interrogation completed that evening and review the data first thing in the morning. The utility of this feature goes beyond data access, however because it may also be used to define a "TASK PATHWAY" for any purpose. Mass update of programs is one example of its utility, let us assume for a moment that you are using a system which does not automatically compensate for daylight savings time. Simply set up a communicator to make the appropriate change in spring or fall, and have the executive program contact your systems to change the system clock on the designated Saturday evening. Given a little time energy managers are astute enough to devise unlimited applications for this function. Finally, it is important to note that this is not limited to EMS communications. The determining factor must be compatibility with such standards as the VT52 and VT100 protocols. As mentioned under program management, Program Update is a vital process. The communicator files can also be used to down load and upload files to other front ends for update purposes. The same process may be used for in house data transfer from a regional facility to corporate, etc.

Database Management: Database management has been defined thus far, yet a crucial point has not been addressed. Data access is the corner stone to this issue. In purchasing an EMS, the user purchases control and information, access to that information must be provided. The user must be able to utilize the data in a format which allows for optimum management of the energy program. The key to this process is Data Transfer from the EMS to a useful format. This process need not produce information in some user or manufacturer defined report format, rather it is necessary to provide a data pathway from the EMS data file to a universal data file. The manufacturer can not anticipate the format in which users may want to format data. Therefore, transfer to universal data files for use with any of the myriad software applications programs on the market is the answer, for the present. It is important to mention that data base management is not limited to system log information. A wealth of information is provided by the EMS and used in equipment maintenance and other facility management functions. These functions are beyond the scope of this paper, though the author must note that controls manufacturers have addressed some discreet functions, ie: maintenance, with software designed for use in conjunction with their systems.

Analysis: Analysis is a crucial process in program management. This is the basis for all decisions which are to be made. Managers must make their own decisions regarding the engineering methods to be applied to the applications under control. The level of sophistaication applied to analysis, and extent to which energy managers consider the many variables affecting specific applications such as: Climate, energy cost escalation, etc. are individual concerns. As regards the controls manufacturer, it is important to provide the data for these functions rather than the software to complete them.

Reporting: Reporting is a subject which could be discussed at great length. Yet, this function has been defined quite well thus far. The product of this process is the window through which the EMS and other programs are viewed. As a result it is of the utmost importance to maximize the opportunity for providing reports. These should be customized for the intended audience rather than standardized, and should employ those charts, graphs, explanations and narratives necessary to convey the desired message. Again, a wealth of options are open to the energy manager to complete this function once the data is available in a universal format.

LINK TECHNOLOGY

The issue of link technology is the basis for this paper on EMS Program Management. In the interest of clarifying any misconceptions, the term will be redefined in the context of program management as outlined thus far. The energy management industry has procreated a plethora of computer systems for purposes of control. Each of these systems has an individual method for user interface. The issue of a link is first and foremost related to communications between a user and more than one of these systems at a time. The link concept has also been classified as a related topic to intelligent buildings. As a result this section will first restate the definition of Link Technology, and second establish the need for it in that context.

Link Technology, as defined in this context, refers to software which provides the capabilities outlined under the preceding sections on Program Management Components and Functions. The need for such software is based upon the incidence of multiple system ownership in the energy industry. There are many causes for a diversity in the EMS mix, including: vendor competition for cost effectiveness and facility or system acquisition. Some of complications associated with system multiplicity are outlined below.

1. Decreased productivity: it is necessary to learn multiple software interface systems, and tie up micro computers to run these systems. If office automation or applications programs may be run on the systems, such will often be interupted to diagnose EMS problems since trouble calls are high priority.

2. No Data Sharing: information from various EMS systems can not be shared for global reports without rekeying to applications programs or manual data merging.

3. Front End Expense: Front ends must be capitalized initially and maintained over time, which results in unnecessary expense.

4. Program Stagnation: The time intensiveness of the issues outlined above, along with the complexity of adding a new system, discourages exploration of new technology. As a result, programs may not keep pace with the state of the art.

5. Non Standardization: EMS interface gear vary in nature from software which will run standard micro computers with proprietary cards, chips, etc., to non standard hardware manufacturered specifically for system interface.

Link is, to a great degree, a response to these issues, and the need for the technology is quite obvious. The need for standardization may be even more clear. But to complete the definition of the term it may be helpful to mention the things that Link Technology is not.

1. Link technology does not replace EMS firmware. It is designed strictly for interface purposes.

2. It does not duplicate EMS control functions.

3. It does not require special equipment, but will run on off-the-shelf micro computers, though there may be specific memory requirements, etc..

4. Link Technology does not require access to the EMS manufacturers source code. The source code or proprietary language and programing of an EMS is not required to allow user interface for communications and programing purposes.

It is now possible to discuss link technology at greater length. There are two basic things to be accomplished here, first is to discuss Link Format and then to provide a framework for Link Evaluation.

Link format refers to the technology which is required to accomplish this function. As mentioned briefly, this concept has been alligned with the discussion of intelligent buildings. There are two basic reasons for this:

1. The concepts are related in that we are talking about interface between computer systems: information management in the sense of data sharing, database functions and analysis, as well as office automation in the area of reporting. However, the utility of the Link is primarily in user interface and information not control. To confuse these issues is to make a critical error in judgement, because it negates the problems which exist in the built environment. To shift the focus to buildings of the future, sidesteps the problems which prompted a call for solutions in EMS controlled facilities of today.

2. The second reason for confusing these issues is that some manufacturers have devised a means for approaching the intelligent buildings market. It is the authors contention, that these entities would like to use that same entree, to encourage wholesale system replacement in the retrofit environment.

The discussion of Link Format is related this point of confusion on intelligent buildings. There are two basic formats which have been suggested to resolve the interface problem. First is to develop a local area network format which would allow for global control, security and office automation via one LAN type system. There are some mini computer based systems on the market which could fit this definition with limited expansion. However, as noted above there are several problems with this format.

1. Long lead times for development, beta testing and implementation ignore present industry needs.

2. The retrofit segment of the industry can not make use of this technology without significant capital investment. Users must purchase the LAN, and replace non-compatible controls and systems. Next the user must determine whether LAN's will be compatible with one another, or the initial problem is simply recreated on a larger scale.

In light of these issues, it is safe to postulate that the network format is less than adequate to meet the industry need.

The alternative Link Format is to accomplish these functions as recommended throughout this paper, via software designed to run on standard PC's. This format is more effective because:

1. The initial investment is substantially less.

2. Research and development along with beta testing and implementation are simplified and occur more rapidly.

3. Updates and enhancements are more easily acquired and put into place.

4. The retrofit environment may make imediate use of the technology.

In light of these issues it is of optimum importance for users to reevaluate their strategic plans. The program objectives should be revised to optimize productivity via Link technology. It is important to reassess program management functions, examine the efficiency of current methods, and apply Link criteria in the evaluation of future EMS program objectives. Define as prerequisites for system interface, that link requirments be fulfilled. In essence, it is of primary importance to establish whether systems currently in use are compatible with the criteria outlined in this paper. Determine a plan of action for systems which are not compatible with link technology based upon the critical nature of control applications and the cost effectiveness of system replacement. EMS specifications should be rewritten to reflect the need for universal interface, via established and standardized protocols. Users should seek out manufacturers who espouse the use of Link Technology, evaluate there product offerings in terms of user requirements and secure copies of software for use with current systems. It is essential to have Link software demonstrated, and verify that it can communicate with your current systems. Evaluate each component of your in house program to reflect the state of the art available, to ensure optimum performance.

Once optimal productivity has been achievied in EMS program management, reconsider the nature of your global program posture. Once techniques have been established for maximizing the value of EMS information available for energy program management, it is possible to consider exporting data. With regard to other segments of your organization, it may be possible to enhance your organizational stature by providing useful information to others. There is no limit to the value of this process, and it further serves to integrate the EMS program into the mainstream of facility management.

FUTURE IMPLICATIONS OF LINK TECHNOLOGY

In essence this treatise has been designed to define an established function EMS Program Management in light of new technology. The concept of universality in an industry which has traditionally employed solely proprietary equipment is of prime importance. The fact that such systems are showing up in the market place, and further that manufacturers are not only discussing these but introducing systems of their own, is revolutionary. There is ample room for postulation in terms of implications for future EMS systems and front end systems. The definition of manufacturers responsibility, and how will it change and stabilize in light of these developments is also of interest. It is the authors view that the product of these developments will be extremely beneficial to the energy community. Though reolutionary in nature, however the industry response will not result in manufacturers publishing their source codes in the trade journals. A simple solution is most likely to prevail: communications, data access and programing will be provided for in universal formats. Manufacturers will quite likely expand the system and front end capabilities of their offerings, however the greater share of the, LINK related, market response will be in the form of software. This is not to negate the network format of link technology, the intelligent building in spite of the current market disfavor, holds tremendous potential.

Link Technology entrees to the market on the other hand, will be oriented towards automation of the program management function. These will be in the form of hardware and software.

Link Hardware refers to systems enhancements beginning with modifications to ensure compatibility with universal communications and interface protocol. Additional hardware modifications might include secondary processors to expand internal logging capability, provide for secondary communications with the outside world, and for data summary and management functions. These would also conduct user defined analyses on system data at the EMS, thus allowing users to upload interim reports with decision rather than raw data.

Future software offerings will certainly incorporate all the features discussed in this paper and open up many new opportunities. The areas of speculation are great, however the ability to conduct full scale program management as outlined herein would be significant. User definintion is perhaps the largest area for expansion to this concept. In this area, there is great potential for software resident databases containing: climate data, utility history, empirical engineering mehtodologies and modeling packages, and statistical analysis packages. Reporting packages consisting of word processors, graphics generators, communications packages, and with video output capabilities would also be quite useful.

In summary the concept of link technology, as defined, is essential to the EMS user. As a result, full acceptance in the industry is inevitable. There will be variations on the manner in which this technology is implemented, however the primary issue remains that users are entitled to have access to their systems via industry standard front ends. Ultimately this is the direction in which every segment of the industry must proceed. For the moment only a portion of the systems on the market have been targeted in this paper, but an important precedent is being set. Perhaps the single most important implication for the future, is that this precedent will ultimately change the face of the entire controls industry.

Chapter 16
MAKING SICK EMCSs WELL

V. A. Williams

I. INTRODUCTION

A. General

EMCS is a challenging area! The actual challenge far exceeds many folks' projected challenge! Users, consultants, contractors and suppliers have not been exempt from these overwhelming "challenges".

Most EMCS contracts are consummated with good intent with reputable and competent "Hi Tech" companies. However, a lack of technical supervision of on-site personnel and/or subcontractors often develops a gap in the implementation of the project. Usually, these gaps are minor in terms of corrective action required, but major in terms of system performance. These gaps create distrust and destroy/prevent any personnel confidence in the system. Personnel often are intimidated by what is perceived as "a higher technology" or "out of my league" attitude. This attitude is often shared or created by the contractors. Training, if any, is usually inadequate and is poorly presented.

Buyers are guilty of using the "low bid" procurement method coupled with short-term contracts because this is the simplest method, even though they may know that this method is not the best.

Vendors are guilty of allowing themselves to be drawn into the circumstance created by themselves and/or the buyer just because of the potential volume of business.

By the time a project has progressed to the point where the buyer and the vendor can begin preliminary acceptance test procedures, they have been "at each other's throats" for so long that neither party will acknowledge the other's state of readiness. Often, they don't even want to see each other, let alone cooperate.

The bottom line is an attitude which will allow only failure and mutual dissatisfaction. When no one wants success, it can't happen.

It is the objective of the EMCS DOCTOR TEAM* to offer a treatment for this attitude illness. This team will seek to act as an independent third party, unencumbered by historical problems, uninhibited by hard feelings and broken promises, whose objective is to make the best of the situation rather than continue an unending disagreement. To be successful at this, one must turn the negative into a positive and move forward.

The EMCS DOCTOR TEAM works to identify minor and major system bugs and to eliminate and correct the mistaken attitudes regarding the technology, utilization, and reliability of the EMCS. Behavior changes are developed by providing the personnel with the necessary training, tutoring and instruction for familiarization, to instill self-confidence and to enhance operational efficiency of assigned personnel. No EMCS is "too technical" or "too complex" to be operated and maintained by well trained and dependable maintenance, operating and supervisory personnel. They simply must have a team of people-oriented, technically competent teachers with the user's objectives and personnel in mind. The EMCS DOCTOR TEAM is such a team.

B. Sources of Problems

Following is a listing of the most common problems which plague EMCS projects:

Contract Deficiencies: In a community in which having the lowest bid price is the only way to win a contract, any imperfection in the contract documents, plans and specifications, becomes a matter of interpretation. The bidder is obliged to assume the lowest cost interpretation, while the buyer (who is generally not the author of the contract documents) usually assumes the more expensive option. These discrepancies often surface months after a contract has been awarded and signal the beginning of the problems. The buyer demands his/her interpretation and the contractor demands more money.

Installation Problems: Many contractors have contracted for the installation responsibility of an EMCS without an appreciation for the complexity and multidisciplinary nature of the system. It always seems easy to someone who has never been directly involved! After the first penetrating question is posed, one may wish he or she had never heard the term "EMCS"!

EMCSs are simple to install only when there are no problems--and who knows of any project that has been completed without any problem?

Attitude Problems: As discussed in the Introduction, there is often a poor working climate between the EMCS project buyer and contractor before the project is completed. Time and ineffective communications often yield a less-than-congenial attitude between the parties of the contract. Each has a reason for the attitude but is not willing to consider the other's position. (This problem is further enhanced by the contracting procedures.)

---

*THE EMCS DOCTOR TEAM is the name Verle Williams gave the team of EMCS analysts that evaluate the EMCS projects.

System Problems: System problems can be divided into three main categories: system hardware, system software and field equipment. The most common complaint of buyers is the lack of operable software. The most common complaint of vendors is that the specification is unclear in defining its requirements.

Usually, both points of view, in fact, have some basis. The buyer may want something that the contract doesn't require. The vendor may also try to deliver less than required in the contract, while emphasizing that the delivered software exceeds the contract requirements.

Documentation: The documentation provided with an EMCS cannot be of any more value than the personnel who receive it. Buyers typically do not know what they need to make the best use of their system and vendors are reluctant to give up any more documentation than absolutely necessary to fulfill the contract.

Training: Like documentation, the EMCS will only be as useful as the operators make it. Vendors have a common complaint that buyers are not staffing with the proper personnel to receive the level of training required by the contract and required to properly operate the system. Buyers insist that training should be made simple enough that any operator can realize beneficial results. The in-depth software training is many times wasted on noninterested, noninvolved personnel.

Maintenance: Proper maintenance of the system is very critical to the successful operation of the EMCS. This aspect of the contract requirements hasn't yet been experienced for most projects, however, since only a few have achieved the "acceptance" milestone.

An important point here is that very few vendors are actually prepared to offer the quality of service expected and required after acceptance of the system. Buyers should prepare themselves before acceptance for the possibility that they may be on their own as far as first level maintenance of their system is concerned.

Interface With Existing Equipment: Many buyers are not convinced that their EMCS will both save them real energy dollars and should not be the source of problems in existing electrical and mechanical equipment.

System failover and failsave mechanisms should be thoroughly tested in each season of use before any assumptions are made as to future success of EMCS failure routines.

C. Sources of Solutions

To accomplish the required system diagnostics and identify solutions to the problems, one must be:

OPTIMISTIC ("It can be done and we can do it.")

Positive feelings about the future of EMCS and a belief in EMCS are mandatory to outstanding EMCS operation.

REALISTIC ("Is it or isn't it?")

Recognize there have been, and still are, many problems with EMCS installations and follow a plan to identify them for timely solution. Also, recognize that there have been, and still are, successful EMCS installations.

OPPORTUNISTIC ("Use the lemon to make lemonade!")

One person's problems are another's opportunities. One must be willing to accept the challenge of these opportunities and methodically work towards a solution.

INDEPENDENT ("Be owing to no one.")

Independent "third party" representatives capable and willing to accept the role of the unbiased professionals who are interested only in identifying the path from the present system condition to the desired operational results will repay their cost many times each year.

II. METHODOLOGY

The following procedure outlines the methodology of a typical EMCS analysis.

A. Site Visit

1. Obtain original specifications, drawings, contract and "as built" documents, as available.

2. Obtain original feasibility study, as available.

3. Analyze The EMCS's present operating condition:

   a. By personal observation.

   b. By discussion with the most knowledgeable personnel.

4. Tour the project for installation procedure and condition.

B. Off-site Analysis

(As an option, depending on the system size and site location, this phase may be conducted on-site.)

1. Analyze original contract documents, as available.

2. Analyze as built documentation, as available.

3. Analyze feasibility study and compare with contract documents, as available.

4. Analyze notes of field interviews and observation of operation.

C. On-site Detailed Analysis

1. For working or partially working system.

   a. Discuss deficiencies with user personnel.

   b. Analyze stated deficiencies.

   c. Analyze data printouts from data environment emulator.

   d. Compare data input values to a known value monitoring point.

   e. Analyze data output signals.

   f. Analyze software deficiencies for possible improvement.

2. Nonworking system.

   a. Attempt to run diagnostics of CCU/CCC/FID/IMUX.

   b. Analyze results of diagnostics.

c. If diagnostics run, analyze software for "roadblocks".

d. Identify and log area(s) of roadblocks.

D. Off-site Analysis

1. Develop full list of present operating status.

a. Good points.

b. Deficiencies.

c. Recommendations as appropriate at this stage.

2. Discuss total status with system supplier, if feasible.

a. Via telephone (initial).

b. In person (informal follow-up conference).

3. Combine all data obtained to date for corrective action recommendations.

E. Preliminary Presentation to Client

1. Review initial operating condition.

2. Review condition of documentation.

3. Review recommendations.

4. Reach agreement regarding future activities and the final presentation.

F. Final Report

The outcome of the Phase One activity is a complete report and recommendation to the client detailing the steps required to realize a successful EMCS. Each of the categories listed in the section entitled "Sources of Problems" is addressed in detail. The state of the EMCS is explained in layman's terms for ease of understanding. Specific recommendations are made.

G. Training

The following sequence of events is implemented for training the EMCS operating and supervisory personnel, as desired by the client.

1. Basics of real-time computers. (How do they work?)

2. Basics of software.

3. HVAC systems and controls.

4. Interactive software, from an operator's point of view.

5. How the EMCS affects the HVAC system control operation.

6. Key points of field installation.

7. Review of the EMCS monitoring and control functions.

8. Analysis of the EMCS reporting capabilities and requirements.

9. Diagnosis of HVAC system problems/failures with the EMCS.

10. Other items as required for site-specific conditions.

(This training includes the necessary tutoring and instructions to ensure thoroughly competent, confident and efficient operator personnel.)

H. Complete Documentation

Prepare complete documentation of the EMCS, as installed, insofar as feasible, including all operator interface commands, hardware manuals and sequence of operation of automatic control systems.

III. SUMMARY

This program can be the answer to many folks' problems. No, it probably won't solve all of everyone's problems. But it certainly can solve many. It is better for one to call in an outsider to help get the EMCS functioning properly and become a happy user than to sit back with the other dissatisfied users and receive little or no benefits from the system.

A properly designed, properly installed, properly operated, and properly maintained EMCS will work and will provide expected results.

SECTION 4

INDUSTRIAL COGENERATION

Sponsored by the Cogeneration Institute of AEE

Chapter 17

FLUIDIZED-BED COGENERATION AT UMC

A. Warden

BACKGROUND

The University of Missouri-Columbia (UMC) is the oldest land grant institution of higher learning west of the Mississippi. Of its 147 years, it has been a cogenerator at least the last 48. With the installation of a 750 KW generator in 1938, UMC began its use of steam turbine electrical generation with this back pressure unit. That unit has just this year been retired from service after producing over 250,000 MWHs of cheap electricity. The cogeneration concept has proven cost effective even through the 60's and early 70's--the era of cheap power! It is in that spirit that the University has recently launched into a 40 million dollar expansion and renovation program to assure that the utility needs of the Campus will be met into the 1990's.

The program calls for adding a 200,000 #/hr boiler ($14 million) to the Power Plant which currently has a steam capacity of 475,000 #/hr in four existing coal fired stoker boilers. UMC's commitment to cogeneration is demonstrated by the fact that during the last boiler and turbine construction project in the early 70's, space was allowed for an additional boiler and turbine.

The program also calls for two additional turbine-generators. One 19.5 MW ($7 million) was added this year and a second 14 MW ($5 million) will be added early in 1988. The program includes about $12 million of improvement to the steam and electrical distribution systems on the Campus.

Over the years, nine generators have been purchased, three of which are currently on line with a combined capacity of 38 MW. The 1988 addition will result in an electrical capacity of 52 MW. Figure 1 shows how the Campus Power Plant will be configured when the current project is complete. The two oldest chain grate stoker boilers with a combined capacity of 150,000 #/hr will supply 300 PSIG steam to the oldest 6 MW turbine-generator. The second largest spreader stoker boiler at 125,000 #/hr will supply 400 PSIG steam to the 12.5 MW turbine-generator. The largest spreader stoker boiler at 200,000 #/hr will supply 400 PSIG steam to the newest 14 MW turbine-generator. Lastly, the new circulating atmospheric fluidized bed boiler at 950 PSIG will supply 200,000 #/hr to the largest turbine-generator to produce 19.5 MW. Progressively, higher pressures have been used to take greater advantage of cogenerating with superheated steam. All of these steam turbine drives are extraction units with various throttle pressures, but all with a common extraction pressure of 60 PSIG.

As the Campus increased in size to almost 8 million gross square feet, heating and cooling needs were supported by both steam and electricity from the Power Plant. Since 1938, the use of 60 PSIG process steam has been encouraged as the favored source of energy on the Campus. The University's teaching hospital was one of the earliest users of a variety of steam powered equipment. Now, two additional hospitals are on line with loads such as autoclaves, water distilling, dishwashing, sterilizing, laundry, cooking, and more. Other areas of the Campus have similar uses today. These include a veterinary hospital, clinics, and animal science laboratories, to mention just a few. The 6,000 bed residence hall system with its domestic hot water requirements adds to the cooking and clean up uses in six cafeterias.

Summer loads are headed by steam absorption chillers which have been a major use of the Campus steam distribution system for many years. By 1980, of the 16,000 tons of air conditioning on Campus, 6,000 tons were steam absorption. The largest chiller units on the Campus (1,000 tons) are now steam absorption type. Every opportunity is seized to insure that additional or replacement chillers are steam powered. The goal is to increase our steam dependence until the winter and summer extraction loads are about equal. This will allow balancing optimum cogeneration efficiency and maximum use of the distribution system capacity.

The first heating plant equipment in the Power Plant was coal fired. In the early years, coal was strip mined only a few miles from the Campus. It was cheap but became less available and was of low quality. In the 1960's gas was so cheap that burners were added and about half the BTU's came from that fuel. An important decision to the University's future utility supply was made at that time. While many similar campus heating plants and industrial boilers were converted to natural gas only--UMC maintained its coal firing capability on every boiler. Later, as natural gas prices rose, the transition back to coal was easy. The University Power Plant burned considerable Illinois coal before 1980 and the quality was good.

In 1980, the University recognized its need to conform to the ever increasing require-

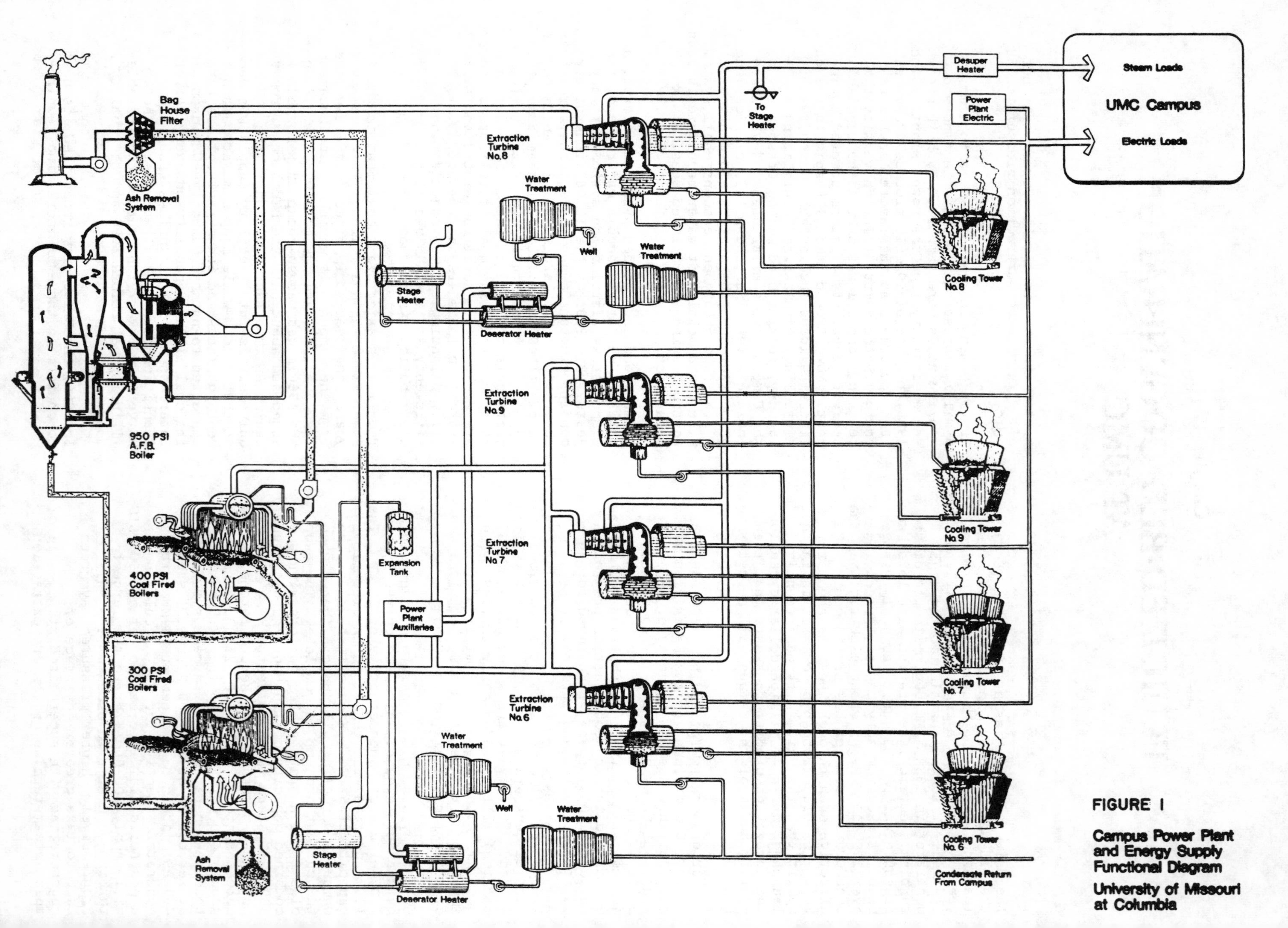

FIGURE I

Campus Power Plant and Energy Supply Functional Diagram

University of Missouri at Columbia

ments to clean up the Power Plant's emissions. At that time, two new 325 foot concrete stacks and two reverse air baghouses were built. This provided compliance but also allowed the Campus to switch back to cheaper Missouri coal, now from modern strip mines about 40 miles away.

THE NEED FOR MORE CAPACITY

Studies made by the University in the early 80's revealed a shortage of steam capacity (given the age of existing equipment and the need for some redundance) and the promise of substantial savings if more cogeneration was added. The studies indicated that savings in excess of a million dollars a year could be realized if UMC generated all its own electricity. With these and other savings already achieved by reduction of demand charges, the current project was initiated by a revenue bond of $23.5 million. Ten year projected savings would allow a $40 million program investment with only inflationary increases in utility costs to the Campus.

Under the current regulations for SO_2 emissions, any new boiler would have to comply with more stringent SO_2 and NOx reductions. The new boiler would either have to have a scrubber with it or be one of the newer atmospheric fluidized bed units. These would provide environmentally acceptable combustion of cheaper, higher sulfur Missouri coal, by using the calcium in limestone to capture the sulfur. Considerable time was devoted to investigating both options, as they appeared to be the only ones viable.

In 1984, planning was complete and the search for new equipment began. Late in 1984, the Missouri Department of Natural Resources gave the University verbal approval to begin designs to add a new boiler to the Plant. They expressed a strong preference for an atmospheric fluidized bed boiler and hopes that the University could demonstrate this technology successfully in Missouri. Early in 1985, the engineering firm of Bibb and Associates of Kansas City, was chosen to design the project. Of all the firms expressing an interest, they were the only ones who had an atmospheric fluidized bed boiler job in their recent experience.

THE SEARCH BEGINS

Specifications were written and Requests for Proposals were solicited for two different options. The first could be a 200,000 #/hr stoker fired boiler with a dry SO_2 scrubber. The second could be a similarly sized atmospheric fluidized bed boiler. Either would be coupled to a 19.5 MW extraction steam turbine-generator. Throttle conditions would be 950 PSIG at 850 degrees Fahrenheit.

Proposals were received in July of 1985. Evaluation took several months and included a "life cycle cost" and "cost of ownership" of each proposal. It was during this analysis that the atmospheric fluidized bed boiler proposals appeared to be lower cost. In a 15 year "cost of ownership" analysis, the stoker and dry scrubber were 20% more than the "circulating" atmospheric fluidized bed boiler. Of the "bubbling" as opposed to the "circulating" atmospheric fluidized bed boilers, the latter evaluated better for the size required, and had an efficiency close to a pulverized coal unit.

The scrubber uses lime to create a highly alkaline spray to treat the boiler gas effluent and absorb SO_2 . It is a process separate from and following the boiler. The atmospheric fluidized bed boiler, on the other hand, introduces the lime as limestone directly into the combustion zone. This is made possible by fluidizing the bed and keeping the coal and limestone thoroughly mixed and in constant contact. While the coal (and sulfur) are burning, the limestone is calcined by the combustor heat, producing reactive calcium oxide that captures SO_2 in the combustion process.

To evaluate and learn more, the UMC Power Plant engineering staff made many inquiries and actual site visits. They learned that dry scrubbers are quite trouble prone and probably worse than baghouses were in their early years. It seemed as though there was as much unknown or unproven about dry scrubbers, as there was about "circulating" atmospheric fluidized bed boilers.

Although we needed to visit some "circulating" atmospheric fluidized bed boiler units, only one was currently operating in the United States. Unfortunately, we were not allowed to visit it because of operating difficulties. The only other operating units were in Europe and Korea. We also learned that only three vendors had actually built one. The other proposals were from vendors who wanted to build their first. A trip to Finland and Ireland was undertaken in September of 1985.

ECONOMIC AND TECHNICAL ANALYSIS

In Finland, we visited two units built by Alstrom--known in the United States as "Pyropower". In Ireland, we visited one unit built by a Battelle licensee. Only two of the units were actually operating, and none were actually using limestone in the process of reducing SO_2 emissions.

The "circulating'" atmospheric fluidized bed boiler was actually developed to handle a broad spectrum of fuels unsuitable for more conventional firing methods. The European interest came about from the desire to fuel with wood waste, peat, and otherwise low grade waste material. Desulfurization was apparently a second thought. The Battelle unit was developed and tested to burn fuels such as coal, kraft liquor, wood waste, municipal waste, sewage waste, delayed coke, fluid coke, char, and rock containing bitumen. Their unit was apparently designed specifically to provide for sulfur capture using limestone.

The Pyropower units used a high velocity combustor which required relatively small particle sizes for coal and limestone feed. The Battelle unit, developed in the United States by Battelle Memorial Institute Laboratories of Columbus, Ohio, uses a dense grinding effect on the coal and limestone. Riley Stoker Corp. of Worcester, Massachusetts, became the licensee of Battelle for industrial and utility boilers in the United States in 1982.

The Limestone Problem

Since SO_2 capture is of paramount importance in the selection of our new equipment, it was disappointing to find that none of the vendors had any currently operating units that could actually demonstrate the process. Neither Pyropower or Riley could produce limestone consumption data that had much credibility. But the Battelle unit seemed better fitted for using the type limestone plentiful in mid-Missouri.

Considerable time was spent in trying to understand the limestone issue. One vendor's design boasted of very low stoichiometric ratio and resultant lower limestone cost. They had apparently done the most limestone testing. Their design, however, could only promise these good results with a relatively fine limestone of specific crystalline structure. Unfortunately, all of our locally available limestone was of a different crystal structure. This might have meant a more costly limestone brought from a distance.

The Battelle/Riley design, however, seemed more forgiving of limestone type. In the dense bed design limestone of a relatively larger size can be used because of the grinding action of the more confined bed material. The limestone is crushed right in the dense bed resulting in more efficient utilization. Because of the less fluid dense bed, the residence time is increased. Both actions serve to enhance the reactivity. This same action serves to "pulverize" the coal which improves its combustion in the same vicinity of the highly reactive Calcium oxide. The fine grinding of the coal increases carbon utilization and results in higher combustion efficiencies.

Similarly, it can be deduced that "fines" of either coal or limestone will be well tolerated. An obvious advantage of this process may be the ability to handle less prepared fuel and limestone. The resulting lower cost may be significant.

THE DECISION

The Battelle/Riley unit, shown in Figure 2, was our final choice. In this patented combustion process, a circulating bed of fine ash and limestone particles are superimposed on a more dense but more confined fluidized bed of larger particles. Fuel and limestone are fed into the combustor just above the dense bed at the bottom. The dense bed serves to grind the materials, promotes thorough mixing, and increases the residence time of the materials. This facilitates efficient combustion as well as good absorption of SO_2 by the calcined limestone. The fluidizing is accomplished by air injected at about 30 feet per second from the bottom of the combustor.

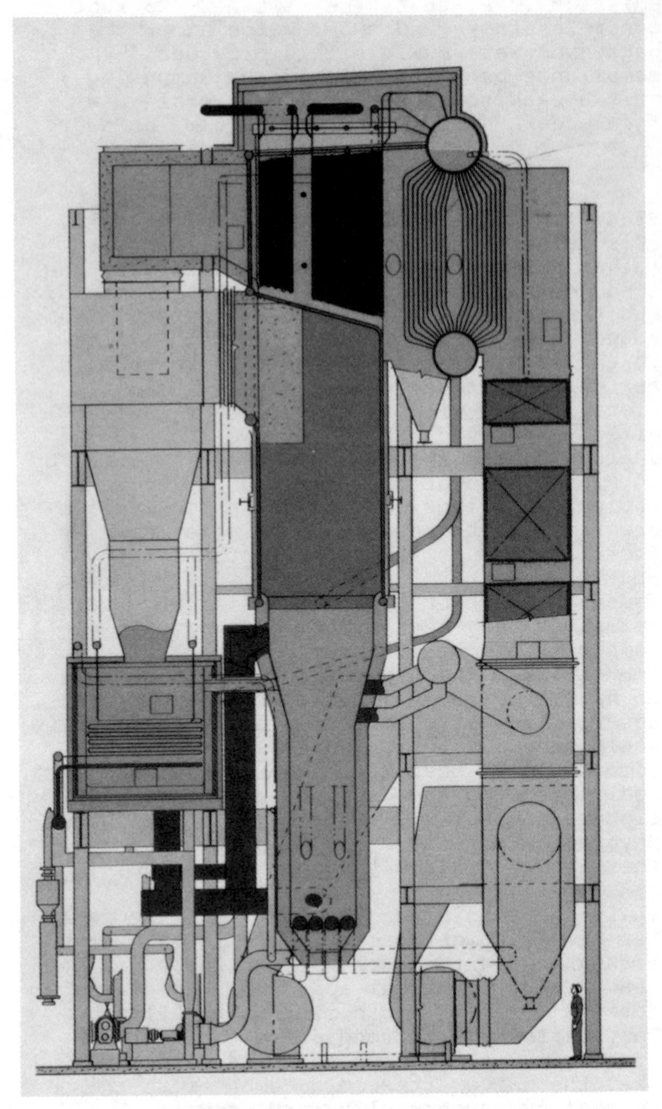

FIGURE 2
RILEY MULTISOLID FLUIDIZED BED
CUMBUSTION STEAM GENERATOR

A hot solids cyclone separates larger particles for recirculation. This recirculation through an external heat exchanger also allows the temperature of the combustor to be controlled at about 1600 degrees Fahrenheit. At this temperature, slag does not form and most of the ash is eventually passed by the cyclone to be captured in the baghouse. Hot gases that carry the fine ash and residue pass through a more or less conventional convection section to produce and superheat steam.

An important feature of the Battelle/Riley unit is the use of an external heat exchanger. This is a low velocity fluidized unit where the majority of the steam is produced from the hot solids separated by the cyclone. Its design maximizes heat transfer surface and uses forced water circulation. Most of the cooled solids leaving the external heat exchanger are reinjected into the combustor to complete their combustion and to help control its temperature.

Although this design is apparently capable of burning a variety of fuels, coal is the only fuel planned for the UMC boiler. The design also appears capable of using types of limestone that others will not readily use. The University is only about 40 miles from a considerable reserve of strip mined bituminous coal that when washed will yield 11,000 BTUs per pound with about 4% sulfur. Limestone is also quite common in the area with three quarries within just a few miles.

THE FINAL RESULT

The goal was to integrate this new boiler technology into our existing power plant. We planned to completely renovate all the existing controls and control systems in current operation prior to the new equipment coming on line. UMC has purchased and installed a Bailey Network 90 "distributed control" plant automation system. It replaced old, and in many cases, obsolete controls with new digital, computer operated systems. This equipment will improve unit control and optimize operating parameters to increase efficiency. In addition, economic dispatch of both boilers and turbines will become possible. This will be particularly important as the atmospheric fluidized bed boiler is completely different than any other equipment on line in the Plant.

Since the role of the Power Plant is to economically provide steam and electricity to the University, the low cost of this cogeneration process is very attractive. More attractive yet will be the economic dispatch of its many units. Since each boiler will have a different cost of steam dependent on its combustion process, size, fuel, operating level, etc., the real time calculation of costs is very important. Loading or unloading needs to be assigned to the units with the lowest or highest incremental unit cost respectively.

Once steam is cost evaluated, then its application to various steam-turbine units can be determined on the basis of greatest economic impact. The extraction steam turbine becomes the target for cost analysis by stage so as to produce as much electricity as possible from the given extraction steam load. With this base loaded, the balance of the kilowatts can be dispatched from the various unit condensing stages, using the least costly units first. These real time computer added decisions hold much promise for further cost saving.

The University of Missouri-Columbia is excited and pleased in anticipation of its new atmospheric fluidized boiler. Coupled with an extraction steam turbine-generator, this new foray into cogeneration should provide better pollution control as well as greater cost effectiveness.

Chapter 18

COGENERATION PROJECT MANAGEMENT

J. W. Egan

INTRODUCTION

During the last eight years Cogeneration has had an amazing rebirth in this country. Principally because of the Federal Public Utility Regulatory Policy Act (PURPA) Legislation and also because of favorable supportive Federal and State Regulation. Many states have also encouraged Cogeneration Development through favorable avoided cost electrical "Buy Back" rates and equally favorable natural gas fuel cost regulation.

Because of this emphasis on Cogeneration, a large number of projects have been designed and constructed in the past seven or eight years. Some of these projects are a credit to our engineering profession and others are not. In an effort to maintain the high integrity of the engineering profession, we as engineers must become real students of the new discipline of Cogeneration Project Management. This paper is written to encourage engineers to become more skilled in the management of cogeneration projects.

DEFINITION

The writer's particular definition of "Cogeneration Project Management" encompasses all engineering activities associated with the design and construction of a cogeneration facility, starting with the feasibility study, and continuing through every phase of engineering and construction activity including the start-up and training of plant operation and maintenance personnel.

EXECUTIVE SUMMARY

Cogeneration Project Management starts with a successful feasibility study. This phase is followed by the preliminary engineering effort, which identifies basic plant configuration and cogeneration cycles, and results in sizing of major equipment. The effort continues through all of the engineering and permitting processes. When the project enters the construction phase, the major effort in the Project Management is then directed to construction management and supervision.

At the completion of construction, the Project Manager's attention is directed to the critical start-up and testing phase.

The Project Manager's responsibility is finished only after the operator training is complete and when the operating and maintenance procedures are in place.

Through the entire project management one of the major responsibilities is budgeting. The Project Manager is responsible for keeping the project on time and on budget.

In the engineering discipline, as well as others, the major problem in project management is communication. Communication is extremely important and without good communications a project is doomed to failure. There are several communication techniques which can be used on Cogeneration projects whether these projects are small or large. A typical method used is the "Project Meeting". Meetings must be scheduled as necessary, during the very preliminary stages of the feasibility study and through the preliminary engineering, engineering design, construction, and start-up phases. These meetings must be well organized, there must be an agenda for every meeting and prompt and detailed minutes must be prepared immediately after every meeting and distributed to all concerned parties.

ENGINEERING PHASE

Feasibility Study

A successful feasibility study will consider all of the major engineering elements in a cogeneration project. These elements include thermal use, electrical use, sizing of basic plant configuration, cogeneration cycles, regulatory considerations, project cost and project economics. Many successful cogeneration feasibility studies employ sophisticated computer programs and usually include a verbal presentation to the prospective owners of the facility to summarize the results of the feasibility study.

Preliminary Engineering

Once the feasibility study has been completed and a decision has been made to fund the project, the preliminary engineering phase can then begin. In this preliminary engineering phase the following efforts are undertaken.

Conceptual Design

This effort involves the mass flow and heat balance diagrams and the process and instrumental drawings, (P&ID).

Once the P. and I.D.'s are complete and the project heat balance is determined, the major equipment on the project can be properly sized.

Prepurchased Specifications

After the equipment has been sized specifications for prepurchased equipment can be prepared.

Request for Quotations

After the specifications are complete the engineer can advertise for quotations from major equipment vendors.

Award of Bids for Major Equipment

After the bids for the major equipment have been received and analyzed, then the awards can be made for the major cogeneration equipment.

Environmental Permitting

The next major engineering activity in the project management of a cogeneration facility is the Environmental Permitting.

This phase includes obtaining all of the permits required for the construction and operation of the facility.

These permits include the following:

Air Quality Permits
Environmental Permits
Federal Energy Regulatory Commission (FERC) Permits
Building Permits

During this phase of the work the engineer will assist the owner in obtaining required permits from the various regulatory agencies. The most crucial permit required is usually the air quality permit. Obtaining this permit can be a very complicated process depending on the particular requirements affecting the specific plant design. Federal Environmental Protection Agency (EPA), State EPA agencies, and the local air quality permitting districts are involved in this permitting strategy. This permitting involves federal and state laws, regulations and almost always requires a certain defined Best Available Control Technology (BACT) for the control of emissions. Since this is a very crucial phase in the project affecting design, the regulatory phase should be started very early in the project, since the time required can be a critical item.

Utility Interface

A critical element in the project management of the Cogeneration Facility is the proper interface with the local utility.

The Utility Interface will include the following items:

Power Sales Agreements
Utility protection considerations
Electrical Utility Upgrades
Gas, fuel supply to the plant

Power Sales Agreements

Depending upon the particular utility involved and whether the cogeneration plant owner's strategy is to sell electrical energy and or capacity to the utility or at a minimum to interconnect with the utility, there are certain agreements that must be negotiated with the utility. The timing of these agreements also can be critical since the utility must be notified early on in the project, regarding the particular characteristics and location of the proposed cogeneration facility.

Utility Protection Considerations

The Electrical Utility Companies are very concerned with the integrity of their electrical generating and distribution systems and have very specific requirements for cogeneration facilities if they are to interconnect with the utility's electrical distribution system. These requirements include the protection for both sides of the system, that is, the utility and the cogeneration, or generating, sides of the plant. When the cogeneration facility is above a certain size, most utilities require specific metering arrangements for gross and net generation and also require telemetering of the generating production of the cogeneration plant to a central utility control center.

Electrical Utility Upgrades

Another major concern is the possibility of utility upgrades to accept the power from the cogeneration facility. These upgrades are often required because of the location of the cogeneration plant and these upgrades require significant time and cost. The planning and construction of these electrical upgrades are often critical and therefore require attention by the project manager early in the process.

Gas, Fuel Supply to Plant

On the fuel side, if the cogeneration plant is to purchase gas fuel from the utility, often the fuel pressure required is higher than the utility has available in the local area. This will require either gas fuel compression at the site or arrangements for the utility to run a separate high-pressure gas service to the facility. This also requires time for the utility to plan and engineer such upgrades. There may also be a significant cost involved.

Detailed Engineering Design

The next significant phase of the project development is the detail engineering design. This engineering design will include the following design elements:

Mechanical
Electrical
Structural
Civil
Architectural
Instrumentation and Control

The Final product of this detailed engineering design effort is the production of a complete project manual. This project manual will consist of the following compnents: all bidding documents; general conditions; all technical specifications; all plans of the various disciplines required to constitute a complete set of plans and specifications.

This project manual will be used to obtain construction estimates or bids for the construction effort and the installation of the cogeneration equipment.

Design Review

When the detail design is complete the next crucial element is a design review. This design review should incorporate a review of the plans and specifications by qualified engineers in various disciplines. This design review would include the following elements:

Coordination
Review for omissions or duplications
Constructability review
Replaceability review
Maintenance and operating review
Budget review

A CONSTRUCTION PHASE

Bid Phase

Under this phase of the work the engineer will organize and execute the following construction efforts:

Invitation of bids
Reciept of bids
Review of bid proposal
Award of bids

Construction Contracts

The construction contracts can be awarded through a prime contractor who will be responsibile for all subcontractors or the engineer and owner can elect to award separate contracts for major divisions of the work, or the project can be constructed under a construction management contract. Whatever procedure is used for the construction contracts the engineer must be involved in the construction monitoring effort.

Construction Monitoring

This monitoring of the construction effort will include the following activities:

Scheduling
Coordination
Budget Control.

Scheduling

The construction scheduling activities and format, which will vary with the size and complexity of the project, is crucial and must be designed and maintained by the Project Manager.

Coordination

The coordination of a cogeneration project can be very complex. This activity will required major attention by the project manager.

Budget Control

The maintenance of the budget goals will be a constant activity of the project manager. During the construction phase this effort will be a crucial concern.

STARTUP AND TESTING PHASE

General

The startup and testing phase of the cogeneration project depending on the size and complexity can be a very involved procedure. The elements involved in this procedure will include the following:

The designation of testing requirements.

Supervision of independent testing labortories when used to perform equipment testing and certification.

Supervision of electrical calibration by independent electrical service companies.

Final approvals of the testing procedures and final acceptance.

The testing and acceptance procedures can involve significant time and planning and the employment of standard American Society of Mechnaical Engineers (ASME) testing procedures for the mechanical elements of the construction of the cogeneration facility and the monitoring and testing of the electrical relay protection systems which are required both for the protection of the cogeneration plant and utility electrical distribution systems.

Controls

The final testing and commissioning of the instrumentation and control systems is very crucial to the final checkout of the cogeneration facility. This must be witnessed by the project manager or delegated to a commissioning specialist. Once the testing of the various components of the system is complete and all of the test reports are available, the project manager must review these testing reports and decide to accept or reject the various components of the system. Once the components are accepted and the final project demonstration is complete the project manager can then generate a certificate of final acceptance. When this certificate is produced the contractors can be paid the final payments and/or retentions and the project can enter into the training and operating phase.

Training

Training of Operating and Maintenance Personnel

At this point the Operating and Maintenance Personnel should receive the final training to operate and maintain the plant. Ideally, the senior operators and supervisors should be brought on board early in the construction phase, so that they are able to witness testing of the various components usually in the manufacturers facilities and to witness the installation of the major equipment and begin to become familiar with this equipment. The regular classroom training of the senior operators can then begin during the startup phases of the work.

Operation and Maintenance Manuals

The project manager must decide if the overall project manuals are to be assembled by a subcontractor or whether this is to be performed by the general contractor, or by the Project Manager's staff. However, a total operating and maintenace manual must be assembled for the entire plant systems.

Operating and Maintenance Procedures

The project manager has the responsibility to develop operating and maintenance procedures for the plant. This plant should then be staffed with qualified, well trained professional operators and maintenance people who understand the procedures implemented by the project manager.

The plant is then ready for the shake down phase of the operation. This shake down phase could consist of several weeks to several months to get through the initial problems that present themselves in any complicated plant operation. It will be necessary for the project manager to remain available during this period to shepard the project into a smooth operating phase.

SUMMARY

When the procedures outlined in this paper are followed the owner will be very pleased with his decision to construct a cogeneration plant, the utility will be happy to have additional electrical power and we as Professional Cogeneration Project Managers will have the satisfaction of helping to conserve our dwindling energy supplies by utilizing this energy to a high efficiency. As design professionals, we will all have the satisfaction of a job well done.

SECTION 5

COMMERCIAL/INSTITUTIONAL COGENERATION

Sponsored by the Cogeneration Institute of AEE

Chapter 19

SMALL-SCALE COGENERATION FOR A SOUTHEASTERN DAIRY

C. C. Ross, J. L. Walsh

INTRODUCTION

This paper provides an overview of the cogeneration system installed by Georgia Tech on a Georgia dairy farm as part of the Energy Integrated Dairy Farm System (EIDFS) Project. The EIDFS is one of six Energy Integrated Farm System projects co-sponsored by the U.S. Department of Energy across the country for the evaluation of energy conservation and alternate energy technologies in agriculture. The State of Georgia and Mathis/P&M Farm were the other co-sponsors for the project. The main goal of the EIFS program was to prove the technical feasibility of these energy technologies while evaluating their economic, social and institutional impact on agriculture.

The major components of Georgia Tech's EIDFS can be seen in the illustration of Figure 1. Although milk is the primary product from a dairy, twice as much manure by weight is produced daily. To make good use of this "resource", Tech installed a full-scale anaerobic digester which accepts manure scraped from the milk herd's free-stall barns and digests the organic material in the waste for the production of methane rich "biogas". The effluent from the digester is separated for bedding material for the herd and liquid fertilizer for nearby cropland. It is this "integration" of various technologies that are meant to complement each other and provide for better economic benefit.

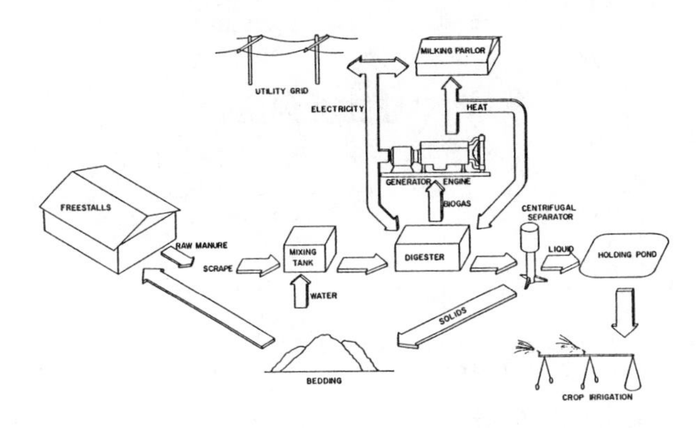

FIGURE 1. GEORGIA TECH ENERGY INTEGRATED DAIRY FARM

It is this biogas that fuels an engine generator set producing electricity and hot water for use by the dairy and occasional sale to the local utility. This paper will detail some of the performance and operational characteristics of this cogeneration system integrated into the dairy operation.

DESIGN CRITERIA

As shown in Figure 2, a dairy operation can present a fairly predictable electrical and thermal energy demand. The major electrical peaks at 10:00 am and 9:00 pm represent the peak of the two daily milking cycles by the dairy. The major electrical demand can be attributed to refrigeration units for chilling the milk (approximately 2400 gallons) prior to transport to a processing plant, vacuum pumps for milking machines, and water pumping.

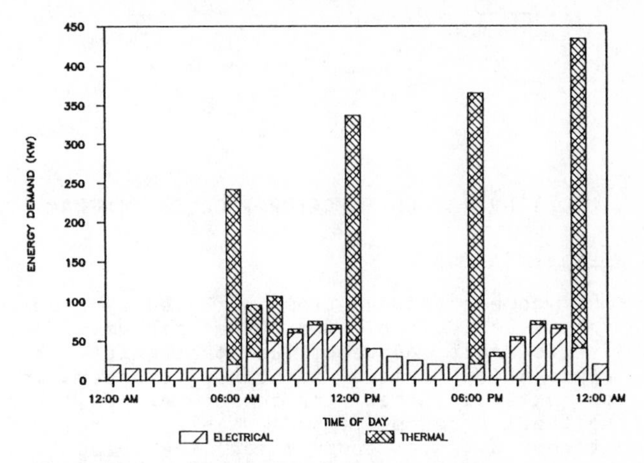

FIGURE 2. DAIRY ELECTRICAL AND THERMAL ENERGY DEMAND

The thermal loads shown in Figure 2 represent hot water requirements by the dairy for prepping (cleaning) the cows prior to milking and the cleaning of milk equipment and storage tanks after milking. These loads are currently met by two refrigeration heat recovery units in series with a 165 gallon propane hot water heater. It is evident from the thermal load shown in Figure 2 that some form of standby or storage is needed to meet these loads.

Both the electrical and thermal loads will vary somewhat with milking herd size and time of year. An average electrical load of 1.80 kWh per cow per day and 4,300 Btu per cow per day average thermal load was measured at this dairy. The total average electrical and thermal loads are approximately 1000 kWh and 2,358,900 Btu per day, respectively. Although both electrical and thermal loads are predictable to a certain degree, they are not easily managed, and, thus, conservation management is not easily implemented. The peaks can be shifted to avoid utility demand charges by changing the time of the milking schedule. However, milking must occur every 12 hours keeping the time between peaks fixed at approximately 12 hours.

COGENERATOR DESIGN

A process diagram for the installed cogenerator system is shown in Figure 3. The major components for the system are the fuel system, the power system, the heat recovery system, the generator, the controls and safety systems, and the utility protection and interconnect system. All of the components with the exception of the interconnect system were purchased from Perennial Energy, Inc. from West Plains, Missouri.

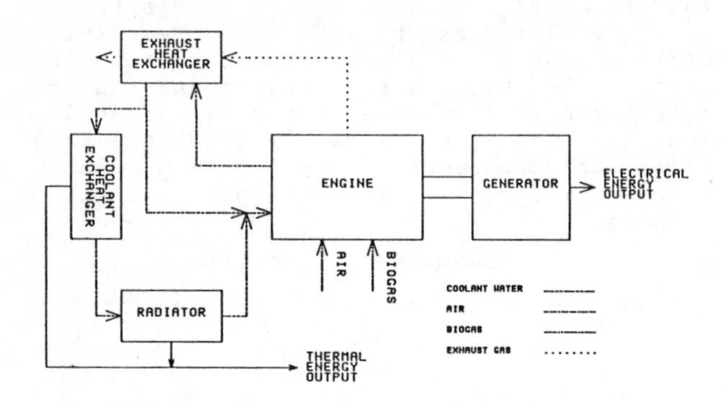

FIGURE 3. COGENERATOR PROCESS DIAGRAM

Fuel System

The cogeneration system is fueled by biogas from a 24,000 cubic foot anaerobic digester. It is this source of fuel that makes this application unique to other cogeneration projects in that the source of fuel is neither produced from a stable source or stored by high compression. The plug-flow digester features an insulated, underground concrete tank with a fixed concrete cover. Biogas is generated by the anaerobic bacterial destruction of organic material in the manure fed into the reactor. This gas collects in a 4000 cubic feet head space in the tank before being treated and consumed by the engine.

The system produces an average of 17,000 cubic feet of biogas per day. This production varies considerably with time of year, type of feed, manure collection efficiency, and dairy herd size. A rule-of-thumb gas production estimate for this system is approximately 45 cubic feet of gas per cow per day.

Table 1 shows a few of the physical characteristics of this biogas. Particularly notable is the reduced energy content of the biogas relative to natural gas. From an operational standpoint, the modest levels of hydrogen sulfide, mercaptans, and moisture can promote not only engine wear and tear but also degradation of gas handling equipment. For this reason, as much of the moisture and mercaptans are removed as possible. Hydrogen sulfide has proven to be less corrosive as the system has not been allowed to cool down for sufficient time to allow for condensation.

TABLE 1
DIGESTER GAS CHARACTERISTICS

COMPONENT	CHARACTERISTIC
Methane (CH_4)	58 % by weight
Carbon Dioxide (CO_2)	41 % by weight
Other (Nitrogen)	1 % by weight
Hydrogen Sulfide (H_2S)	0.540 mg/l
Mercaptans (R-SH)	0.490 mg/l
Water Vapor (H_2O)	19.000 mg/l
Specific Energy	595 Btu/ft^3
Octane Number	100-125

Power System

The engine is a six cylinder Waukesha F817G natural gas engine with modified carburetion and a timing setting of 45 degrees BTDC to compensate for the lower quality biogas fuel. It also is carbureted and connected for alternate fueling from a nearby liquid propane tank. While operating in a generation mode, the engine turns at approximately 910 rpm, or slightly overspeed for the 900 rpm induction motor/generator that it drives.

Table 2 outlines some of the technical data for this engine and generator.

TABLE 2
COGENERATOR TECHNICAL DATA

ENGINE DATA:

Model	Waukesha F817GU
Type	4 cycle, ovhd valve
Number of cylinders	6 in-line
Displacement	817 cubic inches
Aspiration	natural
Compression ratio	9:1
Carburetion	2 Impco, natural gas
Timing	45° BTDC
Continuous BHP @ 900rpm	85 BHP
Maximum BHP @ 2000rpm	190 BHP

GENERATOR DATA:

Model	Marathon 444TS
Type	Induction
Capacity	85 kW
Phase	3
Voltage	480 V
Amperage (full load)	128 @1220 rpm
Efficiency (full load)	91%
Power factor (full load)	80%
Torque (full load)	539 lb-ft @1220 rpm

Generator System

The generator is a Marathon induction generator with a maximum rating of 85 kW. Three phase power is provided at 480 volts with a full-load power factor of 80%. Other details can be seen in Table 2. Being an induction generator, it must receive excitation from the utility grid to produce power and at a frequency synchronous to that of the grid.

Heat Recovery

The heat recovery system consists of an engine exhaust heat exchanger and an external, cooling loop heat exchanger to recover the approximately 437,000 Btu per hour heat rejection from the Waukesha engine. The exhaust heat exhanger boosts the temperature of coolant leaving the engine 10-20 degrees Fahrenheit (the coolant already heated by water jacket heat rejection and oil cooler heat transfer.) As Figure 3 illustrates, the coolant either short-circuits back into the engine to maintain a minimum coolant temperature (165° F) into the engine or passes into a cooling loop heat exchanger. This exchanger (Perfex Model C counter flow, shell-in-tube) can be used to provide process thermal energy to the dairy or any other thermal loads. It is currently used to primarily provide thermal energy to maintain anaerobic digester temperature at 95°-100° F. A full size maximum output radiator is in line to reject any excess energy into a drying room where the separated solids illustrated in Figure 1 are collected and dried. The system has provisions for supply of hot water to the milking parlor.

Gas Cleanup System

Gas cleanup is required to remove mercaptans and moisture from the biogas as it exits the digester. The filter unit is a 21 element Winslow Filter manufactured by Nelson Filter. A Dresser Roots meter is in line after the filter to measure gas consumption by the engine generator. The system also includes a number of water traps for removal of moisture from the biogas.

Controls and Safety System

The engine and generator are protected by a series of relays set to disengage the system in the event of low oil pressure, low coolant level, high engine temperature, starter overcrank, and electrical safety. The control panel also allows for fuel selection, throttle setting, and generator engagement. A warning light and horn are located outside the generator building to alert farm personnel of system malfunctions.

Interconnect/Protection System

Figure 4 shows the interconnect /protection system installed by the local utility, Oglethorpe Power Corporation. The system was required by the utility after its rejection of a duplicate protection system provided by the system vendor, Perennial Energy Incorporated. Although this particular protection package had been widely accepted by other utilities across the U.S., OPC objected to the use of industrial grade (vs. utility grade) relays and contactors instead of breakers to interrupt service and, required magnetic tape metering of demand (kW) and energy (kWh) instead of direct kWh metering.

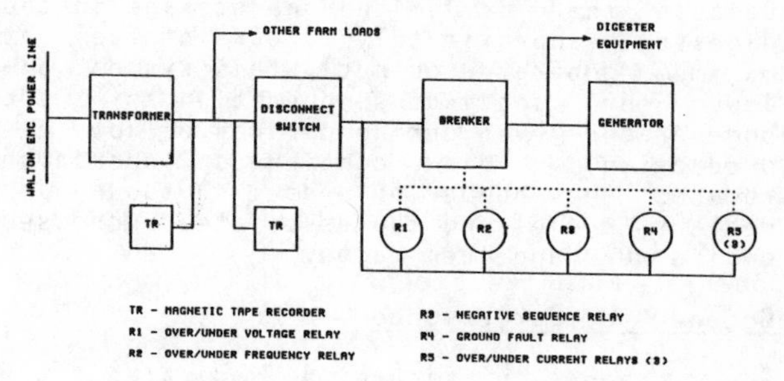

FIGURE 4. UTILITY INTERCONNECT/ PROTECTION SYSTEM

SYSTEM PERFORMANCE

General Operation

Because the biogas has very little storage, it is consumed by the power unit immediately. Gas passes from the digester at a pressure from 6-20 inches water column through the filter system to a regulator which provides gas to the engine carburetion at approximately 4 inches w.c. A maximum/minimum pressure guage determines this operating range as the engine will disengage the generator and enter into a cooldown cycle when gas pressure in the digester drops to the minimum setting. The engine will not restart until after the maximum pressure setting is reached.

The system provides either direct setting of the throttle for various generator outputs or a floating throttle setting provided by a patented throttle control called Tracker-Trol®. This system, designed by Perennial Energy, utilizes a pressure regulator (pressure being an indicator of gas availability) to set the throttle and generator output. Figure 5 illustrates the relationship between digester pressure and generator output. The minimum setting in this particular setting is 6 inches w.c. The diagram also indicates how maximum output is reached around 16.5 inches w.c.

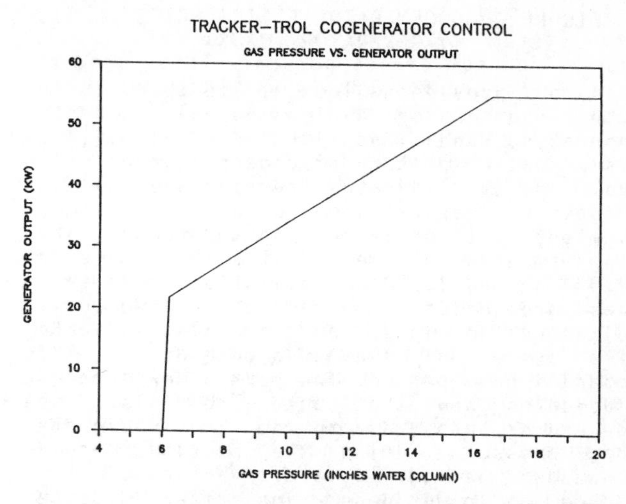

FIGURE 5. EFFECT OF DIGESTER GAS PRESSURE ON GENERATOR OUTPUT

Because there is limited gas storage in the digester (approximately 2 hours of fuel at maximum generator output), this system allows for continuous operation of the cogenerator even during periods of low gas production. This continuous operation reduces the number of system shutdown and restart cycles and the associated increased engine wear and fuel waste.

Cogenerator Performance

The graph in Figure 6 indicates the relationship between cogenerator electrical and thermal energy efficiency and generator load. As expected, the system electrical efficiency drops dramatically as the generator output drops below 20 kW. Consequently, total efficiency also decreases while thermal efficiency remains relatively stable. Since electrical energy has a higher demand (Figure 2) at this operation than thermal, maintaining high electrical efficiency through higher generator loading is desirable. This points out a deficiency in the operation of the Tracker-Trol system which allows the generator output to drop below 20 kW as gas pressure decreases.

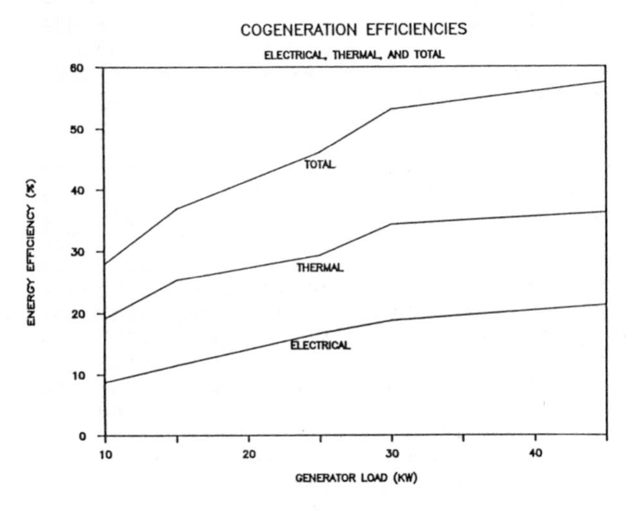

FIGURE 6. COGENERATOR EFFICIENCIES VERSUS GENERATOR LOADS

Figure 7 provides a look at the operation of the cogenerator during normal digester operating conditions with respect to time. A "saw-tooth" pattern of cogenerator electrical output indicates the rise and fall of digester pressure and subsequent adjustment in engine throttle setting to produce varying amounts of electricity. The peaks at 9:30 pm and 11:00 am reflect an increase in gas production after each of the two daily digester loadings. The graph also indicates the system only shut down once during this operational period. The peak after shutdown indicates how the Tracker-Trol raises the generator output due to the rise in digester gas pressure during the previous engine shutdown period. To take advantage of this surge of power generation after digester loading, the digester is loaded one hour before each milking cycle.

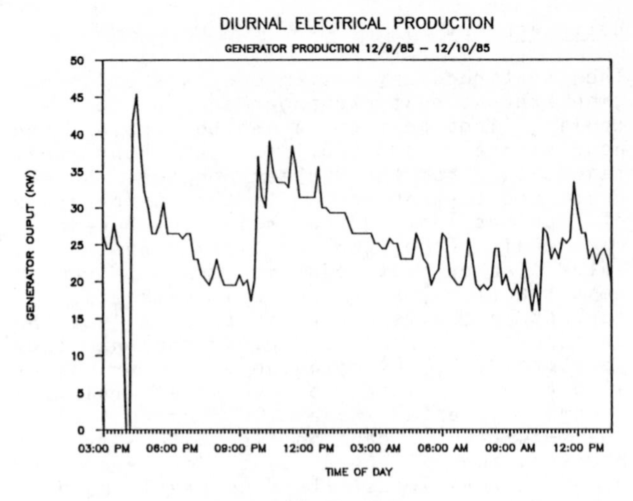

FIGURE 7. COGENERATOR DIURNAL ELECTRICAL PRODUCTION

The cogenerator in effect povides approximately 50% of the dairy's electrical energy requirement. The estimated annual energy savings by the system are shown in Table 3. Of the 560 kWh per day average electrical production, roughly 85% to 100% is used by the dairy with the remainder sold to the utility. On-site use is preferred because the power displaced at the dairy by the cogeneration system costs up to $0.065 per kWh while energy sold to the utility brings only $0.024 per kWh.

TABLE 3
PROJECTED ENERGY SAVINGS

Average Monthly Kilowatt Hours Before Cogeneration Operation	28,200
Average Monthly Kilowatt Hours After Cogeneration Operation	13,260
Average Monthly Kilowatt Hours Saved	14,940
Estimated Annual Kilowatt Hour Savings	179,280

COGENERATOR MAINTENANCE

After 4000 hours of operation, maintenance of the cogenerator system has not been a major problem. Daily maintenance involves checking fluids (coolant and oil), clearing water traps, and recording performance data.

Oil tests are performed at regular intervals to determine metal wear and oil deterioration. The Total Base Number (TBN) is of particular interest in that it reflects the deterioration of the oil due to wash down of hydrogen sulfide, water and mercaptans along the cylinder walls. The operation currently uses Mobil Delvac 1330 (SAE 10W-30) as the lubricating oil, and can get up to 600 hours of operation before oil change.

Other items requiring replacement include the 21 elements from the Winslow Filters for removing mercaptans from the digester gas. Replacement for these appear to be about every 6 months. Spark plugs (J-6 Champions) require replacement only about every 1000 hours.

Repairs to date include replacement of one of the heat exchanger pumps, a valve job, and cleaning the carburetors. Degradation of the interior of gas lines and valves due to the corrosive nature of the digester gas is a condition which will eventually require cleaning or replacement of the exposed components. Estimated annual maintenance costs are shown in Table 4.

TABLE 4
COGENERATION SYSTEM MAINTENANCE COSTS

7,884 Hours Per Year Operation

Item	Quantity	Unit Cost	Frequency hours	Annual Cost
Oil (Gal)	5	$6	600	$94
Oil Filter	1	$10	600	$134
Oildex Filter Cartridge	1	$10	1,000	$79
Wix Coolant Filter	1	$10	600	$156
Air Filter	1	$15	2,000	$63
Spark Plugs	6	$6	1,000	$47
Mercaptan Filter	21	$400	4,000	$788
Minor Overhaul	1	$1,600	16,000	$788
Major Overhaul	1	$5,000	32,000	$1,230
Total				$3,679

COGENERATOR ECONOMICS

The costs for the cogeneration equipment are detailed in Table 5. All of the equipment with the exception of the protection equipment were purchased from Perennial Energy Incorporated of West Plains, Missouri. The protection and metering equipment were purchased from Oglethorpe Power Corporation per their requirement.

TABLE 5
COGENERATION SYSTEM CAPITAL COSTS

COST ITEM:	COST:
Digester Component	$160,000
Engine Generator Component	60,000
Interconnect/Protection	30,000
Solids Separator Component	25,000
Total Capital Costs	**$275,000**

The annual operating costs for the system are listed in Table 6. An allowance is made for operator labor although experience has shown that impact on normal operations is minimal. The basis for the maintenance cost was discussed in a previous section. The annual tax cost is based on experience on other projects as the equipment was still owned by Georgia Tech at the time of the writing of this paper. The liability insurance premium recently escalated to the $2,000 figure shown in the table from a previous premium of $500 per year.

TABLE 6
COGENERATION SYSTEM OTHER COSTS

Time Required (hours) per Day for Operation and Maintenance	0.5
Hourly Labor Rate for Operator	$7.50
Annual Operation and Labor Costs	$1,232
Total Capital Cost of System	$284,000
Tax Percentage of Capital Cost	2.0%
Annual Taxes	$2,000
Annual Insurance Premium	$2,000
Total Other Costs	$5,232

The economics are based on an assumption that the monthly OPC service charge of $60 to $75 is offset by any sales of power to the grid. Although the system has not operated for a sufficient time to produce revenues from capacity payments, the equipment has paid approximately 50% of dairy's monthly electric bill through energy payments alone. It is thus anticipated the capacity payments will be sufficient to cover the balance.

Table 7 provides a summary of the projected annual savings based on reductions in the monthly power bill from the utility. This estimate is conservative in that operation to date has been during months when irrigation has not been required. Higher savings are anticipated during the summer months. The thermal energy being produced is being used for digester heating and drying of the digested solids. Additional savings could be realized if this energy were used to displace liquid propane for hot water heating although additional capital costs would be incurred for installation of the plumbing required.

TABLE 7
COGENERATION ANNUAL SAVINGS

Average Annual Electrical Energy Savings	$11,650
Annual Savings from Replacement of Sawdust for Bedding	$20,000
Total Annual Savings	$31,650

Table 7 also lists an annual savings of $20,000 for the replacement of sawdust with separated digester solids as a bedding material for the dairy herd. Evidently, as the figures show, the bedding has a higher value than the current energy production. However, if the system were operated at full capacity (it currently is operated at 65% capacity), the energy savings would be more substantial. Use of the digested solids as a resource is part of the integration of the energy and resource recovery technologies which must be implemented to make these systems economically viable.

Table 8 summarizes the simple payback for the cogeneration system. This computation does not account for interest or escallation of substitute fuel price. Until recent years, farmers were willing to accept such a payback as the farm was considered a lifetime investment. However, from a business standpoint the long payback of 12.1 years is very questionable.

TABLE 8
COGENERATION ANNUAL PAYBACK

Total System Capital Cost	$275,000
Total Annual Savings	$ 31,650
Total Annual Maintenance Cost	$ 3,679
Total Annual Other Costs	$ 5,232
Net Annual Savings	$ 22,739
SIMPLE PAYBACK (YEARS) (Capital Costs/Net Annual Savings)	12.1

CONCLUSIONS

This project was successful in indentifying many of the technical, economic, and institutional issues which affect cogeneration on an agricultural operation. The economic viability of these systems depend heavily on basically three things:

1) Maximum utilization of all cogenerated energy, both thermal and electrical,

2) Integration of other resource recovery technologies, i.e. solids recovery, and

3) Successful negotiations with the local utility on the technical and contractual requirements of an interconnect to the grid.

REFERENCES

Ross, C. C. and J. L. Walsh. 1985. "Cogeneration on a Southeastern Dairy-The Georgia Tech Experience", Proceedings of 5th Annual Solar and Biomass Energy Workshop, U. S. Department of Agriculture, Atlanta, Georgia.

Stahl, T. 1985. "Energy Cogeneration With Biogass Fuel", Doctoral Dissertation, University of Missouri-Columbia, Columbia, Missouri.

Walsh, J. L. and C. C. Ross. 1984. "Engine Generator-Electric Utility Interface", Proceedings of 4th Annual Solar and Biomass Energy Workshop, U. S. Department of Agriculture, Atlanta, Georgia.

Walsh, J. L., C. C. Ross, and R. M. Lamade. 1986. "Energy Integrated Dairy Farm System", Final Report, U.S. Department of Energy, Georgia Institute of Technology, Atlanta, Georgia.

SECTION 6
COGENERATION FINANCING
Sponsored by the Cogeneration Institute of AEE

Chapter 20

COGENERATION FINANCING IN A CHANGING UTILITY MARKET

R. J. Rudden, W. J. Oliver

The utility industry in the United States is undergoing significant structural changes which will have long-term implications for the cogeneration market. These changes could add additional risk to projects if they are not fully evaluated. An understanding of the nature and direction of change, the attendant risks which result, and the opportunities which are present will enhance the ability of the cogeneration developer and the financial institution to perform their "due diligence", and successfully finance and complete the project.

This paper will discuss the structural changes occurring within the utility industry and evaluate the effects of these changes on several important areas of risk. Our focus is on the power sales agreement, the fuel purchase contract, and the competitive threat presented by the utilities themselves. Finally, we present a series of recommendations to minimize project risk in the changing utility market.

A. Structural Changes In The Utility Industry

Changes occurring within the utility industry which will likely affect cogeneration economics include:

1. Move toward deregulation of the electric utility transmission system. In June, 1985 the Federal Energy Regulatory Commission issued a Notice of Inquiry to evaluate its policies toward wholesale electricity transactions and transmission service with the goal of promoting more efficient allocation of electricity. States are also taking an initiative with regard to requiring wheeling of cogenerated power. We anticipate these trends will continue and will result in a more accessible transmission network for sales of competitively priced cogeneration power.

2. Utilities are reorganizing their operations to integrate demand/supply planning and become more competitive players in the energy market place. The intent of this reorganization is to provide quicker response to market changes and plan for a least-cost demand/supply strategy. Utility Commissions are also mandating least-cost planning on the part of utilities. This will significantly influence the role of cogeneration in the overall supply strategy of the utility.

3. Utilities are diversifying into non-regulated subsidiaries including cogeneration development subsidiaries. These subsidiaries will be competing with cogenerators for project development and power sales markets. The strength these subsidiaries bring to the market place is a wealth of knowledge with regard to the power market, power pool dispatch, operations of facilities, and the ability to attract financing. To compete, developers will require similar information and knowledge.

4. Utility construction strategies are now departing significantly from the more traditional approaches previously employed. Utilities are generally following two tacks. One is the construction of more down-sized, less capital intensive technologies. The second is to joint venture projects with third party developers, including equipment vendors, engineering firms and fuel suppliers. The implications for cogenerators are more and financially stronger competition for developers, and possibly lower capacity payments for future projects.

B. Areas Of Utility Related Risk

The risks that these structural changes present to the contractual process cannot be minimized. The utility contracts affected include the contract for power exchanges and sales between the cogenerator and the utility, the interconnect agreement, and the fuel purchase agreement between the fuel supplier and the cogenerator.

The Power Sale Agreement: The power sale and interconnect agreement between the cogenerator and the utility is a major consideration in performing "due diligence" reviews for project financings. Several components of the power sales agreement influence financing availability. These include the strength of the contract (utility requirements to take power); interconnection costs and requirements; the avoided cost rate including the length of the contract; the mix of capacity and energy sales; and the calculation of avoided cost (actual avoided costs, levelized rates, front-end loaded contracts); standby, and supplementary power rates; reliability priorities; and access to other markets.

Although the Public Utilities Regulatory Policy Act (PURPA) requires electric utilities to interconnect with cogenerators and purchase the power produced, there could be certain obligations or restrictions included in a contract, or utility design and operating constraints, which will add risk to the project. For example, transmission capacity constraints or least-cost purchasing procedures utilized by utilities may permit a utility to refuse power at certain times or under certain operating conditions, or may allow the utility to terminate the interconnection agreement if the cogenerator does not perform in accordance with certain terms of the agreement, such as availability.

Another area of risk is the avoided cost rate. Utilities and State Commissions are expressing concern in a number of states that avoided cost contracts which have established rates in excess of actual avoided cost (front-end loaded or levelized rates) are costly to ratepayers, and do not meet least-cost planning strategies. This concern is particularly acute in service territories which are likely to experience rate shock from new facilities. Also, attractive avoided cost rates which stimulate substantial cogeneration and small power development may result in a situation whereby the utility is paying for its own capacity as well as cogeneration capacity in excess of its needs. Under these circumstances the consumer will experience increasing rates and the Public Utility Commission may be forced to adjust rates downward for those projects which do not have a fixed contract. It is also likely that as market access improves through industry deregulation, only the market sensitive contracts can be guaranteed a market for the power. Finally, tying avoided energy costs to fuel price forecasts has proven very costly to the consumer as fuel prices have dropped but avoided cost payments to cogenerators have not declined in response. The trade-off of providing long-term fixed rates which minimize financing risk versus establishing more market sensitive rates which increase financing risk will receive more attention in the future. Such options as establishing an auction process for cogenerated power sales will achieve market sensitivity but will increase project risk.

Another area of concern is standby and supplementary power rates. Utility action to restructure rates by shifting costs from the energy component to the demand charge has been undertaken partially in response to increased cogeneration and small power development. Higher demand charges ensure that the utility will recover its costs even if its own electricity sales decrease. Cogenerators who are connected to the utility will have to pay these high demand charges whether they require power or not. Project economics are adversely affected through this utility rate restructuring.

Another area of risk is the absence of clearly defined policies that make power wheeling available to cogenerators. As the industry moves to a less regulated environment, increased system access ensures a more efficient allocation of electric power. For example, a cogenerator in the service territory of company A may enter into a contract with company B. Company B needs power and is willing to pay more than A. However, in a number of cases A may not be willing to wheel power or may charge such a high rate as to negatively influence project economics. In general, transmission system access is limited primarily to utility generated power rather than cogeneration or small power production. Risk is increased if market access is not a viable option. States which require wheeling will to some degree alleviate the risk to the extent all producers have the right of equal access.

A final area of concern is cogeneration system reliability. Reliability concerns have focused on two issues: ensuring the project comes on-line according to schedule, and ensuring that the cogenerator produces power during peak requirement periods. The competition between cogeneration projects owned by utility subsidiaries versus purchases from a third party developer highlights this reliability issue. The preference of utilities is to have dispatch control over the project. To the extent that power production from an independent cogenerator can be integrated with utility dispatch, the risk of competition with utility owned facilities is diminished. The facility can more likely be assured of operating at its maximum possible level, and be assured of receiving the full value of avoided capacity costs.

The Fuel Purchase Agreement: The recent change in fuel prices highlights the significant risk inherent in project economics. In fact, one of the major factors influencing project economics is the differential between purchased fuel prices on the one hand and avoided cost and retail electricity rates on the other. Our focus is on natural gas as the primary fuel. The changes that are occurring within the natural gas industry will greatly influence fuel purchase decisions, prices and contract provisions in the future. The risks and potential benefits provided by these changes must to be carefully evaluated.

Traditionally, an industrial firm or other fuel consumer bought gas directly from a local distribution company either at a rate which was tied to the price of oil (interruptible rate) or at a firm industrial rate. The local distribution company purchased the gas from pipelines which transported the gas from the wellhead.

Within the past several years, the gas industry, particularly the transmission segment, has undergone radical change. Order 436, issued by the Federal Energy Regulatory Commission in October, 1985 is designed to change the role of pipelines. In brief, Order 436 encourages pipelines to provide transportation service without "undue" discrimination to local distribution companies and end-use consumers. In essence, Order 436 opens up the transportation system to non-traditional pipeline customers, including cogenerators.

Since spot market prices are currently below contract prices and end-use purchases can avoid rate discrimination, direct wellhead purchases offer cogenerators a great opportunity to reduce fuel costs substantially. However, there are a number of risks inherent in such an approach which must be recognized.

First of all, direct purchase from producers means that the responsibility and organizational burden of fuel management is either shifted to a third party purchaser (broker) or the cogenerator itself. Another concern is reliance on a single source for fuel supply. A contract with an individual producer could result in an interruption of fuel supply if the supplier curtails deliveries during periods of tight supply or has production well problems. A diversity of supply sources, on the other hand, can minimize risk. A third concern is availability of pipeline capacity. The ability of a cogenerator to obtain firm pipeline capacity may be limited by other users who also desire firm capacity. Interruptible off-peak capacity may be more readily available, but such an option requires dual fuel capability. In addition, available pipeline capacity may be rationed by a substantial reservation charge which could negate the economic benefits of low cost fuel purchases. Lastly, another risk to the fuel purchase contract is the establishment of price escalator clauses in the contract. Escalator clauses which are not market sensitive could substantially increase the fuel price relative to the competition and thereby increase project risk.

C. Risk Minimization Techniques

The changing utility environment with regard to both natural gas and electric utilities introduces many complexities in the decision process for cogenerators. As this situation grows in complexity with the movement toward a more market-based energy industry, project risk will increase. A thorough understanding of the risks inherent in this changing environment is absolutely essential if financial institutions and developers are to discharge themselves of their "due diligence" and "prudent man" responsibilities. Based on our analysis, there are a number of options which can be pursued to minimize risk.

1. Where possible, develop the project as an "inside-the-fence" facility as opposed to a "PURPA Machine" which is designed to sell power back to the utility grid. This latter type of project is highly dependent on state and federal regulatory policy with regard to such factors as avoided cost rates, reliability, and contractual commitments. A cliche which is appropriate in describing this risk is "The Government giveth and the Government taketh away." Inside-the-fence projects, on the other hand, must stand on their own economic merits and are not substantially dependent on regulatory and legislative preferences. However, these projects also require unique technical and negotiating skills for fuel purchase contracts, utility interconnect agreements, and standby, supplemental and maintenance power rates.

2. Build in dual fuel capability to minimize reliance on a single fuel source, and to hedge against any differential fluctuation in fuel prices.

3. For "inside-the-fence" projects, evaluate the economics of designing for maximum redundancy to avoid utility standby charges. Cogenerators should weigh the costs and benefits of totally disconnecting from the grid, generating all their own power, and providing all their back up requirements. Cogeneration facilities served by utilities which are undertaking large construction projects would be likely candidates. Excess generating capacity induces high utility demand and standby charges which may make disconnection by cogenerators viable.

4. Where power is sold to the grid a separate set of options emerge which serve to reduce risks. These include:

   - Joint venture these projects with electric utilities or their subsidiaries.

   - Design the project for maximum reliability to avoid any penalty for not meeting reliability standards.

   - Integrate plant operations with the utility to allow for dispatchability by the utility.

   - Design for least-cost output, to ensure the power is competitively priced with other supply sources on the utility system. Although several states allow for various types of contracts with avoided cost rates above actual levels, these contracts are most susceptible to regulatory scrutiny if consumer rates are adversely affected by a larger number of these contracts.

   - Conduct a detailed analysis of the financial status of the utility, the cost of power and fuel mix of existing facilities, its capacity plans, and its diversification goals.

   - Develop a knowledge of other utilities which may serve as an alternate market for power.

   - Understand the wheeling policies of the state, any constraints and opportunities for wheeling power, and the cost of wheeling.

Chapter 21

CREDIT ENHANCEMENT TECHNIQUES FOR COGENERATION PROJECT FINANCINGS

R. D. Feldman, S. L. Hoffman

INTRODUCTION

Market concerns relating to developer creditworthiness and the general state of the energy market are shaping the financing structure for project financings of cogeneration projects. Also affecting cogeneration project financings is the noticeable decline in orders for cogeneration equipment that equipment manufacturers and suppliers are now experiencing. In short, the overall economic outlook for cogeneration financing is in a state of transition from the early financings where the PURPA contract was thought to be sufficient credit support, to the financings of the late 1980's where complex financings with innovative credit enhancement from the developer, utility, equipment supplier and contractor are involved. These market influences have given rise to a number of creative credit enhancement techniques.

Various risk allocation and financial issues arise when we consider what will happen to the financing of cogeneration projects in 1986 and beyond. It is productive to analyze these issues for two purposes: first, to understand the direction of project financing of cogeneration projects, and second, to learn what credit enhancement elements will be necessary to complete a successful financing in the future. We follow and analyze these issues in an effort to insure that the contractual documents drafted, negotiated and executed by the project participants reflect the state of the industry and to thereby avoid delays in closing the financings.

This paper will examine briefly five innovative project finance structures that are appearing and developing in the project finance area: (1) the project finance joint venture, (2) the tenancy-in-common lending structure, (3) the bank letter of credit, (4) the bank line of credit, and (5) the financial guaranty. The purpose of each structure is to weave together credit supports from the developer, equipment manufacturer or supplier, utility, and contractor to develop a financing with sufficient credit enhancement to finance the cogeneration project.

PROJECT FINANCE JOINT VENTURES

One structure that has become increasingly popular, and an area in which we have structured financings, is the joint venture. Joint ventures are frequently formed for a project financing by entities that have neither the financial nor management capability to participate in the project alone, but have the desire to join financial, technology and management resources and share risks in a project with other participants. Such project finance joint ventures are typically financed in part with debt provided on a non-recourse or limited recourse basis with respect to the project sponsors, assuming cash flow is sufficient to enable debt repayment. Lenders generally look to the assets and cash flows of the venture for debt service and repayment of loans. Thus, part of the project risk is shifted to third parties, and if non-recourse, will not appear on the balance sheets of the joint venturers.

Some of the venturers will typically be large companies, each bringing different components to a project financing. For example, a fuel supplier, construction contractor and a developer might come together to develop, construct and operate a project through the vehicle of a joint venture. Another type of joint venture might be made up of large companies and a small company that seeks to introduce a new technology.

1. Typical Provisions

To understand the impact of the joint venture structure, developers of cogeneration projects should become acquainted with the typical provisions contained in the joint venture agreement. When structuring a joint venture, developers and their attorneys must consider the following terms and the manner in which risks will be allocated among the venture members:

(1) capital contributions of the venturers and the financial obligations of the venturers;
(2) management of the joint venture and voting;
(3) distributions of profits and losses and the manner in which distributions would be made;
(4) competition provisions;
(5) default provisions;
(6) assignment or transfer of a venturer's interest; and
(7) termination.

Where one of the venturers possesses a technology that will be used by the joint venture in the project, the technology will need to be transferred to the joint venture in a license agreement. The interests of the technology owner and the venture itself will, of course, conflict. To support the financing, the developer must be sensitive to insuring that the venture has the legal right to use the technology. The technology owner, however, will desire to include events of default under the agreement to insure that the technology owner is able to use the technology if the project does not proceed. It is important, however, that the joint venture have the right to use the technology upon the bankruptcy or other default by the owner.

We will continue to see other agreements we are familiar with in project financings under the joint venture structure. For example, under a services agreement, the joint venture could contract with a venturer (or a third party) to manage or provide other services to the venture. Similarly, the power contract, fuel supply contract, or construction contract could be entered into between the joint venture and one or more of the venturers.

2. Types of Joint Ventures

The joint venture can be structured under various forms. First, a corporate joint venture can be used, in which the venturers, as shareholders, seek to limit their liability. Typically, shareholders of a corporation are not liable for the corporation's liabilities.

Second, a general partnership can be used, in which the general partners are jointly and severally liable for the liabilities of the partnership. To a certain extent, a corporation can use a special purpose subsidiary for this purpose, thereby limiting the extent of exposure to the total amount of the subsidiary's capital.

Third, a limited partnership can be established. Generally, limited partners in a partnership are not liable for the liabilities of the partnership beyond the amount of their investment. This limitation of liability is eliminated, however, where the limited partner participates in the management of the partnership. Therein lies the problem since to avoid liability, the limited partners cannot be involved in management of the partnership.

3. Conflicts of Interest

Conflicts of interest are inherent in the project finance joint venture. We have provided advice to our clients in this area that can be categorized conveniently into two areas: (i) confidentiality and (ii) non-competition.

Confidentiality: The confidentiality of information in a project finance joint venture is an important consideration. Each venturer should carefully consider the type of information that will be available to the other venturers and the extent to which the other venturers must be contractually required to keep information confidential. Confidentiality agreements entered into between one venturer and a third party must also be examined to determine whether the venturer can disclose information to other venturers.

Non-competition: The venturers must consider whether or not a provision should be added to the joint venture agreement relating to competition by any other venturer with the venture. Conflicts can easily develop in this area and the issue of competition should be carefully considered and clearly defined.

4. Capitalization

Finally, it is important to consider the manner in which the joint venture will be capitalized. The project finance joint venture will sometimes be capitalized by the venturers, which from time to time will be supplemented by debt provided by third parties or the venturers themselves. More typically, the trend we have seen is for one venturer to provide equity, another the technology, and still others construction and management expertise. Debt from a bank or other lender is then used to provide the largest part of the financing, which is loaned either to the venture itself or to the venturers individually.

For a joint venture to be in a position to receive debt financing, real equity must be at risk. This "risk" capital will help to convince a third party lender that the venturers have contributed sufficient capital to be genuinely interested in and tied to the success of the project.

If debt financing is made by a venture member, the loans must be made on a subordinated basis to insure the ability to obtain third-party financing secured by the project assets. Even though the value of the project's assets may be more than the principal amount of the loan, we have found that lenders will not make loans on a non-recourse basis to the venturers unless cash-flow projections demonstrate sufficient coverage of debt service.

The timing and form of capital contributions are all subject to negotiation. For example, if debt financing is provided by a venturer, the parties can also consider the possibility of converting the debt into equity in return for an attractive interest rate.

BORROWING AS A TENANCY-IN-COMMON

Generally, project financings of cogeneration projects involve one borrower established for the sole purpose of developing, owning and operating one project. Whether the borrower will be a joint venture, corporation, partnership, or some other entity is governed by a range of issues including tax positions, credit ratings, and other concerns. One form of borrowing that is often overlooked is the tenancy-in-common, in which each participant in the project owns an undivided interest in the project. A tenancy-in-common is not a legal entity, but rather a type of financing. Typically, each participant enters into identical loan agreements in which each agrees to borrow a share of the funds needed to complete the project and grants its share of the project collateral.

This structure of project financing is often attractive to companies that are new to the project finance area and who desire a limit of liability for project risks. Others choose this structure for credit or tax reasons. Lenders approve of this structure because it provides credit support for the project through direct access to the borrowing entities.

BANK LETTER OF CREDIT

A more traditional type of credit enhancement for cogeneration project financings is the bank letter of credit. A bank letter of credit is an unsecured obligation by the bank to pay a specified amount in defined situations. Bank letters of credit have been traditionally used in taxable and tax-exempt bond financings.

The typical structure for a letter of credit transaction includes a reimbursement agreement, wherein the borrower agrees with the bank to pay back any amounts paid out under the letter of credit. Letters of credit usually have a maximum term of ten years.

BANK LINE OF CREDIT

In some situations, a bank line of credit will be sufficient to provide the necessary credit enhancement for a project financing. A bank line of credit is a loan arrangement in which a bank agrees to make available a certain amount of money for a given period of time. Line of credit agreements typically provide that certain financial tests be met before each draw is made. The disadvantage of the bank line of credit is that the bank can cancel the commitment under the terms of the agreement.

GUARANTEES

Project finance credit enhancement is sometimes provided by a guarantee. Guarantees can be given by other project participants, such as in the form of guarantees of payment or performance, and by parent corporations or subsidiaries.

CONCLUSION

The current energy situation, over abundance of PURPA contracts in some geographical areas, and the tax environment will not destroy project financing of cogeneration projects. Rather, the industry will undergo a change in which the financings are increasingly based on new credit supports by different sponsors. The developer and other cogeneration industry participants must understand the changes taking place in the cogeneration industry and adapt financing structures and documents in ways necessary to bring financings to closing.

Chapter 22

RECENT TAX AND REGULATORY DEVELOPMENTS AFFECTING THE COGENERATION MARKET

R. D. Feldman, S. L. Hoffman

INTRODUCTION

The purpose of this paper is two-fold. First, it provides a general overview of the significant tax and regulatory developments during the past year that may have an impact on the cogeneration market in the United States. Second, it will focus on five specific areas that will affect various types of cogeneration transactions:

1. Pending tax legislation and how it would specifically affect cogeneration projects (including the general effect of legislative changes regarding depreciation and investment tax credit);

2. Recent federal developments, including the FERC's Alcon decision and its impact on third-party financing and retail sales;

3. State regulatory trends;

4. Opportunities that may arise from proposed legislative changes to the Fuel Use Act; and

5. The outlook for district heating in light of these federal and state regulatory developments.

To appreciate the current trends in the United States cogeneration market, it is necessary to consider the regulatory and tax context in which the market has grown so dramatically.

The primary impetus for the development of cogeneration in the United States was the Public Utility Regulatory Policies Act ("PURPA"), passed by Congress in 1978 as part of the National Energy Act. PURPA vested the Federal Energy Regulatory Commission ("FERC") with substantial power to issue regulations encouraging the development of cogeneration and small power production facilities. Soon after, the FERC adopted regulations that, among other things, require electric utilities to purchase power from "qualifying facilities" ("QFs") at rates equal to the utilities' "avoided costs," or the cost they would incur to generate or purchase the power if they did not buy it from the cogenerator. The FERC regulations also require electric utilities to sell qualifying facilities power they need in addition to what the Facility generates, or when the Facility is out of service ("Stand-by Power"). As part of the PURPA mandate, each state utility commission was also required to issue rules implementing PURPA to promote development of cogeneration.

In addition to providing incentives for cogeneration through regulatory measures, Congress also sought, through the National Energy Act, to promote cogeneration development through energy tax credits, supplementing the existing investment tax credit ("ITC"). In subsequent years, the Accelerated Cost Recovery System ("ACRS") program further enhanced the front-loading of cash flow from alternate energy projects, and thereby made possible their syndication in tax shelters. The combined effect of PURPA and tax incentives spurred tremendous growth in the development of cogeneration across the nation, particularly in areas like California and Texas where energy prices were heavily dependent on the price of oil.

The PURPA and tax incentives, however, were adopted in the midst of an energy crisis in the United States, when the national perception was of rising oil prices, diminished availability of natural gas, and a serious need to rely on additional sources of generating capacity. As these conditions have changed significantly, there has been an increasing movement, spearheaded in large part by electric utilities, to re-examine the value of cogeneration and to reduce the tax and regulatory incentives to cogeneration development.

In recent years, the cogeneration market has been exposed to a variety of external trends that have changed the nature of the marketplace and pointed to new directions for development. The most significant factors include shifts in fuel prices, shifts in the power requirements of different portions of the electric utility industry, shifts in available tax benefits, and the resultant shifts in the developers available for energy projects.

FEDERAL INCOME TAX DEVELOPMENTS

A. Introduction

Tax considerations have historically played a significant role in the cogeneration marketplace because of the potentially large tax benefits available to owners of gas turbines or other cogeneration equipment. Principal among these potential tax benefits are the investment tax credit ("ITC") and depreciation deductions under the Accelerated Cost Recovery System ("ACRS").

Certain other provisions of the federal income tax law limit the availability of ITC and ACRS, and thus are also important considerations in determining the overall tax consequences of an investment in cogeneration equipment. Principal among these rules are various restrictions upon favorable tax treatment for leasing arrangements involving individual investors as owners or tax-exempt entities as users, including the so-called "Wallop Amendment," which in many cases determines the proper characterization of a contractual arrangement as a lease, sale or something else.

Three caveats apply to the following discussion. First, the discussion is, of necessity, very general. Application of the federal tax rules and effective tax planning is highly dependent on the specific facts of each transaction, and slightly different facts can produce radically different tax results. Thus, the discussion is merely an attempt to discuss basic principles. Second, the usefulness of any potentially available tax benefits is highly dependent on the individual tax situation of the affected taxpayer. If a particular owner has no "tax appetite," because for example it has net operating losses or large amounts of foreign income against which U.S. tax benefits may not be utilized, the availability of tax benefits to it may be meaningless or may mandate consideration of different structures to transfer those tax benefits to another party. Third, the continued availability of generous ITC and ACRS benefits is uncertain in light of the significant tax reform proposals presently before the U.S. Congress. There is gathering momentum in the Congress for significant tax reform, and at the moment it appears likely that tax reform legislation in some form will be enacted in 1986. Particulars of the House and Senate proposals that would affect currently available tax benefits for cogeneration investments are discussed below.

B. Investment Tax Credit (ITC)

1. Present Law: Under present law, a credit against income tax liability is allowed for up to 10 percent of a taxpayer's investment in certain tangible personal property or other tangible property (not including a building and its structural components) used as an integral part of the production or furnishing of electrical energy, gas, and water services, among others. Within these general limitations, the credit is generally available for gas turbines and other assets used in cogeneration projects. However, if the turbine or other asset is deemed to be a "structural component" of a building (generally defined as a component relating to the operation of a building), no credit is allowed.

2. H.R.3838: H.R. 3838 would repeal ITC effective for property placed in service on or after January 1, 1986, subject to detailed transition rules which would allow the credit to be taken for certain property placed in service after this date. A taxpayer would be required to spread any credit earned on transition property ratably over five years, and would be required to reduce its cost basis in the property by the full amount of the investment credit.

3. Senate Finance Committee Proposal: Under the Finance Committee Proposal, ITC would also be repealed effective January 1, 1986. However, since legislative language has not yet been drafted, the transition rules which would apply under the proposal are not yet clear, although the Finance Committee would require a 30 percent reduction in the allowable credit for any transition property.
It is unlikely that turbines or other equipment not presently subject to binding purchase contracts will be eligible for ITC as transition property.

C. ACRS Deductions

1. Present Law: Under current ACRS rules, the cost of depreciable property that is not a building or structural component is generally recoverable over a three, five, 10, or 15-year period, depending on which of several classes of property it falls into. (Depreciable buildings and structural components are generally recoverable over a 19-year period.) Most cogeneration equipment, including gas turbines, would likely be characterized as 5-year property under ACRS and depreciated over that period. However, if the equipment is deemed to be a structural component of a building (determined under standards similar to those applicable to ITC and noted above), it would be depreciated over the 19-year period applicable to the building. In certain cases property used in cogeneration projects may be classified as "public utility property" (generally defined as property used predominantly in the trade or business of the furnishing or sale of electrical energy, water, gas or steam, if the rates for the furnishing or sale have been established or approved on a rate-of-return basis by a governmental body), in which case such property may be classified as 10- or 15-year property.

2. H.R. 3838: H.R. 3838 replaces ACRS with the Incentive Depreciation System ("IDS"). Under IDS all assets are grouped into ten classes. Each class is assigned a depreciation method and a recovery period. IDS is mandatory for all eligible property. Although the wording of H.R. 3838 relating to IDS is vague, it seems to maintain the current law distinction between tangible property, on the one hand, and buildings and structural components on the other. Buildings and structural components will probably be classified as Class 10 property under IDS. The cost of property included in Class 10 is recovered using the straight line method and a 30-year recovery period.

Cogeneration equipment treated as 5-year property under current law could be included in any one of six other classes under IDS, depending on the type of equipment involved and the use to which it was put. For example, under IDS waste reduction and resource recovery plants and related equipment would be included in Class 4, with the cost recovered using the double declining balance ("DDB") method, switching to the straight line method at the time which maximizes the deduction, and a 10-year recovery period. Equipment used in industrial steam and electric generation and/or distribution systems (where the output is used by the taxpayer claiming the ACRS deductions) would be included in IDS Class 7, with the cost recovered using the DDB method and a 20-year recovery period. Although it is not entirely clear under the bill, it is conceivable that cogeneration assets could be treated as electric utility transmission and distribution plants and included in IDS Class 9, under which they would be depreciated on a DDB basis over 30 years.

As in the case of the repeal of ITC, the application of IDS would be effective for property placed in service on or after January 1, 1986, subject to detailed transition rules.

3. Senate Finance Committee Proposal: The Senate Finance Committee proposal would generally retain ACRS, but with some significant changes. Under the Finance Committee proposal, property with a midpoint life of 16 years or greater under the old Asset Depreciation Range (ADR) system (generally equivalent to the useful life of an item of property) would be moved from the 5-year to the 10-year class and depreciated on a DDB basis, switching to straight line at the time most advantageous to maximize the deduction. Utility property with an ADR midpoint

life of 20 years or greater, and steam and electric generators for distribution systems, would be included in the 15-year class, which utilizes a 150 percent declining balance depreciation method. Buildings and structural components would be depreciated using the straight line method over 31 and one half years. No description has been released as yet concerning the transitional rules which will apply for ACRS property under the Senate Finance Committee proposal.

Although it is not at all clear from the limited material available describing the Finance Committee proposal, it appears likely that some cogeneration equipment (if not the majority) will be moved from the 5- to the 10-year class. Such a change would reduce markedly the benefit of the depreciation allowance currently available. However, it is possible that cogeneration assets will remain in the 5-year category; this determination will have to await the release of specific legislative language.

As in the case of ITC repeal, it is unlikley that turbines or other equipment not presently subject to binding purchase contracts will be eligible for ACRS treatment as transition property.

D. Characterization of Contractual Arrangements and Ownership Structures

1. Present Law: The availability to an owner of cogeneration equipment of tax benefits such as ACRS and ITC may depend in large measure on whether the contractual arrangements under which the cogeneration facility is operated, or the ownership structure utilized for the project, are deemed to be leases or service contracts. If the arrangement is a service contract, under present law ITC and 5-year ACRS deductions should be fully available. If, however, the arrangement is deemed to be a lease to the "purchaser" of the electricity, and the deemed lessee is a public utility, a tax-exempt organization or a governmental entity (as may be the situation in either Case A, Case B or Case C), the ACRS recovery period would be substantially lengthened, and ITC may not be available. Thus, under current law it is vitally important to determine the proper characterization of the particular arrangement.

While the characterization issue is fairly fact specific, as a general rule it is better from a tax standpoint to have an arrangement characterized as a service contract than as a lease. There are several judicial and administrative decisions on this issue, as well as recently enacted statutory provisions in the Internal Revenue Code. One of these provisions is section 7701(e)(3)-(4), commonly known as the "Wallop Amendment." Under the Wallop Amendment, a contract involving a cogeneration facility will not be classified as a lease so long as the service recipient or a related entity does not (i) operate the facility, (ii) bear any significant financial burden if there is nonperformance under the contract, (iii) receive any significant financial benefit if the operating costs of the facility are less than the standards of performance or operation under the contract, or (iv) have an option to purchase any portion of the facility at a fixed and determinable price other than fair market value. If this safe harbor can be satisfied, the dangers inherent in the characterization issue often can be avoided.

If an arrangement involving a cogeneration facility is characterized as a lease, under the tax law an additional inquiry must be made to determine whether or not the arrangement is in fact a lease or amounts to a sale of the equipment or facility to the lessee. If it is determined to be a sale, the tax benefits expected to be realized by the putative owner will be disallowed and instead will be realized by the "lessee." A discussion of the general principles of the lease versus sale analysis is beyond the scope of this memorandum.

2. H. R. 3838 and Senate Finance Committee Proposal: Neither H.R. 3838 nor the Senate reform proposal include any changes to the characterization rules presently contained in the Internal Revenue Code. However, to the extent that these reform proposals would eliminate ITC and substantially lengthen the period over which cogeneration assets may be depreciated, the characterization issue could be rendered substantially moot. This is because under the reform proposals there would be much less of a distinction between the recovery periods applicable to property deemed to be public utility property or property leased to a tax-exempt entity and property which does not fall into either of these categories.

E. Impact of Possible Changes in Tax Law On Cogeneration Marketplace

Because tax benefits may be utilized only by the owner of an asset, structures employed for investment in cogeneration equipment are dictated in large measure by the need to place ownership with the individual or corporate participant in the transaction who has the largest tax appetite.

The pending legislative proposals would, if enacted in their present form, undoubtedly have a significant impact on the relative tax appetites of potential owners of cogeneration equipment and, accordingly, on the structures used to secure tax benefits. Although it is not yet possible to gauge with certainty the impact of any finally-enacted tax legislation on the cogeneration marketplace, it is possible to make some general observations.

The elimination of ITC and the likely reduction in the benefits offered by ACRS will reduce the attractiveness of owning equipment to those individuals or entities interested in obtaining large immediate tax write-offs. As a result, there will undoubtedly be some narrowing of the pool of investors who are likely to have an interest in owning cogeneration equipment.

In addition to reducing the amount of immediately available tax benefits, the pending legislative proposals would also impose a minimum tax on corporate investors that have high book income but invest in equipment to obtain large tax writeoffs which are then used to reduce tax liability. Such a change likely will reduce the presence of large institutional investors in the marketplace. The pending proposals, particularly the Senate bill, also would limit the ability of individuals to utilize tax benefits obtained through investments in syndicated partnerships which purchase cogeneration equipment. Thus, it appears likely that the post-tax reform pool of investors will be comprised of those entities who are interested in ownership of cogeneration equipment primarily for reasons other than utilization of tax benefits.

It is important to note that, while ITC would be eliminated by the proposed legislation, depreciation deductions would continue to be available, albeit over a longer period. Accordingly, some tax benefits will continue to be available for investments in cogeneration equipment, but these benefits will be of interest to a smaller number of taxpayers than is the case under current law. Traditional structures for transferring ownership of equipment and the related tax benefits, such as leveraged leasing, will continue to be available under the current law guidelines, but also will be of interest to a smaller pool of investors.

It is difficult to gauge the impact of this tax-driven reduction in the pool of equity capital and equity investors on other aspects of the cogeneration marketplace, such as pricing. To the extent that cogeneration facilities are either encouraged under other provisions of U.S. law or are otherwise desirable from an economic standpoint, there will still be a market for turbines and other cogeneration equipment. Price should continue to be dictated by supply, demand and competition, rather than by tax considerations. In the absence of a larger pool of equity investment capital, however, manufacturers may have to be willing and able to utilize structures where they retain some sort of ownership interest with more frequency than might be the case under current law.

F. Summary

It should be evident from the foregoing that tax considerations have played an important part in the development of the cogeneration marketplace, particularly as to the availability of financing, and they will undoubtedly continue to be important in the future, although perhaps less so. The outcome of the legislative debate is of crucial importance, and it will not be possible to gauge the impact on various investment structures in the marketplace until the scope of any legislative package is agreed upon by the House and Senate, enacted and signed into law. At present, it is anticipated that a final bill will be ready for signature by the President sometime in August. Although this timetable may be somewhat optimistic, there is general agreement among observers of the legislative process that a tax proposal of some sort will be enacted before the end of this year.

If legislation similar to H.R. 3838 or the Senate proposal is ultimately enacted, there will undoubtedly continue to be some tax benefits available for owning cogeneration equipment, although they may not be as striking or as immediately realizable as they have been under current law. In addition, the structures used for investment may vary, and there may be less equity investment capital available, particularly if individuals are driven out of the marketplace. It would, therefore, be imprudent to place a great deal of emphasis on tax benefits in developing a marketing strategy for entry into the U.S. cogeneration marketplace.

FEDERAL REGULATORY DEVELOPMENTS AND TRENDS

A. Alcon

At the federal level, the most significant development is the FERC's decision in Alcon. In Alcon, the FERC concluded that an electric utility is required under federal law to sell Stand-by Power "only to a QF and to the owners and operators of a QF." The FERC also suggested that projects which purchase and resell Stand-by Power to non-utility end users would run the risk of losing their status as qualifying facilities under PURPA.

Alcon concerned a pharmaceutical manufacturer that had entered into an agreement with a developer for the construction and installation of cogeneration equipment on the manufacturer's property to meet its overall needs for electricity and steam. The parties agreed that the developer would own and operate the equipment as lessor and that the lessee/manufacturer would purchase the electricity and steam. The manufacturer sought qualifying facility status for the facility and a determination from the FERC that it would be entitled to Stand-by Power. Because the FERC found that the manufacturer was neither an owner nor an operator, it concluded that the manufacturer would not be entitled to Stand-by Power.

Although Alcon generally impairs the ability of cogenerators to use third-party financing for the development of projects, for several reasons these types of arrangements can still go forward. First, by concluding that an electric utility must sell Stand-by Power "to a QF and to owners and operators of a QF," the FERC left open many issues concerning the circumstances under which participants in a cogeneration project would be entitled to Stand-by Power. It is not clear under Alcon what is required to be deemed an "owner" of the qualifying facility. The FERC did not indicate whether ownership of an equity interest in a company that owns the qualifying facility or ownership of a portion of the cogeneration equipment would be sufficient. Likewise, the FERC did not address the question of whether a split in ownership of facility components (e.g., boiler and turbine) would allow an end-user to receive Stand-by Power. Moreover, Alcon leaves open the possibility that an "operator" of the qualifying facility might be entitled to Stand-by Power; in other words, that a split of the ownership and operation functions between two entities might allow both to receive Stand-by Power. Alcon did not articulate a standard for determining whether a party is an "operator." Thus, it is possible to structure around the Alcon problem.

Second, Alcon is limited to the question of entitlement to Stand-by Power under federal law. It does not rule out the possibility that the utility may be obligated to provide Stand-by Power as a matter of state law. At least one state, Pennsylvania, has taken the position that, regardless of Alcon, electric utilities in that state are required to furnish electric service to all customers within their service territories.

Finally, the Alcon decision has engendered considerable controversy and is still pending before the FERC on a petition for rehearing. Thus, the possibility exists that the FERC could reverse its position.

B. Qualification Issues

The FERC has also recently focused more closely on qualification issues regarding cogeneration projects. The FERC regulations impose certain requirements concerning efficiency standards and use of thermal output in order for a project to qualify for PURPA benefits. The FERC has increasingly been skeptical as to the bona fides of qualified cogeneration projects, in terms of the thermal application. This has been reflected in decisions emphasizing the requirement that the thermal application be a bona fide one, and indicating that the project's independent economic justification will have to be shown in circumstances where it is owned by an affiliated person.

This should not adversely impact the projects

contemplated since, as we understand it, each will make substantial steam sales to non-affiliated end-users.

C. FERC's Gas Transmission Order

Not all the FERC action this year has been unfavorable. A recent FERC rule (Order No. 436), intended to reshape the natural gas pipeline industry, may provide economic opportunities for the cogeneration industry. The new rule encourages natural gas users to buy gas in the field, rather than from natural gas pipelines. The resulting availability of competing energy suppliers will place downward pressure on the field prices, making it less expensive for gas-fired cogenerators. The attraction to industrial customers of conservation through cogeneration may be enhanced.

Under Order No. 436, a pipeline that offers transportation services to its customers must offer non-discriminatory transportation on a firm basis to anyone. Thus, a cogenerator served by a pipeline offering transportation may secure natural gas from any seller it chooses, and the pipeline must deliver that gas, to the extent that it has capacity available. Expedited FERC approval will be granted to a pipeline for new services and facilities, if the pipeline is willing to undertake the financial risks associated with the venture, even if by-pass of a local gas utility is entailed -- an option clearly envisioned by the Order.

A gas-fired cogeneration facility will no longer need to buy its supply from the local utility or the pipelines to which it is connected. Gas may be purchased in the field, through brokers, or from other pipelines. These purchasing options appear at a time of considerable softening in prices. Gas-fired cogenerators that are located near open-access pipelines may be able, under the new regime, to negotiate long-term contracts for lower-priced gas from this new variety of sources.

It is possible that some of the effects of the rule on cogenerators may be adverse. Utility customers of open-access pipelines may be able to decrease the cost of their gas supply. In turn, this will decrease the prices paid to cogenerators, based on the avoided costs of the utility. The downward impact on avoided costs may be more widespread if the rule triggers a dramatic decline in the wellhead price of natural gas, as the FERC hopes it will do. Several major gas pipelines are currently active in the cogeneration industry. It will be informative to watch their strategies in response to the FERC Order.

D. Legislative Action on PURPA

There is also the possibility of legislative action concerning PURPA. Recently, the Senate Committee on Energy and Natural Resources announced that it will hold hearings on June 3, 1986 concerning implementation of PURPA. According to the notice, the hearing will focus on the growth of cogeneration and small power production since passage of PURPA and will consider whether there is a need for any modifications. The Committee has called for testimony on the price paid by utilities for power from qualifying facilities, the effect of such purchases on the operation and reliability of utility systems, and the environmental impacts of construction and operations of qualifying hydroelectric facilities.

STATE REGULATORY DEVELOPMENTS AND TRENDS

A. General Trends

Certain general trends are taking place in cogeneration across the United States that should be considered in assessing that market. They include:

1. Avoided Cost Rates: The first concerns avoided cost rates. Overall, as result of declining oil and gas prices, utility avoided cost rates have been experiencing a downward trend. This has been particularly true in certain areas of the country, such as California and Texas, where the electric utilities traditionally have relied heavily on oil and gas in their generating mix.

2. Avoided Cost Methodology: The second major trend concerns the development by state utility commissions of standard methodologies for determining utility short-run and long-run avoided cost rates. PURPA established the general requirment that cogenerators are entitled to rates equal to a utility's "avoided costs," which essentially are the energy and capacity costs that the utility avoids or defers when the cogenerator comes on-line. However, PURPA left it to the states to decide how a utility's "avoided cost" should be calculated.

The states have dealt with this in several different ways. Some, like Florida, New Jersey, New Mexico, and Texas have adopted the "proxy unit" approach, which looks to a hypothetical generating unit to determine long-run avoided cost rates. Others, like New York, have relied on complex computer simulation models to project what avoided cost rates will be in the future. Ideally, these various methodologies should yield a similar result which accurately reflects the utility's avoided costs. In practice, however, different methodologies may lead to relatively higher or lower rates. In New York, for example, the adoption of the PROMOD III methodology, which employed certain input assumptions that are were favorable to the New York electric utilities, led to a noticable decline in avoided cost rates compared with previous estimates. This, in turn, may have the effect of discouraging some cogenerators from pursuing projects in New York.

The decline in avoided cost rates is linked with another development in certain jurisdictions: use of decremental pricing. Under this approach, which has been followed in Maine, avoided costs are calculated for "decrements" of a certain level or percentage of the utility's peak load. The utilities calculate a per kilowatt hour cost including both capacity and energy. This per kilowatt hour cost is then used to determine the total amount of money that the utilities may expend in arranging for purchases of power for that decrement. When the decrement has been met, the process is started again for a new decrement. Time is an important factor for projects under the decrement approach because future decrements may be at lower avoided cost rates.

3. Standard Power Sales Contracts: The third major trend is the general movement toward standardized contracts for the sale of power to electric utilities. More and more state utility commissions have recognized that cogenerators often face difficult and protracted negotiations with electric utilities to obtain contracts that will support the financing requirements of a project. Consequently, these commissions have encouraged the development of standard contracts which are available to cogenerators and call for little or no

negotiation. California was the leading state in this area. The other states that have adopted standard contracts include Connecticut, Florida, and Virginia. Several other states, including Massachusetts, New Mexico, New York, New Jersey, and Nevada are in the process of considering standardized contract terms. Assuming that the terms of the standard contract allow satisfactory financing, the existence of a standard contract may be a significant incentive for prospective cogenerators to develop projects in that particular state.

4. Sales to Non-Utilities: The fourth major trend concerns the permissibility of sales of power by cogenerators to non-utility entities. These "retail sales" arrangements, which may be especially attractive in regions where electric utility rates remain high despite declining avoided costs, were not specifically addressed by PURPA. An increasing number of states, including New York, California, and Texas have allowed such sales under certain circumstances (e.g. sales to an adjacent user). Where retail sales are permitted, cogenerators may have an attractive alternative to selling power to the local utility.

Of course, as noted above in the discussion of Alcon, there may be structural issues to resolve concerning the provision of "Stand-by Power" to end-users under a retail sales arrangement.

5. Wheeling: The fifth major trend concerns transmission or "wheeling" of cogenerated power to neighboring utilities. Several states, such as Florida, Indiana, and Texas, have required utilities to provide wheeling service to cogenerators within their service territories.

6. Milestone/Bidding Requirements: The sixth significant development is the implementation of a milestone or competitive bidding procedure in areas where there is excess capacity and substantial cogeneration development. California recently instituted a milestone procedure in which cogenerators must meet certain project goals within specific time-frames in order to preserve their right to sell power to the electric utility under their contract. Competitive bidding has not been officially adopted by any states yet, but several states including Massachusetts and Texas have actively considered it.

7. Miscellaneous: Finally, although they cannot be considered major trends, certain other state developments affecting rates warrant mention. One is the adoption of a statutory "floor" rate which all cogenerators must be paid for a certain period. This has been done in New York, Minnesota, and Iowa (there is still litigation pending over whether this is permissible in Iowa). Another is the establishment of favorable rates or policies for certain projects. Connecticut, for example, has passed a law requiring utilities to to pay municipally-owned resource recovery projects the same rate that it ordinarilly would charge the municipality.

CONCLUSION

A. Tax Developments

Although federal income tax considerations have been an important factor in the development of the U.S. cogeneration marketplace, particularly with regard to the structuring of investments in cogeneration projects, it is likely that tax considerations will be of less importance in the future. Pending legislative proposals would, if enacted, repeal the investment tax credit, lengthen in many cases the depreciable lives of cogeneration equipment and reduce or eliminate the benefits which may be obtained by offsetting tax losses generated by investments in cogeneration projects against other income. These changes will likely reduce both the rate of return available for cogeneration investments and the pool of investors (both corporate and individual) willing to commit capital to cogeneration projects. Nevertheless, some tax benefits for ownership of cogeneration equipment will remain, albeit with less current value. Traditional structures for obtaining ownership of equipment (and thus the tax benefits), such as leveraged leasing, will continue to be available.

B. Regulatory Developments

Recent federal and state regulatory developments have both positive and negative implications for the cogeneration marketplace. On the one hand, the FERC's decision in Alcon has inhibited the development of projects where the end-user of a project's output is not the owner or operator of the project. On the other hand, state trends toward the development of standard methodologies for determining avoided cost rates, standardized forms of power sales contracts, a more permissive approach to "retail sales" arrangements, and stricter "wheeling" requirements applicable to utilities are all likely to encourage the development of cogeneration in the future. External factors such as the recent drop in fuel prices and shifts in the capacity needs of electric utilities will have an effect on future regulatory developments.

Chapter 23

MAJOR CONTRACTS FOR COGENERATION AND SMALL POWER PROJECTS

J. W. Pestle, E. J. Schneidewind

This paper outlines the major considerations applicable to the principal contracts for a cogeneration or small power project, namely the power sales contract, the fuel contract, and the design/build contract.

In particular, this paper addresses the requirements that these contracts must meet for a successful, nonrecourse or project financing of a cogeneration project (where the lenders or leasing company look solely to the revenues of the project for the return of their capital). Due to this form of financing, the contracts must minimize the various risks and adverse consequences that might occur. These same considerations are applicable to projects financed on more conventional bases because if the risks are minimized, the likelihood of the project achieving its projected results and returns are enhanced.

The specific matters addressed in this paper are:

"MAINTAINING THE SPREAD" THE INTERRELATIONSHIP OF THE FUEL AND POWER SALES CONTRACT

I. Project makes money on the spread between the cost of fuel and the price of energy sold.

A. The key is to protect the spread against

1. Electric/thermal revenue decline without corresponding fuel price decreases, and

2. Fuel price increases without corresponding electric/thermal rate increases.

3. Declines due to poor heat rate/capacity factor (see below).

II. Maintaining the spread is helped by factors such as:

A. A floor on energy rates, either

1. Absolute; or

2. Carried (if rate drops below floor, utility pays floor rate and shortfalls are later repaid to the utility with interest).

B. Consistent underlying economics (so as to prevent divergences):

1. For example, the electric rate is based on coal prices and the cogeneration plant is coal-fired.

2. The electric rate is based on gas prices and the cogeneration plant is gas-fired.

C. Financially strong fuel vendors

1. Who for this reason can absorb decreases in fuel prices below their cost of production, at least for a period of time

D. Diversity in and actual alternate sources of supply

1. Spreads risk.

2. Project should have an express contractual right to go to alternate suppliers if existing suppliers cannot meet specified price and terms.

E. Use of true wastes or by-products where the use of the substance as fuel is a no cost (or cost reduction) item to the fuel supplier, rather than a revenue item

1. Wood

2. Bagasse

3. Municipal solid waste

4. Waste coal

5. Etc.

F. Energy rate based on less volatile solid fuels

III. Specific mechanisms

A. Simple indexing--fuel price varies with electric price:

1. Either based on total electric price rate change (energy and capacity), or

2. Based on energy portion only.

B. Subordination of fuel payment to loan/lease payment and reserves:

1. Totally.

2. Up to X% (similar to retainage).

C. Suspense/tracking account:

1. Deferral of a portion of fuel payments, with or without interest, so as to maintain the spread in the event of revenue shortfall/decrease in energy rates below a specified level.

D. Profit and loss sharing with fuel vendor:

1. Equity interest.

2. Contractual.

IV. Fuel Purchase requirements: Must track actual plant operations

A. No or low minimum purchase requirements.

B. Purchase requirements are only those actually needed for actual operation.

1. Purchases decrease and increase as plant actually operates no matter what the cause is:

a. Mechanical failure.

b. Operator error.

c. Negligence by owner.

d. Intentional actions by owner (e.g. - intentional shut-down of plant for financial reasons).

C. Purchase obligation ceases if plant stops operation.

V. Term of Fuel Supply contract

A. In comparison with

1. Power sales contract and

2. Term of primary financing

B. Absolute term of fuel contract

1. 5, 10, 15 years or beyond and

2. Market price projections for that term

"GETTING THE BTU'S"
THE FUEL PURCHASE CONTRACT

I. Fuel specification described in detail

A. Btu content

B. Moisture

C. Ash

D. Sulfur

E. Other

F. Remedies for noncompliance

1. Reject fuel.

2. Fuel supplier replaces with complying fuel.

3. Automatic fuel price adjustment to keep project economics constant.

II. Price

A. Price adjusted automatically to maintain project net revenues constant if there is a deviation from the fuel specification.

1. The project is buying useful btu's. The price should be on a per mmbtu basis (e.g. - btu/lb).

2. Table or formula for other major variable factors, such as moisture content.

3. Specified remedies for deviation from environmental requirements (e.g., compliance coal fails to EPA specification).

B. The price should be a delivered price (seller of fuel to absorb any transportation price changes, up or down).

C. Price mechanisms have to correspond with power sales contract, as described above.

III. Other provisions

A. Measurement of fuel to conform to specifications

1. Who does the measurement.

2. Sampling method

3. Specific standards for measurement (ASTM or equivalent)

B. Delivery means carefully specified

1. Type of railcar (rotary coupler or bottom dump)

2. Truck delivery standard specified (to meet dumper specification), if applicable

C. Extensive default and remedy provisions favorable to cogenerator

D. Agreement to provide financial institutions with all data needed on seller of fuel that is necessary for a project financing

E. Term of contract to be short initial term with renewals at cogenerator's option. Allows cogenerator to switch if fuel delivery is unsatisfactory/market price should drop

F. Delivery schedule provisions:

1. "Look-ahead" notification of likely requirements for next several months.

2. Obligation on fuel supplier to maintain a specified minimum inventory of fuel at the cogeneration plant.

"SELLING THE POWER"
THE POWER SALES CONTRACT

I. Power Sales Contract Goals:

A. High rates are only part of the goal.

B. Rates must be financeable -- predictable with downside risks minimized.

1. Downward fluctuations minimized/prevented.

2. Risks of nonpayment removed.

3. Risks of rate change minimized/removed.

4. In summary -- goal is a contract with complete assurance that the stated rate will be paid for all hours of operation for the life of the contract.

C. Typical type of solution for financeable projects.

1. Negotiated rate where upward fluctuations are traded to utility in return for removal of downward fluctuations. Results in a firm, fixed rate, often at a discount from projected rates.

(a) A high but fluctuating rate is thus discounted to a lower fixed rate.

(b) Avoided costs escalating (but not decreasing) at a percentage of full avoided cost escalation.

(c) Other.

1. Resulting rate is ratepayer neutral or favorable.

D. Specific rate design matters.

1. Seasonal rates vs. flat rate year round.

2. Time of day rates (on-peak, intermediate peak, off-peak).

3. Utility fees for administering PURPA contracts.

4. Contract adders for pollution decrease.

E. Methodology: The contract should specifically spell out the precise methodology used to compute the rates so as to prevent future disputes/aid financeability.

F. Rate Security: Assurance that the contract as written will stay in effect for the life of the contract.

1. "Contract or rate" -- Can the contract be revisited/reopened by the parties or by the Public Service Commission?

(a) Can PSC reopen contract even if the contract does not allow same/parties do not want it? If so, what are the standards?

(b) If allowed in the contract, under what circumstances and what are the standards?

2. Contract enforceable even if PURPA or state regulations changed/repealed (not a PURPA contract).

3. Pass through -- utilities ability to pass through costs to the ratepayer.

(a) Express approval on this in advance very desirable

(b) PSC approval of contract in advance as just, reasonable, in the public interest and complying with PURPA.

(c) Can contract be reopened/unrecovered costs charged back to the project if the utility cannot pass through costs?

4. General language of force majeure clauses should not allow the contract to be opened under the preceding or other analogous circumstances.

5. Loss of QF status.

(a) Does the utility still have to purchase?

(b) If so, for how long (during any appeals; while the project has QF status restored)?

(c) If so, on what terms?

(d) Agreement to have contact approved as wholesale contact by FERC.

G. Curtailment: Minimize situations/hold project harmless in event of utility inability/lack of requirement to purchase (transmission line de-energized or overloaded, system emergency, testing interconnect equipment, light loading).

1. Cap on number of hours per year when need not purchase.

2. Some/all of the rate (e.g. -- capacity payment) is paid during times of curtailment.

II. Interconnection: Interconnection requirements can be a major hurdle. Must be expressly dealt with in the power sales contract or related contracts.

A. What is required for interconnection?

1. Dual feeds to the utility's transmission system?

2. What is the point of connection to the utility's existing system -- and thus length of needed transmission lines?

3. Islanding issues (project and some customers cut-off from rest of utility grid):

(a) Does project continue to operate?

(b) Surge protection.

(c) Frequency maintenance.

(d) Voltage limits.

(e) Load following ability.

(f) Does this make the project a utility?

(g) How is billing handled?

4. Telemetry/telecommunications requirements: Is direct, secure, redundant telemetry and phone connection with utility dispatcher required?

5. Amount and types of other protective and safety equipment.

B. Provision and cost of interconnection equipment:

1. If provided by a private contractor, how to assure that the utility's standards for the interconnection equipment have been met?

2. If the utility supplies the interconnection equipment:

(a) Will its price meet the lowest competitive private bid?

(b) Will it commit to a fixed price, schedule and adequate delay damages for its provision of the interconnection equipment?

(c) Who resolves the above issues if the utility and project can't?

C. Is the project required only to pay for interconnection costs incurred at the time the installation is placed on line, or repair, replacement or additional interconnection costs in later years as well? If future costs are included are there any dollar limits on them?

D. Will transmission bottlenecks require payments by the project to remove the transmission bottleneck?

III. Indemnities/Non-Interference Clauses:

A. Scope -- where circumstances on the utility's system harm the project and vice versa.

B. Equivalence -- are they truly a two way street? Should they be?

C. Are the risks imposed on the project insurable (important for financing)?

D. Non-interference and indemnity can be quite important if there is a risk that islanding or the project tripping off line can lead to surges harming other customers, or if interferences on the company's system reduce the power factor, and thus the output, of the project.

IV. Station Power:

A. Will it be produced by the project or bought at retail?

B. How is this affected by the utility's retail demand ratchets and standby rates?

V. PSC Approval/Ratepayer Pass Through:

A. Is the power sales contract contingent on Public Service Commission approval? Even if not, does the contract (and will the utility) allow advance Public Service Commission approval?

1. Advance approval minimizes the risks of later rejection/alteration of the contract by the Commission as imprudent or violating PURPA.

2. Approval aids financing, especially with a weak utility.

3. Utilities may oppose such approval as infringing on their management prerogatives or moving the Public Service Commission out of its reviewing role.

4. But approval may give the commission more ability to reopen the contract (against the cogenerator's wishes) later.

B. Must/can/will advance rulings be obtained from the State Commission on the ability of the utility to pass through all costs to its ratepayers?

1. Similar issues to number A above.

2. If obtained this minimizes one of the biggest risks for the utility and the project -- that part way through the contract the utility cannot pass through its costs. This may result in the utility trying to alter the contract.

VI. Other Issues:

A. No or minimal limits on project's ability to assign the contract are usually necessary for financing.

B. Billing and prompt (20-30 days) payment terms very helpful--reduce working capital needs.

C. Contract term must be significantly longer than term of expected financing.

D. Default provisions must provide adequate notice and ability to cure.

E. Does the utility require an option to purchase at the end of the contract?

1. Price.

2. Terms.

F. Dispatchability.

1. Does the utility desire/require this?

2. Can the project accommodate this?

G. Coordination of maintenance and planned outages between the utility and project.

H. Provision by the utility for emergency purchases from the project if project not already operating at full capacity.

1. Required by utility?

2. Provision for dumping excess thermal energy.

3. Effect on qualified facility status.

4. Rate (X% over fuel costs).

5. Telemetry/telephone notification.

I. Utility arrange/assist in wheeling power if project located in another utility's service territory.

"BUILDING IT TO WORK" THE DESIGN-BUILD CONTRACT

I. Two main concepts:

A. Construction Phase: Strong contract provisions/assurances on the cost and schedule for completing the project.

1. Developer has only a limited amount of funds, and no more, with which to complete the plant and bring it on line.

B. Operation Phase: Strong contract provisions/assurances that the project will operate as planned -- producing X kwh of electricity for sale per year while burning no more than Y amount of fuel.

1. Heat Rate: That if provided X tons of coal/Y mcf of gas/etc., the plant will produce at least a certain number of kwh of electricity.

2. The number of kwh of electricity actually generated per year is the product of rated output x capacity factor x 8,760. Requires assurances that:

(a) That the plant will have the rated output planned (e.g. at least a 25 mw plant), and

(b) That it will meet or exceed a specified capacity factor (e.g. 85%).

C. Implementing these concepts involves a combination of

1. Contractual performance standards and responsibilities on vendor and

2. Remedies, bonuses and penalties.

II. True turn-key contract approach

A. The vendor delivers a fully operable plant meeting the specified scope of work by a certain date for a certain amount of dollars.

B. Place total responsibility for bringing the project to completion on the vendor.

1. The contract is all inclusive on items which must be done to bring the plant to completion.

2. Few, if any, provisions in the contract for price increases or schedule changes.

3. Extremely limited force majeure clause (e.g. strikes do not excuse performance).

4. Construction contract is keyed to a general scope of work document ("A plant which will produce 25 MW with an 85% availability factor when provided with fuel meeting a certain specification") and not to a detailed design. The scope of work requires building a plant to a performance specification with general quality standards as opposed to a detailed design specification.

5. Responsibilities of the developer and owner minimized

C. The results should be similar to the developer/owner buying an existing plant: Most or all of the risks of the construction phase (cost increases, schedule delays, not meeting specifications) are placed on the vendor.

D. Typical problem areas in allocating responsibilities/risks include:

1. Sub-surface/hidden conditions.

2. Obtaining and complying with permits.

3. Subsequent law changes.

4. Strikes (vendor or sub-supplier).

5. Utility interfaces.

III. Performance Test

A. Goals

1. To show compliance with contract standards; trigger penalties/remedies of non-compliance; lead to closeout of contract.

2. To provide substantial assurance to the owner/lender/lessor that the plant will perform as intended for a long time.

B. To achieve these goals, have the performance test resemble reality.

1. Long duration.

(a) 30-90 days

(b) Two 30-day tests, six months apart.

2. Performed under actual operating conditions.

(a) Operators who will actually run the plant.

(b) No more than actual number of operators specified in operating manuals (no additional help.)

(c) No special equipment.

(d) In accordance with all operation manuals, vendor instructions, warranty requirements and the like.

3. Comply with all environmental and other laws.

4. Vendor to perform the test when it believes shakedown is sufficiently complete.

5. Plant performance during test determines whether the contract is met, applicable bonuses and penalties.

C. Typically measure many plant parameters during the performance test, especially those relating to

1. Output level.

2. Fuel used.

3. Heat rate.

4. Emissions

D. Detailed specifications on the performance test must be included in the contract covering such matters as:

1. Design conditions for the plant.

2. Method of correcting from actual test conditions to design conditions.

3. Condition of the plant at start and stop of test (inventories at various portions of the process).

4. How the plant will operate with respect to intermittent factors (cycling equipment and the like)

E. Instrumentation and measurement

1. What is measured?

2. By what instruments?

3. To what standards (ASTM #X, etc.)

4. With what precision?

5. With what adjustments?

6. Record-keeping requirements.

F. Type of Reports/Data/Computations to be supplied to Owner/Lender/Lessor by Vendor.

G. General formulas to be used in computing key variables carefully spelled out.

IV. Remedies/Bonuses/Penalties

A. Goal. Penalty (and perhaps bonus) arrangement that holds project's over-all economics constant against the major project risks of delays and failure to perform as intended.

1. Reality. It may not be possible to obtain complete contractual protection on all points from the vendor.

2. The owner, interested third parties and/or financing institutions will likely have to take some of the residual risks in return for cash payments or expected future payments/rate of return.

B. Schedule: Goal is a fixed completion date with delay damages equal to cost to owner of any delays after a specified date, such as:

1. Interest on construction loan

2. O & M costs (operators and equipment being paid for even though the plant is not generating revenues)

3. Loss of tax benefits due to delays.

C. Failure to Meet Performance Test Standards.

1. First and most important remedy is obligation of vendor to promptly fix plant to meet standards.

(a) Best for all parties and especially for owner/lender/ lessor as the monetary damages described below may not be sufficient to totally compensate all parties for failure to meet specifications.

(b) Dollar and time limits on vendor's responsibility to re-perform and correct problems are usually a major issue.

2. The secondary remedy is dollar penalties/ liquidated damages for failure of the project to meet the performance tests standards.

(a) "Buy-down" of the plant so that the cost per kilowatt (cost/KW) is held constant if the rated output is not met for any reason, e.g.

(i) Inability to produce output at contract level (20mw rather than 25mw plant)

(ii) Environmental constraints.

(b) Similar "buy-downs" if heat rate is higher than provided for/capacity factor is not met

(i) The reality is that the discounted present value of the lost income stream due to either of these factors is very large and there is a likely inability to get liquidated damages approximating this disaccounted present value

(ii) Reinforces the need for a conservative design and extensive first obligation on the vendor to make the plant work.

D. Bonuses for project exceeding specifications.

1. Desired by vendor but risky for the owner due to the vendor's ability to "skew" matters to achieve some bonus whereas the actual plant may not be deserving of same.

2. A likely intermediate position is a partial bonus determined based in part on the performance test and part on the actual operating characteristics over time.

V. Many other factors to be covered in the contract

A. Detailed warranty provisions.

1. Scope

2. Duration (several years on major equipment)

3. Wrap around by main vendor

B. Limitations on liability

C. Owner's rights

1. Review and comment.

2. Receive data

3. Participate in meeting/negotiations

4. Observe inspections.

D. Coordination and priority among design contract documents.

E. Clear specification of external interfaces to be met

1. Raw water qualities
2. Air discharge
3. Water discharge.
4. Electric utility interface.
5. Gas utility interface.

"INTERFACES AND CONSISTENCY" MAKING SURE THE CONTRACTS MEET AND MATCH

I. Financing/Legal Perspective

A. The project is a "paper project" where the contract package represents the project. All the contracts must fit together perfectly and be consistent with no over-laps and no gaps on all matters material to the project.

1. If the contract package, scopes of work, assumptions, interfaces and the like in the various documents are not all consistent or do not match, there is a significant risk that the project will not be completed or operated as planned.

B. Solution: Structure the project from the start for consistency, no overlaps, no gaps; and at the appropriate time (neither too early nor too late) the developer, lawyer and engineer must carefully review the entire document package for consistency and gaps.

II. Typical Issues.

A. Fuel Contract and Design Build Contract: Consistency between the two on

1. Fuel specification

2. Delivery method

3. Schedule for deliveries.

B. Power Sales Contract and Design Build Contract.

1. Usually complicated issues as to who does what on connecting plant to utility grid.

(a) Standards

(b) Timing

(c) Respective roles of the parties on review/ comment; approval; construction and cost responsibility.

(d) Typically applicable to

(i) Meters

(ii) Line to utility grid

(iii) Transformers

(iv) Relays

(v) Disconnects and the like

2. Typical example: Is the project output metered on the high side or low side of the output transformer? If on the high side, have the transformer losses been included in the performance standards for the plant?

3. Power Delivery Characteristics

(a) Wave forms

(b) Frequency Limits

(c) Nominal voltage and ability to increase/ decrease same within utility's scheduled limits for same.

(d) Reactive supply and ability to make power factor leading/lagging within utility's scheduled limits.

C. Design-Build Contract and Its Attachments.

1. Reluctance on the part of lawyers to examine the scope of work, general technical requirements, performance, test documents, design documents and the like. Similar reluctance by technical experts to examine legal documents.

2. Each must examine the other's documents in detail. Typically find actual/potential inconsistencies or ambiguities which should be resolved at the time, not later via a conflict/priority of document provision.

D. Correspondence of Design Build Contract With External Environment.

1. Raw water characteristics.

2. Air permit requirements.

3. Water permit requirements.

4. Easements and rights-of-way.

---

* Mr. Pestle is a partner in Varnum, Riddering, Schmidt & Howlett specializing in cogeneration and electric utility matters. The firm has been actively involved in over 40 cogeneration and small power production projects nationwide representing municipalities, developers, trade associations and lenders. Mr. Pestle is a graduate of Harvard College, Yale Graduate School and the University of Michigan Law School.

** Mr. Schneidewind is a partner in Varnum, Riddering, Schmidt & Howlett specializing in cogeneration, telecommunications and regulated utility matters. He is the immediate past chairman of the Michigan Public Service Commission and as such was responsible for the financial restructuring of Consumers Power Company following the cancellation of Consumers' Midland Nuclear Power plant after $4 billion had been expended upon the plant. Mr. Schneidewind is a graduate of the University of California at Berkley and the University of Michigan Law School.

SECTION 7

COGENERATION REGULATORY ISSUES

Sponsored by the Cogeneration Institute of AEE

Chapter 24

ACCESS BY COGENERATORS TO UTILITY TRANSMISSION SYSTEMS

J. D. Greenwade

Background Perspective

Houston Lighting & Power Company (HL&P), over the last three years, has spent more than one billion dollars on cogeneration purchases, making HL&P one of the largest buyers of cogenerated power in the country. HL&P's service area contains a dense concentration of refining and petrochemical plants. Since the enactment of the Public Utility Regulatory Policies Act of 1978 (PURPA), the decline of natural gas prices, and the proliferation of favorable tax advantages for cogenerators, large industrial companies have literally jumped on the cogeneration bandwagon and have become major producers of electricity.

By the end of 1985, cogeneration provided 14 percent of HL&P's energy fuel mix, which represents 18 cogeneration facilities capable of producing approximately 3000 MW. Three of these facilities have 10 year firm capacity contracts for a total of 820 MW of firm capacity. The other 15 cogenerators are providing "as available" power; that is, whenever the cogenerator desires to sell energy to us. This summer up to 850 MW of additional as-available power could be purchased from cogenerators, with the actual amount varying with the economics of the transaction. These cogeneration facilities, plus those under construction or in planning stages will represent approximately 25 percent of our energy fuel mix well into the 1990's (see figures 1A, 1B, and 1C ENERGY FUEL MIX). Our firm capacity contracts will meet our needs through the end of this decade. The Public Utility Commission of Texas (PUC) does not require us to contract with cogenerators for more firm capacity then we need; therefore, we have a large quantity of "as available" cogeneration that could be wheeled or transported to other utilities in the state that need it, or purchased by us. In 1986, over 1200 MW of cogenerated power will be wheeled from cogeneration facilities to utilities outside our service area. We believe that wheeling to other utilities is essential for the development of cogeneration in the State of Texas.

Transmission Access: Cogeneration & Wheeling

Transmission access represents the availability of an electric utility's transmission system to anyone wishing to utilize it. The interconnection of non-utility parties to the transmission network presents many additional concerns to the utility. The utility has a fundamental obligation to serve, whatever the load, on any day, and at any hour. The planning, design, construction, and operation of generation and transmission systems is an extremely complex, time consuming, exorbitantly costly process. A cogeneration facility interconnected on the transmission system becomes an integral component of that system and any flaw in the design, construction, or operation of that facility jeopardizes the reliability of the entire grid.

Transmission access exists in one of three forms in Texas - cogeneration, wheeling between electric utilities, and wheeling between cogenerator and electric utilities.

In the sense of transmission access, cogeneration would include those large industrial customers who have become major suppliers of electricity, requiring interconnection to their local utility's transmission network. This would not include small power producers, wind farms, or solar installations which would be interconnected to the utility's distribution system.

The most common wheeling arrangement is wheeling between electric utilities. This type of wheeling has been done for many years to transfer power for contracted purchased power sales, economy power purchases, or as the result of equipment problems, severe weather, or other emergencies.

In Texas, almost all wheeling occurs within the boundaries of the Electric Reliability Council of Texas (ERCOT). All wheeling between ERCOT members is under the jurisdiction of the PUC's Substantive Rule 23.67, "Wheeling Service for Transmission of Firm Power." Wheeling between electric utilities within Texas but outside the boundaries of ERCOT is under the jurisdiction of the Federal Energy Regulatory Commission (FERC).

ERCOT consists of six investor-owned utilities (Central Power & Light, Houston Lighting & Power, Southwestern Electric Service, Texas Utilities Electric, Texas-New Mexico Power, and West Texas Utilities Companies), a state agency (Lower Colorado River Authority), and numerous municipalities and cooperatives that are all operated within the state of Texas, and are all interconnected with each other on the Texas grid. (See figure 2A - ERCOT SYSTEM TERRITORY). The Texas grid is one of three separate interconnected transmission systems in the nation, and the only grid that exists entirely in one state. The Eastern grid extends from the Eastern Seaboard to the Plains States, and the Western grid extends from the Pacific Coast to the Mountain States. (See figure 2B - U.S. GRIDS).

Cogeneration and wheeling between cogenerators and electric utilities within ERCOT is covered in the PUC's Substantive Rule 23.66, "Arrangements Between Qualilfying Facilities and Electric Utilities", a comprehensive set of rules and regulations that govern cogenerator-electric utility transactions. Some of its main provisions follow:

1. Utilities are not required to contract with cogenerators for capacity in excess of the utilities' forecasted load requirements.

2. Utilities may negotiate contracts with cogenerators at less than full avoided cost.

3. Capacity payments to cogenerators will be based on the cost of avoidable generating units.

4. Capacity payments can be adjusted based on how well the cogenerator's capacity is an equivalent quality substitute for the utility's own generation.

5. The host utility must wheel the cogenerated power out of its service area if the cogenerator contracts to supply power to another utility. Cogenerated power that is wheeled must be greater than 1 MW at a voltage of 60 KV or higher.

6. All utilities whose transmission systems are impacted by the wheeling of cogenerated power are entitled to compensation from the cogenerator.

7. All metering and interconnection costs are the responsibility of the cogenerator.

8. Utilities are required to place cogeneration projects which use municipal waste, or renewable fuel sources at the top of their priority lists.

Cogeneration rates

HL&P purchases both firm and non-firm cogenerated power. Firm capacity and energy purchases are based on the avoided cost of building and operating a lignite generating unit. The energy portion of the payment is based on both lignite and gas fuels - energy quantities comparable to the output of a lignite generating unit are purchased according to lignite fuel costs; energy quantities produced by cogenerators in excess of a lignite unit are purchased according to gas fuel prices.

HL&P purchases only energy from non-firm cogenerators. Energy payments are based on the hourly avoided energy rate determined from HL&P's GENSOM-AC computer model. The hourly avoided energy rate is calculated by modeling operation of the system with and without non-firm cogeneration. The difference in cost between the two cases represents the avoided energy rate. Cogenerators are paid based on their production for each hour.

Wheeling Rates

Comprehensive regulations in the PUC's Substantive Rule 23.66 established a two-tiered rate structure for wheeling. Two types of transactions are defined - Planned Capacity Wheeling and Available Capacity Wheeling.

Planned Capacity Wheeling (PCW) is the wheeling of firm power. Under a PCW contract, the cogenerator would be obligated to provide scheduled capacity to the purchasing utility for a period of three years or longer. Utilities generally incorporate PCW into their annual planning schedule. PCW is non-interruptible except in a case of a system or area emergency where continued wheeling would contribute to the emergency.

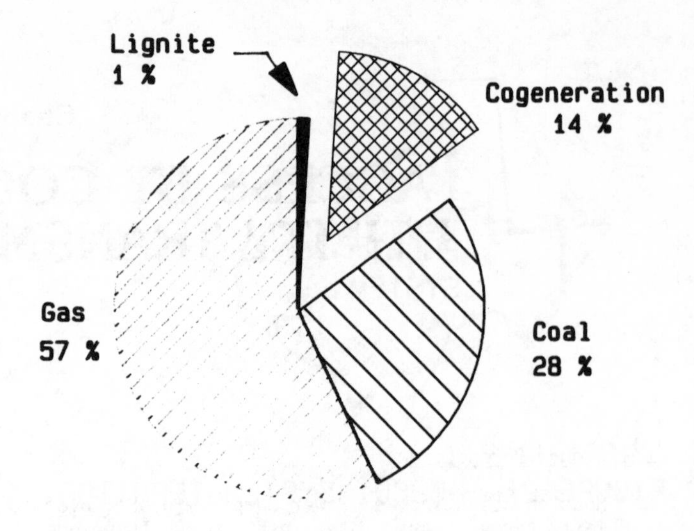

FIGURE 1A - ENERGY FUEL MIX <1985>

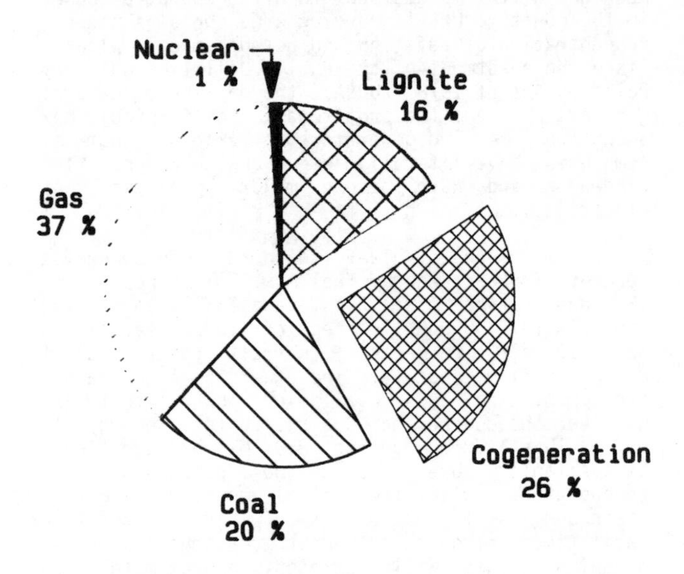

FIGURE 1B - ENERGY FUEL MIX <1987>

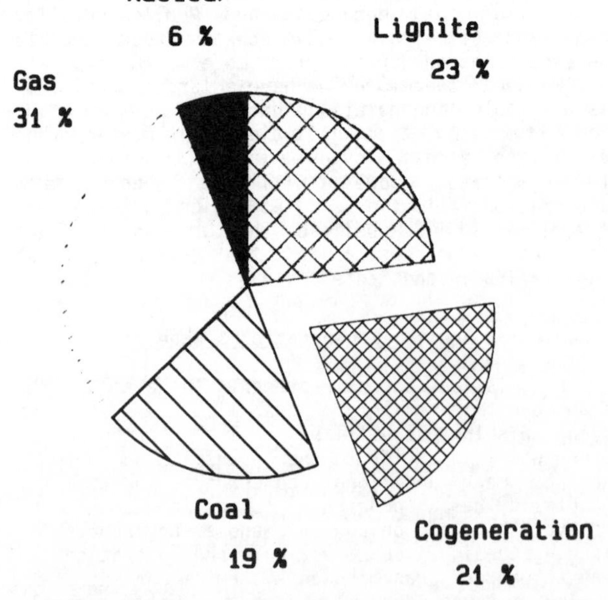

FIGURE 1C - ENERGY FUEL MIX <1994>

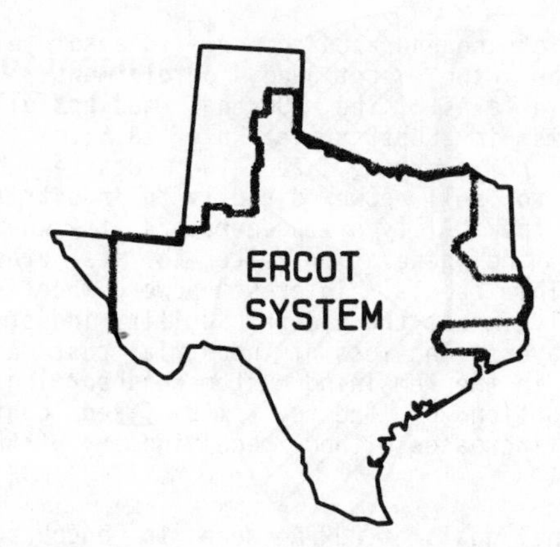

FIGURE 2A - ERCOT SYSTEM TERRITORY

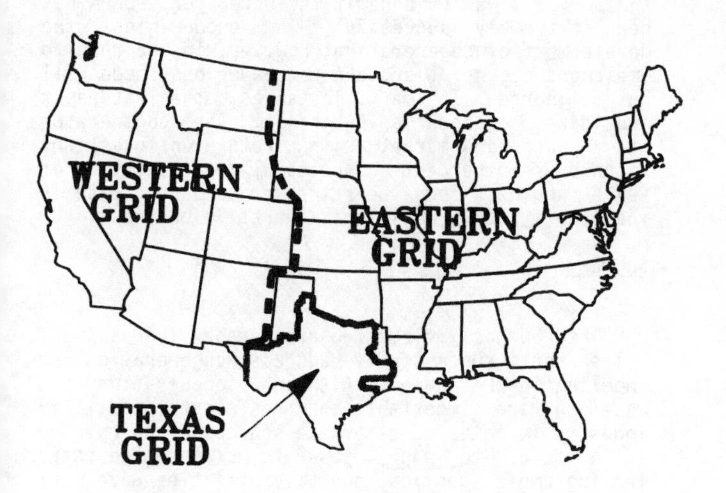

FIGURE 2B - U.S. GRIDS

Impacted utilities are responsible for the cost of any system improvements for PCW transactions.

Available Capacity Wheeling (ACW) is the wheeling of non-firm power. This type of transaction provides power to the purchasing utility without any guarantee of availability. ACW is usually a very short-term contract, less than a year. Utilities do not generally utilize ACW in their annual planning schedule.

The cogenerator or the purchasing utility is responsible for the cost of any system improvements involving ACW transactions.

In both PCW and ACW transactions, the cogenerator is responsible for compensating all utilities with impacted transmission systems. This compensation or "facilities use" charge is equal to the system impact multiplied by the wheeling rate. The wheeling rate is determined by each utility based on its annualized transmission investment in dollars, and is filed with the PUC.

Two methods are used to determine the impact on transmission systems - the contract path method and the MW-mile method.

Under the contract path method, which is utilized in PCW transactions, the cogenerator selects the utilities that will be on the path from the host utility to the purchasing utility. The impact under this method is equal to the contract capacity. This is the simplest method, but it can be inconsistant with the actual flow of power. Power flows over all possible paths, and is not limited to the selected route (see figure 3 - WHEELING).

The MW-mile method utilizes load flow calculations (before and after the transaction) to determine the impact. The impact is equal to the sum of the products of the increase in power flow per line and the length of the line in miles. This method is used in PCW for those impacted utilities that are not on the contract path, and in ACW for all impacted utilities.

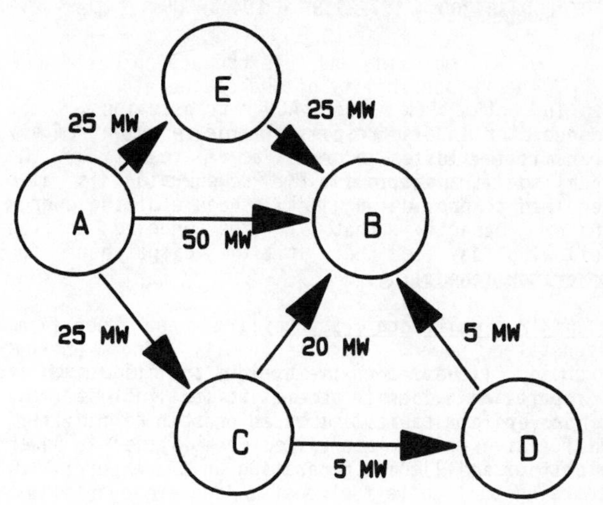

FIGURE 3 - WHEELING

Example of PCW Calculation

Texasgulf Chemical, an industrial customer in HL&P's service area, has a PCW contract to wheel 70 MW to Texas Utilities. HL&P is on the contract path, and nine other utilities in ERCOT that are not on the contract path are also impacted. The facilities charge is calculated as shown below:

As an impacted utility on the contract path, HL&P's facilities charge is equal to the impact (or contract MW) multiplied by the facilities rate

HL&P facilities charge = 70 MW x $960/MW
= $67200

The following impacted utilities are not on the contract path, and the facilities charge is equal to the impact in MW-Miles multiplied by the facilities rate.

Utility	Impact (MW-Miles)	Facilities Rate [1] ($/MW-Mile)	Facilities Charge ($)
CPL	1347	6.3992	8619.72
LCRA	1253	3.6317	4550.52
CPSB	822	2.5025	2057.06
WTU	572	6.4150	3669.38
BEPL	475	6.1717	2931.56
COA	453	4.2592	1929.42
STEC	413	4.2642	1761.11
TMPA	133	12.0733	1605.75
MEC	36	3.1492	113.37
		TOTAL =	$27237.89

[1] Facilities rates vary from one utility to another.

The total Facilities Charge Texasgulf would pay under a PCW contract is:

TOTAL = $67200 + $27237.89 = $94437.89

In both PCW and ACW transactions, the cogenerator is also responsible for repayment of any transmission losses incurred as a result of the wheeling transaction. The cogenerator is also required to provide an hourly schedule of the energy and/or capacity that will be wheeled on the following day to the utility dispatcher for generator scheduling.

Issues Facing Electric Utilities

Many issues are involved in the discussion of transmission access. These issues include many controversial topics such as system reliability, fuel diversification, special interest power wheeling, and PURPA reform.

Cogenerated power and the wheeling of cogenerated power have a direct impact on the reliability of the system. The operation of an electrical system and the planning process to ensure that adequate supplies of power are available over the long-term are further complicated by the addition of large amounts of non-firm cogeneration. The utility has no control over the business environment of the cogenerator, and has no guarantee that the cogenerator will remain in business. The utility, however, has a fundamental obligation to serve the customers' electrical requirements, and must rely on the continued construction of traditional central power plants to fulfill their long-term commitments.

Natural gas, currently with favorable prices and ample supply, fuels nearly all of the cogeneration projects on the Gulf Coast. HL&P has reduced the cost of electricity by purchasing gas on the spot market. However, this situation of readily available and cheap gas may not last. In recent years, Texas has seen natural gas curtailments and rapidly rising prices. A return to those volatile times could cause many cogenerators to cease operation. Utilities must continue to diversify their fuel sources and not become overly dependant on natural gas. Cogenerators should also seek out alternate fuel sources as well as alternate backup fuel sources.

Wheeling of cogenerated power is absolutely essential for the continued development of cogeneration in Texas. The PUC has successfully addressed this in Substantive Rule 23.66. Two issues that are emerging are the desire of cogenerators to sell power directly to industrial end users and the ability of cogenerators to wheel power from the generation site to its other facilities. This special interest power wheeling would adversely impact the electric utility industry and its ratepayers. The loss of industrial customers would result in the remaining customers absorbing a greater proportion of the system's fixed costs through rate increases without receiving any of the benefits.

The original goals of PURPA were to encourage conservation of electric energy sources, promote efficient use of facilities and resources by electric utilities, and ensure that consumers had equitable electric rates. The intended result of these goals was to benefit the ratepayer. PURPA has been extremely successful in encouraging the development of cogeneration; however, in the rush to implement cogeneration, the ratepayer has been all but ignored. In many instances, the ratepayer subsidizes cogeneration purchases. The cogenerator has a guaranteed market, with a return on investment often over 30 percent. Successful implementation of PURPA would allow the ratepayer to participate in the benefits offered in this lucrative business.

Summary

The PUC has implemented a comprehensive set of rules that successfully address cogeneration and wheeling in the state. Although cogeneration and wheeling are important to the electric utility industry in Texas as alternate sources of energy and as a means to supply power to areas of the state lacking ample supplies, electric utilities have many concerns over their proper utilization.

ACKNOWLEDGEMENTS

The following individuals provided technical information in the preparation of this paper:

Lloyd G. Pond, Jr., P.E. - Manager, Electrical Systems Division, HL&P

Michael E. Connolly, P.E. - Supervising Engineer, Electrical Systems Division, HL&P

David R. Bobo - Engineer, Electrical Systems Division, HL&P

APPENDIX A - COGENERATION IN HL&P'S SERVICE AREA

PROJECT	CONTRACT(MW)	NAMEPLATE CAPACITY	FUEL TYPE	CONTRACT TYPE
Air Products	4.1	4.1	Nat. Gas	Non-Firm Energy
Amoco Chemical	37.1	37.1	Nat. Gas	Non-Firm Energy
Amoco Chemical[1]	15	40	Nat. Gas	Non-Firm Energy[2]
Bayou Cogen.	360	312	Nat. Gas	270 MW Firm Capacity
Capitol Cogen.	375	375	Nat. Gas	Non-Firm Energy[3]
CoGen Lyondell	465	518	Nat. Gas	Non-Firm Energy
Diamond Shamrock	250	225	Nat. Gas	225 MW Firm Capacity
Diamond Shamrock	75	75	Nat. Gas	Non-Firm Energy
Dow Chemical	1300	1300	Nat. Gas	300 MW Firm Capacity[5]
Enterprise Product	5	5	Waste Heat	Non-Firm Energy
Imperial Sugar	1	4	Nat. Gas	Non-Firm Energy
NASA	0.6	0.23	Wind	Non-Firm Energy
Plaza del Oro	0	0.5	Nat. Gas	None[4]
Rice University	0	3.2	Rice Hulls	None[4]
Stauffer Chem.	0	1	Waste Heat	None[4]
Stauffer Chem.	5	6.5	Waste Heat	Non-Firm Energy
Texasgulf Chem.	0	78	Nat. Gas	None[6]
Texas Petro-Chem.	5	35	Nat. Gas	Non-Firm Energy
Uncle Ben's	0	1.4	Rice Hulls	None[4]

[1] In Texas-New Mexico Power's service area.

[2] Wheels excess power to HL&P.

[3] HL&P contracted to wheel power to Texas-New Mexico Power (Texas City, 306 MW & City of West Columbia, 90 MW).

[4] Self-generator.

[5] Dow Chemical wheels power to Texas Utilities (450 MW).

[6] Texasgulf wheels power to Texas Utilities (70 MW).

Chapter 25

STATE COGENERATION POLICIES AND THE TRANSITION TO A DEREGULATED ELECTRICITY MARKET

J. Clarkson, J. Kopfle

As with the airline, trucking, and telephone industries, deregulation of the electricity supply industry will provide the consumer with lower prices and better service. Although there will be inevitable dislocations at first, with some winners and some losers, the most efficient companies will survive.

The deregulation effort will not occur overnight, however. During the transition period, rules and laws are required on the state level to stimulate the development of cogeneration and other alternatives to the monopoly - regulatory system and its almost total reliance on large, central station power plants for satisfying customers' needs.

To date, cogeneration has been the most important alternative for utilities in supply planning.

COGENERATION POLICY TRENDSETTERS

There is considerable variation in cogeneration policy in different states, due to different electricity supply situations, regulatory philosophies and other factors. Some states and utilities have been openly hostile to cogeneration, while others have taken the lead and actively encouraged it. Some original and farsighted policies have evolved out of this process and provide good examples of the ways in which cogeneration and small power production can be included in utility supply planning.

Three states which have been particularly active in setting cogeneration policy are California, Connecticut and Florida. One reason is all three have fairly high power rates because a large part of their capacity is oil and gas fired. The three states have taken somewhat different approaches, however, and the following sections describe some of the specifics of those approaches.

1. California

California was the first state to implement the Public Utilities Regulatory Policy Act (PURPA) in a comprehensive manner. PURPA was enacted into law in 1978 and was meant to encourage cogeneration by exempting cogenerators from utility regulations and by requiring utilities to purchase power from cogenerators at the utility's avoided cost and provide backup power service to cogenerators at reasonable cost. Even in California, cogeneration development did not begin in earnest until 1983.

In September of 1983, the California Public Utility Commission (CPUC) required the state's utilities to enter into 10-year contracts with qualifying cogeneration or small power facilities (QF's). The 10-year contracts were important because they allowed firms to finance projects by guaranteeing a positive cash flow. California's Standard Offer #4 resulted in a tremendous amount of cogeneration interest because it provided for long term contracts and three payment options: 1) increasing energy payments over the life of the contract; 2) levelized energy payments; and 3) energy payments based on the utility's actual cost of oil or gas. These options gave cogenerators flexibility in developing projects. Capacity payments were also available for firm power delivery.

California has also passed a law allowing cogenerated power to be sold to users on the same site or adjacent sites. This law expands the options available to cogenerators and improves the chances of developing a viable project.

Based on these policies and the opportunity to avoid high cost rates, the Pacific Gas and Electric Company and Southern California Edison signed contracts for over 15,500 MW of cogeneration capacity between September 1983 and April 1985. An additional 7,000 MW is under consideration. If all of these cogeneration and small power plants were to come to fruition, they would supply about 25 percent of the state's electricity needs. Due to this tremendous response, which will satisfy California's needs for increased power supply for many years, Standard Offer #4 was terminated in April 1985. The CPUC made a new, lower standard offer, effective July of 1986.

2. Connecticut

In Connecticut, as in California, the state regulatory body, the Department of Public Utility Control (DPUC), has taken the lead in cogeneration policy.

As of December 1985, Connecticut Light & Power (CL&P) had 649 MW of cogeneration and small power capacity either on line or under contract. At that time, the DPUC ordered CL&P and the United Illuminating Company (UI) to come up with 30-year avoided cost forecasts for use in negotiating contracts for cogenerated power. This order, along with CL&P and UI's attractive avoided cost offers, resulted in a flood of interest in cogeneration projects. From December of 1985 to April 1986, inquiries were received from QF's for 1,669 MW of capacity, making a total of 2,318 MW of cogeneration in operation, under contract or under discussion. If all this capacity were to develop, it would increase the generating capacity of CL&P and UI by 35 percent.

CL&P is now concerned that avoided cost payments for this large amount of capacity will cause serious harm to their customers and is requesting that it be allowed to reduce its long term avoided cost offers.

The first 649 MW which CL&P had under contract was included in their Block I, which had the highest avoided cost payments. Block I is now filled, and CL&P is negotiating with cogenerators for its Block II requirements. In Connecticut as in California, as more capacity is contracted for and becomes part of the utilities' supply planning, avoided cost offers decrease. Also, the recent natural gas and oil price drops have lowered significantly the cost of the Connecticut utilities' most expensive power. This drop in avoided cost offers indicates that the "window of opportunity" for cogenerated power is closing.

Connecticut has come out with several other rules which have helped to bring about a favorable climate for cogeneration. These rules include:

a. Requirement that utilities offer 30 year contracts.

b. Requirement that utilities offer four payments options:

- -levelized capacity, actual energy
- -projected capacity, actual energy
- -projected capacity, projected energy
- -front end loaded options

c. Requirement that utilities bargain in good faith.

d. Mandatory wheeling of cogenerated power to other utilities in state or out, or to other facilities owned by the QF.

e. Regulations regarding both firm and non firm standby power.

When firm standby service is provided, the cogenerator is not assessed the full demand charge, but only a portion of it, based on the capacity requirements that service imposes on the system. The rationale behind this practice is as follows. Out of a group of cogeneration facilities, the probability of all of them being down at the same time is small. Thus, there is essentially no chance that the utility will be required to provide standby service to all cogenerators simultaneously. It is unfair for a cogenerator to be required to pay a full year's demand charge because it required standby power for a few minutes.

Studies have found that standby power imposes less demand cost per unit of energy on the system than the industrial class as a whole. Therefore, total rates for standby service should be equal to or less per kWh than standard industrial rates. Also, the demand component of a cogenerator's standby power rate should be based on duration of use, not merely maximum peak, because of the operating characteristics of a system of small cogeneration facilities.

Regarding maintenance (i.e., non-firm standby) service, if certain conditions are met, the customer is required to pay only an energy charge and not an additional demand charge. These conditions include: the maintenance should occur either during off peak hours or during a low load month; the customer should provide advance notice of the dates of its planned maintenance; and the Power Company must confirm that the period will be acceptable.

f. Legislation dealing with payments to municipal resource recovery facilities, standard contracts, security requirements, risk of disallowance of contracts, and other issues.

3. Florida

Since it relies on oil and gas-fired plants for a good bit of its power, Florida has tried to encourage cogeneration, although it has not been as aggressive as California and Connecticut.

On May 1, 1984, the Florida Public Service Commission (PSC) proposed a 1¢/kWh wheeling tariff statewide. This rate was meant to encourage cogeneration and was favorable, as it was well below the average tariffs filed by the state's utilities. However, the Federal Energy Regulatory Commission (FERC) later ruled that they, not the PSC, have authority to set wheeling rates.

In October of 1985, the PSC issued regulations dealing with wheeling. The regulations require utilities to wheel cogenerated power if they have the capacity and if the wheeling will not adversely affect service to other customers. Utilities must file their wheeling rates with the PSC and maintain them up to date. Also, utilities must provide wheeling to other facilities owned by the cogenerator (self service wheeling) if it can be demonstrated that this will not result in higher costs for other customers.

However, the PSC ruled that retail sales of electricity to other customers will not be allowed. The regulations appear to state that any sale of electricity in which the owner of the plant and the user of the electricity are not identical is illegal. This is the case in many other states as well and precludes third party financed projects, in which the power plant is owned and operated by a financing entity selling power to the host site. The PSC staff had recommended that third party arrangements be allowed as long as ratepayers were not adversely affected, but the PSC ruled otherwise. This ruling has not been tested in court, however, and may not be the final result.

In addition to the wheeling legislation, a helpful tool is Florida Power Corporation's interruptible electric contract. This contract can be useful for cogenerators, especially those who use the power onsite and have energy management capability. The contract allows a customer to set a new billing demand each month, rather than the typical case in which a demand ratchet is set in the summer for the entire year. Using the cogeneration system, demand control, operation during off peak hours, etc., a customer can lower its demand charge significantly and reduce its overall power cost.

Finally, one innovation in Florida has proved advantageous for that state's utilities and may have long term implications for the cogeneration market. Since 1978, Florida utilities have used a unique brokerage system to buy and sell power. Eighteen utilities are now involved; the arrangement is entirely voluntary and is financed through a monthly fee. Utilities enter quotes to buy or sell electricity on an hourly basis. The highest bid to buy is matched with the lowest offer to sell, and the transaction price is the average of the two. All the other offers are then matched up in this manner until all the required power is sold. Although the majority of the transactions are on an hourly basis, contracts up to one week are also offered.

The advantage of the system is that it allows utilities which have excess power to find a willing buyer and utilities which need power to buy it easily. In 1985, the system transferred 3.2 million MWh of power, and saved Florida utilities $60 million. Both the Florida PSC and the FERC support the system.

Although this system does not affect cogeneration at present, it may well increase opportunities for wheeling cogenerated power. By having in place a means to easily transfer power from one system to another, cogenerators in the future should be able to sell their power to the utility which needs it most. It makes no sense for a cogenerator to be forced to sell power to a local utility which does not need it, when there are other utilities in the state which could use the power. Also, having a system in place which continuously transfers power statewide, utilities can no longer make the argument that wheeling cogenerated power is impractical for technical reasons.

"IDEAL" STATE COGENERATION POLICIES

Often legislators, utility commissioners and utility executives complain that they have no idea on how to begin the process of deregulating the electricity market. Following is a summary of the best policies from California, Connecticut, Florida and other states which can be implemented to encourage cogeneration development and assist in the transition to a free market.

1. Require utilities to provide wheeling service to other utilities and other customers at fair prices when transmission capacity is available. Cogenerators should be able to sell their power to the end user who can best use it. As mentioned previously, Florida has implemented mandatory wheeling requirements.

2. For firm commitments of power, which will reduce the need for future generation facilities, capacity payments should be paid. As utilities become more comfortable with cogenerated power and consider it when planning future capacity needs, they should have no problem with paying capacity payments.

3. Rules for standby service, similar to those adopted in Connecticut, should be used. The cogenerator should not be assessed the full demand charge when standby service is provided.

4. As allowed in California, cogenerators and small power producers should be allowed to sell power to users in the immediate area and avoid utility regulations. Due to the fears of utilities that they will lose customers, it is not likely cogenerators will be allowed at present to sell power to users outside of their immediate area. However, as the utility industry becomes more deregulated, this restriction should be lifted and cogenerators allowed to sell power to whomever they choose.

Another point regarding retail sales is that third party financed projects should be allowed to sell power to the company on whose site the project is located. In several states, this is not allowed, since the company which owns the plant and the company which uses the power must be the same.

5. Cogeneration should be sought several years before it is needed and encouraged through reasonable but attractive avoided cost offers. Starting the process of obtaining cogeneration capacity 10-years before it is needed would not be at all unreasonable, since that is about the lead time for a large, central station power plant. Also, it takes several years for the process of soliciting cogeneration projects, working out avoided cost rates, negotiating contracts and actually getting the projects on line.

One of the problems has been that when utilities do begin to solicit cogeneration capacity several years before it is needed, avoided costs are too low to be attractive. A solution used successfully by California and some New England states has been to offer long term (up to 30-year) contracts which include capacity payments. Front-end loaded rates, which put more of the avoided cost payments in the early years of the contract have also been offered. Front-end loaded rates are typically calculated on a discounted basis, so that the net present value of the utility's payments over the life of the contract is no more than for a contract based on estimated actual avoided costs. The main advantage of long term contracts is that they are very attractive to financiers, since they can be used to guarantee a positive cash flow. As cogeneration capacity is contracted for the offers can be reduced, allowing the utility good control over the amount of cogeneration which occurs in its area.

BEYOND PURPA

The policies described in the previous sections, PURPA in particular, have stimulated a tremendous amount of cogeneration development in recent years. These policies are still needed in most states to encourage cogeneration and thus begin the process of deregulation of the electricity market.

In some cases, however, PURPA is artifically stimulating the growth of cogeneration and causing consumers to pay more for their electricity than they would otherwise. In these cases, it may be time to open up the power market and allow the cogenerator to freely compete with the utilities for electricity customers. Since in many cases the retail price of electricity is higher than the utility's avoided cost, open access to the power market will be incentive enough for projects to be developed. Once cogeneration development has a good start, it is no longer necessary to encourage "PURPA machines" (projects justified only by high avoided cost payments).

With a chance to compete with traditional power suppliers, the cogeneration projects already on line and those yet to be built will demonstrate that there is the potential for innovation and entrepreneurship in the stodgy power market. Other nontraditional methods of supplying electricity needs, such as power pools and demand management, will also be used increasingly in the years to come. The consumer will be the ultimate beneficiary of this new, more open market.

SUMMARY

California, Connecticut and Florida have stimulated the growth of cogeneration through their implementation of PURPA and other innovative policies. These policies can be used as examples for other states which have not yet encouraged cogeneration. The ultimate goal of these efforts is to deregulate the electricity market. However, laws and regulations such as PURPA are a necessary first step in making the transition from a regulated monopoly system to a deregulated market.

Once cogeneration development has begun, PURPA can be phased out, and cogenerators allowed to compete freely in the power market. With the freeing of the market will come new competitors and some dislocations. However, in the long run everyone's standard of living will increase as resources are employed more efficiently under management honed by the rigors of competition.

Chapter 26

COGENERATION AND SMALL POWER: STATE REGULATORY DEVELOPMENTS

C. P. Benagh

I. INTRODUCTION

1985 and 1986 have been years of retrenchment in many areas of cogeneration. The impact of falling oil prices, pending tax law changes, and potential changes to PURPA itself have led to uncertainty. One the other hand, there has been substantial progress in other areas, such as wheeling, contracts, and standard offers. Some of the more important changes at the state level will be reviewed here.

II. WHEELING

On September 30, 1985, the Texas Public Utility Commission ("TPUC") adopted a mandatory wheeling rule, 16 TAC 23.66(d)(4), requiring utilities to offer transmission system access to qualifying facilities over 10Mw for the transportation of electricity to other utilities in Texas. In large part, this regulation was made possible by Texas' isolation from the interstate grid. The utilities are required to file tariffs on a per-Mw basis for firm and a per-mile basis for as-available capacity. Access must be offered, under the terms of the rule, for a term at least as long as the term of the power purchase contract.

On March 5, 1985, in the Florida Public Service Commission (FPSC) issued a proposed rule on "self-service wheeling" (transmission service from a QF to other facilities owned by the QF's owner). Proposed Rule 25-17.882 would have made self-service wheeling required only when the owner and/or operator of the QF or the transmitting utility "demonstrates that the provision of this service will not result in any adverse economic impact on the utility's general body of ratepayers." All "retail sales" of energy or capacity by a QF to an entity which is not a public utility would have been prohibited by proposed Rule 25-17.883.

Although the FPSC adopted the proposed Rules in Order No. 14143, the FPSC Staff's recommended that (i) each investor-owned, municipal and REC utility be required to provide transmission service from QFs to other electric utilities, (ii) the FERC should initially determine whether a wheeling transaction would occur in interstate or intrastate, commerce, (iii) the owner operator of the QF would bear the costs of transmission service, (iv) utilities could deny, curtail or discontinue transmission service when such service would adversely affect the utility's customers, legislation should be adopted authorizing retail sales by unregulated entities pursuant to certain terms and conditions established by the FPSC, separate proceedings should be instituted to establish the appropriate rate for (intrastate) "self-service wheeling" and standby and backup rates for each utility.

The FPSC adopted the Staff's recommendations with minor modifications in Order No. 15053 issued on September 27, 1985, and ordered all electric utilities ti file wheeling tariffs by January 2, 1986.

These rates, when filed, ranged from \$1.148/KW/month - \$1.225/KW/month for firm service and between 2.5 mills/KW - 1.57 mills/KW for interruptible capacity. Florida Power and Light filed controversial tariffs on a voltage basis.

In Order No. 14339 issued on May 2, 1985, in Docket No. 830377-EU, the FPSC established an "interim nonfirm wheeling rate" of one mill per KWh to apply only to transmission service which (a) occurs in intrastate commerce and (b) involves wheeling QF power from one utility to another ("self-service wheeling" was excluded). Florida utilities were required to amend their cogeneration tariffs by June 2, 1985.

III. STANDARD OFFERS AND LONG-TERM CONTRACTS

In April, 1985, the California Public Utility Commission suspended the interim Standard Offer #4, pending development of long-run standard offer. In July, 1985, the CPUC adopted a generation resource plan methodology for determining long-run avoided costs. The methodology specifies the most cost-effective way for the utility to generate power needed to meet its system requirements in the absence of a QF. Different price offers would then, be made available to the QF: (i) If the utility were able to defer or cancel future plants because of QF power, the QF price would be keyed to the capital and operating costs of those avoided plants; (ii) if the QF did not displace any future utility resources, the price would be based on the short-run marginal cost of the utility.

Now the PUC is developing a final long-run offer, with contract terms and payment options, to complement the adopted costing methodology. Compliance filings, with prices and terms, hearings are expected in July, 1986.

In March, 1986, the CPUC also suspended Standard Offer #2 (for fixed capacity payments with fluctuating energy payments, pended final avoided cost formulae.

Another dramatic development in California is the finalization of the Qualifying Facility Milestone Procedure, intended to ensure that transmission capacity is available to those projects most likely to generate power.

In January, 1985, the CPUC adopted an Interconnection Priority Procedure for use in areas with transmission constraints: 1) $5/kw fee which was refundable at the time the QF went on line or applied to the special facilities (interconnection) charges; 2) establishing a critical technology path with targets; and 3) filing a comprehensive project questionnaire before signing a standard offer. Revised in December, 1985, the QF Milestone Procedure, as it is now called, not only tracks how many QFs with signed interim Standard Offers #4 actually come on line, but is also incorporated into those interim Standard Offers #4 that are effective in areas where transmission constraints already exist. Thus, this is becoming a tool for rationing transmission capacity.

In New York, the statutory requirement that electric utilities enter long-term contracts has been brought into focus by Case 28793, Niagara Mohawk Power Corporation - Long-Run Avoided Costs. On August 26, 1985, the New York Public Service Commission ordered the recalculation of Niagara Mohawk's long-run avoided cost rates to on-site generators. (Earlier estimates had come out of of a 1984 settlement.) Although, the NYPSC suspended Niagara Mohawk's obligation to make payments under the long-term settlement rates pending recalculation, the PSC required Niagara Mohawk to make available its existing long-term settlement rates for fifteen years available to hydroelectric facilities of up to 20 megawatts for sales commencing not later than December 31, 1987.

The PSC, in 1984, had instituted a proceeding to establish long-run avoided costs for the other six major electric utilities. Niagara Mohawk's future rates are also developed in this proceeding, and issued in the Spring of 1986.

These rates, reflecting falling oil prices and lowering avoided cost payments as much as 41%, are discouraging development in New York.

On September 12, 1985, the Massachusetts Department of Public Utilities ("DPU") issued an Interim Order in Docket No. 84-276, the ongoing review of the Commonwealth's regulations under the PURPA of 1978.

The DPU held that standard offers and long-term fixed price contracts are necessary to encourage QF development. The DPU found that the absence of such contracts created a non-price barrier to cost-effective generation and threatened the maximization of the Department's goal of achieving optimization of the electric supply industry.

The DPU has proposed regulations requiring utilities to solicit small power offers each year and to contract through a competitive bidding process (with projects larger than 1 MW). Projects smaller than 1 MW are to receive standard offers.

In Texas the Texas Public Utility Commission ("TPUC") rules, 16 TAC § 23.66(g), required that each generating utility file a calculation of avoided cost of capacity and energy related to an identified avoidable unit by December 31, 1984. The filing had to reflect a ten-year forecast of anticipated purchases of firm capacity from cogenerators and a standard set of terms and conditions for purchase. By the end of 1985, the majority of the cases were settled by stipulations incorporating agreed avoided cost calculations, terms and conditions, and projected purchases.

In Connecticut, the Department of Public Utility Control ("DPUC") took major steps toward the encouragement of cogeneration. In Docket No. 85-04-16 (Dec., 1985).

The DPUC established standard long-term contracts for investor-owned utilities -- Connecticut Light and Power Company and United Illuminating Company. Under these contracts, QFs have the option of 10-, 20-, or 30-year contract terms and the option of current, projected, or levelized energy payments and projected or levelized capacity payments.

Any natural gas or oil-fired QF that plans to provide firm capacity and receive capacity payments must have dual fuel capability. QFs must post security, ranging from 10-20% of the avoided cost payments, as a condition of receiving front loaded payments from a utility. Contracts for QFs located outside the state are subject to the same conditions applicable to fossil-fueled QFs. Out-of-state QFs may be also required to provide higher levels of security in order to obtain levelized capacity payments.

The DPUC adopted a "proxy plant" method for establishing avoided capacity costs using the cost of plant that would have been built but for the QF contract. Avoided energy costs reflect the cost of the most costly, lease efficient, and last dispatched generating units on a utility's system, rather than at average on-peak and off-peak costs.

The DPUC also recommended that the removal of the prohibition against electric utility ownership of QF's to the extent permitted by PURPA, and removal of the prohibition against gas utility ownership of QFs, provided that such QFs are dual-fuel capable and purchase gas under a tariff.

In September, 1985, the New Hampshire Public Utilities Commission ("NHPUC") updated the short- and long-term avoided cost rates for power purchases from qualifying cogeneration and small power producers. The order was the first annual update of such rates.

In December, 1985, the New Jersey Department of Energy issued its final Energy Master Plan. The plan is based upon the avoidance of a hypothetical 600 Mw coal plant to go on-line in 1992 and oil or gas-fired generation in the interim. The plan is utilized by the New Jersey Board of Public Utilities in developing avoided cost rates.

Jersey Central Power and Light ("JCP&L") has issued a term sheet for contracts for the purchase of long term energy and capacity from cogeneration and resource recovery facilities. JCP&L is important since it is the New Jersey utility most in need of capacity, due to its reliance on power from Three Mile Island. Under this offer, cogenerators with 200 Mw must contract for the delivery of firm capacity for at least twenty years. JCP&L will pay 65 mills/kWh delivered (1985 dollars) with variations designed to encourage production during peaks.

There are to be two components of the rate -- a fixed portion (26-29 mills/kWh) which will remain unchanged throughout the life of the agreement, and a variable portion which will be indexed to provide for escalation throughout the life of the contract.

In Oklahoma, the Oklahoma Commerce Commission ("OCC") has retained its Rule 58(H), permitting the revision of tariffs and contracts pertaining to cogeneration. However, the OCC has waived this regulation with respect to at least one major (300 Mw) plant.

Similarly, the Minnesota Public Utilities Commission approved the use of standard offers in early 1986. In many respects like the California model, the standard offers feature levelized capacity payments and levelized, floating, or fixed escalation energy payments.

Under a 10-year agreement with Northern States Power, power producers smaller than 5 Mw receive levelized capacity payments of $9.51/kW/month for projects coming on line in 1986 and $10.67/kW/month for projects starting in 1987. Twenty-year contracts will bring $11.51/kW/month for 1986 start-ups and $12.91/for start-ups in 1987. The maximum 33-year contract will pay $13.42/kW/month and $15.06/kW/month respectively for 1986 and 1987 start-ups.

Projects larger than 2 Mw on the Northern States system are only eligible for fluctuating energy rates -- currently $12.81/MWh off-peak and $21.35/MWh on-peak, keyed to NSP's fuel costs and operating and maintenance expenses for the Sherburne-3 coal plant. Projects smaller than 2 Mw can choose energy rates that are levelized or which follow a fixed escalation. With levelized energy payment, a 10-year contract beginning in 1986 calls for energy payments of $14.78/MWh off-peak and $24.63/MWh on-peak; a 10-year contract beginning in 1987 would pay $14.98/MWh off-peak and $24.97/MWh on-peak. With a 20-year contract, a small power producer would receive $16.56/MWh off-peak and $27.60/MWh on-peak beginning in 1986; a 20-year contract beginning in 1987 would pay $16.71/MWh off-peak and $27.84/MWh on-peak. Levelized energy payments under 30-year contracts will be $18/MWh off-peak and $30/MWh on-peak for 1986 start-ups and $18.08/MWh and $30.13/MWh for 1987 start-ups.

If power producer chooses energy payments with fixed escalation rather than levelization, it will receive $17.72/MWh off-peak and $29.53/MWh on-peak for the tenth year of a 1986 start-up; $18.43/MWh off-peak and $30.72/MWh will be paid in the tenth year of a 1987 start-up. Payments in the twentieth year of a 1986 project will be $26.23/MWh off-peak and $43.72/MWh on-peak. For a 1987 project, twentieth-year payments will be $27.28 off-peak and $45.47 on-peak. In the thirty-third year, 1986 projects will be paid $43.68/MWh off-peak and $72.79/MWh on-peak; 1987 start-ups will be paid $45.42/MWh off-peak and $75.70/MWh on-peak.

Projects that deliver less than 100 kW will continue to be paid Northern States' avoided cost rate. Currently, this amounts to: winter off-peak 1.84 cents/kWh, on-peak 2.73cents/kWh; summer off-peak 1.61 cents/kWh, on-peak 2.43 cents/kWh. Projects smaller than 40 kW are paid 5.61 cents/kWh in winter and 5.84 cents/kWh in summer. Projects larger than 5 MW must continue to negotiate individual contracts.

Northern States has also filed its wheeling rates. For transmission voltage service, the company will charge $15.39/kW; for primary distribution $30.39/kW and for secondary distribution $36.99/kW.

The standard offers for the other utilities are not as favorable or extensive as Northern States'. A major difficulty with the Minnesota system is that all standard offers are to be revised every two years. It is unclear how extensive such revisions will be or how realistic it is to expect development in Minnesota given this uncertainty.

In December, 1985, the New Mexico Energy and Minerals Department filed a proposed rule with the State Public Service Commission to establish standard methodologies for calculating long- and short-run avoided costs rates for purchases of energy and capacity by utilities from qualifying facilities. In addition, the proposed rule directs all utilities to make available to qualifying facilities a uniform standard contract for the utilities' purchase of electricity.

Under the proposed rule, short-run avoided energy costs are to be based on current marginal energy costs for the most recent three-month period, or, for future years, upon the transactions methodology established in the particular proceeding. Utilities' current shortage costs are to form the basis of the short-run avoided capacity cost calculation.

Long-run avoided costs are to be calculated using a proxy unit method. Because planned additions to a utility's existing resource base entail costs which are considered avoidable, the long-run avoided cost proxy is set to equal the total cost associated with a utility's next planned resource addition. For avoidable baseload additions, long-run avoided energy costs are to include both variable operating costs and capitalized energy costs. For avoidable peaking (or demand-driven) additions, long-run avoided energy costs are to be based on short-run marginal energy costs. Long-run avoided capacity costs for both baseload and peaking additions are to be based on the total fixed costs of a combustion turbine.

The North Carolina Utility Commission ("NCUC") on January 22, 1985, issued its third order to determine the rates for sale and purchase of electricity between electric utilities and QFs. The NCUC declared that, although long-term levelized rates are important to the financing of QFs because they assure a constant income flow, such rates represent a risk to ratepayers because they "require greater overpayments during the early part of the contract period and they are necessarily more difficult to forecast accurately." The NCUC, therefore, limited the availability of five, ten and fifteen-year levelized rates to hydroelectric facilities and those QFs with generating capacities of five megawatts or less. In the case of small QFs, stated the Commission, a default on a long-term contract posed little risk to utilities. Furthermore, the Commission stated its belief that offering the long-term contract as standard options would encourage their development and offset their lack of skills and resources in negotiating contracts with utilities.

In Virgina during 1985 buyback rates were set by dividing capacity costs by the number of peak hours that the utility's planned unit would have operated. A QF that operates more peak hours automatically receives a higher capacity credit. This mechanism recognizes the higher reliability associated with cogeneration. A typical utility coal-fired powerplant may have a reliability factor of about 70%. Cogenerators, particularly gas fired cogenerators, tend to have reliability factors in excess of 90%. Idaho followed a similar path earlier in 1985, by setting capacity payments for a cogeneration facility at a premium over its dispatchable capacity due to the higher reliability of the cogeneration facility.

Early in 1985, the Special Counsel to the Louisiana Public Service Commission issued a proposed ruling concerning the establishment of avoided cost rates for Louisiana. These proceedings are important, as Louisiana has substantial cogeneration potential. The proposed order addressed three issues:

(1) the interconnection of a utility to cogenerators,

(2) the rates to be paid for buyback power under avoided cost principles; and

(3) the rates to be paid by cogenerators to the utility for supplementary, backup and maintenance power.

Under the proposed order, Gulf States Utilities is to submit avoided cost rates based on the avoidance of Nelson 5, a 540 MW coal-fired unit scheduled for service in 1994. This "capacity component" is not available until 1994 or even later, if the date on which Nelson 5 is scheduled to enter commercial operation changes. In addition, it is to be discounted by 40% to "allow for uncertainty and the increased risk to ratepayers resulting from the requirement that the utility enter long term contracts for future periods embodying capacity costs." Finally, the capacity component of the rate will not be fixed in the order, but will vary depending upon the amount of capacity offered by qualifying facilities in each year, with capacity payments to be based upon the cost of the 540 MW plant, but if more than 540 MW are offered, prorated over all the megawatts offered.

Short term avoided cost payments are to be based on avoided energy costs only. The order would discount the computer-generated avoided cost levels by 10%, to account for the possibility of currently unquantified reductions in marginal energy costs due to future power purchase agreements with other utilities. Finally, the order would grant fixed long term energy prices for a period of up to five years only, even though contract terms would go up to 20 years.

In partial response to a petition of Dow Chemical, the order would permit such sales only to the extent that there are transmission facilities to support them. Dow wanted the right to "sell" up to 200 MW, using 100 MW in house, and transmitting up to 100 MW more through an existing 100 MW transmission line. Under the proposed order, Dow could only "sell" up to the capacity of the transmission line.

The rates set for standby, maintenance and interruptible service under the order are more favorable to development. Standby rates are only $.95/kW/month, with charges for actual use to be based on the prorated firm rate. This rate is available only for 72 hours. After 72 hours, standby service is available at the same energy rate, but the capacity charge, prorated, is multiplied by 1.75. Scheduled maintenance is to be billed at the off-peak rate.

In Idaho, the Public Utility Commission has ordered an interim reduction in the buyback rate for the utility of over one-third of its value, from6.78 cents per kWh to 4.42 cents per kWh for thirty-five year contracts, in one instance. The PUC decided that the power surplus in the Northwest to be far greater than it had originally envisioned it to become when the Commission first established its buyback rates in 1983.

IV. RETAIL SALES

At the request of the Georgia Public Service Commission, in September, 1985, the Attorney General of Georgia issued a formal opinion that under current Georgia laws, cogenerators may not make retail sales of electricity in Georgia except to electric suppliers.

The current Georgia statutes state, "Any person may operate a cogeneration facility without being subject to the jurisdiction or regulation of the Georgia Public Service Commission if such person uses all of the electric energy,steam, or other form of useful energy produced at such cogeneration facility. The electric energy shall not be sold to any other person except as provided in Code Section 46-3-53." In turn, Section 46-3-53 declares, "Any person may operate a cogeneration facility and sell any excess electric energy to an electric supplier without being subject to the jurisdiction or regulation of the commission . . . ."

In a similar vein, in an order issued March 5, 1985, the Florida Public Service Commission has proposed that retail sales of electricity by cogenerators be prohibited:

> "(1) Qualifying facilities may not engage in retail sales. A retail sale occurs when a Qualifying Facility sells energy or capacity to an entity which is not a public utility.
>
> (2) Any customer, including a Qualifying Facility, may choose to provide its own electrical service. A Qualifying Facility will be considered to be serving itself so long as the ownership of all entities to which it supplies energy or capacity is identical to the ownership of the Qualifying Facility."

Moving in the opposite direction, the New York Public Service Commission determined that a cogeneration facility serving customers within one mile of the plant are exempt from regulation as electric utilities under New York Public Service Law, Case 29157, Petition for Declaratory Ruling.

New York Public Service Law provides a specific exception from utility type regulation of certain cogeneration facilities engaging in the retail sale of steam and electricity, which provides that the owners of such facilities are not to be deemed "electric corporations" or "steam corporations" so long as the steam or electricity from the cogeneration facility is "distributed solely from one or more of such facilities to users located at or near a project site."

Following the FERC PURPA regulation requiring the aggregation of small power producers within one mile from ach other (for purposes of determining whether the project exceeds the statutory size limitations for small power producers), the NYPSC ruled that because the end users of electricity and steam would all be within one mile of the production facilities, they should be deemed to be "near" the project site.

V. CONCLUSION

In sum, the developments of the past year have been mixed. Falling oil prices have adversely affected avoided cost calculations. On the other hand, cogeneration and small power production seem to be becoming an integral part of the electric generation industry.

SECTION 8

FUTURE DIRECTIONS IN COGENERATION

Sponsored by the Cogeneration Institute of AEE

Chapter 27

HAVE FALLING OIL PRICES WIPED OUT THE ALTERNATIVE ENERGY MARKET?

J. D. Weesner, M. Whiting, Jr.

The alternative energy industry, which includes such non-traditional sources of energy as cogeneration, biomass, geothermal, hydropower, wind, and solar, was created out of the energy crises of the 1970's. The National Energy Act of 1978 established a new class of independent power producers which were exempt from regulation as electric utilities provided they employed non-traditional methods of producing electricity, either cogeneration (a more efficient way to generate power) or renewable resources. Effectively, this was a limited first step toward the deregulation of the electricity industry.

However, as oil prices have dropped from over $35 to under $15 per barrel, the basic premise of the alternative energy industry has been called into question. In addition, special tax incentives for wind, solar, and biomass investments expired at the end of 1985, reducing their economic attractiveness.

A Bright Future

Despite these changes, the future for alternative energy has never looked brighter, although the shape of the industry will be different than expected a few years ago. Alternative energy facilities can be built more quickly and cheaper than conventional central station power plants. By comparison, they can be constructed in 1-3 years versus 8-10 years for even coal-fired utility plants and at a cost of around $1,000 per kilowatt versus over $2,000 per kilowatt. Adding to these lead time and cost advantages is the high efficiency of cogeneration facilities, which convert 70% to 80% of the fuel input into useful energy products compared to only about 32% for standard utility-type plants. With these substantial advantages, investments in well-conceived alternative energy projects can be very profitable.

While certain types of alternatives, such as wind and solar energy, depended on tax breaks to be economical, others like cogeneration represent sound investments regardless of tax treatment. In fact, the amount of alternative energy projects applying for certification by the Federal Energy Regulatory Commission has increased steadily from about 400 megawatts in 1980 to over 11,000 megawatts in 1985.

This upward trend will continue into the future. In recent years electric utilities have cancelled far more power plants than they have ordered, and now few utilities have plans to construct new facilities once current ones under construction are completed. With unpredictable load growth and uncertain cost recovery on new plants, few utilities are willing to take the risk of investing in expensive new power plants. Despite the dearth of new construction, the demand for power continues to grow, though only at 2% to 3% per year compared to the 7% rate of the postwar years through 1973. Even at these low growth rates, the current surplus of capacity will be worked off by the early 1990's in many regions. With a decade-long lead time for new central station power plants, utilities have already passed the point at which they could have met this growth by building their own new facilities. On the other hand, the much shorter lead time of alternative energy projects enables them to be one of the few ways in which the looming capacity shortage of the 1990's can be avoided.

Huge Potential for Alternative Energy by 2000

Independent power producers presently supply about 7% of the United States' electricity, primarily through industrial cogeneration facilities. By the year 2000, alternative energy has the potential to provide at least 20% of our power, meeting about one-half of the growth in electricity demand over the next 15 years.

This new supply will come from resources that have long been available, but have been ignored because of their small size and utilities' obsession with building ever-larger power plants in the pursuit of the new elusive economies of scale. With the newly created competition in power supply, creative entrepreneurs have invigorated the once-sleepy electric industry, developing a multitude of efficient, low-cost generating facilities:

- Cogeneration projects, which produce both electrical and thermal energy more efficiently than conventional energy systems, are blossoming at the sites of large energy users, such as industrial plants, hospitals, colleges, and apartment buildings.

- Municipal waste-to-energy facilities are generating cheap power and helping to solve serious landfill problems.

- Wood-fired power plants are utilizing this abundant, low-polluting renewable resource.

- Geothermal plants are tapping the heat of the earth in California, Nevada, and elsewhere.

- New technologies, spurred by the opportunities created by deregulation, are being developed to economically utilize wind, solar energy, and other renewable, but diffuse energy resources.

Though alternative energy projects individually are small by utility standards, collectively they represent a huge potential for economically supplying new power demands.

Low-Cost, Low-Risk Electrical Power

A major Southwestern utility balks at purchasing large amounts of power from cogeneration facilities at a cost of less than 3 cents per kilowatt-hour, while continuing to build a nuclear power plant that its Public Utility Commission says will produce 17-cent power! Despite this obstruction, new cogeneration projects continue to be announced in this area, which could easily supply all of the utility's demand growth beyond the year 2000. This situation is typical of other regions as well, where alternative energy can generate electricity at much lower cost than new conventional coal-fired and nuclear power plants.

As promulgated in federal and state regulations, the power from alternative energy facilities is sold to utilities at the cost that they have avoided by not having to produce the same amount of power themselves. This can be contrasted to traditional electric utility regulation, where the price of power is established by an allowable return on the utility's investment. Thus, alternative energy is priced at the value of the power produced, while utility rates are based on the cost of production.

The value-based pricing of alternative energy is much better for the ratepayer, as he will never pay more for the power than it is worth. The risk of cost overruns and inefficient operations is borne by the owner of the project, not the ratepayer. On the other hand, under the current regulatory scheme, utilities are given the contrary incentive to incur cost overruns, because the more they invest, the more they earn. This cost-plus system exposes the ratepayer to substantial risks of construction cost overruns and poor operation. The result has been the rate shock phenomenon, where the ratepayer pays the high cost of the utility's mistake.

Many Benefits

In addition to providing economical new generating capacity with a short lead time, alternative energy has many other local and national benefits. Most of all, it represents a wise use of our natural resources. Cogeneration is the most efficient way to generate electricity, converting 70% to 80% of its fuel input into useful electrical and thermal products, as compared to an average of only 32% for conventional electric utility power plants. Other alternative energy projects utilize renewable resources, such as biomass and hydro, which reduce consumption of our valuable and finite fossil fuel resources. Even in times of falling oil prices, we must adopt a long-range view in order to forestall a recurrence of the costly energy crises of the past.

In the 1970's energy forecasters wildly overestimated growth in power demand, as they failed to appreciate the potential for price-induced conservation. The result was that many utilities badly overbuilt, resulting in reserve margins of 50% or greater, compared to an optimum of about 20%. Since utilities are paid based on their invested capital, the cost of this overinvestment was absorbed by the ratepayer. Even today, forecasting the need for new generating capacity is a vexing problem. Demand projections are only accurate two or three years ahead, while the lead time on new central station power plants is 8 to 10 years. Given the huge size of utility investments, a forecasting error of only one percent compounded over a number of years can result in hundreds of millions of dollars of excess capacity on one hand, or a power shortage on the other. Overlaid onto this dilemma is the penchant of many state public service commissions to determine after the fact whether or not a utility's investment decision was prudent, making cost recovery on these multi-billion dollar investments highly uncertain. Having spent the last fifty years in a low-risk regulated environment, what utility would "bet the company" on a new construction program under these conditions?

Alternative energy represents one solution to this planning dilemma. These facilities can be built quickly in smaller increments, allowing generating capacity to be closely matched to demand. With alternative energy no longer will the ratepayer have to absorb the huge cost of mistakes in demand forecasting, and utilities can avoid risky investments in new plants.

Need for Fair Treatment

Utilities, because of their monopoly power in the markets for electricity, are in a position to block the development of alternative energy. By being a single buyer with many suppliers (a monopsony), they are able to delay and mold it to their liking. This must not be allowed to happen.

As their generating monopoly has started slipping away, utilities have adopted a number of practices to protect themselves from competition and to cast doubts in the minds of potential end users about the viability of alternatives. For instance, they have:

- Adopted rate tariffs that penalize operating cogeneration systems or that give special deals to potential cogenerators to keep them from dropping off the system;

- Denied or threatened to deny standby power to end users which buy cogenerated power from projects owned and operated by third parties;

- Established back-end loaded rates in long-term purchase contracts to make alternative energy projects less economically attractive in the early years, as compared to their own front-end loaded cost recovery;

- Established excessive security requirements for long-term contracts, requirements that they themselves do not have to meet.

These arcane regulatory issues are little understood, but are vitally important to the long-range success of alternative energy. The extent that the United States benefits from the low-cost, low-risk power supplied by alternative energy will depend in large measure on how effectively these issues are resolved.

To ensure fair treatment for alternative energy, federal and state regulators must be vigilant in identifying and blocking these practices. However, this is a difficult task, given the large resources of utilities compared to small, entrepreneurial alternative energy developers and given the traditionally cozy relationship between regulator and regulated.

Summary

Alternative energy has the potential to supply as much as half of the United States' growth in electric demand beyond the year 2000 at a lower cost and at lower risk to the ratepayer than new conventional utility power plants. It has many national and local benefits and is a sound, long-range approach for the wise use of our natural resources, a goal which we must not lose sight of in these times of falling fuel prices. It represents a new threat of competition to electric utilities, which have adopted a variety of practices to delay and shape it to their will. However, in the long run, alternative energy is one important piece of the solution to our energy challenges of the 1980's, 1990's, and beyond, and it must be ensured of fair treatment to realize its full potential benefit for the nation.

SECTION 9

ENERGY MANAGEMENT IN THE HEALTH CARE INDUSTRY

Sponsored by the American Society for Hospital Engineering

Chapter 28

TOTAL FACILITY ENERGY MANAGEMENT

R. E. Hobbs

Successful Energy Management cannot be measured by a few projects, no matter how significant the energy savings. Large facilities today are comprised of extensive energy consuming systems. For every energy project developed, two more projects remain to be discovered.

The successful Energy Manager is in the driver's seat completing ten projects, then twenty, thirty, and still looking and finding more projects. Nothing is assumed to be as efficient as possible, and no part of any system is ignored.

The successful Energy Manager is willing to take risks, not of being fired, but to use imagination, study engineering theory, exercise common sense, develop concept designs, calculate savings, sell projects to management, control designers, study equipment performance, pre-select contractors, manage the contractor efforts, solve the inherent problems along the way, and then optimize the project after acceptance when the designers and contractors all walk off.

Once the successful Energy Manager establishes his credibility, his problem becomes finding enough time to get the projects rolling as he dreams them up. He sees what others don't. As they say in the North, only the lead dog sees new scenery.

ENERGY MANAGEMENT

What is Energy Management? It's all inclusive of Energy Conservation, Load Shifting, Load Sequencing, and Alternative Energy Sources.

There is no "cure-all" for successful Energy Management; not cogeneration, not thermal energy storage, not energy management systems, not trash incineration, or anything else. Successful Energy Management is a combination of all the energy technologies currently being promoted, in a well planned program that does not eliminate the potential for future projects. As an example, planning a cogeneration project for full heat and/or electrical demand after a modest (10%) energy conservation effort, may preclude additional energy conservation, just to achieve the predicted savings in the cogeneration feasibility study.

There is always potential for more Energy Conservation in the best of Energy Management Programs, even with a 39% per square foot reduction in energy consumption.

ENERGY COST SAVINGS

The cost savings generated through Energy Management cannot be equaled by any other means. Every dollar saved in the energy budget is a dollar for profit. New product revenues generate only a few percent in profits and require many years to payback capital investments while the majority of energy management programs generate a thirty plus percent energy cost savings annually. The return on investment for energy management can seldom be equaled.

The Energy Cost Savings during 1985 at Mercy Hospital & Medical Center reached $1,417,000. Based on a 4% profit margin, revenues would had to have been $35,425,000 greater in 1985 to off-set the higher energy costs with no conservation. The Energy Cost Savings since 1975 reached a total of $4,702,000 by the end of 1985, with a total capital investment of $3,072,000 during the same period.

During 1986, another $260,000 will be invested in energy conservation that will save $118,182 per year. More projects are being planned for 1987, and there is still no end in sight.

THE STARTING POINT

Energy Consumption can not be managed until the actual energy consumption is known. Most facility managers know the total energy consumption each month and may find some data to compare their facility consumptions to other similar facilities. Even armed with that information, it is of little value in a good Energy Management Program.

The average time-of-day energy demand is needed for each energy source for every month of the year. This can be as simple as taking meter readings every fifteen minutes one workday each month. Electronic monitoring is more accurate but may not be immediately affordable. Then an inventory of all energy consuming devices, with run schedules, is needed to determine where energy is being used. The comparison of energy actually being required, and the energy being consumed, quickly indicates the losses within the facility. The waste will be significant and a little detective work can lead to a large number of projects, plugging steam leaks, recovering condensate, insulating piping, turning off security lights during the day, resetting thermostats, repairing air handler temperature controls, replacing steam traps, and of course closing the by-passes around steam traps.

Yes, no matter how conscientious you think maintenance personnel are, these things will be found in years to come. Through 1983 the natural gas, for steam use, was reduced over 30% at Mercy, but with the "boss's" assistance, a hand-over-hand survey was conducted on the steam system and repairs were made to those impossible to repair leaks. Just that one, full facility survey helped net a 42% reduction in natural gas use between 1983 and 1984. Just conducting a survey and actually seeing the condition of equipment, controls, set points, and the distribution systems has the potential of reducing energy consumption 20%.

The inventory then provides the needed information for additional energy savings. The run times on each device not only provides information leading to the development of a project priority list to get the greatest savings first, but allows the Energy Manager to ask "why" equipment is being run so many hours, especially chillers. Later it will be shown how chillers are often run just because its always been that way.

Without a first hand knowledge of his facility, the Energy Manager cannot realize his full potential. It may require getting dirty and interrogating maintenance personnel, but it will also achieve respect both for the Energy Manager and the Energy Management Program.

ABOUT MERCY

Mercy Hospital began its history in 1890 when two Sisters of Mercy opened two rooms in a downtown San Diego hotel. Over the years Mercy has grown from the only hospital in San Diego to the largest civilian hospital in San Diego and Imperial counties.

The current twelve story, 320,000 square foot hospital was constructed in 1966 providing 523 licensed beds and all acute care hospital support services. Small additions were made through the years followed by the addition of a 137,000 square foot Ambulatory Services Addition in 1982. Other facilities served by the main plant include a 66,000 square foot charity clinic and mental health facility constructed in 1960, and multiple facilities constructed before 1927 totalling 94,000 square feet.

All the facilities comprising the Mercy Hospital & Medical Center are services from central electrical, steam, and chilled water distribution systems. The central distribution systems became an invaluable asset to optimumly utilize the entire complex for co-generated electricity and recovered heat.

Medical support services include:

- 13 Operating Rooms
- 5 Delivery/Operating Rooms
- 9 X-Ray Suites
- 1 Computerized Tomography Unit
- 1 Magnetic Resonance Imager (.6 tessla)
- 72-80% Census
- 14 Bed Surgical Intensive Care
- 10 Bed Medical Intensive Care
- 12 Bed Neo-natal Intensive Care
- 24 Bed Oncology Unit
- Computer Center

Plant support services include:

- 3 Boilers (1-750HP, 1-250HP, 1-180HP)
- 4 Centrifugal Chillers (250 Ton each)
- 1 Hi-Pressure Steam Absorption Chiller (200 Ton)
- 655HP Fan Capacity
- 698HP Pump Capacity (425HP Standby or Alternated)
- Hot Water Heating (443,000 SF)
- Steam Heating (174,000 SF)
- Critical Area Chill Water Loop (55,000 SF)
- Non-Critical Area Chill Water Loop (468,000 SF)
- 8,500 LB/Day Laundry (6 Days/Week)

WEATHER IMPACT

San Diego weather is tempered by the Pacific Ocean, resulting in cool summers and warm winters. Summer days do reach temperatures in the 90-s and sometimes 100-s. The weather conditions are changing with a significant (100%) increase in cooling degree days and a significant (57%) decrease in heating degree days as the following graphs show.

COOLING DEGREE DAYS

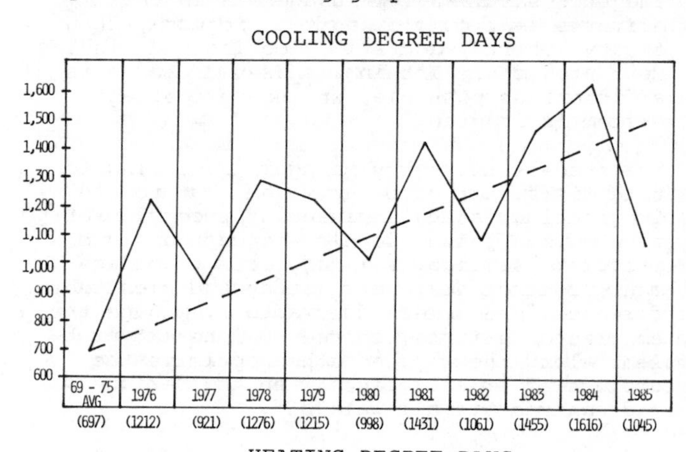

HEATING DEGREE DAYS

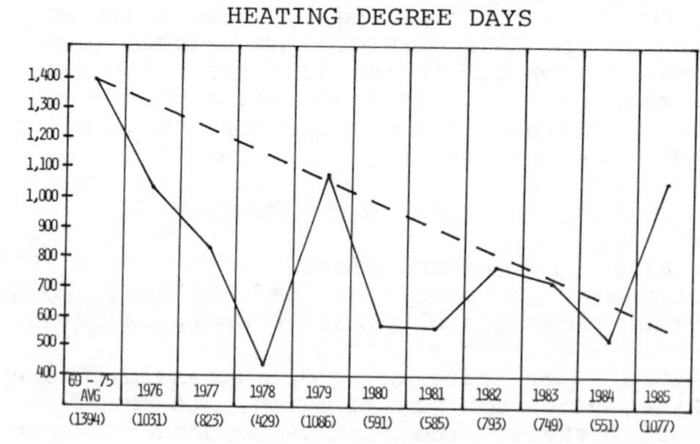

It became apparent that the changing weather conditions had negatively impacted the energy conservation efforts. Meeting the cooling requirement was far more energy intensive than providing heat.

Base load chiller operations are required 8,760 hours per year (continuous service) for the critical area loop. The non-critical loop chiller hours began to follow the cooling degree days after 1978. The graph on the next page shows a direct relationship between the chiller hours and the cooling degree days above.

COMBINED CHILLER HOURS

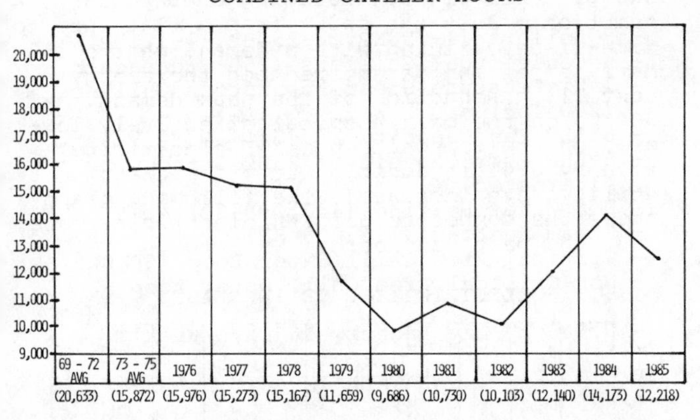

The average electricity consumption per chiller-hour is 166 KWH. The last six year ratio of non-critical chiller hours to cooling degree days has been 2.3. The calculated cooling electricity consumption per degree day was 382 KWH. The increases in cooling degree days have hindered the overall energy conservation efforts by burning-up energy savings to meet the increased degree day cooling loads.

CHILLER ENERGY CONSERVATION

It should be noted that conservation began in 1973 when chiller hours were reduced. Prior to that time, all chillers were run during the summer months and steam/hot water heating was used to control temperatures. During the years 1973-1978 only half the chillers were run during the summer months and again the heating systems were used to control temperatures. In 1979 the chillers were only operated as required, and at the minimum capacities needed to maintain an adequate cooling temperature, and the heating systems were secured during summer months.

Chiller operations are manually optimized based on the daily temperature and comfort levels within the hospital. Until 1983 the thermal wheel effect of the building had helped to reduce chiller operating hours. During the past three years the temperatures have remained high all night, when in previous years the day-night differential was 30+ degrees.

Installation of a 220,000 gallon chilled water storage tank in 1982 provided an artificial thermal wheel. Electrical demand was reduced 300KW through this project and variable-air-volume system installations providing a $122,000 energy cost savings in 1983.

TOTAL ENERGY CONSUMPTION

A new 137,000 square foot Ambulatory Services Addition was occupied in phases from 1981 to 1983 increasing the facility size by 28.5%, and the cooling degree days increased by 52%. Overall, the facility size increased 32.2% from 1975 to 1985 while the total electricity consumption in 1985 was 1.3% below that in 1975. The following graphs show the annual electricity and natural gas consumptions during the years 1975 to 1985.

TOTAL FACILITY ELECTRICITY (KKWH)

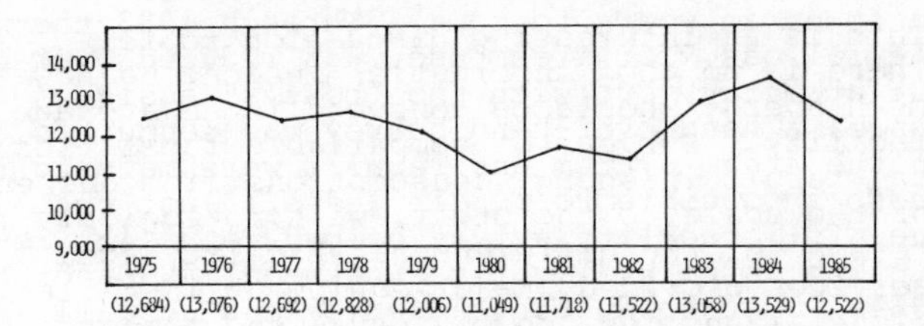

TOTAL FACILITY NATURAL GAS (MBTU)

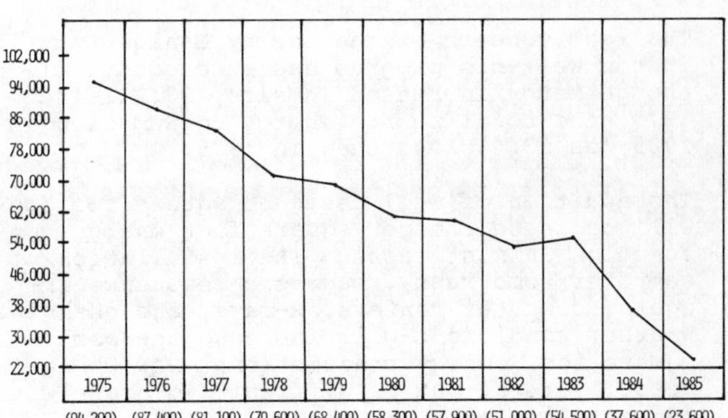

The natural gas conservation program was only slightly impacted by the 1983 occupancy of the Ambulatory Services Addition. It was put back on track with the 1984 hand-over-hand steam system survey, and cogeneration heat recovery in 1985 achieved additional savings.

Combining the energy values of natural gas and electricity consumed by the facility shown an interesting trend. Electricity is included below, both by the heat value needed to produce it (source) and the heat value at the point of delivery (delivered).

TOTAL FACILITY ENERGY

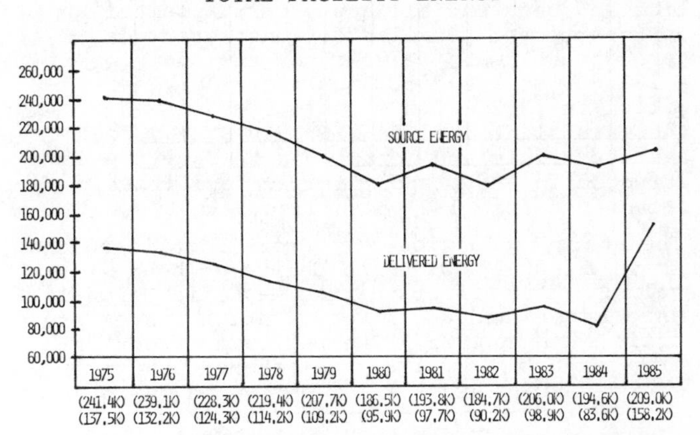

The Source heat value is based on the heat value required to generate electricity and the Delivered heat value is the heat value contained in the electricity delivered to the facility.

The addition of a Magnetic Resonance Imager slightly increased the Source energy consumption in 1985, while the addition of an 800KW Cogeneration system greatly increased the Delivered energy consumption through on-site generation. Even though the total energy consumption increased slightly, cogeneration and a shift to absorption chilling reduced the 1985 energy costs by $514,000.

SQUARE FOOTAGE ENERGY CONSUMPTION

This is an interesting discussion topic. There is no good information indicating how much energy should be consumed in an average facility. Surveys of comparable facilities can result in energy consumptions from one end of the scale to the other, with no logical reason for the differences. Facility age, services provided, major equipment installations, laundries, degree days, and number of energy conservation measures, seldom leads to an explanation.

The real concern of the Energy Manager must be in how well his program has succeeded. Although Mercy increased in size, 32.2% since 1975, the total source energy consumption in 1985 was 13.4% less than in 1975.

The addition of well designed square footage will decrease the per square foot energy consumption in most cases. The installation of computer tomography, magnetic resonance imagers, computer centers, x-rays, and changing weather conditions will increase the per square foot energy consumption. How these actually total out is difficult to argue without metering each new change.

The per square foot energy consumption provides some indication of success and of course is the basis used by the U.S. Department of Energy programs. The following graph shows the energy consumption per square foot experience in the Mercy energy program.

ENERGY CONSUMPTION (000 BTU) PER SQUARE FOOT

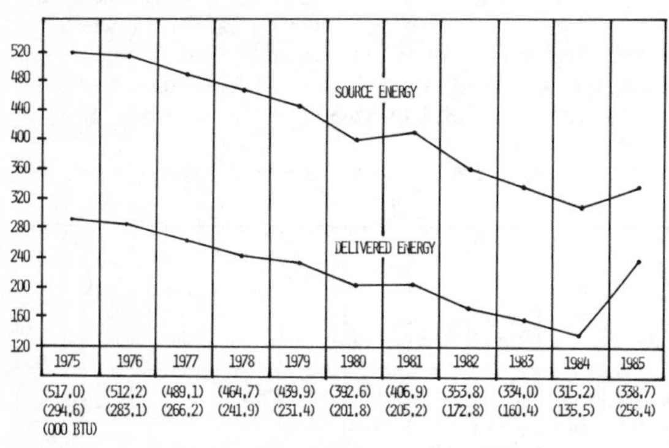

The energy reduction per square foot is again shown for the source and delivered heat values. The affects of the Magnetic Resonance Imager and 800KW Cogeneration system are again seen in 1985. The per square foot energy reduction by 1984 had reached 30% for source energy and 54% for delivered energy. In 1985 the energy reduction was only 34.5% and 13.0% respectively. The significant change in delivered energy begins to show the need to evaluate conservation results on source energy.

ENERGY RATES

The successful Energy Manager must become very familiar with the utility rate structures. The introduction of time-of-day pricing, demand charges, base load pricing, and standby charges have caused significant increases in energy costs. Knowing the rate structures, and his energy demands and consumptions, the Energy Manager can reduce energy costs without reducing energy consumption. Just the shift from a flat rate to time-of-day pricing with a demand charge in Mercy's parking garage reduced the energy cost 21%. Reduction of the peak demand, by 300KW, on the main hospital effectively lowered on the composite per KWH electricity rate by 0.6% in addition to off-setting an 8% utility rate increase. The following graph shows the composite per KWH electricity rate over the past ten years.

ELECTRICITY RATE INCREASES

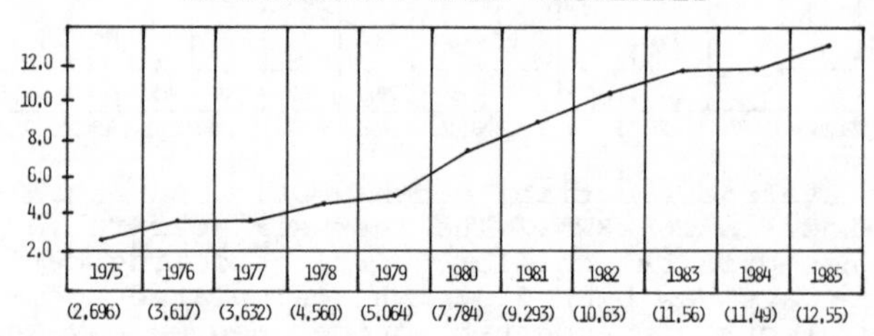

The purchased electricity costs in 1985 were as follows:

Peak Demand Charge	$7.31 /KW
On-Peak Energy Charge	12.934 ¢/KWH
Semi-Peak Energy Charge	12.334 ¢/KWH
Off-Peak Energy Charge	9.934 ¢/KWH

and the composite electricity cost, total electricity cost divided by total kilowatt hour consumption, was 12.55 ¢/KWH.

Natural gas rates have decreased in the past two years as deregulation and increased reserves have favored the user.

NATURAL GAS RATE INCREASES

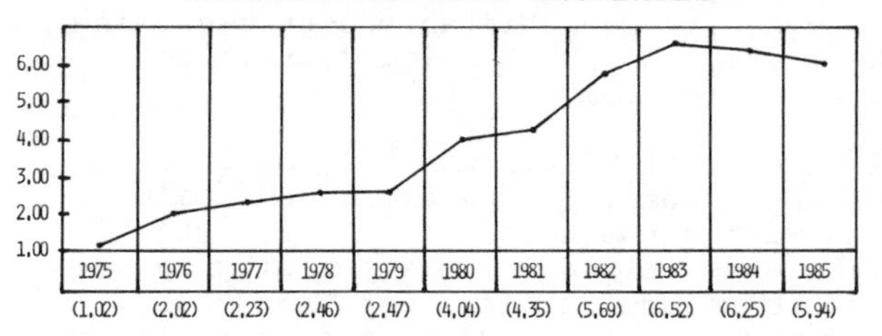

Energy Rates developed, by the distributing utility, are a reflection of the actual energy cost whether produced by the utility or purchased and wheeled, the return on capital investment in the distribution system, maintenance of the system, and the cost of maintaining the peak capacity available for customer peak demands which all occur at the same time of day. We the customer place a great burden on the utility to provide reliable power and as a result must bare the cost of that burden.

ENERGY COST SAVINGS

Energy savings has never been the motive behind any Energy Management Program. Energy Cost is, and always will be, the driving force behind Energy Management. Capital investments are not made without a projection of the Return on Investment or Simple Payback. A good Energy Management Program can provide the best return on capital investment as the following energy cost savings graph shows.

ENERGY COST SAVINGS

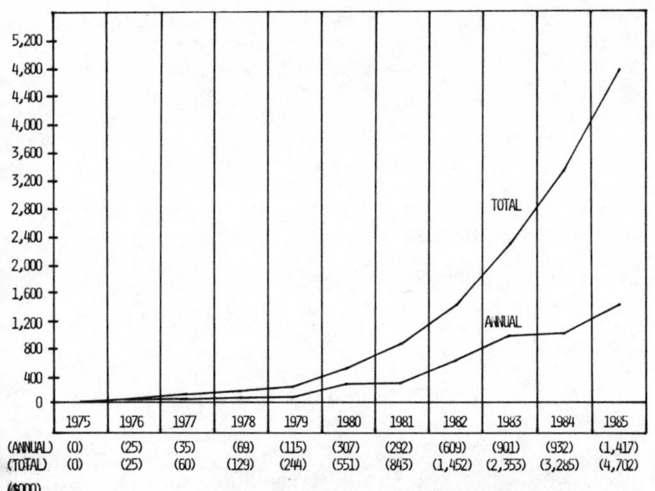

Each year the avoided energy cost savings increases as new projects are implemented and the energy rates increase. The cumulative total savings from year to year increases almost exponentially. During the ten years of this graph, only $3,072,000 was invested to achieve an energy cost savings of $4,702.000.

ENERGY SAVINGS VS. MAINTENANCE

Following the trend in maintenance costs over the past nine years began to show an interesting relationship to the success of the energy program. Maintenance cost increased significantly in 1980 as the low-cost, no-cost projects were implemented. Again in 1981 and 1982 the cost went up, in support of the new 137,000 square foot addition as much of the interior work was deleted from the construction contract to save money, and maintenance foot the bill. It should be noted that maintenance costs only include normal engineering cost centers and common areas of hospital complex. All work directly related to patient care was transferred to other cost centers.

TOTAL PLANT MAINTENANCE COST ($000)

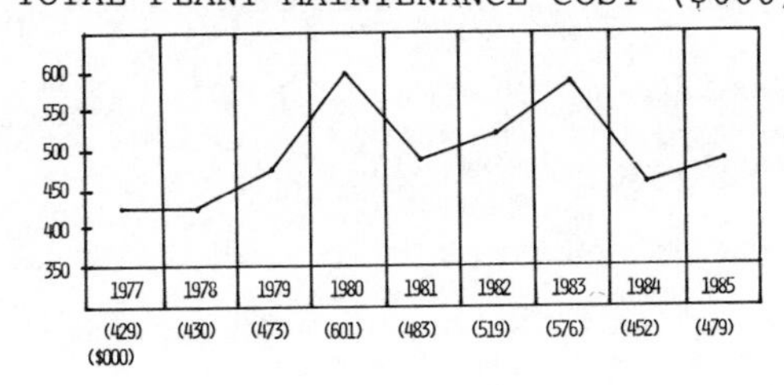

The plant maintenance costs take a different appearance when related to square footage.

PLANT MAINTENANCE COST PER 000 SQUARE FOOT

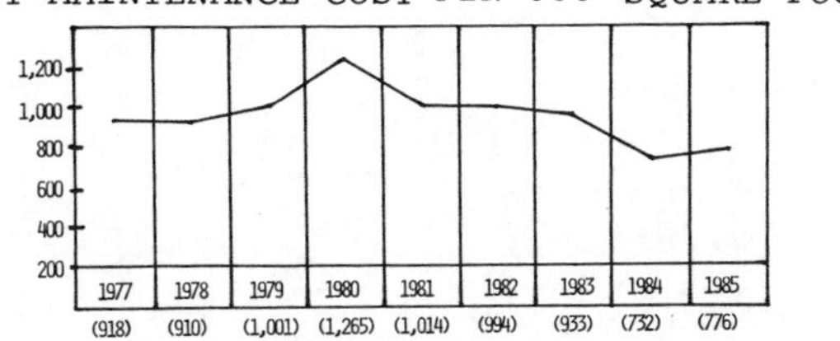

The low-cost, no-cost projects (primarily maintenance and repair) increased the maintenance budget by $125,000 in 1980 but reduced the source energy consumption by 6.7% and the delivered energy consumption by 10.5% for the period 1979 to 1981. That maintenance investment represented a $258,000 energy cost savings during the same period.

TOTAL ENERGY COST REDUCTION

It is often said "I keep reducing my energy consumption, but my bill keeps going up". That statement is true and it can easily be substantiated by the earlier graphs showing annual electricity and natural gas rate increases exceeding 50%. Effective Energy Conservation Programs dampen those drastic rate increases, and even though the total energy bill is still going up, it's not going up as fast as it would without Energy Conservation.

Everyday I thank my Utility Company for those rapid rate increases because it presents a greater challenge for me. The Mercy energy cost in 1985 was one-half what it would have been, if the 1975 per square foot energy consumption had remained the same over the last ten years.

It seemed strange that the utility rates in San Diego were increasing much faster than other parts of the United States, with San Diego now boasting the second highest energy cost in the country. But it's not. The rest of the country is now experiencing rapid energy cost increases while San Diego's costs are stabilizing. San Diego was just leading the way.

The Mercy Energy Management Program has not been able to realize reductions in the total energy cost for the past two years as the graph below shows.

TOTAL ACTUAL ENERGY COST ($000)

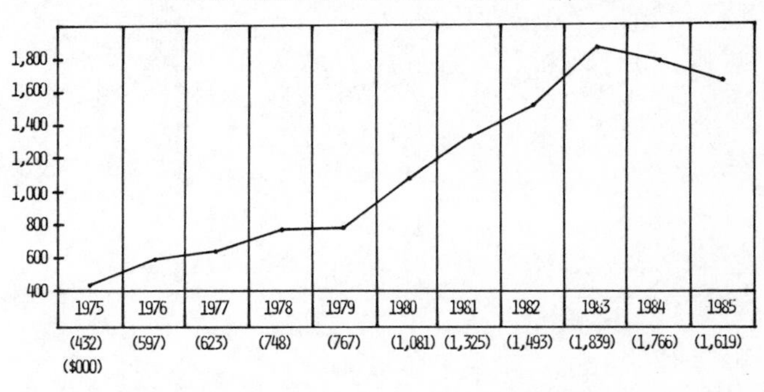

The Energy Manager's job is becoming more difficult as the prices at the gasoline pump are going down. This energy price indicator gives management the wrong impression on the utility energy cost and now the emphasis on energy cost savings is dropping. This is gradually leading to energy conservation complacency. Utility energy rates are not following the gas pump prices because so little of the electricity rate actually covers energy cost. Like any other major industry, utilities have tremendous fixed overhead costs that must be factored into their final product, energy.

The Energy Manager must continue to develop new projects in preparation for the next round of energy cost increases that are sure to come within the next three or four years.

SECTION 10

ENERGY CONSERVATION OPPORTUNITIES FOR HOSPITALS AND SCHOOLS

Sponsored by D.O.E., Office of Institutional Conservation Programs

Chapter 29

GENESEE HOSPITAL OPERATES EFFICIENTLY

D. McGeddy, L. G. Bellenger

INTRODUCTION

Hospitals are energy-intensive facilities because most of the HVAC equipment must operate continuously and because there are stringent requirements governing air circulation rates, pressure relationships, temperature, and humidity. This applies particularly to operating rooms. In New York State, operating rooms require 25 air changes per hour with 5 air changes per hour of outside air.

The Genesee Hospital is one of six hospitals located in Rochester, New York. It includes 13 operating rooms served by two central HVAC systems which operate continuously. Surgical procedures at the hospital are scheduled for approximately sixty hours per week, leaving the operating rooms empty for over one hundred hours per week. Consideration was given to deactivating the HVAC systems during unoccupied periods, but the medical staff rejected this alternative after reviewing problems experienced at other hospitals which had implemented this change.

INNOVATIVE PROCEDURES

In order to reduce the energy used by the operating room systems, the hospital implemented measures to vary the air flow and use of outside air according to occupancy and weather conditions. Permission was requested and received from the New York State Department of Health to use the federal standard of 15 air changes per hour with 100% outside air when outside air conditions made that selection more economical than the state requirements of 25 air changes per hour with 20% outside air. Variable speed drives were installed on the supply and return fans to control the air flow and permit changing from 25 air changes per hour to 15 air changes per hour and back again. An energy management system was installed to monitor space conditions and control the heating and cooling coils and humidifiers as well as the variable speed drives.

Through the use of the energy management system, the HVAC systems run as efficiently as possible. During unoccupied hours, the systems operate at 15 air changes per hour with full return air. During occupied hours, the energy management system monitors outside air conditions and determines whether to operate at 15 air changes per hour with 100% outside air or at 25 air changes per hour with 20% outside air. The HVAC systems serving the operating rooms typically operate at full outside air and the lower air flow when the outside air temperature ranges from 35 to 70°F and operate at 20% outside air and the higher air flow when the outside air temperature is above 70°F or below 35°F.

To guarantee that the systems always provide the required amount of outside air and supply air during occupied conditions, a lighting interlock was installed on the lights in the operating rooms. The systems will automatically return to occupied conditions whenever any one of the operating room lights is turned on. Status lights in each operating room and at the nurses' station keep the staff informed of the condition of the HVAC systems at all times.

This energy management project is an unusual application of an existing technology. It combines the use of an energy management system and variable speed drives to control the operation of HVAC systems serving operating rooms with stringent environmental and air flow requirements. To the best of our knowledge, it is a unique application of outside air, supply air, and environmental control.

TRANSFERABILITY

Since operating rooms throughout New York State have the same air change requirements, and since similar requirements are in effect in the rest of the states, the techniques used in this project can be readily used by other facilities. The project used existing technology and engineering capabilities in an innovative way that can be duplicated by other hospitals interested in reducing energy consumption and costs.

As a result of the success of this project, a similar modification already has been made to the HVAC system serving the X-ray area at Genesee Hospital. During unoccupied periods, the outside air dampers are closed, the supply fan is deactivated, and the return fan provides a reduced air flow to the space. An interlock with the X-ray equipment ensures that the system will return to the required air quantities during an emergency and during normal occupancy periods. These revised procedures are controlled by the energy management system.

ENERGY SAVINGS

As expected, this project has significantly reduced steam consumption throughout the year. Reduced air flow and use of return air during unoccupied periods and variable air flow and outside air quantities during occupied periods has reduced steam consumption for preheat, reheat, and humidification. These changes also have reduced electrical consumption for fan energy and refrigeration.

The savings can be identified by comparing hospital energy consumption before and after the project was implemented. Table 1 compares electrical and steam consumption for the period of May, 1984 to April, 1985 with electrical and steam consumption for the same months the previous twelve years.

The cost avoidance shown was calculated by multiplying the monthly savings by the average unit cost for that month and totalling the results. The energy consumption figures were obtained from the monthly utility bills and include the entire hospital. The operating rooms and X-ray area are included in Carlson Building. Although Carlson Building occupies only 33% of the hospital complex by size, steam submeters show that it uses 50% of the steam consumed by the hospital. All of the savings obtained during the period shown are attributed to the retrofit project, and steam consumption in Carlson Building has been reduced approximately 34%.

Genesee Hospital funded this project through energy savings and a $150,000 federal matching grant. While the total cost of the project was $369,714, the cost to the hospital was only $261,714. The figures stated in the table show that the hospital recovered those costs through steam savings alone in the first twelve months following installation.

COMMUNITY IMPACT

This successful project provided direct economic benefits to both the hospital and the community it serves. The hospital benefited by the cost avoidance achieved from reduced steam and electrical consumption and the improved ability to stay within the operating budget. Between June, 1984 and May, 1985, the average rate for purchased steam rose from $16.11 per MLB to $20.36 per MLB, which is an increase of 25%. By comparison, the average rate in 1978 was $6.21 per MLB. By implementing this project to reduce consumption and therefore obtain better control of operating expenses, the hospital provided a benefit to the organizations and individuals who pay for the operating expenses through their medical bills.

	Steam MLB	Electricity KWH
Before (5/83-4/84)	83,711.2	17,876,706
After (5/84-4/85)	69,657.5	17,616,786
Savings	14,053.7	259,920
Percent Savings	16.8%	1.5%
Cost Avoidance	$269,902	$13,230

TABLE 1. ENERGY SAVINGS

Chapter 30

ENERGY CONSERVATION ON SPACESHIP EARTH

C. E. Bailey

For decades, energy came from fossil fuels. Like air and water, we took it for granted that it would be a never ending source of supply. As the supply began to diminish, the public was not made aware of the oncoming crisis. The value of energy based on its scarcity was not reflected in energy costs. Consequently, its conservation was not regarded as a necessity. While the scientific world was aware of the urgency of developing alternatives for energy sources, and was working continually to find substitutes, the reaction of the public was skepticism. Through various means of community relations and public education, this imbalance of price and value is rapidly being corrected. Although there is still a great deal of energy waste and complacency on energy matters by a public, long accustomed to unlimited resources in a land of plenty, the pendulum is slowly swinging in the opposite direction. Immediate low cost problems are getting attention from both the commercial and industrial sectors, as well as the private sectors. Management is beginning to look at their own facilities in an effort to correct the mounting energy waste problems. Not only must we correct these inefficiencies within our respective organizations, but we must also face the fact that our fossil fuel sources are dwindling at a rapid pace. Conservation and control are important factors in balancing our present economic environment. Seeking out alternative energy sources is a top priority. Exploration into solar energy, co-generation and photovoltacs are a few of the areas targeted for extensive scientific research and testing programs.

Energy Management offers a wealth of opportunities--from computerized energy management systems, to simple heat recovery systems such as the exhaust hood. From co-generation to a simple adjustable shower head nozzle. The varieties of innovative and creative solutions are endless!

In the Pinellas County School System in 1979, the projected cost of energy through the mid 80's showed an escalation of costs which, at the present rate of usage indicated a topping out point of twelve million dollars. School administrators recognizing an urgent need to regulate and direct energy use and management, employed the services of an energy management specialist from private industry and instituted the Office of Energy Management in Pinellas County Schools in 1983.

A county plan was developed based on the Florida Governor's Energy Office NECPA program. The School Board committed total support to the program. Top administrators as well as personnel at all levels were involved in active participation in the program. An Energy Management Committee was appointed to interpret the School Board policies. Local Energy Management Teams were formed and together with the Project Manager, Energy Manager, Maintenance Department, Plant Operators and Purchasing personnel the program began its action agenda. A policy manual for principals, The Energy Management Manual was produced. The manual outlines a program by which energy costs can be cut. It includes a checklist for teachers, cafeteria workers and custodians. By involving the entire school staff in the program, rather than creating a management program directed by administration, more interest was stimulated. Schools responded with enthusiasm.

There are five major factors that influence the level of energy used in school facilities. They are interrelated and must be activated concurrently for maximum efficiency. The major factors are:

1. External climatic conditions;

2. Mandated education programs and activities which must be implemented;

3. Building components and features including floors, ceilings, walls, roofs, windows and landscaping;

4. Energy-using systems and equipment, such as heating, cooling, lighting and ventilation;

5. Occupant habits and facilities utilization, by school personnel, as well as hours of operation.

The Energy Management Department kept computerized records of year-to-date usage and target comparison which were provided to principals in a monthly report indicating progress in cutting energy usage. The staff was available at all times to assist principals in implementing the program through personal consultations, plant surveys, identification of areas of concern and suggestions for solutions.

An incentive program was an important part of the package plan. The kilowatt target concept of the Energy Rebate Program was set up. A kilowatt target based on demand times hours of usage was assigned to individual schools. A school using less kilowatts than its assigned target or is equivalent to its target would be eligible for a monetary rebate of $1.50 per student enrollment. Each year, the school with the largest percent of decrease in energy use receives a plaque plus a cash rebate. Second and third place winners receive a certificate of merit plus a cash rebate. All schools on target or below receive cash rebates.

"See the Light? Save it, Florida, Turn it Off." This Florida state slogan developed by the Governor's Energy Office was adapted to Pinellas County Schools' program and "Turn it Off" became a familiar sign and slogan in the schools as students, teachers and staff scrambled to turn down, thermostats, turn off appliances, copiers, typewriters and desk lamps when not in use. The dress code even came under scrutiny and occupants of buildings were encouraged to dress comfortably for the 68° heat/78° cooling temperature levels.

The maintenance department implemented many changes to conserve energy. All incandescent lights were eliminated. Outdoor lighting was changed to high pressure sodium. Metal Halide fixtures were installed in large indoor areas such as gymnasiums and auditoriums. Emergency lighting was turned off when buildings were not in use. Dusk-to-dawn lights were used outdoors (1.3 years payback). Conditions of diffusers were monitored as well as efficiency of lighting locations. "Gang" cleaning as opposed to sporadic cleaning was encouraged. Classroom lighting in thirty-seven schools was upgraded as well as some kitchen lighting and equipment. Rate studies were made to determine lowest cost available. Air-conditioning chillers were cleaned regularly. Energy use went down in thirty-five schools using disposable dishes. Incandescent exit lights were replaced with fluorescent tubes. Lighting was reduced in corridors. Electric motors were replaced by energy efficient ones. Electric heating was converted to natural gas.

Projected electric costs for 1984/85 were at the twelve million mark, but actual dollars spent amounted to $6,276,085.00. In 1978/79, 94,930,000 kilowatt hours were used, while in 1984/85 only 87,105,000 were used. In 1979, the projected cost of energy through the mid 80's showed an escalation of costs, and at the present rate of usage indicated that it could top out at twelve million dollars. Through the energy saving methods employed by the Pinellas County School System, the escalating cost trend has been reversed and costs decreased during inflation years. Even with added electrical costs such as air-conditioning and lighting for fifty-one elementary schools and the building of seven new schools and eleven new media centers, actual expenses decreased from 94.3 million to 87.1 million.

Dr. Scott Rose, Superintendent of Pinellas County Schools has stated, "Energy management is necessary to offset rising costs of energy which would, if not checked, interfere with other school system priorities, including market competitive salaries for employees. Competition for the scarce resources of our school system necessitates that each employee be conscious of potential waste and work to eliminate waste."

Last year energy costs projected beyond actual expenditures were budgeted for across-the-board salary increases for employees of Pinellas County Schools. The incentive plan for school rebates for energy savings is highly successful with additional schools reaching their target kilowatt hours each year. We've "seen the light" in Pinellas County Schools, and we're "turned on" about "turning it off."

OBJECTIVES OF THE ENERGY MANAGEMENT PROGRAM

1. To significantly reduce the existing energy consumption.
2. To record added equipment usage so records are accurate without restricting the educational program.
3. Provide an accounting procedure which will measure reduction of utility energy consumption and related cost avoidance.
4. Generate an awareness in the education process of energy cost and show methods of efficient usage.
5. Maintain a history of utility/energy usage in terms of both quantities and cost for each school and administrative centers.
6. Provide information for new construction and repairs/replacement equipment, with the latest energy saving data.
7. Report status of energy projects and see that projects are scheduled and kept current.

FACILITY UTILIZATION

1. Turn it off! The single most important energy factor in a facility is hours of operation.
2. Schedule cleaning and maintenance activities during daylight hours, when practical.
3. Conduct an operations analysis of the facility's use and, whenever possible, consolidate activities to reduce building usage. Analyze all activities in terms of the cost/benefit considering energy consumption.
4. When elimination of rescheduling of activities is not possible, use lights and HVAC equipment only in those areas where occupied by employees or students.
5. Adjust schedules so rooms are in continuous use. Use the right size room for the number of people and task.
6. Evaluate for possible elimination nonessential tasks and instructional elements that consume excessive amounts of energy.
7. Turn off heating and cooling systems, or turn off registers in unoccupied areas (i.e.; storage areas, corridors, etc.).
8. Where possible reduce facility operating hours by consolidating evening or weekend activities into the weekday schedule.
9. Evaluate all extracurricular activities in terms of energy consumption. Reduce activities when possible or consolidate into areas which consider energy efficiency.
10. In scheduling large assemblies, consider utilizing a time or day which has the least impact on the heating and cooling system.
11. Except as specifically approved by the principal or facility administrator, restrict the use of facilities for non-school related functions to non-air conditioning areas. Such usage shall be analyzed on a case-by-case basis and exceptions made as appropriate.

PRINCIPAL'S CHECKLIST

__ Make sure thermostats are set at 68° in winter and 78° in summer.

__ When outside temperatures are moderate, turn off heat and air conditioning units and use open windows or air handlers for ventilation.

__ Make sure doors and windows are kept closed while heat or air conditioning is on. Drapes on windows that receive direct sunlight should be closed when air conditioning systems are on and at night during the winter.

__ Consider reducing the number of breakfast and lunch periods, and use the cafeteria at full capacity whenever possible.

__ Do not use assembly areas, such as the auditorium or gymnasium, for small groups that can comfortably meet in smaller areas.

__ Avoid holding assemblies at times when heating and cooling demands are high. In the winter, hold assemblies in the middle of the day. Summer assemblies should be held in the early morning.

__ Schedule as many activities as possible outdoors. Avoid using auditoriums and gyms for pep rallies and other activities that can take place outdoors.

__ Schedule the use of classrooms and other spaces to reduce energy consumption. Do not allow teachers or students to use vacant classrooms. Use the fewest number of rooms necessary for summer and night programs. Schedule teachers into one room for preparation periods, and place support staff in fewer rooms, if possible. Turn off the room size HVAC units and close the registers when the room is not in use.

__ Avoid fire drills when the outdoor temperature is below 45°F or above 85°F.

__ Do not allow the use of portable electric heaters.

__ Schedule classes to maximize the utilization of classroom space in the permanent buildings. Avoid classroom vacancies during any period of the day.

__ Maintain user logs for all reproduction machines.

__ Establish a window, door and transom check at the end of each school day to insure that they are closed.

__ Implement a lighting policy. Keep lights off where space is unused.

__ Schedule office hours to make the most of natural daylight.

__ Reduce night lighting of buildings. Replace old security lights with the sodium vapor type.

__ Use portable units for support services rather than as classrooms, when possible.

__ Reduce the movements of students and staff in and out of buildings.

__ Close off unused storerooms and combine storage areas.

__ Centralize food preparation in the school kitchen. Eliminate office refrigerators, hot-plates and other such food preparation appliances.

__ When repainting buildings, specify light, reflective colors.

__ Establish a resource center for energy education in your school.

__ Solicit feedback from students and staff on energy conservation.

CUSTODIAL SERVICES CHECKLIST

__ Check for proper thermostat settings and function.

__ Check for overheated and overcooled areas.

__ When possible, turn off air conditioners thirty (30) minutes before the end of classes, but continue to ventilate until classes end. Shut down equipment when school is not in session.

__ Check all building insulation, caulking and weather stripping. Repair caulking and weather stripping as necessary.

__ Secure all attic and roof hatches.

__ Inspect heating and air conditioning equipment periodically. Replace worn seals, fittings, traps, etc. Check ducts for leakage. Check the hydronic systems for leaks and damaged valves.

__ Insulate ducts and hydronic system pipes which pass through uninsulated areas.

__ Adjust dampers to reduce the number of air changes per hour to the legal minimum.

__ Replace ceiling tile when dislodged.

__ Turn off power ventilators and exhaust systems when not needed.

__ Isolate unoccupied spaces from heating and cooling systems.

__ Keep door closers in good working condition.

__ Inspect windows and doors for proper closing.

__ Repair damaged windows and doors immediately.

__ Turn off lights in unused spaces.

__ Measure lighting levels throughout the facility. Remove unnecessary lamps and ballasts.

__ Adjust security light timers to coincide with changes in sunrise and sunset.

__ Keep refrigerator compressors and condensers clean.

__ Inspect drinking fountains for proper operation and leaks.

__ Check all plumbing for leaks.

__ Reduce hot water temperatures to 105° except in food preparation areas.

__ Disconnect all unused electrical equipment.

FOOD SERVICES AND CAFETERIA CHECKLIST

- ___ Plan menus to minimize cooking, especially in warm weather.
- ___ Keep refrigerators and freezers as full as possible.
- ___ Batch cook for more than one meal at a time whenever possible.
- ___ Do not open oven doors except when cooking is complete. Use timers.
- ___ Do not use ovens as space heaters.
- ___ Make sure appliances are completely off when not in use.
- ___ Keep ice makers in proper working order. Servicing should be done by qualified personnel.
- ___ Do not operate ice makers when school is not in session or during vacations.
- ___ Use dishwasher machines and racks only when full. When hand washing dishes, use a full sink or pan. Do all rinsing at one time.
- ___ Turn on steam tables thirty (30) minutes before use and keep them covered. Turn off steam tables and food warmers as soon as possible.
- ___ Set refrigerators at recommended operating temperatures. Lower temperatures reduce equipment life and waste energy.
- ___ Keep stored products away from cooling coils.
- ___ Turn off light when leaving walk-in refrigeration units.
- ___ Allow hot foods to cool in shallow containers before placing them in refrigerator.
- ___ Remove unnecessary packaging on refrigerated items. Packing retards product cooling.
- ___ Keep a daily record of refrigerator and freezer temperatures. Report any critical variations to maintenance personnel.
- ___ Make sure there is adequate ventilation around condensers and compressors. If air flow is restricted, equipment life is reduced and energy is wasted.
- ___ Follow manufacturer's recommendations to defrost freezers.
- ___ On gas ranges, adjust the flame so it is blue. A yellow-orange tip means the flame should be turned down. If you cannot get a blue flame by turning the flame down, clean the burner with a stiff wire brush. If the flame is still too yellow, have a service representative adjust the gas-to-air mixture.
- ___ Clean encrusted food from gas burners by soaking burners in water and a good grease solvent. Boil burners in a solution of salt, washing soda, or detergent at least twice a year.
- ___ Keep kitchen hood filters clean.
- ___ Keep the ovens clean to maximize heat transfer to the food. Don't forget to clean the heating elements.
- ___ Check oven temperatures with a thermometer. Have thermostat recalibrated if necessary.
- ___ Keep pots and pans covered when cooking.
- ___ Adjust gas flame to just cover the bottom of the pot. Match pot and element size on electric units. On all ranges, the base of the pot should be in complete contact with the heating surface.
- ___ When food boils, turn heat down to simmer position. More heat will not cook the food faster; it will only waste energy.
- ___ Preheat ovens only when baking. Bake with a full oven whenever possible.
- ___ Request that the Maintenance Department check water temperatures on the dishwashers and set them at the proper temperatures.
- ___ Cook at the lowest temperature that gives satisfactory results. Slow cooking not only saves energy, it reduces meat shrinkage and preserves nutrition.
- ___ Use exhaust and hood fans only during food preparation.
- ___ Make sure ranges are completely off when not in use.
- ___ Keep lights off in dining area when not in use. Heat or cool the dining area just before and during serving hours only.
- ___ Turn off lights when leaving storagerooms and unoccupied restrooms.

SPECIAL PROCEDURES ARE REQUIRED FOR CONVECTION OVENS:

- ___ Always use the fan when using the oven.
- ___ Set the oven time and temperature at the recommended settings. Times may be reduced after the oven has been used. When reducing the time, make sure the meal is properly heated.
- ___ When using convection ovens, do not thaw meals, but move them quickly from the freezer to the preheated ovens. Ovens must be preheated and work more efficiently with a full load.

TEACHER'S CHECKLIST

- ___ Do not block classroom air supply and return grills with furniture or displays.
- ___ Keep classroom doors, windows, and transoms shut when heat or air conditioning is on.
- ___ Open windows when outside temperatures are moderate and heating or air conditioning is off.
- ___ Close and lock all windows, doors and transoms when leaving the classroom at the end of the day.
- ___ Use natural light whenever possible. When air conditioning is on, close the draperies or shades on windows that are subject to direct sunlight.
- ___ During winter, open drapes on south-facing and east-facing windows to take advantage of solar heat gain. Close the drapes at night to conserve some of the heat (providing that this action is consistent with school policies regarding security).
- ___ Avoid reproducing printed materials whenever possible.
- ___ Do not cover or adjust thermostats.
- ___ Report faulty thermostats and other equipment.
- ___ Wear warm clothes in cold weather and encourage students to do the same.
- ___ Hold classes outdoors when weather is pleasant.
- ___ Combine classes when practical, especially when using air conditioning equipment.
- ___ Involve students in monitoring energy usage.

Chapter 31

"ENGINEERING" EFFECTIVE ENERGY FINANCING

S. J. Hansen

The advent of private sector energy financing has given new life to institutional energy needs and forgotten audits. For energy engineers who wish to work with non-profit institutions, alternative financing is the wave of the future. It offers exciting opportunities and broader markets -- if engineers can learn to deal with it effectively.

FUNDING FUTURE

The funding future for energy efficiency points away from the traditional sources. Local or state funds usually require voter authority or legislative appropriations and always increase the level of indebtedness. Debt service payments draw down the institution's ability to fund other activities. Money that goes for energy work is money that cannot buy teaching supplies, fix up the city parks, or buy the hospital a new CAT scanner. Using tax dollars for something as amorphous as energy, particularly in an era of soft fuel prices, is increasingly hard to sell.

Federal support through the U.S. Department of Energy's Institutional Conservation Program, popularly referred to as the Schools and Hospitals Matching Grants program, is limited. Even if the annual dire "phasing out" predictions never become a reality, the program at current funding levels would need years and years to make much of a dent in the market. To date, grants for energy conservation measures have reached only small percentage of the institutional market. And, the program still requires a match of state or local funds with all the attendant drawbacks just mentioned.

Another factor also works to make alternative financing even more attractive: the cost of delay. In the U.S. DOE project, "Positive Cash Flow Financing in the Institutional Sector," which is under the direction of Hansen Associates, we have analyzed energy financing options for cities, school districts, a university, a community college, and a hospital.[1] This analysis considered internal financing, bonds, and private sector financing. Typical bonding procedures revealed a two year lag from inception to fruition. The cost of that delay is the mirror image of the Simplified Cash Flow formula and can be calculated:

$$CoD = I - [E_n + F_n + O_n + M_n]$$

where,

CoD = Cost of Delay
I = Initial investment
E = Differential electric costs
F = Differential fuel costs
O = Differential operations costs
M = Differential maintenance costs
n = A specified period of time, usually the fiscal year

Figure 1 displays the cash flow potential of several alternative financing arrangements using the same parameters: initial investment of $100,000, energy savings at $30,000/year, and a 5 percent energy cost inflation. The figure also contrasts the financial effect of doing nothing (null) and using the bond approach (bond) with its inherent delays. While there can be short delays with alternative financing options -- bureaucratic decision-making can be slow -- these are not reflected in Figure 1.

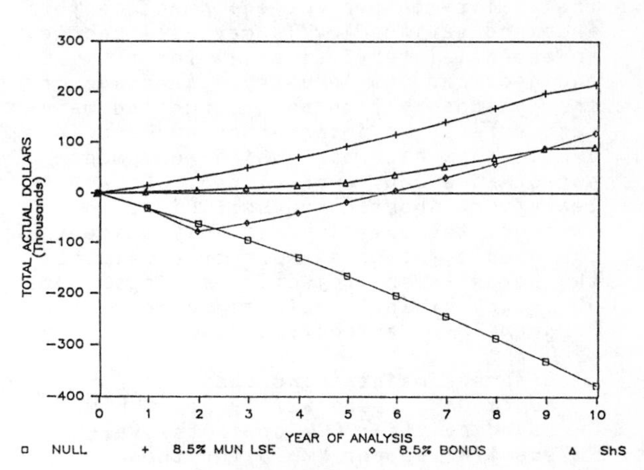

FIGURE 1
ALTERNATIVE FINANCING OPTIONS AND THE COST OF DELAY

Doing nothing is obviously a costly proposition. The cumulative loss over the ten year period for the given parameters is nearly $400,000. The figure also clearly indicates that financing energy work through bonds does not always compensate for the cost of the delays incurred, even when the institution can keep 100 percent of the savings.

The cash flow in Figure 1 considers only the direct net financial energy benefit to the institution; it does not consider the operations and maintenance differential, the value of the money, indebtedness, or the other factors which impact the institution. The effects of these other factors need to be included in the institutional deliberations. When all the ramifications are weighed, it is becoming increasingly apparent that the institution can justify using its own funds for energy work only when it has the capital <u>in hand</u> as well as the expertise, commitment, and organizational momentum to sustain the energy effort.

All indications, therefore, are that private sector financing will become an increasingly important source of energy funds in the non-profit sector, particularly as public administrators become more comfortable with the concept and more assertive in setting their own ground rules.

ALTERNATIVE FINANCING AND THE ENERGY ENGINEER

As the non-profit sector moves more aggressively into energy financing, the impact on the character of energy engineering will be more pronounced. Public administrators are risk adverse. As they seek higher comfort levels, they will rely more heavily on the engineers' guidance with a consequent higher risk level for engineers. Our research suggests that the engineer's predictive ability will become even more critical. The ability to project equipment performance and savings levels may well become an essential survival skill for the engineer and the industry. A decade of energy conservation experience and manufacturers' test information has provided a good data base upon which equipment performance can be predicted. As we learn more about energy efficiency, however, the data increasingly point to the people factor as more critical than the hardware in projecting savings. One DOE study of Institutional Conservation Program ECM grantees found:

> Grantees maintaining their energy audit O&Ms spent $27.79 per MMBTU saved by their ECM projects, versus $147.52 per MMBTU for those that did not maintain their O&Ms. Those that pursued O&Ms beyond the energy audit spent $27.60 per MMBTU saved.[2]

In other words, about $.80 cents out of every dollar saved in an effective energy program was attributed to energy efficient O&M practices. While this ratio may prove to be high, it highlights the significance of non-predictable human behavior in projecting energy cost savings. A non-predictable determinant of this magnitude in a discipline that relies on prediction heightens the level of vulnerability for energy engineers.

The energy financing industry is rife with risk factors. The energy engineer that seeks to do business in the non-profit sector needs to be able to identify those risks and develop strategies to manage his or her share of them.

The first step is to gain some appreciation of the whole realm of energy financing and to sense the manner in which specific engineering recommendations can impact the process. The following draws from the Positive Cash Flow project's research to date, including an overview of alternative financing and a discussion of the risks in energy financing. The paper concludes with a consideration of how these findings impact on the energy engineering profession.

Alternative Financing Options

An Alternative Financing Commission was formed as part of the DIE Positive Cash Flow project. The Commission consists of representatives of the energy service industry, insurance, end-users, state energy offices, and state level policy makers.[3] The Commission's first task, which proved to be an exceedingly difficult one, was to define alternative financing. The Commission finally decided that the range of activities usually described by the term "alternative financing" would more clearly convey the two relatively distinct aspects of the process if both the terms alternative financing and performance contracting were used. The working definitions of these two terms used in the project are:

> **ALTERNATIVE FINANCING** refers to any source or method of financing energy cost savings programs other than public funds or normal capital budgeting procedures.
>
> **PERFORMANCE CONTRACTING** refers to a procedure whereby the energy service company agrees to perform engineering and design, equipment purchase and installation, project financing, monitoring and maintenance services; and customer payments for these services are usually scaled to actual reductions in energy costs. Individual contracts may include any combination of these factors. [4]

The term "alternative financing" is used as an energy efficiency financing rubric to avoid the confusion that frequently results from using shared savings as a generic term and as a specific financing scheme. Because the firm and the institution usually share in the savings in some fashion, the popular press tends to use the term "shared savings" as an all encompassing term for alternative financing arrangements. Those involved in energy efficiency financing generally refer to shared savings as a particular financial arrangement in which equipment is leased through a percentage of the savings. The term "shared savings" is used in this paper in its narrowest interpretation as defined below.

The following are descriptions of the energy efficiency financing procedures which are generally considered when developing alternative financing options:

Tax-exempt leasing, or municipal leasing: Structured like a simple loan, tax-exempt leasing is, in essence, a lease-purchase agreement. The interest income to the lessor is tax-exempt. Ownership of the property can pass to the lessee at the beginning of the lease. Language to satisfy restrictions against multi-year liabilities may be needed in some states.

Vendor financing: Used to obtain specific equipment. Energy equipment suppliers guarantee to the institution that the equipment payments will not be more than the avoided energy costs.

Shared savings: A lease arrangement with payment predicated on a percentage of the energy savings. The private firm assesses the institution's energy savings potential and provides the capital for cost-effective measures. The institution and the private firm share in the avoided costs. This particular financing arrangement does not always provide the extended services, carries a high debt service level for the firm, and represents what appears to be a progressively smaller portion of alternative financing market.

Third party or joint venture financing: Generally limited to large projects which produce energy, such as cogeneration, this approach usually involves the design, finance and construction of the project by a private firm. The firm may operate the generating plant and sell energy to the institution.

Tax-exempt bonds: Given an economically sound project, the annual debt service of the bonds may be less than the savings realized through reduced energy consumption -- resulting in an immediate positive cash flow. To make tax-exempt bonds a viable alternative financing procedure, state budgeting procedures may need to be modified to incorporate this investment option.

Revenue bonds: These bonds are generally secured by the anticipated revenues generated by the funded project. Energy efficient projects are designed to cut costs, not generate revenues; therefore, they generally don't fit this pattern. Such procedures are possible, however, if a private firm intervenes between the institution and the bonding authority. Tax reform measurers currently before the Congress could reduce the viability of this funding approach.

Chauffage: Total energy management of a facility is provided by a third party. The firm purchases, installs, operates, and maintains most or all components and usually assumes responsibility for paying the utility bills. The institution pays a flat fee, monthly or annually, usually based on a percentage; e.g., 90 %, of the base year energy costs.[5]

These types of financing procedures were essentially set by industry in the early days of energy financing. As the industry has become more sophisticated and public administrators more aware of the funding opportunities, lines have blurred and hybrids, such as tax-exempt leasing with a shared savings wraparound, have become more common. In fact, we are now seeing hybrids of hybrids as financing schemes are forced to respond to a range of user conditions. Many of these conditions are inherent in the other aspect of energy financing concerns: performance contracting.

Performance Contracting

In addition to capital formation and energy expertise offered, the contractor may assume other functions. The New York State Energy Research and Development Administration has noted the breadth of the contracted services commenting, "Performance contracting approach transfers to the contractor a portion of the financial commitment, risk, and project management functions building owners typically face in mounting energy-related capital improvement projects."[6]

The transfer of a portion of risk, as noted by the New York agency, is a critical component of performance contracting, for it requires a level of contractor performance as a function of payment.

Research to date has also revealed that the more traditional definition of performance contracting cited above does not fully convey the strong emphasis on service emerging in the energy financing movement. Performance contracting goes beyond the method of financing and establishes a professional relationship that offers improved facilities and management services as well as reduced energy costs. In effect, energy savings are increasingly "paying the freight" for other services the institution critically needs.

Alternative Financing Cautions/Difficulties

The complexity of serving the engineers' public sector client through private sector financing becomes clearer if the concerns of the public administrator are weighed. To facilitate analysis, the prevailing concerns identified in our research are grouped into four categories; financial, procedural, technical and legal.

Financial: Administrators must weigh the real cost of private sector financing. The firm makes a profit by investing in the institution's energy efficiency improvements. The public administrator must determine if the same financial benefit will accrue to the institution. To do so, the administrator must assess the costs and benefits, including:

- o expertise provided, including engineering and monitoring;
- o maintenance benefits;
- o opportunity value of the money;
- o avoided indebtedness;
- o risk management; and
- o other services which energy service companies offer.

A financial analysis should include:

- o the availability of capital to the institution;
- o the ROI rate required to use funds other than those available; such as an endowment fund;
- o cash flow conditions, including outside influences;
- o economic projections and estimates of user savings; and
- o institutional risk; e.g., the degree to which the institution is required to make payment, take equipment ownership, assume maintenance responsibilities, etc.

Technical: Factors related to technical concerns include:

- o existing condition of energy consuming systems and viability of modifications or replacement;
- o the potential for cost-effective structural modifications;
- o sophistication of current controls and potential benefit of a microprocessor-based energy management system installation or upgrade;
- o implications for more sensitive controls on existing mechanical systems; and
- o the energy-related technical expertise of operation and maintenance staff.

Procedural: Procedural issues that public administrators need to consider include:

- o the necessity of bidding, writing specifications and Request for Proposals procedures;
- o means to evaluate proposers;
- o analyzing/developing payment formula;
- o remedies by owner; e.g., repairs, improper maintenance;
- o insurance, guarantees, maintenance; and
- o termination provisions.

Legal: Sources of legal constraints that could impact financing procurement include:

- o building and safety codes;
- o conflicts with other contracts; i.e., labor union agreements;
- o state procedural requirements; i.e., multi-year obligations, accounting procedures, etc.
- o the degree to which control over a public building's operations can be relinquished to a third party; and
- o owner's liability.

Emerging User Determinants

No longer content with industry established molds, potential users are building their own packages and issuing Requests for Proposals based on their institutional needs. Most of the energy service companies (ESCo) have shown a willingness to respond to these hybrids.

Many of the provisions coming from the potential users grow out of the cautions/difficulties already cited. Others reflect specific needs of the end-user seeking energy financing and services. The more paramount of these emerging determinants are:

Ownership: The institution has a number of choices, including:

- o leasing without any ownership consideration;
- o leasing with a buy-out clause;

- lease/purchase with ownership taken at end of contract;

- accepting ownership upon satisfactory installation and "refinancing;"

- hybrids that vary with structural modifications and equipment; e.g., taking ownership of window treatment while leaving ownership of the computer-based energy management system with the private firm.

Payment: A range of options to pay the energy service company are available, any of which could include a declining balance buy-out option. They include:

- a fixed fee, which could be based on a percentage of the base year or related to the capital investment;

- a variable fee as a percentage of savings;

- a scaled fee declining as the firm recovers its investment;

- a fixed fee guaranteed not to exceed savings; with reimbursement of any payment above savings on a quarterly or annual basis;

- a specified fee and split of the savings in excess of the fee;

- all or nearly all the savings going to the firm until a specified dollar figure is reached followed by a savings split; or

- a tax exempt lease paired with separate service agreement with a lease payment guarantee.

Maintenance: Energy efficiency experience has shown that the quality of maintenance is frequently as critical as the hardware. Many institutions do not have the manpower and/or technical sophistication to service the new equipment -- or even exercise energy efficiency practices on existing equipment. Therefore, public administrators are beginning to stipulate some maintenance provisions, including:

- the firm to include maintenance and automatic update on all equipment they install for the life of the contract;

- under the same or separate agreement, the firm provides maintenance on new and specific existing equipment;

- the firm provides training on new equipment; and/or more comprehensive O&M training in energy efficiency practices; and

- a emergency response procedures are defined by its criticality to the operation.

The industry appears very supportive of the move to incorporate maintenance in the agreement. In fact, manufactures offering vendor financing are increasingly apt to require maintenance as a condition of the guarantee.

Related services: Administrators are becoming aware of related services that enhance operations and/or save energy, including:

- computer software programs to perform energy accounting, preventive maintenance, financial analysis, etc.;

- materials or support for board, administrators, or staff briefings;

- public information support; or

- energy education guidance.

Non-energy related needs: Energy savings may cover the costs of non-energy related equipment or services with ESCos assuming a "general contractor" role, including:

- structural work or HVAC equipment replacement, that may be energy related, but not cost-effective;

- full scale maintenance services; or

- instructional equipment such as classroom computers.

Risks: Public administrators by virtue of their "fishbowl" existence tend to be risk adverse. This prompts a risk management strategy that assigns risks to a third party; in energy financing, an ESCo. As administrators become more sophisticated in energy financing, they are beginning to weigh the high cost of some risk shedding and may retain lower level risks and some financial benefits. Risk/trade off considerations include:

- equipment ownership;

- maintenance;

- fixed fees that are not guaranteed; or

- communications/organizational (political) concerns.

To put all these determinants in some workable form, a guide that public administrators might use as a preliminary assessment of their energy needs and financial options was drafted. The determinants cited above were analyzed within the context of the conditions found at our Positive Cash Flow research sites. The working draft of this self-assessment instrument is shown in Figure 2. The project's Alternative Financing Commission has urged that the self-assessment items might ultimately serve as the basis for a user's manual.

1. Do we have a significant opportunity to reduce energy costs? Do we have the necessary commitment to get the job done?

2. Should we consider all our facilities or only the highest energy consuming buildings?

3. What should we use as return on investment parameters?

4. How should we measure cost-effectiveness? Simple payback? Life cycle costing? Other?

5. Do we have the reserve funds to get started? What should the hurdle rate on the interest be? Do we have the energy expertise to use our own funds effectively; i.e., recent energy audits, specific energy saving equipment, etc.

6. Should we raise the money through bonds? Could we include energy work with a new construction and/or renovation package? What would the effect be on our level of indebtedness? What is the likelihood of receiving voter authority? Would we draw down on voter willingness to tax themselves?

7. Considering past efforts how long would it take us to get the engineering work done, obtain the voter approval, bid the job and get it installed? At 20 percent potential energy cost savings, what would this delay cost us?

8. Should we consider the services and financial support of an energy service company? How much sooner could they act than if we were to raise the funds and do the work ourselves? Could we maintain an equivalent energy management focus to sustain savings without them?

9. Are there any legal restrictions on our use of private sector energy financing? Would a one year contract that is automatically renewed satisfy multi-year obligation limitations?

10. Could we keep the energy savings for educational programs and service or would it go back to the county or state government? Would the savings be restricted to certain budget categories? If we wanted to, could we have the energy service company supply us with equipment, such as computers, in lieu of monies for our share of the savings?

11. Do we want to own, lease/purchase, or lease (through shared savings) the equipment and/or capital modifications needed to reduce energy consumption? Is a combination of financial options appropriate?

12. What are the relative risks associated with the various financial options? With ownership? Maintenance and repair? Projected energy costs? Technical expertise?

13. If we go to the private sector for energy efficiency financing, what is the opportunity value of <u>our</u> money? What are the implications for avoiding a millage election, increasing the local and state tax burden, indebtedness?

14. How much would we be paying the energy service company out of our utility savings and how would that compare with the benefits we'd receive?

16. Are we large enough; e.g., 10 buildings or $100,000 annual utility bill, to provide the economic incentive to a private firm? If not, could we join with another institution in our community to attract this service?

17. Could we secure a more financially beneficial package by collaborating with other institutions in the area?

18. Are there other services from an energy service company that we should consider, such as:

    __ monitoring and field support;
    __ operations and maintenance training;
    __ preventive maintenance software;
    __ general maintenance services;
    __ non-energy related equipment or construction;
    __ energy education support;
    __ public/staff information assistance;
    __ other____

19. Do we have the internal financial, procedural, and energy expertise to do the job or should we seek outside guidance? From the state? Another institution? Our state or national association? Consultants? Manuals?

20. How much are we losing every day if we do nothing?

FIGURE 2. INSTITUTIONAL SELF-ASSESSMENT GUIDE

RISK AS A FUNCTION OF ENERGY FINANCING

As work progressed in the Positive Cash Flow project, it became increasingly apparent that risk plays a major role in financing decisions and in the structuring the financing package. Research indicated that perceived risks, whether real or not, cause public administrators to resist private sector financing. On the industry side, risk limits available financing.

Every facet of energy financing appeared to have a risk factor. For instance, a primary function of a contract is to identify and assign risks. Insurance is a protection against risk. Those who keep or accept risk expect financial compensation.

Conversely, risk dictates money conditions. The greater the risk to the investor; the higher the cost of money. As the cost of money climbs, the reliance on technical expertise is greater. The risk to the energy engineer climbs accordingly.

Figure 3 depicts some preliminary findings regarding the more established financing schemes and the risks associated with each scheme for investors/ESCos and owners. The risk appears in bold; the cost of assigning that risk appears in brackets [ ].

Financing Scheme	Types of Risks: To Owner	Types of Risks: To investor/ESCo/ manufacturer
Shared savings	[Larger portion of cost goes into debt service; less into energy benefits. Projects underfunded.]	**Uncertain level of payment**
Vendor financing	[Vendor influence on equipment selection. Limitations on broader service.]	
	Manufacturer may not guarantee all capital projects. Or, manufacturers may require maintenance.	**Vendor risk to extent guarantee is not compensated for.**
Tax-exempt leasing	[Obligations to lessor are protected by ESCo for compensation.]	**ESCo guarantees savings**
	Level of risk rests on ESCo stability.	

bold face --risk
bracketed [ ] remarks --cost of risk shedding

FIGURE 3. RISK ANALYSIS BY FINANCING SCHEMES

Quantifying Risks

Risks do have a price. Insurance actuarial tables draw on a massive body of data to put a price on certain risks. Energy financing has yet to assemble that kind of experience data. However, some gross indicators are available.

The method of financing dictates the acceptable level of payback. A comparison of the cost of money for shared savings vis a vis tax exempt leasing and its ramifications illustrate the point. Shared savings poses a high risk investment to the ESCo and the investor. Tax-exempt leasing typically requires the owner to make fixed payments; thus, reducing investor/ESCo risk levels. In one case, the cost of shared savings money was 21 percent while the cost of tax-exempt leasing was 8.5 percent. The risk is greater when the debt service is a higher percentage of savings. If the ESCo has a bigger risk, it will take an additional cut to compensate for that risk. As a reflection of risk, then, the costs of doing business mount.

The higher debt service and cost of doing business requires a better ROI, which, in turn, forces the combined ECM payback down by about one-third. For instance, a tax-exempt package may include all ECMs with 3 year payback or less while the shared savings approach in the same facility would consider only measures with a payback of 2 years of less. The end result: the institution pays more under shared savings in relation to its energy benefits and its energy opportunity goes underfunded. In aggregate, it is a cost the institution pays for risk protection. You can put a dollar figure to it.

Key Risks and Management Strategies

Performance contracting by definition forces a high level of performance on the participating engineers. It presumes some accountability regarding projected savings. It places on the energy engineer responsibilities which do not necessarily fall on engineers in other disciplines.

In private sector financing, the engineer's recommendations are magnified in the way financial packages are structured, where payment is a function of those savings. The engineer's projections become the fulcrum upon which perceived risks, debt service levels and the extent of work teeter. The energy engineer is exposed to professional risks not covered by an errors and omissions policy. From our research, some risks that impact on energy engineering have been identified. They are listed below along with suggested ways to reduce risk exposure.

Operations and Maintenance: Since the savings potential is strongly affected by the O&M staff's manpower and capabilities, these considerations become risk factors inherent in the engineering approach. Consider:

- o an assessment of the O&M manpower and capabilities; predicate savings projections on training and/or additional personnel with specific skills; and/or
- o limit equipment design to a level of sophistication the owner's O&M staff will be able to handle.

Energy price risk: Energy prices are apt to continue to fluctuate. Consider:

- o couching strongest projection language in reduced consumption figures only;
- o perform sensitivity analyses to determine the project's viability using various assumptions regarding future energy prices; reflect the cost-effectiveness of certain recommendations using this range of assumptions;
- o resist pressures to make a project look good with greater energy price escalation; and
- o encourage ESCos entering into shared savings schemes to share price drop risk in contract language.

Energy demand risk: Demand charges constitute the highest cost of energy; so consider:

- o investigating contemplated changes in building use or function;
- o assessing the impact certain occupancy and energy consuming equipment changes would have; e.g., closing a portion of a building, adding a classroom of computer, or scheduling a computer science class during peak demand.

Equipment performance risks: Consider:

- o the existing equipments' ability to respond to tighter controlling; e.g., duty cycling;
- o new equipment warranties and their provisions; and the cost-effectiveness of additional warranty coverage.

Bidding risks: Non-profit institutions are generally required to accept the low bid. Low bids do not always assure the quality of equipment and service required to fulfill the engineer's projections. The engineer can manage this risk and help the institution achieve greater savings if he or she will provide specifications in the detail necessary to assure quality.

Engineering/technical risk: With colleagues, compile data and assemble an "actuarial table" of savings for specific measures which take into account certain risk variables.

All of our research underscores the crucial role that engineers must play in the evolution of new approaches to energy financing. The quality of engineers predictive skills can allay owners concerns and go far to enhance the vital role that the private sector must play in financing energy efficiency projects in non-profit institutions. The energy financing industry, the engineering profession and the clients they serve are dependent upon the engineers' ability to identify and manage the risks that are implicit in the effort to project energy savings. Risk definition and management may very well be the keys to the new world of energy management.

REFERENCES

1. U.S. Department of Energy. Positive Cash Flow Financing in the Institutional Sector: Interim Report. Washington, D.C., 1986.

2. __________. An Evaluation of the Institutional Conservation Program. Washington, D.C., 1983. p. 3-32.

3. Alternative Finance Commission members are Robert Bartley, Delaware Energy Office; Don Borut, International City Management Association; Howard Bozich, Impact Management Systems and National Association of Energy Service Companies; Dwight Connor, National Conference of State Legislatures; Daniel Frederick, Association of Professional Energy Managers; James Hyatt, National Association of College and University Business Officers; Kent McGuire, Education Commission of the States; Tom Olchefske, VISTA Energy Service (insurance); John Schooley, Energenics; Dón Tharpe, Association of School Business Officials; and Darryl J. Tramonte, Commercial Energy Systems.

4. U.S. Department of Energy. Positive Cash Flow Financing in the Institutional Sector: Interim Report. Washington, D.C., 1986. p. 5.

5. Truman Esmond & Associates, Inc. Using Shared Savings Arrangements for Energy Capital Investments: A Guide to Decision-making. Barrington, Illionois: American Hospital Association, 1986.

6. New York State Energy Research and Development Authority. Performan Contracting for Energy Efficiency. Albany, New York. 1984. p.1-1.

Chapter 32

ALTERNATIVE FINANCING FOR ENERGY CONSERVATION: THE AUGUSTA COLLEGE EXPERIENCE

P. Burks, J. Weisman

Since the apparent end of the oil shocks and constant price rises of the 1970s and early 1980s, energy conservation within institutions is not quite the "hot" topic it once was. By the early 80's institutions, like the rest of us, were feeling safe about energy - the prices were continuing to rise, but we felt more comfortable about our energy resources.

The Institutional Conservation Program (ICP) provided a new impetus for conserving energy. And yet, many administrators, though acknowledging their interest in reducing their energy costs, were reluctant and often unable to come up with the large capital expenditures needed to make their buildings more energy efficient. The 50-50 grant program has been attractive to many institutions, but many more said that even 50% of a large project was tough to come up with.

Augusta College was the first institution in the country to have approved a payment plan for energy conservation measures that, at least in this case, solved all the major problems: the University received the energy retrofit measures it needed, and none of its own money was spent on the $215,000 project.

There are many forms of alternative financing and many names for it - shared savings, performance contracting, paid from savings. Augusta College is participating in a paid from savings program.

Augusta College received $107,903 in federal funds to install a computerized energy management system in 13 buildings. The College was to match that amount. Unfortunately, cutbacks from the State Board of Regents resulted in Augusta College being unable to obtain the matching $107,903 for the project.

Working with their engineering consultants, the State Office of Planning and budget, the Atlanta Support Office of the Department of Energy, the State Department of Administrative Services and our office, Augusta College began the process of developing a paid from savings project. When no federal funds are used, the options for such an arrangement are numerous. However, by using federal funds, several special requirements were introduced that had to be overcome before the project could be approved by the Department of Energy. It was these obstacles that had prevented the use of ICP funds with paid from savings arrangements.

First of all, the development of the RFP was crucial - it had to cover all the needs of the institution, meet the requirements of the U.S. Department of Energy and the State Energy Office, and adhere to Georgia laws.

Augusta College sought to install computerized energy management system in 13 campus buildings. The RFP required that the selected system do the following:

- schedules HVAC systems on and off based upon: time of day
  - time and day combinations
  - time and date combinations
  - occurrence and pre-defined conditions
  - outside/inside air temperatures
- demand cycling
- late start optimization
- enthalpy control
- optimization package
- analog temperature sensing
- duty cycling
- high temperature alarms.

The RFP asked for two prices: (1) a lump sum purchase and (2) a paid from savings price. The lump sum purchase price was the contractors price to install the required system in a normal fashion. The paid from savings prices was the contractor's price to install the required system and receive payment based on a percentage-of-savings price.

One critical aspect of the project was the ownership of the equipment. In many shared savings arrangements, the vendor retains ownership of the system. In this case, and in order for the project to be approved by the Department of Energy, the RFP required that the equipment become the property of the College upon installation and acceptance by the college engineer.

Under the financial provisions of the RFP, the contractor would receive the 50% federal share upon installation and after 30 days of effective operation and after acceptance by the Augusta College engineer. The institution's share would be paid from 70% of savings based upon three previous years' actual experience. That 70% will be paid until the paid from savings purchase price is reached or for three years, whichever happens first. The 70% payments were schedule to begin within 30 days of receipt of the first utility bill after acceptance. If the 70% savings does not pay for the system after three years, payments will cease and equipment remains the property of the college.

The contractor, through the RFP had to agree to operate the equipment during a 30-day testing period; to train four Augusta employees to operate the system; and to warrant and maintain the system for the paid from savings period plus one full year. Once again, the contractor had to agree to pass title to Augusta college upon acceptance and upon payment of 50% of the lump sum purchase price by the Department of Energy. (Please note: the 50% of the project cost to be paid by the federal share is 50% of the lump sum cost - not 50% of the paid from savings cost.)

Seven responsive proposals were received by the college in the summer of 1984, and a service company was awarded the contract. The system was complete by July of 1985.

The total energy cost of the college in 1983 was $445,000 and the estimated savings were projected at $88,000 a year. The total project cost was $240,000. The savings results were lower than expected until the winter of 1985/86, during which savings slightly exceeded estimates. Based upon the activity so far, the service company expects to recover their investment costs within 20-24 months.

This project has been a success for Augusta College. They have a $240,000 system and none of their own funds were expended. In less that three years, the College will also reap the benefits of 100% of its energy savings. And they are conserving energy as well as money.

Chapter 33

RELATIONSHIPS WITH ENERGY SERVICES COMPANIES

D. Keck

The Florida Governor's Energy Office is currently working with four selected school districts to identify and resolve the legal, adminstrative, and technical impediments to utilizing energy services companies to implement energy conservation projects.

School districts and similar institutions normally purchase equipment through the process of requesting funds for specific purposes in their budget. They advertise and usually award a contract with the lowest priced bidder. These contracts are for short periods of time and are primarily for equipment and installation. Contracts with energy services companies, however, are usually long-term arrangements in which service is a major factor. Therefore, a school district must consider the personal interaction between themselves and an energy services company.

The resources of energy services companies can be brought to the aid of public school districts through energy conservation projects and innovative financing. Energy service companies have available the money, time, expertise and ability to guarantee results, if a compatible relationship can be developed between school districts and energy services companies.

Prior to becoming seriously involved with an energy services company, a school district, or any institution, should determine whether they need such a service. By analyzing current energy usage and existing energy using systems, a school district will be able to identify potential energy savings. Next, an institution should evaluate whether they have the available funds to invest in the initial costs of engineering, equipment purchase and installation to achieve the energy savings. If a school district has the capital to invest and is willing to accept the risk and responsibility involved in installing, operating, and maintaining the equipment to obtain the energy savings, they do not need an energy services company. When an institution recognizes the need to involve an outside source to install and maintain energy conservation equipment to achieve energy savings, they have identified and accepted the first step necessary toward initiating a compatible relationship.

Any institution considering an agreement with an energy services company must ask themselves what motivates an energy services company to assume the risks and provide the initial investment in an energy savings project. It is the profit to be gained from the company's ability to accurately predict energy savings and successfully install changes in the facility which will create savings large enough to more than cover the cost of the project. The energy services company's initial savings predictions, using a conservative energy inflation rate, and their ability to actually produce these savings guarantee the company a profit. The engineering expertise of energy services companies, their administration of energy conservation projects, their maintenance of the equipment, their ability to raise capital, as well as their assumption of risk for the success of the project, made them over a two billion dollar industry in 1984 with expectations to hit four billion dollars by 1987. When an institution accepts and understands that energy services companies expect a reasonable return on their investments and that in reality the institution will ultimately provide this reimbursement, the second component in establishing a relationship has been accomplished.

To establish the communication necessary in a successful relationship, the needs, expectations and goals of each party must be identified. The success or failure of a project will to a large extent depend on how well the needs and expectations of the institution are presented. One method of accomplishing this communication is to develop and distribute a Request for Qualifications, or RFQ. An RFQ asks energy services companies to submit statements regarding their qualifications to successfully implement the planned energy conservation project. In their response, companies detail their ownership, interests, and past experience. The RFQ may ask for certain preliminary information such as what sub-contractors and what types of equipment the company will use; how training, maintenance and services will be provided; and may even include an example exercise using a representative building to see how the firm would apply energy conservation techniques in a specific situation. The RFQ process allows the institution to evaluate interested energy services companies and determine whether each company would be qualified to successfully complete the project. The institution must have a good idea of what will be required in their subsequent Request for Proposal and contract, and include this information in the RFQ.

Interested companies can use this information to determine whether or not they will be able to comply with all requirements and needs before responding to the RFQ. The Request for Qualification process provides many advantages to the school districts or institutions and to the energy services companies and sets the stage for clear communication in the relationship. Through the RFQ process, energy services companies can be found that are qualified and interested in performing a project.

Qualified companies compete to obtain energy service business from institutions through the Request for Proposal, or RFP, process. The RFP provides the school districts or institutions with a procedure to evaluate and compare several companies' approach to a project, as well as the technical merits and financial benefits of each. The RFP process should only be entered into when there is reasonable certainty that the project can be accomplished. The institution should be committed to enter into a contract when an acceptable energy conservation proposal is obtained from a qualified company. The costs for responding to the RFP will be borne by the energy services companies. It should be recognized that the RFP process will incur certain costs to the institution for development, distribution and evaluation expense.

To ensure clear lines of communication, the RFP specifications must be technically correct and sufficiently detailed so that all parties--institutions and energy service companies--have the same interpretation of the information. The institution issuing the RFP may provide information of the facilities' energy costs and consumption, existing energy systems and the projects being considered. Energy services companies responding to the RFP should be encouraged to independently calculate these items as a part of the RFP process. The RFP might specify the format and content of responses to include technical information, a list of recommended energy efficiency measures for all buildings in the project, the technical (engineering) and management approach to meeting the school districts' energy efficiency objectives for all buildings, and any additional recommendations by the energy services company. The technical aspects can include the cost and amount of energy savings attributable to the energy conservation measures, service and maintenance procedures. The financial information required by the RFQ should be also requested in the RFP, except that it must be provided for all buildings in the project, not just a representative building. It can also include information on purchase option terms for the school districts and on tax benefits the company would expect to receive as a result of the project. The more complete and detailed the Request for Proposal, the clearer the lines of communication that are established.

The partnership between the institution and the energy services company is sealed in the contract. Therefore, a contract is most successful when all parties participate in its development. The institution and the energy services company should both have a clear understanding of each other's decision-making process and the criteria for a successful contract. The interests of the institution and the energy services company must be kept in mind during the negotiation and writing of the contract. The ultimate goal of the contract is to define the rights, obligations and risks of each party, and the consequences if obligations are not met. The mutual agreement between the institution and the energy services company to enter into this relationship must be approached in an orderly sequence to achieve the compatibility necessary in a long-term relationship.

The risks must be considered prior to finalizing the contract. Some of the risks associated with investments in energy conservation projects are:

- If the energy audit and calculated savings are not accurate, the savings will not materialize.
- If capital improvements and equipment do not perform according to expectations due to misapplication, improper installation, improper maintenance or obsolescence, savings will not be realized.
- If energy prices do not rise according to projections, or the project costs are more than anticipated, savings will be reduced.
- Any change in energy use, particularly due to occupancy, will affect the projected savings.
- An institution should consider the effects of loss of control and flexibility in the use of energy systems and in the use of the facilities.
- A facility should consider the capabilities of their own staff and the potential conflicts with energy services company employees. How will the new energy conservation project affect current employees' jobs? Are there administrative restraints to making changes? Organized labor may need to be considered.

In addition to the above, other considerations are:

- Some institutions see energy conservation and energy services contracts as a way to eliminate ongoing management problems. The energy services company may be more successful than the school district in getting management support and supplying expertise in designing, upgrading, installing, operating and maintaining energy conservation projects.
- On the other hand, an institution looking for a private company with which to team may want to determine

how closely and cooperatively the company staff plans to work with the institution's personnel, particularly facility managers and engineers. Will the company use the institution personnel's knowledge of buildings?

- It may be to the institution's advantage to give added weight to proposals that provide the most net benefit while incurring the least risk. Risk reduction might include a guaranteed level of energy savings in dollars or units of consumption.

- The financial arrangements a company proposes in the response to the RFP may place constraints on the types of improvements that can be implemented. Thus, they are critical to the project's success. The company may also be limited by a lack of technical knowledge or lack of exposure to a wide variety of equipment and manufacturers.

- All innovative financing agreements should deal with the energy services company's return on their investment and the savings payback to the institution.

- In evaluating the benefits of financial options, financing charges, total costs of the project over time, dollar savings, operation and maintenance costs, and net present value should all be considered.

- Special attention should be paid to the estimated annual energy savings and the private company's compensation related to the savings attributable to be energy conservation improvements. Energy savings estimates can be influenced by cost of energy, consumption, energy systems efficiency, building use and occupancy, and project maintenance.

- It is advisable to investigate information contained in the proposals, particularly with respect to new technology and in innovative financing situations. Is the information provided realistic and valid? Cost and performance assumptions, energy consumption formulas used to determine energy cost savings, and cashflow analysis will all affect the success of the energy conservation project.

- The institution should monitor the progress of the energy conservation project's implementation. Were the energy services company's projections on target? If the monitoring includes checking invoices--were the cost projections accurate?

In Florida, forty-seven schools were selected within the four county districts and divided into two groups. An RFQ was developed and issued. Four finalists were selected for each group from the responses to the RFQ, and were provided a copy of the RFP. The finalists were given an opportunity for on-site inspections and prepared their responses to the RFP. These responses were evaluated by the committee and recommendations presented to the individual school boards. An Energy Services Agreement is being prepared for each county with their selected contractor. The selected contractor has 90 days to validate his proposal and submit final recommendations prior to a contract being negotiated. They must, however, remain within 90% of their original savings estimates.

In summary, it is important for institutions to remember that contracts with energy services companies are usually long-term arrangements. Establishing a compatible relationship is an important component which should be considered by the institution at the very beginning.

The State of Florida is preparing a working manual which will be a valuable tool to other school districts interested in repeating our process. The manual will contain model documents of the RFQ, RFP, Energy Services Agreement and Energy Services Contract.

Chapter 34

WHERE HAVE WE FAILED? PROBLEMS IN FACILITIES OPERATION AND MAINTENANCE

R. F. Burch

The George Washington University is located in Washington, D. C. four blocks west of the White House out Pennsylvania Avenue. We have 66 buildings totalling 4.4 million square feet. Included are twelve residence halls capable of housing 2800 students, a 500 bed hospital, a medical school, a law school, an excellent and improving business school and lots of other nice things.

It is a safe area for people to live and work and when my daughter was a student there, I felt very comfortable about her being there night and day. Our buildings are clean and very well maintained, and because I have had such splendid support from my bosses all the way to the Board of Directors, we have relatively little deferred maintenance. The District of Columbia is a marvelous place for a young person to live and study and I suggest you send your youngsters to the George Washington University to get a wonderful education.

The Physical Plant Department which I head has 450 employees responsible for all phases of operation and maintenance of the campus. It is also responsible for energy conservation.

I became employed there in May 1970 and late that year brought in a consultant to study one building to see if we could reduce electrical costs there. In essence he said to turn it off when it wasn't in use. We did so and found it good and started manually turning off the airhandlers in our other major buildings soon after that. We felt that having the ability to turn off things remotely would be much more effective, so we put in an energy management system serving about 80% of our gross square footage and had it active by the summer of 1973. We would have done it earlier but as we had neither tunnels nor ducts under city owned streets we had to wait for the development of the modem. It took us months to get the thing working reliably, and we said frequently that the only thing worse than having an EMS was not having one. But we did and it has been mostly a good experience.

The point I am making is that we were active and quite effective in the energy conservation business long before the OPEC countries edged themselves into the picture. For example, we brought two buildings totalling 750,000 square feet on line in the summer of 1973 and they went into unoccupied turn-off immediately. I can't tell you how much we saved using unoccupied turnoff because we never operated any other way.

The energy conservation measures we have undertaken fit all the cliches in the book and a few are quite interesting. We did windows and storm windows and these can be a Neverdo. Rule! Never put storm windows on a college dormitory. They won't be closed and you lose all advantage. Instead put in new thermally efficient prime windows. We reduced lighting and took out incadescents, and we put in one room with SPECULAR SILVER REFLECTORS. We even put in a device that sniffs the ambient air in a heated parking garage and turns on the exhaust fans only when the carbon monoxide and gasoline vapor content reaches a certain level. That saved about 53,000 CFM's of heated air because the fans have not come on since. It was indeed a worthwhile project, but we professionals in the field of facilities operation and management have found ourselves quite frequently in the soup in the name of energy conservation. Therefore, I, as an informed user, am attempting today to put a tiny drop in a very large bucket with the label, "Feedback to Energy Engineers" on it. We are justifiably proud of the energy conservation measures we have taken and their effect. However, in many cases, our work has exacerbated old problems, created new ones, and saved neither energy nor money. I would like to surface some of these problems; to discuss some of our failures.

At least 75 percent of all problems I have as a facilities maintainer and operator are caused by defective design and construction practices. Age, abuse, vandalism, weathering are all pikers in comparison to the damage bad design and construction can cause. This covers all disciplines and trades and old things as well as new. Roofs and brickwork are a very large problem to me and they have been used for centuries without any really great change. There is no reason for these old things to be badly designed, but they are with alarming frequency. Energy conservation, though, has presented us with a new set of operation and maintenance problems that makes me want to shout for us to pull back. We are buying and selling snake oil in more ways than we need to and than we can afford.

For example, I have never seen or known of a fully functional variable air volume system. Our first one came on line in 1973 using the vortex damper system and the vortex damper has never functioned from the first day and getting it to do so would have been prohibitively expensive. The quality of the duct work was so bad that the controls which operate by sensing static pressure differentials never did so.

We are taking over a new building now and I have reconciled myself to taking out of service most if not all of the variable speed drives. Eleven of eighteen are beyond hope. Once again we have the problem of sleazy duct construction that will not permit enough static pressure differential for the controls to sense. Further the drives are so difficult to maintain and service so expensive to get that we are better off to change to two speed motors. These are products of good reputation, by the way, and I am disheartened. Incidentally, I have spoken to others active in my field and they, too, report similar situations.

If a designer is listening or reading, I earnestly counsel you not to propose any use of variable air volume systems because I don't think you can deliver a working product. Since you won't and probably shouldn't heed what I say, at least specify that all duct work will be pressure tested as each floor is completed and see to it that it is done before anything is covered up.

If an owner is listening and a designer proposes a VAV system, say no unless he specifies a stringent test procedure. Here is another Neverdo. Never allow the air-balance contractor to be affiliated with either the engineer or the contractor. Make certain he works for you, reports to you and inspects the duct work for you while it is being installed. Let him conduct the pressure test.

If anyone finds this to be insulting, so be it. I have had enough experience to know it is the prudent thing to do. There was a certain amount of bitter truth in the old joke that went, "How many people does it take to prepare an air balance report? Three. In a hotel room. Two to play gin while the third drinks it and fills out the report."

Duct work is a scandal that we have put out of sight above ceilings and in shafts for years. Losses of thirty percent are quite common and all this air goes into the ceilings and shafts that conceal it. Thus far I have never heard of a successful method of sealing ductwork as a retrofit thing. I have often wondered, though why someone didn't develop a plastic film coated on one side with a heat actuating cement. One section of duct could be removed and the film formed into a tube of the same circumference as the inside perimeter of the duct. Then the tube could be blown through the duct for its length and the air temperature raised to activate the cement thereby sticking the plastic to the sides of the duct. Fiberoptic devices could be used to inspect inside the duct if necessary. Until that time, though, only good design and construction will solve the problem and my plea now is that people will recognize ductwork for the problem that it is. Incidentally, misuse of flexible duct is widely done. This exacts a terrible toll in loss of capacity and usually can be prevented with adequate inspection.

Another neverdo. Never expect to use an emergency generator except in the most dire emergencies. They can be tested only between 8:30 and 8:35 A.M. on Saturday mornings. This is because they deliver noise or fumes into sleeping areas or air intakes 100 percent of the time. We have 12 diesel emergency generators that we could use in a demand curtailment program sponsored by the Potomac Electric Power Company. Aggregate demand reduction would be 1500KW. Only one of those generators is usuable for the purpose without doing so much work at such expense that it would be foolish. That one we can use by spending a mere $10,000. We are doing so because it was installed with 38 KW of connected load while its capacity is 155KW. Operating a diesal engine under no load or low load conditions is quite destructive, and periodic testing and exercising is mandatory if it is to function properly. We are spending to preserve the generator. Incidentally, we will use it in the curtailment program.

Our Potomac Electric Power Company (PEPCO) is working very hard on this. They have installed instrumentation to permit monitoring and have entered into agreement with us and others for us to curtail our use during those times when their load peaks in the summer. At PEPCO's direction we shed load for a maximum of 6 hours for a maximum of 15 times per year. Such a program extends radically the time before an electrical utility has to build new generating capacity. It is a wonderful concept, and it is irritating to have generating capacity that is not usuable to reduce load because of poor engineering.

Cogeneration is being oversold in my opinion. I think there is going to be a lot of embarassment, lying or both going on about the things that have been badly done. There is an aura of aluminum siding and blue suede shoes about it.

We have two energy managment systems, and we have worn out two before this. Their first cost was about $500,000. They are a wonderful thing but in solving one category of problem they have created at least one other. People tend to overlook all costs except the first costs. It is sort of assumed that the savings they can generate are free and clear. Not so.

On our systems are fourteen buildings totalling 2,150,000 square feet. To operate them on a three shift basis we have 4 Energy Management System Operators. Wages and fringes cost $110,000 per year. Contract maintenance of the two systems costs $78,000 per year. Thus we must save at least

$188,000 per year if we are going to break even with the operation and maintenance costs. I am convinced we do so though I can't prove it, but I am also convinced many people do not because so frequently the systems become merely super-sophisticated time clocks. I think they frequently become an end rather than a means to an end. It is a thing that niggles at me. Am I as a facilities manager really capable of using the technology and equipment available to me? My answer is a qualified yes in my case because I do worry about it and therefore nag my very able subordinates. But the owner of a plant less compently staffed than mine has no real way to ensure reasonable use. So I must say that energy management systems frequently fail to achieve their potential.

That brings me to another failure. We simple folk who operate and maintain systems are given state of the art equipment to operate, and when things don't go well we are frequently told that we don't know what we are doing; that the problem stems exclusively from our own shortcomings. Sometimes true. However, much of the problem is because we are in a point and push situation vis-a-vis the designer. He points us in the direction of the equipment and pushes us off to operate it. We should have a statement of the designer's philosopy of operation. We should have it far ahead of turnover date along with all manufacturer's manuals (It is surprisingly difficult for us to get operating manuals ahead of time) The point I am trying to make is that energy engineers must expand from pure design and telling how to operate. Otherwise much opportunity is lost. The energy management system becoming a time clock is a prime example.

Energy conservation measures have contributed greatly to indoor air pollution which is not necessarily a failure but is certainly a problem. The literature is full of information on the subject and one sees notice after notice about seminars on the matter. I attended one and it was quite useful. In the past few years we have had several incidents at the University and I have come to the conclusion that we should not necessarily take general measures to preclude indoor air pollution but should move aggressively to solve each case on its own merits.

Our protocol for solving an indoor air pollution problem is about as follows: interview the people in the area, all of them, to define what they are sensing; be obviously concerned; if necessary, obtain assistance of industrial hygenists or the equivalent to determine if the thing sensed is generally hazardous or merely obnoxious. Decide what you are going to do and do it in a way to cause enough bother to the occupants to impress on them the fact that you are doing something. The latter is very important because conditions are frequently very subtle and sometimes imaginary. The psychology of the matter must be considered. Incidentally, we use this same psychology when we are doing pest control in buildings. Nothing subtle. Above all, don't ignore the complaints. They won't go away for the problem really exists in many cases.

I know that designers may not really know the magnitude of the mistakes they have made. When they are made aware of mistakes, they do what comes naturally for survival and blame the constructor or the operator; frequently rightfully so. But the ultimate solution must start with the professional engineers. They must design and specify so that an owner who is not a professional has a reasonable expectation of getting a building that will function as it is supposed to function. Frankly, this needs to be an effort of the profession rather than the individual, and my purpose here is to tell the profession that it is in trouble with much of what it has done in energy conservation design. Too many energy conservation measures are not achieving thier potential!

The problem has been exacerbated by the constructor who has no experience to fall back on when faced with new systems, new equipment and new expectations for old things. For example, leaking ducts were no bid deal in the old days as the lack of static pressure with which to control was not such a factor. There was energy loss of course but energy was cheap. They, too, have had to come too far too fast, and there was insufficient direction from the design professionals to change their set.

Vendors have contributed immeasurably to the problem. Too much has been sold that failed rapidly, became obsolete overnight, or did not meet expectations. Maintenance problems are frequent and getting service, parts and advice is difficult and expensive. I have been sold snake oil, so I tend to see snake oil on everything. A classic example would be the energy saving fluorescent tubes that came on the market several years ago. We bought and installed heavily and wondered why our ballast failure had escalated. Then I read an article in "Energy User News" that explained that old ballasts plus new tubes equalled rapid failure of old ballasts. We don't use those tubes anymore. In fact, we have come to the conclusion that most retrofit lighting conservation measures are not worthwhile. I have become very cautious here, and I feel that many things with lighting for new construction are not economically prudent.

Finally, we come to the operator who is expected to operate systems with which he is not familiar using concepts he has never heard of. Rarely is he given a statement of the designer's operating philosophy and has to learn through self training and trial and error. But the buck stops there. Nearly always the operator has to find the problem through trial and error and without much help from either the designer or the constructor. Sensibly, though deplorably, neither wants to admit any culpability whatsoever.

I fervently hope that the lower energy prices we are having now persist for enough time to permit us to slow down drastically if not outright stop many of our more sophisticated attempts at energy conservation. We need a time for analysis and learning from mistakes. The energy engineering industry needs to go back to the boiler room and learn from the people who operate and maintain. These people, who are rarely degreed engineers, are accustomed to solving the problems they have been given, but it is time to stop asking so much of them of things of this nature. Instead ask them to help define the problems so that mistakes of the past can be avoided in the future. Energy engineers must achieve their potential if things they design are going to achieve theirs.

Chapter 35

A UNIVERSITY ENERGY INTERN PROGRAM

E. Steinhardt

PREFACE

It is a pleasure to have this opportunity to describe the Energy Intern Program. The program, which has just completed its fourth year, permits undergraduate mechanical engineering students at West Virginia University to perform their senior design projects in industry. The projects are energy related. Information and actions resulting from projects have saved significant amounts of energy and money. The program is a result of a cooperative effort involving the United States Department of Energy, the West Virginia Fuel and Energy Office which is a division of the Governor's Office of Community and Industrial Development, West Virginia University, and industries across West Virginia.

The following paper is not a technical presentation. Rather, I prefer to describe the program, to discuss some of its many successes, to mention a few failures, and to respond to anticipated questions. Most of all I hope to convey my enthusiasm for the program. As the professor involved in the program, it is for me not just a course or program, it is an engineering lifestyle.

THE ENERGY INTERN PROGRAM

Most bachelor of science programs in engineering across the country require that students complete a semester-long design project during their senior year. This is to demonstrate that they can function as engineers. Although the terminology "design" is used, the real emphasis is on execution of a complete engineering project. The students should be able to identify a problem and to develop a set of information, device, or system that best solves that problem. The solution should consider all aspects extending from the technical and economic to the social and humanistic.

The senior design project in our mechanical engineering program is undertaken during the last semester. The students usually take other courses at the same time; consequently, the project is equivalent to three hours credit in semester programs involving twelve to eighteen hours credit.

Prior to the initiation of the Energy Intern Program in our department student projects had two weaknesses. The projects were limited to the innovative thinking of the faculty and students as to being relevant and interesting. It was quite difficult to identify year after year exciting and meaningful projects, particularly when one was at a university and supposedly away from the real world. The projects were also limited by the laboratory facilities available at the university.

During the Fall of 1982 through the auspices of the West Virginia Fuel and Energy Office our department began developing a program whereby mechanical engineering students could work on energy related design projects in industry. A team of three to five students would work with a company. For most of the companies the students would initially prepare an energy audit. Through preparation of this audit the team would identify energy related design projects which it would pursue for the remainder of the semester. As a few of of the larger companies would have a specific energy project in mind from the beginning the students at these companies would work on the identified project from the onset.

Although the number of visits to the company made by the students would vary, a typical number would be ten. These would be made to gather data and perform studies or experiments that could only be performed at the company. The majority of the work would be done at the university. A student would work about ten hours per week on the design project. The students would prepare two reports: an interim and final report, and give an oral presentation of their results. Throughout their project the student would be working closely with members of the company so that the company was continually aware of activities.

The companies would pay the travel expenses of the students which would be basically car mileage. As most companies would be within a few hours driving distance of the university, the students could go and return on the same day. In some cases the companies would be located far from campus but near the homes of students so that the students could stay at home overnight. (In actual operation of the program some companies have also provided meals, supplies, and a work space. Safety equipment has also been provided.)

The Fuel and Energy Office would provide support to develop the program and to cover the added faculty involvement. Compared to a typical course or student project, this program would require more intensive faculty involvement. The support would also cover travel expenses of faculty.

The Energy Intern Program was anticipated to offer advantages to both students and companies. The students would gain a relevant experience in industry related to energy management and the design of energy related systems. The companies would receive specific recommendations as to how they could operate in a more economic and energy efficient manner. This would include detailed engineering studies which documented the specific energy and money savings associated with changes in operation, management, and the purchase of new equipment.

PROGRESS OF PROGRAM

The program was first presented in Spring 1983. Forty-six students and ten companies participated.

The Energy Intern Program became very successful. During the last three years the program has expanded. Additional companies have participated. Some companies which have previously participated have invited new design teams in to investigate additional energy systems. Typically fifteen companies now participate annually in the program. The annual dollar value of energy saved by each team is typically in the tens of thousands of dollars. Some teams working at large facilities have saved their company hundreds of thousands of dollars.

Although the names of companies who have participated in the program would be too long to list in this paper, it may be of interest to the reader to see the diverse list of participating, West Virginia industries:

1. Steel
2. Chemical
3. Refractory Materials
4. Glassware
5. Fiber-glass
6. Mining Equipment
7. Electric Power
8. Scrap Metal Recovery
9. Rubber Tire
10. Small Manufacturing
11. Building Products

Although the emphasis of the program is industry, design teams have also been involved in energy projects for other groups. These include:

1. City Governments
2. Hospitals
3. Historical Buildings
4. State Government
5. Inventors
6. State Parks
7. Department Stores
8. National Chain of Discount Retail Stores
9. Energy Research Centers

INITIATING A PROGRAM

Initiating an Energy Intern Program is not that difficult, but it does take effort and time to contact companies at the beginning. If this is done by mail the initial response may be small. The key step is to be invited to visit the company. Once that personal contact is made and one can describe the program face-to-face with the company personnel, the company is all for the program. In our case both the West Virginia Fuel and Energy Office and ourselves worked to identify the first companies. This was done by mail and telephone. Now that the program is established the office continues to help us by directing company inquiries our way.

A comment about the rapport between our department and industries made through this program: It is excellent. Typically in situations outside our program, companies are suspicious of a university. A university usually tells a company that it can do great things for it; all it needs is a million dollar contract. The Energy Intern Program relieves this initial tension and distrust. The focus is on the students. Later, a sponsored project may be mutually developed, but there is no requirement to do so. I am pleased that through the Energy Intern Program our department has established an excellent relationship with West Virginia industries. We are good friends and we feel comfortable contacting each other.

SOME SUCCESS STORIES

Essentially each one of the design projects is a success story with the students providing energy saving and money saving information to the company. There is also the impact upon the students through the engineering design experience they have gained as well as the appreciation they have as to the significant energy and money savings associated with proper energy management and the use of energy efficient systems.

The following are a few of the success stories. There are many more. The company names are omitted. In discussing success stories it should be noted that some projects may not have been as glorious as others, but they provided the company with meaningful information which often that company could not have obtained in any other way.

Steel Manufacturer

Students were asked to evaluate the operation of steam accumulators which were part of the energy recovery system for steel made using the basic oxygen process. After evaluation of the recovery system the students discovered that the accumulators were not being operated correctly. Because of the thermodynamics involved what appeared to be the correct time to open and close certain valves was actually incorrect. Over a year's time tens of thousands of dollars were being lost in wasted steam. The most impressive part of this story is that about two weeks after the students' oral report to the company I happened to visit the company and asked what they thought of the students recommendations. Officials of the company responded, "We've already made the changes."

Chemical Plant

As part of their design project at a particular chemical plant students performed an energy audit. Included in their audit the students identified the energy and associated dollars lost through steam leaks. The students felt concerned that their analysis indicated that nearly one million dollars was being lost annually. When they reported this information to the company, the company indicated that it had suspected that this was the case and that was their ulterior motive in having the students work at the plant. The company needed the students' independent evaluation of the situation.

Glass Manufacturing Plant

A plant making glassware wished to investigate whether a new material could be used for their molds. They were concerned that the interior of iron molds had to be coated at the end of the day and then the mold fired overnight so that glassware made the next day would not stick to the mold. A considerable amount of energy was used in this firing process. The plant wished to investigate a carbon mold which would not require overnight firing. In their own studies, the company found the carbon mold produced a good surface finish, but that occasionally the glass stuck to the mold and the piece was ruined. The students identified that the heat transfer characteristics of iron and carbon were different, and that the transient interface temperatures between the carbon and glass were critical. Using computer aided design they were able to design a new mold configuration that eliminated the sticking program.

Electric Power Station

Students were requested to develop two new monitoring systems for an electric power station. One would monitor air leakage into the condensers; the other would monitor (sample) fly-ash particles. Personnel at the power station were quite impressed by the students' work. Within the short period of a semester, the systems was designed, the equipment ordered, installed, calibrated, and the systems were in use. The students had successfully completed in four months projects involving over $100,000 in equipment purchases.

National Chain of Discount Retail Stores

Like many chains of stores, one national chain with stores in West Virginia has that many of its stores are identical. The students used a computer energy analysis program to model the store. Various operating schedules and energy conserving modifications were investigated. The impressive aspect is that with the number of stores involved, the value of the energy alternatives identified by the students became most significant.

POSSIBILITY OF FAILURE

The energy related design projects undertaken by the students are real engineering projects which require that the students perform as engineers. The industries need the information. This realism places an added burden on the students. There have been two situations where the students were not ready for this responsibility. In the one case it was an individual student who was not ready to carry the responsibility. As the student's work would impact the work of teammates, it was necessary to dismiss the student halfway through the project. The project was completed successfully without the student. In another case a team of students was not ready for the responsibility. It was necessary to apologize to the company for the lack of progress. The following semester a new team worked with the company and did an excellent job.

GENERAL COMMENTS

I am very confident that this program has had a significant, beneficial impact on our nation's energy interests. Industries have obtained and used energy related information with savings in the millions of dollars. Engineering students have had meaningful engineering design experiences and also gained awareness that proper design and management saves energy and money. This energy awareness will be used throughout their careers. Having had four years experience with the program the following comments come to mind:

Participating in the program has had a major impact on the students. The energy awareness has already been mentioned. Another impact is the engineering experience they gain. The students are graduating seniors. During their interviews for full-time employment the students have the opportunity to describe their work on the projects and essentially show this as engineering experience. Over the course of the program many students have been offered permanent employment with the companies where they did their senior projects. Significantly, almost all of the students have used the experience gained in their project as a selling tool during job interviews. The students can demonstrate that they have engineering design experience in addition to a degree. During one of my discussions with the personnel managers of a national manufacturing company they described how they were now identifying that successful participation in senior projects such as the Energy Intern Program was a better indicator of future success at their company than grades or student activities.

Related to the impact on students I am particularly impressed by one event involving a group of students who I knew to have excellent academic records. One of the students had straight A's, and the others were very close to that. The students were having problems getting started with their project--identifying what were their project goals--identifying what were the things that should be done first. In discussing the predicament with the students I learned that the real problems was that they had never had an experience like this before. Previously they always had the feeling that the professor knew all of the answers or the answers were "in the back of the book". The Energy Intern Program was their first real experience as engineers.

Directing an Energy Intern Program is not a simple matter. It takes a unique type of professor. The environment is not just one of lecturing to students. It is one of being a chief engineer and engineering manager for about fifteen projects per year. It involves working with the students to get the job done and done on time. It involves not knowing in advance what the next step will be. Often the professor feels the added responsibility of knowing that the students, the department, and the university will be evaluated by the quality of the work accomplished. The program is heavily dependent on the style and personality of the professor. It is not one where the direction of the program can be assigned like a thermodynamics or kinematics class.

The Energy Intern Program is a valuable one for students and industry; however it can be an expensive program for a university in that the faculty involvement required is quite high. Within our own department we have had some debates as to whether we can afford such a program. We all agree that the experience for students is invaluable, but some argue that a simple lecture type course would be more economical for the department. Without the financial support of the West Virginia Fuel and Energy Office it would be difficult to continue the program.

All of the projects undertaken in the Energy Intern Program have been interesting. Some have been quite unique. One group of students worked during the winter at a year-round resort. They evaluated whether a system which used waste heat from an ice skating rink to heat an outdoor swimming pool was energy efficient. They also investigated the most economical way to make snow. In working at the resort the understanding was that if the weather should turn bad (if it should snow), they could stay overnight at the resort and naturally use the ski facilities. For some strange reason the students always scheduled to visit the resort the day that a significant snowfall was expected. Another group of students did energy studies for a historical building. The unique part of their work was that any energy modifications recommended could not alter the historical appearance of the building. Storm windows and weather stripping were out. The students also had the experience of analyzing a circa 1850 heating and ventilation system. Two groups of students have had the opportunity to evaluate patents related to energy conservation. In the one case a solar-coupled heat pump was involved. In the other a novel roof-solar collector system was evaluated. The last unique experience I will cite involves the fact that today both men and women are studying to be engineers. Both are involved in the Energy Intern Program. One coed had a unique "temporarily transforming" experience when she started her project at a chemical plant. She found that for safety reasons contact lenses and make-up could not be worn. Imagine her expression as she learned of this requirement.

Some people have asked whether the Energy Intern Program competes with the work of consulting engineers. The answer is no. In the situation where the work requires the attention of a consulting engineer, the students are actually performing the function of a preliminary study or design team. They are providing preliminary answers which should be verified by a professional. Additionally, often the students are identifying situations and solutions which convince the company that it is worth investigating the situation further and hiring professional engineers to do so. In a sense the Energy Intern Program allows a company to look at certain situations with little financial risk in order to identify if further detailed studies appear beneficial. In this regard some projects undertaken by the students may be classified as "what if?" engineering.

This paper has not disclosed the names of particular companies. It is surprising how often the students become involved in company confidential information. It is not that national secrets are at stake. It is just that in manufacturing there are many situations where one company is happier if a competitor doesn't know exactly how their product is made. Companies have even asked for identification on the premise that impersonating a university professor or student may be a convenient way to get into their plant and learn their processes.

THE FUTURE

The Energy Intern Program is now firmly entrenched in our department. Industries like it. It has reached the status of one company telling another and creating new clients for us. The students like it. Underclass students inquire about participating when they are seniors. We are in the process of expanding the program to meet more of industry's needs. As it meets the present needs of industry, has a significant bearing on energy conservation, and is within our capability, the immediate expansion is in the area of computer integrated manufacturing and computer aided design.

FINAL COMMENT

The Energy Intern Program would not have come into existence and remained a success without the personal encouragement as well as financial support of the United States Department of Energy and the West Virginia Fuel and Energy Office. I wish to thank these agencies. Their efforts have had a significant effect upon industry, West Virginia University, the students, and me.

SECTION 11

INDUSTRIAL ENERGY MANAGEMENT PROGRAMS

Chapter 36

STEAM TRAPPING SYSTEM OPTIMIZATION

G. Lehman

The cost of operating a steam system includes boiler operation costs, steam distribution system losses, steam utilization losses and inefficiencies, steam trapping system losses and inefficiencies, condensate return system losses, system maintenance costs, and steam and condensate system leaks.

The steam trapping system offers an important opportunity for cost reduction.

STEAM TRAP MANAGEMENT PROGRAM

Steam traps play an important role in the operation of a steam system and in the conservation of energy.

In all systems which produce or transport steam, or use steam to provide heat or motive power, condensate is formed as the steam's latent heat is used. This condensate must be removed to prevent steam system damage and inefficiency. Steam traps are used to provide for the removal of condensate while keeping steam within the system.

All steam traps will eventually fail. Most traps fail because of wear of the mechanical parts of the trap through normal operation. Others will fail because of the flashing of condensate as it passes through the trap, which can wire draw the valve and seat of the trap. Still others fail because of the stresses of steam service, such as water-hammer, rapid temperature fluctuations, carbonic acid corrosion which can damage the mechanism, and fatigue of the trap parts.

In addition to the failure of properly applied steam traps, many traps fail to provide the expected performance because the trap is used in a service for which it was not designed. Such misapplications can involve relatively easy to identify problems such as undersizing in process service, or the use of a steam trap in a steam system which has a higher pressure than the trap is designed to withstand. Other misapplications can be more subtle, such as the use of a trap which does not operate efficiently when it must discharge into a condensate recovery system with relatively high back-pressure.

The Steam Trap and Steam Leak Management Programs are often the most neglected portions of the total steam and condensate systems. Therefore a comprehensive steam trap management program often provides one of the best Returns on Investment of the available non-capital system improvements.

In almost any plant with a steam system there are usually many traps compared with the numbers of other types of equipment, and normally little thought is given to traps unless they disrupt operations or the steam plumes annoy management.

Steam traps are small, relatively inexpensive and short-lived components of the steam system. This steam trap population in most cases represents an opportunity for cost effective energy conservation.

The establishment of an effective steam trap management program provides a rapid return on investment, with costs usually recovered in two to three months. The key to achieving these savings is an effective steam trap management program.

Steam Trapping System Costs

The costs associated with the steam trapping system include:

- The direct cost of trap operation which varies by trap type and size
- The direct cost of steam losses from failed steam traps and steam leaks
- The direct cost of maintenance manpower to inspect and maintain the trap population
- The direct cost of trap and materials inventories
- The indirect costs caused by the effects of failed closed steam traps, such as increased corrosion and water-hammer damage
- The indirect cost of production interruptions and off specification products
- The indirect cost of operator time spent correcting upsets caused by faulty traps

The cost of steam leaking through a failed steam trap can in one day exceed the cost of a new trap including installation. The reduction in the efficiency of steam-using equipment caused by traps which have failed closed can also waste more money in one day than the cost of the replacement trap including installation.

Effective steam trap system management provides for efficient operation by minimizing steam trap system costs through the reduction of steam losses through failed traps and steam leaks to an acceptable minimum, and reduces overall maintenance costs through the elimination of freeze-ups, the reduction in corrosion rates, and the elimination of water-hammer damage.

In order to implement any program, clear goals must be established. The goal of the steam trap management program should be to achieve the minimum total cost for the operation of the steam trapping system.

One of the most important aspects of achieving this goal is to set the optimum survey and repair/replacement frequency rates. This rate depends upon the severity of service, the time in service, the types of traps selected, the cost of steam, and maintenance costs including materials and manpower. This optimum survey and repair frequency rate will vary from plant to plant.

One steam trap manufacturer recommends trap inspection frequencies based upon system pressure as follows:

Pressure	Frequency
0 - 30 PSIG	Annual
30 - 100 PSIG	Semi-annual
100 - 250 PSIG	Quarterly or monthly
Over 250 PSIG	Monthly or weekly

This chart does not take into consideration some of the more important system conditions, and in our opinion, should not be rigorously followed. Other considerations include:

Steam temperature, since superheat can reduce the life of traps

Trap capacity, since larger capacity traps may lose more steam when they fail

The importance of the trap application, and the cost of trap failure in critical applications

The time it takes to effect trap repairs after a survey has been completed. It makes little sense to resurvey steam traps when repairs from the previous inspection have not been completed, or in some cases even begun

The timely repair or replacement of failed traps obviously provides most of the economic incentive for the development of a steam trap management program, but the program should not be allowed to stop with that alone.

Even assuming that the optimum survey frequency rates have been determined, a successful and effective steam trap system management program is not easy to establish or maintain. This is partially true because an effective program must do more than identify and repair failed traps. Other steam trapping problems which must be addressed include:

Misapplication by size: Sizing involves more than pipe or connection size. Traps should be sized based on the condensate load and steam system variables, not the inlet pipe size.

Misapplication by type: Each trap type has certain operating characteristics which may or may not be desirable in a given application. Those characteristics which are desired for a given service should be determined first, and then those characteristics used to select the optimum trap for that service.

Misapplication by temperature or pressure limits: Often traps are used outside the design pressure and temperature operating limits, and care should be taken to ensure that those limits are followed.

Condensate return system problems: These can include such things as high backpressure, water-hammer, and improper general piping practice.

Inaccessibility of traps: If a trap is not readily accessible, survey and repair may be difficult or impossible, resulting in very high failure and steam loss rates for such traps.

Master trapping: Master trapping involves the use of a single trap to drain more than one source of condensate. Because the pressure drop through each of these sources is certain to be different, one of the sources will be drained, while condensate will back-up in the others. This can cause increased corrosion rates, reduced heat transfer rates, and increase the probability of freeze-ups.

Series trapping: Traps should never be used in series.

Piping practices which can prevent condensate drainage: Practices such as installing the trap above the equipment to be drained, and attempting to lift condensate after a modulating control valve should be identified and corrected.

Lack of isolation valves: If the shut-off valve for a trap is not easy to locate, maintenance costs will increase because of lost time, and steam losses may increase because repairs are not made.

Improper trap installation: Sometimes traps are installed improperly. We have seen many examples of mechanical traps, for example, installed upside-down.

Leaking bypass valves

Dirt, scale and corrosion

Missing traps: Locations where traps should be installed should be identified, and properly selected traps installed. Often these locations are drip stations, where it is imperative that condensate be removed from the steam lines to prevent water-hammer damage, or control valve erosion caused by flashing condensate.

Potential freeze problems: Piping design on both sides of the traps should be examined. Tail pieces after sub-cooled discharge traps and risers in the discharge line are examples of how piping practices can cause freeze-ups.

Missing or defective insulation

Associated steam leaks

Trap support and bracing

All of the above listed trap system deficiencies should be identified and corrected as part of an effective steam trap management program.

Identification of Failures

Obviously, a basic part of a steam trap management program is the accurate identification of failures. Because of the numerous steam trap types, and the varying modes of operation of some of these types, steam trap testing requires a high degree of competence from the technicians.

Without this expertise, only a small portion of the steam trapping system problems will be identified and corrected, and in many cases repairs will be made to traps which are operating properly, wasting maintenance money.

High quality training is essential for the technicians to be able to identify problems and recommend corrective action. However, training is not the only requirement. Technicians should spend much of their time testing steam traps because field testing is part science and part art. If the technicians do not constantly practice their "art", they will soon lose the ability to accurately identify problems.

Some steam trap manufacturers offer training seminars which are quite educational, and which do not attempt to sell that manufacturer's products. In addition, some independent steam trap testing firms offer training.

All trap testing technicians should be able to identify the trap type and model from the trap body configuration. The determination of the type of trap, the data from the test equipment, combined with the technician's knowledge of how that particular type of trap can operate, should allow the technician to accurately determine whether or not the trap is properly operating.

Difficulties can arise if the technician is familiar only with the primary mode of operation for each trap type, and is not familiar with the other modes of operation. He may therefore assume that the trap has failed because the discharge mode is different from what he expected. Traps that are operating properly and which do not require attention, may be replaced. These unnecessary replacements add to the cost of maintaining the steam trapping system.

In some cases, comprehensive steam trap management programs have reduced the numbers of traps purchased each year while at the same time lowering the average failure and steam loss rates.

Technician training and expertise is also vital if the more subtle indirect system losses are to be reduced. These indirect losses can approach the cost of direct steam loss through steam leaks and faulty traps.

STEAM TRAP TYPES AND CHARACTERISTICS

Effective steam trapping practices have a direct impact upon the efficiency of any steam or condensate system. Because the selection of appropriate steam traps is complicated, judgement and experience are vital elements in getting optimum results from a facility's steam traps.

To ensure maximum steam trap life and steam system efficiency, steam trap type and size must be properly matched to each application. It is important to emphasize that there is no "UNIVERSAL" steam trap which will provide efficient operation in all applications.

Most facilities will require several types of steam traps, in various sizes, to provide efficient steam trapping. The user must have knowledge of the various types of traps available to properly select and specify the traps to be used.

In addition to the failures caused by the steam system stresses and the failures caused by the misapplication of traps, many failures are caused by piping errors. Just as steam traps must be properly typed and sized, they must also be properly installed to help reduce steam system losses and steam system damage caused by water-hammer and corrosion.

Proper steam trap selection, sizing and installation require the close cooperation of the facility engineering and maintenance staffs, trap manufacturers, and often, independent steam trap specialists. Steam traps are no longer a "commodity" item which can be selected by purchasing agents who are unfamiliar with the complexities of trapping, and who merely select the lowest cost trap offered by the vendors.

There are three basic categories of steam traps, each using a different principle to differentiate between steam, non-condensable gases and condensate. These are:

THERMODYNAMIC - Which are operated by kinetic energy

THERMOSTATIC - Which are operated by temperature

MECHANICAL - Which are operated by differences in density between steam and condensate

Since the method of operation is a vital component for the success or failure of a trap in a specific application, and affects the initial cost, repair cost, operating cost, and affects the method which must be used to test the trap, proper trap selection must be based upon a careful consideration of all trap characteristics.

In addition to the general method of steam trap operation, the specific details of trap design, materials, construction, workmanship, and manufacturers warranty have a direct impact on trap reliability. We recommend that you discuss specific applications with several steam trap manufacturer's to determine which trap is best suited for your facility.

Following is a discussion of the various types of steam traps and what are, in our opinion, the advantages and disadvantages of each.

Thermodynamic Steam Traps

Thermodynamic traps are operated by the principles of thermodynamics and fluid dynamics. They include Disc, Piston, Lever and Orifice types.

Thermodynamic traps do not discriminate between steam, air and other non-condensable gases, and therefore must have a path to bleed those gases from the system. This bleed can consist of the cross-hatching of disc traps to the pilot flow of piston and lever types.

The thermodynamic operating principles are simple, with only one and sometimes no moving parts. These traps are normally small and rugged.

Disc Traps: Disc traps have a single operating part, a flat disc which lifts from the valve seat to open and is forced onto the valve seat for closure.

During startup, the pressure of the cold condensate and non-condensable gases pushes the disc from the valve seat. This opens the trap, allowing the discharge of the condensate and non-condensable gases.

Discharge continues until hot condensate (near steam saturation temperature) enters the trap. This condensate will flash in the trap chamber causing an increase in pressure above the disc and a decrease in pressure below the disc caused by the high velocity flow. This combined action forces the disc onto the seat, closing the trap.

The pressure of the flash steam operating on the whole area of the disc will keep the trap closed against the pressure of the steam and condensate systems operating on the small inlet and outlet orifices on the underside of the disc.

Heat losses from the trap, and leakage through the cross-hatching under the disc, will eventually cause the flash steam pressure above the disc to decay, allowing the disc to open and begin the operating cycle again.

This cycle will repeat, thus giving the disc traps their characteristic full open, then full closed operation.

Piston Traps: Like the disc trap, the piston trap has a single operating part. In this case, a piston which lifts from the seat to open the trap, and drops onto the seat for closure (although in this case with a pilot flow).

During startup, the pressure of the cold condensate and non-condensable gases lifts the piston, allowing the discharge of condensate and non-condensable gases.

Discharge continues until the hot condensate (near steam saturation temperature) enters the trap. This condensate will flash in the control chamber. This increase in volume chokes the flow through the control orifice, increasing the pressure in the control chamber. This increase in pressure, acting on the larger upper surface of the piston will force the piston down onto the valve seat.

The pilot orifice allows a relatively small flow of condensate, non-condensable gases, or steam, to continue to pass through the control chamber.

When cooler condensate enters the control chamber (assuming that the condensate flow is greater than the pilot flow), control chamber pressure will drop, allowing the piston to rise from the seat to repeat the cycle.

Piston traps, then, operate in a semi-cyclic fashion, without the tight shut-off of the disc trap.

Because of the weight of the piston (which must be lifted by the pressure of the condensate), piston traps have a low differential pressure limitation. Care must be exercised when using piston traps downstream of modulating control valves, in low pressure service, and where high back-pressure may be present.

If insufficient differential pressure is available to lift the piston, the trap will operate on pilot flow only, significantly reducing trap capacity.

Lever Traps: Lever traps have many similarities in operation to the disc and piston traps. They operate in the same manner as a piston trap, but with a tilting rather than a reciprocating motion.

During startup, the pressure of the condensate and non-condensable gases lift the lever valve in a tilting motion, allowing the discharge of condensate and non-condensable gases.

Discharge continues until hot condensate (near the steam saturation temperature) enters the trap. This condensate will flash in the control chamber, causing an increase in pressure above the lever and a decrease in pressure below the lever caused by the high velocity flow. This combined action forces the lever onto the seat, closing the trap.

The pilot flow allows a relatively small flow of condensate, non-condensable gases, or steam, to continue to pass through the control chamber. When cooler condensate enters the control chamber (assuming that the condensate flow is greater than the pilot flow), control chamber pressure will drop, allowing the lever to be lifted from the seat, repeating the cycle.

Lever traps, then, operate in a semi-cyclic

fashion, but without the tight shut-off of a disc trap.

Because of the weight of the lever, lever traps have a low differential pressure limitation. Care must be taken when using lever traps downstream of modulating control valves, in low pressure service, and where high back-pressure may be present.

If insufficient pressure is available to lift the lever, the trap will operate on the pilot flow only, significantly reducing the trap capacity.

Orifice Traps: Orifice traps consist of one or more orifices in series and have no moving parts.

Single orifice traps typically have very small orifices, in the range of one tenth the diameter of thermodynamic or thermostatic trap orifices.

The operating principle is that water (condensate) flowing through the orifice is restricted, thus backing up some of the condensate and preventing the flow of steam through the orifice. Flow through the orifice is choked by flashing condensate.

The orifice is somewhat self regulating. That is, if the condensate load is less than the orifice was designed for, the condensate will be hotter, causing more flashing, which in turn will further restrict flow. If the condensate load is greater than the orifice was designed for, the condensate will back up and cool. This cooling will reduce flashing, thus allowing a greater condensate flow.

Orifice traps, then, have a constant discharge, not the cyclic discharge of other thermodynamic types.

Thermostatic Steam Traps

Thermostatic traps are operated by changes in temperature and include Bellows, Diaphragm, Bimetallic and Expansive Element types.

Thermostatic traps respond more slowly to changing operating conditions than some other types of traps because of the heat stored within the trap materials and the condensate within the trap. A short cooling leg is usually sufficient to overcome this disadvantage.

Thermostatic operating principles are simple, and these traps normally have only one moving part (more than one if the individual elements of a bimetallic stack are counted).

Bellows Traps: Bellows traps are often called balanced pressure thermostatic traps because the bellows contains a volatile fluid which closely parallels the temperature-pressure relationship of the steam saturation curve. The pressure created inside the bellows by this fluid as it vaporizes from the heat of the condensate closes the trap against the pressure of the steam system.

During startup, the bellows is contracted away from the seat, allowing the discharge of condensate and non-condensable gases. Discharge continues until hot condensate enters the trap, heating the bellows and the volatile fluid. The fluid vaporizes and expands, causing the bellows to expand and close the valve.

The trap will remain closed until the condensate, the bellows, and the volatile fluid cool. This cooling condenses some of the fluid, reducing the pressure inside the bellows. This reduced internal pressure allows the external pressure (from the steam system) to contract the bellows away from the seat. This opens the trap and begins the cycle again.

Reduced temperature from a steam and non-condensable gas mixture will also cool the bellows and fluid, allowing the discharge of these gases.

Bellows traps will cycle under most operating conditions. They may however, throttle or modulate during light load operation.

The discharge temperature from this type of trap is determined by the fluid within the bellows. This temperature can range from very close to steam saturation temperature to significantly subcooled temperatures. However, the temperature of discharge will tend to follow the steam saturation curve.

Some bellows traps use a variation of this method of operation, in that the bellows is down stream from the seat. This exposes the bellows to atmospheric pressure rather than the steam system pressure. These traps do not follow the steam saturation curve, but instead discharge condensate at a nearly constant temperature regardless of steam system pressure. The discharge temperature in this case is primarily determined by the condensate load, and is typically in the 190 degree Fahrenheit range. These traps normally operate in a constant discharge mode and may therefore be dirt sensitive. Additionally, because of the normally low temperature of operation, these traps can not be expected to vent air and non-condensable gases.

Another bellows trap variation is the dual-range thermostatic trap. In this type, a short stroke bellows is used to open the pilot valve of the trap. As long as cool condensate and non-condensable gases flow through this pilot valve, thermodynamic pressure within the steam system will open the pilot operated valve. Once the condensate is near the steam saturation temperature, the flash steam produced by the reduction of pressure through the pilot orifice will force the pilot operated valve closed.

This type of trap has a large turn-down ratio and will provide tight shutoff. As a caution, the pilot operated valve may be dirt sensitive.

The failure mode of bellows traps is determined by the design of the bellows. Either a FAIL OPEN or FAIL CLOSED design is possible. The failure mode is determined by the natural free length of the bellows.

In the case of a fail open design, the natural free length of the bellows will cause it to contract away from the seat if the bellows is ruptured. The bellows in a fail open design is usually filled with alcohol or ether, so that the boiling point of the fluid is well below the boiling point of water. These traps may not closely follow the steam saturation curve over a wide pressure range.

In the case of the fail closed design, the natural free length of the bellows will force the valve down onto the seat, closing the trap. The bellows in a fail closed design is normally evacuated, and filled with a water/alcohol mix. These traps can normally follow the steam saturation curve very closely.

Diaphragm Traps: Diaphragm traps are a modification of the bellows type traps described above. However, instead of a large bellows with many convolutions or welded elements, a single element is used.

Operation of this type of trap will closely parallel the operation of the bellows traps. The normal operating mode is cyclic. However, they may throttle under light load conditions.

Diaphragm traps are normally designed to fail open, but the limited travel of the valve from the seat may allow the trap to become plugged more easily than a bellows design with a longer valve travel length.

Some types of diaphragm traps have a variety of capsules which can be interchanged, allowing discharge temperature to be tailored to the application.

Like in the bellows design, some diaphragm traps use of variation of the basic design in which the capsule is downstream rather than upstream of the orifice. This exposes the diaphragm to discharge pressure only, not the steam pressure. These traps then, do not follow the steam saturation curve, but instead discharge at a near constant temperature which is determined primarily by the condensate load.

Care should be exercised in the use of this variation because of the normally substantial subcooling, limited air handling capability, and sensitivity to dirt. Some designs of this type are not suitable for use with closed condensate return systems.

Bimetallic Traps: Bimetallic traps use the temperature of the condensate in the trap to bend bimetallic elements against the force exerted by the steam pressure on the valve. There are many different configurations of bimetallic traps. These configuration differences may cause significant differences in operation.

Since a basic bimetallic element is a nearly linear device, most manufacturers use several types of bimetal or special shapes to cause the trap to approximate the steam saturation curve over the operating range.

Because of the relatively large thermal mass of the bimetallic element, response to system changes can be slow. Additionally, these traps are sometimes affected by back pressure which reduces the net opening force on the valve, possibly increasing the amount of subcooling.

During startup, the bimetallic element is relaxed, allowing the steam system pressure to open the valve, discharging cold condensate and non-condensable gases. As warmer condensate reaches the trap, the element warms and change shape, exerting a closing force on the valve.

Depending upon the orifice and valve design, the trap will either throttle down so that a near constant discharge is permitted, or the trap will close tightly because of the thermodynamic forces operating on the valve.

If the trap throttles, the system will tend toward a near constant discharge, with the heat of the condensate maintaining the temperature of the element, and the trap will respond to slight load changes. If tight shut off is achieved, the condensate in the trap and the element will cool, allowing the discharge of condensate and a resumption of the cycle.

Because of these design differences, some designs will modulate under all load conditions, and others will cycle under most load conditions. Because of the thermal mass of the bimetallic element, and the thermodynamic forces required to force the valve fully open and fully closed, except in the case of "snap" traps, the cyclic design traps will normally throttle under light condensate loads and cycle under heavy condensate loads.

In some bimetallic traps, a single element is used, with the valve attached directly to the element above the seat or orifice. This type of trap is commonly called a "snap" trap because it will cycle open and closed, giving a cyclic discharge much like a disc trap, but at a lower temperature.

Expansive Element Traps: Expansive element traps are characterized by a constant discharge temperature for a given condensate load, regardless of steam system pressure.

Various elements are used, and they may be liquid or solid. In all cases, the response to changing conditions is relatively slow, and dependent upon the thermal mass of the element.

During startup, the element is contracted, allowing the discharge of cold condensate, air and non-condensable gases. Discharge continues until warmer condensate heats and expands the element, moving the valve toward the seat. The trap will reach an equilibrium condition, discharging condensate continuously at a nearly constant temperature. Only rarely will traps of this type cycle, and then only under very light load conditions, before returning to the modulating mode.

The operation of these traps is regulated solely by the condensate temperature. As the condensate temperature increases, the element expands to close the valve. Lower condensate temperatures will cause the element to contract, opening the valve. That is, as the condensate load increases, condensate will backup further into the system, allowing more cooling before the condensate enters the trap. As the element cools and contracts opening the valve slightly wider, the condensate flow through the trap will increase. This increase in flow will allow less condensate cooling and the element will heat, closing the valve slightly.

Care must be exercised when using these traps. They should only be used where the subcooled discharge of condensate, with the resulting backup of condensate, and the slow response to load changes, is acceptable.

Mechanical Steam Traps: Mechanical traps are operated by the difference in density between steam and condensate. All use a float (whether open or closed) to operate a valve, or to act as the valve.

Mechanical traps include Inverted Bucket, Open Bucket, Float, and Float and Thermostatic (F&T) types. All operate at, or near, the steam saturation curve, because trap operation is dependent upon the condensate level, and not temperature and pressure.

All respond quickly to changing loads, and most have a substantial turn-down ratios. However, without a separate mechanism to discharge air and non-condensable gases, mechanical traps have limited venting capacity.

Since all mechanical traps depend upon a condensate level inside the trap for proper operation, all are position sensitive. This position sensitivity can result in some mechanical traps failing to operate at as little as 10 degrees from vertical, although some will operate as far as 40 degrees from vertical.

Inverted Bucket Traps: Inverted bucket traps use an open inverted bucket as the float. As in all mechanical traps, these operate on the difference in density between steam and condensate.

The inverted bucket is usually attached to the valve by a lever mechanism. When the inverted bucket sinks toward the bottom of the trap body, the valve is opened. Since the linkage (if any) is designed with some "play", inverted bucket traps can operate in either a cyclic or modulating mode under some conditions.

In all cases, regardless of the appearance of the external piping, the inlet piping discharges under the inverted bucket, and the valve and seat are at the top of the trap. All inverted bucket traps have a bleed hole at the top of the bucket.

During startup, the inverted bucket rests on the bottom of the trap body because of its own weight. The valve is open, allowing the discharge of cold condensate, air and non-condensable gases. As the condensate enters the trap, a liquid level is formed which provides a water seal around the inverted bucket. Since the bucket is filled with air and non-condensable gases, the weight of the bucket is overcome by the buoyant force of these gases in water, and the bucket rises closing the valve.

The air and non-condensable gases trapped under the bucket are bled through the hole at the top of the bucket, allowing condensate to enter. the bucket loses buoyancy and sinks, opening the valve.

If the amount of air and non-condensable entering the trap is greater than the vent capacity of the bleed hole, the trap can air-bind and fail closed. Some manufacturers have alleviated this problem by using larger bleed holes, or thermostatic elements to enhance venting capability.

Once the valve is open, discharge continues until all of the condensate has been removed from the system, and steam enters the bucket. Steam, being less dense than water, will increase the buoyancy of the bucket causing it to rise and allowing the valve to close.

The trap will then remain closed until enough steam is vented through the bleed hole and condensed to allow the bucket to sink, opening the valve, and starting the cycle again.

The slack, or play, in the linkage allows the steam pressure to snap the valve closed after the bucket has risen within the trap body. Steam pressure acts to keep the valve closed until the bucket has lost enough buoyancy to pull the valve off the seat.

As the steam pressure is increased, the closing force applied to the valve is increased. Since the mechanical advantage applied by the fulcrum and lever cannot be changed as the steam system pressure increases, the total force applied by the steam pressure must be reduced to allow the weight of the bucket to open the valve when the trap is used in higher pressure service. This is done by reducing the size of the orifice. Therefore, in order to maintain the proper relationships between the closing force of pressure on the valve, and the opening force of the weight of the bucket multiplied by the mechanical advantage, orifice sizes must be changed to match steam system pressure.

Since the orifice must be sized to match the MAXIMUM steam system pressure anticipated, care must be taken to ensure that adequate capacity is still available at lower pressures.

Though the normal operating mode of an inverted bucket trap is cyclic, equilibrium can be reached, and the trap can enter either of two constant discharge modes. In the "dribble" mode, the bucket hovers in the middle of the trap, allowing the valve to cycle rapidly open and closed. Discharge appears to be constant, and is normally very light.

Inverted bucket traps can also enter a constant, or modulating discharge mode if the inlet steam pressure is very low, if the discharge pressure is high, if the differential pressure is low, or if the orifice is sized for the proper pressure, but the condensate load is very light. In this mode, the bucket moves up and down too rapidly for the valve to open and close, thus the valve stays partially open.

One variation of the inverted bucket trap described above is the free floating bucket. This trap has no linkage, and the bucket itself acts as the valve.

Another variation of the inverted bucket trap is the Differential Controller. This is simply and inverted bucket trap with an additional discharge path, designed to allow continuous discharge from the trap for use in systems where the condensate must be lifted from a drain point below the trap.

Open Bucket Traps: The open bucket type of trap is an older, and in our opinion, obsolete design.

Open bucket traps consist of a trap body which encloses the open bucket. The valve is attached vertically above the bucket, normally with rigid linkage. A siphon tube, which has the valve seat at the top, extends downward, surrounding the valve and valve linkage. Most open bucket traps have a separate thermostatic air vent at the top, or an equalizing line (which complicates the piping) from the top of the trap to the inlet steam line so that non-condensable gases can be vented.

During startup, the open bucket rests on the bottom of the trap body, and the valve is fully open. The thermostatic element is also open, allowing the discharge of air and non-condensable gases. When condensate enters the trap, it is deflected around the open bucket by a baffle. this allows the trap body to fill with condensate, causing the empty bucket to rise, closing the valve. Because air and non-condensable gases can be removed by the thermostatic element, condensate will continue to enter the trap.

When the liquid level exceeds the level of the top of the open bucket, condensate spills into the bucket causing it to lose buoyancy and sink, opening the valve. Condensate is then discharged until steam enters the trap. The steam rises to the top of the trap, displacing the liquid from the bucket by forcing the liquid out through the siphon tube and valve. The bucket becomes buoyant, rises and closes the valve. This cycle is then repeated.

Without the thermostatic element or balancing line, or if the thermostatic element fails closed, the trap will air bind and fail closed.

Float Traps: Float traps are one of the oldest trap designs, but are still used, and are not considered to be obsolete.

A float trap consists of a closed float attached to a valve by mechanical linkage. During startup, this float rests on the bottom of the trap, closing the valve. Air and non-condensable gases must be removed from the system by either a separate thermostatic air vent, an equalizing line, or be manually vented.

As condensate enters the trap, the liquid level rises, lifting the float and opening the valve. As the flow of condensate changes, the liquid level will change, which will in turn lift or drop the float to adjust the valve to the new flow rate.
Since the valve is move to adapt to changing condensate loads, this trap will function in a modulating mode.

The valve is located below the water level, which provides a water seal which prevents the loss of live steam. This, however, prevents the venting of air and non-condensable gases, so that external provisions must be made as indicated above.

Float and Thermostatic Traps: Float and Thermostatic traps are a modification of the float trap, in that the thermostatic air vent is an integral part of the trap. This eliminates some of the problems experienced with float traps.

Mechanically the operation is the same as the float trap with the exception of the thermostatic element which will vent air and non-condensable gases during startup, and during normal operation.

The thermostatic element will be open during startup, until steam enters the trap and heats the element, expanding it and closing the valve. This element will remain closed until air and non-condensable gases concentrate in the top of the trap, lowering the temperature of the steam/air mixture, opening the element and discharging the mixture. The thermostatic element will then close.

A variation of the float and thermostatic trap with mechanical linkage is the free float or ball float trap. In this type, no linkage is provided, and the float itself acts as the valve.

Since a float and thermostatic type trap contains two elements, each is subject to failure. The float and its associated linkage normally fail closed, while the thermostatic element can fail either open or closed, depending upon design.

IDEAL STEAM TRAP CHARACTERISTICS

We at Energy Efficiency Consultants, Inc. believe that ideally a steam trap should have the following characteristics:

Be capable of removing condensate from the system at the desired temperature

Provide long and reliable service

Have low overall cost, including:
- purchase price
- repair cost
- operating cost

Be self draining and freeze proof if properly installed (outdoors)

Be resistant to corrosion and water hammer damage

Be able to operate against high back pressure if used in a closed condensate return system

Be able to remove air and non-condensable gases during startup and normal operation

Fail in the desired mode

Each application should be identified, and the desired trap characteristics for that application specified. Then by evaluating the operating characteristics of the various types of traps, the type which is most appropriate for that application can be selected.

Once the generic type has been identified, the trap should be properly sized, and a manufacturer selected to determine exact model.

Items which should be considered in the selection of a steam trap manufacturer include: general reputation, experience at your facility with that manufacturer, other experience by your corporation with that manufacturer, the warranty offered, and the level of support offered to your engineering and maintenance staffs.

It is also likely, in our opinion, that no one manufacturer will be able to supply the optimum trap for all of the applications in a given facility.

REQUIREMENTS FOR AN EFFECTIVE STEAM TRAP SYSTEM MANAGEMENT PROGRAM

Because steam traps will continue to fail, a steam trap management program must be ongoing. That is, it is not a one pass program to fix identified problems. Inspections must be performed on a regular basis (with schedule determined by individual facility characteristics), and the repairs should immediately follow the inspection.

It is important to recognize that no steam trap system management program can reduce the failure rate to zero, but an acceptable minimum can be achieved through an aggressive and cost effective program.

Five things are required in order to achieve an effective steam trap management program.

Management Commitment

This is the first and most vital of the five requirements. Without this, personnel will not be assigned to the program and kept on the project because there are always other problems within the plant that can take precedence over the trap program.

This management commitment must be ACTIVE and not passive, and it must be clearly communicated to all levels in the facility.

Another function of management in this type of program is to prevent some personnel from taking the institution of this type of program as a reflection on their performance. There must be recognition of the fact that possibly poor initial system condition can be attributed to lack of funding and the lack of availability of all the tools necessary for the maintenance department to adequately maintain the system.

All departments must recognize that they work for the same company, and avoid the temptation of blaming others for existing conditions and previous system problems. The objective is simply to correct the existing deficiencies to make the facility operate more efficiently.

Funding

Someone must pay the initial costs for the implementation of an effective steam trap system management program.

Often, the maintenance department must pay for the inspections and repairs, while the operations department is credited with the energy and cost savings.

Costs and savings must be evaluated plant-wide, not by department. All involved must remember that they work for the same company, and avoid these inter-departmental obstacles to energy savings.

An aggressive, on-going steam trap management program does not cost money. It saves money, equipment, manhours and energy.

Expertise

The third requirement is expertise. Without expertise in steam trap systems, only the major problems will be identified and corrected. In many plants, this is less than half of the systems problems.

As mentioned previously, in the identification of failures, training alone is not enough to ensure that the technicians are able to accurately identify failures and other system problems. They must have the time to practice their art.

If the other system problems are not identified and corrected, the subtle problems, which do not cost money through direct energy loss, but which nevertheless cost money, will remain.

These indirect losses can approach the cost of the direct energy losses through trap failures and steam leaks.

Access to Technology

The fourth requirement for a successful program is access to all available technology. No one manufacturer of steam traps, in our opinion, offers optimum solutions to all steam trapping problems. Usually a mix of steam trap types and manufacturers is required to finely tune the steam trap system.

Remember, there is no "UNIVERSAL" steam trap. All traps have advantages and disadvantages. These must be weighed to select the technology which provides the most benefit, at the least cost, to the facility.

Documentation

The fifth requirement is documentation. Without documentation, which will quantify costs and savings, management commitment will be lost. Without management commitment, the program will be lost.

All five elements are necessary. If any one element is missing, the program you establish will be severely limited in effectiveness, and will not provide full benefit to your company.

TRAP SYSTEM MANAGEMENT ALTERNATIVES

There are four primary types of steam trap system management programs available.

In-house Program

With an in-house program, essentially all of the items previously discussed are performed by company personnel.

There are potential limitations to such a program for several reasons. These include: changes in plant priorities, loss of key personnel because of transfers, difficulty with savings documentation, and personnel training.

Outside Survey with In-house Repair

This is typically the first type of program that companies choose. The difficulties usually involve the timeliness of repair work because of limited materials availability, and the mechanics being pulled off the job because of other maintenance priorities.

Other difficulties include control over the installed trap and the piping configuration. Typically, the mechanics and supervisory personnel are not specialists in steam trapping systems, so details get lost and often the wrong type of trap is installed.

Outside surveys should include at the minimum:

- Tagging and identification of all steam trap stations
- Detailed report of trap type, size, function, and pressure
- Trap map to provide location data
- Identification of the other system problems previously discussed

Outside Survey with Outside Contractor

The utilization of an outside survey company and a separate outside mechanical contractor to do the repairs will often provide better results than the complete in-house program or the outside survey with in-house repair.

The primary advantage for the facility is that the mechanical contractor will not have other priorities in the plant and can proceed without interruption to make the necessary repairs.

Limitations to this type of program include delays in initial repair work because of the time required for competitive bidding. However, once repair work starts, it can proceed rapidly.

Another limitation can be the coordination of efforts between the survey company, the mechanical contractor, and the client facility.

Turn-key Programs

There are two primary types of turn-key steam trap system management programs. These are the negotiated survey and repair frequency, and the guaranteed performance level.

In the negotiated survey and repair frequency type of program, the facility essentially assumes the risk of optimizing the total program to minimize total cost. As we mentioned earlier, optimum survey frequency depends upon many system variables, and should be carefully considered to maximize savings. The tendency for the client facility in this type of program is to look only at the cost of the program, and not at the benefit.

Since the cost goes up as the survey frequency increases, the tendency is to limit this frequency because of a lack of recognition of the fact that overall costs go down to some minimum level as survey frequency increases.

There is of course the law of diminishing returns, and incremental costs from increased survey frequency rates (beyond the optimum) will actually increase total cost.

The guaranteed performance level program, on the other hand, shifts the burden of identifying optimum survey and repair frequency rates to the contractor. Since in this case, the contractor will guarantee that at no time will the failed trap rate exceed a given percentage, or the maximum loss rate, the contractor must determine the most cost effective means of achieving the desired result.

The disadvantage to the facility is that apparent cost may be higher than the apparent cost of the other programs. It is important to keep in mind that this type of program may yield the highest net savings because of the expertise applied.

A turn-key program provides additional benefits such as:

- Review of trap applications to minimize initial trap cost, inventory cost and losses when traps fail
- Evaluation of basic trapping philosophy, for example, subcooling or not, in-line repairable or throw-away
- Evaluation of steam trap piping standards to minimize costs

The use of skilled and specialized manpower can ensure that the program will be successful over the long term.

A steam trap system management program of any type can be one of the best investments a plant can make. The worst thing a facility can do about steam trap system management is nothing.

Chapter 37

ENERGY MANAGEMENT AT AN ALCOHOL PRODUCTION PLANT

W. C. Turner, N. R. Knight

A relatively large plant in Amsterdam, Montana converts wheat and barley into alcohol in a very energy intensive production process. Experiencing very large and rising energy costs, management of the plant decided to do something about it and contacted Montana State University for help.

This paper describes the process over about a 12 month time frame. First, the "easy" savings were obtained. Then, the more capital intensive items were examined. Savings are quite large and some novel ideas were tried. Many of the ideas should have widespread applicability.

The plant manufactures alcohol from grain grown locally. The final product (alcohol) is sold and the effluent is used by local livestock farmers as sileage. The plant employs a moderate number of local people, uses products grown locally, and uses the effluent locally. Consequently, the plant is quite important to the local economy and management really wanted to make it profitable.

The flow through the plant is presented in Figure 1. Significant amounts of energy are used throughout the process with the majority in the form of steam (gas and coal fired).

Figure No. 1

Flow Diagram

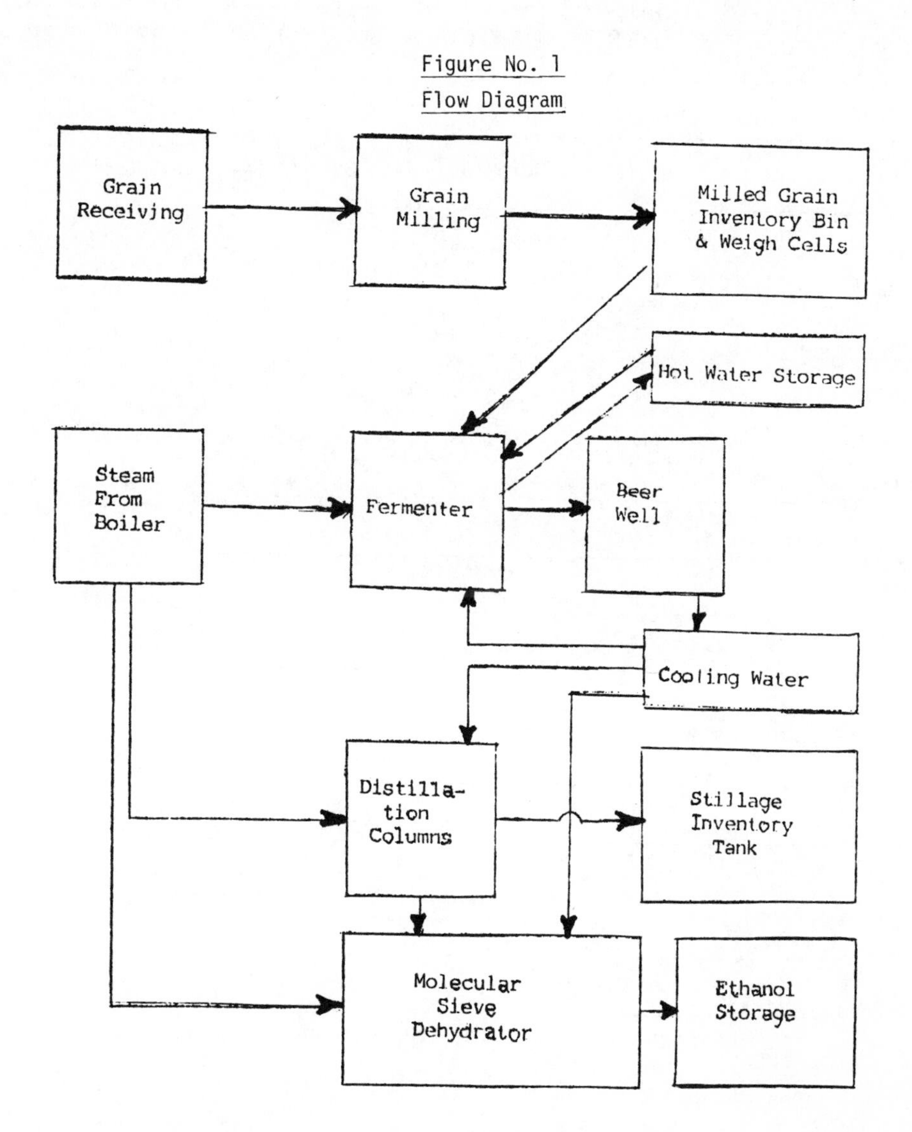

Energy Consumption

The total energy consumed (and its cost) is presented in tabular and graph form in Table 1 and Figures 2, 3, and 4. Although the absolute value is only moderate, the energy cost has a dramatic impact on total profitability (relative energy costs are high). As will be shown, the first phase was able to reduce the total energy costs by about 12%, mostly through insulation.

Table 1

ENERGY CONSUMPTION AND COST
1984 - 1985

	NATURAL GAS			ELECTRICITY			TOTAL	
MONTH	MCF	MMBTU	$	KWH	MMBTU	$	MMBTU	$
OCT	1,463	1,463	6,556	101,200	345	2,619	1,808	9,175
NOV	1,543	1,543	6,897	91,040	311	3,200	1,854	10,097
DEC	858	858	3,828	129,440	442	4,255	1,300	8,083
JAN	1,745	1,745	7,209	102,080	348	4,054	2,093	11,263
FEB	1,690	1,690	6,982	116,080	396	4,367	2,086	11,349
MAR	1,946	1,946	8,052	113,520	387	3,301	2,333	11,353
APR	2,591	2,591	10,722	108,880	371	3,172	2,962	13,894
MAY	675	675	10,688	109,680	374	3,190	1,049	13,878
JUN	1,493	1,493	6,178	102,960	351	3,018	1,844	9,196
JUL	2,785	2,785	11,524	115,520	394	3,549	3,179	15,073
AUG	2,314	2,314	9,575	103,120	352	3,240	2,666	12,815
SEP	3,021	3,021	12,500	114,320	390	3,579	3,411	16,079
TOTAL	19,103	22,124	100,711	1,307,840	4,462	41,544	26,586	142,255

NOTES: 1 MCF = 1,000 CUBIC FEET of NATURAL GAS
1 MMBTU = 1,000,000 BTU

Figure 2

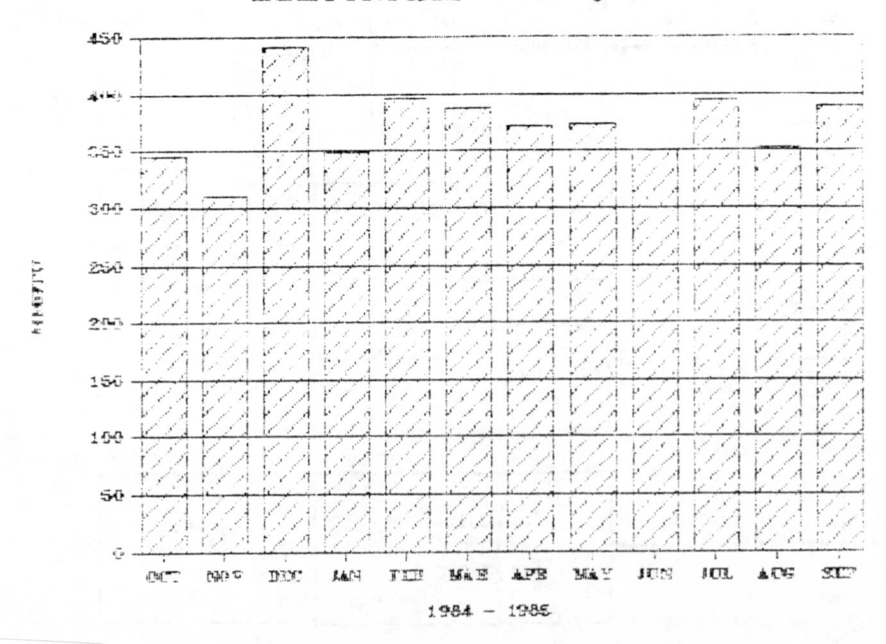

Figure 2

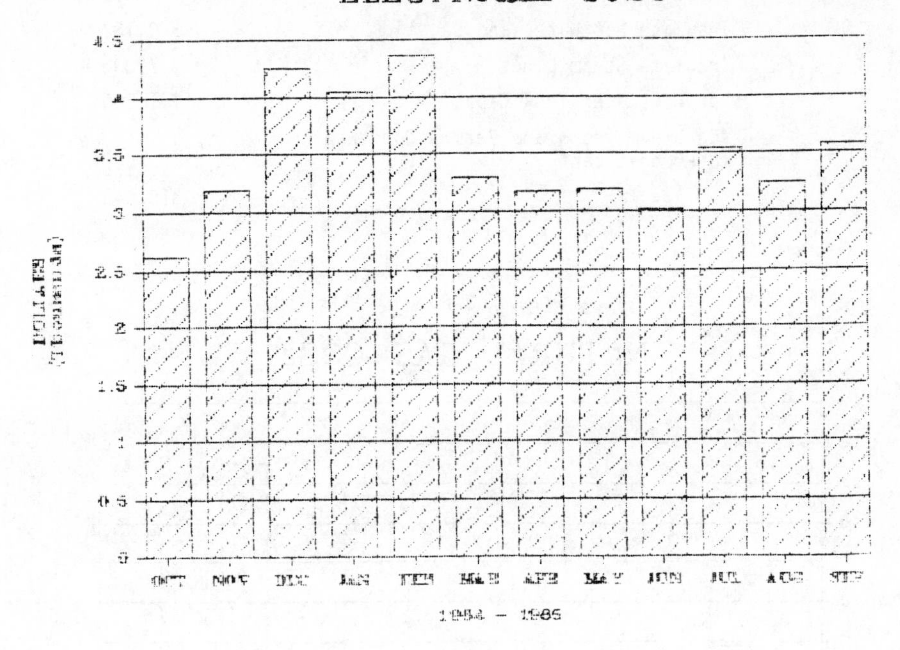

Figure 3

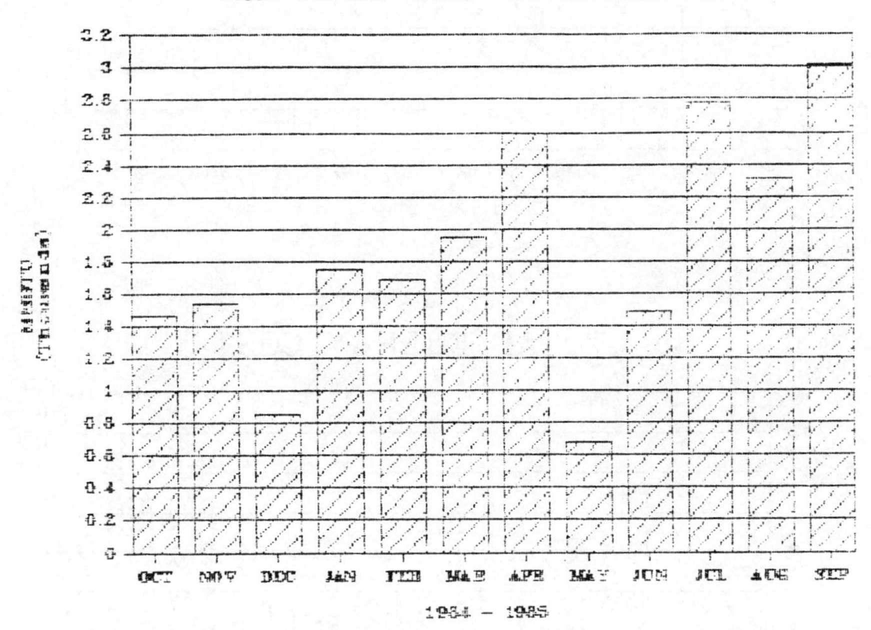

Summary of Results

This report contains recommendations that represent a substantial potential for savings if implemented. The recommendations, if implemented, have the potential to save an estimated 12% of the company's total energy usage. Management is still in the process of forming recommendations concerning the regulation of the boiler air flow. They are also still in the process of analyzing the situation concerning the 125 psig to 50 psig pressure reduction on the high pressure boiler. Two of the biggest opportunities include combustion air optimization and steam pressure reduction. The boiler is presently incapable of controlling air flow very closely - some retrofit will be required. Below is a summary of findings in this report.

Recommendation	Description	Annual Savings
1	Insulate Preheat Tank	$ 512
2	Insulate Hot Water and Caustic Tanks	$ 9,132
3	Insulate Steam Lines	$ 7,030
4	Add Hot Water Tank Capacity	$ 1,500
5	Add Steam Traps and Return Condensate to Preheat Tank	$ 560
		$19,643

Figure 3

NATURAL GAS COST

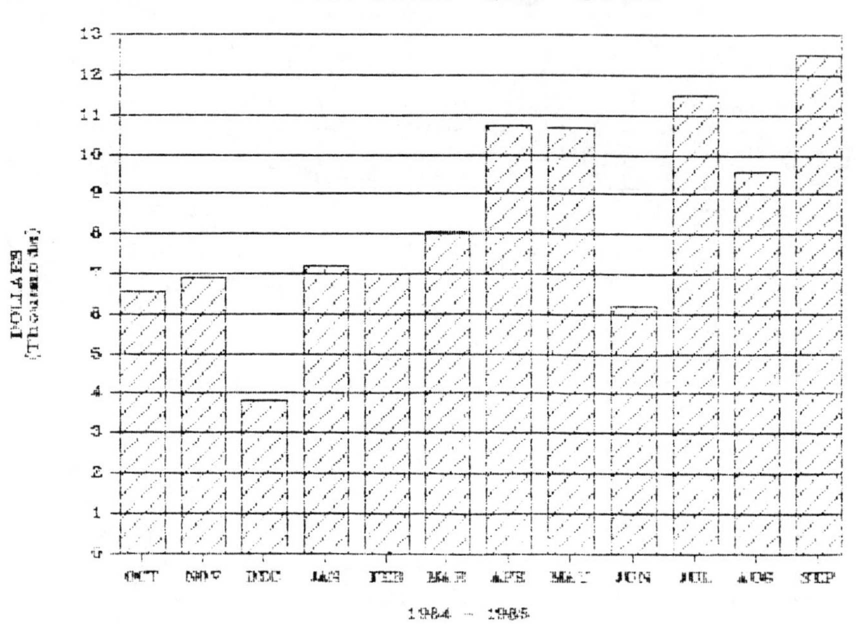

Figure 4

TOTAL ENERGY COST

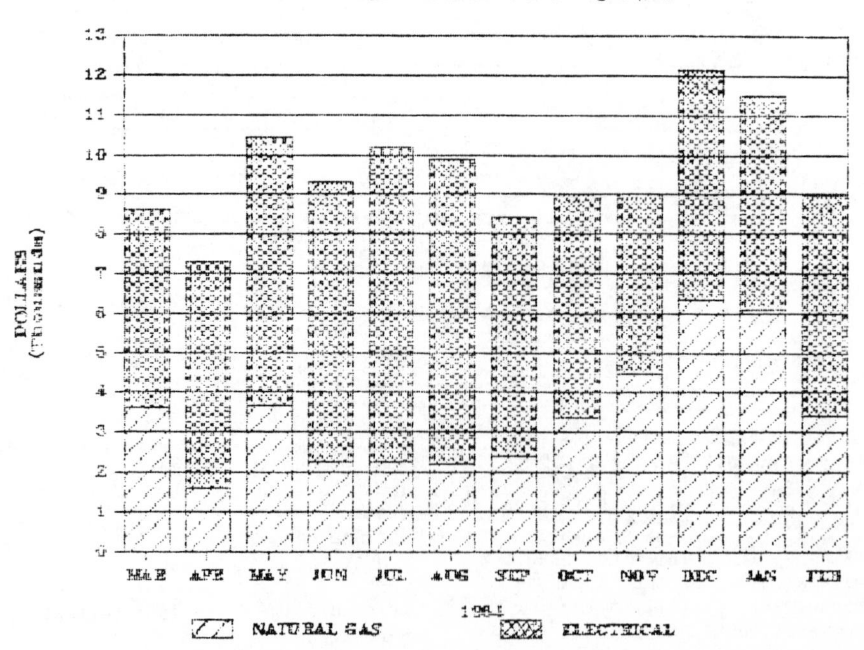

ECO # 1

Title: Insulate High Pressure Boiler's Preheat Tank

Summary: Much heat is being lost through the sides and uncovered top of the preheat tank. This tank should be covered and insulated in order to minimize the heat loss.

Data:

Avg. Ambient Temperature	60 F
Tank Surface Temperature	130 F
Tank Diameter	48 in.
Tank Heighth	68 in.
Surface Resistance-Rs	0.48 hr-sq.ft-F/BTU
Proposed R-Value-Ri	5.00 hr-sq.ft-F/BTU
Boiler Efficiency	80%
Hours of Operation	8760 Hr/Yr
Cost of Natural Gas	$4.22/MCF

Annual Savings: Installing a moisture resistant layer of insulation which will bring the insulation level to proposed R-value.

(Tank Surface Area)x(Surface Temp. - Ambient Temp.)x (1/Boiler Efficiency)x(Hours of Operation)x(1/Surface Resistance - 1/Proposed R value)x(1MCF/1x10^6 BTU)x (Cost of Natural Gas)

=(84 sq.ft)x(130 F - 60 F)x(1/.80)x(8760 hr/yr)x (1/0.48 hr-sq.ft-F/BTU) - (1/5.0 hr-sq.ft-F/BTU)x (1MCF/1x10^6 BTU)x($4.22/MCF)

= $512/yr.

Implementation Costs: Cost of Insulation and Installation.

Insulation Cost $2.06 sq.ft (1985 Mechanical Means Cost Data Book)

Total Cost = (84 sq.ft)x($2.06/sq.ft)

= $173

Simple Payback = Implementation Cost/Annual Savings

= ($173/($512/yr)

= 0.34 years (4 months)

ECO # 2

Title: Insulate Hot Water and Caustic Tanks

Summary: The surface temperature of these tanks indicates that much heat is being lost through the uninsulated sides and tops of the tanks.

Data:

Avg. Ambient Temperature	60 F
Surface Resistance-RS	0.48 hr-sq.ft-F/BTU
Boiler Efficiency	80%
Hours of Operation	8760 hr/yr
Cost of Natural Gas	$4.22/MCF

Hot Water Tank

Surface Area 1033 sq. ft (Sides and Top) 20 ft tall, 14 ft dia.
Surface Temperature 130 F

Caustic Tank

Surface Area 466 sq.ft (Sides and Top) 135 in. tall, 128 in.dia.
Surface Temperature 130F

Energy Savings: Installing Insulation - Fire & Water Resistant Backed Fiberglass

(Area Hot Water Tank + Area Caustic Tank)x(Surface Temp. of Tanks - Ambient Temp.)x(1/Boiler Efficiency)x (Hours of Operation/yr)x(1/Surface Resistance - 1/Proposed R value)x(1 MCF/1x10^6 BTU)x(Cost of Natural Gas)

= (1033 sq.ft + 466 sq. ft)x(130 F - 60 F)x(1/.80)x (8760 hr/yr)x(1/0.48 hr-sq.ft F/BTU)-(1/5.0 hr-sq.ft F/BTU)x(1 MCF/1x10^6 BTU)x($4.22/MCF)

= $9,132/yr

Implementation Cost: Insulation and Installation

Cost of Insulation - $2.06/sq.ft (1986 Mechanical Means Cost Data Book)

Total Cost = (1499 sq.ft)x($2.06/sq.ft)

= $3,090

Simple Payback = Implementation Cost/Annual Savings

= $3,090/($9,132/yr)

= 0.33 yrs (4 months)

ECO # 3

Title: Insulate Steam Lines

Summary: Much heat is being lost through uninsulated steam lines. These lines should be insulated to minimize the heat loss.

Data:

Avg. Ambient Temperature	60 F
Hours of Operation	8760 hr/yr
Boiler Efficiency	80%
Cost of Natural Gas	$4.22/MCF

Current Piping (50 psig Lines)

6.0 in. pipe	60 ft	@ 290 F
1.5 in. pipe	50 ft	@ 190 F
1.0 in. pipe	100 ft	@ 190 F

(15 psig Lines)

6.0 in. pipe	120 ft	@ 250 F
1.0 in. pipe	20 ft	@ 150 F

Energy Loss - Bare Pipe (See Note 1)

((1140 BTU/hr-ft)x(60 ft)+(150 BTU/hr-ft)x(50 ft)+ (104 BTU/hr-ft)x(100 ft)+(860 BTU/hr-ft)x(120 ft)+ (70 BTU/hr-ft)x(20 ft))x(8760 hr/yr)x(1/.80)x(1 MCF/ 1x10 6^BTU)x($4.22/MCF)

= $8,821/yr

Experience with the calculations has shown us that we can expect to save 90% of this amount by applying insulation to an uninsulated surface. The expected annual savings would then be:

= $7,939/yr

Cost of Insulation

Calcium Silicate - Pipe Insulation
Cost Per Linear Foot

6.0 in. pipe	\$7.10 /ft	(1985 Mechanical Means Cost Data Book)
1.5 in. pipe	\$4.71 /ft	
1.0 in. pipe	\$4.55 /ft	

Total Cost = (60 ft)x(\$7.10/ft)+(50 ft)x(\$4.71/ft)+(100 ft)x(\$4.55/ft)

= \$1,117

Simple Payback = Implementation Cost/Annual Savings

= \$1,117/(\$7,939/yr)

= 0.14 yrs (1.7 months)

Note 1: Values for Heat Loss through Bare Pipes were obtained from a table in the following reference:

Energy Management Handbook, Turner, Wayne C., Published by John Wiley & Sons, 1982: P. 489

ECO # 4

Title: Add Hot Water Tank Capacity

Summary: The plant uses 26,000 gallons of hot (140 F) water for each batch of product. Currently, the plant has 23,000 gallons of hot water capacity. During the cool-down period of the production cycle cooling water passes through the fermenters to cool the product. This cooling water reaches a temperature of 140 F and is deposited into the hot water tank. When the hot water tank is full the excess cooling water is sent to the cooling ponds. This water contains usuable heat, but there is not enough capacity to hold it. When starting the next batch, the 23,000 gallons of hot water is placed into the fermenter tanks and 3,000 gallons of makeup water is brought in to make up the difference to 26,000 gallons. This makeup water must be heated to the desired temperature of 140 F. We suggest adding AT LEAST 3,000 more gallons of hot water capacity and configuring the system so that any excess hot water above the 26,000 gallons needed for a batch can be placed into the caustic tank which is used for flushing the fermenters between batches. This will create increased savings due to the decrease in the heat that is used to heat the water for the caustic tank.

Data:

Cooling Water Temperature	100 F
Ambient Water Temperature	55 F
Specific Heat of Water	1.0 BTU/lb-F
Weight of Water	8.4 lb/gal
Boiler Efficiency	80%
Cost of Natural Gas	\$4.22/MCF

Savings per Batch - Adding ONLY 3,000 gallons of Capacity

(3000 gal/batch)x(8.4 lb/gal)x(100 F - 55 F)x(1 BTU/lb-F)x(1/.80)x(1 MCF/1x10^6 BTU)x(\$4.22/MCF)

= \$6.00 / batch

Annual Savings = (\$6.00/batch)x(220 batches/year)

= \$1,320/yr

Tank Cost = \$3,000 (1985 Mechanical Means Cost Data Book)

Simple Payback = Tank Cost/Annual Savings

= \$3,000/(\$1,320/yr)

= 2.27 yrs

ECO # 5

Title: Add Steam Traps and Return Condensate to Preheat Tank

Summary: Near the Dehydrators there are two 1 inch steam lines that travel through the dehydrators and return to the feed water preheat tank on the high pressure boiler. These lines, although at a very low pressure, return steam to the preheat tank. We recommend that traps be placed on each of these lines in order to hold back any usuable heat instead of re-pumping the heat through the system. Also near the dehydrators is a small drain line that deposits a small stream of hot water into the cement trench in the plant. The temperature of the stream was measured as 200 F. We will calculate the savings using a conservative estimate that the flow rate of the water is 10 gal/hr. We did not try to quantify the savings due to installing the steam traps.

Data:

Condensate Stream Temperature	200 F
Makeup Water Temperature	55 F
Flow Rate	10 gal/hr
Hours of Operation	8760 hr/yr
Boiler Efficiency	1/.80
Cost of Natural Gas	\$4.22 /MCF

Energy Savings:

(200 F - 55F)x(10 gal/hr)x(8.4 lb/gal)x(1 BTU/LB-F)x(1/.80)x(8760 hr/yr)x1 MCF/1x10^6 BTU)x(\$4.22/MCF)

= \$ 563/yr

Implementation Cost:

Allow \$150 for piping to return line which runs near the dehydrators to the preheat tank.

Simple Payback = Implementation Cost/Annual Savings

= \$150/(\$563/yr)

= 0.27 years (3.2 months)

SECTION 12
THERMAL STORAGE

Chapter 38

25kWh BARIUM HYDROXIDE LATENT HEAT STORAGE PILOT UNIT

S. Krause

ABSTRACT

A 25 kWh barium hydroxide phase change heat storage pilot unit with direct heat exchange - probably the first studied in technical dimensions - is described. The storage temperature of 78 °C and the large attainable storage capacities of up to 125 kWh/m^3 should make the system attractive for low temperature process heat storage and for the storage of factory waste heat for heating purposes. The present discussion includes the device, examples of charging and discharging characteristics, the applied direct heat exchange and other heat exchanges, heat losses, material degradation effects, and the practical operating range, with favorable issues in all respects. The storage unit has by now been operated for 20 months.

INTRODUCTION

The advantages of latent heat storage as compared to sensible heat storage are the large storage capacities and storage at nearly constant (phase change) temperature. Among the considerable number of possible storage media proposed and tested[1,2], salt hydrates combine relatively easy handling with large. heats of fusion. Barium hydroxide octahydrate is particularly outstanding: the capacity of 125 kWh/m^3 we attained is about twice the capacity of Glauber's salt or water (latent), and about 5.2 times the capacity of warm-water heat storage at the same temperature span. Its storage temperature around 78 °C appears very suitable for short-term storage of low-temperature process heat and of factory waste heat for heating purposes.

The necessity to charge and discharge makes heat transfer the vital element in heat storage technology. In salt hydrate latent heat storage, the so-called direct heat exchange within the bulk of the medium is considered to be most effective, permit the largest storage density, and avoid irreversible sedimentation of anhydride from the salt hydrate during the melting process (charging). Since 1957[3], this concept has been applied for low-temperature heat storage by many investigators using liquid hydrocarbons as the heat transfer fluid. Those investigators mostly envisaged applications in house heating, together with collectors of heat pumps. Therefore, for their technical-size developments, they selected salt hydrates with phase change temperatures between 25 and 48 °C only, in one case 58 °C. Detailed reference to those studies and media, and to the few commercial developments, was made in a previous paper[4].

After a thermoanalytical investigation of the medium and subsequently testing it together with the direct heat exchange in a laboratory-scale storage unit[5,6], a 370 kg barium hydroxide latent heat storage pilot unit capable of storing approximately 25 kWh[4] was built and has by now been operated for 20 months during the first half of which 40 complete charging/discharging cycles were performed. The aims of the tests were to demonstrate the feasibility of the storage medium and technology, to obtain a basis for the construction of larger practical units, and to provide the information needed for economical analyses and technical planning of thermal systems using such storage units.

Some of our test results comprising discharge and temperature curves, arbitrary variations of the discharge power, subcooling, repeatability, and others, were already described[4]. In particular it was pointed out that the usual problems connected with the application of direct heat transfer - salt carryover, oil inlet blockage, subcooling, etc. - were less evere with barium hydroxide and/or could be solved by simple means. This paper concentrates on data of interest to prospective appliers.

Because the equipment used for charging was so far limited to medium powers, the discharge behaviour is emphasized here. More powerful equipment for charging is presently being installed, but the medium-power-charging results already suggest that charging in general will be as feasible and simularly describable as discharging.

EXPERIMENTAL APPARATUS AND PARAMETERS

The storage medium was composed of 92 w/o $Ba(OH)_2 \cdot 8H_2O$ and 8 w/o water. The heat transfer medium for the direct heat exchange was BP Energol WM2 oil. The main properties of both media were given previously[4].

The experimental setup is shown in FIG. 1. The storage tank was made from 3 mm stainless steel plates and covered loosely but with a rubber sealing by a flat lid. This way and considering also the prevailing temperature near 78 °C, the escape of oil and water vapor from the space under the lid could be kept negligible and the pressure in that space maintained near atmospheric. The 385 l (overall volume) tank contained 370 kg of the storage medium capable of storing about 25 kWh[4] of thermal energy. This is pilot size compared, e.g., with typical one-day heating and storage requirements of 120 to 250 kWh of one to two-family residences.

Charging and discharging were accomplished by means of two closed-cycle heat transfer circuits (FIG. 1A),

(1) a "storage circuit" with heat transfer medium WM2 oil, and

(2) an "applier's circuit" with heat transfer medium water,

with three comprised heat exchanges (FIG. 1A),

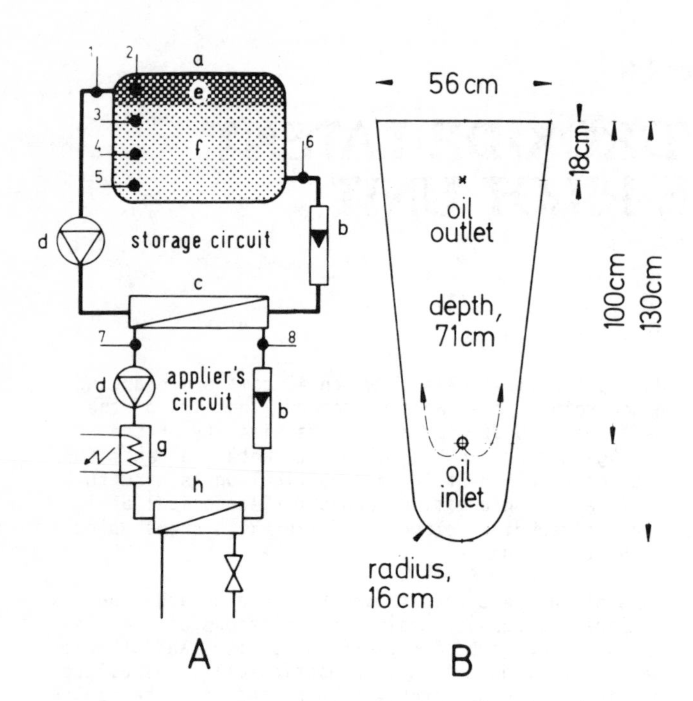

FIGURE 1. EXPERIMENTAL APPARATUS. A, SCHEMATIC; B, ACTUAL CONTAINER GEOMETRY. a, STORAGE TANK; b, FLOW METERS; c, INTERMEDIATE HEAT EXCHANGER(S); d, PUMPS; e, HEAT TRANSFER OIL; f, STORAGE MEDIUM; g, ELECTRIC HEATER FOR SIMULATION OF CHARGING; h, APPLIER'S HEAT EXCHANGER FOR SIMULATION OF DISCHARGING; 1 THROUGH 8, TEMPERATURE SENSORS.

(1) the "direct heat exchange" medium-to-oil, for charging and discharging,

(2) the "intermediate heat exchange" between the storage and applier's circuits, for charging and discharging, and

(3) an "applier's heat exchange" from the applier's circuit to external cooling water for discharging, or an electric heater in the applier's circuit for the simulation of charging.

In industrial applications, the applier's circuit may eventually be omitted. Then the applier's heat exchanger takes the place and assumes the problems of the intermediate heat exchanger, and only two heat exchanges are involved.

In the direct heat exchange, the oil was pumped into the storage medium through 34 holes, rose there in the form of bubbles exchanging heat, and was then returned to Heat Exchanger (2) from the oil layer on top of the medium.

Directly adjusted experimental parameters:

$\dot{m}_{oil}$ = mass flow of heat transfer oil through the storage volume,

$\dot{V}_{cw}$ = volume flow of tap cooling water of 6 ^{o}C through the applier's heat exchanger,

number of equal 0.2 m^2 intermediate heat exchangers of the shell-and-tubes type connected in parallel. Either one or two of these were used in the tests.

Main indirectly adjustable experimental parameters:

ΔT_{oil} = difference between the oil temperatures at outlet (T_1) and inlet (T_6) of storage tank (indices refer to numbered positions in FIG. 1A),

(1) $\Delta T_{oil} = |T_1 - T_6|$, and

$\dot{Q}$ = thermal power in charging or discharging.

ΔT_{oil} and by

(2) $\dot{Q} = c_{oil}\ \dot{m}_{oil}\ \Delta T_{oil}$ (c = specific heat)

also $\dot{Q}$, depended on $\dot{m}_{oil}$ and on the external heat exchange periphery, in particular on $\dot{V}_{cw}$ and the number of parallel intermediate heat exchangers.

EXAMPLES AND COMPARISON OF CHARGING AND DISCHARGING

FIG. 2 presents typical charging and discharging curves. Charging immediately followed discharging.

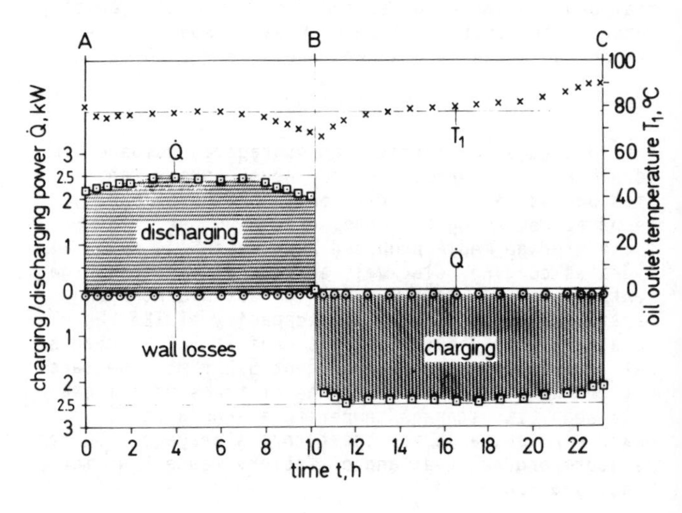

FIGURE 2. EXAMPLE OF DISCHARGING AND CHARGING STORAGE UNIT AT THERMAL POWER OF 2.5 kW. A = START OF CRYSTALLIZATION, B = ALL MEDIUM SOLID, C = END OF MELTING.

The charging curve was obtained with the largest power of the actually installed electric heater (g in FIG. 1). The discharge power was chosen approximately equal to the charging power for this comparison. The adjustable experimental parameters were kept constant both during charging and discharging. The experimentally determined heat losses over the walls (see below) are also shown.

FIG. 2 shows that the exit temperature T_1 of the heat transfer oil as most important for future users, remains nearly constant and in the vicinity of the phase change temperature T_{PC} over a large portion of the charging or discharging period. Deviations of T_1 from T_{PC} may be caused by

(1) contributions of sensible heat (free water in medium),

(2) insufficient heat transfer to solid parts of the medium,

(3) decreasing heat transfer because of decreasing contact hights.

Effect (1) is an intrinsic physical property of the medium. Together with Effect (3) it is responsible for the decrease and subsequent increase of T_1 near time B of Fig. 2. The increase of T_1 near time C is mainly attributable to Effect (2) because some of the solid medium tends to stick to the upper inner walls of the tank where only little of the heat transfer fluid passes which instead already heats the liquid portion of the medium to temperatures above T_{PC}. Substantial reductions of Effects (2) and (3) may be expected after suitable improvements of the geometry of the tank and the oil flow in it.

FIG. 2 shows also that the thermal power remained essentially constant over the discharding and the charging periods, as important for future applications. This is due to the constancy of the adjustable parameters and the excellency of the direct heat exchange as discussed below.

The shaded areas in FIG. 2 are the net heat extracted or stored in the storage unit over the discharging or charging period, respectively. They are approximately equal for discharging and charging. The small difference is due to different contributions of sensible heat. Evidently, for equal thermal powers, the charging time must be larger than the discharging time because of the wall losses.

HEAT TRANSFER CHARACTERISTICS

Efficiency of Direct Heat Exchange

FIG. 3 is a simultaneous representation of three experimental discharge curves and the corresponding average contact hights for the direct heat exchange between the rising oil droplets and the remaining liquid portion of the storage medium above the layer of crystals already deposited below in discharging. It is seen that while the contact hight diminishes rapidly, the discharge power remains constant or nearly constant over a large portion of discharge. This already demonstrates the effectiveness of the applied direct heat exchange.

A quantitative criterion for the direct heat exchange is the often used self-explanatory overall heat transfer coefficient

$$\xi = (T_1 - T_6) / (T_{PC} - T_6) \tag{3}$$

as obtainable from the measured temperatures T_1, T_6 and T_{PC}. In FIG. 4, ξ is plotted as a function of $\dot{m}_{oil}$ comprising a large number of discharge tests.

Near the beginning and during the major portion of a discharge (upper curve), the efficiency ξ is excellent. Its decline with increasing $\dot{m}_{oil}$ is small and may be explained by the decreasing period pf dwell available for the heat transfer, of the ascending oil droplets in the liquid storage medium. This in turn is mainly due to the increased upward motion of the storage medium itself as induced by frictional forces between bubbles and medium. It may also be enhanced through an increase of the mean bubble size with $\dot{m}_{oil}$, with subsequent increase of the upward velocity although after a maximum, the upward velocity may decrease again[8]. Since points for different ΔT_{oil} are on the same (upper) curve of FIG. 4, contrary to $\dot{m}_{oil}$,

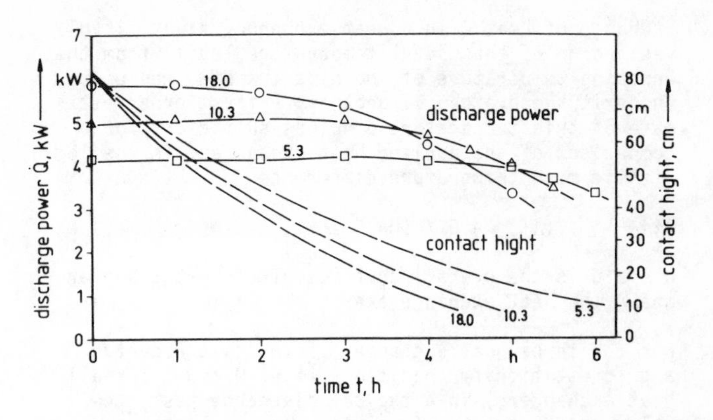

FIGURE 3. DISCHARGE CURVES AND CORRESPONDING MEAN CONTACT HIGHTS FOR THE DIRECT HEAT EXCHANGE. V_{cw} = 1750 l/h, 2 INTERMEDIATE HEAT EXCHANGERS. PARAMETER, m_{oil}.

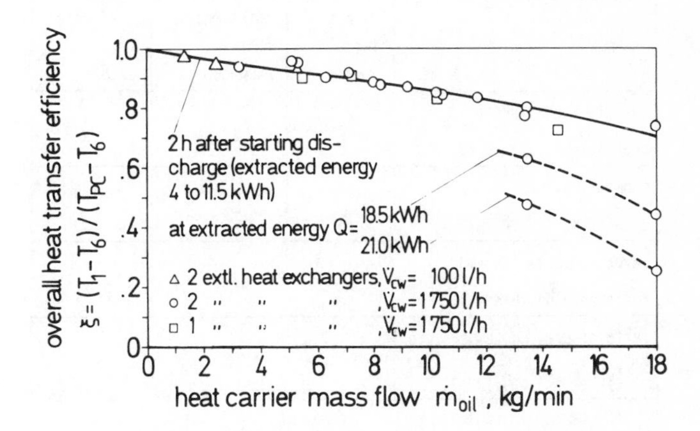

FIGURE 4. OVERALL HEAT TRANSFER EFFICIENCY OF DIRECT HEAT EXCHANGE IN DISCHARGING.

ΔT_{oil} did not influence ξ within the range of the present experiments. From a plot of T_1, T_6 and T_{PC} (FIG. 5 of our previous paper[4]) and Eq. (3), it is easily seen that the decrease of ξ with $\dot{m}_{oil}$ is intrinsically connected with a slight unfavourable decrease of the application-relevant oil outlet temperature T_1.

The upper curve of FIG. 4 is practically free of the influence of the above mentioned contact hight because for all $\dot{m}_{oil}$, the liquid-solid interface has essentially not yet risen above the level of the oil entrance orifices (FIG. 1B). The effect of a decreased contact hight is demonstrated by the lower curves of FIG. 4 which were taken for two larger extracted energies (18.5 and 21 kWh) near the end of discharging (total extractable energy = 25 kWh[4]) when the oil entrance orifices were already below a thick solid layer of the storage medium (through which the oil flows by means of channels). It is seen that towards the end of discharging, the efficiency decreases considerably but still appears satisfactory up to relatively large $\dot{m}_{oil}$ and hence discharge powers.

Comparison of Applied Heat Exchanges

Exchange of heat $\dot{Q}$ in a heat exchanger always involves a drop of the useful temperature level, from the entering temperature of one heat transfer medium to the exit temperature of another. A first order estimate of this temperature drop, as sufficient for a comparison of the applied heat exchanges, is the logarithmic mean temperature difference

$$(4) \qquad (\Delta T)_m = \dot{Q} / (UA)$$

where U is the overall coefficient of heat transfer and A the heat exchange area.

For the three heat exchanges of the test appartus, and for stationary conditions (i.e. $\dot{Q}$ equal for all heat exchangers) in a typical discharge test, the relevant quantities of Eq. (4) were evaluated and summarized for comparison in TABLE 1. For other discharge tests, these quantities differ quantitatively but the order-of-magnitude relations between them remain similar.

	direct heat exchange	intermediate heat exchanger	applier's heat exchanger
overall heat transfer coefficient U, $W/(m^2K)$	400	120	3200
geometrical heat transfer area A, m^2	.4	.4	.1
Inverse overall thermal resistance UA, W/K	160	48	320
ratio of driving temperature difference, ΔT_m	1 :	3.3 :	.5

TABLE 1. COMPARISON OF HEAT EXCHANGES IN A TYPICAL DISCHARGE TEST $\dot{m}_{oil}$ = 7.3 kg/min, $\dot{V}_{cw}$ = 1750 l/h, $\dot{Q}$ = 4.4 kW, 2 INTERMEDIATE HEAT EXCHANGERS.

TABLE 1 shows that the intermediate heat exchanger represents the by far largest overall thermal resistance and consequently requires the largest driving temperature difference. This heat exchanger therefore contributes most to the overall detrimental drop of the useful temperature. Its large thermal resistance is mainly due to the oil side, the water side and the intermediate wall contributing only 1/13 and 1/350, respectively. The intermediate heat exchange may certainly be improved for future applications and will probably constitute the most expensive element in the heat exchange periphery of a storage system.

Wall Losses

FIG. 5 is an example of how the wall insulation affects the useful extractable energy and discharge time. The storage-ambient temperature difference was 78 °C - 20 °C. The extractable heat is the area under the $\dot{Q}(t)$-curve. About 13 % more energy (shaded area) may be extracted from the container with a 7.5 cm insulation than with a 1.3 cm insulation, until the discharge power has dropped to 1/3 of the original value.

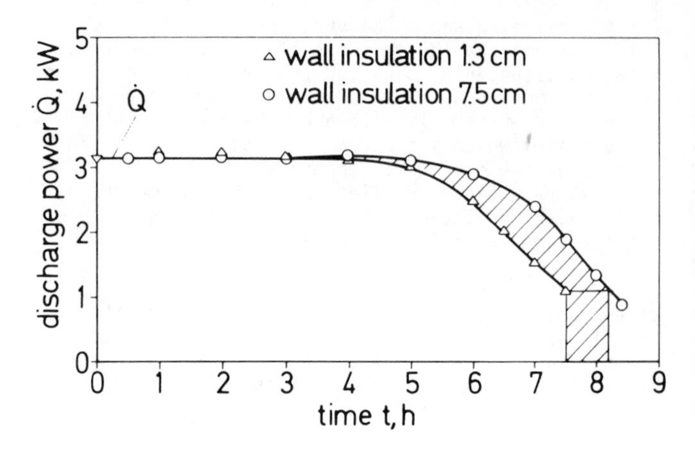

FIGURE 5. EXAMPLE OF INFLUENCE OF HEAT INSULATION ON EXTRACTABLE ENERGY. INSULATION WAS AF/ARMAFLEX TYPE 99 WITH HEAT CONDUCTION COEFFICIENT .04 W/(mK) at 20 °C. $\dot{m}_{oil}$ = 7.3 kg/min, $\dot{V}_{cw}$ = 1750 l/h, 1 INTERMEDIATE HEAT EXCHANGER.

The wall losses are practically independent of the discharge power but increase with time. Thus, since a complete discharge takes longer for smaller thermal powers, the percentage of the accumulated heat losses, of the 25 kWh storable in the container, increases as the discharge power decreases. Concurrently, the total discharge time is increasingly reduced in comparison with the theoretical no-loss case. This is depicted in FIG. 6. The curves of FIG. 6 are based on experimental determinations of the heat losses (from the measurable heat input required to obtain stationary conditions, i.e. constant storage temperatures chosen just above T_{PC} for convenience). It is seen that with a reasonable insulation of 7.5 cm, the share of the wall losses and the subsequent reduction of the discharge time remain negligible for discharge powers larger than 1.0 kW, and tolerable for discharge powers down to less than 0.5 kW.

Because of smaller surface-to-volume ratios, the relative wall losses will be still smaller for larger storage units as required in practical applications.

DEGRADATION OF MATERIALS

Four degradation effects were observed in the involved materials:

(1) escape of about .5 l of water per month from the storage medium past the sealing of the lid. The lost water may be replaced easily.

(2) continuous conveyance of part of the 1 - 2 % barium carbonate impurity contained in the commercial barium hydroxide, by the circulating heat transfer oil. The additional formation of barium carbonate from barium hydroxide and CO_2 from the ambient air appears to be effectively inhibited by the lid of the container.

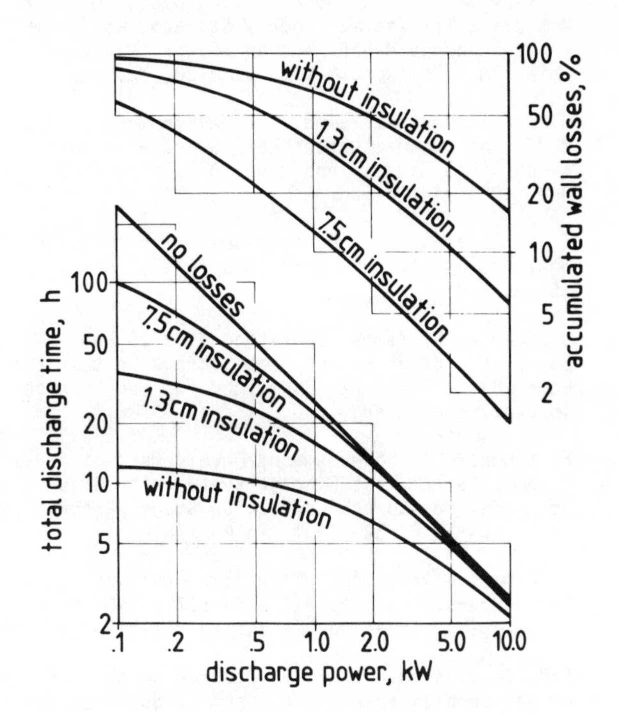

FIGURE 6. WALL LOSSES AND TOTAL DISCHARGE TIMES AS FUNCTIONS OF THE DISCHARGE POWER AND THE WALL INSULATION, FOR THE 25 kW PILOT UNIT. SEE FIG. 5 FOR TYPE OF INSULATION.

(3) formation of large-molecule hydrocarbons from oil, oxygen, and possibly barium, with subsequent deposition at the triple intersection of container wall, heat transfer oil, and storage medium. This product may be removed in yearly intervals.

(4) dissolution of iron from the container walls with subsequent formation of iron compounds in the storage medium. The iron content in the medium reached 13.7 g after 18 months of operation. Assuming constant-rate uniform erosion for simplicity, this corresponds to a decrease of the wall thickness of 3/100 mm in 20 years. A detailed metallographic investigation of the wall surface will follow the current tests.

These effects appear to be harmless in any respect and have so far not influenced operation and performance of the storage unit.

LIMITS OF THE STORAGE UNIT

Assuming constant c_{oil} in the operating range of the storage unit, Eq. (2) may be represented by straight lines ΔT_{oil} = const in a $\dot{Q}(\dot{m}_{oil})$ diagram. These lines are characteristics of the heat transfer oil only. FIG. 7 is such a diagram with experimental points and estimated operational limits enclosing the permissible operational range, for the tested storage unit. The experimental points were obtained varying the three parameters $\dot{m}_{oil}$, $\dot{V}_{cw}$ and number of intermadiate heat exchangers. Four operational limits were identified.

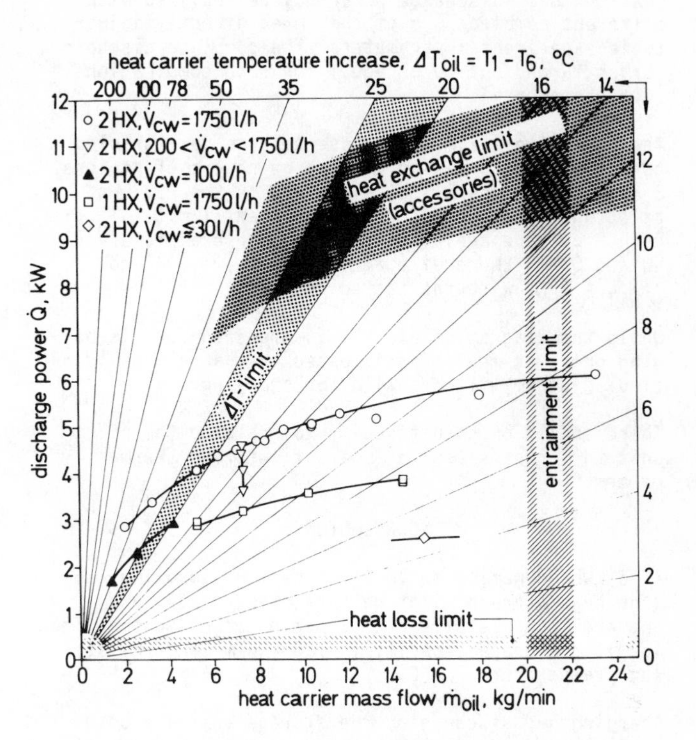

FIGURE 7. EXPERIMENTALLY REALIZED OPERATING CONDITIONS AND PRACTICAL OPERATING LIMITS OF TESTED STORAGE UNIT.

Beyond the entrainment limit, the heat transfer oil would carry along some of the storage medium with subsequent irreversible deposition in, and obstruction of, the cooler flow ducts. Below the heat loss limit, the heat losses over the container walls become intolerably large (see FIG. 6). The ΔT-limit is the temperature difference ΔT_{oil} of the heat transfer oil which may be accepted by the applier of the storage unit (house heating application assumed in FIG. 7). As a heat exchange limit, the maximum Q of the direct heat exchange could be taken which would be obtained assuming ideal intermediate and applier's heat exchanges with zero temperature drop. This Q as a function of m_{oil} is obtained combining Eqs. (2) and (3) into

$$Q = c_{oil}\, m_{oil}\, \xi(m_{oil})\, (T_{PC} - T_6), \tag{5}$$

inserting the tap cooling water temperature for T_6, and using $\xi(m_{oil})$ from FIG. 4. This limit, however, proves to be far beyond the above ΔT-limit. Understandably, the technical or economical limits of the other heat exchangers will be reached first, in particular those of the intermediate heat exchanger. The heat exchange limits given in FIG. 7 are the estimated discharge powers for a maximum number of between 5 and 8 equal intermediate heat exchangers of the type used in the tests.

The first two limits are strictly internal to the storage unit, the other two are internal-external being also attributable to the periphery and the future application. The limits are diffuse rather than sharp lines because they depend on the type and rigor of the applied criteria. They may be pushed outwards by future improvements of the storage unit.

It is evident from the experimental curves of FIG. 7 that the same discharge power may be realized with different combinations of the three directly adjustable experimental parameters. The complete discharge curves turned out to be equal for such combinations (not shown here).

The operational limits enclose a large permissible operating range. Maximum discharge powers of at least 8 kW should be easily attainable with the 25 kWh pilot unit. Because of the entrainment limit, ΔT_{oil} cannot be made arbitrarily small. For example $\dot{Q} = 6$ kW and $\dot{Q} = 3$ kW require at least $\Delta T_{oil} = 8$ K and $\Delta T_{oil} = 4$ K, with the tested unit.

While the diagram of FIG. 7 was prepared for discharging only, it may be anticipated that an almost identical diagram will be valid for charging.

There should be no difficulty to scale up the pilot unit to larger sizes, oil mass flows, and thermal powers.

CONCLUSIONS

A 25 kWh "dynamic" or "active" barium hydroxide latent heat storage pilot unit has been tested and operated successfully over a period of 20 months. The specific storage capacity is 125 kWh/m^3 and the storage temperature 78 ^{o}C.

Charging and discharging the storage unit are both possible at essentially constant power and constant exit temprature of the heat transfer oil.

The efficiency of the direct heat exchange between the storage medium and the heat transfer oil is excellent through the major portion of a discharging process, and satisfactory for the remainder. The bottle neck of the heat transfer is the heat exchanger between the oil circuit and the applier's circuit. The heat losses may be kept small applying conventional insulation.

Some small degradation effects in the involved materials were identified. Negative influences of these on behaviour and performance of the storage unit have not been observed.

For discharging the storage unit, approximate power and operational limits are given which enclose a satisfactory range for possible applications. The charging power was so far limited to 2.5 kW but the experience made suggests that charging with larger powers will not present any difficulties, and charging will be subject to limits very similar to those given for discharging.

There should be no difficulty to scale up the pilot unit to larger sizes, oil mass flows, and thermal powers.

Despite previous discussions[9,10], there is still considerable uncertainly as to whether and where latent heat storage may be applied with technical and economical advantages. The present and previous results should permit respective studies on barium hydroxide latent heat storage in particular thermal systems.

ACKNOWLEDGEMENT

The author is indebted to H. Kanwischer for the chemical analyses of the storage medium.

REFERENCES

1. K. Kauffmann, I. Grundfest, Congruently Melting Materials for Thermal Energy Storage. Natl. Center for Energy Management and Power, Philadelphia, PA, USA, Report No. NCEMP-20, Nov. 1973.

2. H. Kanwischer, R. Tamme, The Development of Media for Dynamic Latent Heat Storage in the Low Temperature Range. Report No. DFVLR-FB 84-03, Dec. 1983, in German.

3. T.L. Etherington, A Dynamic Heat Storage System. Heating, Piping, Air Cond., 12 (1957), pp. 147-151.

4. S. Krause, R. Tamme, Operation of a 25 kWh Barium Hydroxide Latent Heat Storage Unit in the Power Range 2 - 6 kW. Submitted for publication in J.of Solar Energy Engg., Trans. ASME.

5. F. Lindner, K. Scheunemann, Development of a Dynamic Latent Heat Storage System with Glauber's Salt up to the Production Stage. Report No. DFVLR-FB 81-32, 1981, in German.

6. R. Tamme, Development of Dynamic Heat Storage in the Temperature Range 314 K to 353 K (40 ^{o}C to 80 ^{o}C), Int. Solar Forum, Berlin, 1982.

7. F.N. Peebles, H.J. Garber, Studies on the Motion of Gas Bubbles in Liquids. Chem. Engg. Progress, 49 (1953), pp. 88-97.

8. D. Seeber, Heat Exchange and Its Optimization for Latent Heat Storage. Investigation of the Heat Transfer between Salt Hydrate Solutions and Droplet Swarms. Dipl.-Ing. Thesis, University of Stuttgart, Germany, Sept. 1978, in German.

9. B. Shelpuk et al., Technical and Economical Feasibility of Thermal Storage, RCA Report No. ATL-CR-76-04 for ERDA, June 1976.

10. D. Lecompte, D. Mayer, Design Method for Sizing a Latent Heat Store/Heat Exchanger in a Thermal System. Applied Energy, 21 (1985), pp. 55-78.

Chapter 39

METHODOLOGY AND STUDY OF THREE PROPOSED COLD THERMAL STORAGE SYSTEMS FOR A U.S. NAVY SHORE FACILITY

J. F. McCauley

INTRODUCTION

About the time of Christ after the first Persian invasion of India a magnificent fortress, known today as the Red Fort, was constructed on the dry Delhi plateau. It was so large that cavalry mounted on elephants could engage in combat for sport on the fort's parade grounds.

In order to humidify and cool the ruler's quarters and the quarters of his harem, natural draft ventilation was directed through water sprays and into their living spaces. Here one of the earliest forms of air conditioning can be found and today is demonstrated for tourists.

During the era of the Revolution an inventor, Thomas Jefferson, introduced to America the practice of storing ice formed during the winter in semi-underground ice houses. It was used for cooling liquid refreshment and food preparation during the hot humid summers encountered in the Central and Southern portions of North America. Blacks were then in slave bondage and provided inexpensive labor to gather the ice. The idea caught on and most of those who could afford an ice storage house built one.

These perhaps were the first successful attempts at thermal storage known to man.

Today we can assemble sophisticated HVAC and thermal storage plants producing thousands of times more units of comfort than could our predecessors but not without an economic sacrifice. HVAC and thermal storage plants cost money. And one must choose from the various technologies which system meets the cost/benefit restraints for the project.

This paper deals with an organization's experience in attempting to retrofit existing HVAC systems with accepted cold thermal storage technology equipment.

The HVAC equipment ranges in size from 25 to 550 ton chillers of the reciprocating, centrifugal and screw genuses. The types of storage systems studied are water, ice and eutectic salts; with single, dual and multi-tank storage arrangements.

Early in the study we determined water storage best suited our needs and we proceded to study the pros and cons of tank arrangements in detail.

BACKGROUND

The Naval Aviation Supply Offices Scenario

Thermal storage is a concept aimed at reducing the electric utility costs associated with operating HVAC water chillers such as at the Naval Aviation Supply Offices facility in Philadelphia, Pennsylvania.

The capacity for temporary storage of thermal energy enables at least partial decoupling of the chiller from the building cooling load for large parts of the cooling period.

Arrangement of chiller operation during off-peak periods permits the activity to take best advantage of the provisions in the electric rate structure. Specifically, demands can be leveled off, thereby reducing demand charges. Also, usage during periods of high energy costs (peak periods) can be minimized. These savings opportunities are most significant when applied to buildings which currently are cooled by the electric chiller during the period of peak daytime rates and have few or no nighttime cooling requirements.

Three existing building systems at NASO exhibited characteristics inviting thermal storage study in conjunction with their HVAC systems.

Building No. 36, an administration office, is cooled by a 400-ton electric centrifugal chiller. The chiller load is primarily for comfort cooling and is typically required in service only eleven hours a day. It therefore was considered to be an ideal candidate.

Building No. 4, which comprises offices and computer areas, has a 360-ton electric centrifugal chiller. It also is characterized by loads primarily confined to the period from 6:00 AM to 5:00 PM.

Finally, Building Nos. 2 and 3, which contain large computer areas and some offices, share a commonly connected chiller system comprising three large electric centrifugal chillers at 550 tons, 500 tons and 200 tons, and one electric reciprocating chiller with a capacity of 25 tons. Although Building No. 2, the Data Processing Center, contains computer equipment which requires a continuous cooling load, most of the load from Building No. 3 dissipates at night. Because this comfort cooling portion of the system load accounts for over fifty percent of the system capacity, it was considered a viable candidate for application of the thermal storage concept.

METHODOLOGY OF THE STUDY

An Activity Energy Plan study performed at NASO under the sponsorship of Northern Division, Naval Facilities Engineering Command, uncovered a need for a detailed study of air conditioners over 50 tons. Therefore, an Act-Up Phase I* Study was authorized for the Activity,

---

*Act-Up: Air Conditioning Tune-Up Study. Act-Up Phase I studies cover air conditioning units over 50 tons capacity. Act-Up Phase II studies cover A/C units 50 tons or less.

with Northern Division overseeing the effort.

The Architect/Engineering firm selected to perform the study uncovered what seemed to be a natural opportunity to further enhance several air conditioning systems at NASO. Although they did not do so formally, they stated that thermal storage and the cooling systems of several buildings appeared compatible. They pointed out the very large electrical operating cost savings potential of thermal storage systems.

Recognizing the Phase I study offered excellent energy conservation opportunities, the Activity has acted to cut energy costs. The study we are discussing, now known as a Specialized Energy study (SES), is the outcome of the Act-Up Phase I study recommendation. The astuteness of the A/E performing the Act-Up I study and his deliberations with the Activity Public Works Officer were prerequisite to Northern Division's again soliciting proposals for the thermal storage study as described herein.

BLDG. NO. 36 AND PROPOSED THERMAL STORAGE TANK

BLDG. NO. 36, 400 TON CENTRIFUGAL CHILLER

The methods used to assess the technical and economic feasibility of the potential thermal storage systems are explained below.

Engineering Field Survey and Data Acquisition: Data was collected which relates to the operation and physical characteristics of existing HVAC equipment at NASO. This data and field investigation covers the following:

- Metered electrical consumption from the main base meter,
- Hourly demand profiles for typical days during the cooling season,
- Operating schedules (peak-shaving, daytime-energy--use reduction),
- Operation and equipment information for the centrifugal chillers,
- Drawings and layouts of the chilled water and HVAC systems,
- Building construction data such as wall and roof construction and area and window type and area,
- Occupancy and equipment-use schedules for existing buildings,
- Interior load data for occupancy, lighting and computer and office equipment loads and
- Tentative locations for the thermal storage systems.

Computer Analysis: The data collected during the field survey was analyzed by the DOE-2.1C computer program. The building envelope, building occupancy schedules and interior loads were simulated using actual Philadelphia weather. A building was first simulated as it currently exists and then simulated with the thermal storage system. The spare capacity of the chiller plant, which is available during off-peak hours, will be put into simulated use to supply chilled water to the thermal storage system. Again, the simulated chiller plant will be shut down during the peak cooling period and chilled water obtained from the thermal storage system to meet the building loads. It is expected the thermal storage plant will reduce the peak electrical demand and the electrical costs by operating the chillers during periods when utility rates are minimal.

Cost Estimates: The cost of installing thermal storage equipment was estimated for each system analyzed. The costs include storage tanks and their support structures, chilled water piping, pumps and controls.

Operating Schedules: The options in operating schedules hinge directly on the nature of electric rate schedules and building electric load profiles. With ratchet demand charges* and time-of-day rates (such as those at NASO), the scheduling objectives in thermal storage concepts are as follows:

- Peak Shaving: Levelize electric demand throughout the 24-hour day, thereby reducing peak KW charges and
- Daytime Energy-Use Reduction: Reduction of energy use during peak-rate daytime periods.

If chiller power requirements constitute over half the daily electric peak load and/or there are significant off-peak loads, the ideal storage operating schedule could call for some chiller operation during the day. This cooling could be provided in parallel with "storage tank discharging" to eliminate the chance of establishing a new peak at night.

At NASO, however, the ideal candidate buildings are characterized by steep profiles with nearly all air conditioning, lighting and miscellaneous electric loads currently disappearing at night (5:00 PM to 6:00 AM). Furthermore, power requirements for chilling the water constitute less than half the daytime total electric loads. Therefore, by rescheduling chiller operations as completely as possible to nighttime (off-peak) hours, the 24-hour electric peak can be reduced by the full amount of eliminated daytime chiller demand. Rescheduling can transfer a maximum amount of KWH usage from the high-cost daytime period to the low-cost nighttime period. This was the approach considered in evaluating the thermal storage concepts described below.

---

*Ratchet demand charges: see "A Favorable Electrical Power Rate Structure" - p. 4

Three Technical Concepts And Their Economics

There are many ways to plan a thermal storage plant. In general, the approaches to implementing a thermal storage system involve combining the following components:

- Heat transfer equipment (centrifugal, reciprocating and/or screw-type chiller compressors),
- Storage media (water, ice, eutectic salts),
- Containment systems (single- or multi-container)

Heat Transfer Equipment: There are three generic types of refrigeration equipments readily available for use with a thermal storage system. Screw, reciprocating and centrifugal chillers are all capable of producing temperatures adequate for chilled water, ice or eutectic salt thermal storage systems. However, each also has limitations.

Each type is available with direct expansion (DX) evaporators. Also available are screw type and centrifugals which use flooded evaporators to evaporate the refrigerant. Direct expansion refrigeration systems are not recommended because they use thermal expansion valves and evaporator superheat in a delicate balance of variable suction and discharge conditions to get unevaporated refrigerant out of the suction gas. When this fails, the liquid remaining in the suction gas can be quite damaging to a reciprocating compressor. Consequently, the reliability of DX machines used in thermal storage applications is not high.

Screw machines (also called helical rotary machines) are a positive displacement type. They offer many attractive performance characteristics, including a nearly constant refrigerant flow rate, low noise, low speed, high thermal efficiency and low discharge temperature. This last point qualifies the screw-type chiller as an icemaker. However, the low discharge temperature comes at a high price. The 20 degree F suction temperature necessary to build ice on a coil requires about 30 percent more input energy than does the 42 degree F evaporator temperature that produces chilled water.

Reciprocating machines, too, are of the positive displacement type. Because pressure rise has only a slight influence on the volume flow rate of the compressor, a reciprocating chiller can maintain nearly full cooling capacity even on days when wet-bulb temperatures are above design conditions for the machine. This type of chiller is also capable of making ice. It can, however, be subject to the same energy penalties as the screw compressor in the ice-making temperature ranges. Another disadvantage of the reciprocating chiller is its capacity limit. The largest readily available machine of this kind is only about 200 tons. Because reciprocating chillers commonly use a DX evaporator, they do not work well in thermal storage applications. The varying suction and discharge conditions under which thermal storage systems operate can damage the compressor.

Centrifugal machines are the most widely used commercial HVAC chillers. Their popularity stems from their reliability, energy economy and ability to respond to fluctuating load conditions. Centrifugal chiller reliability is partially due to the use of flooded evaporators. These drop unevaporated refrigerant out of the suction gas, thus protecting the compressor. Because centrifugal machines are not of the constant displacement type, they offer a wide range of capacities continuously modulated over a limited range of pressure ratios. Thus, centrifugal chillers are desirable for both close temperature control and energy conservation because of their wide load handling characteristics (with nearly proportionate changes in power consumption).

However, centrifugal chillers face initial and operating costs when used for ice-making. These costs are not encountered when the chilled medium does not undergo a state (solid/liquid) change. A water/glycol solution is required as the heat transfer medium to make ice. The addition of the initial glycol cost and the cost of periodically replacing the glycol solution make ice storage systems driven by centrifugal chillers even more expensive than they already are.

Thermal storage for a new construction project presents options that cannot be considered for retrofit applications such as those at NASO. In new construction, the heat transfer equipment can be selected with thermal storage in mind. For instance, in new construction a screw or centrifugal chiller compressor could be sized exactly for the load and choice of storage medium.

In retrofit construction, as is the case at NASO, the designer must use existing chillers unless those units are old and ready for replacement. At NASO, the chillers serving Building Nos. 2, 3, 4 and 36 are not ready for replacement. But by using storage system options of chilled water or eutectic salts, NASO could take full economic advantage of the existing equipment and would not have to install new heat transfer media or glycol. The following section further discusses important issues involving the various types of storage media.

Storage Media: Water is the most common storage medium. It provides a capacity of 1 btu per lb-degree F in the liquid state and 144 btu per lb when changing from liquid to ice at 32 degrees F. Whether the additional thermal storage capacity associated with the phase change offers a net benefit depends largely on the specific application.

The efficient production of ice may require refrigeration equipment different from conventional HVAC chillers. When properly selected, ice-making systems can operate at efficiencies comparable to HVAC chiller systems. But with retrofit HVAC applications such as those at NASO, the ice-making approach would add to the initial cost of the project, unlike using existing equipment to chill water for storage in the liquid state.

Containment Systems

Schemes for containing chilled water in thermal storage systems focus primarily on balancing vessel volumes and costs with the need to keep warm (unchilled) water separate from chilled water. (The separation is necessary to ensure that the chillers operate at favorable evaporator temperatures during the off-peak hours.) Three different approaches are commonly taken:

Single Tank: The first approach utilizes a single tank with no excess volume but with a flexible bladder dividing the enclosed space (see Figure 1). With this approach, the volume of water in the tank remains constant while the relative amounts of warm and chilled water vary. During the night (off-peak period), warm water from the upper storage volume is pumped through the chiller and into the lower part of the tank. At 6:00 AM the lower tank (cooled water) is lined up to discharge through the cooling coils and back into the upper tank to be chilled during the night. The cycle repeats itself.

Dual Tank: The second approach utilizes two tanks, each sized to contain the full volume of the chilled water to be generated during off-peak hours. During the day (on-peak period), one tank is filled with return (warm) water while the other tank is emptied of chilled water to satisfy loads. At night (off-peak period), the warm water is pumped from the full tank, through the chillers, and into the empty tank in preparation for the cooling loads of the next day. Problems with this approach include the hazard of air being drawn into the system as either tank empties. Also, this approach requires installation of a total tank volume which is twice that needed to contain the system water at a given time. This may not be possible in retrofit projects where space for tank installation is limited.

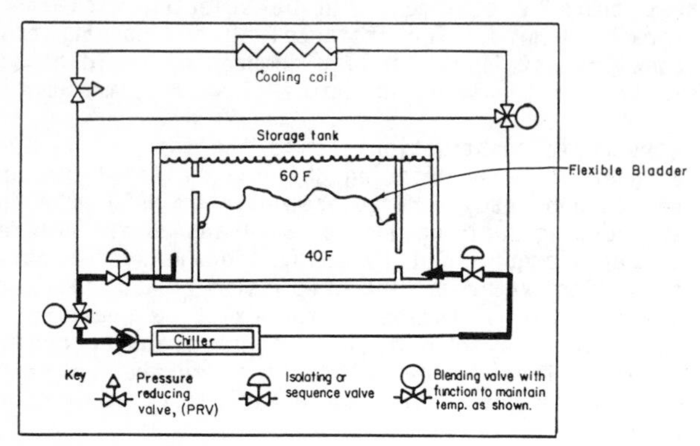

a) Tank charging mode

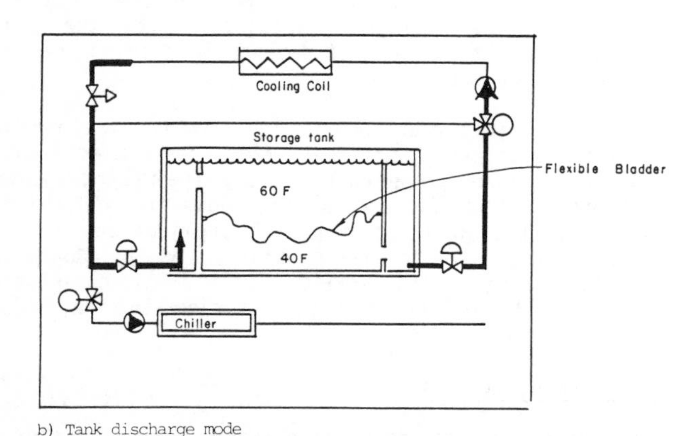

b) Tank discharge mode

FIG. 1. CHILLED WATER STORAGE, SINGLE TANK WITH FLEXIBLE BLADDER

Multiple Tank: The third approach would partially alleviate the requirement for excessive storage volume. A larger number of tanks, perhaps six, might be used, each with a capacity one-fifth of the total system volume. See Figure 2. During the off-peak nighttime hours, warm water from the tanks flows through the chiller and into the empty storage volume. When cooling needs occur the following day, chilled water is delivered to the cooling coils. The warm water discharged from the coils fills the available storage volume over the course of the day, and at night the system repeats the cycle. In this way, separation between warm and chilled water can be maintained with only 20 per cent excess storage volume. The hazard of air being drawn into the system remains, however, and the cost and complexity of tank construction and piping assembly increase.

The single tank approach was selected for NASO to minimize first costs and space requirements for tank installation.

A Favorable Electrical Power Rate Structure

The electric company power rate structure may include part or all of the following elements:

- Time-of-day rate adjustment,
- Seasonal rate adjustment,
- KWH energy rate,
- KW demand charge
- KW demand ratchet clause and
- Customer charge.

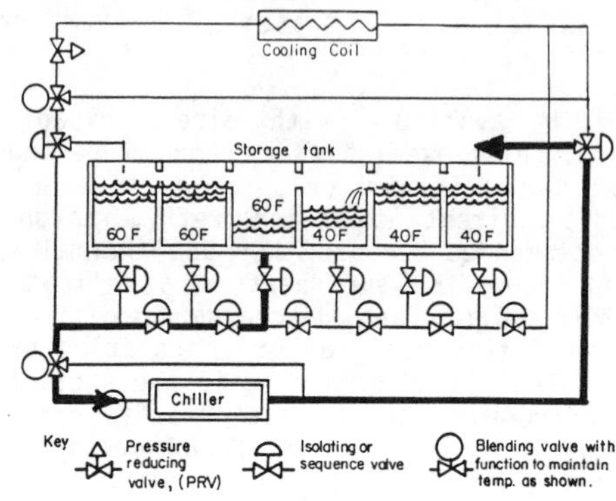

a) Charging mode

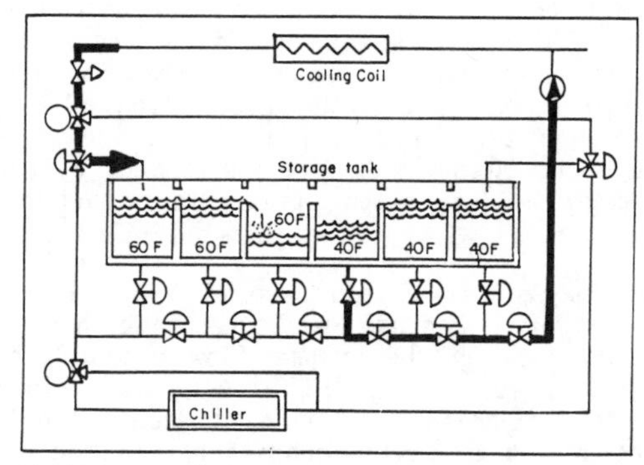

b) Discharge mode

FIG. 2. CHILLED WATER STORAGE, MULTIPLE TANK SYSTEM

NASO is provided electric service by the Philadelphia Electric Company under their high tension power rate. This rate comprises charges and credits for electric energy use according to a time-of-day and seasonal structure. On-peak hours are defined as 8:00 AM to 8:00 PM, Monday through Thursday. Friday on-peak hours are from 8:00 AM to 4:00 PM. All other hours are off-peak, including weekends and holidays.

The time-of-day energy use is but one component of the monthly electric bill. A customer service charge and peak power demand constitute the remaining charges. Kilowatt-hours are billed at three incremental rates. The first 150 hours times the KW demand is charged at \$0.0739/KWH. The second 150 hours times the demand is billed at \$0.0556/KWH. The balance of the monthly KWH usage costs is \$0.0376/KWH. Each kilowatt of monthly peak demand is billed at \$5.37/KW. The customer charge is \$220.45 per month.

Kilowatt-hours consumed during on-peak hours receive the additional on-peak charge of $0.0057/KWH from June through September. The off-peak credit for kilowatt-hours used in the off-peak period during these months is $0.0021/KWH. The months of October through May have an on-peak and off-peak charge and credit of $0.0022/KWH and $0.0021/KWH, respectively.

The peak KW demand is billed according to the season. The billing demand for each month of the October-through-May period is 80 percent of the highest demand recorded during the June-through-September period. Billing demand for each month of the June-through-September period is the actual peak KW occurring during the month. Table 1, following, summarizes the rate schedule.

TABLE 1. ELECTRIC RATE SCHEDULE

Billing Category	Charges (in $) Per Mo	Per kW	Per kWh	Per On-peak kWh	Credit Per Off-peak kWh
Customer service	$220.45				
Demand		$5.37			
Energy					
1st 150 hrs x demand			$0.0739		
2nd 150 hrs x demand			0.0556		
Additional Wage			0.0376		
June through September (Summer Months)				$0.0057	$0.0021
October through May (Winter Months)				0.0022	0.0021

NORTHERN DIVISION'S TECHNICAL CHOICE

Building Nos. 2, 3, 4 and 36 were analyzed both with and without thermal storage. For brevity, however, only Building No. 36 analysis will be presented since what applies to Building No. 36 applies to all.

Existing Systems: Building No. 36 is currently served by a variable air volume system which is run in the cooling mode from May through September. The chilled water coils are fed by a 400-ton centrifugal chiller operating from 6:00 AM to 5:00 PM and providing cooling to the 117,000 sq. ft. space dedicated to general office type use. The building is occupied from 7:00 AM until 6:00 PM weekdays. Because the chiller and fans are shut down at night, this schedule is well suited to using the unoccupied hours to generate and store chilled water for the cooling needs of the next day.

The daytime cooling loads are caused by various factors, significantly heat generated by lighting, office equipment and personnel. Other loads include: conduction through the building envelope, solar gains through windows and heat introduced with outside air through infiltration and ventilating air. Another source of heat is the gain from building mechanical equipment such as air conditioning, refrigeration and air handling equipment and domestic water heaters.

Occupant density is approximately 85 square feet per person, the lighting level is 1.65 watts per square foot and office equipment uses about 0.75 watts per square foot. Because of the total heat load of the building structure and its contents, heat is stored in walls and furniture during the day. When the mechanical system fans are shut down at about 5:00 PM, ventilation is eliminated. Because heat stored in the building structure and contents is released into the building during the night, temperatures inside the building remain relatively warm despite cooling outside temperatures. Early morning solar gains contribute to the interior heat level. Consequently, cooling is sometimes needed at 6:00 AM or 7:00 AM to bring the interior temperatures of the building down to comfort range preparatory to employee arrivals. Even if cooling is not required before the workday starts, loads are rapidly generated as people arrive and lights and equipment are energized.

Figure 3 represents the hourly cooling load profile on a typical summer day. Building No. 36 was still warm when the chiller came on-line at 6:00 AM to cool the building in anticipation of the work day. The daily peak occurred during the second hour of chiller operation due to the increased cooling load of the work force, lights, office equipment and solar gains.

As the cooling system caught up with heat gains, the cooling load dropped steadily throughout the remaining morning. Greatly reduced gains occurred when equipment was turned off and people left the building at midday. As a result, the cooling load bottomed at 1:00 PM and then climbed as afternoon activity increased, peaking at 3:00 PM.

Figure 5 depicts the hourly electric demand profile for Building No. 36 on a typical summer day. The base electric load consists primarily of nighttime lighting. Demand took a jump at 6:00 AM when the 400-ton chiller switched on to begin cooling the building. Demand climbed steeply when lights and equipment were turned on to accommodate the workday. A morning peak was established at 10:00 AM when office activities were in full swing. The profile registered a dip as workers turned off machinery and left the building for lunch. Electric demand again increased as people returned to work. The peak demand of the day occurred at 3:00 PM.

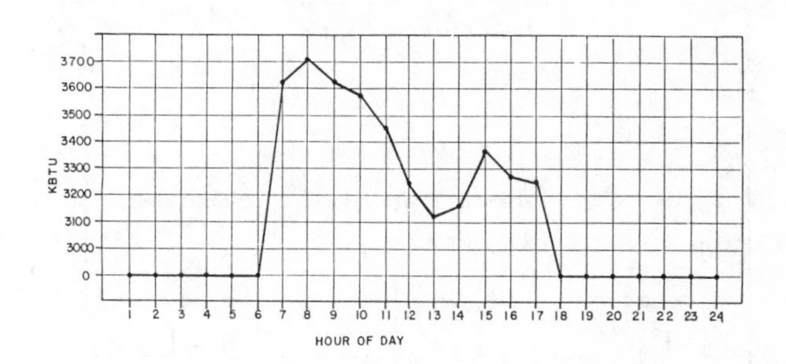

FIG. 3. BLDG. NO. 36, HOURLY COOLING LOAD PROFILE - TYPICAL SUMMER DAY

Proposed Storage System: The chilled water storage system investigated in the study employs the existing 400-ton chiller to generate chilled water during the 5:00 PM to 8:00 AM off-peak electric period. This system produces 800 gallons of water per minute cooled an average 10 degrees F in one pass through the chiller.

An insulated storage tank located above the ground and capable of holding 705,000 gallons is divided into upper and lower sections by a movable membrane. While the tank is charging, the chiller receives 50 degrees F to 60 degrees F water from the upper section and supplies the lower section with 40 degrees F to 50 degrees F chilled water. The membrane moves up inside the tank as the upper water volume diminishes and the lower section volume increases.

During the day, cooling loads demand chilled water from the lower tank section and circulate it through the cooling coils of the Variable Air Volume (VAV) air handlers. It is returned to the upper section of the storage tank 10 degrees F to 14 degrees F warmer than when it left the lower section. As the volume of the lower section is depleted and the volume of the upper section grows, the membrane moves down inside the tank. At the end of the working day, the volume of chilled water has been drawn off and is again ready for the tank charging mode of operation. The cycle repeats daily, with the charge mode beginning Sunday evening at 8:00 PM and ending Friday with the shutdown of building operations. The system sits idle over the weekend until the charge mode begins again on Sunday in anticipation of the workweek. This daily cycle is in use from May 1 through September 30.

Figures 1 and 4, respectively, illustrate the tank membrane system and the proposed configuration of the storage system.

Figure 5 depicts the hourly electric peak demand profile for Building No. 36 with and without a storage system, on a typical summer day.

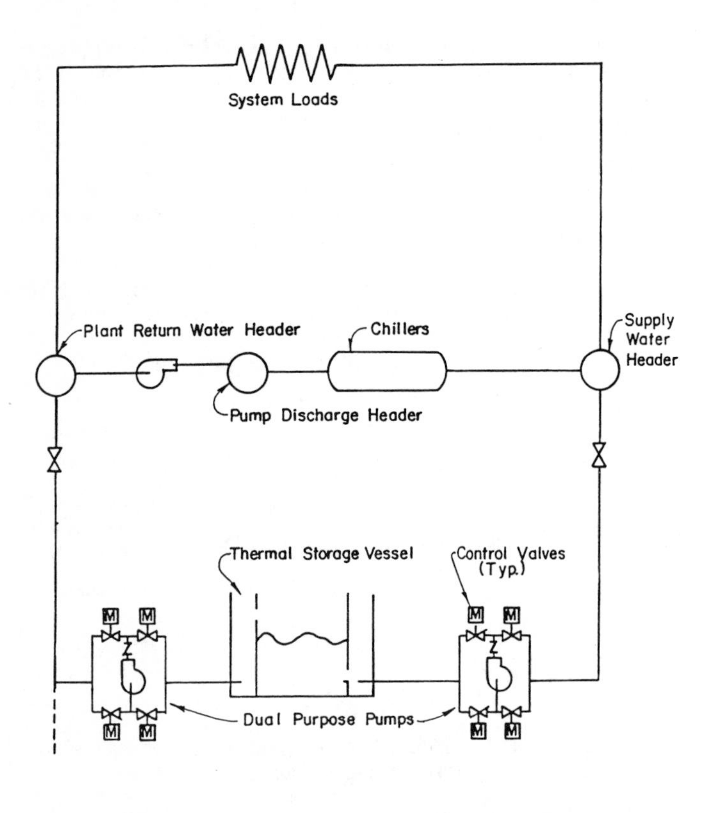

FIG. 4. PROPOSED THERMAL STORAGE SYSTEM

Summary of Energy Cost Savings: Cost savings could be realized by shifting chiller operation from on-peak electric hours to off-peak, taking advantage of the lower off-peak electric rates. Additional cost savings could be obtained by reducing kilowatt demand during the period that the facility-wide peak occurs. This peak occurs during the day when lighting and equipment demand are concurrent with peak cooling loads. Shifting the operation of the chiller in Building No. 36 would reduce the building peak power demand by the amount of power drawn by the chiller (up to 271 kilowatts). Consequently, both the facility-wide daytime demand and the kilowatt demand charge would drop correspondingly.

Tables 2 and 3 summarize the base case and storage case electrical usage respectively and present a summary of electrical data. The storage system reduces on-peak usage by 166,172 kilowatt hours, the total electrical usage by 13,646 kilowatt hours and the building peak kilowatt demand from 593 to 332 kilowatts.

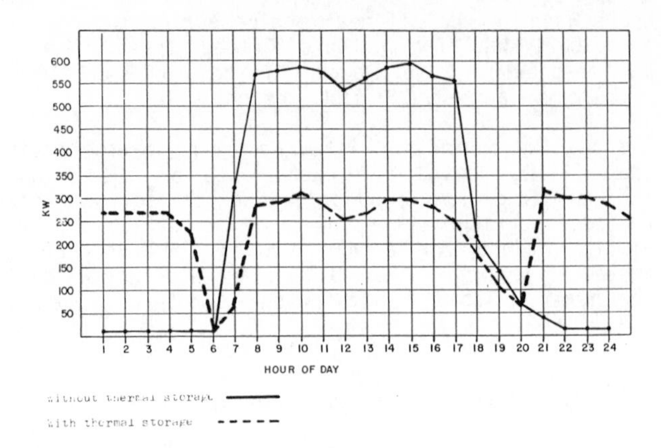

FIG. 5. BLDG. NO. 36, PEAK ELECTRIC DEMAND PROFILE WITH AND WITHOUT THERMAL STORAGE, TYPICAL SUMMER DAY

TABLE 2. BUILDING NO. 36, COOLING SEASON ELECTRICAL LOADS, BASE CASE SUMMARY

Month	Peak kW	On-peak kWh	Off-peak kWh	Total kWh
May	524	86,121	22,930	109,024
Jun	854	91,249	29,815	121,064
Jul	590	105,446	25,919	131,365
Aug	593	98,022	26,889	124,911
Sep	587	90,062	22,798	112,860
Total	593	470,900	128,351	599,224

TABLE 3. BULIDING NO. 36, COOLING SEASON ELECTRICAL LOADS, STORAGE CASE SUMMARY

Month	Peak kW	On-peak kWh	Off-peak kWh	Total kWh
May	311	59,140	42,029	101,169
Jun	322	60,677	58,966	119,643
Jul	332	64,650	66,563	131,213
Aug	322	60,179	64,536	124,715
Sep	318	60,082	48,756	108,838
Total	332	304,728	280,850	585,578

Table 4 displays the electric cost savings delivered by the chilled water storage system. Savings in the noncooling season are the result of the 80 percent ratchet clause in the utility rate structure. Reducing the cooling season peak demand by 261 kilowatts causes the billing demand during the noncooling season to drop by 80 percent to 209 kilowatts. The total cost savings realized by the storage system are 37,894 dollars per year.

Storage System Cost Estimate: The cost of the proposed chilled water system is estimated at 450,000 dollars, based on 1985 material and labor costs. This value was derived by using standard engineering cost estimating methods. Individual component costs were taken from "MEANS 1985 Building Construction Costs Data" or were quoted by equipment suppliers. Table 5 summarizes component costs.

TABLE 4. BLDG. NO. 36, ELECTRICAL COST SAVINGS WITH THERMAL STORAGE

Month	Savings (1985$)
Jan	2,993
Feb	2,993
Mar	2,993
Apr	2,993
May	3,392
Jun	4,055
Jul	4,037
Aug	4,201
Sep	4,251
Oct	-0-
Nov	2,993
Dec	2,993
Total	37,894

TABLE 5. BLDG. NO. 36, THERMAL STORAGE MACHINERY COST ESTIMATE

NAVFAC 11013/7 (1-78) Supersedes NAVDOCKS 2417 and 2417A — COST ESTIMATE — DATE PREPARED 11-13-85 — SHEET 1 OF 1

ACTIVITY AND LOCATION: BLDG. 36, CHW STG. CONCEPT W/SINGLE TANK & BLADDER
CONSTRUCTION CONTRACT NO.:
IDENTIFICATION NUMBER:
PROJECT TITLE: NAVFAC, NORTHDIV NASO, PHILADELPHIA, PA
ESTIMATED BY: GT
CATEGORY CODE NUMBER:
STATUS OF DESIGN: [ ] PED [ ] 30% [ ] 100% [ ] FINAL [X] Other (Specify) Feas Stdy
JOB ORDER NUMBER:

ITEM DESCRIPTION	QUANTITY		MATERIAL COST		LABOR COST		ENGINEERING ESTIMATE	
	NUMBER	UNIT	UNIT COST	TOTAL	UNIT COST	TOTAL	UNIT COST	TOTAL
STEEL TANK	1	EA					LS	146,000
FOUNDATION							LS	46,200
BLADDER							LS	50,000
TANK INSULATION	9,500	SF	.09	855	.25	2,375		3,230
PUMPS	2	EA	5,100	10,200	1,500	3,000		13,200
INSULATED PIPING	500	LF	48.15	24,075	21.60	10,400		34,875
VALVES/FITTINGS							LS	7,000
ELECTRIC POWER WIRING							LS	1,750
CONTROLS							LS	5,000
SUBTOTAL								307,255
OP & L (27.05%)								83,112
CONTINGENCY (15%)								58,555
TOTAL								448,922
ROUNDED TO								450,000

S/N 0105-LF-010-1371 — U.S. Government Printing Office

BASIS FOR DECISION ON EXERCISING A PROJECT DEVELOPMENT OPTION

Thermal storage systems were investigated as economical means of reducing the cost of space cooling at the Naval Aviation Supply Office. Building Nos. 2, 3, 4 and 36 were studied as prospective sites of storage systems. The preceding are detailed discussions of benefits to be derived from Building No. 36 HVAC modification with a thermal storage system. It is typical of the other three buildings with respect to thermal storage.

Chilled water was selected as the storage medium because of its lower first cost in retrofit applications compared to other available storage media. The Philadelphia Electric Company provides power to NASO through the High Tension Rate. This rate structure is conducive to the nighttime generation of chilled water which can be stored and used to address the cooling loads of the following day. The chilled water approach allows the use of existing chillers to charge storage tanks.

The costs of installed components for ice and eutectic salt systems for Building No. 36 are higher (28 and 36 percent, respectively) than the chilled water storage system cost estimated for this building. Savings-to-investment ratios and simple payback periods will therefore be less attractive for these systems than for a chilled water system.

The results of this study indicate chilled water storage delivers an annual dollar savings on electric costs for each building and building complex of $37,894, $44,464 and $65,515 respectively for Building Nos. 36; 4; 2 and 3.

The electric cost savings resulting from installing a thermal storage system are substantial. However, the cost of retrofitting buildings with chilled water storage systems are also substantial. Chilled water storage systems exhibit economies of scale. The installed costs of the 705,000 gallon systems studied at Building No. 36 is $0.64 per gallon. Tanks of larger size, however, start to require additional structural considerations which increase the costs disproportionately to the 705,000 gallon tank.

Another factor influencing storage system economics is the amount of time during the year the system operates. The cooling season for Building No. 36 is only five months. During the remaining seven months, the system sits idle and generates no electric cost savings. In contrast, the system serving Building Nos. 2 and 3 is operated year-round, producing cost savings every month.

The higher system cost per gallon of storage, combined with seven months of idle time each year, spells relatively long payback periods for chilled water storage systems serving Building No. 36. The system serving Building Nos. 2 and 3, on the other hand, enjoys a shorter payback as a result of a system economy of scale and year-round usage.

The Navy uses the Savings/Investment Ratio (SIR) as their economic guide in qualifying projects for funding. Energy Conservation Projects with SIRs greater than 2.5 are considered valid from the viewpoint of taxpayer dollars equitably spent in shore facility projects. Table 6 highlights the techno/economics of the three projects.

TABLE 6. SUMMARY OF STORAGE SYSTEM SAVINGS

Building	On-peak kWh Saved	Peak Demand Saved	Dollars Saved	Savings-to-Investment Ratio (SIR)
2 & 3	1,085,944	399	65,515	1.02
4	188,819	313	44,464	0.80
36	166,172	271	37,894	0.94

Conceding electrical costs could increase and possibly economically justify thermal storage, one must realize that there is a straight line relationship between electrical costs and the SIR in this project. Therefore, to attain an SIR of 2.5 (other factors being equal), electrical costs would have to increase by a factor of almost 1.6 for the Building No. 36 project to qualify economically.

As well as qualifying economically, the project must also qualify technically. A legitimate need for the Energy Conservation Project must be demonstrated also. In the above case a technically viable, legitimate need has been demonstrated. But the Economic Analysis indicates the Government can better invest capital elsewhere.

Some of us feel we could substitute underground wells as a holding (storage) place for water at 45 to 55 degrees F. When wells are drawn on, air handler chillers would only be required to cool the water 5 to

10 degrees F. The solution is not as simple as it seems. It involves environmental, forensic and electro/mechanical barriers of formidable magnitude. However, storage wells open a door for us when thermal storage closes a door to further investigation.

Summarizing our efforts in this thermal storage study, we find that capital investment in retrofitting Navy equipment at NASO is not compatible with the minimum savings expected of an Energy Conservation Project.

The industrial community, however, may consider an investment in a cold thermal storage plant like this because of various tax incentives it enjoys, which of course are unavailable to government. The tax credit for investing in new machinery and the tax credit for energy conservation investment, combined, could render this or similar cold thermal storage schemes very attractive. My intention in presenting the paper was not to express how a good idea can fail in the acid environment of dollars and cents realism but rather to offer our experience with a project's failure. Hopefully, industrial practitioners of engineering, working within less rigid economic restraints, will have more success.

SUMMARY

Methodology of the Study

A discussion on Northern Division's procedure in studying the feasibility of using thermal storage in conjunction with three large HVAC chillers at the Naval Aviation Supply Office, Philadelphia, PA was executed.

Technical Concepts

We have discussed the science of three cold thermal storage systems and the relative merit of each from the view of capital investment, maintenance and electrical cost saving.

A Favorable Electrical Power Rate Structure

The necessity for an electric company to offer a rate structure permitting low cost operation of refrigeration equipment during off-peak hours was scrutinized.

Northern Division's Technical Choice

A discussion of the pros and cons of the technology and economics of the three thermal storage system sciences was undertaken. They were considered as they relate to NASO chiller plants. Attention was given to the choice of retaining or replacing the existing chillers as each thermal storage system may demand.

Basis for Decision on Exercising a Project Option

The project's bottom line, after assuring the technical feasibility of thermal storage at NASO, was the Saving-Investment Ratio. This is used throughout the Navy Shore facility complex as a "go-no go" tool for determining energy saving project viability.

ACKNOWLEDGEMENTS

A thank you is offered to Lieutenant Commander J. L. Donofrio, Public Works Officer, along with Robert Bloch, P.E. and the able staff of engineers and their support personnel at the Naval Aviation Supply Office, Philadelphia, Pa.

Also thank you Bruce Bechard, P.E. and the staff of EMC Engineers, Inc., contracted to perform the thermal storage study, for producing an outstanding report upon which the author relied in preparing the preceeding paper.

Special thanks is extended to my colleagues and managers whose capable critique rendered the paper worthy of presentation here at the World Energy Engineers Congress, 1986.

And also, thank you Mr. Dick Koral, AEE for your encouragement to undertake the writing of this paper.

Chapter 40

THERMAL STORAGE WITH EMS CONTROL – AN IN-HOUSE APPLICATION

M. J. Herro, R. Roach

This paper will describe an in-house application of ice thermal storage controlled by a centralized energy management system. The combined system is installed and operating in the newly remodeled Trane Company's Technology Center in La Crosse, Wisconsin. The paper will begin by giving an overview of the building and it's energy management system. A description of the thermal ice system layouts will be followed by a discussion of the basic design considerations. Various aspects of the three thermal storage operating conditions will then be presented, with an emphasis on energy management control sequences. Finally, a description of other energy management features implemented at the Technology Center will be reviewed.

BUILDING OVERVIEW

The newly expanded Trane Technology Center is located in La Crosse, Wisconsin near the east bank of the Mississippi River. This northern location has an average of 7540 heating degree days and 683 cooling degree days. For this region the design dry bulb cooling temperature is 91 deg. F and wet bulb is 75 deg. F.

The Technology Center's structure consists of 2 floors above and 1 floor below grade with a total area of 193000 square feet. Indirect task lighting is used to provide illumination for the modular furniture setting. The walls of the building, made up primarily of insulated metal panels, have an overall R value of 21. There are two mechanical rooms in the ground floor which contain the air handling units, water chillers, back up electrical generator, and electrical distribution equipment. A separate room, adjacent to one of the mechanical rooms, is used to house the 17 ice storage tanks and associated piping. The ice tank system was first put into operation in the fall of 1985.

ENERGY MANAGEMENT SYSTEM OVERVIEW

An energy management system (EMS) equipped with equation processing is used to control and monitor the thermal storage system components. Equation processing is a user definable control program within the software of the EMS. The routines are written in a language similar to elementary Fortran statements. In addition to the thermal storage points, there are 700 other points being controlled and monitored at Trane's 5 manufacturing and office buildings. The Technology Center's EMS is a Trane TRACER 1000 system which is capable of direct digital control (DDC) and many other software programs. Constant on line information about the HVAC system can be monitored and/or controlled from any of six C.R.T. screens located throughout the South La Crosse manufacturing complex. There is a small C.R.T. screen located in each of the two mechanical rooms at the Tech. Center which aid in troubleshooting the HVAC system. A centralized C.R.T. and printer also serve the building's automation needs. Two remote stations in each mechanical room contain the terminations and computer cards to control and monitor the equipment. The smart remote stations monitor and send signals (0-10 volt or 4-20 mA) to the electronically controlled device actuators.

THERMAL SYSTEM

Figure 1 shows a simplified sketch of the piping arrangements for the Technology Center's ice storage system.

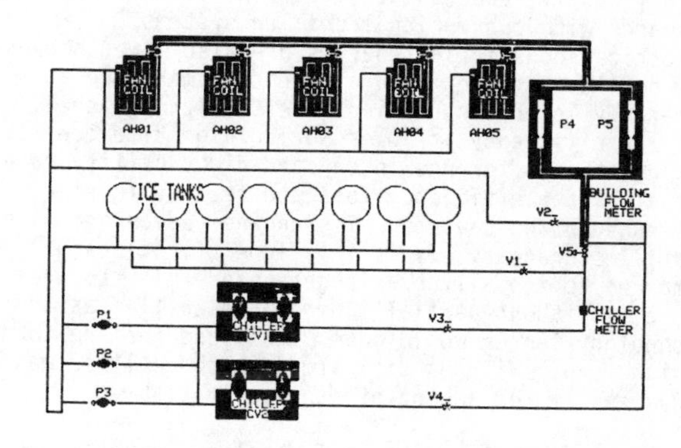

FIGURE 1. ICE STORAGE SYSTEM PIPING

There are two chillers shown in this system. Chiller #1 is a 185 ton centrifugal chiller with the capability of producing 45 deg. chilled water/glycol to the coils or 24 deg. chilled water/glycol to the ice tanks. Chiller #2 is a stand by chiller capable of producing 45 deg. water/glycol, but is not equipped to produce water cold enough to freeze water. There are two 30 HP building chilled water pumps (P4, P5), and three 30 HP pumps (P1, P2, P3) for the chillers. Each chiller has one dedicated pump, with the third acting as an automatic standby to the two chiller pumps.

The 17 thermal storage ice tanks, manufactured by CALMAC, are the foundation of the building's thermal storage system. Each tank stands 82 inches high and has a diameter of 74 inches. The cylindrical insulated tank contains spiral wound plastic tubing surrounded by water. The piping for the tanks is done in a reverse return design to insure even charging and discharging of the ice. During nighttime ice making a 24 degree water/ glycol solution is circulated in the tubes. This solution extracts heat from the the 850 gals. of water in each tank which causes the tank water to freeze. All 17 tanks are frozen solid at the end of a night ice charging cycle. During the day the ice in the tanks is melted to provide building cooling. To do this, the circulating water/glycol gives off heat to the melting ice mass. The solution is cooled to 32 degrees and is then mixed with building return water to deliver 45 deg. water to the air handling chilled water coils.

It is important to understand the basic design considerations of a thermal storage system in order to effectively control the operation.

THERMAL SYSTEM DESIGN CONSIDERATIONS

There are two types of load management designs which can be used with ice storage systems. A full storage system has enough capacity to meet design day load conditions. The other alternative is a partial storage system, which is the type in place at the Technology Center. In partial storage systems the storage capacity is downsized to meet only part of the building cooling load. The chiller provides the other portion of the cooling to meet the building load.

There are valuable savings which can be realized with a partial storage system. A partial storage system significantly reduces the electrical demand charges compared with conventional chiller systems. Electrical consumption charges are also lower because the chiller is being used at night to make ice at generally lower consumption rates. Although the chiller efficiency is lower during nighttime ice making, the difference in day and night utility rates outweighs the efficiency loss and results in electrical consumption savings. Yet another advantage of a partial storage system is it's lower first costs compared to installing a larger sized full storage system. Without partial storage the chiller at the Technology Center would have been sized for the total design load. With partial storage, the chiller was downsized by the amount of storage available.

On a cooling design day the Technology Center's 185 ton centrifugal chiller will run continuously in conjunction with the discharging ice in order to satisfy the occupied period peak load of 350 tons. This situation is typical of partial systems, where the full load cannot be met by the chiller alone. The load could be handled by the ice alone, but caution must be used to avoid discharging all of the ice too quickly. If the ice is all melted and the load is still high, the chiller will not be able to meet the peak cooling load later in the day.

With this type of system it is essential to use logic and foresight to insure cooling requirements are met for the entire day. This decision making process is most effectively handled by an advanced energy management system. It is also important to examine the total cooling requirements over a daily occupied period in order to formulate an effective cooling control strategy.

For a 10 hour occupied period, the total building load is designed to be 3350 ton - hours. Figure 2 shows a simple load analysis for a 10 hour design occupied period using the partial storage ice system.

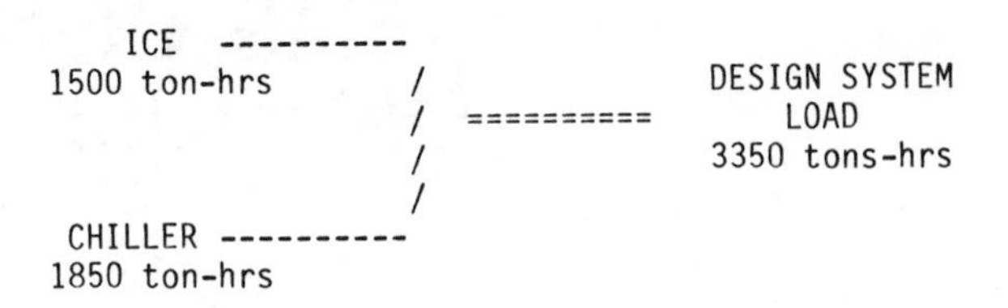

FIGURE 2. SIMPLIFIED LOAD ANALYSIS

There are many days in the spring and fall when the load is such that the chiller does not need to be turned on at all. Other situations occur when only the chiller needs to be run for a portion of the day in order to achieve the daily cooling requirements. With so many different conditions possible, a well planned control sequence needs to be devised.

THERMAL SYSTEM OPERATION MODES

In order to develop an energy management control strategy it is necessary to define the different operational conditions that will exist. This section will concentrate on 3 different operational modes; 1) Ice making only 2) Ice discharging only 3) Ice discharging plus chiller producing 45 deg. water. One additional situation involves using the back up chiller for second shift cooling while chiller #1 is simultaneously making ice for the following days cooling needs.

Operation Mode #1 - Ice making only

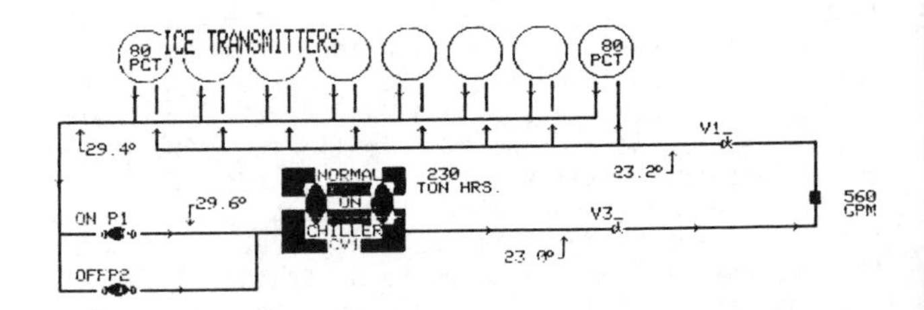

FIGURE 3. ICE MAKING ONLY MODE

A simple isolated flow loop is used for the ice making mode. There are three valves that the energy management system has to position properly to insure that a full load of ice can be made. Valves V3 and V1 are opened and the building loop valve is closed. Two additional functions need to be done to make the ice. The first is to switch the chiller from its normal setpoint of 45 deg. to the low setpoint of 24 degrees. The next step is to start pump #1. All of these steps are performed by a simple EMS equation processing routine, which is executed once a day at 9:00 pm. Once the chiller is running it takes approximately 1-2 hours to pull the storage tank temperatures down to 32 degrees. This time period depends on what the tank water temperature is at start up. As the ice begins to build up on the plastic tubes in the storage tanks the return water/glycol temperature hovers at approx. 31.5 degrees. This causes the chiller to remain loaded during the major portion of the charge cycle. Towards the end of the charge cycle (as the tanks approach total freeze up) the return water/glycol temperature finally begins to fall. Figure 4 shows a trend log which depicts the return water/glycol pulldown characteristics during the ice making mode.

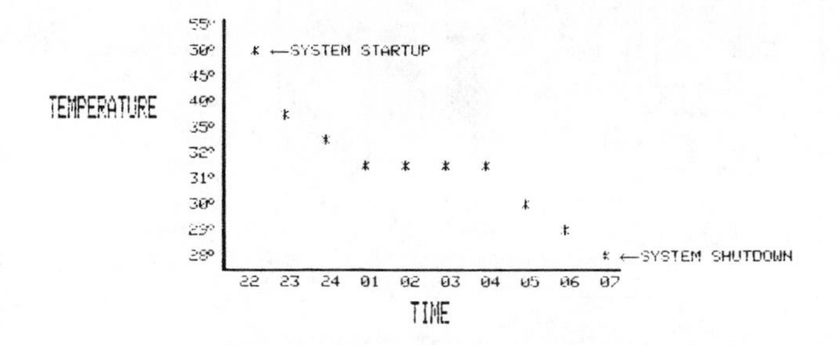

FIGURE 4. TREND LOG OF RETURN H2O/GLYCOL (TEMPERATURE VS. TIME)

The amount of time to complete the charging of the tanks after the tanks reach 32 deg. is approximately 8 hours. The EMS system stops ice charging with an analog auto response program which monitors the return water/glycol temperature. When the water/glycol reaches 28 degrees, the program shuts off pump #1. This drops out the evaporator flow switch and the chiller shuts down. Another software program, called binary auto response, is then initiated by the status change of pump #1. This program executes an equation processing routine which positions the valves and the chiller setpoint back to the position normally used for building pulldown in the morning.

Operation Mode #2 - Ice discharging only

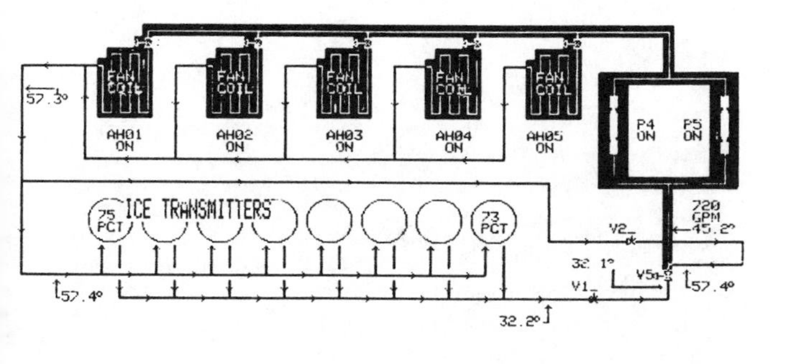

FIGURE 5. ICE DISCHARGING MODE

In the ice discharging mode there are three valves and one pump that need to be controlled. Valves V1 and V5 are opened, valve V2 is modulated and pump #5 is turned on. There are two situations in which only ice would be used to cool the building. In the first, the thermal storage forecasting program determines that there is an adequate number of ice ton-hours to meet the daily load, therefore ice only is used for the daily cooling needs. The second situation to use ice only would be during times of high electrical demand. As the electrical demand rises to near peak levels, the load shed program of the EMS shuts down the chiller for a set period of time or until the demand comes back down. While the chiller is being shed, the ice system picks up the building load.

In partial storage systems it is sometimes necessary to operate both the chiller and ice at the same time in order to satisfy the daily building cooling needs.

Operation Mode #3 - Ice discharging plus chiller at 45 deg.

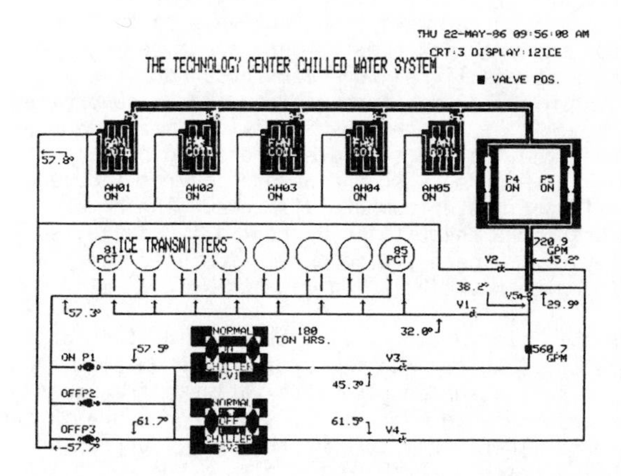

FIGURE 6. ICE DISCHARGING & CHILLER AT 45 DEGREES MODE

There are many decisions that have to be made when two systems are trying to satisfy a common cooling load. These decisions are made by using an equation processing routine, which is a small computer program within the EMS tailored to the situation being controlled.

In mode #3 the thermal storage prediction program has determined the daily load to be greater than the ice storage capacity. It will be necessary to operate the chiller in order to make up the shortfall in ton-hours needed for the day. The chiller will be used to do the initial morning pulldown for the building. When the building space temperature is down to approx. 75 degrees, a separate equation is executed which keeps a log of the chiller ton-hours produced. This equation will continually compare ton-hours produced to the ton-hours required minus the stored capacity. Once the stored capacity plus the ton-hours produced equals the predicted load, the chiller is shutdown and the system switches to discharging ice only.

There are times when the instantaneous load is greater than the capacity of the chiller. The equation processing routine monitors this instantaneous load and automatically opens electronic valves to discharge ice when the excess load situation occurs. Water flow meters are used to determine whether ice is needed to supplement the chiller in meeting the instantaneous load. The chiller pump is only capable of delivering 560 GPM to the building, so when the building load flow meter rises above 560 GPM the program opens valve V1 and the excess building load is pulled from the ice storage tanks.

An electrical demand limiting feature is also implemented into the program. The program scans the current electrical demand and shuts down the chiller, for a specified time period, when the demand is near peak. Ice discharge is now handling the whole cooling load. If the ice level ever reaches a critical low point, which is the point where the daily ice would run out too quickly, an alarm is generated and the chiller can then be restarted.

The thermal storage system is only one of many operations controlled by the energy management system at the Technology Center.

OTHER EMS CONTROL APPLICATIONS

The Technology Center's energy management system is used in many other ways to effectively control and monitor the HVAC equipment. There are a total of 7 remote stations linked together throughout the building with 123 monitored points and 85 controlled points. All of the remotes are called smart remotes. In these remotes the schedules and setpoints are stored in the remote so the remote can run independently if the master computer is down. The remote stations serve the total electronically controlled HVAC system. There are no pneumatics used for control within the building.

A variable air volume (VAV) system is in place at the Technology Center. The VAV system uses an air monitoring station coupled with variable frequency drive inverters to maintain 1" static pressure in the ductwork. There are 150 electronically controlled VAV boxes which distribute the air to the space. A portion of the VAV temperature setpoints are editted through the EMS C.R.T. screen which gives the EMS the capability of resetting space temperatures.

A direct digital control (DDC) strategy controls the cooling valve, heating valve, and mixing box dampers at each of the main air handling units (Figure 7). Using DDC software, the control of discharge air temperature is accomplished with very good accuracy and reliability. Each 0-10 dc volt signal comes from the analog output card located in the remote station. Reset of the discharge air is done during the morning warm up periods in order to bring the spaces to proper temperature in a short period of time.

DISCHARGE TEMP
59.1
D-2 POSITION OPEN
O.A. TEMP 71.0DEG
O.A. HUMID 17.6RH
OUTSIDE AIR DUCT
ON
SUPPLY
HEATING
COOLING
MIXING SP58.0
HEAT SP57.0
COOL SP59.0
DDC SETPOINTS
OCC/UNOCC OCC
MIX-REL DDC
OVERRIDE 2KC OFF
MIXING BOX
ENTHALPY
EAST VENT
DAMPER 2KA SHUTDOWN OFF
COOLING FLAG
RETURN AIR
HUMID
TEMP
RELIEF DUCT
ON
RETURN
35.7
74.2
DELTA CFM
OFF

FIGURE 7. AIR HANDLING GRAPHIC

One of the main advantages of a building controlled by an EMS is the centralized monitoring capabilities. Being able to monitor a building's HVAC system, security points, and electrical demand is a very useful tool for a building operator. Figure 8 shows a graphic of one of the mechanical rooms located in the Technology Center.

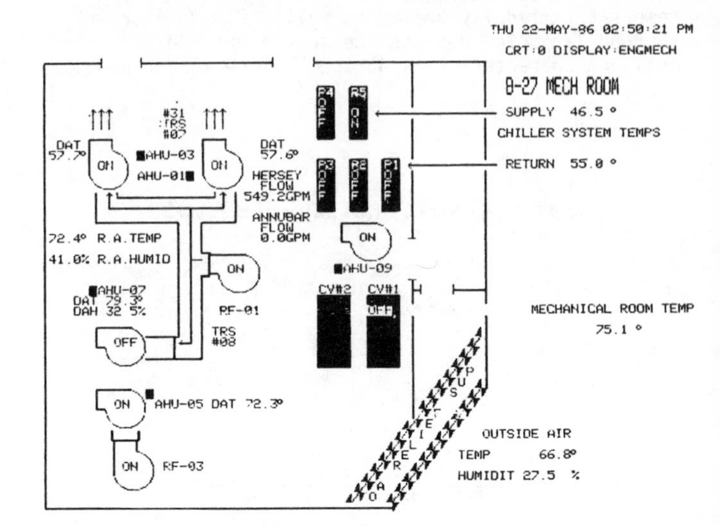

FIGURE 8. MECHANICAL ROOM GRAPHIC

This type of graphic can be monitored from any one of the systems C.R.T. screens. The response time to HVAC problems is greatly improved because of the operator notification capabilities of the system. This alarm feature is very useful for security points which monitor the open/close status of entry doors.

CONCLUSION

Thermal storage control with an energy management system has proven to be a very useful and exciting way to optimize ice system performance at the Trane Technology Center. Proper control and monitoring of a thermal ice storage system can best be accomplished by utilizing a complete energy management system. The EMS allows the operator to develop good working knowledge of the entire thermal system.

Chapter 41

THERMAL STORAGE OPTIONS FOR HVAC SYSTEMS

B. N. Gidwani, M. G. Mirchandani

ABSTRACT

With the ever-increasing cost of electricity and the high demand charges levied by utility companies, thermal storage for cooling is rapidly becoming a widely recognized method to lower cooling costs. There are three major types of thermal storage systems:

- Ice Storage: This utilizes the latent heat of fusion of ice for thermal storage. During off-peak periods, the refrigeration system is used to build ice. The ice is melted to produce chilled water when cooling is required.
- Chilled Water Storage: Chilled water is generated and stored during off-peak periods and used for cooling during on-peak hours. Since this method is based on the specific heat of water rather than the latent heat of fusion of ice as in ice storage, it requires about 4 times the storage capacity of an equivalent ice storage system.
- Salt Storage: This system utilizes eutectic salts which freeze and melt aroung 47°F. Existing chillers can be easily retrofitted for salt storage or chilled water storage. For ice storage systems, a direct refrigerant system or glycol chillers are suitable.

This paper discusses the details of each system, their advantages and disadvantages, and applications.

INTRODUCTION

With the escalating cost of electricity and high demand charges levied by utility companies, thermal storage is rapidly becoming a widely recognized method to lower cooling costs.

In conventional cooling systems, all equipment and piping is sized to meet peak instantaneous load. These systems would run at peak load during design conditions to satisfy existing loads. The concept of thermal storage as applied to cooling systems is that instead of using equipment designed to handle peak loads, a smaller unit is installed. This unit would operate throughout the day storing additional capacity during off-peak hours and using the stored capacity during on-peak periods. This results in smaller equipment, and smaller pipe and duct sizes. In addition, by producing cooling capacity during off-peak hours, the kW is shifted from on-peak periods resulting in demand charge savings. Also, many utility companies have time-of-use or time-of-day rates in which nighttime off-peak energy consumption is cheaper than other periods. Therefore, thermal storage would also save energy charge as expressed in cents/kWh.

Buildings with sharp load profiles are ideal applications for thermal storage. There are two types of storage systems: full storage and partial storage. In a full storage system, the chiller runs during off-peak periods to maximize the savings in on-peak period demand and energy consumption. During the on-peak period, the storage system needs to be sized to handle the entire on-peak cooling load. This system has a higher initial cost due to larger chiller and storage system as compared to the partial storage system in which the chiller continues to run during on-peak periods supplementing the storage capacity. Before choosing between the two types of storage systems, an economic assessment should be made considering the initial equipment cost and the annual energy costs.

There are three storage mediums commonly in use today: Chilled Water Storage, Ice Storage, and Salt Storage.

This paper presents the details of each of the above three storage mediums, their relative advantages and disadvantages, applications and cost considerations.

Chilled Water Storage

This system uses one or more tanks located in the cooling system as shown in Figure 1. Chilled water is generated at night by the chiller and flows through the tank, thus charging it. During on-peak period, warm return water enters the tank, displacing chilled water into the system. The principal advantage of the chilled water system is that it is easily retrofitted to existing chillers and does not sacrifice chiller efficiency. However, this medium of thermal storage requires a very large space since it utilizes sensible heat for storage. For a system operating at a 15°F temperature difference, the storage would be 15 Btu per pound of water. The major problem with existing chilled water systems has been in the area of blending the chilled water with the warm return water. Several techniques ranging from membranes to multi-tanks have been used to prevent temperature blending in the storage tank. Membranes are a source of maintenance problems whereas multi-tank systems result in high initial costs.

Ice Storage System

Ice storage systems fall into two different categories. First there are the static systems in which ice is formed on the evaporator coils inside an ice bank. The storage capacity of the ice bank is a function of the ice thickness. The ice bank generally consists of a serpentine pipe coil submerged in water in an insulated box. There are no moving parts within the ice bank. Design evaporating temperatures range from 10°F to 25°F depending on desired ice thickness, ice build-time, and heat transfer area.

The second kind of ice-storage system is the dynamic system in which ice is produced in crushed or chunk form and fed into large storage tanks. Water is circulated through the tank during on-peak periods to produce chilled water for cooling. Static systems are more popular since they are available as factory-assembled packaged units which provide ease of installation and a lower initial capital cost.

Since the latent heat of fusion is used for ice-storage, a pound of ice stores 144 Btu's of cooling energy as compared to 15 Btu's per pound for a chilled water system. This results in a storage capacity of about one-fourth that required for chilled-water. Other advantages include less weight, easier controls than water-storage systems and greater reliability. A disadvantage of ice-storage systems is that they cannot be easily retrofitted to existing chillers because existing chillers are typically designed for about 42°F water, whereas evaporator temperatures required for ice-storage systems are 10 to 25°F. Another aspect of ice-storage systems that warrants attention is that the lower evaporator temperature results in a slightly higher kW/ton for the system causing some penalty in cooling efficiency. Figure 2 illustrates a typical ice-storage system.

Salt Storage

This system utilizes salt hydrates which are mixtures of inorganic salts and water that are capable of freezing and melting at a pre-selected temperature. Salts are available that are capable of the above phase change at 47°F. Typically, the salts are sealed in plastic containers which are stacked in layers in a large tank. There are gaps between the containers which allow water to flow between the layers. During off-peak periods, chilled water is passed through the tank freezing the salts in the containers. The circulating water does not come in direct contact with the salt at any time. During the "melt-down" cycle (on-peak periods), the warm water from the building circulates through the tank, melting the salt and in turn is cooled to meet the cooling load. The latent heat of fusion of the salt-solution is about 40 Btu/lb. The tank size required is about one-third that required for water-storage. Other advantages of salt-storage systems are that they do not sacrifice chiller efficiency and they are easily retrofitted to existing chillers. Since salt-storage is a relatively newer technology, it does not have a proven storage track record unlike the other two storage mediums. Moreover, since the lowest water temperature possible is 47°F, humidity requirements of the building should be considered before specifying salt-storage. Also, the added cost of salt containers should be considered in the economic analysis. Figure 3 illustrates a typical salt-storage system.

SIZING THERMAL STORAGE SYSTEM

The first step in sizing a thermal storage system is to develop the peak-day load profile. This can be done utilizing chiller logs where available, or using load estimation software, or computer simulation of load based on ambient conditions. Table 1 presents a typical peak day load profile calculated using an hourly computer simulation model. No chiller logs were available, but it is known that

- Maximum Load = 674 Tons
- Design Day Temperature = 93°F DB
- Minimum Load = 236 Tons
- Temperature at Minimum Load = 40°F DB

The cooling load in tons is

$$\text{Minimum Load} + (\text{Maximum Load} - \text{Minimum Load}) \times \frac{(\text{Hourly Temp.} - \text{Temp. at Minimum Load})}{(\text{Design Day Temp.} - \text{Temp. at Minimum Load})}$$

Having obtained the peak-day load profile, the next step is to size the thermal storage capacity. The total daily cooling capacity required is 14,102 ton-hours. During summer months (May 1 to September 30) the on-peak hours on a weekday are effective from 12:30 p.m. to 6:30 p.m. If both chillers were to operate only during partial-peak and off-peak hours - 6:30 p.m. to 12:30 p.m. (18 hours) - the available capacity is calculated as follows:

$$18 \text{ Hours} \times 2 \times 337 \text{ Tons} = 12{,}132 \text{ Ton-Hours}$$

However, there is still a remaining cooling capacity of

$$14{,}102 - 12{,}132 = 1{,}970 \text{ Ton-Hours}$$

which will have to be generated during on-peak hours on a peak summer day. This load can be met by running one chiller for

$$\frac{1{,}970 \text{ Ton-Hours}}{337 \text{ Tons}} = 5.85 \text{ Hours}$$

Say 6 hours from 12:30 to 6:30 p.m.

Therefore, on a peak summer day the chiller operation can be summarized as follows:

- 6:30 p.m. to 12:30 p.m. (18 hours) - both 337 ton chillers run at full load.
- 12:30 p.m. to 6:30 p.m. (6 hours) - one 337 ton chiller runs at full load.

Even on a peak summer day, thermal storage helps in shifting 368 kW (one chiller) from on-peak to off-peak and partial-peak hours in the example.

Having computed the peak summer-day load profile and the proposed chiller operation, the size of the thermal storage system can be estimated. From 6:30 p.m. both chillers operate. Every hour the chiller runs (6:30 p.m. to 12:30 p.m. in the above example), it produces 674 tons of cooling and the air conditioning load required for that hour is used. At 1900 hours (6:30 p.m. to 7:30 p.m.), 674 tons of cooling is produced and 632.7 tons of air conditioning are required. The available capacity at the end of 1900 hours is

$$674 - 632.7 = 41.3 \text{ Tons}$$

At the beginning of 2000 hours (i.e., at 7:30 a.m.), 41.3 tons of cooling capacity is available from the previous hour. 674 tons are produced till 8:30 p.m. and 616.15 tons are used. Therefore, the available capacity at the end of 2000 hours (i.e., at 8:30 p.m.) is

$$41.32 + 674 - 616.2 = 99.2 \text{ Tons}$$

Table 2 presents an hourly dynamic profile of the available capacity at the end of each hour. From 12:30 p.m. to 6:30 p.m. only one chiller is operating. As can be seen from the table, the thermal storage system should be capable of storing at least 1992 ton-hours which is the maximum available capacity that would occur on a peak summer day.

SAVINGS CALCULATIONS

Figure 4 shows the peak day load profile and the proposed chiller operation with thermal storage. The energy savings will result from the following:

- Demand Savings =

  $$\sum (\text{kW Shifted})_i \times (\$/\text{kW})_i$$

  and,

- Energy Charge Savings =

  $$\sum (\text{Existing kWh Charge})_i - (\text{Proposed kWh Charge})_i$$

  Where,

  i = Each Month

ECONOMIC ANALYSIS

To assure that thermal storage is an attractive project for a particular installation, a complete life cycle cost analysis should be performed. In addition to the energy savings there are a number of other factors that need to be addressed. The various factors to be considered in the life cycle analysis are:

- Capital cost of the thermal storage system.
- Any rebate or incentives that can be obtained from the Utility.
- Avoided cost, if any, for a new or backup chiller.
- State energy tax credit savings, where applicable.
- Energy and demand savings.
- Annual operating and maintenance costs.

Figure 5 illustrates the various factors involved in the life cycle cost analysis.

In summary, it is imperative for the designer of any thermal storage system to consider the various storage technologies and systems, and to evaluate them for the particular application as discussed in this paper.

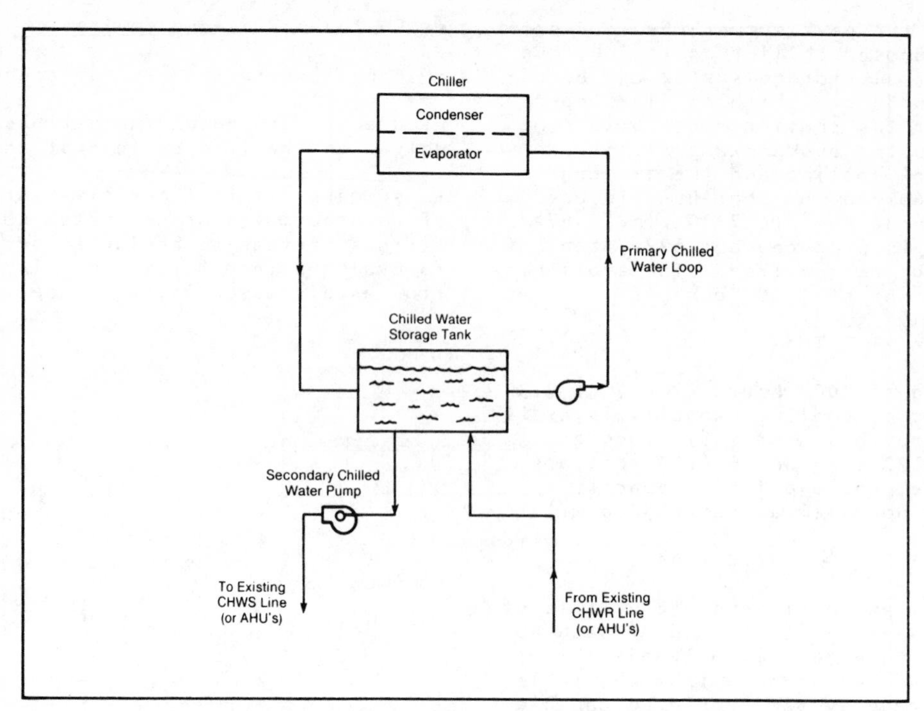

FIGURE 1 SCHEMATIC OF CHILLED-WATER-STORAGE SYSTEM

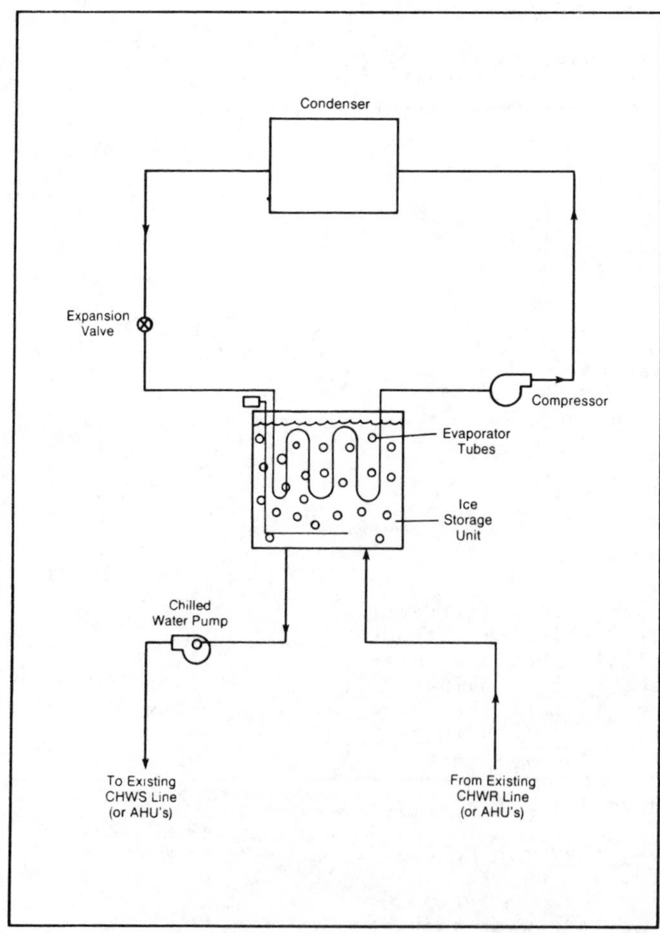

FIGURE 2 SCHEMATIC OF DX ICE-STORAGE SYSTEM

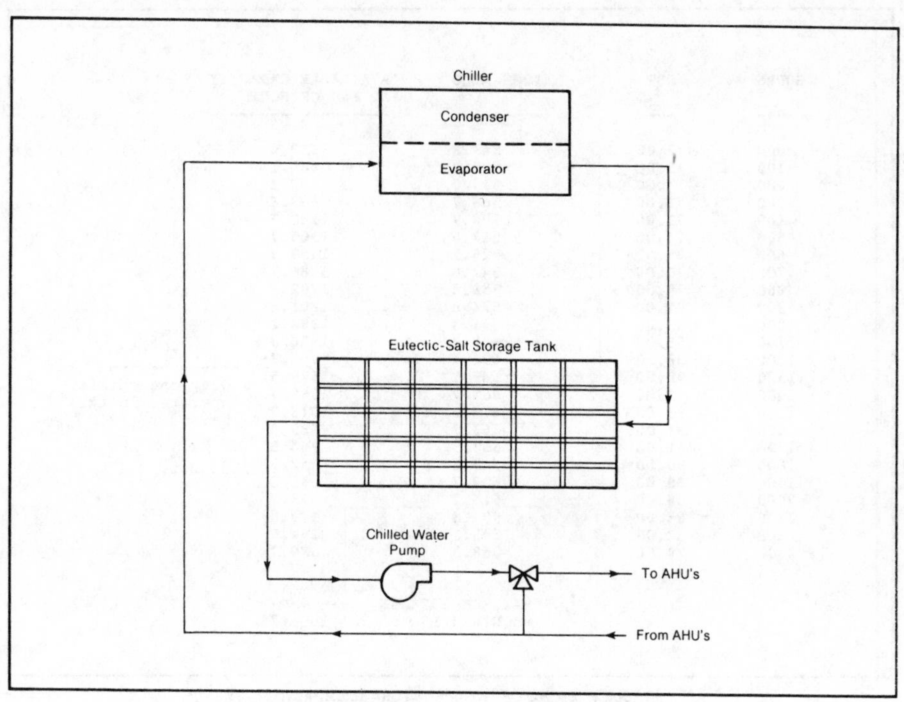

FIGURE 3 SCHEMATIC OF SALT-STORAGE SYSTEM

HOURS	TEMPERATURE DBT	WBT	COOLING CAPACITY (TONS)
000	77.00	66.00	541.77
100	75.00	66.00	525.25
200	74.00	65.00	516.98
300	73.00	65.00	508.72
400	73.00	65.00	508.72
500	74.00	65.00	516.98
600	75.00	65.00	525.25
700	77.00	66.00	541.77
800	79.00	66.00	558.30
900	81.00	67.00	574.83
1000	83.00	67.00	591.36
1100	85.00	68.00	607.89
1200	88.00	69.00	632.68
1300	90.00	70.00	649.21
1400	92.00	70.00	665.74
1500	93.00	70.00	674.00
1600	92.00	70.00	665.74
1700	91.00	70.00	657.47
1800	90.00	69.00	649.21
1900	88.00	69.00	632.68
2000	86.00	68.00	616.15
2100	84.00	68.00	599.62
2200	82.00	67.00	583.09
2300	79.00	67.00	558.30

Total Peak Day Ton-Hours: 14,101.70

- **Temperature at Minimum Load** 40°F DB
- **Temperature at Design Day** 93°F DB
- **Minimum Load** 236 Tons
- **Maximum Load** 674 Tons

TABLE 1 TYPICAL CALCULATION OF PEAK DAY LOAD PROFILE BY AN HOURLY SIMULATION MODEL

HOURS	DBT	TONS REQD	AVAILABLE CAPACITY AT END OF HOUR
000	77.00	541.8	512.4
100	75.00	525.2	661.1
200	74.00	517.0	818.2
300	73.00	508.7	983.4
400	73.00	508.7	1148.7
500	74.00	517.0	1305.7
600	75.00	525.2	1454.5
700	77.00	541.8	1586.7
800	79.00	558.3	1702.4
900	81.00	574.8	1801.6
1000	83.00	591.4	1884.2
1100	85.00	607.9	1950.3
1200	88.00	632.7	1991.7*
1300	90.00	649.2	1679.5
1400	92.00	665.7	1350.7
1500	93.00	674.0	1013.7
1600	92.00	665.7	685.0
1700	91.00	657.5	364.5
1800	90.00	649.2	52.3
1900	88.00	632.7	41.3
2000	86.00	616.2	99.2
2100	84.00	599.6	173.5
2200	82.00	583.1	264.5
2300	79.00	558.3	380.2

Only one chiller operates in this period. (1300–1800)

*MAXIMUM STORAGE REQUIRED IS : 1991.7

TABLE 2 SIZING OF THERMAL STORAGE CAPACITY

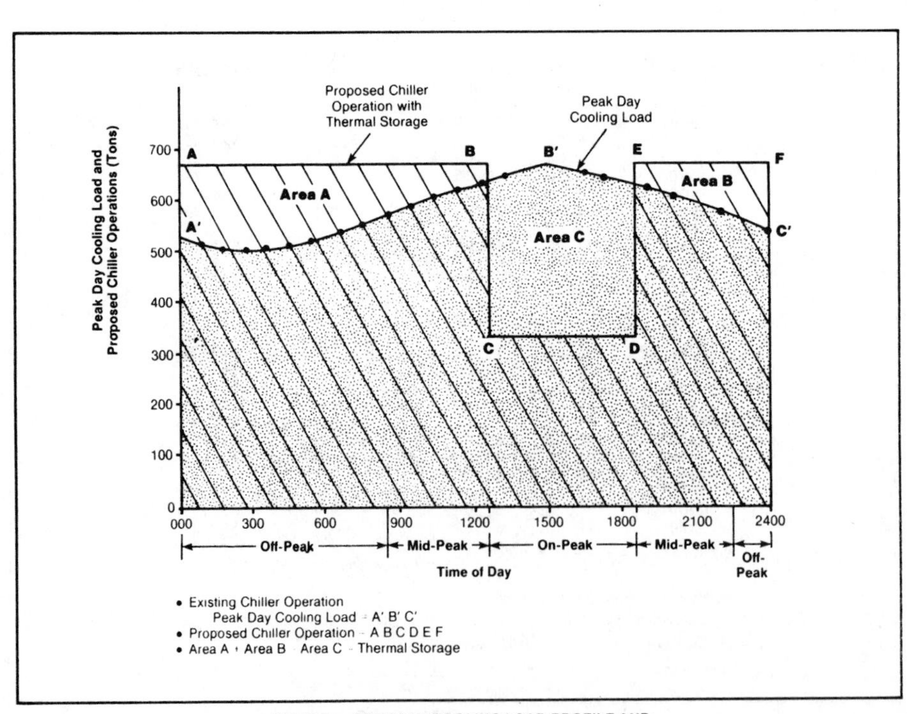

FIGURE 4 PEAK DAY COOLING LOAD PROFILE AND PROPOSED CHILLER OPERATION

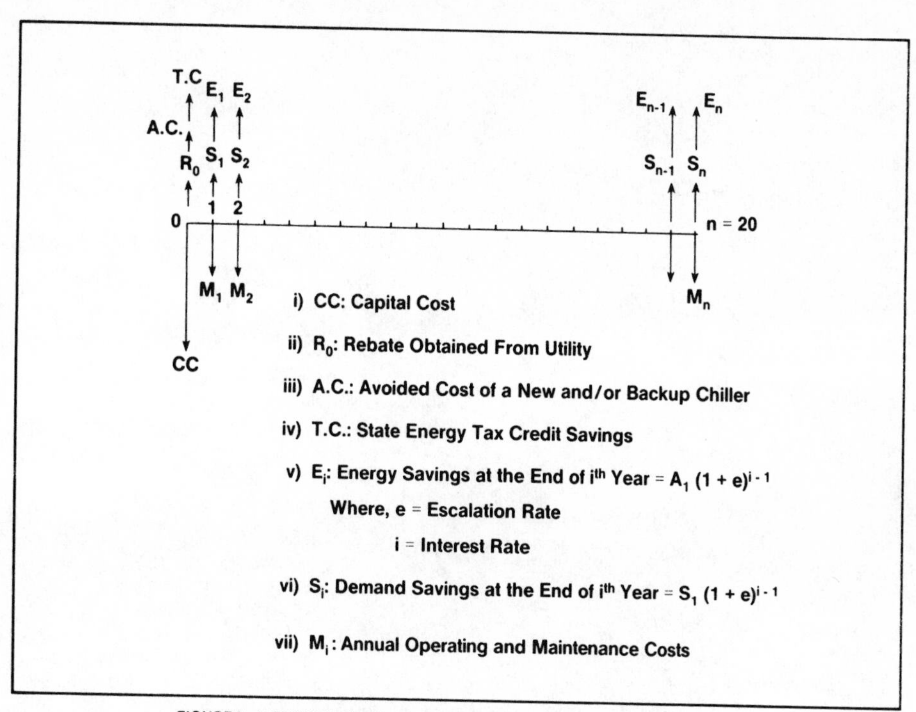

FIGURE 5 LIFE CYCLE COSTING FOR VARIOUS THERMAL STORAGE OPTIONS

Chapter 42

ANALYSIS OF THERMAL STORAGE OPTIONS

B. Bechard, E. A. Evans

A thermal storage system can be compared to a rechargeable flashlight battery. The thermal battery stores heating or cooling energy for use at a later time. The storage medium may be water, ice, eutectic salts, or other media such as rocks. The storage medium is heated or cooled (charged) during periods of low energy usage and is discharged during periods of high energy usage. The cycle is then repeated. Most thermal storage systems operate on a 24-hour cycle; however, weekly or yearly cycles are not uncommon. Thermal storage systems provide a means to decouple the use of thermal energy from the thermal load being served. Thermal storage options used for chilled water storage will be analyzed in this paper.

Thermal Storage Benefits

Thermal storage systems provide many benefits, including reduction of utility costs and increased reliability. A summary of these benefits is provided below.

- Lower Demand Costs: The peak electrical demand for most facilities coincides with the peak cooling demand. The peak electrical demand and the demand charge for the peak months can be reduced considerably by storing cooling energy during off-peak hours. Depending on the utility rate structure, this might also reduce the demand charges for each month of the year.

- Lower Electric Consumption Costs: Many utility companies offer reduced electric rates during off- peak periods. A thermal storage system allows the owner to take advantage of these rates.

- Reduced Equipment Sizes: A building initially designed with a thermal storage system may have a smaller chiller installed. Because the off-peak periods are generally longer than the on-peak periods, a smaller chiller can run longer to generate the same cooling energy. If the storage medium is ice, the temperature differences in the system may be increased, and the sizes of the air and water distribution system can therefore be reduced. This results in lower initial costs for the equipment and lower operating costs.

- Increased Reliability: Facilities with large computer centers which must be air conditioned will benefit from thermal storage. Critical computers usually have a UPS or emergency generator to provide power during short power outages. Often, the chiller serving the computer area does not have emergency power. A thermal storage system can provide emergency cooling for computer centers and thereby increase their reliability and operating time.

- Increased Efficiencies of Chiller Systems: A chiller sized to meet peak building loads will operate below its peak efficiency most of the time. A chiller which is charging a thermal storage system can operate at peak efficiency all of the time. When the storage tank is fully charged, the chiller can be shut down.

CANDIDATES FOR THERMAL STORAGE

Thermal storage systems are not economical in every situation. A careful engineering analysis of each specific case is required to determine its economic benefits. The following criteria should be considered before detailed analysis is completed. If the project meets these criteria, the potential for an economical project is high.

Load Profile

The load profile for the facility being considered for thermal storage must have peaks and valleys. If the load is constant for a 24-hour period, there is little benefit in providing thermal storage. A typical office building has a load profile which is ideal for thermal storage. Figure 1 shows the breakdown for the various load elements for a typical office located in Philadelphia. The chiller load, lighting load, and office equipment load vary considerably during the 24-hour period. The chiller load also varies seasonally and adds significantly to the daily electric peak.

Electric Utility Schedules

Some electric utility schedules are better suited for thermal storage than others. More and more utility companies are penalizing the electric users with high demand charges during peak times and rewarding the off-peak users by lowering kWh costs and demand charges during off-peak hours. This type of utility contract provides an excellent opportunity to maximize thermal storage benefits. A high-demand charge during peak use hours usually is enough incentive to economically justify a thermal storage system. A lower kWh cost during off-peak hours is icing on the cake. Some utility companies are offering large incentives to facilities who install peak avoidance systems. This could amount to $200/kW-$300/kW in a lump sum amount for avoided demand. These incentives can significantly impact the overall economics of a thermal storage system.

Table 1 provides a summary of typical utility schedules for various areas of the country. Note that Philadelphia has a high demand charge but very little difference between on- and off-peak kWh costs. San Diego has a lower demand charge but a greater difference between on- and off-peak rates.

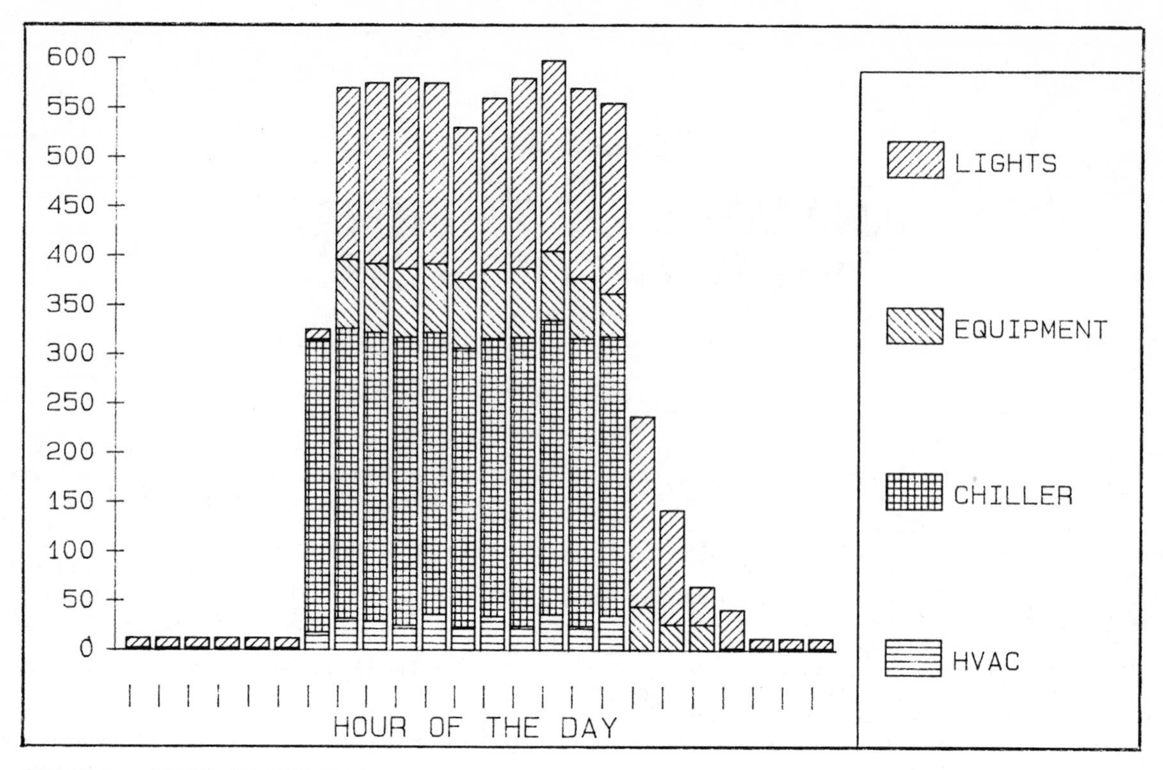

FIGURE 1. HOURLY kW DEMAND PROFILE FOR PEAK COOLING DAY

City	Effective Demand Charge $/kW	On Peak $/kWh	Off Peak $/kWh	Demand Ratchet	Peak Avoidance Incentives
Denver	6.15	0.0367	0.0248	None	None
Phil.	13.45	0.0433	0.0355	80% of summer peak	$0.0021/kWh off-peak credit
San Diego	7.81	0.12934	0.05898	None	$225/kW up-front cash

TABLE 1. ELECTRIC UTILITY CONTRACTS FOR VARIOUS LOCATIONS

ANALYSIS OF THERMAL STORAGE OPTIONS

Options to consider when designing a thermal storage system include storage system type and size, and chiller system type and size. The advantages of the various options are presented below.

Storage Media

Three types of media are commonly used in thermal storage systems: water, eutectic salts, and ice. All three have advantages and disadvantages. Some are more suited to new construction, and some are more suited to retrofit applications.

Water systems are the most common and, in a retrofit application, usually provide the best economics. Water systems operate at temperatures which allow use of existing chiller and air-side equipment without any changes. A large volume storage tank is required; this could be a problem where space is limited.

Several schemes have been developed for water storage which separate the cold supply water from the warm return water. The simplest but costliest method is to provide two tanks; one for cold water storage and the other for warm water storage. During the charging mode, water is pumped from one tank through the chiller to a second tank. During the discharge mode, the water is pumped from the cold tank to the building load and back to the warm storage tank.

Another method is to provide a series of six to eight smaller tanks. (See Figure 2). One tank is initially empty. Chilled water is pumped from the first tank to the building load and then returned to the empty tank. When the first tank is empty, it is then used as the warm water storage tank. This method, however, requires a costly valving system and a complicated control system to open and close valves. It does reduce the space required for storage when compared with the two-tank systems.

Figure 3 shows a third method of chilled water storage. This method utilizes a single storage tank with a flexible bladder separating the warm and cold water. As water is pumped from one side of the bladder and returned to the other, the bladder moves up and down. This method provides the most economical approach to chilled water storage.

Using ice as a storage medium can reduce the size of the storage tank considerably. One pound of water will store 16 Btu of cooling energy when cooled from 60°F to 44°F. If one pound of water is cooled from 60°F to 32°F and changed to ice, it will store 172 Btu of cooling energy. In theory, ice would utilize about 10% of the storage volume needed by a water system to store the same amount of cooing energy. In practice, however, only about 50% of the water in a tank can be frozen.

Unfortunately, the cost of the ice storage system will not be reduced in proportion to its size. The cost of ice builders, additional piping, and brine solutions

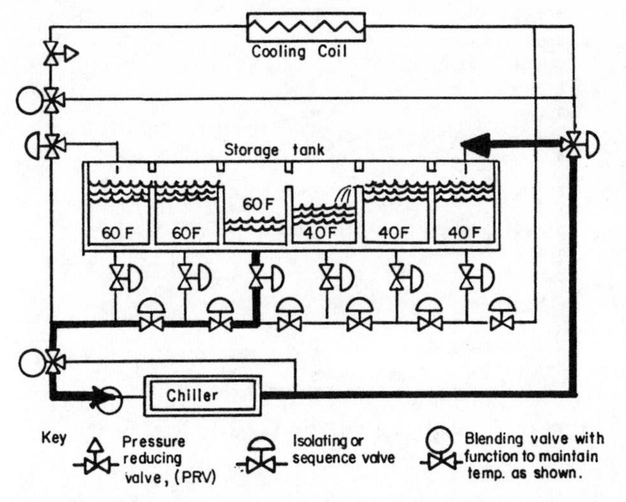

a) Charging mode

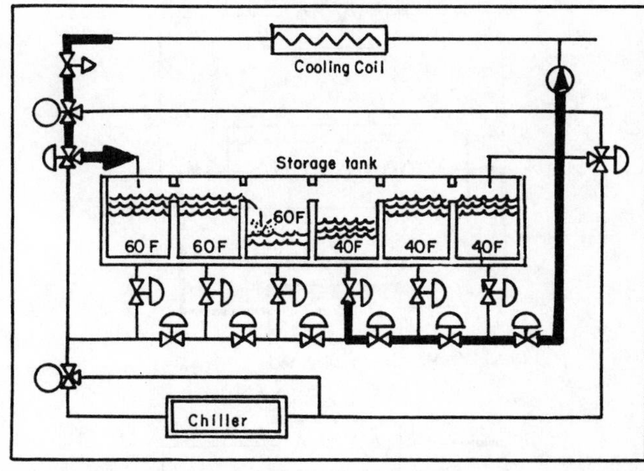

b) Discharge mode

FIGURE 2. CHILLED WATER STORAGE: MULTIPLE TANK SYSTEM.

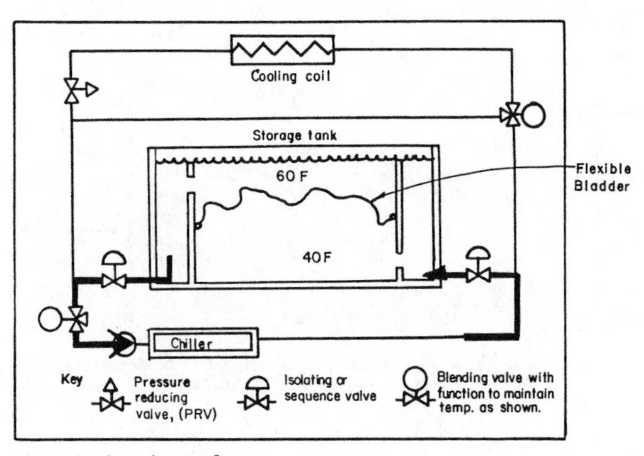

a) Tank charging mode

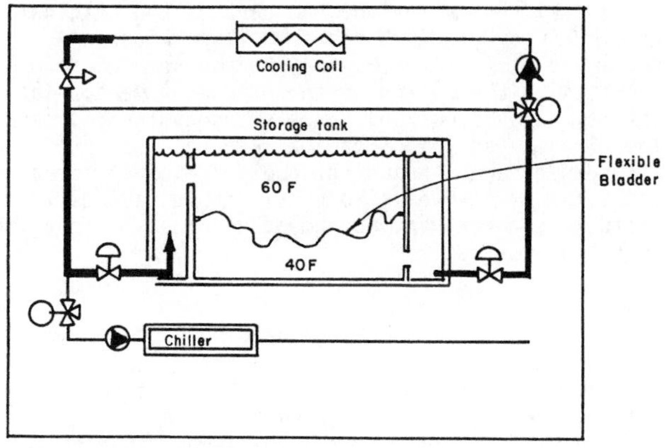

b) Tank discharge mode

FIGURE 3. CHILLED WATER STORAGE: SINGLE TANK WITH FLEXIBLE BLADDER

offset the cost of the smaller storage tank. Direct expansion systems reduce the cost somewhat, but these systems are very difficult to operate and maintain, and are not recommended. Figure 4 shows an ice storage system which utilizes a brine solution and a heat exchanger to separate the chiller water loop from the brine.

While the ice storage method has the advantage of a smaller storage volume, it has the disadvantage of requiring considerably lower compressor operating temperatures. This decreases the compressor operating efficiency considerably. These losses can be offset by other factors which will be discussed further on.

The use of eutectic salts as storage medium provides the advantage of low storage volume, similar to ice storage systems, but without the loss of compressor efficiency.

Eutectic salts are similar to the "blue ice" in packages which are available in sporting goods stores and commonly used to keep picnic lunches cold. These salts have the advantage of freezing at temperatures between 40°F and 50°F. The phase change provides about 40 Btu/lb of energy storage. This is not as good as ice but much better than plain water. Eutectic salts come in plastic containers which are stacked inside a storage tank. The chilled water is circulated directly over the containers, so no heat exchangers are required. The only drawback with this system is the initial cost of the eutectic salt. Table 2 provides a summary of the cost for the three storage systems discussed, each sized for 4400 ton-hours of capacity.

Chiller Systems

The type of storage medium selected, as indicated earlier, depends on whether the thermal storage system is a retrofit or a new installation. With a retrofit, the chiller and air-side equipment are usually designed for chilled water of approximately 40°F-45°F. The thermal storage system must accommodate these design restrictions. A selection of chilled water storage or a eutectic salt solution would be recommended for a retrofit application.

Using an ice storage system for a retrofit is usually not advisable. A severe penalty would be paid in chiller efficiency by going to the lower temperature. Figure 5 shows the reduction of efficiency and capacity which results from lowering the suction temperature of a typical centrifugal compressor.

The fact that the chiller will operate only at night will not appreciably increase the operating efficiency. A common misconception is that the lower night temperatures will reduce condenser water temperatures. The condensing water temperature, however, follows the outside wet-bulb temperature. Figure 6 is a graph plotting the outside dry-bulb and wet-bulb temperatures for a typical summer day. The wet-bulb temperature varies little when compared with the dry-bulb swing.

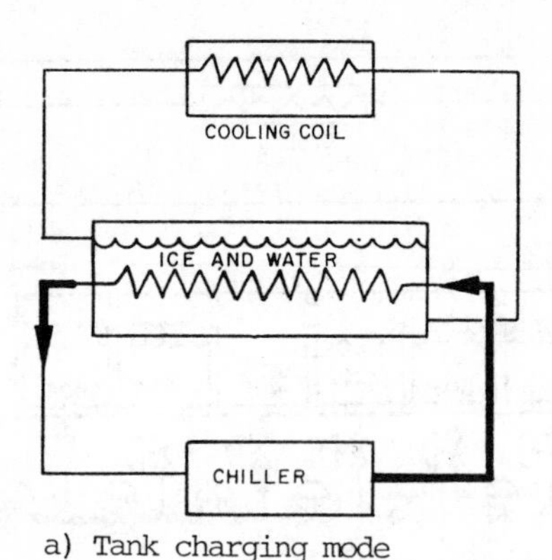

a) Tank charging mode

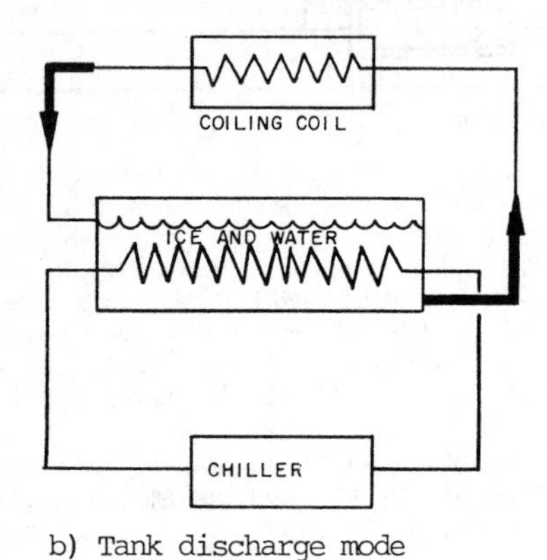

b) Tank discharge mode

FIGURE 4. ICE STORAGE SYSTEM WITH BRINE AND HEAT EXCHANGER

ICE STORAGE SYSTEM	
4400-ton-hour insulated storage tanks	$355,740
Pumps	12,376
Piping	13,817
Valves, wiring, controls	12,688
TOTAL	$394,621
EUTECTIC SALT STORAGE SYSTEM	
4400-ton-hour insulated storage modules	$396,000
Pumps	13,728
Piping	18,135
Valves, wiring, controls	14,300
TOTAL	$442,163
CHILLED WATER STORAGE SYSTEM	
475,860-gallon insulated storage tank	$117,168
Concrete foundation	30,912
Bladder	41,600
Pumps	13,728
Piping	18,135
Valves, wiring, controls	14,300
TOTAL	$235,843

TABLE 2. SUMMARY OF STORAGE COSTS

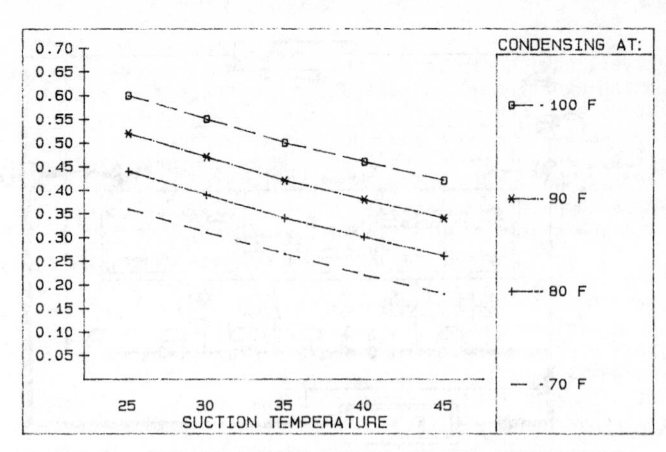

FIGURE 5. CHILLER kW/TON VERSUS SUCTION TEMPERATURE

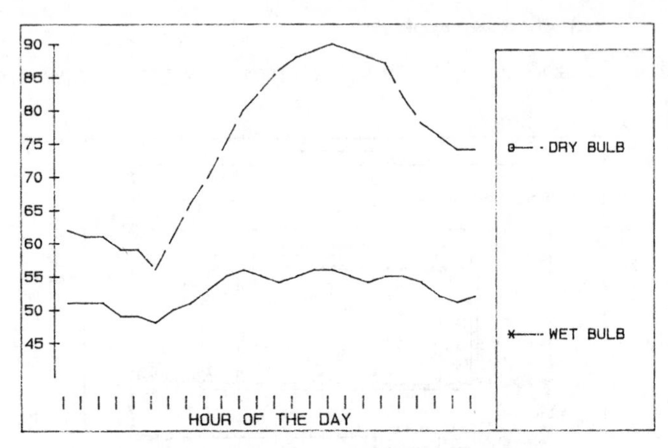

FIGURE 6. TYPICAL HOURLY PROFILE OF SUMMER DRY-BULB AND WET-BULB TEMPERATURES

The penalty of lower chiller efficiency which results from ice storage systems can be overcome if the ice storage system is designed as part of the original, total HVAC system. The lower chilled water temperatures (32°F-34°F) can provide some additional benefits in the design of the HVAC equipment. The chilled water flows and pumps sizes can be reduced. The air-side equipment can be selected for lower supply air temperatures, reducing supply CFM, duct sizes and fan sizes. This leads to considerable savings in capital cost for HVAC equipment and results in reduced operating costs.

COMPUTER MODELLING

Varying climatic conditions affect the performance of cooling towers. The energy consumption of HVAC equipment is influenced by hour-by-hour changes in solar intensity, ambient wet- and dry-bulb temperatures, and effects of the internal loads of a building due to occupants, lighting, and equipment. Predicting the cost of building operation is further complicated when the utility serving the building is billing for electricity use based on a time-of-day rate structure. Such a combination of variables presents a complex problem to the thermal storage analyst. Hourly computer simulation can make the job easier.

Sophisticated building energy models such as DOE 2.1 have the capability of simulating a wide variety of heating and cooling systems, including thermal storage. Analysis results can be very reliable, but they are only as good as the data input to the program. If you have a good grasp on how the building is currently using energy and can generate a good facsimile with the computer, then your thermal storage results should be reliable. The more you know about current energy use (e.g., annual and monthly consumption, hourly profiles of peak day use), the more accurate will be your base case computer simulation; consequently, your thermal storage system simulation will yield accurate results.

The point of installing a thermal storage system is to save money. Most of the savings are usually realized from avoided demand charges. The rest are due to off-peak electric energy rate differentials. However, as we shall see, this isn't always the case. The magnitude of the electric loads that can be shifted to off-peak hours will define peak demand savings for thermal storage systems. The effects of time-of-day energy use can be determined by comparing daily demand profiles of the base case to those of the storage case. The computer can be used to generate these profiles and to calculate electricity use by time of day for every day of the year.

TWO THERMAL STORAGE STRATEGIES

Two strategies for application of thermal storage systems are presented here. The first employs a tank large enough to store cooling energy to handle the entire building load for the peak cooling day. The second employs a tank that will store only enough energy to meet part of the load.

For illustrative purposes, consider this thermal storage candidate: a three-story, 117,000 ft^2, commercial office building located in Philadelphia. After considering first costs and compatibility of alternate storage media with the existing chiller, chilled water was selected as the storage medium. This building is currently served by a variable-air-volume system which is run in the cooling mode five months a year, May through September. The chilled water coils are fed by a 400-ton centrifugal chiller operating from 6:00 a.m. to 5:00 p.m. and providing cooling to spaces dominated by general office-type use. The building is occupied from 7:00 a.m. until 6:00 p.m., Monday through Friday. Because the chiller and fans are shut down at night, this schedule is well-suited to using the unoccupied hours to generate and store chilled water for the cooling needs of the next day.

The daytime cooling loads are created by various factors: internal heat generated by lighting, office equipment, and building occupants; gains from heat conduction through the building envelope; solar gains through the windows; and outside air introduced into the building by mechanical systems.

Occupant density is approximately 85 ft^2/person. The lighting level is 1.65 W/ft^2, and office equipment uses about 0.75 W/ft^2. Because of the thermal capacitance of the building structure and its contents, heat is stored in walls and furniture during the day. When the mechanical system fans are shut down around 5:00 p.m., ventilation is eliminated. Heat stored in the building structure and contents is released into the building during the night, and temperatures inside the building remain relatively warm despite cooling outside temperatures. Early morning solar gains contribute to the interior heat level. Consequently, cooling is sometimes needed at 6:00 or 7:00 a.m. to bring the interior temperatures of the building down to the comfort range by the time people start arriving for work. Even if cooling loads do not occur before the workday starts, loads are rapidly generated when people arrive, and lights and equipment are energized.

Figure 1 represents the peak-day hourly electric load profile for this building before installation of the storage system. The components of the electric load are chiller load, lights, office equipment and HVAC equipment. The chiller load represents about 50% of the peak demand and also represents the load which can be shifted to off-peak, night-time hours by using thermal storage.

Full Storage

The non-chiller electric loads of this building are roughly equivalent to those imposed by the chiller. Without changing the operation of the building, peak demand can be nearly halved by relegating chiller operation to strictly nighttime thermal storage charging. To accomplish this, storage must be sized to accommodate the entire cooling load experienced on the peak day.

The cooling load for the design day defines the ton-hours of cooling that must be delivered by the HVAC system; storage system losses (e.g., tank heat gains, stratification, unrecoverable stored energy) must be accounted for. The achievable temperature drop across the chiller under design day conditions greatly influences the size of the required storage volume.

The design day cooling load for this building (estimated from the data in Figure 1) is 3517 ton-hours. Assuming design day storage system losses of 30% and a temperature difference of 16°F, the required water storage volume is 411,121 gallons. The closest standard-size tank is 475,860 gallons.

The existing 400-ton chiller generates chilled water during the off-peak electric period (8:00 p.m. to 8:00 a.m.). This system produces 560 gpm of water cooled an average of 16°F in one pass through the chiller. The water is stored in a single tank with a bladder similar to the system shown in Figure 3.

Figure 7 depicts the hourly electric peak demand profile for the storage case. The entire chiller load has been shifted to off-peak hours.

CALCULATION OF SAVINGS

As Figure 8 demonstrates, the storage system shaves the kilowatts drawn by the chiller and cooling tower from the base case daytime peak and shifts the demands of this equipment to the off-peak period. The DOE 2.1 analysis program can predict the peak demand for each month resulting from this shift as well as the number of kilowatt-hours of electrical energy consumed during the peak and off-peak periods over the course of the cooling season.

The nature of the cost-impact analysis of storage systems requires hour-by-hour determination of electricity use. For this reason, computer models that perform hourly system simulation provide a much more accurate assessment of thermal and economic performance than do other methods. Computerized design tools intended for use in sizing equipment can provide reliable estimates of peak kW demand effects of storage systems, but they do not present an accurate picture of on-peak versus off-peak electricity consumption. In certain utility service areas, savings resulting from the shift of energy use to off-peak hours exceed peak kW savings. Therefore, hourly energy simulation is highly recommended.

With monthly peak kW demand data and totals of on-peak and off-peak electricity use in hand for both the base case and the storage case, the energy and dollar

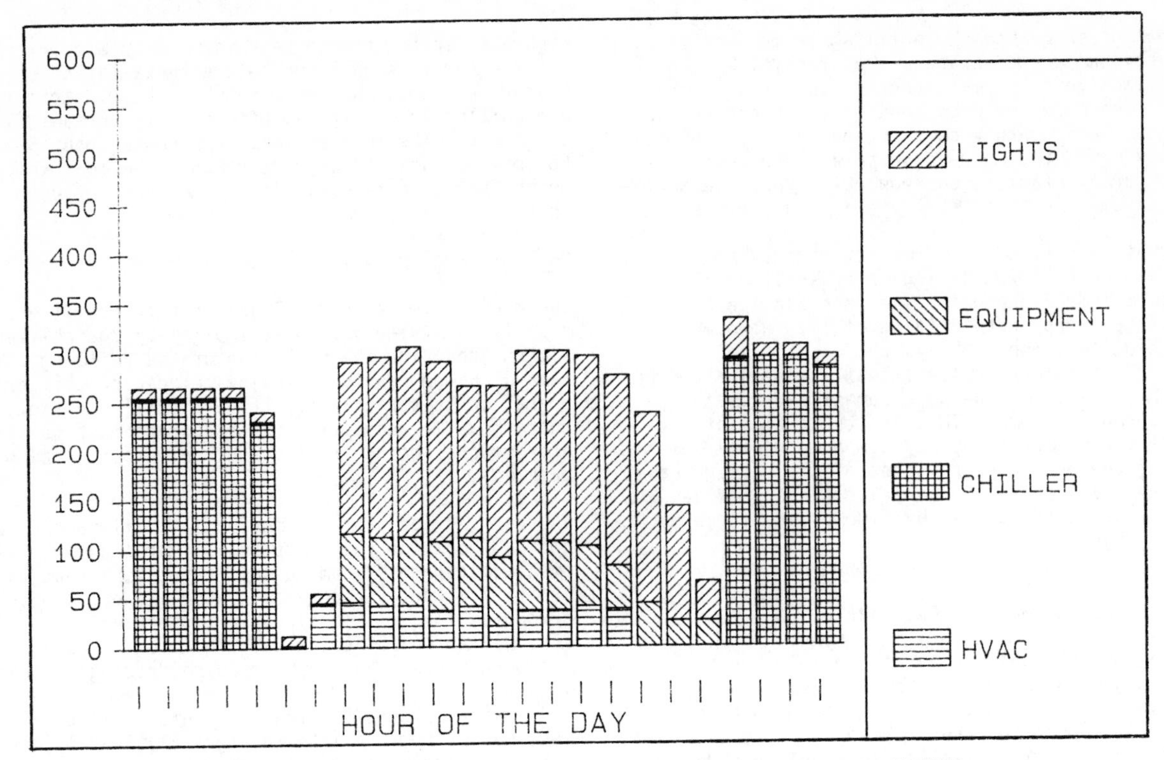

FIGURE 7. HOURLY kW DEMAND PROFILE ON PEAK COOLING DAY WITH FULL STORAGE SYSTEM

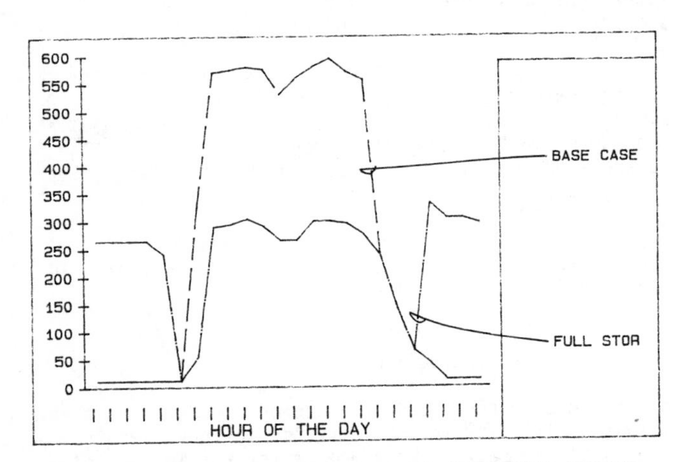

FIGURE 8. PEAK kW DEMAND PROFILES: BASE CASE VERSUS FULL STORAGE

savings delivered by thermal storage can easily be determined. Even complex utility rate structures are easily analyzed with the use of appropriate computer software.

Table 3 presents the monthly cost savings generated by this storage system. Full storage enables this Philadelphia Power and Light customer to avoid $33,934 in demand charges each year and $3,960 in energy charges. The system will pay for itself in less than six years.

Partial Storage

The next case involves a storage system sized to address only part of the building cooling load. The chiller generates chilled water during off-peak hours but only in an amount that covers about half of the design day load. On high cooling-load days, the chiller operates in parallel with the storage tank. During medium cooling-load days, the chiller operates at part-load to augment storage in meeting cooling needs. On low cooling-load days, the storage tank covers the cooling requirements by itself.

The advantage of the partial storage approach is the lower first cost when compared with the full storage system. The tank is roughly half the size of the full storage tank, and the total system cost is about 30% less than for full storage in a retrofit application. Front-end savings are even greater in a new construction project, because the chiller can be downsized to half the capacity required by full storage or a conventional cooling plant. In this case, system costs are about 40% lower.

To size the partial storage tank and chiller, the design day cooling load is divided by 24 to get a levelized load over a 24-hour period. The resulting tonnage represents the chiller capacity. Ton-hours of

Month	Full Storage	Partial Storage
Jan	$ 2,993	$ 1,227
Feb	2,993	1,227
Mar	2,993	1,227
Apr	2,993	1,227
May	3,392	1,859
Jun	4,055	1,945
Jul	4,037	2,033
Aug	4,201	1,924
Sep	4,251	2,206
Oct	0	0
Nov	2,993	1,227
Dec	2,993	1,227
TOTAL	$37,894	$17,329

TABLE 3. MONTHLY COST SAVINGS: PHILADELPHIA

storage are then defined by the number of off-peak hours the chiller will operate each night.

For our example building, partial storage volume is 225,045 gallons after accounting for system losses. The closest standard-size tank is 225,582 gallons.

Figure 9 depicts the effect of partial storage on the peak electric load profile. As with the analysis of full-storage systems, the computer is an invaluable tool in assessing the merits of partial storage. Again, it is very important to be able to quantify the electrical energy use during peak and off-peak hours.

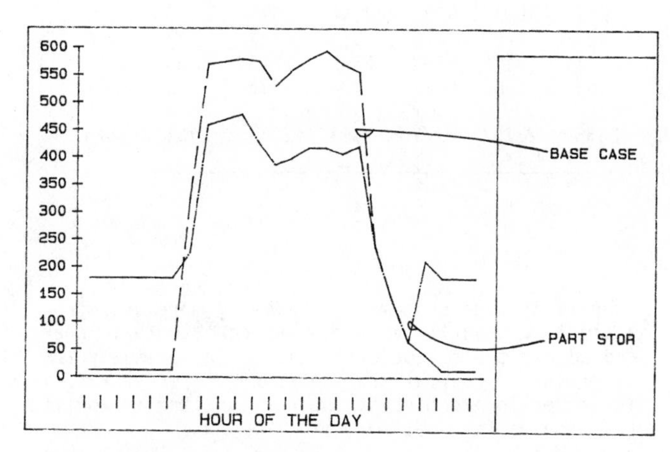

FIGURE 9. PEAK kW DEMAND PROFILES: BASE CASE VERSUS PARTIAL STORAGE

Table 3 presents the monthly cost savings provided by this partial storage system. Demand charges and energy charges in the amount of $14,903 and $2426 are avoided by using this system. These smaller savings relative to full storage are offset by the 29% lower retrofit system cost to yield a nine-year simple payback.

The ease of analyzing these systems with a fully-capable computer model and utility rate calculation package makes optimization of storage systems quick and efficient.

EFFECT OF A DIFFERENT RATE STRUCTURE

To illustrate the impact of the utility rate structure on system economics, full- and partial-storage systems for this same building were modelled in San Diego. San Diego Gas and Electric has rates that are very favorable for load management systems like thermal storage. In addition, an up-front cash incentive based on the amount of displaced demand makes San Diego a very attractive thermal storage market.

The procedures described previously were employed to size full- and partial-storage systems to address the design day cooling load of 3,069 ton-hours in San Diego.

Figure 10 demonstrates the kW demand shaved from the base case operation by a full-storage system. Figure 11 shows the demand displaced by a partial-storage system.

Table 4 contains monthly cost savings delivered by both of these storage systems. Full storage enables the San Diego Gas and Electric customer to avoid $14,667 in demand charges and $30,237 in energy charges each year. Partial storage yields savings of $7,136 and $22,962 respectively. Note that in these cases, the avoided energy charges are greater than demand charge savings. This fact underscores the importance of having the capability to track electricity use hour-by-hour to accurately assess costs arising from the time-of-day rate structure. The San Diego Gas and Electric rate structure includes peak, intermediate, and off-peak energy charges as well as peak-period and intermediate-period demand charges. Hourly simulation with a sophisticated computer program gives the analyst the capability to accurately assess utility costs.

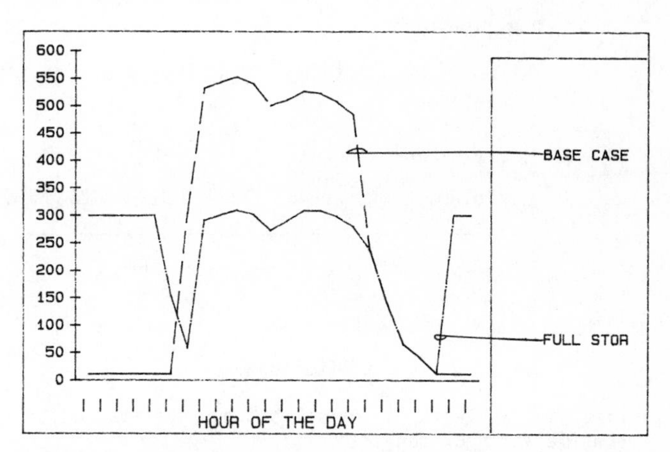

FIGURE 10. PEAK kW DEMAND PROFILES: BASE CASE VERSUS FULL STORAGE (SAN DIEGO)

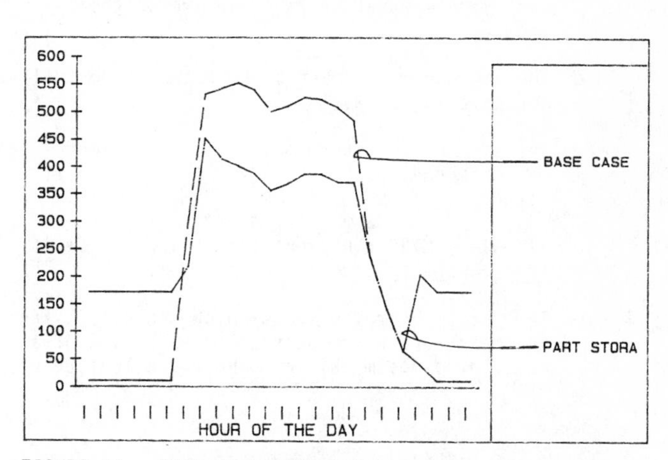

FIGURE 11. PEAK kW DEMAND PROFILE: BASE CASE VERSUS PARTIAL STORAGE (SAN DIEGO)

Capital incentives offered by San Diego Gas and Electric for kW peak avoidance systems are $225/kW of displaced cooling demand for retrofit application and $350/ton storage capacity for new construction. These cash subsidies amount to $54,675 for full storage and $22,500 for partial storage retrofit systems serving this building. These systems offer three-year and four-year simple paybacks.

If this were a new construction project, payback economics would benefit from larger utility subsidies amounting to $350 per ton of storage capacity for both full- and partial-storage systems. Subsidies for this building would total $120,050 for the full-storage option and $47,250 for partial storage. In addition, the chiller and cooling tower serving the partial-storage tank could be down-sized to realize another $26,709 in savings. The end result is a two-year payback for full storage and a three-year payback for the partial-storage system in San Diego.

	Jan	Feb	Mar	Apr	May	Jun	Jul	Aug	Sep	Oct	Nov	Dec
FULL STORAGE												
Peak kWh	$2591	2166	2589	2891	2803	2827	3455	3281	3053	2980	2584	2536
Intermed.	700	643	755	909	1248	1371	1673	1667	1475	1311	742	740
Off-Peak	-1005	-791	-982	-1319	-1514	-1792	-2351	-2187	-2054	-1734	-1152	-943
kW Demand	813	1155	1021	1254	1191	1495	1755	1399	1817	1475	1438	926
TOTAL	3099	3172	3383	3735	3728	3901	4532	4160	4291	4032	3612	3259
PARTIAL STORAGE												
Peak kWh	$2590	2165	2588	2889	2801	2761	3001	3182	2844	2875	2525	2535
Intermed.	270	266	327	334	418	382	245	378	313	382	277	299
Off-Peak	-704	-583	-745	-1003	-1066	-1271	-1517	-1503	-1397	-1215	-889	-736
kW Demand	812	526	1021	395	362	463	646	322	708	436	519	926
TOTAL	2968	2374	3191	2615	2515	2335	2375	2379	2468	2478	2431	3024

TABLE 4. MONTHLY COST SAVINGS: SAN DIEGO

CONCLUSIONS

Effective analysis of thermal storage systems requires consideration of many factors:

- The utility rate structure must be analyzed to determine whether it is conducive to thermal storage.
- The storage media must be selected to best fit the existing situation.
- The size of the storage tank can be selected to maximize savings or provide the best overall return.
- Secondary HVAC equipment can be down-sized if ice storage systems are considered.
- The yearly energy savings which can result from thermal storage are best analyzed by use of a computer program utilizing hourly calculations.

Thermal storage systems are becoming more and more attractive as utility companies increase their charges and adjust their rate structures. The best way to determine if thermal storage is right for your facility is to retain a competent engineering firm to analyze the problem for you.

REFERENCES

Specialized Energy Study: Thermal Storage Systems. E M C Engineers, Inc., Technical Report. Denver, Colorado: 1986.

Thermal Storage. ASHRAE Technical Bulletin. Atlanta, Georgia: 1985.

"Thermal Storage Systems." Heating/Piping/Air Conditioning, Vol 57, No.1 (January 1985), pp. 133-151.

Chapter 43

THERMAL ENERGY STORAGE FOR MUNICIPAL BUILDINGS

D. S. Teji, R. J. Balon

ABSTRACT

In 1985 the City of Phoenix received federal grant money to perform applied research in thermal storage. The research, as reported in this paper, completed four primary tasks:

1. A review of the state of the art in thermal storage technology;

2. A survey of municipal buildings to assess thermal storage opportunities and select a demonstration site;

3. Design and installation of a demonstration system; and

4. Monitoring and payback analysis of the demonstration system.

The research revealed that in typical municipal buildings cool storage could save 40 to 60 percent of the cost of air-conditioning, when a time-of-use utility rate is in effect. At the best sites, a payback of 3 to 6 years could be obtained. At the demonstration site, cool storage saved $1650 per year, which was 51 percent of the previous cost of air-conditioning the building. The payback period on this project was 5 years.

Constraints that exist to the immediate installation of thermal storage in many buildings are also discussed. The air-conditioning compressors at most sites are not suitable for making ice, which is the preferred medium for cool storage in retrofit situations. Locating space for storage in existing high-rise buildings can also prove a problem. Finally, thermal storage installations have a high first cost. The utility incentives for thermal storage must be strong to produce a short payback on the investment.

INTRODUCTION

Over the last 25 years, electricity has become the energy source of choice for the heating and cooling of large commercial buildings. A major side effect of this practice has been a steady escalation in the size and sharpness of utility demand peaks. Most buildings tend to experience their peak cooling load at a similar hour of the afternoon, and their peak heating load at a similar hour of the morning. This coincident demand for electricity taxes the capacity of the utility to keep up, and can even lead to "brownouts", temporary shortages of electricity. The utilities have begun to react by offering rates and incentives which encourage night time or "off-peak" use of electricity in place of daytime or "on-peak" use. By doing so, the utilities hope to increase the load factor of their existing power plants, and postpone the burden of constructing new, much more expensive plants.

Conventionally heated and cooled office buildings have limited potential for taking advantages of off-peak rates, except for the possibility of thermal energy storage. This concept involves the use of electricity during the hours when it is cheapest, to charge a hot or cold thermal reservoir. The reservoir is then used to heat or cool the building during the hours when electricity would be most expensive to use. In this way, thermal storage reduces peak electrical demand, and takes advantage of utility rate incentives, without sacrificing the comfort of building occupants.

In 1985 the City of Phoenix carried out a one year applied research program in thermal storage for its buildings. The work was divided into three phases:

* Phase One - Background Research

* Phase Two - Building Survey

* Phase Three - Demonstration

This paper summarizes the major results of each phase.

PHASE ONE - BACKGROUND RESEARCH

The purpose of this phase was to discover all information about thermal storage presently available. In fact information is still scanty, as thermal storage has just emerged from its infancy as a modern air-conditioning alternative. The utilities themselves have taken primary responsibility for generating both qualitative and technical information on thermal storage and dispersing it to the public. To date, the most comprehensive source of information is the Electric Power Research Institute (EPRI) Commercial Cool Storage Design Guide and related publications [1,2,3,4]. (EPRI is the research organization representing electrical utility companies throughout the U.S.) Individual utilities which promote thermal storage also prepare technical manuals and hold seminars for the engineering and development communities. In 1984 the major centers of thermal storage activity were Chicago, San Diego and Dallas. They were joined by Phoenix in 1985 when both local utilities here announced new and major thermal storage incentive programs.

Technology Assessment

Reliability: Storage systems installed in the 1970's tended to be trouble prone, with problems stemming primarily from operator inexperience, faulty time clocks and manual controls, compressor abuse and failure, leaking storage vessels and inaccurate ice thickness controls. By 1985 nearly all of these problems have been eliminated or minimized. Most of the progress can be attributed to standardization and packaging of complete storage systems, using more appropriate refrigeration equipment and better engineering. In new construction at least, the technology of cool storage is ready for use.

Retrofit Application: Thermal storage technology is more difficult to apply in retrofit situations. Existing refrigeration compressors are often not suitable for making ice, the preferred medium for retrofit applications. The major alternative medium, chilled water, requires about five times as much space as ice and locating room for it is problematic. Newer technologies which ease retrofit problems include brine ice-banks [5] which can be used with some existing reciprocating chillers to freeze ice at 32 deg F. Eutectic salts storage [6] holds additional promise for easing retrofit problems:

* It is compact because it stores cooling in the form of a phase change, like ice, but

* The phase change temperature is 43 deg F, rather than 32 deg F, which permits it to be used with any existing air-conditioning chiller.

Thus, cool storage technology is beginning to seriously address the retrofit market.

Operating Strategies

Most sources name the choice of control strategies for thermal storage as "full storage" or "partial storage", and sometimes "demand-limiting storage" is also mentioned. Most sources attempt to define these terms by illustrating how the strategy might be implemented for a particular utility rate for a particular building under theoretical design day conditions. The definitions are consequently ad hoc, "for this case only". In reality, there is no simple definition of each strategy which will apply to all situations. The meaning of the terms subtly shift, depending on the building load profile, the utility rate, and even the time of year.

To illustrate the effect of the utility rate on the control strategy, consider the following comparison. Figure 1 illustrates "full storage" under a time-of-use utility rate. The "off-peak" hours in this instance have been defined as 7 p.m. to 11 a.m. daily. During these hours the refrigeration compressors are allowed to operate at full load, to charge storage or to meet the building load directly. During the remaining, on-peak hours the compressors are shut down. Thus the compressors use only the cheaper, off-peak energy to cool the building all day.

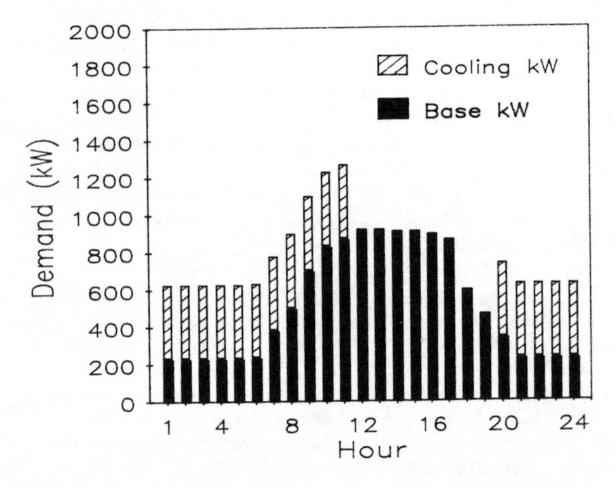

FIGURE 1. FULL STORAGE UNDER A TIME-OF-USE RATE.

In contrast, Figure 2 shows a "full storage" strategy for the same building under a conventional utility rate. Under a conventional rate there are no off-peak hours. The objective, accordingly, is only to limit the peak demand experienced by the building. Thus, the refrigeration compressors are controlled so as not to operate during hours of high demand in the building.

Comparing Figures 1 and 2 demonstrates that the structure of the utility rate indeed has a major influence on defining "full storage". In this example, the utility rate affects the amount of storage required, the size of the refrigeration plant, the hours of compressor operation and the nature of the controls. Moreover the picture is becoming more complex than this simple example suggests. Time-of-Use rates often have "wrinkles" which further complicate the picture, for example:

* "Shoulder Rates"; an intermediate period between full on-peak and full off-peak rates,

* "Off-Peak Weekends" where energy charges are lowered all day Saturday and Sunday,

* "Sliding Demand Windows" which make the on-peak demand hours different from the on-peak energy hours,

* "Ratchet Clauses" which set a minimum monthly demand based on the maximum annual demand, and

* "Seasonal Rates" where the rate charges and rate structure may change from summer to winter.

Each of these features may affect "optimal" control of the storage system. But in addition to accommodating these complexities of utility rate structures, the control strategy may change with changing loads on the building. For example, a system designed for partial storage at design conditions may in fact operate as a full storage system for most of the year when the cooling load is not so high. Most sources gloss over these complexities and, at present, no comprehensive treatment of control strategies exists. Consequently, some trial and error must still be expected in developing a control strategy.

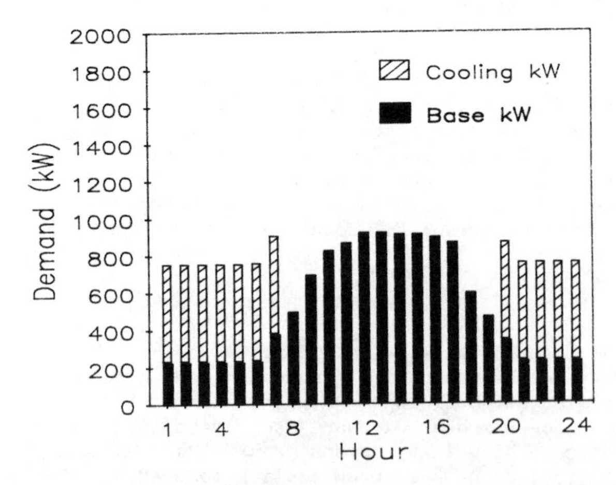

FIGURE 2. FULL STORAGE UNDER A CONVENTIONAL RATE.

PHASE TWO - SURVEY OF CITY BUILDINGS

Table 1 summarizes results of the cool storage survey of city buildings. The first column gives the building name and the second gives the estimated storage capacity required for demand-limiting storage. The unit of storage capacity is the "ton-hour", which is the cooling produced by one ton

TABLE 1. RESULTS OF COOL STORAGE SURVEY OF CITY BUILDINGS.

Building Name	Storage Size (Ton-Hrs)	Retrofit Cost	Incentive Payment	Annual Savings	Payback (Years)
Police Bldg.	2720	$ 255,000	$ 102,000	$ 45,000	3
Municipal Bldg.	3800	$ 360,000	$ 93,000	$ 42,000	6
Plaza Municipal	2400	$ 230,000	$ 74,500	$ 22,000	6
Central Library	2000	$ 225,000	$ 70,000	$ 25,000	5
Art Museum	500	$ 56,000	$ 16,250	$ 3,150	10
Police Academy	500	$ 64,000	$ 13,750	$ 4,100	9
LEAP #3	300	$ 48,000	$ 16,500	$ 3,500	8
Field Engineering	500	$ 75,000	$ 21,250	$ 3,800	10
Adult Center	300	$ 22,000	$ 14,750	$ 2,000	4
Little Theater	500	$ 64,000	$ 20,000	$ 3,000	11
Pueble Grande Museum	200	$ 35,000	$ 9,500	$ 1,500	12
Police Briefing Sta.	300	$ 38,000	$ 9,000	$ 2,600	9
Fire Academy	150	$ 24,000	$ 9,000	$ 1,700	8
Century Library	200	$ 16,000	$ 7,500	$ 4,500	5
Fire Support Service	100	$ 22,000	$ 4,500	$ 1,200	10
Fire Station #21	70	$ 12,000	$ 2,000	$ 600	12

of refrigeration operating for one hour (12,000 Btu's of heat removal). Storage sizes range from 3800 ton-hours for the Municipal Building (city hall) down to 70 ton-hours for a small fire station. The third column holds the estimated cost of installing the required storage. This cost includes adjustments for the scale of the projects; the cost per ton-hour declines with increasing size. The cost also reflects how extensively the existing HVAC system must be modified; existing direct expansion (DX) systems must be converted to chilled water distribution during a thermal storage retrofit. The fourth column lists the expected incentive payment from the utility, based on $250 per kW shifted off-peak. The fifth column shows the annual savings calculated for the building after storage has been installed and a time-of-use rate is in effect. The last column shows the payback for the retrofit, after allowing for a 6 percent annual rate of escalation in electricity prices.

The paybacks range from 3 to 12 years with a roughly even distribution between these extremes. Before the utilities announced their incentive program for thermal storage, the payback on storage retrofits was 17 years or more. The incentives and time-of-use rates have turned this situation around so that paybacks are now 12 years or less. In the most favorable cases the paybacks are in the range of 3 to 6 years.

The type of existing HVAC equipment at a building strongly influences the payback. All storage systems at present require a chilled water distribution system. If the existing distribution system at the building is not chilled water then the system must be converted to chilled water. Such a conversion can be moderately to prohibitively expensive, depending on the details of the existing air-distribution system. Among the surveyed buildings the most costly retrofits would be those with packaged DX air-conditioners, carrying a conversion cost of $150 to $220 per ton-hour. Compare this cost with a range of $73 to $128 per ton-hour for buildings with existing chilled water systems. The type of existing HVAC system can make a difference of a factor of two in the cost of a storage retrofit.

Even in buildings with chilled water distribution, complications can arise. Storage must be located at or below grade because of its weight, requiring that space be located for it around the outside of the building. Ideally the refrigeration equipment room will also be located on the first floor or basement of the building. Otherwise, interfacing the storage with the refrigeration compressor may be expensive or impractical.

PHASE THREE - DEMONSTRATION

System Selection

Ice was selected as the storage medium for the following reasons:

* Space was at a premium in all the buildings which were being considered for a retrofit.

* Chilled water storage tanks above ground would be unsightly while burying would require extensive tearing up of facilities.

* Ice banks are available as manufactured units with know cost. The cost of chilled water storage, on the other hand, depends heavily on site-specific factors and would not be known until late in the design process. This delay would complicate budgeting and planning the project.

Among ice builders one must further choose between brine-type and direct expansion (DX) type. Both types build ice on the outside of a "coil" of pipes or tubes by circulating a coolant on the inside of the tube. The DX type ice builders use refrigerant directly as the coolant. Thus, in a DX ice builder the ice-holding pipe coils are physically the evaporator of the refrigeration cycle. A brine ice builder, on the other hand, uses an anti-freeze mixture of water and glycol as the coolant inside the tube coil. The glycol mixture or "brine" is cooled to subfreezing temperature by a standard, packaged air-conditioning or refrigeration chiller. For the demonstration project we selected brine-type ice banks, with the following reasons:

* The brine ice bank could make use of the existing reciprocating chiller at the test site.

* Using a secondary coolant isolates the chilled water loop from the storage water, preventing contamination.

* Brine ice builders behave reliably. They produce even "build up" and "burn off" of the ice in storage, avoiding the problems of "tunneling" and "bridging" common in DX ice builders.

Overall, brine ice builders provided the quickest and least expensive avenue to use for this particular demonstration project.

Building Selection

The building selected to receive a retrofit was a branch library with approximately 6000 square feet of conditioned area and a peak cooling load of 18 tons. Century Library was selected because it was small enough to be retrofit within the budget of $20,000, because its existing chiller and chilled water distribution system could be used with minimum modification, and because it had a representative load profile for city buildings.

Peak electrical demand at the library was 55 kW, over half of which (30 kW) came from air-conditioning equipment. The annual electric bill, prior to the retrofit, was $10,522, with approximately $3,300 going toward cooling.

Electric Rate Description

Table 2 shows the existing, conventional electric rate on which previous year's charges were based. The conventional rate features a declining block rate structure. This structure lowers the rate for electricity as usage increases, irrespective of the time of day and the actual cost to produce the electricity. An expanding first block and seasonally adjusted rates are also incorporated.

Table 2. Existing Electric Rate at Century Library.

Customer Type:	General Commercial Class	
Energy Charge:	Summer	Winter
First 4,000 kWh	$ 0.0747 /kWh	$ 0.0615 /kWh
Next (75 x Peak kW)	$ 0.0747 /kWh	$ 0.0615 /kWh
Next 50,000 kWh	$ 0.0472 /kWh	$ 0.0437 /kWh
All Additional kWh	$ 0.0357 /kWh	$ 0.0300 /kWh
Demand Charge:	$ 2.78 / kW	$1.55 / kW

Table 3 shows the optional time-of-use rate to which the building was converted. Notice that the declining block structure is gone, replaced by a division of rates according to the time of day. This type of structure more accurately reflects the utility's cost of producing electricity. To further reflect its costs the utility has chosen to retain its summer/winter rate split, and includes different hours as "on-peak" in the different seasons. Weekends are off-peak in the winter but not in the summer.

Table 3. Optional Time-of-Use Rate.

Customer Type:	Experimental, Thermal Storage	
On-Peak hours:	Summer - 12 noon to 10 p.m. DAILY Winter - 7 a.m. to 10 p.m. M - F	
Energy Charge:	Summer	Winter
All On-Peak kWh	$ 0.0743 /kWh	$ 0.0528 /kWh
All Off-Peak kWh	$ 0.0294 /kWh	$ 0.0294 /kWh
Demand Charge:		
On-Peak Demand	$ 4.15 / kW	$ 2.84 / kW
Off-Peak Demand	No Charge	No Charge

Selection of the Storage Size

The cooling load calculations for Century Library indicated a total daily cooling load of 203 ton-hours. Of this total, about 70 percent or 140 ton-hours would occur during on-peak hours (12 noon to 10 p.m.). Thus, full storage could theoretically be accomplished with 140 ton-hours of storage capacity. However, an allowance of 10 percent was made for losses from the storage tanks and piping, bringing the requirement up to 154 ton-hours. Next, discrete tank sizes had to be selected. The CALMAC storage tanks selected for this project come in nominal sizes of 60, 90 and 100 ton-hours. However, the two smaller sizes are designed for quick charging and discharging and were not appropriate for this application. Two of the 100 ton-hour tanks were therefore necessary to cover the anticipated load. On the surface then, storage rated at 200 ton-hours was installed to meet a cooling load of 140 ton-hours, which appears to be an overdesign of 42 percent. In reality, the 100 ton-hour tanks could effectively supply 90 ton-hours at full load, because of limitations in heat transfer. Thus, an available 180 ton-hours (2 x 90) was installed to meet an anticipated cooling load plus losses of 154 ton-hours, producing a 17 percent "safety factor". Most engineers currently design storage systems with a safety factor of 15 to 25 percent. Thus the factor of 17 percent used in the design was not unreasonable.

System Piping and Control

Figures 3 and 4 illustrate the final design for the ice storage retrofit of Century Library. Figure 3 shows the charging cycle for the ice bank. The charging cycle begins at 10 p.m. and continues through the night until storage is fully charged. In this cycle the ice bank receives coolant from the chiller at 26 deg F, uses the coolant to freeze ice at 32 deg F, and discharges the coolant at 32 deg F. Next, an automatic diverting valve diverts the flow of coolant from its normal path through the building and sends it directly back to the chiller. This process continues until the ice bank is frozen solid and latent heat transfer ends. When latent heat transfer is complete the discharge temperature from the ice bank will begin to fall below 32 deg F. When the discharge temperature falls to 29 deg F a thermostat shuts down the chiller and the coolant pump and ends the charging cycle.

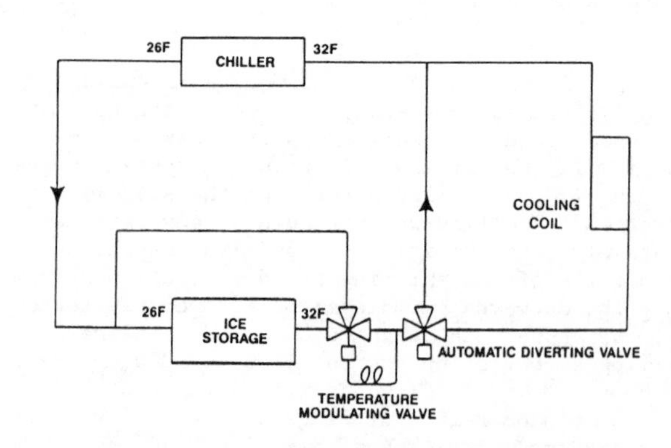

FIGURE 3. CHARGING CYCLE.

During the next day (8 a.m. to 10 p.m.) the system discharges the storage to cool the building. As shown in Figure 4, the automatic diverting valve switches flow back to the cooling coils of the building. The temperature modulating valve mixes 34 deg F coolant from the ice storage with return coolant from the building to produce 44 deg F coolant for the cooling coils in the building. At this time the chiller may be fully on, fully off or part-loaded, depending on the control strategy being used. Figure 4 shows the case in which the chiller is allowed to operate at part-load and supply part of the cooling load simultaneously with the ice bank (partial storage). If the chiller were now turned off the 60 deg F return temperature from the building would go on to the ice bank without a reduction in temperature. The motorized temperature modulating valve would react and proportion the flow so that the ice bank picks up the entire building load (full storage). Finally, if the chiller is allowed to operate at full load it will chill the coolant down to 44 deg F by itself. The modulating valve will sense no need for supplemental cooling and will bypass the ice bank (conventional operation). This system design has the following advantages in retrofit situations:

* Full storage, partial storage and conventional operation can be activated as desired from this single design.

* The existing chiller can be used to make ice and to cool the building directly when required by the control strategy.

* The existing chilled water distribution system, consisting of cooling coils, 3-way valves, air-distribution fans and circulating pump, can be used without modification because the temperature and flow rate of the coolant is the same before and after the retrofit.

The master control for the storage system was a Honeywell "W7000" energy management system, already being used at the building. Output channels of the EMS microprocessor were wired to relays controlling the chiller, motorized valves, thermostats, air-distribution van and coolant pump in the ice-storage system. The channels could then be programmed with the on/off times dictated by a given control strategy. The EMS microprocessor has a self-contained battery backup which will maintain the correct time and program information in the event of a power interruption. Good storage system design requires a power backup feature on all time controls. Thus, linking the storage system to the existing EMS system for the building was a convenient and reliable method of controlling the storage system.

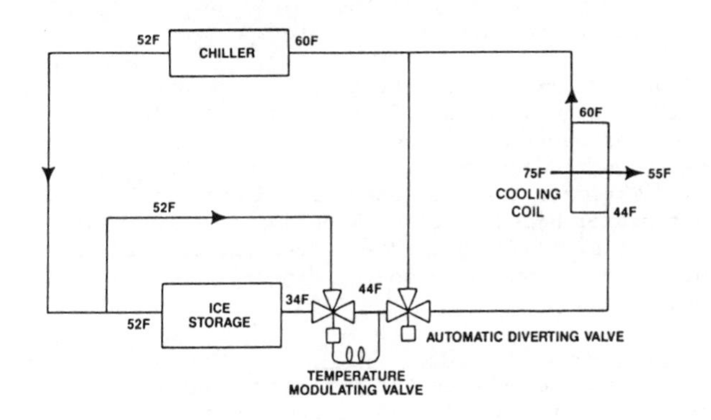

FIGURE 4. DISCHARGING CYCLE (PARTIAL STORAGE MODE).

Instrumentation and Monitoring

The installation was fully instrumented to monitor the thermal and electrical performance of the ice storage system. An IBM-PC microcomputer was used to conduct datalogging from the various instruments which included wattmeters, flowmeters and thermocouples. The PC read data from the instruments continuously and recorded average values to disk every 15 minutes, 24 hours a day. The data was recorded in a LOTUS 1-2-3 compatible format for later analysis using this spreadsheet software.

The system was monitored for 6 weeks of severe summer weather conditions. During the course of the experiment the system was operated in all three possible modes; full storage, partial storage and conventional operation. The findings are presented below.

Results

Figures 5 and 6 portray a typical day during which the system was monitored. Figure 5 shows the ambient air temperature recorded on site at the library. Figure 6 shows the hourly cooling load on the building, recorded on the same day. The cooling load is nearly flat, a feature characteristic of buildings which are not cooled at night, and which have heavy construction and little window area. The load peaks near 10 a.m. because of the "pull down" in temperature which must be accomplished after air-conditioning resumes in the morning.

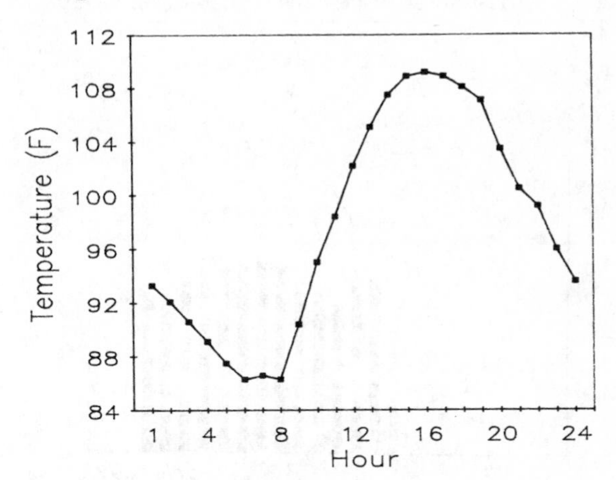

FIGURE 5. AMBIENT TEMPERATURE.

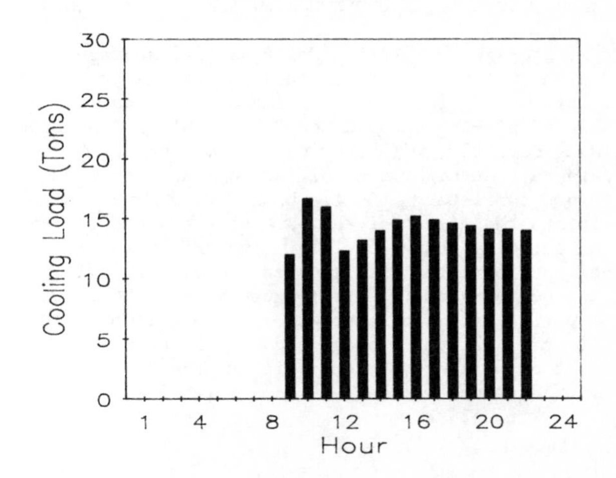

FIGURE 6. BUILDING COOLING LOAD.

Conventional Operation: Figures 7 and 8 profile the electrical consumption of the building under conventional chiller operation. Figure 7 shows the total electrical demand while Figure 8 isolates the energy used by chiller. Compare Figures 6 and 8 and observe how the chiller electrical demand is tied to the building cooling load. Under conventional operation the chiller must follow the load almost exactly. Since the bulk of the air-conditioning load occurs during peak hours (12 noon to 10 p.m.) so does the bulk of the chiller energy consumption. In fact the chiller consumed 75 percent of its daily energy during "on-peak" hours.

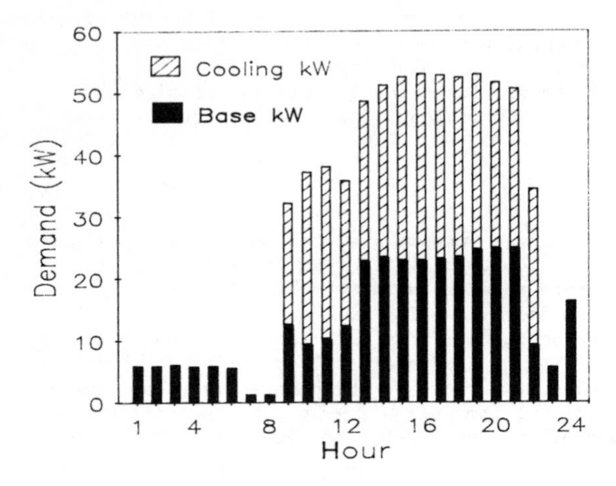

FIGURE 7. BUILDING kW UNDER CONVENTIONAL OPERATION.

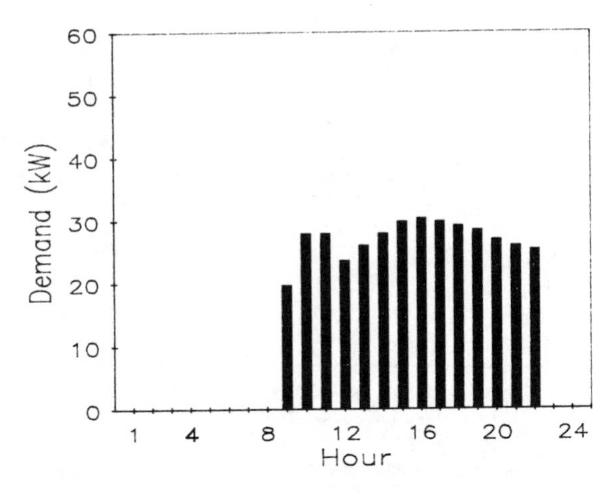

FIGURE 8. COOLING kW UNDER CONVENTIONAL OPERATION.

Partial Storage Operation: Under partial storage operation the chiller was allowed to operate at part-load during the daytime. The chiller was then capable of picking up about half the cooling load from building directly, with the ice bank making up the difference. At night the chiller continued to work at part-load to recharge the ice bank. Figures 9 and 10 illustrate the effect of the partial storage strategy on the building energy profile. The effect is to "level out" both the chiller energy use (Figure 10) and the building energy use (Figure 9) over 24 hours. Hence partial storage is sometimes also called "load levelling". Partial storage reduced the on-peak consumption of energy by the chiller from 75 percent down to 38 percent. The peak demand level was reduced from 55 kW to 45 kW.

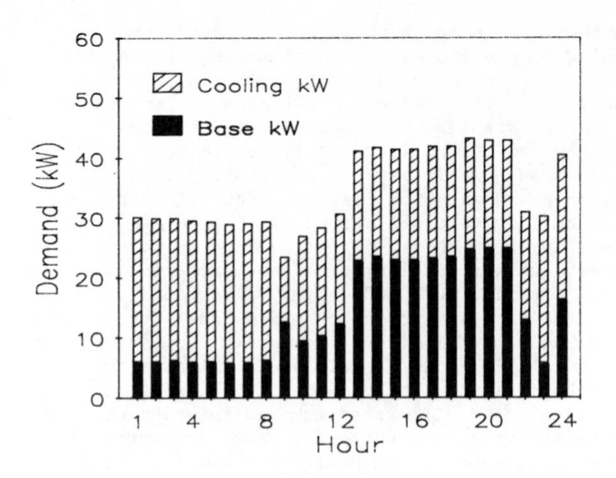

FIGURE 9. BUILDING kW UNDER PARTIAL STORAGE.

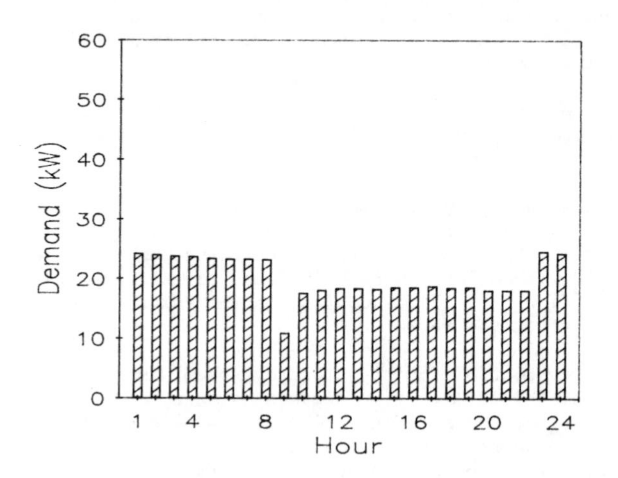

FIGURE 10. COOLING kW UNDER PARTIAL STORAGE.

Full Storage Operation: Under the full storage strategy the chiller was not allowed to operate during the peak hours of 12 noon to 10 p.m. daily. The ice storage alone served the cooling needs of the building during these hours. During the hours of 8 a.m. to 12 noon the building required cooling, but off-peak rates were still in effect. There would be no point in cooling the building from storage during off-peak hours, so the chiller was allowed to operate as a conventional system for these 4 hours and meet the cooling load directly. During the remaining 10 hours (from 10 p.m. to 8 a.m.) the chiller operated at full capacity to recharge the ice storage banks.

Figures 11 and 12 portray full storage operation. Full storage successfully removed all chiller energy consumption from peak hours. The recorded peak demand has been reduced by over half, from 55 kW down to 25 kW. The fact that off-peak demand reaches 59 kW does not matter because off-peak demand does not count under the time-of-use rate. Overall, only 28 percent of the total building energy consumption remains on peak.

Changes in Chiller Efficiency: The average efficiency of the chiller changed only slightly between conventional operation, full storage and partial storage. The specific energy use (kW/Ton) of the chiller rose by 3 percent under full storage and by 7 percent under partial storage. Most of the increased energy use under partial storage was due to the inefficiency of part-load operation for the existing chiller.

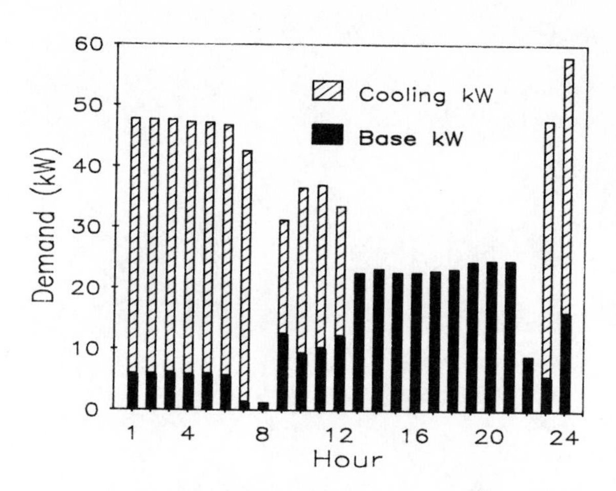

FIGURE 11. BUILDING kW UNDER FULL STORAGE.

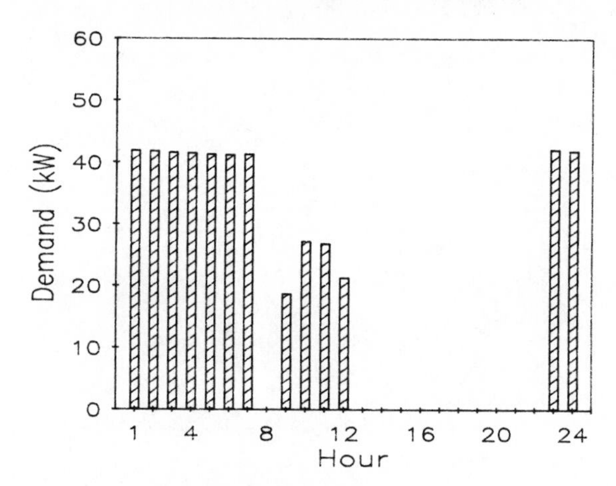

FIGURE 12. COOLING kW UNDER FULL STORAGE.

Changes in Total Cooling Energy with Storage: The total energy used for cooling per day rose 23 percent under full storage and 28 percent under partial storage. Contributing factors consisted of the decrease in chiller efficiency described above, thermal losses from the ice banks and piping, and additional run time on the circulating pump and condensing fans. The increased energy consumption was included in calculation of annual cooling costs and deducted from the system savings.

Annual Savings and Paybacks: Comparing first cost to annual savings, the full storage system would pay for itself over a five year period:

Total Cost of Installation	= $ 16,000
Utility Rebate	= $ 7,500
Annual Operating Savings	= $ 1,650
Payback Period (16000-7500)/1650	= 5 years

Both the time-of-use rate and the cash rebate were necessary to make the payback period attractive. Without the time-of-use rate the savings in operating cost would have almost negligible. The payback period would have been completely unacceptable, on the order of 45 years. With the time-of-use rate the savings jumps to over half the annual cost of air-conditioning. But even with these impressive savings the high first-cost of storage would have made the payback period 10 years. The incentive payment from the utility was needed to bring the payback period down to 5 years, an acceptable time for us.

CONCLUSION

Technology Assessment

* Thermal Energy Storage technology is ready for widespread application, but is not yet completely mature.

* Thermal Storage savings are significant. Savings of 40 to 60 percent in the operating costs of air-conditioning systems are possible.

* Strong utility incentives, including time-of-day rates and rebates are needed to make thermal storage attractive.

* Retrofit options are often limited because of

  -- Incompatibility with existing equipment
  -- Lack of space for storage

* The number of types of systems and equipment vendors is increasing rapidly.

Suggestions for Application

The following procedure is offered for consideration as a possible path to use in investigating thermal storage opportunities:

1) CONSULT YOUR LOCAL UTILITY company at the outset for information on thermal storage incentives. The utility may offer cash incentives, time-of-use rates, preliminary feasibility studies and so on. If the utility has no incentive program, thermal storage will not be economical (at least for retrofits) in your service area.

2) RANK BUILDINGS BY PRELIMINARY FEASIBILITY. Create a list of buildings ranked by preliminary feasibility. First rank the buildings by the type of existing HVAC system:

   First Priority - Chilled Water Systems.
   Second Priority - Central DX Systems.
   Third Priority - Multiple, Packaged DX.

   Within each category, further rank the buildings by the location of the existing equipment and the availability of space for storage. The ideal situation will have the existing equipment room located near ground level with space for storage immediately adjacent, either on-grade or under a lawn or parking surface.

3) ROUGHLY ESTIMATE THE COOLING LOAD over on-peak hours. An estimate accurate to 25 percent can be obtained from examining the operating log of the refrigeration equipment or by analyzing the monthly electric bills for the building.

4) ESTIMATE PAYBACKS. At this point, obtain rough payback figures for one or two buildings from each of the priority categories. Use rules of thumb for the unit cost of storage and the annual operating savings. This step will indicate which categories are attractive.

5) DO A FULL ENGINEERING STUDY on buildings with attractive paybacks. Compare the basic system alternatives; chilled water, ice and eutectic salts, on feasibility and payback.

6) OBTAIN COMPETITIVE BIDS on the final design.

7) INSTALL THE SYSTEM. If possible, install and test the system in the off-season for cooling.

ACKNOWLEDGEMENTS

Funding for this project was provided by the Energy Task Force of the Urban Consortium for Technology Initiatives under a grant from the federal Department of Energy. A copy of the complete, 120 page report on the project may be obtained for a small charge. Contact:

Publications and Distribution
Public Technology, Inc.
1301 Pennsylvania Avenue, NW
Washington, DC 20004

Phone (202) 626-2443

Request document number DG/85-307 02/86-100: Thermal Storage Strategies for Energy Cost Reduction.

REFERENCES

1. EPRI EM-3371: Commercial Cool Storage Primer. Electric Power Research Institute, P.O. Box 50490, Palo Alto CA 94303. January 1985. To order phone (415) 965-4081.

2. EPRI EM-3981: Commercial Cool Storage Design Guide. May 1985. Phone (415) 965-4081.

3. EPRI EM-4125: Current Trends in Commercial Cool Storage. July 1985. Phone (415) 965-4081.

4. EPRI EM-4405: Commercial Cool Storage Presentation Material. Volume 1: Seminar Handbook. February 1986. Phone (415) 965-4081.

5. CALMAC Manufacturing Corporation, Englewood NJ 07631-0710. Phone (201) 569-0420.

6. TRANSPHASE SYSTEMS INC. Thermal Energy Storage Systems. Huntington Beach CA. Phone (714) 841-4010.

Chapter 44

"DO-IT-YOURSELF" DDC FOR THERMAL STORAGE

J. R. Sosoka, K. W. Peterson

INTRODUCTION

There were two primary goals for this project. The first was to develop a highly reliable and accurate control system that was suitable for unsupervised remote operation. The second was to develop non-proprietary user generated control software that could be modified for use at other similar sites. This paper will discuss the advantages of industrial microcomputers for some applications, but the main thrust will be related to the programming considerations. The programming not only had to provide local control, it had to allow for communication and remote trouble shooting.

HVAC SYSTEM

Air System

The air side of the system consists of air handlers with heating and cooling coils. Three way valves are used to modulate the water flow. All of the building systems are controlled using discrete electronic modules.

Hot Water/Chilled Water System

A simplified flow diagram of the hot water/chilled water system is contained in Figure 1. Basic heating and cooling is provided by means of a heat recovery chiller. This chiller has two condensing circuits and two reciprocating compressors. Normally the chilled water flows from the cold storage tank through the evaporator section and back to the cold storage tank. In the case of hot water the hot water flows through the condensing sections where it is heated and then flows back to the hot water tank. The circulating water systems for the building systems takes water from the storage tanks, circulates it through the systems and then returns it to the tank. There are provisions for mixing water from the tanks with return water. Under

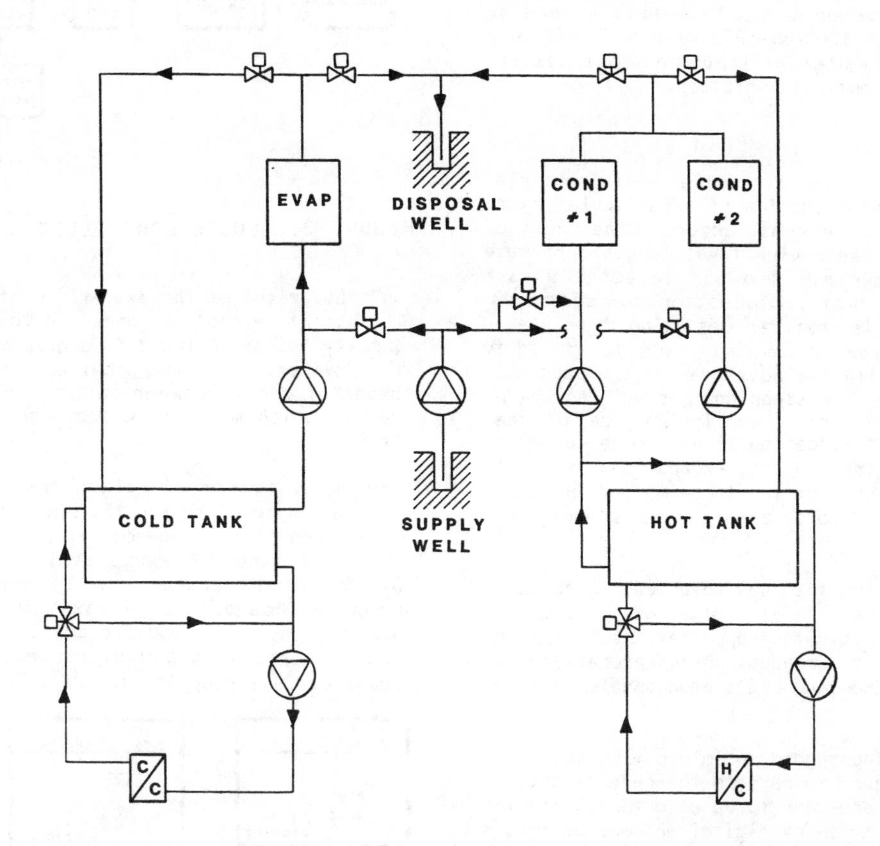

FIGURE 1. SYSTEM FLOW DIAGRAM

conditions of light load the temperature of the building supply water can be reduced so that the temperature differential in the storage tanks can be maximized.

When the water in either the cold tank or the hot tank is at its limit, but the other supply still needs to be conditioned further, the well water can be brought into operation. For instance, if the hot water tank is satisfied but additional cooling is required for the cold tank, the well water will be circulated through the condensing section. The condensing water pumps will be shut down during this operation and the appropriate valve changes will be made to accomodate the flow of well water. The well water flows through the condensing section to a disposal well where it is returned to the aquifer.

Storage is accomplished with two large cylindrical fiberglass tanks installed underground. Both tanks have distribution headers, top and bottom to facilitate stratification.

The valve actuators in this system are electric and are motorized for operation in both directions. The valves are also equipped with end switches in order for the control system to know whether they are open or closed.

While the simplified diagram shows only single pumps, all of the building pumps and the hot water and chilled water pumps are duplicated to provide redundancy.

CONTROL SYSTEM

Inputs and Outputs

Flow sensing is accomplished by means of capacitance type electronic flow sensors. Temperature sensing is done by means of 1000 ohm RTD with 4-20 milliamp transmitters. The digital inputs and outputs are all isolated with optical isolators.

Control Computer

The control computer is an off-the-shelf industrial microcomputer. The selection of a particular micro was dependent upon several factors. The first of these was that it had a high level language to make it easier to program. The one selected uses a structured BASIC that includes control commands. Secondly, since this computer was going to be placed in a mechanical room it had to be rugged. It had to be able to live with the power variations caused by equipment starting and stopping, as well as major fluctuations due to poor power in the general area. Because of the site location it had to be able to withstand wide temperature excursions as well. Furthermore, because of the large motors in close proximity, it had to be able to resist magnetic field problems.

The industrial micro that was selected is actually designed to work in all of these types of environments. Typical applications include controlling electric furnaces, batch processing out on the factory floor and unattended panels out in oil fields.

In addition to being rugged the micro also had to be modular. In order to perform the needed control functions it was necessary to be able to select the proper number and types of digital and analog inputs and outputs. Also, for future expansion or change, it was desirable if the types of inputs and outputs could be easily changed and expanded.

Finally, a high degree of accuracy and repeatability was desirable. Since this unit would be operating unattended - service and operating personnel are located about fifty miles away - it was necessary that the sensor readings provide a true indication of the system conditions. Also, because this is a storage system, it is necessary that temperature readings be accurate in order to minimize energy consumption and to make maximum usage of the thermal storage. Another requirement was that the unit be able to communicate easily with another computer. The other computer is used as a communication link to off-site locations as well as a data acquisition device.

The industrial micro that was used for this project consists of a main computer board which can handle up to 16 digital I/O's and 12 analog inputs and up to six expansion boards. Figure 2 shows the basic structure for the main board. It should be noted that the A/D conversion is done with a 14 bit device in order to provide a high level of accuracy. There is space available in ROM so that once an application program has been developed it can be placed in EPROM to save space in RAM. The main board has a counter to accomodate pulse type digital I/O's.

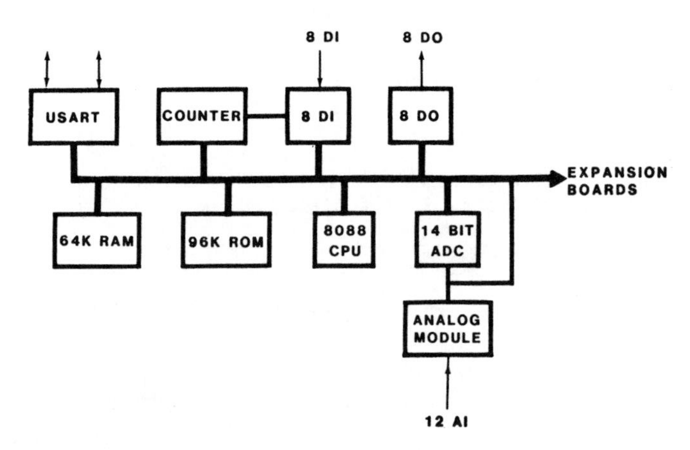

FIGURE 2. LOCAL CONTROLLER

In the case of the system for this project the industrial micro is connected to a PC. The PC greatly increases the data acquisition capability of the system. It also provides a much more flexible means of remote communication. Figure 3 shows one way in which multiple micros can be grouped into a system.

The total number of points that can be installed with a single micro and the six expansions will vary depending on the type of I/O's required. Figure 4 shows the types of boards available. A combination of up to six boards can be added to the basic computer board. For a maximum point count four digital I/O boards and two combination boards can be added to the main computer board for total point count of 24 analog inputs and 288 digital I/O's.

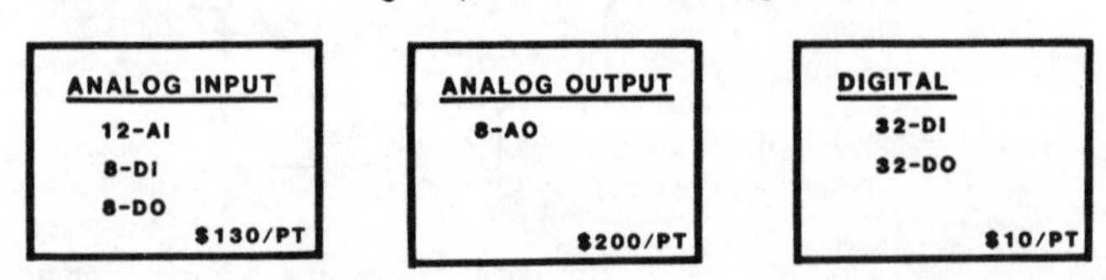

FIGURE 4. EXPANSION BOARDS

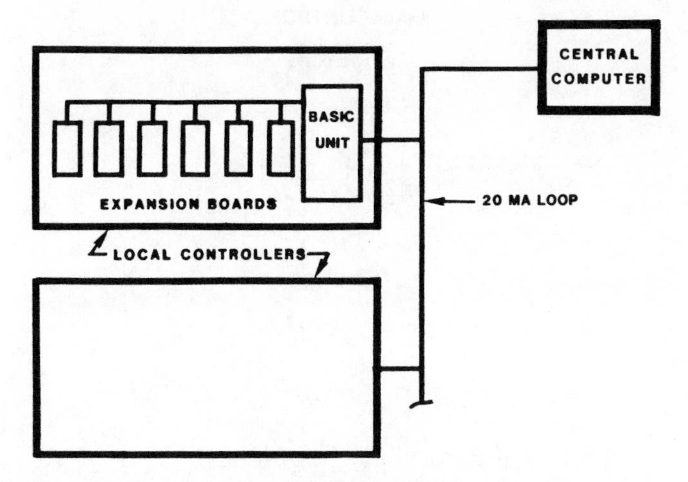

FIGURE 3. SYSTEM CONFIGURATION

PROGRAMMING

General

While not for everyone, there are applications where user developed software can be very beneficial. The situations where this normally holds true is for critical applications, projects where the controls will be staged in over a period of time, or where the user has a number of similar applications. Actually, a considerable quantity of public domain control software is starting to become available. There are also custom software packages that can be used with a variety of micros. As more users continue to develop their own software, hopefully, a means of exchanging information between users will develop. The ability to do the control programming in BASIC has greatly facilitated the development of user control software.

Software

The purpose of the software is to start and stop the various pieces of equipment, control the chilled water and hot water tank temperatures, perform lead-lag on various pumps, track alarms and provide a user interface which would not interfere with the control. The software is divided into two parts, control code and communications code. The control code runs continuously, controlling the thermal storage system, while the communications code is strictly interrupt driven. The communications software provides the required user interface for the industrial microcomputer via a standard RS-232 port. This paper, however, is concerned mainly with the control software.

The majority of the information required to operate the control system is stored in three main arrays partitioned in the battery backed RAM. The first stores information pertaining to the analog input points. The second array maintains all the information needed for the digital inputs and outputs. These arrays contain information such as analog or digital channel numbers corresponding to each point, alarm flags to track which points are in alarm, and current status of each point. The last array stores the setpoints for the control procedures and alarms.

The control software for the thermal storage facility was developed with a structured form of BASIC. The sequence of operations for the thermal storage system provides the following four main modes of operation:

1. IDLE MODE (IM) In which the chiller does not operate.

2. CHILLED WATER - HOT WATER MODE (CW-HW) The chiller is used to cool the chilled water and heat the hot water.

3. CHILLED WATER - WELL WATER (CW-WW) In which the chiller is used to cool the chilled water and the condenser heat is rejected to the well water.

4. WELL WATER - HOT WATER MODE (WW-HW) In which the chiller absorbs heat from the well water passing through the evaporator and transfers it to the hot water flowing through the condensers.

These different modes of operation, however, have many similarities. Therefore, to minimize memory usage and increase speed, the sequence of operations was broken down into similar low level tasks required to operate the different modes. Small procedures were then written to handle these tasks.

The control software is modularized into the various procedures and functions. These procedures and functions contain the low level control algorithms. Procedures and functions are the essential building blocks of a structured and modular program. Both are self-contained blocks of statements designed to perform a specification and may operate on arguments passed to them as parameters or on global data.

Functions differ from procedures, however, in that they always return a result, that is an integer, real number or string. An example is a low level function used to read temperatures in degrees Fahrenheit. The function reads the voltage input on the specified channel and returns the result in degrees Fahrenheit.

Alarms for the facility are divided into three categories: analog, digital and miscellaneous alarms. All alarms are stored in a single 255 byte string. The string is capable of storing thirty alarms at a given time. They are stored in the string until the alarm buffer is cleared. This is automatically done after the alarms have been received by an operator. Alarm flags are also utilized to insure the same alarm is not repeated before being acknowledged. Lastly, a critical alarm flag is used to flag a critical condition in which the thermal storage system should be kept in IDLE mode. A valve failing to open or close when commanded is one example of a critical alarm condition. This flag is used to prevent such catastrophies as dumping the tank water down the dispersion well or dead-heading a high head capacity pump. The critical alarm flag will keep the system in IDLE mode until it is reset by an operator, either locally or remotely.

There are three main control procedures and one main supervisory procedure for the facility. These four procedures correspond to the four different modes of operation. These main procedures follow the sequence of operations. They implement the many low level procedures and functions to perform a sequence of tasks as shown in Figure 5.

The first procedure operates when the system is in the IDLE mode. It is the "traffic cop". It is responsible for determining which mode to operate. The listing and flowchart for this procedure are shown in Figures 6 and 7, respectively. If the chilled water needs to be cooled or the hot water needs to be heated, or both, this procedure directs the system to the appropriate mode of operation. This procedure also performs lead-lag on the chilled water and building pumps. The lead and lag pumps are automatically switched every month. The procedure maintains the current analog and digital statuses and checks for alarm conditions. It also checks for the critical alarm flag which is used to keep the system in IDLE until the alarm flag has been reset by an operator.

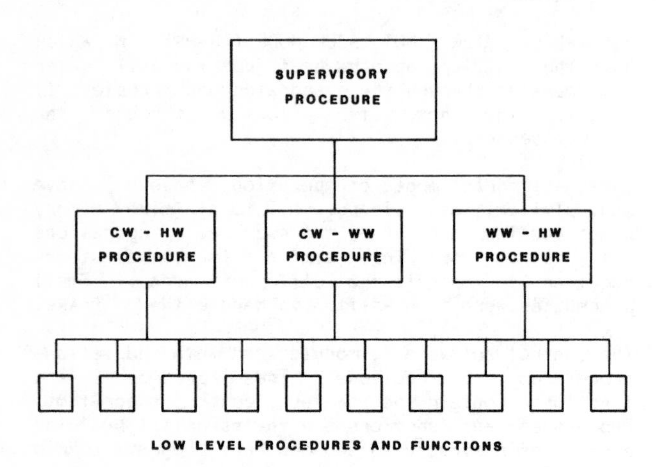

FIGURE 5. CONTROL SYSTEM HIERARCHY

Procedure CONTROL

```
INTEGER:    I,M,D,Y,MONTH
EXTERNAL:   CHWHW, CHWWW, WWHW
EXTERNAL:   LEADLAG, CRITALARM,DISCAN,AISCAN,PUMPS,RAI,SP,OVERFLOW
EXTERNAL:   MODEON,OVRIDE,DISTATUS,ALS$,SAI,SOFTOVER,READDIO,SETDIO

   1 rem ----> main control loop for the system
   2 rem ---->
   3 rem ----> set lead pumps and lag pumps
  10 GDATE(MONTH,D,Y)
  20 LEADLAG
  30 GDATE (M,D,Y) : IF M<>MONTH THEN 10
  35 rem ----> scan all inputs
  40 DISCAN : AISCAN
  45 check tank temperatures against alarm setpoints
  50 IF RAI (3,0)>SP(4) THEN ALS$(1,3,21,0)
  60 IF RAI (11,0)<SP(5) THEN ALS$(1,11,22,0)
  70 IF DISTATUS(42)<>1 THEN ALS$(0,42,4,0)
  80 rem ----> check for overrides
  90 IF DISTATUS (19)<>1 OR SOFTOVER THEN 30
  95 rem ----> check main bldg pumps
 100 PUMPS
 115 rem ----> check for critical alarm and overflow
 110 IF CRITALARM OR OVERFLOW THEN 30
 120 IF RAI (3,0)>SP(1) THEN 140
 130 IF RAI (10,0)>SP(3) THEN I=4 ELSE I=3
 140 IF RAI (10,0)>SP(3) THEN I=2 ELSE I=1
 150 ON I GOTO 1000, 2000, 3000, 4000
1000 rem ----> chilled water - hot water mode
1010 IF MODEON(1) THEN CHWHW : GOTO 30
1020 IF MODEON(2) THEN 2000 ELSE 3000
2000 rem ----> chilled water - well water mode
2010 IF MODEON(2) THEN CHWWW
2020 GOTO 30
3000 rem ----> well water - hot water mode
3010 IF MODEON(3) THEN WWHW
3020 GOTO 30
4000 rem ----> handles fallout
4010 GOTO 30
```

FIGURE 6. PROCEDURE CONTROL LISTING

The other three main control procedures are used to provide the sequence of operations required for the CW-HW, CW-WW and WW-HW modes described earlier. After the procedure has implemented a particular mode, it will maintain the current analog and digital statuses and continuously check for alarm conditions. The tank temperatures are checked against their corresponding setpoints. The flowchart in Figure 8 shows the criteria to maintain the CW-HW mode. When the tank temperatures are within setpoint limits the system goes back into idle.

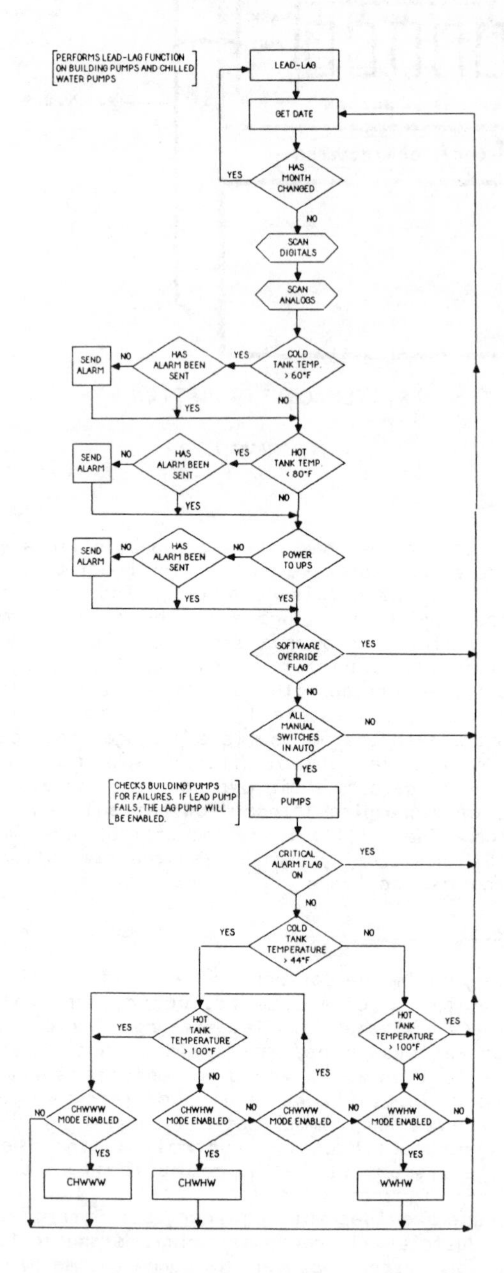

FIGURE 7. MAIN CONTROL FLOWCHART

In order to facilitate the servicing of the equipment a Hands/Off/Automatic switch was provided for each piece of equipment including the motorized valves. These switches are monitored by the computer. To protect the system, if any of these switches are taken out of the AUTO position the computer will automatically put the system into the IDLE mode.

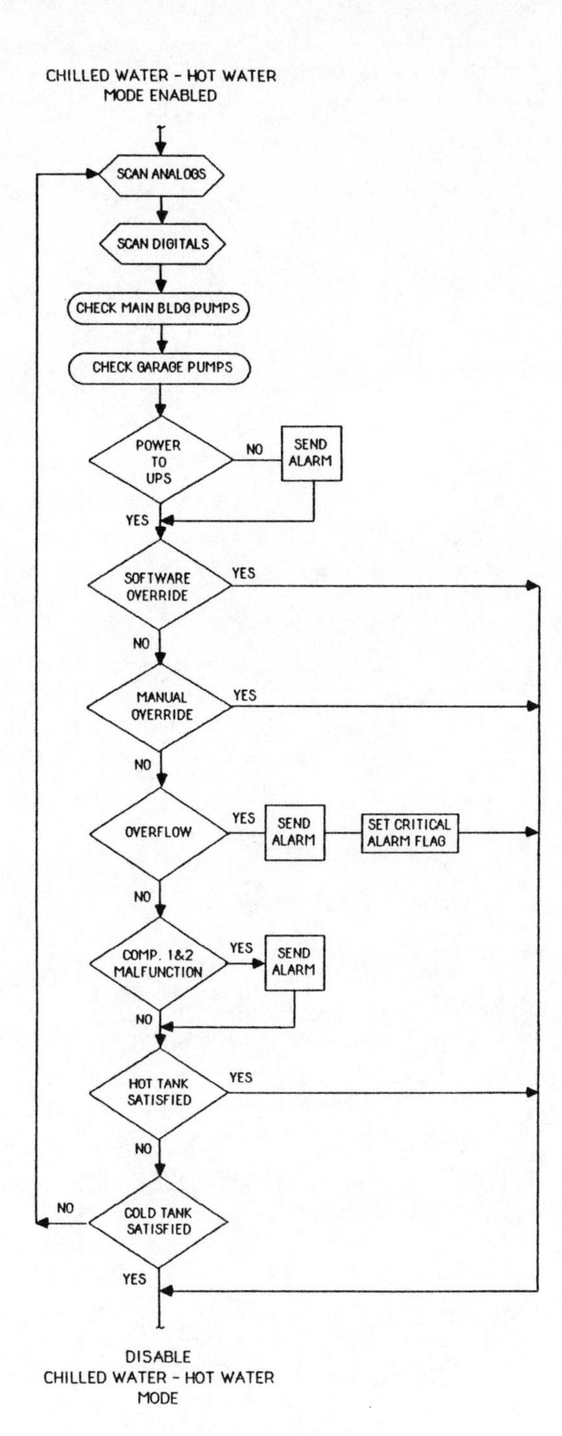

FIGURE 8. CW-HW MODE FLOWCHART

<u>Program Considerations</u>

The main advantage of utilizing low level procedures and functions in the software structure is that each can be tested as an individual task. Once de-bugged, the procedure or function can then be added to the programmer's control toolbox.

Control software is usually required to wait a specified time period before looking for a response from an output. This response could take less than a second or over ten minutes. Therefore, the monitoring and supervision should not be put on hold during this period. Figure 9 shows an example of a procedure which monitors analog and digital status while it checks for tank overflow, software or manual overrides and maintains the building pumps. This procedure utilizes lower level procedures and functions to perform all these tasks.

Procedure TD

```
EXTERNAL:  AISCAN,DISCAN,DISTATUS
EXTERNAL:  SOFTOVER,PUMPS,OVERFLOW
INTEGER ARG:  I1, I2

   1 rem ----> time delay procedure
   2 rem ----> I1 = seconds   I2 = 0,1 (leaving mode, entering mode)
   3 rem ----> distatus (19) - manual override
  10 ZTIMER
  20 DO
  30    AISCAN : DISCAN
  40    IF OVERFLOW THEN EXIT
  50    IF I2 AND SOFTOVER OR DISTATUS (19) = 0 THEN EXIT
  60    PUMPS
  70 REPEAT IF TIMER < I1
```

FIGURE 9. PROCEDURE TD LISTING

CONCLUSION

While the use of industrial microcomputers for control purposes is not for everyone, there are times that they can be used to advantage. It should be noted that these systems are designed to be programmed by the user for their particular application. There is also a significant amount of public domain software being developed for HVAC applications. All of this should help to reduce the programming cost.

The gains in accuracy and flexibility of implementation must be weighed against the increased involvement required by the user. This involvement is required for both programming and servicing. There are, however, an increasing number of control consultants and contractors that can provide support for these projects. For some applications the nonproprietary systems could be substantially less expensive. In any case, there seems to be a growing interest in this approach. This trend should continue as more people become familiar with computers and more public domain software is developed. Development of proprietary general control software for nonproprietary hardware systems will also increase the interest in the use of "Do-It-yourself" DDC.

SECTION 13
ELECTRIC GENERATION ALTERNATIVES

Chapter 45

TURBINE VERSUS GRID POWER: CONTROVERSY IN CALIFORNIA

M. Lobnitz

INTRODUCTION

It is ironic that major offshore oil and gas reserves in the United States are associated with a coastal environment which due to a combination of meteorology and terraine features produces conditions ideal for ozone formation. If air quality in California is viewed as a limited resource, it becomes obvious that pollution control measures implemented within the petroleum industry must be a cooperative effort, lest the first project is permitted at the expense of future offshore activity.

Nowhere is this fact more evident than in the Northern Santa Maria Basin, where results of air quality impact analysis for the first offshore platform predicted state and federal ozone violations with the potential to impede any development in the area. One of the proposed solutions to this problem is the utilization of grid power as a replacement for gas turbines and other offshore combustion sources that emit ozone precursors to the atmosphere. However, there are many aspects of platform electrification which need to be explored prior to its implementation in the coastal waters of San Luis Obispo County.

This paper discusses the application of grid power to offshore platforms, covering such topics as; air quality tradeoffs in the use of turbine versus grid power, availability and reliability of grid power, concerns regarding the safety and reliability of process modifications, policy and regulatory issues, economic analysis and long-term resource recovery potential.[1]

PROJECT AND AREA STUDY DESCRIPTION

Cities Service Oil and Gas Corporation has applied to develop oil and gas reserves (OCS Lease P-0409) in the northern Santa Maria Basin of California. The proposed project, known as the San Miguel Project, involves the construction of an offshore platform (Platform Julius), an onshore oil treating facility, and associated onshore and offshore pipelines. The proposed project would be the first offshore oil development project in the northern Santa Maria Basin (see Figure 1).[1]

Platform Julius would be installed approximately 9.5 miles west of Point Sal. It would have the capacity to produce a maximum of 50,000 barrels of wet oil. Most of the natural gas produced along with the wet oil at the wellhead would be reinjected into the reservoir; the remainder will be used as fuel for turbine generators which generate platform electrical power.

Three subsea pipelines would be constructed to connect Platform Julius with an onshore oil processing plant. One pipeline will transfer wet oil from the platform to the processing plant. Another would return to the platform produced water separated from the wet oil at the processing plant. The third pipeline would deliver diesel fuel to the platform for turbine use during the first six months of operation when produced gas is unavailable, for use in emergency equipment, and for use as diluent for the wet oil pipeline whenever necessary. The pipelines are located offshore along an eleven-mile corridor; the remaining onshore portion would extend another 6.8 miles to the onshore processing plant.

The onshore processing plant would be located near the Union oil refinery at Nipomo Mesa (Figure 1). Alternate locations for the processing plant are the Douglas, Callendar and Flintkote sites. The plant is designed to process 50,000 barrels of wet oil per day. A 24 mile-long interconnect pipeline would be constructed by Celeron Oil and Gas Company to transport the dehydrated crude oil from the processing facility to a pump station near Sisquoc. At the pump station, the interconnect pipeline would tie into an interstate pipeline system. The interconnect pipeline has the capacity to transport 180,000 barrels per day of crude oil.

Although the installation of Platform Julius would mark the first offshore oil development project in the northern Santa Maria Basin, additional development in the area is anticipated. To accommodate this future development, the Cities platform was designed to allow future pipeline hookups from platforms on nearby leases and pipelines were sized to handle additional production from the area.

In order to evaluate the impacts of area development, it was assumed that six hypothetical platforms would be developed on OCS tracts within the Northern Santa Maria Basin. To accommodate production from this offshore development, there would be two 50,000 barrel per day additions to the oil processing plant proposed for the Cities Project. A 30 MMSFCD gas plant would be constructed, along with future processing additions with capacities of 30 and 65 MMSFCD, to process the natural gas produced. Alternate locations for the area study oil and gas processing plants are similar to those considered for the proposed project.

INITIAL MODELING RESULTS[2]

Emissions from the platform, pipelines and processing plant were calculated for both the construction and production phases. Emissions were developed for worst hour scenarios, normal hour scenarios, and upset conditions. The worst hour emissions represent the highest emissions that can reasonably be expected to occur from a given activity. Normal hour emissions represent a more frequently experienced emissions which would occur during periods of high activity. Upset emissions occur infrequently during abnormal events such as breakdown of equipment or shutdown conditions.

Three different atmospheric dispersion models were used to simulate the transport and diffusion of pollutant emissions. The Offshore and Coastal Dispersion (OCD) model was used to evaluate the impacts of inert

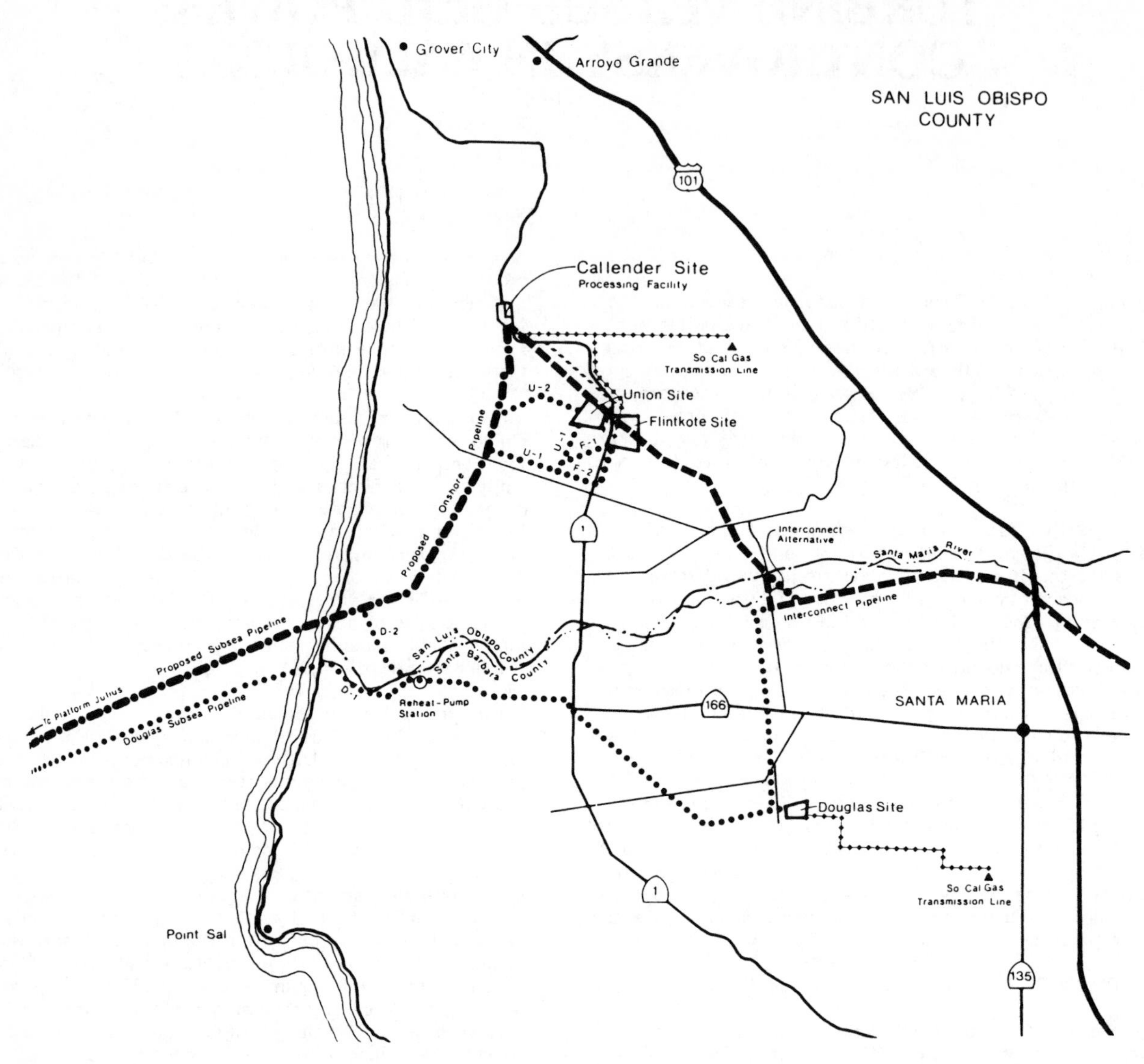

FIGURE 1: LOCATION OF SAN MIGUEL PROJECT COMPONENTS

pollutants on offshore sources of emissions at the shoreline as well as at receptors located inland at critical terraine locations. As this analysis represented the first use of this version of OCD in a major EIR/EIS, comparison runs using a modified version of the COMPLEX 2 model were performed. This model has been used frequently in past offshore EIS's and produces conservative model predictions. Both of the models described are hourly, steady-state Gaussian dispersion models based on point sources. To evaluate the project impact on ozone production, a photochemical model based on the trajectory (Lagrangian) formulation was used. The model selected was TRACE (Trajectory Model for Regional Atmospherics, Chemistry, and Emissions).

Use of the trace model requires the development of meteorological trajectories. Seven trajectories were constructed from actual meteorological data on days in which relatively high ozone concentrations were measured in the study region. Table 1 describes the trajectories developed.

Preliminary modeling results for the TRACE modeling of worst hour emissions are summarized in Table 2. Violation of the state ozone standard of 10 pphm is predicted to occur for five of the six trajectories. However, only 3 of these cases (trajectories 1, 3, and 6) show a standard violation produced by project emissions. In the other two cases, standard violations are exceeded by the future baseline (a projection of future pollutant concentrations predicted for the period in which the project is implemented). The results of trajectory 5 show that a violation of the federal ozone standard of 12 pphm is predicted to occur as a result of the future baseline emissions. The projected incremental increase in ozone is considerably lower using normal hour emissions, but a state standard violation is still predicted for trajectories 3 and 6.

To ameliorate predicted impacts in trajectories 3 and 6, mitigation measures were applied to the platform which included injection timing retard on crew and supply boat engines, limits on testing of emergency equipment, and a vigorous inspection and maintenance program for piping components.

An alternative to mitigating emissions from the turbine-powered platform was to replace gas turbine power generation with electricity from the Pacific Gas and Electric grid. This purchased power could also be used to power an electric crane and two electric heaters on the platform, further reducing emissions.

Tables 3 and 4 compare the predicted ozone impacts of mitigated turbine and grid power option on trajectories 3 and 6. In both trajectories 3 and 6, a state standard exceedance is predicted during worst and normal hour emissions scenarios for the turbine powered platform, but the exceedance is eliminated in the grid power case.[3]

When the comparison of turbine versus grid-powered platforms is extended to the area study, no federal ozone violations are predicted, but modeling results indicate that the addition of one or more area study platforms in combination with gas processing and expanded oil processing at Union is sufficient to produce state standard violations. The incremental ozone increase caused by the turbine power platform emissions is generally 10 to 20 percent greater than that caused by the grid power platforms. However, in adding the area study platforms into the TRACE simulations, preference was given to those platforms located closest to Platform Julius and in the center cell of the trajectory. Addition of area study platforms for the grid power option in a different configuration, such as positioning them in the lateral cells of the trajectory might have generated a different result (not have violated the state Standard).

OTHER TECHNICAL ISSUES

Air quality impact is not the sole criterion for imposing platform electrification on a project proponent. Public policy, engineering feasibility, and economics also need to be considered. This section will explore those issues in detail with respect to the Cities project.

Public Policy

To oversee the EIR/EIS document production for the project, a Joint Review Panel (JRP) was formed. The JRP is chaired by the County of San Luis Obispo and consists of three voting representatives (MMS, San Luis Obispo County and the State Lands Commission) and three non-voting participants (the California Coastal Commission, the County of Santa Barbara, and the Governor's Office of Offshore Development). MMS is the federal agency preparing the EIS under NEPA and the County is the lead agency preparing the EIR under CEQA.

Platform Julius would be constructed in OCS waters and is under the jurisdiction of the Minerals Management Service. MMS is responsible for mitigating project impacts to meet federal standards. Any further mitigation it would impose would be on a voluntary basis to minimize projected impacts. Both the MMS and the State Lands Commission receive revenues from oil production and are concerned that the potential for future development is maintained. San Luis Obispo County has jurisdiction over the onshore portions of the state and local level. When offshore emissions contribute to onshore standard violations jurisdictional issues become complex. At this point, there is no indication from any of the agencies how this issue will be resolved.

Technical Feasibility

Table 5 lists the comparative features of turbine-powered and grid powered platforms. According to Cities Service, if grid power were used, the platform would require a minimum of three turbines as the primary power source for initial drilling and production.[4] According to the current project schedule, drilling operations would commence before grid power could be provided to the platform by PG&E, as the permitting process for the transmission system takes approximately two years.[5]

In addition, three turbines are required to support minimum platform operations during an extended grid power down-time scenario such as substation or subsea power cable maintenance. Because of the high viscosity of the reservoir crude oil, it is essential that this oil be continuously heated and pumped through the system. If heat or motive power were lost for an extended period of time, the crude oil could set in the lines and equipment and at best an extensive recovery period would be required to resume production.

Cities feels this level of redundancy is necessary because of the unreliability of the grid. However, PG&E asserts that grid power availability is at least 99.5%.[5] PG&E would install a spare subsea cable to the platform for protection against cable failure and would keep emergency transformers and switching equipment onhand which can be shipped to any state site within 12 hours.[6] Although PG&E's efforts result in high grid power reliability, they do not protect the platform from catastrophic events such as the power outage which occurred recently in Santa Barbara County when a barge anchor being dragged along the ocean floor severed both power cables connecting an offshore platform to an onshore substation.[6]

TABLE 1. DESCRIPTION OF TRACE TRAJECTORIES

Trajectory	Project Components Assessed	Impact Area
1	Callendar and Union Oil Processing	N. Santa Barbara County
2	Callendar Oil Processing	S. SLO County
3	Platform Julius	Santa Ynez Valley
4	Douglas Oil Processing	S. SLO County
5	Callendar Oil Processing	S. SLO County
6	Callendar, Union and Flintkote Oil Processing; and Platform Julius	Santa Ynez Valley
7	Platform Julius	S. SLO County

TABLE 2

PEAK OZONE IMPACTS FOR THE SAN MIGUEL PROJECT - WORST HOUR EMISSIONS

(pphm)

Trajectory		Present Baseline	Future Baseline	Project Increase	Peak Impacts	Project Sites in Trajectory
	Overwater Impacts	*10.66	* 10.72	0.18	* 10.90	Callendar
1	Shoreline Impacts	*10.31	* 10.39	0.09	* 10.48	
	Onshore Impacts	9.81	9.95	0.11	* 10.06	
	Overwater Impacts	7.68	7.62	0.08	7.70	Callendar
2	Shoreline Impacts	8.70	8.65	0.21	8.86	
	Onshore Impacts	9.98	* 10.07	0.03	* 10.10	
	Overwater Impacts	3.92	3.92	0.74	4.66	Julius
3	Shoreline Impacts	4.56	4.56	2.11	6.67	
	Onshore Impacts	***	9.63	0.97	* 10.60	
	Overwater Impacts	7.36	7.35	0.39	7.74	Callendar
5	Shoreline Impacts	8.89	8.78	-0.02	8.76	
	Onshore Impacts	***	**12.54	0.16	** 12.70	
	Overwater Impacts	7.09	7.05	0.12	7.17	Callendar
6	Shoreline Impacts	8.00	7.98	1.08	9.06	Julius
	Onshore Impacts (1600)	9.76	9.71	0.72	* 10.43	
	Onshore Impacts (1700)	***	* 10.15	0.71	* 10.86	
	Overwater Impacts	4.68	4.68	5.27	9.95	Julius
7	Shoreline Impacts	5.13	5.08	4.42	9.50	
	Onshore Impact	8.77	8.62	0.72	9.34	

* Equals or exceeds the State Standard of 10 pphm
** Exceeds the State Standard and the Federal Standard of 12 pphm
*** Present baseline not calculated for this hour.

TABLE 3

PREDICTED OZONE IMPACTS OF FULLY MITIGATED TURBINE AND GRID POWER OPTION ON TRAJECTORY #3

	WORST HOUR		NORMAL HOUR	
	a. Peak Overwater Impacts		a. Peak Overwater Impacts	
	Peak O_3 (pphm)	Increase (pphm)	Peak O_3 (pphm)	Increase (pphm)
Future Baseline Scenario Emissions	3.92	--	3.92	--
Mitigated Turbine Power	4.72	0.80	4.67	0.75
Mitigated Grid Power	4.55	0.63	4.57	0.65
	b. Peak Shoreline Impacts		b. Peak Shoreline Impacts	
	Peak O_3 (pphm)	Increase (pphm)	Peak O_3 (pphm)	Increase (pphm)
Future Baseline Scenario Emissions	4.56	--	4.56	--
Mitigated Turbine		1.98	6.52	1.96
Mitigated Grid Power	6.57	2.01	6.03	1.47
	c. Peak Onshore Impacts		c. Peak Onshore Impacts	
	Peak O_3 (pphm)	Increase (pphm)	Peak O_3 (pphm)	Increase (pphm)
Future Baseline Scenario Emissions	9.63	--	9.63	--
Mitigated Turbine		0.68	10.10	0.47
Mitigated Grid Power	9.93	0.30	9.75	0.12

TABLE 4

PREDICTED OZONE IMPACTS OF FULLY MITIGATED TURBINE AND GRID POWER OPTION ON TRAJECTORY #6

	WORST HOUR		NORMAL HOUR	
	a. Peak Overwater Impacts		a. Peak Overwater Impacts	
	Peak O_3 (pphm)	Increase (pphm)	Peak O_3 (pphm)	Increase (pphm)
Future Baseline Scenario Emissions	7.08	--	7.08	--
Mitigated Turbine Power	7.03	-0.50	7.04	-0.04
Mitigated Grid Power	7.05	-0.03	7.05	-0.03
	b. Peak		Peak Shoreline Impacts	
	Peak O_3 (pphm)	Increase (pphm)	Peak O_3 (pphm)	Increase (pphm)
Future Baseline Scenario Emissions	7.88	--	7.88	--
Mitigated Turbine Power	8.87	0.99	8.64	0.76
Mitigated Grid Power	8.27	0.39	7.97	0.09
	c. Peak Onshore Impacts		c. Peak Onshore Impacts	
	Peak O_3 (pphm)	Increase (pphm)	Peak O_3 (pphm)	Increase (pphm)
Future Baseline Scenario Emissions	9.71	--	9.71	--
Mitigated Turbine Power	10.15	0.44	10.01	0.30
Mitigated Grid Power	9.90	0.19	9.78	0.07

TABLE 5

COMPARATIVE FEATURES OF TURBINE-POWERED AND GRID-POWERED PLATFORMS

Feature	Turbine-Powered Platforms	Grid-Powered Platforms
Turbine Generators		
Number	5[a]	3[b]
Power Output (MW)	12	N.A.
Energy Production (MW-hours/year)	105,000	N.A.
Gas-Fired Oil Heaters		
Number	0	0
Maximum Heating Rate (MM Btu/hour)	N.A.	N.A.
Electric Oil Heaters		
Number	0	2
Maximum Heating Rate (MM Btu/hour)	N.A.	19.9
Energy Consumption (MW-hours/year)	N.A.	51,700
Diesel Crane		
Number	2	0
Electric Crane		
Number	0	2
Energy Consumption (MW-hours/year)	N.A.	820
Grid Power Requirements		
Maximum Demand (MW)[c]	N.A.	18.2
Energy Consumption (MW-hours/year)	N.A.	158,000

a One of the five would be used as a backup.

b To be used as backup only.

c Not including transmission system losses.

N.A. Not Applicable

Another technical barrier to grid power is that Cities has already fabricated the platform modules and there would be safety and structural problems associated with retrofitting them to grid power. From a policy standpoint, this argument is questionable because it is the responsibility of the applicant to ensure that its project is permittable prior to the outlay of capital for equipment fabrication. However, PG&E has proposed that a transmission platform could be constructed as an alternative to an onshore substation which could accommodate both the equipment required for grid retrofit on Platform Julius and the future expansion of platforms as evaluated in the area study.

Economic Concerns

Cities Service prepared an evaluation of the economics of platform electrification, entitled "Alternate Power Review", which they submitted to the JRP and which was subsequently reviewed and reanalyzed by Jacobs.[7] Economic impact on project feasibility could not be directly analyzed because production curves and financial data for the project are proprietary information. However, relative impact of the two alternatives could be assessed.

Capital costs for the power cable system typically range from $16.4 million to $18.1 million. Cities estimates its total operating costs to be $606 million and $582 million for grid and turbine power options, respectively. Under the turbine option, gas-fired equipment could be operated on natural gas produced from the reservoir at minimal cost to Cities. However, the cost of purchased power may be partially offset by reduced operation and maintenance costs associated with converting most of the major platform equipment to a standby basis.

Cities performed a Best Available Control Technology (BACT) analysis for the two options and estimated that in the turbine option, the cost per pound of NO_x removed was $0.16 and converting to grid power would increase the cost per pound to $27.58.[4] However, the base case for this analysis was the level of NO_x emissions remaining after the application of BACT to the uncontrolled turbines. When this analysis is performed starting with uncontrolled emissions in both cases, the cost per pound of NO_x removed for the grid power cases is reduced to $8.88 (which is still over fifty times the cost of NO_x removal in the turbine power case).[7] On the other hand, if the platform modules were not already fabricated, grid power would be an alternate design and there could be a potential for lowering capital costs by reducing the capacity of standby equipment.

Based on data presented by Cities in the APR, imposition of grid power will reduce project life by 6 to 8 years.[4] However, the projected loss in terms of oil production is approximately 7.1 percent and this estimate does not anticipate the potential for increased production if more of the produced gas is reinjected into the reservoir or an increase (or decrease) in the real price of oil relative to the price of electricity over the life of the project.[7] In addition, the Cities analysis does not consider the loss of government revenues if no further development were allowed other than the Cities project.

CONCLUSIONS

The Cities San Miguel project is an interesting case study of regional air quality issues. Decisionmakers associated with permitting the project must evaluate whether the technical and economic barriers to implementing platform electrification outweigh the air quaility benefit to be derived from it. If grid power were imposed on the project, would it be an unfair burden to the applicant or a necessary measure to ensure that further development can occur in the basin? Are there other pollution control measures that could be applied to existing sources county-wide to reduce ambient pollutant levels and more evenly distribute the financial burden among those responsible for deteriorating the air quality resource, or should the penalty rest upon the applicant which would cause the air basin to violate existing state and local standards?

In determining air pollution control requirements, an agency must have the ability to enforce the measures imposed. In attainment areas, the burden of air pollution control usually rests with the applicant projected to violate standards because there are no other legal means other than ambient air quality standards to maintain air quality. Once an area is designated as "non-attainment", federal regulations require an agency to develop an air quality attainment plan in which measures are developed to be applied to existing and proposed projects in order to return the air basin to attainment status. In the case of the Cities project, there are trajectories for which the future baseline is predicted to exceed the state standard before any project emissions are considered. There has been no action taken to redesignate the status of the area because the future baseline is only a projection of future conditions and not based on actual monitoring data. Thus, applicable air quality regulations give no firm guidance as to how this case should be resolved. The agencies involved face a difficult decision based on the complexity of the issue.

REFERENCES

1. URS Company, 1985. Cities Service Oil and Gas Corporation and Celeron Pipeline Company of California, San Miguel Project and Northern Santa Maria Basin Area Study. Draft Environmental Impact Statement/Draft Environmental Impact Report. OCS EIS/EIR MMS #85-0106, Volume I.

2. Jacobs Engineering, Nov. 1985. Cities Service San Miguel Project and Northern Santa Maria Basin Area Study EIS/EIR. Technical Appendix Air Quality/Meteorology, Vol. II.

3. Applied Modeling and Jacobs Engineering, May 1986. Cities Service San Miguel Project and Northern Santa Maria Basin Area Study Final EIS/EIR. Supplemental Area Study (To Assess the Air Quality Impacts of Turbine Versus Grid Power).

4. Cities Service, Jan. 1986. Alternative Power Review Platform Julius San Miguel Project.

5. Anderson, W., Nov. 1985. Letter from PG&E to J.D. McDevitt, Bechtel Inc.

6. Anderson, W., April 1986. Letter from PG&E to D. Butler, Jacobs Engineering.

7. Jacobs Engineering, May 1986. A Review of the Cities Service Alternative Power Review (January 13, 1986).

SECTION 14
LOAD MANAGEMENT

Chapter 46

ASSESSING DEMAND-SIDE MANAGEMENT OPTIONS FOR UTILITY STRATEGIC RESOURCE PLANNING: A MICROCOMPUTER APPLICATION

D. L. Norland

Demand Side Management (DSM) programs are increasingly being examined by utilities and state public service commissions as part of strategies to meet consumer electricity needs and at least cost. Unfortunately, comprehensive analysis of conservation and load management opportunities in utility strategic planning is new to the industry and managers often lack the tools and data necessary to do the job. Some sophicated tools for such planning have been developed, but they typically require large amounts of detailed load data. The Alliance to Save Energyhas developed a simple, easy-to-use computer program that is a DSM screening tool. As a screening tool, the program allows users to make basic analyses and judgements about the economics of DSM options and the impact of conservation programs.

The tool - called CONPRO for CONservation PROgram Impact Estimation Model - aids utility planners in determining how much resource expenditure on conservation and load management programs is "optimal" - or maximizes utility program goals. In a case study done by the Alliance with General Public Utilities (GPU), the goal was to find the level of expenditures on a generic rebate program targeted to all customer classes that resulted in the lowest present value of future revenue requirements over the next 20 years. CONPRO, however, can handle other specifications of utility DSM program objectives.

While CONPRO can do complete program revenue requirement impact analyses, it has many features that allow the analyst to do partial or specific subanalyses. These features include the ability to:

- o Evaluate impacts of DSM programs on utility loads, revenues, costs, rates, and revenue requirements.
- o Calculate the magnitude of economic DSM alternatives to society or individual consumers and display the resulting load curves along with the utility's load forecast.
- o Calculate DSM option costs of conserved energy (CCE) or demand (CCD) [The CCE or CCD equals the levelized cost of each kWh or kW saved over the life of the option.]
- o Calculate and print or graph DSM supply or resource curves for any time period.
- o Calculate market penetration of DSM alternatives over time.

This paper is divided into two parts. In the first part preliminary results from the GPU case-study will be used to illustrate the calculation of the magnitude of economic electricity conservation and load management alternatives (ECAs) from two different perspectives, comparing them to the utility's load forecasts. Part one is organized in two parts (1) an overview of the defition of the opportunity for economic conservation, and (2) conservation opportunity measurement results from the GPU project. The second part of the paper discusses the calculation of market penetration of DSM alternatives and the evaluation of DSM program impacts CONPRO can make.

PART I. CONSERVATION OPPORTUNITY

Concept

Conservation Opportunity (CO) is defined as the maximum amount of conservation and load management that is economic from the perspective of the consumer or society. Consumers individually or as a whole (society viewpoint) evaluate the economics of conservation and load management investments. This methodology evaluates all ECAs using the next present value (NPV) method. By the NPV method, all investment benefits and costs are discounted by either society's or the consumer's discount rate. The present value of the costs are subtracted from the present value of the benefits. Positive results for an ECA indicate that the "yield" of the ECA is greater than the consumer's or society's discount rate and the ECA is economic.

While the ranking of ECAs by NPVs is useful when making investment decisions, in this paper we are only concerned with identifying the number of ECAs, and their corresponding kWh or kW savings, that qualify as economic investments. These ECAs could be viewed as an inventory of conservation and load management alternatives which at least meet minimum requirements for consumer or societal investment versus spending money on consuming more electricity.

Society Viewpoint: For society, ECAs are economic if the investment is positive at society's discount rate. From this viewpoint, benefits equal the utility's avoided costs[1] due to the electricity savings from the ECA investment and costs equal the ECA's incremental purchase price.

Society is faced with many choices to meet its energy service needs, especially with regard to eletric services. For example, in the area of lighting, commercial building owners may light a hallway using several 40 watt fluorescent lamps. An alternative might be tu use new efficient 32 watt lamps. The cost savings resulting from the lower generation and consumption of electricity constitute the main benefits to society from the conservation investment. These cost savings are primarily fuel savings in the short term and, if the total savings from conservation and load management is large enough, fuel and capacity savings in the form of delayed, down sized, or cancelled power plants in the long run. These are measurable costs avoided by the utility.

In our methodology, it is assumed society uses a single discount rate. This discount rate reflects society's time value of money in making long-term collective investment decisions. In this study, we chose the yield on long-term government securities as a proxy for society's discount rate.

Individual Consumer Viewpoint: Individual consumers vary considerably in the benefits they idenify with conservation investments and the discount rates they apply in investment evaluation. Even so, ECAs are still economic whenever their NPVs are positive where benefits equal the consumer's electric bill savings and costs equal the ECA's incremental purchase price.

When consumer make conservation investments they do not receive benefits in the form of the savings in the utility costs; rather, they receive a reduction in their electric bills. Benefits to the consumer will almost always be different than the benefits to society because the utility's average rates are its average embedded costs while the utility's avoided costs equal its marginal costs. Depanding upon the relationship between a utility's avoided costs and its average rates, the benefits to a consumer could be perceived to be higher (average rates > avoided costs) or lower (avoided costs > average rates) than those perceived by society.

Because there are a large number of individual consumers for any given utility applying many different discount rates, calculations of CO from the consumer's viewpoint require a representation of the variation in discount rates using a discount rate distribution for each customer class--residential, commercial, and industrial.

In our methodology, up to seven discount rate categories may be specified for each customer class. For the individual consumer's viewopoint, instead of applying one discount rate as in the society viewpoint, each ECA's economics are evaluated for each of the seven customer class discount rate categories. The conservation and load reductions are counted in calculating CO only for those customers segments who obtain a positive NPV result.

Conservation Opportunity Over Time: Conservation Opportunity, whether from the viewpoint of society or individual consumers, will change over time due to growth in the customer population and the economy and the rate of ECA investment. As new growth and the turnover of existing electricity-using devices takes place, CO will grow. This growth in CO is important to utility analysts and can be calculated each year given assumptions about ECA useful lives, replacement rates, and growth in number of customers.

In CONPRO, CO is calculated year-by-year for both the society (COs) and consumer (COc) viewpoints for 20 years. CONPRO also projects the current electricity consumption of the utility over 20 years assuming growth in the customer population (or floorspace for the commercial class and production output for the industrial class) occurs but that the stock of electricity-using devices remains constant in terms of efficiency and consumer utilization. This projection, called ULceu (Utility Load--constant efficiency and utilization), is used as a reference point to subtract and graph COs and COc.

Figure 1 shows what the plot of COs and COc over time might look like in comparison to ULceu. In Figure 1, COc and COs are subtracted from ULceu to produce the utility load in kWh or kW that would result if all economic ECAs were implemented. ULcco is the utility load that would result if all ECAs economic from the consumer viewpoint were undertaken and ULsco is the utility load that would result if all economic ECA investment from society's viewpoint were undertaken.

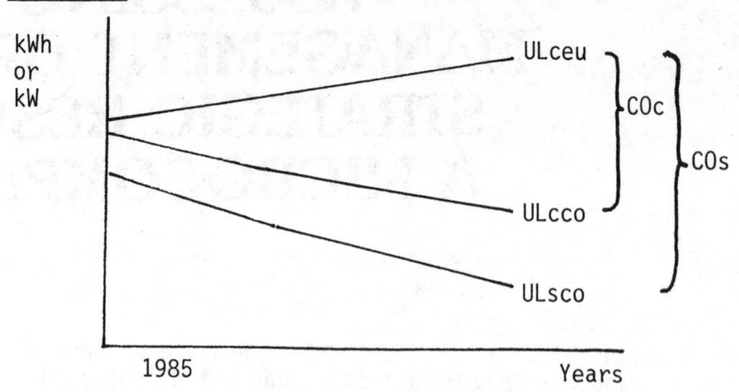

Figure 1. (Conservation Opportunity Over Time Society and Consumer Viewpoints)

MEASUREMENT

Conservation Opportunity in the case-study with GPU was calculated for annual energy, summer peak demand, and winter peak demand over a 20 year horizon. Preliminary results for GPU's Pennsylvania Electric subsidiary are used here for illustration.

Data Requirements: To make the CO estimates two data sets are required: (1) a common set of utility customer class rates, end-use characteristics, energy and demand forecasts, discount rate distributions and utility marginal costs and (2) an inventory of conservation and load management options by customer class and end-use. An example of the information required in the common data set for class end-use characteristics is shown in Table I. Here data for nine end-uses on number of customers with the end-use, growth rate in customers with the end-use, and summer and winter annual kWh and peak kW usage are displayed. This data is used to develop the ULceu reference load forecast. Similar data, including end-use load factors, was developed for eight end-uses in the commercial sector and six end-uses in the industrial sector.

Data requirements for CONPRO require specification of ECA option characteristics. While many utilities have not as yet developed the necessary data, most utilities with the use of in-house and secondary data could develop it without a substantial investment in resources. For example, each ECA option for a given customer class requires information on applicable end-use; investment type (i.e., retrofit, normal replacement, etc.); units per customer; unit incremental costs; useful life; percent of customers for which the option is technically applicable; current level of market penetration; year of ECA option market introduction; total, seasonal, and on- and off-peak energy changes. For the GPU project, 76 ECAs werw identified and specified. The breakdown of the ECAs by customer class was: 26 for residential, 28 for commercial, and 22 for industrial. One example of the ECA input data for each class is shown in Table II.

Conservation Opportunity Results: Given the ECA characteristics and discount rate information, each option can be evaluated as to its economics for each customer class or for society as a whole. As discussed, an ECA is considered economic if its net present value is positive for any given discount rate category. Alternatives that are economic enter the market based on their replacement characteristics. Figure 2 illustrates for Pennsylvania Electric the annual energy, summer peak demand, and winter peak demand load curves CONPO produces and compares to the utility's load forecast.

The top curve in each case, labeled ULceu Utility Load (Constant Efficiency and Utilization), equals the load that would occur due to economic growth (i.e., population, new homes and appliances, etc.) with electric-using device efficiency and utilization held constant at 1985 levels. This curve is calculated and portrayed as a reference point.

The second curve, ULcco (Customer Conservation Opportunity), is the load one would expect if GPU's customers made all ECA investments they found economic. The third curve, ULsco (Conservation Opportunity - society) is the load one would expect if society invested in all ECA options it found economic. The magnitude of the savings each year that is economic to customers (or society) is subtracted from ULceu to produe load forecast ULcco or (ULsco). In each case the

Table I.
Pennsylvania Electric Company
End-Use Data: Residential Class

End-Use	Number of Customers w/End-Use	Growth Rate in Customers w/End-Use	Average Use Per Customer w/End-Use: Summer kWh	Winter kWh	Summer Peak kW	Winter Peak kW
Other & Light	463,000	0.6	750	750	0.27	0.41
Refrig.	540,043	0.6	680	580	0.15	0.10
Water Heat	180,107	1.4	1,700	1,850	0.70	1.00
Space Heat	41,670	1.6	-	8,316	-	3.89
Cooking	275,485	1.3	740	440	0.10	0.10
Dryer	265,762	1.5	275	665	-	-
Freezer	236,130	0.9	590	505	0.15	0.10
Window A/C	111,120	1.6	200	-	0.20	-
Central A/C	14,816	1.5	200	-	0.60	-

Table II.
Pennsylvania Electric Co.
Example ECA Data
Residential, Commercial, and Industrial Classes

	Residential	Commercial	Industrial
ECA Description	High Efficiency Side-Door, Manual Defrost Refrigerator	Replace Standard F40 watt Lamp and Ballasts with High Efficiency Units	Replace Standard Efficiency Motors with High Efficiency Motors
End-Use	Refrigeration	Lighting	Motors
Investment Category	New + Normal Replacement	New + Normal Replacement	New + Normal Replacement
Unit	Refrigerator	Lamp	Hp
Units/Customer	1	68	64
Cost	$30	12.668 cents/Ft^2	$2,664,000 (Total)
Cost Basis	Incremental	Incremental	Incremental
Use Life (Years)	20	10	7
% of Customers w/End-Use	7	100	100
% of Market Penetration	1	25	20
Year of Product Introduction	1984	1977	1977
kWh Reduction:	per/unit	per/Ft^2	(1000's)
Winter On-Peak	69	0.238	13,468
Winter Off-Peak	69	0.119	13,468
Summer On-Peak	84	0.238	13,468
Summer Off-Peak	84	0.119	13,468
Total	306	0.716	53,872
Diversified kW Reduction:	per/unit	(1x10^{-3})/Ft^2	(TotalkW)
Winter Peak	0.087	0.190	19,111
Summer Peak	0.089	0.178	18,440
Non-Diversified kW Reduction:	per/unit	(1x10^{-3})/Ft^2	(TotalkW)
Winter Peak	n.a.	0.254	32,603
Summer Peak	n.a.	0.238	31,459
Facility Size (Sq. Ft.)	n.a.	2684	n.a.
Number of Facilities	n.a.	n.a.	4625

customer economic load forecast is above the societal forecast because we have assumed, for somer customer categories, much higher investment hurdle rates for ECA options. The fourth forecast displayed is the utility's forecast (ULfor). This forecast typically is derived by traditional econometric procedures.

Looking at Figure 2a, Annual Energy, we find the ULceu, ULfor, and ULcco curves for the year 1985 all start between 10,700 and 11,100 GWh (Note: the ULceu and ULfor curves start from a common point in 1984). The ULsco load forecast begins at 9,900 GWh. Thus, while consumer opportunities are in line with the utility load forecast, potential conservation (due to immediate retrofit opportunities for some ECAs) show a potential from society's viewpoint of approximately 1,200 GWh (or 10.8 percent).

Over time conservation potential increased compared to holding electricity usage constant at 1985 efficiency and utilization levels (ULceu). By the year 2004, projected utility sales would have risen to 14,000 GWh without efficiency changes. Conservation investment considered economic to individual consumers, if entirely undertaken, results in sales of about 12,800 GWh (or a 11.7 percent reduction from the ULceu level). If all of society's economic ECAs are undertaken the load reduction would be about 17.2 percent (or 2,500 GWh).

For Pennsylvania Electric, our preliminary results show that the utility's sales forecast produces in the year 2004 an almost indentical forecast to the society Conservation Opportunity forecast. Essentially, Pennsylvania Electric is currently forecasting long-term sales to fully capture societal economic ECA

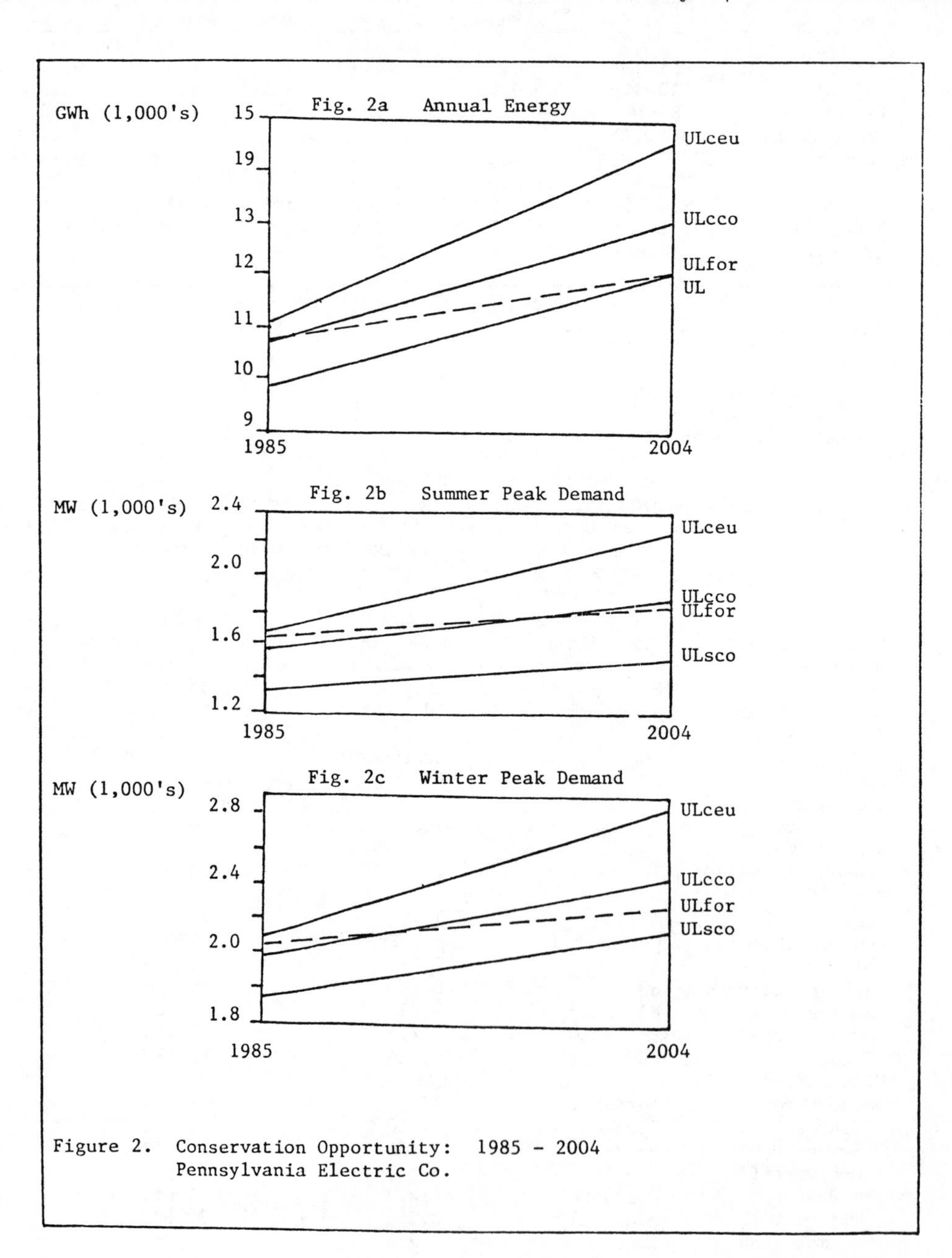

Figure 2. Conservation Opportunity: 1985 - 2004
Pennsylvania Electric Co.

opportunities, while we project the likely forecast based on consumer discount rate behavior to lead to a higher forecast. At this point it is conjective whether GPU is underforecasting total sales or we are overstating consumer discount rates. What our analysis does shows is that GPU's annual sales forecast assumes an average customer discount rate of 7.5 percent (the proxy for the societal discount rate we used). This provides additional information to GPU to re-examine its sales forecast. If our view were considered the better of the two upon further analysis, it would tell GPU that to achieve its present sales forecast, conservation programs producing an 800 GWh reduction in energy by the year 2004 would be required.

Examiniation of the summer and winter peak forecasts presents a slightly different picture. In these cases, forecasted peak tends to fall near or slightly below the ULcco forecast (or individual consumer CO forecast). This indicates additional peak reduction opportunities are available through conservation and load management programs moving the forecast closer to the societal line.

PART II. MARKET PENETRATION AND PROGRAM IMPACT ANALYSIS

Measurement of Conservation Opportunity is only one stage in the process of assessing DSM options in utility resource planning. Ideally, a utility would like to know the rate at which its customers are adopting such options on their own and what impact any utility programs including DSM option will have on its load curve and costs and revenues. CONPRO includes two routines that conduct these types of analyses. First, CONPRO allows the analyst to specify and estimate the rate of market penetration of DSM options given a list of options and assumptions about average customer class investment hurdle rates. Second, given a base case load shape calibrated for the current rates of DSM option market penetration, CONPRO can generate new load curves for any utility DSM program capable of being modelled for affecting the cost or return-on-investment of DSM options to its customers.

These two features of CONPRO will be discussed in turn. Because the quantitative analyses of these two areas in the GPU project are still underway the discussion will only be descriptive of CONPRO's operation. Quantitative result from the GPU project will be used to illustrate CONPRO's features at the conference.

Market Penetration: To estimate market penetration of DSM option, CONPRO utilizes a market penetration model developed by Mansfield and Blackman [2] that assumes the rate of market penetration of a device is highly correlated with the relation of the device's profitability to the industry's average profitability criterion.

The Blackman penetration model calculates market shares over time according to:

$$(1)\quad \ln\left[\frac{m}{L-m}\right] = -\ln\left[\frac{L}{No} - 1\right] + \phi\,(t-t_1)$$

where:
- m = market share at time t,
- L = long-run upper market share limit, and
- No = initial year's market share.

In this equation L, No, and ϕ are provided and the equation is solved year-by-year for m - the market share. The initial market share and the year of product introduction can be obtained from two sources -- vendors and manufacturers of the product and utility customer service representatives.

ϕ is defined as the market response parameter. This parameter is estimated from:

$$(2)\quad \phi + z + 0.53\,\pi - 0.27\,S$$

where:
- π = required industry payback/actual payback of the device
- S = original cost of investment x (100)/ average firm asset value, and
- z = constant

In calculating π, required paybacks can be obtained from secondary or primary research from audits and surveys of conservation investment behavior of customers. As can be seen, the lower the actual payback the higher the π value and the value of the market response parameter. The higher ϕ is, the faster the device will penetrate the market. S is the ratio of the device investment cost (x 100) to the average firm asset value. Blackman found that the higher the cost of the innovation, the slower it would penetrate the market though the effect is small compared to the profitability ratio of the device. z is a constant related to the industry's propensity to innovate -- values which Blackman derived using factor analysis relating market penetration rates to other measures of innovative activity (i.e., patents, R & D expenditures, etc.).

Assessing Program Impacts: Penetration curves developed for DSM opportunity using the penetration model serve as a base case projection of market penetration assuming the utility does not become involved in promoting conservation investment. However, utilities are very interested in the impact and cost-effectiveness of, for example, incentives promoting such investment. A cash rebate is a type of incentive CONPRO can evaluate. The impact of a cash rebate can easily be estimated because it can readily be incorporated in the penetration model by recalculating the payback to the customer after an incentive is provided.

Once the value of the incentive is established for each conservation opportunity it is subtracted from the device's original cost to determine the net investment cost. The payback period is then recalculated. The change in the payback period alters the devices profitability to the customer and hence its rate of adoption and ultimate market penetration (unless the device would have penetrated the market to 100 percent without an incentive). The long-run maximum market penetration may also be adjusted upward for lower paybacks by estimating the additional conservation opportunity resulting from the change in DSM option economics.

Figure 3 provides an illustration of the impact a cash rebate program might have on a device's market penetration curve. The Base Case market penetration curve shows the rate of market penetration for a device in the absence of a utility incentive program. If cash rebates are offered in 1985 some customers will accelerate their investment that could have made the investment otherwise and some customers make the investment who would not have done so in order to take advantage of the favorable economics associated with the device and the cash rebate. The total of these two effects is shown as the Conservation Program Case. We assumed that the program would end after four years. At that time some new investment is captured, but the rate of market penetration slows until those customers investing in the device who did not take advantage of the rebate program begin to do so.

The annual changes in electricity demand and energy induced by the cash rebate conservation program affects the cash flows of the utility. Reductions in cash flows occur in savings in fuel costs in the short run and distribution system/new generating capacity construction and operating costs in the long run. These are benefits attributable to the conservation program.

Offsetting these benefits are several costs. Two direct costs are conservation program administrative costs and cash rebate payments. An additional cost to be calculated for some regulatory tests is the lost revenue to the utility resulting from the induced conservation of the utility's program.

By obtaining data on utility costs and rates, market penetration of DSM options, and customer response to utility programs, CONPRO can estimate the load forecasts corresponding to the two market penetration cases shown in Figure 3. Changes in the rate of market penetration of DSM options are then translated into changes in utility cash flows and regulatory tests such as the society test, utility test, and non-participating customer test can be calculated to determine utility program cost-effectiveness for any utility program goal.

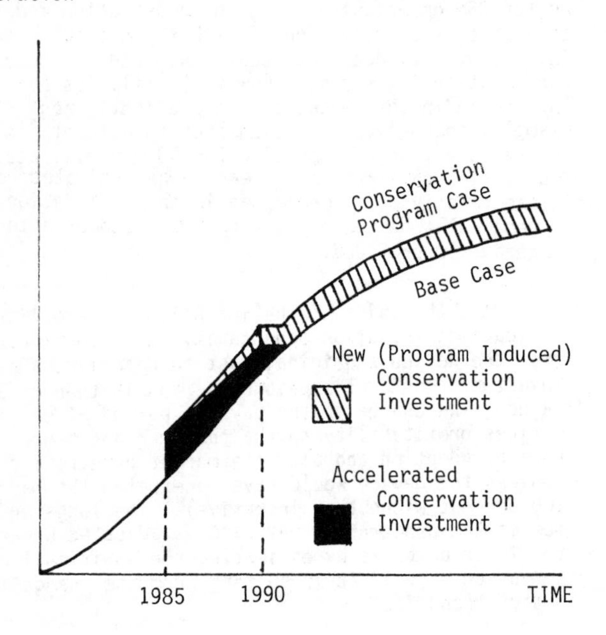

Figure 3. Economic Analysis
Illustrative Market Penetration Analysis
(5 Year Program)

CONCLUSION

CONPRO provides utilities a simple, but comprehensive tool for screening conservation and load management options and programs. In addition, it provides information that can be used to check the implicit assumptions underlying utility energy and peak forecasts. Overall, CONPRO helps utility management utilize end-use and conservation and load management option data to improve their demand-side management decision-making and test program cost-effectiveness.

REFERENCES

[1] The benefits to society may be greater than just the utility's avoided costs where external benefits such as reduced environmental damange are included. For the most part such costs are difficult to quantify and are often ignored. CONPRO could include such benefits (if quantified by the user) by treating them as additions to the utility's marginal costs. They would be added because if electricity is generated these additional costs will be incurred by society.

[2] A. Wade Blackman, Jr., "The Market Dynamics of Technological Substitutions," Technological Forecasting and Social Change, 6, 41-63 (1974).

Chapter 47

AN EFFECTIVE LOAD MANAGEMENT PROGRAM FOR THE CITY OF COLLEGE STATION

C. K. Shear

ABSTRACT

In 1984 and 1985, the City of College Station completed two successful voluntary Load Management Programs. The premise of the program was that if College Station residents were informed of the benefits of a lower demand peak, then they would voluntarily reduce energy consumption during known peak periods. Savings derived from both years amount to almost $900,000.00 with expenditures of less than $20,000.00.

INTRODUCTION

Electrical load demand management is one of the prime opportunities available to electrical suppliers and wholesale customers to reduce the overall cost of producing and distributing power. Demand reduction comes as the result of wise management of power and therefore, helps not only the consumer by reducing costs, but also, the supplier by decreasing system demand during peak load situations.

Faced with the realization of higher wholesale electric costs, in April, 1984, the City of College Station sought out various ways to keep utility costs down as much as possible. One of the more promising alternatives was a Load Management Program. Two facts made this proposal appealing: 1) College Station's electrical supplier's (Gulf State Utilities) rate structure includes a 75% ratchet clause on demand. 2) College Station's consumption records for the past five years showed that historically the utility system had ratcheted its demand peak during the billing period of August 20 to September 20 and the time period of 4 P.M. to 8 P.M. daily. More specifically, four out of five years the demand peak fell on the Wednesday following the opening day of Texas A&M University. The only exception was when it rained on that day, and the demand peak fell on the following Thursday.

It was the brain child of North Bardell, City Manager, to implement a voluntary Load Management Program. His premise was that if College Station residents were informed of the benefits of a lower demand peak, then they would voluntarily reduce energy consumption during this period.

The first year's program was implemented from August 20 to September 20, 1984. It was hoped that this program could save the City $250,000.00 over a twelve month period. In actuality the City saved $405,889.12 in wholesale electric costs.

The second year's program was implemented from August 20 to September 20, 1985. It was determined that if no form of load management had been or would be implemented, the City would reach a peak demand of 96MW. A goal of a 10% reduction was set. In actuality the demand of 83.5MW was reached. This equates into an estimated savings of $482,200.00.

IMPLEMENTING THE PROGRAM

Background

College Station is a municipal utility with a population of 52,260. It is also the home of Texas A&M University which enrolls approximately 32,000 students. Although the University does not purchase power from the city, many students move into College Station and open utility accounts. Also, many local businesses main clientele consist of A&M students.

College Station purchases electricity wholesale from Gulf States Utilities and resells the power to local commercial and residential customers. (There are no industrial electricity customers.) As with most large electricity consumers, College Station's contract with its supplier includes a ratchet clause whereby the City is billed each month a minimum of 75% of its peak demand for the preceding 11-month period.

The first step was to find out the time of year College Station's demand peak occurred. It was discovered that College Station was a summer peaking utility and that the peak fell during the billing period of August 20 to September 20. (See figure 1.) This is not difficult to understand considering that during this period College Station experiences the highest temperatures and maximum use of air conditioning for the year. Another primary reason is the increased activity that accompanies the start of the fall semester at Texas A&M University.

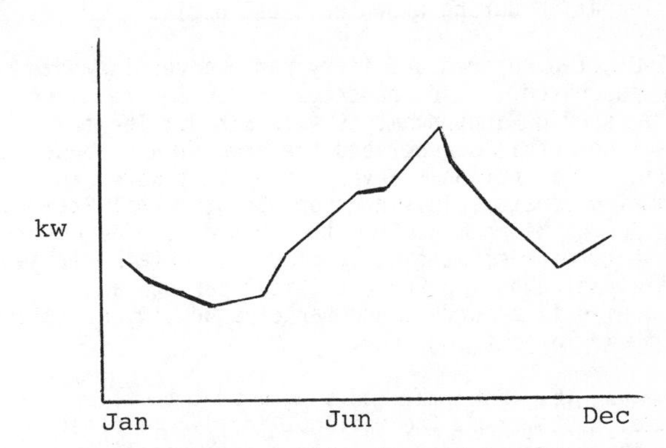

Fig. 1 1983 monthly demand peaks

The second step was to find the particular time of day the peak occurred. When graphed, the pattern was similar to that of other summer peaking utilities. It was discovered that the highest peak generally occurred around 6:30 P.M. (See figure 2.)

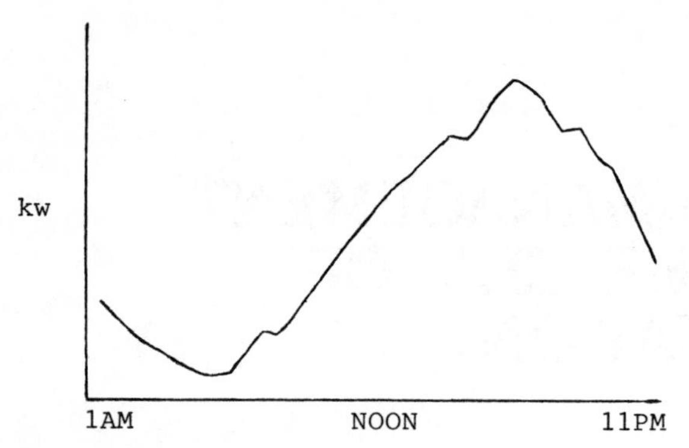

Fig. 2 Aug. 31, 1983 peak demand

It was decided to target the whole period of August 20 to September 20 with a more concerted effort placed on the week after Texas A&M University started fall classes. For optimum savings, the program was run from 4 P.M. to 8 P.M. daily.

The Load Management Program was launched in five directions with each segment intertwining with the sum. They are as follows: 1) residential participation, 2) commercial participation, 3) City participation, 4) the media, and 5) voltage reduction.

Residential Participation

After a study of the 1984 Load Management Program's facts and figures, it was determined that the residential sector was the largest contributor to the success of the program. Due to this fact, a large portion of the time and funds were directed towards informing the public with the need and benefits of a Load Management Program.

In 1985, thirty-five television spots were purchased and twenty were aired as public service announcements. Four commercials were produced. One featured Senator Lloyd Bentsen in a straight shot of him sitting behind his desk requesting citizen participation. The second featured Senator Phil Gramm in a similar production. The other two were segmented commercials containing North Bardell, City Manager, describing the program and several Councilmen showing various ways to reduce electrical consumption. These latter two consisted of Bardell closing with a "thank-you segment". The commercials were strategically placed to obtain citizens' participation during known critical periods.

In 1985, two hundred and fifty radio advertisements were purchased. Also, hundreds of ten second, live public service announcements were aired. The thirty second commercials described the program and requested public participation. Seven commercials were produced featuring Senator Lloyd Bentson, Senator Phil Gramm and five Energy Management Committee members. The advertisements were strategically placed to obtain citizens' participation during known critical periods and (according to a surveys and market study) when stations had their largest audience.

On August 16, 1985, mail-outs were sent to all residential customers. The mail-out included a flier describing the program and a list of suggestions on how to participate. A total of 12,430 letters were mailed. Also, every new customer connected during this period was handed this information.

Starting August 4, 1985, and ending September 13, 1985, all utility bills were stamped with a message promoting the Load Management Program. On August 31, 1985, every residential door was tagged with a door tag describing the program and listing ways to participate.

Fliers were handed to all elementary and high school students on the first day of school to take home to their parents. Project coordinators also participated in a teachers' orientation meeting to inform teachers of the program.

A three hour radio remote was held at a local mall on August 31, 1985. Councilmen and staff were used in twelve two minute live commercials.

Project coordinators participated in a Texas A&M University Off-Campus Student Seminar. Students were informed on the importance of the Load Management Program and energy conservation.

A large poster was displayed in the main lobby of City Hall. A sign was also placed at the local mall. It was changed daily to show the previous day's demand peak.

A post-Load Management Program telephone survey showed that 88% of College Station homes participated in the program. An even larger number (92%) felt that the program was beneficial. These percentages are much larger than the planning committee had anticipated. It is one of the main reasons why the City exceeded the goal by 2.5MW.

Participants in the survey were also questioned about the various means in which they heard about the program. The results are as follows:

Television.......47%
Newspaper........47%
Mail-Outs........33%
Door Tags........20%
Radio............17%
Friends..........09%

*Note: Participants were allowed to state more than one way in which they heard about the program.

Commercial Participation

A concerted effort was made to inform College Station's commercial electrical customers of the benefits of not only College Station's Load Management Program, but also on how their own load management program could be implemented. In 1985, two Demand Reduction Seminars were conducted - one on August 5 and one on August 6. Brochures concerning the seminar were mailed to all commercial customers on July 10. Newspaper advertisements were run a week prior to the seminar. Also, every medium and large commercial customer was contacted by phone and informed of the seminar and the Load Management Program.

Both years seminars' attendance were disappointing. In 1985, over 125 people said they would attend, and less than 30 people actually did.

Beginning on August 7, 1985, project coordinators visited with the top 25 electrical users. The City's and individual load management programs were discussed.

On August 16, 1985, mail outs were sent to all commercial customers. The mail out included a flier describing the program, a list of suggestions on how to participate and a poster promoting the Load Management Program. Although an exact number is not known on how many posters were displayed, it was difficult to go anywhere in town without seeing a poster.

Several businesses informed their employees on the

benefits of the Load Management Program. For instance, Texas Instruments held department meetings and passed out a flier that they produced.

Although an exact number has not been ascertained, it is known that many commercial customers reduced their electrical consumption during peak periods. However, many felt that restricting electrical usage would have an adverse effect on customer and employee relations. The majority of all commercial customers participated by promoting the program.

City Participation

The key to city staff participation is to get top management involved. This was an easy task since the program was the brain child of North Bardell, City Manager. Management involvement was maintained by keeping him informed and by requesting his help in many of the activities.

On August 8, 1985, North Bardell sent a memo to all city employees, informing them of the benefits of the Load Management Program. It also encouraged them to cooperate fully with the Energy Department.

On August 13, 1985, a meeting was held with city directors, department heads, and designated contact persons. Project coordinators requested names of contact persons for each facility and a plan spelling out various ways in which energy consumption would be reduced during peak periods.

City participation was exceptional. Plan of actions were widely encompassing and workable. City facilities not only helped reduce the demand peak by lowering electrical consumption, but also by projecting an image of leadership for the entire community.

The Media

The City's goal was to keep the media informed. A week before the program began, the various reporters that covered "City Hall" were contacted individually. Lines of communications were set up for quick news releases during critical periods and for daily updates.

One main tool that was used was a remote meter that was hooked up to GSU's power source. It provided the City with current demand information. Thus, the City was able to determine critical periods and inform the media with current information.

In 1985, project coordinators participated in nine television interviews. They ranged from a quick reminder of the Load Management Program to a magazine type format interview. Several interviews were broadcasted on all three news shows - 6 o'clock, 10 o'clock, and morning. Also, the local television news team was very helpful in broadcasting "alerts" on short notice during critical periods.

In 1985, project coordinators participated in fifteen newspaper interviews. The local newspaper was very helpful by considering the program a "hot" news story. Articles were generated almost daily. They also published a daily graph that showed the previous day's peak. Articles were also printed in local organization's news letters.

In 1985, project coordinators participated in twenty radio news interviews. Several interviews were developed into two or three news stories. Project coordinators also participated in six morning radio talk shows. Local radio reporters were very helpful in broadcasting "alerts" on very short notice during critical periods.

The media played a key role in the success of the program. More news stories were presented than paid advertisements.

A key to the successful use of the news media was to keep them informed and to be enthusiastic. They were very eager to present current news stories and provide information to the public that they wanted to hear. It was a snowballing effect. The more information the public heard; the more they wanted to keep current. The more they wanted to keep current; the more the news media wanted to do a story.

Voltage Reduction

The City of College Station has employed voltage reduction on its primary distribution system to aid in the reduction of peak demand loading for the last seven years with favorable results. Nominal voltage at the City's electrical substations is typically maintained in the range of 125-127 volts (120 volt-base) during times of peak system loading. During the Load Management Program, the system was monitored daily via recording chart devices installed at each of the City's substations. During peak periods, voltage reduction was employed from 4 P.M. to 8 P.M. Output voltage levels were manually lowered via the power transformer load tap changer control to 120-122 volts which was the City's overall goal to realize an approximate four percent reduction in voltage level during the peak load period.

A major portion of the City's distribution feeder system has been constructed since 1976. The City's feeder circuits are constructed using 477 MCM AAC conductors and average approximately three miles in length. Feeder loading are generally, maintained at or under 50 percent of the conductor thermal rating to facilitate possible load transfer between circuits during emergencies. In general, conductor loading and not voltage drop constraints is the main criteria used in the design of the City's feeder circuit capacity and the load levels to be placed thereon. No major feeder voltage drop problems have occurred even during peak periods when voltage levels have been reduced. This type of load shedding program very likely would be implementable on an electric system for which voltage drop conditions are a major system design criteria. The City regularly monitors voltage levels at the ends of its distribution feeder circuits during the periods of voltage reduction to be certain that adequate customer service levels are still being maintained.

The City estimates that the peak load reduction during the September 1985 billing period from voltage reduction was three to four percent. This translates to an overall load reduction of 3,000 to 4,000 KW.

The City considers voltage shaving to achieve peak load reduction to be a beneficial program. The City is currently installing a Supervisory Control and Data Aquisition System (SCADA) that will be utilized to assist in automatic system control to achieve maximum possible load reduction during peak load periods in the future.

CONCLUSIONS

The City of College Station's Load Management Program is a great success. Evidence of this accomplishment can be seen in the fact that the summer peak has been lowered to approximately the winter's peak demand. (See figure 3.)

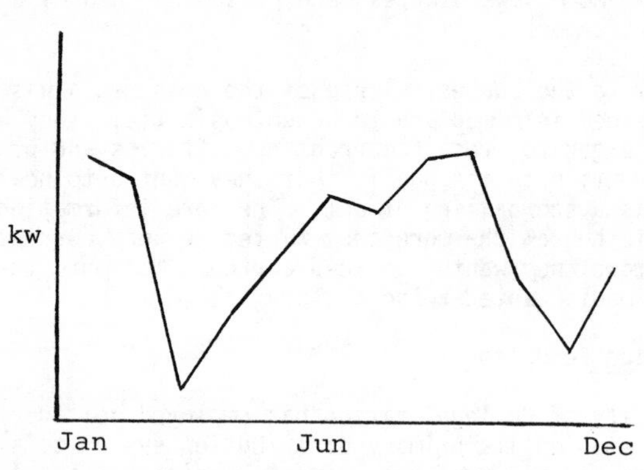

Fig. 3 1985 monthly demand peaks

Further evidence can be seen in the fact that the demand actually declined between 4 P.M. and 8 P.M. daily. (See figure 4.)

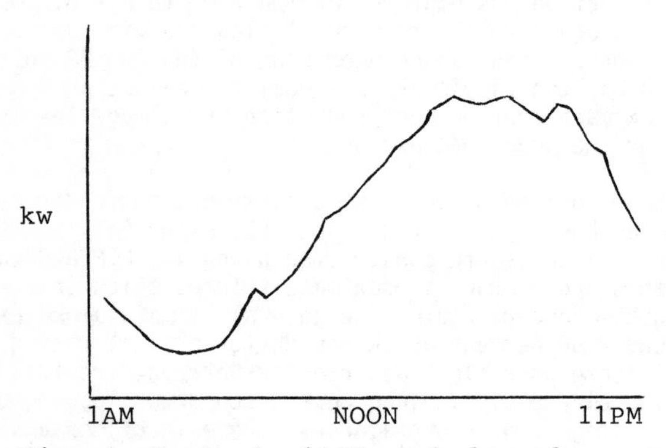

Fig. 4 Sept. 3, 1985 peak demand

The success is even more amazing if you take into consideration weather conditions. During the critical days of 1985, College Station experienced record high temperatures and no rain. The highest demand fell on Sunday, September 1, 1985. That day set an all time high temperature record of 106 degrees F. It is also interesting to note that this was the first time the highest demand peak fell on a weekend. The rest of the week had unusually high temperatures, but the demand was lower due to the amount of information that had already been scheduled to be distributed on known historic peak days.

The success of the program can be attributed to two reasons. The first is the amount of people who knew of the program. A phone survey has shown that 98% of College Station's electrical customers knew about the Load Management Program. This is extremely high when you take into consideration that there were 7,500 new electrical connects from the end of July, 1985, to the beginning of September, 1985.

The second reason is that the 88% of the electrical customers who participated knew of easy ways to reduce their demand. The City made a concerted effort to make this program as simple and painless as possible. The City not only pushed for participation but also gave simple suggestions on how to do it. Many comments were to the effect that some recommendations had never been thought of before.

In conclusion, College Station's Load Management Program is a viable option for demand control. The City will save a little less than $900,000.00 in two years with expenditures of less than $20,000.00. It is easily implementable and can be adapted to any city.

Chapter 48

POWER FACTOR CORRECTION USING CAPACITORS

M. Heis

Power Factor is the relationship (phase) of current and voltage in AC electrical distribution systems. Under ideal conditions, current and voltage are "in phase" and the power factor is 100%. If inductive loads are present, power factors of less than 100% will occur.

The worst offender of good power factor is the lightly loaded induction motor. Motors fully loaded will typically have power factors of 80% or better. Motors lightly loaded may have power factors of 40% or less. Fractional horsepower motors have much lower power factors than larger motors. High efficiency electric motors have better power factor ratings.

Although motors are usually identified as the biggest offender of good power factor, other inductive loads can be just as guilty. Transformers, ballasts and other equipment with coils of wire wound in various ways around cores cause poor power factor. Transformers and ballasts operating unloaded will produce very low power factors.

Power used by AC electrical systems has two components: real power and reactive power. Power factor is simply a name given to the ratio of actual (real) power being used in a circuit, expressed in watts or kilowatts (KW) to the power which is apparently (real + reactive) being drawn from the line, expressed in volt-amperes or kilovolt-amperes. Because of reactive power, sometimes called "wattless power", current is increased.

Apparent power is easily defined as the voltage applied to a circuit multiplied by the current which is drawn. This is measured in volt-amperes and includes any reactive power that may be required by the load.

$$\text{Apparent Power (Volt-Amperes)} = \text{Volts X Amperes}$$

The actual power in watts consumed by an electrical load is the product of the load current, the applied voltage, and a third factor - the cosine of the phase angle, θ (power factor).

$$\text{Power (Watts)} = \text{Volts X Amperes X Cosine } \theta \text{ (Power Factor)}$$

The cosine of the phase angle accounts for reactive power. It appears in the equation because either inductance or capacitance causes a time difference between the peak of the AC voltage applied to the load and the peak of the AC current drawn by the load.

In inductive circuits, the voltage peak occurs first, and the current is said to lag. In capacitive circuits, the current peak occurs first and the current is said to lead. In purely resistive circuits with no inductance or capacitance, the current and voltage peaks occur simultaneously, and are said to be "in phase". Here the angle θ is equal to zero and the power factor is 1 or unity.

$$\text{Power Factor} = \frac{\text{Actual Power}}{\text{Apparent Pow.}} = \frac{\text{Volts X Amperes X Cos.}\theta}{\text{Volts X Amperes}}$$

$$= \text{Cosine } \theta$$

EFFECTS OF POOR POWER FACTOR

The effect of low power factor is increased current flow. Power losses in transmission lines and feeders increase with increased current flow. Power losses are proportional to the square of the current.

Transformers and generators are rated in KVA. The available KW power is greatly reduced with poor power factors. The useful output is reduced below the nameplate rating. Voltage regulation is poorer with low power factor. Motors and other electrical equipment will run less efficiently.

A direct cost of poor power factor is higher electric bills. The most common way electric utilities charge for low power factor is to compute electric demand in KVA rather than KW. There are many other ways that utilities may enter power factor into the rate schedule. Most local utilities will explain the effects of low power factor on their billings. Usually the utility will also calculate cost savings and provide needed data for power factor correction projects.

BENEFITS OF CORRECTING POWER FACTOR

The real benefit of improved power factor is reduced current flow in the electrical distribution system. Reduced current flow means reduced power losses.

$$\text{\% Reduction Of Power Losses} = 100 - 100\left(\frac{\text{Original PF}}{\text{New PF}}\right)^2$$

Improved power factor will result in improved voltage regulation due to reduced line voltage drop. This benefit will result in more efficient performance of motors and other electrical equipment.

High power factors result in more KW working power for the same KVA load. Transformers will have more system capacity for additional loads. More loads can be added before the existing transformers become overloaded. System capacity can be released on fully loaded transformers and distribution equipment.

Lower utility bills can be a direct result of power factor improvement. If demand charges are based on KVA, significant savings can be realized in reduced demand. Some utilities penalize for poor power factor in both demand and usage charges. Savings are even more significant in these cases. In addition to reducing any utility penalty charges, KWH usage will be reduced as a result of reduced system losses.

METHODS OF CORRECTING POWER FACTOR

1. Capacitor Banks

   Capacitor banks may be installed on the primary or secondary side of the plant power transformer. If electric bill penalties are the only concern, the total capacitor requirement can be installed in one bank on the load side of the metering equipment. This method does not increase the capacity of the plant distribution system. Another disadvantage is the requirement for elaborate switching devices to prevent leading power factors during low loads.

2. Capacitor Units At Load Centers

   Capacitors can be installed at load centers, usually motor control centers, and switched with the loads. This method increases the load capabilities of the plant electrical distribution system. The power factor is corrected at the load center and back through the distribution system. Better voltage regulation is obtained for the system transformers. Engineering is simplified and costs of installation are reasonable.

3. Individual Capacitors Across The Load Terminals

   Capacitors can be connected directly across the terminals of larger motors thereby eliminating the cost of separate switches. The capacitor ratings may be selected directly from Table II, which requires knowing only the type, horsepower, and speed of the motor. This method requires more capacitor units and generally higher installation costs. The power factor is corrected at the motor and back through the distribution system.

4. Synchronous Motors

   Synchronous motors are sometimes used to correct power factor. Large motors of this type have the same electrical effect on the distribution systems as capacitors. This method is seldom used outside of industrial plants.

5. Correction By The Electric Utility Company

   Some electric companies will install capacitors and charge their customers. Generally the capacitors are installed on their own lines and do not correct the power factor within the customer plant. The only purpose of this method would be to reduce the penalty on the electric bill. The utility would benefit with improved power factor in their distribution system.

SPECIFICATIONS FOR CORRECTING POWER FACTOR

The first step in developing a specification is to choose a method. My perferred method in commercial buildings, where HVAC equipment is responsible for poor power factor, is to install capacitors at the load centers. I have found this method to be both economical and effective. Other methods are effective and should be considered. However, I will only discuss the load center method.

Commercial buildings normally have motor control centers for fans, compressors and pumps. This equipment is normally operated during the building's normal occupied period. A capacitor unit can be installed with a disconnect, contactor, and start/stop station at the motor control center. The contactor can be operated manually with the start/stop station, automatically with a time clock, or interlocked with a motor starter. Capacitor units can also be installed on larger individual loads like chillers. Table II can be used to size the capacitors on individual motor loads. Read the limiting factors given under Table II before installation.

Decide how much improvement in power factor is needed. Usually 90 - 95% power factor is considered good. Study your electric bills or other data and use the information given in the "Determining Your Capacitor Requirements" section of this paper. Table I is used along with that section. Some electric utility companies have power factor penalties for power factors below 95%. Others use 85 or 90% as the required power factor. Most utility companies seem to require 90%. The power factor can be corrected up to 100% but the payback becomes unattractive. When determining the total capacitor requirement, remember that leading power factor should be avoided. Leading power factor occurs with overcorrection. Overcorrection normally occurs when the inductive loads are switched off with the capacitors still on line.

A good method of locating capacitors is to have some fixed at the main switch gear, some at the motor control centers, and some on large motors. The example proposal on the following page is a typical installation using this method. One 75 KVAR capacitor unit is installed on the service level using an existing spare switch. This unit is fixed ("on" continuously). This unit provides the capacitance needed for the after-hours lighting, transformers and other inductive loads. Capacitors on MCC #1, #2, #A, #B are switched with building's fans and pumps. These capacitor units are installed with disconnects, contactors, and start/stop stations. The 50 KVAR unit on MCC #E is fixed ("on" continuously) and provides capacitance for the air compressors and domestic water pumps. The 50 KVAR units on the chillers are switched with the chillers except for one fixed unit.

The installation provided for "on peak" power factor correction of 91% and "off peak" power factor correction of 99%. The local electric utility provided the data needed to determine "on" and "off" peak sizing for the capacitors. The installation resulted in a payback of less than one year. The electrical contractor took less than a month from date of order to final check-out.

SWITCHING REQUIREMENTS

The National Electrical Code requires that power capacitors, other than those directly connected across motor terminals, have a separate disconnecting means to permit their removal from the circuit as a regular operating procedure, or for maintenance purposes. The code also requires that the continuous current carrying capacity of the disconnecting device and of the capacitor circuit conductors shall be not less than 135% of the rated current of the capacitor. See Table III for selection of cable and switch information.

SPECIFYING CAPACITORS

There is a large selection of capacitor manufacturers. I feel that the following requirements can be met by most of them.

1. Capacitors will be factory installed and wired in dust-tight metal enclosures with a baked enamel finish. Integral mounting brackets shall be provided to facilitate wall or floor mounting. Nameplates shall be attached to enclosures giving name of manufacturer, rated voltage, KVAR rating

and number of poles (phases).

2. Each capacitor unit will contain discharge resistors to bleed off residual voltage after power is removed from unit.

3. Capacitors shall contain no PCB dielectric fluid. Fluid shall be biodegradable.

4. Individual capacitor cells shall be factory assembled in the metal enclosures and wired in a ______phase, ______volt, configuration with termination provisions within the enclosure to facilitate field connection to system wiring.

5. Each capacitor cell shall be furnished with a built-in UL recognized pressure sensitive interrupter.

6. Capacitors shall be fused with current limiting replaceable fuses. Fuses will be factory installed in enclosures.

7. Capacitors will have blown fuse indicator lamps. Lamps shall provide for quick external inspection for blown fuses.

May 3, 1985

TO: John W. Galbreath Corporation
21st Floor
1st National Bank Center
Cincinnati, Ohio 45202

RE: Capacitor Installation
1st National Bank Center

ATTN: Mr. Mel Heis

P R O P O S A L

We are pleased to submit, for your consideration, the following proposal covering all electrical work for the installation of capacitors at the above mentioned location.

As per site "Walk thru" with Mr. Mel Heis, the following Capacitors are to be furnished and installed:

3--50KVAR---27th floor Chillers (1-line side, 2-load)
2--75KVAR---27th floor MCC #1 & #2
2--75KVAR---12th floor MCC A & B
1--50KVAR---12th floor MCC-E
1--75KVAR---Service Level (using existing 200Amp. Spare)

TOTAL PRICE LABOR & MATERIALS------------ $13,875.00

All capacitors to be installed with fused disconnects (Except Service Level).

All 75 KVAR Capacitors are to be furnished with Contactor Size #4, with control transformer (120v secondary), Stop/Start Button, and indicatiing Light.

All work to be performed in a neat and orderly manner, with power "tie-ins" at Building Convenience.

Thank you for the opportunity to bid on this work, and if we can be of any furthhr service, don't hesitate to call.

Respectfully submitted,

Fred Stang, President

Determining Your Capacitor Requirements

The total KVAR rating of capacitors required to improve a plant power factor to any desired value may be calculated very easily by using the several basic formulas below, and by applying the appropriate multiplier selected from Table I.

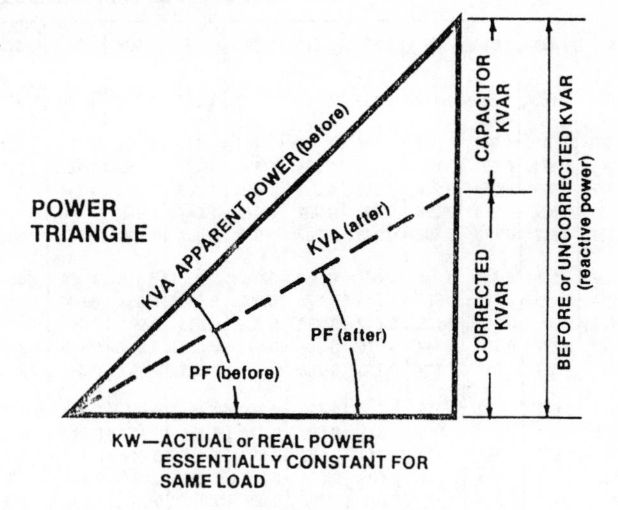

Formulae:

1. $PF = \frac{KW}{KVA}$ or $KW = KVA \times PF$ or $KVA = \frac{KW}{PF}$

2. Capacitor KVAR = KW × Table I Multiplier

3. $KVA\ (3\ phase) = 1.73 \times \frac{I(amps) \times V\ (volts)}{1000}$ or $I\ (amps) = \frac{KVA \times 1000}{1.73 \times V\ (volts)}$

Examples:

1. A plant with a metered demand of 196 KW is operating at a 52% power factor. What capacitor KVAR is required to correct the present power factor to 95%?
   a. From Table I, Multiplier to improve PF from 52% to 95% is, 1.314
   b. Capacitor KVAR = KW × Table I Multiplier Capacitor KVAR = 196 × 1.314 = 257.5 say 260 KVAR.

2. A plant load of 425 KW has a total power requirement of 670 KVA. What size capacitor is required to improve the present power factor to 90%?
   a. Present $PF = \frac{KW}{KVA} = \frac{425}{670} = .634 = 63.4\%$ say 63%
   b. From Table I, Multiplier to improve PF from 63% to 90% is .749
   c. Capacitor KVAR = KW × Table I Multiplier = 425 × .749 = 318 say 320 KVAR.

3. A plant operating from a 480 volt system has a metered demand of 258 KW. The line current read by a clip-on ammeter is 420 amperes. What amount of capacitors are required to correct the present power factor to 90%?
   a. $KVA = 1.73 \times \frac{I}{1000} \times V = 1.73 \times \frac{420}{1000} \times 480 = 349$ KVA
   b. Present $PF = \frac{KW}{KVA} = \frac{258}{349} = 73.9$ say 74%
   c. From Table I, Multiplier to improve PF from 74% to 90% is .425
   d. Capacitor KVAR = KW × Table I Multiplier = 258 × .425 = 109.6 say 110 KVAR.

COURTESY OF FEDERAL PACIFIC

Table I KW Multipliers for Determining Capacitor Kilovars

Original Power Factor in Percentage	Desired Power Factor in Percentage																				
	80	81	82	83	84	85	86	87	88	89	90	91	92	93	94	95	96	97	98	99	1.0
50	0.982	1.008	1.034	1.060	1.086	1.112	1.139	1.165	1.192	1.220	1.248	1.276	1.306	1.337	1.369	1.403	1.440	1.481	1.529	1.589	1.732
51	0.937	0.962	0.989	1.015	1.041	1.067	1.094	1.120	1.147	1.175	1.203	1.231	1.261	1.292	1.324	1.358	1.395	1.436	1.484	1.544	1.687
52	0.893	0.919	0.945	0.971	0.997	1.023	1.050	1.076	1.103	1.131	1.159	1.187	1.217	1.248	1.280	1.314	1.351	1.392	1.440	1.500	1.643
53	0.850	0.876	0.902	0.928	0.954	0.980	1.007	1.033	1.060	1.088	1.116	1.144	1.174	1.205	1.237	1.271	1.308	1.349	1.397	1.457	1.600
54	0.809	0.835	0.861	0.887	0.913	0.939	0.966	0.992	1.019	1.047	1.075	1.103	1.133	1.164	1.196	1.230	1.267	1.308	1.356	1.416	1.559
55	0.769	0.795	0.821	0.847	0.873	0.899	0.926	0.952	0.979	1.007	1.035	1.063	1.093	1.124	1.156	1.190	1.227	1.268	1.316	1.376	1.519
56	0.730	0.756	0.782	0.808	0.834	0.860	0.887	0.913	0.940	0.968	0.996	1.024	1.054	1.085	1.117	1.151	1.188	1.229	1.277	1.337	1.480
57	0.692	0.718	0.744	0.770	0.796	0.822	0.849	0.875	0.902	0.930	0.958	0.986	1.016	1.047	1.079	1.113	1.150	1.191	1.239	1.299	1.442
58	0.655	0.681	0.707	0.733	0.759	0.785	0.812	0.838	0.865	0.893	0.921	0.949	0.979	1.010	1.042	1.076	1.113	1.154	1.202	1.262	1.405
59	0.619	0.645	0.671	0.697	0.723	0.749	0.776	0.802	0.829	0.857	0.885	0.913	0.943	0.974	1.006	1.040	1.077	1.118	1.166	1.226	1.369
60	0.583	0.609	0.635	0.661	0.687	0.713	0.740	0.766	0.793	0.821	0.849	0.877	0.907	0.938	0.970	1.004	1.041	1.082	1.130	1.190	1.333
61	0.549	0.575	0.601	0.627	0.653	0.679	0.706	0.732	0.759	0.787	0.815	0.843	0.873	0.904	0.936	0.970	1.007	1.048	1.096	1.156	1.299
62	0.516	0.542	0.568	0.594	0.620	0.646	0.673	0.699	0.725	0.754	0.782	0.810	0.840	0.871	0.903	0.937	0.974	1.015	1.063	1.123	1.266
63	0.483	0.509	0.535	0.561	0.587	0.613	0.640	0.666	0.693	0.721	0.749	0.777	0.807	0.838	0.870	0.904	0.941	0.982	1.030	1.090	1.233
64	0.451	0.474	0.503	0.529	0.555	0.581	0.608	0.634	0.661	0.689	0.717	0.745	0.775	0.806	0.838	0.872	0.909	0.950	0.998	1.068	1.201
65	0.419	0.445	0.471	0.497	0.523	0.549	0.576	0.602	0.629	0.657	0.685	0.713	0.743	0.774	0.806	0.840	0.877	0.918	0.966	1.026	1.169
66	0.388	0.414	0.440	0.466	0.492	0.518	0.545	0.571	0.598	0.626	0.654	0.682	0.712	0.743	0.775	0.809	0.846	0.887	0.935	0.995	1.138
67	0.358	0.384	0.410	0.436	0.462	0.488	0.515	0.541	0.568	0.596	0.624	0.652	0.682	0.713	0.745	0.779	0.816	0.857	0.905	0.965	1.108
68	0.328	0.354	0.380	0.406	0.432	0.458	0.485	0.511	0.538	0.566	0.594	0.622	0.652	0.683	0.715	0.749	0.786	0.827	0.875	0.935	1.078
69	0.299	0.325	0.351	0.377	0.403	0.429	0.456	0.482	0.509	0.537	0.565	0.593	0.623	0.654	0.686	0.720	0.757	0.798	0.846	0.906	1.049
70	0.270	0.296	0.322	0.348	0.374	0.400	0.427	0.453	0.480	0.508	0.536	0.564	0.594	0.625	0.657	0.691	0.728	0.769	0.817	0.877	1.020
71	0.242	0.268	0.294	0.320	0.346	0.372	0.399	0.425	0.452	0.480	0.508	0.536	0.566	0.597	0.629	0.663	0.700	0.741	0.789	0.849	0.992
72	0.214	0.240	0.266	0.292	0.318	0.344	0.371	0.397	0.424	0.452	0.480	0.508	0.538	0.569	0.601	0.635	0.672	0.713	0.761	0.821	0.964
73	0.186	0.212	0.238	0.264	0.290	0.316	0.343	0.369	0.396	0.424	0.452	0.480	0.510	0.541	0.573	0.607	0.644	0.685	0.733	0.793	0.936
74	0.159	0.185	0.211	0.237	0.263	0.289	0.316	0.342	0.369	0.397	0.425	0.453	0.483	0.514	0.546	0.580	0.617	0.658	0.706	0.766	0.909
75	0.132	0.158	0.184	0.210	0.236	0.262	0.289	0.315	0.342	0.370	0.398	0.426	0.456	0.487	0.519	0.553	0.590	0.631	0.679	0.739	0.882
76	0.105	0.131	0.157	0.183	0.209	0.235	0.262	0.288	0.315	0.343	0.371	0.399	0.429	0.460	0.492	0.526	0.563	0.604	0.652	0.712	0.855
77	0.079	0.105	0.131	0.157	0.183	0.209	0.236	0.262	0.289	0.317	0.345	0.373	0.403	0.434	0.466	0.500	0.537	0.578	0.626	0.686	0.829
78	0.052	0.078	0.104	0.130	0.156	0.182	0.209	0.235	0.262	0.290	0.318	0.346	0.376	0.407	0.439	0.473	0.510	0.551	0.599	0.659	0.802
79	0.026	0.052	0.078	0.104	0.130	0.156	0.183	0.209	0.236	0.264	0.292	0.320	0.350	0.381	0.413	0.447	0.484	0.525	0.573	0.633	0.776
80	0.000	0.026	0.052	0.078	0.104	0.130	0.157	0.183	0.210	0.238	0.266	0.294	0.324	0.355	0.387	0.421	0.458	0.499	0.547	0.609	0.750
81		0.000	0.026	0.052	0.078	0.104	0.131	0.157	0.184	0.212	0.240	0.268	0.298	0.329	0.361	0.395	0.432	0.473	0.521	0.581	0.724
82			0.000	0.026	0.052	0.078	0.105	0.131	0.158	0.186	0.214	0.242	0.272	0.303	0.335	0.369	0.406	0.447	0.495	0.555	0.698
83				0.000	0.026	0.052	0.079	0.105	0.132	0.160	0.188	0.216	0.246	0.277	0.309	0.343	0.380	0.421	0.469	0.529	0.672
84					0.000	0.026	0.053	0.079	0.106	0.134	0.162	0.190	0.220	0.251	0.283	0.317	0.354	0.395	0.443	0.503	0.646
85						0.000	0.027	0.053	0.080	0.108	0.136	0.164	0.194	0.225	0.257	0.291	0.328	0.369	0.417	0.477	0.620
86							0.000	0.026	0.053	0.081	0.109	0.137	0.167	0.198	0.230	0.264	0.301	0.342	0.390	0.450	0.593
87								0.000	0.027	0.055	0.083	0.111	0.141	0.172	0.204	0.238	0.275	0.316	0.364	0.424	0.567
88									0.000	0.028	0.056	0.084	0.114	0.145	0.177	0.211	0.248	0.289	0.337	0.397	0.540
89										0.000	0.028	0.056	0.086	0.117	0.149	0.183	0.220	0.261	0.309	0.369	0.512
90											0.000	0.028	0.058	0.089	0.121	0.155	0.192	0.233	0.281	0.341	0.484
91												0.000	0.030	0.061	0.093	0.127	0.164	0.205	0.253	0.313	0.456
92													0.000	0.031	0.063	0.097	0.134	0.175	0.223	0.283	0.426
93														0.000	0.032	0.066	0.103	0.144	0.192	0.252	0.395
94															0.000	0.034	0.071	0.112	0.160	0.220	0.363
95																0.000	0.037	0.079	0.126	0.186	0.329
96																	0.000	0.041	0.089	0.149	0.292
97																		0.000	0.048	0.108	0.251
98																			0.000	0.060	0.203
99																				0.000	0.143
																					0.000

Example: Total KW input of load from wattmeter reading 100 KW at a power factor of 60%. The leading reactive KVAR necessary to raise the power factor to 90% is found by multiplying the 100 KW by the factor found in the table, which is .849. Then 100 KW × 0.849 = 84.9 KVAR. Use 85 KVAR.

COURTESY OF FEDERAL PACIFIC

Suggested Maximum Capacitor Ratings for T-Frame Motors When Switched with Capacitors

TABLE II: Suggested Maximum Capacitor Ratings for T-Frame NEMA Class B. Motors*

INDUCTION MOTOR RATING (HP)	NOMINAL MOTOR SPEED 3600 R/MIN CAPACITOR RATING (KVAR)	3600 R/MIN LINE CURRENT REDUCTION (%)	1800 R/MIN CAPACITOR RATING (KVAR)	1800 R/MIN LINE CURRENT REDUCTION (%)	1200 R/MIN CAPACITOR RATING (KVAR)	1200 R/MIN LINE CURRENT REDUCTION (%)	900 R/MIN CAPACITOR RATING (KVAR)	900 R/MIN LINE CURRENT REDUCTION (%)	720 R/MIN CAPACITOR RATING (KVAR)	720 R/MIN LINE CURRENT REDUCTION (%)	600 R/MIN CAPACITOR RATING (KVAR)	600 R/MIN LINE CURRENT REDUCTION (%)
3	1.5	14	1.5	23	2.5	28	3	38	3	40	4	40
5	2	14	2.5	22	3	26	4	31	4	40	5	40
7.5	2.5	14	3	20	4	21	5	28	5	38	6	45
10	4	14	4	18	5	21	6	27	7.5	36	8	38
15	5	12	5	18	6	20	7.5	24	8	32	10	34
20	6	12	6	17	7.5	19	9	23	10	29	12	30
25	7.5	12	7.5	17	8	19	10	23	12	25	18	30
30	8	11	8	16	10	19	14	22	15	24	22.5	30
40	12	12	13	15	16	19	18	21	22.5	24	25	30
50	15	12	18	15	20	19	22.5	21	24	24	30	30
60	18	12	21	14	22.5	17	26	20	30	22	35	28
75	20	12	23	14	25	15	28	17	33	14	40	19
100	22.5	11	30	14	30	12	35	16	40	15	45	17
125	25	10	36	12	35	12	42	14	45	15	50	17
150	30	10	42	12	40	12	52.5	14	52.5	14	60	17
200	35	10	50	11	50	10	65	13	68	13	90	17
250	40	11	60	10	62.5	10	82	13	87.5	13	100	17
300	45	11	68	10	75	12	100	14	100	13	120	17
350	50	12	75	8	90	12	120	13	120	13	135	15
400	75	10	80	8	100	12	130	13	140	13	150	15
450	80	8	90	8	120	10	140	12	160	14	160	15
500	100	8	120	9	150	12	160	12	180	13	180	15

Applies to three-phase, 60 Hz motors when switched with capacitors as a single unit.

*Taken from IEEE STD 141-1976.

Percent AR is the percent reduction in full-load line current due to capacitors. A capacitor located on the motor side of the overload relay reduces current through the relay. Therefore, a smaller relay may be necessary. The motor-overload relay should be selected on the basis of the motor full-load nameplate current reduced by the percent reduction in line current (percent AR) due to capacitors.

The capacitor size specified in the above table will increase the full load power factor to 95%, and larger sizes should not be used without consulting the Federal Electric Company.

Points to Consider when Sizing Capacitors

Two limiting factors must be considered when capacitors are to be switched with a motor as a unit. The first is overvoltage due to self-excitation, and the second is transient torques.

Self-excitation voltage: When a motor is disconnected from the line, it will normally rotate for a short time before coming to rest. A capacitor connected to this motor will still be supplying magnetizing current, which will excite the motor. Under these conditions, the motor and capacitor act like a generator and produce a certain voltage because of this "self-excitation". The magnitude of the voltage that can be produced is determined by two things—the rating of the capacitor being used and the speed of the motor involved. It is not uncommon for this "self-excitation" voltage to reach 150% of rated voltage if too large a capacitor is being used.

Transient torques: Perhaps even more important than overvoltage is the transient torques that can occur if the motor happens to close back into the line before coming to a complete rest. If the motor is still rotating and acting like a generator, the resulting transient torque may be as much as 20 times the full load torque.

Because of transient torque and overvoltage considerations, most motor manufacturers provide recommendations concerning the maximum capacitor KVAR that should be switched with a given motor. These recommendations are conservative enough to avoid endangering the motor, and will ordinarily result in a corrected power factor of approximately 95-98% at full load.

To avoid nuisance blowing of fuses when capacitors are connected directly across the motor terminals:

1. Motors should not be subject to plugging or reversing duty.
2. Motors should not be operated such that rapid restarting occurs.

COURTESY OF FEDERAL PACIFIC

Table III Guide for Selection of Cable and Switch

240 Volt, 3 Phase

Capacitor Rating		Minimum Cable Sizes (Note 1)	Safety Switch	
KVAR	Amps		Rating Amps	Fuse Amps
0.5	1.20	14	30	3
1	2.41	14	30	6
2	4.82	14	30	10
3	7.23	14	30	15
4	9.64	14	30	20
5	12.0	12	30	20
7.5	18.0	10	30	30
10	24.1	8	60	40
15	36.1	8	60	60
20	48.1	6	100	80
25	60.1	4	100	100
30	72.2	3	200	125
35	84.0	2	200	150
40	96.2	1	200	175
45	108	1/0	200	200
50	120	2/0	200	200
60	144	3/0	400	250
75	180	250	400	300
80	192	300	400	350
90	217	350	400	400
100	241	(2) 2/0	400	400
105	253	(2) 2/0	600	400
120	289	(2) 3/0	600	500
135	325	(2) 4/0	600	600
140	337	(2) 4/0	600	600
150	361	(2) 250	600	600

480 Volt, 3 Phase

Capacitor Rating		Minimum Cable Sizes (Note 1)	Safety Switch	
KVAR	Amps		Rating Amps	Fuse Amps
1	1.20	14	30	3
2	2.41	14	30	6
3	3.61	14	30	6
4	4.81	14	30	10
5	6.01	14	30	10
7.5	9.02	14	30	15
10	12	12	30	25
15	18	10	60	35
20	24.1	8	60	50
25	30.1	8	60	60
30	36.1	8	60	60
35	42.2	6	100	80
40	48.1	6	100	80
45	54.1	4	100	90
50	60.1	4	100	100
60	72	3	200	125
75	90.3	1	200	150
100	120.4	2/0	200	200
120	145	3/0	400	250
125	150	4/0	400	250
140	169	250	400	300
150	180	250	400	300
175	210	300	400	350
180	216	300	400	400
200	241	(2) 2/0	400	400
225	270	(2) 3/0	600	450
240	289	(2) 4/0	600	500
250	300	(2) 4/0	600	500
300	361	(2) 250	600	600
350	421	(2) 300	800	800
400	481	(2) 400	800	800

600 Volt, 3 Phase

Capacitor Rating		Minimum Cable Sizes (Note 1)	Safety Switch	
KVAR	Amps		Rating Amps	Fuse Amps
5	4.81	14	30	10
7.5	7.22	14	30	15
10	9.62	14	30	20
15	14.4	10	30	25
20	19.2	10	60	35
25	24.1	8	60	40
30	28.9	8	60	50
35	33.6	6	60	60
40	38.5	6	100	70
45	43.3	6	100	80
50	48.1	6	100	80
60	57.7	4	100	100
75	72.2	3	200	125
100	96.3	1	200	150
120	115	2/0	200	200
125	120	2/0	200	200
140	135	2/0	400	225
150	144	3/0	400	250
175	168	4/0	400	300
180	173	4/0	400	300
200	192	250	400	350
225	217	350	400	400
240	231	350	600	450
250	241	(2) 2/0	600	450
300	289	(2) 3/0	600	500
350	337	(2) 4/0	600	600
400	385	(2) 250	800	800

NOTE

1. Cable sizes are based on three single-conductor, 600 volt, copper, 90°C insulated, cables per raceway

COURTESY OF FEDERAL PACIFIC

SECTION 15
ENERGY UTILIZATION IN GOVERNMENT

Chapter 49

ENERGY EFFICIENCY AT THE POST OFFICE

B. Rowe, J. Flynn

The U.S. Postal Service in San Diego County won the 1985 Corporate Energy Management Award presented by the San Diego Chapter of the Association of Energy Engineers. This paper reviews the energy management initiatives that helped earn this prestigious award.

SCOPE OF ENERGY OPERATIONS

The U.S. Postal Service operates over 100 buildings in San Diego County. They range in size from under 1,000 square feet to almost 500,000 square feet.

These facilities are spread out over almost 4,300 square miles and are located in a variety of climate zones from Mount Laguna to the Anza-Borrego Desert to the Shores of La Jolla.

These facilities provide the full range of postal services and usually operate extended hours, often around the clock.

ENERGY COSTS

These buildings used 18,122,416 kilowatt hours of electricity and 68,410 therms of gas last year. The total cost was $2,229,000 for electricity and $42,072 for gas -- an average of 12.3¢ per kilowatt hour and 61.5¢ per therm.

Gas and electricity are provided by San Diego Gas & Electric. Their electric rates were 3rd highest in the U.S. last year -- right behind New York City and Long Island.

ENERGY ACCOUNTABILITY

When operating a large number of remotely located facilities, it's important to keep close track of their energy consumption on a continuing basis, so timely corrective action can be taken whenever consumption gets out of control.

Utility service is provided through 103 electric meters and 56 gas meters. A copy of all monthly utility bills for each facility is accumulated in the Energy Management Office and input to a FASER computerized energy accounting and reporting program.

Four monthly reports are generated by FASER for distribution to division heads and facility managers.

Division heads receive a report for all facilities under their control that covers total energy usage and costs for the past month and the current fiscal year to date. They also receive a report that breaks down total usage and costs by individual facilities. This report also compares the performance of the individual facilities to goals set at the beginning of the fiscal year.

Annual and monthly consumption goals are set by upper management based on past consumption, adjusted for operational changes and a reasonable conservation goal that averages about 5 percent.

The first of two monthly facility manager reports covers monthly and fiscal year-to-date energy usage and costs, plus the status of goal achievement by fuel type. The second report compares total usage and costs within the range of fuel types and quantifies cost avoidance.

ENERGY ANALYSIS

The facility manager receiving a monthly report showing usage in excess of 20 percent over goal must respond in writing within 10 days, explaining the cause and corrective action planned or taken. When usage is more than 20 percent under goal, a congratulatory letter is sent by upper management.

Facilities with usage in excess of 20 percent over goal for two months in a row are visited by the Energy Coordinator to ascertain the reasons for excess usage and to stimulate necessary corrective action.

Facilities are also rated on energy cost per square foot by the four climate zones -- coastal, inland, mountain and desert.

Where a facility's average cost per square foot exceeds the prescribed zonal maximum, a 30-day demand analysis (15 minute intervals) is ordered. Study of this data usually reveals the cause of the excess consumption. If not, an energy audit is ordered.

CONSERVATION HIGHLIGHTS

The two main areas of energy usage at San Diego Postal Service facilities are lighting and HVAC, with the majority of HVAC energy used for cooling.

Lighting Conservation

All exterior lighting has been changed out to efficient lighting sources, mostly HPSV. Most dock lights have been converted to HPSV from incandescent and fluorescent and photocelled.

Essentially decorative exterior incandescent lighting has either been removed or converted to PL fluorescent fixtures, mostly PL-7s.

Post office box lobbies operated on a 24-hour basis have been equipped with motion sensors set at a 3-minute delay on shut-off. This has resulted in about a 75 percent reduction in lighting energy consumption.

Conference rooms, restrooms and other lightly occupied spaces are also being converted to occupancy sensor control.

Most interior incandescent lamps have been removed, and where needed, replaced with fluorescent PL lamps.

Extensive delamping through the total removal of fixtures and ballasts has been accomplished where lighting is either excessive or not required. Lowering of fixtures mounted higher than necessary has often facilitated removal of as much as half of the fixtures.

Existing fluorescent lighting is being retrofitted with high-efficiency reflectors and electronic ballasts.

Cooling Conservation

Conservation modifications at three coastal post offices have permitted permanent removal of air conditioning systems -- one of the heaviest energy cost items in the San Diego area. These modifications have included reducing the cooling load contribution of excessive and inefficient lighting and installation of louvered windows, ceiling fans (over 400 so far), and attic ventilators. This reduced energy costs in one of these post offices by 85 percent.

Reflective roof coatings are currently being tested in cooperation with San Diego State University's Energy Engineering Institute to determine their cooling load reduction capabilities.

Most thermostats are being replaced by Accu-stats, so that tamper-proof heating and cooling setpoints can be established within an 11-degree deadband (65° - 76°). The cooling setpoint is extended to 78° in facilities with ceiling fans.

Four 365-day programmable thermostats are currently being installed for test purposes.

Economizers are being specified for all new installations of packaged air conditioning units. An economizer retrofit program is set to begin in Fiscal Year-1987.

ENERGY MONITORING & CONTROL

A powerline EMS installed in one of the smaller post offices delivered in excess of 35 percent energy savings last year. Current plans are to install similar systems in a wider range of facilities.

ALTERNATE ENERGY STRATEGIES

With San Diego's high utility costs and heavy peak demand problems, many different energy alternatives are proving cost effective.

This year's #1 energy project at the San Diego Postal Service is to install a thermal energy storage system at the main postal facility. Preliminary analysis shows a 1.9-year simple payback (including a utility financial inducement of $75,000).

Cogeneration is also being investigated, however lack of sufficient thermal loads and heavy off-peak consumption appear to limit its application.

Solar domestic water heating worked effectively in one facility with electric water heating, however only limited use of relatively low temperature water makes solar non-competitive with gas water heating at this time.

ENERGY SAVINGS

Since 1973, the U.S. Postal Service in San Diego County has reduced its energy consumption per square foot by over 60 percent.

San Diego currently ranks 2nd lowest among postal service divisions in the 13 western states in BTUs per square foot. Only Long Beach ranks higher, and all their facilities are located in the more climatically moderate coastal zone.

EXECUTIVE LEVEL PROGRAM SUPPORT ... A main reason for the success of energy conservation efforts at the U.S. Postal Service in San Diego County has been the consistently high level of executive support given the energy management program. San Diego Postmaster Margaret Sellers is a strong believer in efficient management of all postal resources, including energy. She was recognized last year by the Southern California Energy Council when they presented her an "Energy Recognition Award" for her executive level support of energy management in Southern California.

SECTION 16

PRIVATIZATION OF ENERGY PROJECTS

Sponsored by the Privatization Council

Chapter 50

THE MARKET FOR PRIVATIZATION: THE STATE REGULATORY ENVIRONMENT

R. D. Feldman

INTRODUCTION

In the next decade, the vast majority of "privatization" will occur at the state and local levels, resulting from a series of economic choices, rather than any broad ideological commitments. It will also be service-based as well as asset-based. Obviously, privatization is most likely to occur where the legal statutory environment is supportive both in terms of the absence of institutional barriers and in terms of economic incentives.

In the context of privatization statutes, the objectives of this paper are two fold: first, to provide an overview of the initiatives previously taken and, secondly, to outline the most productive lines of development for markets. For example, one particular development could modify any projections presented here concerning ad hoc lines of privatization development: the emergence of revolving funds and their integration with private sector involvement. The Clean Water Act Amendments essentially envisage the transition of the construction grants program into a series of state revolving funds (SRFs), with broad capacity to create leverage. If regulations governing these "SRFs" embrace privatization, the water treatment field could become an area of wholesale privatization. In addition, some 12 states have instituted resolving funds for infrastructure development and others have them under contemplation. These too could serve as a fertile seedbed for systematic privatization. If the private sector wants privatization to happen through revolving funds, it must take the initiative.

STATE PRIVATIZATION STATUTES

It is useful to analyze state statutes in terms of three factors:

(1) How does privatization varies the current way in which governments do business?;

(2) How have states provided incentives for privatization?;

(3) How public and private parties not covered statutorily are dealt with.

1. Privatization: Modifying Current Modes of Doing Business

Privatization of facilities or services obviously represents a new way of doing business for municipalities to the extent it goes beyond merely contracting from year to year for a particular private company or establishing a regulated utility arrangement. Essentially, privatization reflects the hypothesis that through carefully crafted contractional arrangements, the benefits of long term contracts and free market arrangements can be obtained without corruption or economic abuse of the market. Privatization reflects a transaction in which a municipality divests itself of certain risks as a service provider, which historically have been associated with exercise of the public power, and a private sector entity accepts some additional facets of the public trust and the public responsibility to provide service.

To achieve this, states have exempted persons entering privatization contracts from utility regulation in specifically indentified fields, such as the operation of water treatment facilities. Generally, the private sector quid pro quo is undertakings regarding non-discrimination to public service users and compliance with safety requirements. Removal from such utility status does, however, deprive a private company of its organic right to just and reasonable, non-confiscatory rates. But, such rates may be negotiated contractually and, in some jurisdictions, bolstered by a rate covenant.

Utility status is, of course, supported by the monopoly conferred. In the privatization context, careful compliance with antitrust laws through legislation is necessary to confer comparable benefits.

Municipal procurement of services has long been recognized as giving rise to potential corruption. Recognition of and concern over such possible activity has been expressed, for example, in the limitations on long term contracts and requirements for conferring contracts on the lowest bidder. In the privatization context, however, particularly where a complex service is involved, municipalities have realized that the cheapest alternative may not always be the best option. To evaluate possible choices, governments have evolved an elaborate statutory qualification and request mechanism for qualification and proposal procedures, which seek to qualify only selected vendors, then establishing comparability for selection among them. This has been particularly true where a packaging of services/design/build/construct/ operating has been appropriate, and the successful bidder is correlatively intended to also assume the associated developmental risks.

Finally, states historically have been concerned that in connection with a procurement, their credit and financial strength will be lent or gifted to private parties, for their own unearned gain, rather than for public benefit. Traditionally, this concern has been reflected in state debt limits, pay-as-you-go requirements, restrictions on indirect credit supports, and requirements relating permissible debt levels to asset cost. Incurrence of debt other than in industrial development bonds frequently requires public approval and/or may be subject to forms of budgetary monitoring. Any contractual arrangements amounting to the incurrence of debt may be made subject to state regulation.

State privatization legislation has basically opened to private parties the issuance of debt instruments backed primarily by specific resource generating sources, such as user charges. These parties, having municipal government approval, are able to collect such charges for privatization purposes without violating any state constitutional strictures.

For example, in Louisiana, service charges for sewage system use may be applied to satisfy such debts; Utan provides for similar pledging of taxes and assessments, specifically contemplating the introduction of rate covenants. Alabama exempts contractual arrangements from being treated as debt within the meaning of its state constitution, for any requirements that contracts shall only be payable out of that fiscal year's revenues, and from provisions insulating government users from damages for failure to make payments when due.

Alternatively, several jurisdictions create a some new of jurisdictional entity which can issue debt secured by revenues derived from the operation, leasing or sale of waste water treatment facilities. In Alabama, the "governmental utility serivce corporations" enjoy this power. Other state statutes link similar constitutional liberalization provisions with the use of industrial development bonds by appropriately empowered jurisdictions.

2. Facilitation of Privatization by State Statutes

The first facilitation statutes, dealing primarily with solid waste resource recovery, focused on the removal of critical barriers to privatization. Essentially this process has had to be repeated in the water treatment context. Implicitly, it seems generally to have been believed that enough economic opportunity was available for both the private and the public parties, specifically in terms of power sales revenues, tax benefits and risk assumption undertakings. Thus, states were reluctant to provide any major incentives other than the removal of regulatory barriers.

Even prior to the impending shifts in the tax benefit equation and the gradual erosion of many electric power markets [both of which threaten to impair privatization], there has been a greater tendency among states and municipalities to encourage privatization legislatively through other economic benefits, provided they did not adversely affect their budgetary bottom lines. Examples included exemption from various taxes otherwise imposed locally on private parties, such as state taxes and license and recording fees. Some states empowered special purpose authorities to become magnets for a variety of sources of funds, both public and private, to be used to fund ancillary costs, while contracting with private parties to provide a service.

Over the longer term, if privatization is recognized as an attractive option, states may have to consider other strategies, such as the provision of low cost or free land and the abatement of other taxes. This strategy is most likely to be employed as part of a broader state agenda designed to encourage private infrastructure development to complement a strategy of encouraging economic development. Indiana, for example, has encouraged the establishment of an overall state privatization program to encourage privatization in a variety of other contexts.

Obviously, to the extent a state has not only proclaimed, but implemented a privatization assistance program, a good market has been created. It would be a mistake, however, to lose sight of the careful scepticism both public and private parties have employed in approaching privatization even when incentives are available. From the public side, both economic and political concern surface when statutory protections for the community existing under prior law are repealed. This concern expresses itself in virtually every state statute, appearing both as a provision for due process in the choice between competing developers and the maintenance of some sort of continued public responsibility for public oversight and review of the private contractor's performance. New Jersey has, for example, statutorily described the terms which must be addressed in entering into any contract.

Private developers need to evaluate these provisions from two different standpoints. On the one hand, the level of public hearings and detail can reach such proportions that the investment prospects are defeated. The presence of these procedures does serve, however, to validate the privatized non-competitive process and to protect the contractor from subsequent allegations of impropriety. It should not be assumed, though that these procedures will provide contractors with blanket insulation from the governmental process. Not generally recognized at the time of development of privatization legislation, for example, was the need to account for the requirements of environmental legislation. Many states enacted environmental impact statement procedures which is equally applicable in privatization work as in it is with completely publicly developed projects. The respective timing of required compliance with these statutes and the overall procurement process requires careful scrutiny to avoid major delays.

3. Non-Statutory Concerns

While statutory analysis is helpful, it should be recognized that most state privatization statutes do not address many essential management concerns municipalities fundamentally have with respect to privatization transactions and which necessarily also affect the economics of private developers. Among the most important are the following:

- o rights to expand the facility and/or to modify the nature of the service;
- o responsibility for dealing with force majeure and change in law events which modify capital and operating costs;
- o responsibility for retaining existing workers or for the non-union status of new workers;
- o responsibility for assuming payment obligations with respect to prior governmental advances; buying out

facilities which have been funded with government grants in connection with a refinancing; and dealing with pre-existing liens arising from earlier government related financings;

o indemnification and assumption of aspects of liability with respect to the facility;

o entitlement to ownership of the facility at the end of the basic or renewal terms;

o protection of the right to use the technology and rights to the operating benefits from improvements of technology over the term of the agreement.

These questions are frequently not addressed by state statutes and must be hammered out early in the negotiating process if an agreement is ultimately to be reached.

4. Conclusions Regarding State Statutes

Because of the continued novelty of privatization and the significant modification in traditional practices it represents, privatization is more readily attempted in states where legislation, even if imperfect, has already been enacted. Alternatively, if the enactment of legislation is central to the structure of a privatization transaction [as will always be the case, for example, where a long term service contract is contemplated] this should clearly understood by the parties.

Nor should it be assumed that the presence of a privatization statute will be satisfactory to meet all of the minimum legal requirements of the project. Particularly if the venture is not of the same type as provided us for in the initial passage of the legislation, it is possible that not all barriers to the proposed privatization application are removed. This can be particularly true in the case when privatization legislation was promulgated to deal with the development of environmental facilities and is used in the context of very different types of facilities such as transportation or for services, such as correctional services.

Additionally, the potential for bureaucratic mischief in the implementation of the legislation -- the potential for delay and even derailment -- should be considered. For example, some states, such as New Jersey, have enacted elaborate privatization mechanisms, only to find that the level of due process and environmental review is enough that, when taken together with tax uncertainties, relatively few projects will been undertaken.

An evaluation of the state market, whether or not supportive legislation has been adopted, in terms of whether real bases of support for privatization have been identified, should be undertaken by potential privatization backers. Again, in the environmental context, the nature of the driving factors can be identified readily: non-availability of landfills, special state legislation, implementation of Federal laws. Similar bases of support -- whether out of concern with cost, mismanagement, economic development or reduction of heavy budgetary outlays -- must be identified in the hospital, correctional, energy transportation or other privatization areas in order to assess the seriousness with which legislation will be implemented.

In determining whether such motivations are present, the burdens placed upon the developer in order to take advantage of the impetus towards privatization must be considered. In the environmental privatization field, this has become clear enough, in terms of compliance with laws, absorption of unforeseen casualties and subsoil circumstances and accepting technological risks. The problems continue to be refined and recycled in the contexts of third party credit support and the strength of the balance sheets of project developers. In the non-environmental privatization field, while similarities in the types of risks to be dealt with exist -- insofar as they relate to construction, operation, health and safety -- there are also important differences to be considered. On the positive side, non-environmental areas sought to be privatized frequently have already also been performed in the private sector -- the parameters for measurement of what may be required by way of performance in energy or transportation already is quite clear. By contrast, privatization in some of these areas breaks ground in a legal sense. For example, in the correctional field, novel issues of rights of prisoners are raised. Would-be privatizers may be required to make concessions with respect to those areas in order to achieve their desired goals. Finally, the suitability of privatization legislation from a target market standpoint must be examined in terms of its impact on the financing of projects must be examined. This includes both a conventional analysis of the afforded incentives plus a more project specific consideration of whether the contemplated risks the private developer assumes in privatizing a project are compatible with those against which the capital markets will either lend or advance equity. Because privatization is so frequently project financed, all of these factors must receive intense consideration. But privatization need not always be accomplished on a project financing basis. It is the pattern which has been common with respect to solid waste resource recovery and water treatment facilities, because from the developer's standpoint, this approach serves to insulate the developer from risks of one project from the risks of other projects. The price for such insulation, however, is the financial community's absolute demand that provisions be made for all risks, even those of the most remote contingency. It is as if the words "what if" were engraved the lintels of the conference room doors at project financing banks. The privatization developer thus may find itself torn between the demands of what amounts to special legislation on the part of financing institutions and for enlistment and dedication to public service on the part of communities. Consequently, because of the nature of privatization financing, target markets where a "cookie cutter" approach exists are limited, and assumptions as to their existence merely because privatization legislation permitting service contract based financing is available should not be made.

REVOLVING FUNDS

In theory, the delays plaguing the closing of privatization transactions could be minimized or avoided if a central governmental lending facility for all privatization transactions existed. In that case, specific lending standards would be set; the allocation of risks would be clear; credit risks could be uniformly analyzed; and subject to the vagaries of lawyers, even documentation could be standardized. In fact, two types of revolving fund concepts with potential in this regard have surfaced, although it should be noted that each is principally public finance directed in its orientation, and will require considerable adaptation to be suitable for significant support for privatization. The first category of revolving funds are focused exclusively on the water treatment field, in which, currently, 12 states had operational revolving loan programs and 11 more had operational loan or bond bank programs. During 1986, the EPA expects as many as 12 more states to have proposed legislation to create bond banks and revolving loan programs. Currently before Congress is a proposal to institutionalize state organization and operation of revolving funds as a substitute for the construction grants program. The second category of revolving fund is the infrastructure bank concept first raised two years ago before the Congress, and perhaps only temporarily lost in the cloud of tax and fiscal reform. It is not inconceivable that it may re-emerge at the Federal or the state level, where analogs to it have been proposed, particularly as the effects of the budget crunch become clearer. To gain a quick overview of revolving fund proposals, it is useful to delineate their generic elements, differentiating them from related concepts with which they are frequently confused, and to focus on how particular fund proposals could be related to privatization.

There are four generic elements of a revolving fund program:

(1) an initial infusion of capital into the fund, either through a loan or grant or other capital construction;

(2) leveraging of that capital infusion, either by requiring matching grants or other capital contributions from the revolving fund sponsors, and from earnings resulting from the investment of such capital infusion;

(3) loan of the resulting fund on a basis contemplating repayment on specified terms;

(4) provision for partial repayment of the initial capital infusion, and possibly for its further recycling through the fund.

The key variables affecting how these basis elements are configured include:

- How the initial capital infusion is raised; how, if at all, the source of these funds will be repaid; and what the priority is for funding of different structures. If the fund is a two-tiered structure, for example, this question can arise twice at the Federal and again at the state level. The effective leverage on initial capital advanced will be affected by these decisions.

- The conditions on which money in the fund is advanced, such as the term, the nature of the sinking fund requirements, the mandatory coverage ratios, and, most importantly, the procedures to anticipate and prevent problems. The nature of the credit support for additional obligations incurred by borrowers also will affect the amount of leverage gained from the fund. For example, greater leverage could be obtained from the fund if it could guarantee or serve as security for, rather than merely fund, the debt obligations of the entities.

- The extent to which future payments of loans outstanding may be utilized as collateral for bond issuance, constituting some form of securitization.

- The extent to which private funds may be involved in the leveraging of funds directly or indirectly made available from revolving funds.

The revolving fund concept continues beyond that of the Bond Bank, which has been extant for several years. Bond Banks buy the bonds of smaller localities using the proceeds of state bond issuance. They essentially represent an effort to achieve indirectly a higher bond rating [or any credit rating at all] for numerous pooled credit sources for municipalities desiring to sell debt than an exercise in leveraging available funds for public projects.

States have taken a variety of approaches to revolving funds. With respect to fund sources of capital, some states such as Georgia have simply contemplated contribution of general tax revenues, while several others have identified either a stream or source of funds or the creation of special bonding rights. Washington State, for example, has established a Public Works Trust Fund, capitalized by dedicated taxes levied on water, garbage utilities and on property.

The scope of the revolving funds and their terms have varied considerably. Georgia is confined to a waste water fund; Washington State's extend to major capital maintenance and also certain infrastructure. Low interest loans or guarantee of municipal bonds is permissible. Significant in this regard is the New Jersey program which extends to private entrepreneurs developing projects and can provide guarantees to finance infrastructure projects.

(1) they cannot create initial capital without either imposing special or additional taxes or using up state general obligation debt capacity;

(2) they cannot guarantee local debt or debt of an infrastructure bank without creating credit risks;

(3) they have not been interfaced with efforts to introduce privatization and consequently do not explore risk absorption possibilities outside of the financial context;

(4) they do not relate specifically to the existing Federal grant programs under the Clean Water Act, particularly as related to the financing of facilitation.

CLEAN WATER ACT AMENDMENTS

The Clean Water Act Amendments' currently under consideration by Congress, introduce the revolving fund concept in the scenario where the Federal program for providing grants to fund publicly owned treatment works (POTWs) is being cut back, from 75 to 55 percent, with the additional responsibility being shifted to the individual states.

Accordingly, the Amendments propose to create State Water Pollution Control Revolving Funds (SRFs) and to transfer the construction grants program to them in two stages. First, under Title II, categorical grants for POTWs would be reduced, and money would instead be provided to states to make low interest loans available through the SRFs to local communities for construction of specified treatment facilities. SRFs initially would be capitalized by states by converting Title II construction grants into capitalization grants for SRFs. Second, under Title VI, after a five year phase-in period, the SRFs would provide a base for the future financing of waste-water facilities. Federal capitalization grants for SRFs would become available for this purpose commencing in 1989.

Those states which entered into agreements with the Federal Administrator to organize SRFs would receive capitalization grant awards proportionate to the construction grant allotments currently made. The agreements would require state provision of a 15 percent matching contribution into the revolving fund, and would be required to include a schedule for grant repayment by the SRF. States would be required to apply funds first to meet the 1988 municipal compliance deadline before using them for the other permitted purposes.

The government's intention is that the SRFs will revolve in perpetuity, because loans will only be made to projects generating a revenue stream to support repayment of financial assistance. Basically, 20 year loans at or below market rate are contemplated.

Additionally, and of potential great significance, the fund would be permitted to undertake certain key activities which would enhance its leveraging capability beyond the level necessarily acceptable in a bond bank:

(1) guarantee or insure local debt obligations;

(2) guarantee a loan pool operated by a large intermunicipal agency;

(3) secure the issuance of additional bonds with the SRF and the revenues it is anticipated it will receive -- thereby enhancing its liquidity. States are required to establish plans for SRF usage, which may be modeled on the current construction grants plan.

The SRF approach could revolutionize municipal water treatment finance. The extent of its effectiveness may turn on its ability to be linked with future privatization efforts -- a possibility which is not necessarily precluded although clearly not explicitly contemplated by the Clean Water Act. The key issues will turn on the feasibility of public/private partnerships receiving SRF funds. These include the feasibility of the following:

(1) the commingling of SRF funds with IDB funds in financing;

(2) the extent of the repayment requirement of prior grant funds in connection with fund operations and the availability of SRF or private funds for that purpose;

(3) the availability of a private security interest in a project, or improvement to a project partially financed with SRF funds;

(4) the susceptibility of a project which has received SRF funds to being municipal lease financed on an installment sale-type basis;

(5) the feasibility of a private party entering into a service agreement with respect to the operation of a project which has received SRF funds and remaining eligible to receive tax benefits; and

(6) the introduction of the concept of allocating risk of default, change of law, or other risks between SRF fund recipients and private developers. In terms of market creation, the nature of both Federal and state regulations governing the SRFs are of the greatest importance if the privatization opportunity in the water treatment field is to remain open. For these new regulations to work effectively, they will have to be not only with state privatization statutes but with the regulations emerging to implement the new regulations governing the extent of private involvement with different types of industrial development bonds.

INFRASTRUCTURE BANK PROPOSALS

Over the longer term, greater recognition also may be afforded to the warnings of the Congress's Joint Economic Committee and the Congressional Budget Office that a broader based "infrastructure gap" imperils the ability of communities both to deal with the problem of decaying facilities and to provide the necessary framework for future economic growth. This analysis led to a proposal still languishing before Congress for a National Infrastructure Act which would establish a Federal "bank" revolving fund. That fund would make 20 year repayable grants to states, which, in turn, would establish their own revolving funds to make interest free loans to particular projects. Repayment would be assured through the creation of a sinking fund. Some proposals would empower the resulting State funds to utilize grants or funds from other state/Federal or state programs as well. Analogous infrastructure bank type proposals, on a broader basis than water treatment, and funded by state taxes or by bonding have been established in several states. Some of these proposals would invest the funds with power to guarantee the obligations of municipalities within the states. The potential of infrastructure funds is likely to be a major topic in the report of the Private Sector Advisory Committee on Infrastructure Financing, which conducted extensive hearings on infrastructure financing problems during the past year.

What is the significance of these statutes from a market standpoint? It has frequently been suggested by critics of privatization that it is a mistake to present it as a large scale alternative to conventional public financing. On the other hand, it remains to be properly understood by public policymakers that increasing the velocity circulation of a reduced amount of infrastructure funds will not close the infrastructure gap and that private capital, particularly if leveraged, can be helpful in that regard. It is problematic to target as a major state market those states with revolving infrastructure or water treatment funds unless they acknowledge this and are prepared to systematically work with private capital. There are ample precedents for such public/private arrangements, albeit styled as loan guarantees, insurance, partial grants or reconstruction finance loans. They have come under some measure of reproach as subsidies which distort the market plan.

Privatization's linkage with revolving funds will only have a long term effective life if based on participation in projects which meet conventional marketplace lending tests e.g., coverage based on the user charges which communities are prepared to pay. Before predicating a marketing strategy on the revolving funds a state has organized, its long term viability must be assessed along the analytic lines as as suggested in this paper as appropriate for state privatization statutes.

CONCLUSION

In conclusion, it should be clear that the marketplace for privatization -- a form of "peaceful revolution" -- is statutorily driven and will only occur where legislators follow words with actions. Even then, the nature of the bargain being struck -- explicitly in terms of the statutory requirements and implicitly in terms of the benefits anticipated from the private sector as a consequence of the statute -- must be examined. Where the prime vehicle for privatization is believed to be a revolving fund, its true relationship with private sector economics must be examined carefully.

Overall, although it is possible to structure privatization strategies accommodating state needs as well as Federal tax laws, what is also required is recognition that in privatization, it is not merely the legal framework, but also the business objectives of the parties which must be accommodated if transactions are to be closed.

Chapter 51

PRIVATE FINANCING FOR MUNICIPAL ENERGY PROJECTS: THE EVOLUTION OF PRIVATIZATION

J. Casselman

INTRODUCTION

The term "privatization" has become a fixture in the American legal and financial vocabulary. As with other such terms, it is not susceptible of precise definition, but it has evolved in response to clear trends in law, finance and business.

The purpose of this article is to review briefly those trends and to develop an understanding of the term "privatization". To serve this broad purpose, the comments which follow are necessarily general. We will see, however, that the general trend toward privatization of municipal utility projects, and particularly energy related projects such as cogeneration, district heating and municipal solid waste to energy facilities, focuses on a very real working relationship between the public and private sectors which is beneficial to both.

The public sector will benefit from the injection of private risk capital into municipal energy projects, especially in the current era of dramatically reduced government spending for public projects in general. The public sector will also benefit from economies in construction and operation of projects which are not burdened with pervasive public procurement procedures. The private sector will also benefit from privatization of municipal energy projects if it succeeds in constructing and operating such projects on an efficient and profitable basis. In its drive to maximize the return on its investment, the private sector can be expected to use its best efforts in supplying services to municipalities. The public will also benefit from achieving a certain measure of energy independence.

ROOTS: INDUSTRIAL DEVELOPMENT BONDS

The roots of privatization trace back several decades to industrial development bond financing. A number of states passed laws permitting government entities to issue bonds, the proceeds of which could be used to finance facilities for private business. The Federal tax laws were changed to permit the interest income on these bonds to be exempt from taxation so that the interest rate would be relatively low. See Exhibit A for a schematic representation of such a financing.

The use of "public money for a private purpose" was intended to attract industry to geographic regions which were commercially underdeveloped. Industrial development bond financing then spread in the early 1970's to other uses, notably for pollution control equipment for private business facilities required to meet increasingly strict pollution standards. The public health and welfare would be served by this use of bond financing.

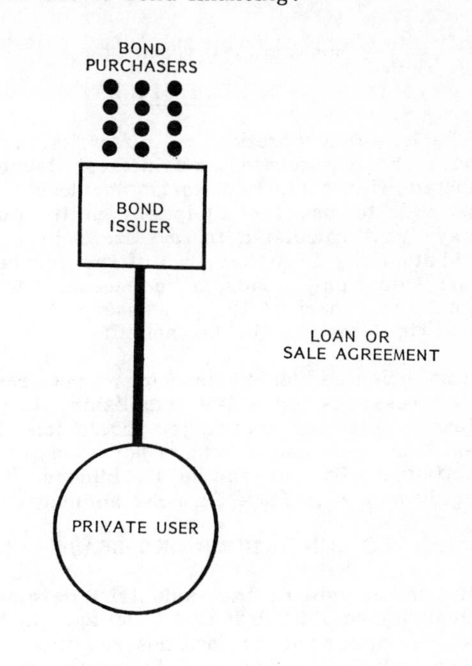

INDUSTRIAL DEVELOPMENT BOND FINANCING

EXHIBIT A

TAX ORIENTED PRIVATE FINANCE

In the 1960's, the tax oriented leasing transaction was beginning to take shape in the private sector.

The essential element of leasing is "third party tax benefit utilization". If a corporation needs financing for additional capital equipment in order to conduct its business, but for any reason does not have sufficient taxable income from which to deduct the depreciation and interest expense associated with that equipment, then it may arrange for an unrelated corporation which has sufficient taxable income to buy the equipment and lease it to the user corporation. See Exhibit B for a schematic representation of tax oriented lease financing.

Adapted from an article published in Strategic Planning and Energy Management, Summer 1985

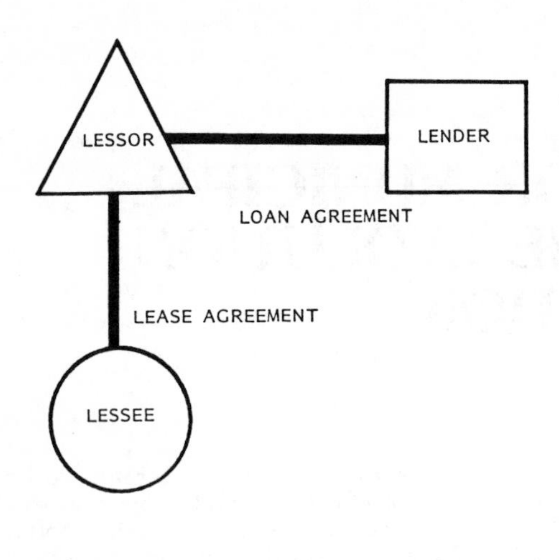

TAX ORIENTED LEASE FINANCING

EXHIBIT B

The lessor corporation can offset its taxable income with the depreciation and interest deductions associated with the equipment. The lessee corporation is able to use the equipment in its business and pays rent calculated to amortize debt in an amount substantially less than 100% of the purchase price of the equipment. This is so because the lessor has paid for a part of the purchase price in return for the right to take the tax benefits.

Tax oriented lease financing grew rapidly when Congress enacted a law establishing the investment tax credit to encourage acquisition by private enterprise of capital equipment to expand business activity. By the mid-1970's billions of dollars of equipment were lease financed annually.

COMBINED BOND AND LEASE FINANCING

It became evident that industrial development bond financing and tax oriented leasing could be combined where equipment or facilities qualified under state and Federal law for bond financing and were to be used by a corporation unable to use tax benefits. The lessor corporation would borrow the proceeds of a bond issue, purchase the equipment or facilities and lease it to the lessee corporation. The lessee benefited economically not only from third party tax benefit utilization, but also from lower interest rates associated with tax exempt debt.

Representative types of facilities susceptible to combined finance were port facilities (e.g. - chemical and petroleum storage tanks), airport facilities (e.g. - flight simulators for training commercial pilots), solid waste disposal facilities (e.g. - resource recovery plants) and power production facilities (e.g. - cogeneration facilities producing both electricity and steam for a municipal district heating system). By the late 1970's and early 1980's some of these facilities were financed with combined bond and lease transactions.

Furthermore, some of these facilities, particularly those which produced energy, were financed on project finance principles. In a project financing, there is no creditworthy obligor directly liable to repay an investor. Instead, the investor has recourse only to the revenues produced by the operation of the facility, project or equipment being financed for repayment of his investment. The investor determines whether to make his investment primarily on the potential for revenue production of the facility, project or equipment. See Exhibit C for a schematic representation of a tax oriented lease project financing.

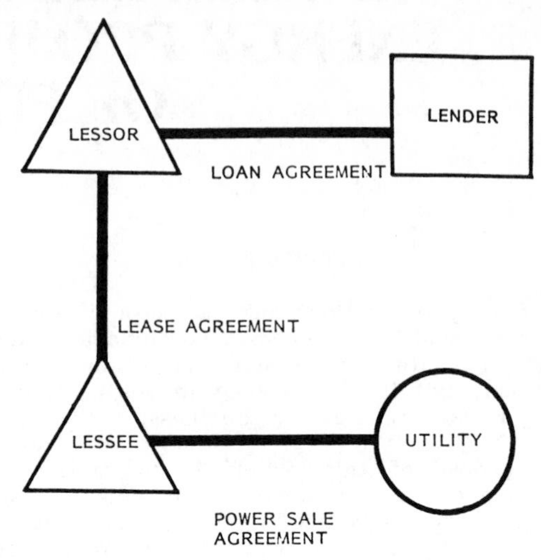

TAX ORIENTED LEASE PROJECT FINANCING

EXHIBIT C

With this development, the term "privatization" began to take on meaning. Ports, airports and waste disposal are usually considered to be in the domain of governmental entities, yet certain facilities in that domain were being financed, owned and operated by private business.

PRIVATE ACTIVITY IN FINANCINGS NOT TAX ORIENTED

In the 1970's, a separate trend emerged uniting the public and private sectors where no tax benefits were taken by any party.

Municipalities would contract with private firms for the design and construction of facilities, such as water treatment facilities, which would be owned by the municipality. The facilities were financed by bonds backed by the municipality's credit. The private corporations were paid a fee for services provided, but took no risk related to the successful operation of the facility over time. Occasionally, a private firm would be paid a fee to operate the facility for the municipality, but again without entrepreneurial risk or reward.

A variation on this type of arrangement, however, did involve entrepreneurial risk and reward. In this variation, the facility would be financed by bonds backed by a private corporation's credit and the corporation would take legal title to the facility. The corporation would then operate the facility for a fee intended to compensate the private corporation for its risk on the financing and to provide incentive for profitable operation.

The municipality would have an option to purchase the facility, exercisable prior to maturity of the bonds at a price calculated to retire the bonds early, or at maturity for a nominal amount, $1 for example. In either case, the tax laws prohibited the use of tax benefits where control of ownership rested with the municipality.

In these transactions, the private operators took entrepreneurial risk. They pledged their credit to amortize the bonds used to finance the facility, built the facility and undertook to operate it profitably. In return, they received a fee out of operating profits as their entrepreneurial reward.

As with municipally owned facilities, the municipality obtained the benefits of private expertise in the design, construction and operation of facilities. The municipality could also expect greater effort by the private operator to realize economies and efficiencies to assure profitability.

Most important to the municipality, the municipality had the option to take title to the facility, once it was established by private enterprise.

INFRASTRUCTURE SALE/LEASEBACK

In the early 1980's, the principle of third party tax benefit utilization began to be used for facilities not operated by a private corporation. In these transactions, infrastructure facilities owned and operated by a governmental unit or other tax-exempt entity were sold to private investors and leased back to the original owner. The private investors in these transactions each became an owner for tax purposes and were able to utilize tax benefits associated with the facilities. This development was prompted by the increased value of tax benefits resulting from the Economic Recovery Tax Act of 1981.

A city museum was the subject of such a sale/leaseback transaction and other transactions for city hall buildings were proposed across the country. A sale/leaseback transaction for a county sewer collection system was planned but never closed.

With the infrastructure sale/leaseback transaction, the term "privatization" took on a new meaning: tax ownership by private enterprise of facilities used by a governmental unit or tax-exempt entity, not by a private user.

THE TAX REFORM ACT OF 1984

Congress enacted changes to the tax law on the general subject of leasing in the Economic Recovery Act of 1981 and the Tax Equity and Fiscal Responsibility Act of 1982. Congressional attention continued to focus on leasing in 1983 and 1984 and, in particular, largely because of the infrastructure sale/leaseback transaction, on leasing as it related to tax-exempt entities. The Tax Reform Act of 1984 contained special provisions applicable to, among other things, solid waste disposal facilities and cogeneration facilities.

The thrust of those tax-exempt entity leasing provisions of the Tax Reform Act was that tax benefits would be available in financings where private enterprise was taking meaningful business risk in using the property financed, even if the private user was providing services to a tax-exempt entity for a fee and the tax-exempt entity exercised some minimal control over the property. We may call this a "qualitative rule" with respect to the privatization phenomenon, intended to permit tax benefit utilization in the right kinds of transactions.

Congress also enacted two "quantitative rules" related to privatization. The first rule established for each state an annual limit on the dollar amount of tax-exempt industrial development bonds which may be issued. The second rule reduced the amount of tax benefits available with respect to property financed with tax-exempt industrial development bonds. Both rules were intended primarily to increase the flow of funds into the Federal treasury.

The qualitative rule is consistent with the intention of those in the private sector who wish to build, own and operate facilities which provide services to municipalities. As indicated above, that intention is to employ business expertise and to assume business risk for the profit potential inherent in those activities.

PRIVATIZATION STATUTES

State laws have also been passed to accommodate privatization. In 1984, the Alabama legislature passed Act No. 84-314 to establish a privatization policy for that state. The City of Auburn, Alabama shortly thereafter entered into a privatization agreement with an engineering firm to upgrade and expand the capacity of an existing wastewater system which had aged and become increasingly unreliable. More than twenty other states currently have privatization statutues either enacted or pending. Many are aimed specifically at water treatment facilities inasmuch as the federal Clean Water Act of 1972 mandated compliance with certain pollution control standards by 1988 and federal grant money to build required treatment facilities has been severely restricted.

State privatization statutes vary as to types of facilities covered and the effect of legislation. In general, these types of statutes remove privatization projects from public utility regulation, permitting more beneficial tax treatment and fewer restrictions on business operations. This regulatory pattern is similar to that applicable to small power producers operating cogeneration and other alternate energy facilities.

CONCLUSION

Privatization has evolved in response to the need for the construction of new municipal utility projects, including energy related projects. Concomitant population growth, an aging municipal infrastructure, reductions in the availability of public sector funding and the need for energy efficiency and cost containment have fostered an atmosphere of cooperation between the public and private sectors. The search for new technologies to deal with problems of pollution control and energy efficiency has created new opportunities for private enterprise to provide vital community services.

These basic economic and business considerations are the driving forces behind the trend toward privatization. Developments in law and finance are increasingly accommodating the privatization phenomenon. Privatization permits the dedication of private capital and private enterprise to the solution of our pollution control and energy efficiency problems in the public sector.

SECTION 17
ENERGY MANAGEMENT STRATEGIES

Chapter 52

MARKETING AN ENERGY MANAGEMENT PROGRAM TO TOP MANAGEMENT

R. J. Redpath

Recent top selling management authors tend to agree on the proposition that 95% of the workplace people want to do the right thing. These authors go on to explain how management impedes this desire by perpetuating inefficiencies and that result in frustration.

If we accept this premise and dwell on it briefly: 95% of the people probably includes management. One might believe that top management with lucrative stock options and high salaries might have a larger percentage of "let's do it right" people.

Then why is it so difficult, and in some cases, impossible to sell these good people on an energy management program. In the mid-1970's, we experienced (and some still do) difficulty in selling the latest demand controller or flu gas analyzer. Certainly, co-generation projects have not been an easy task to father into even the wealthiest companies. They need a champion. Going back to Feudal times, the Ivanhoe champion carried someone's cause to battle. If you think about that, the champion didn't have that great of a job description.

As a Vice President of the Ralston Purina Company and our outside activity group, Ralston Technologies, I champion what I believe are good opportunities in both hard- and soft-engineered projects. Hard simply refers to devices - lighting substitutions, demand controllers, and other more efficiency-promoting devices. Soft is a little more difficult to define. Soft is systems, methods, and providing opportunity to the people who want to do it right.

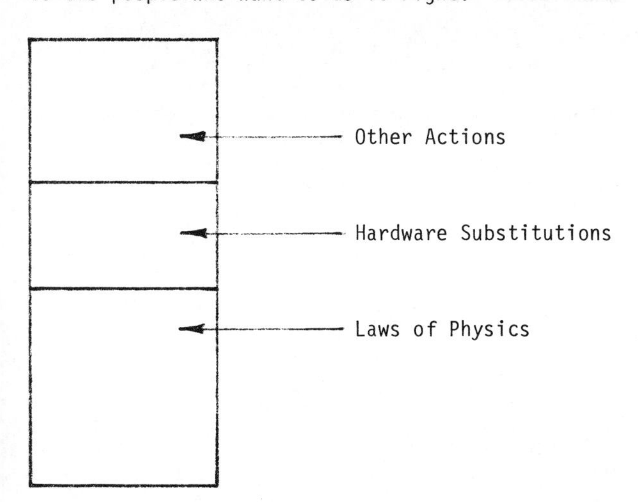

FIGURE 1. ENERGY COMPONENTS

The above graph indicates these components of energy use: the energy required to do the work dictated by the laws of physics; energy saved by substituting more efficient hardware; and energy lost by other actions. Dwelling on other actions for a moment - what other actions? How much energy was used during clean-up over the weekend? Lost per ton of product during "normal" production? If you pull up data, surprisingly, these other actions cause wide variances, and when corrected for degree days and production still vary widely. The conclusion is energy use is not being managed. Note we have not identified the actions that caused the variations but statistically hint that these actions are consuming energy. Further conclusion infers that an energy management program is needed.

Now, if you think selling hard projects, with their return on investment calculated, to top management is difficult, how about a program to get at undefined other actions? I believe our friend Ivanhoe had a clearer job descrption.

The key to gaining support from top management is marketing versus selling. You can sell good hard energy projects today because top management wants them. That's sales; i.e. want meets offer.

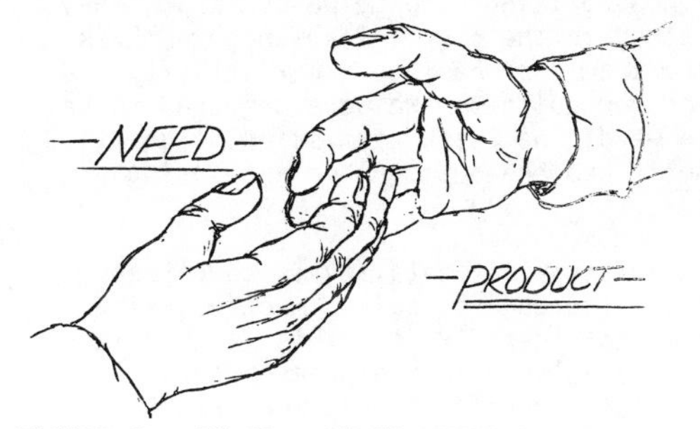

FIGURE 2. SALES = WANTS MEETS OFFER

Marketing is entirely different.

NO CLEAR DEFINITION OF THE WANT.
NO PREVIOUS EXPERIENCE WITH WHATEVER WILL BE SOLD.
OFFER NEEDS TO BE DEFINED.

FIGURE 3. MARKETING

You must know your market. First, what kind of people are they and who around them may stop your idea. Most ideas are killed in the middle; no one wants to look close-minded or stodgy in the beginning nor does anyone put down success. It's the lonely middle where ideas are sterilized. The idea terminator might be a plant manager who is threatened by it. Energy management programs are in their very nature threatening. They seek to improve the management of energy use of those who have been previously paid to manage the facility's resource.

Marketing requires a champion or champions. Champions want good causes. Consequently, the first sale has to be to the champion. Many good technical people lose this round to the first error. They go to a potential champion or, worse, their boss, and present "self-explanatory" data. They expect the elegant technical data to do the job. Sometimes that works, but energy management is hard to define.

In identifying a market, you are creating the product or convincing the customer of a need. More emphasis on convincing your potential customer, in our case top management, is necessary. You must use your champions to get to top management. The champions must have credibility. The upper manager is comfortable supporting gut feelings and new ventures without finite numbers when someone he trusts supports the issue. To inspire your champion, you may have to show unusual courage of conviction yourself. Most important, you must show your confidence in a human fashion.

In the selling of our first management program, we approached several champions. We picked a gutsy plant manager who was comfortable with taking on new challenges. His plant was the leader in energy reduction. We approached the people between the plant and top management telling them we would assume all cost risk. Surprisingly, once we did that, they were willing to share the risk. Top management was informed of the team's probe into a new activity aimed at saving new dollars. We were prepared to be forgiven; note we did not seek permission. The team then quietly proceeded to gather data using a Compac computer.

The American manufacturing mentality is to gather data, look at the scoreboard, call a meeting, find out what went wrong, then fix it. This is a regressive process. The Ralston Technologies program looks for good production, identifies what went right, looks at energy usage, then resets targets. This encourages people to go for a positive goal and to suggest ways to achieve it. The data is boiled down by the computer and presented in a human fashion. The program is created by the very people who use it.

The above process was explained to our champions and subtly to upper management. By dwelling on positives, we were able to reduce the threat the program presented to people who already knew they are doing a good job. They did not necessarily believe that a major improvement was possible; and in most cases, just went along with it because it sounded like something we should have been doing. Most participants, especially hourly wage people, will more than likely come forward at the end and say, "I didn't think this thing was worth a dam in the beginning, but now I am convinced it works." These very people become future champions.

Remember, few people kill a reasonable idea in the beginning once a group has said it believes in it. But watch out as it progresses. We are quiet in our application. As soon as positive results occur, we are quick to inform management and other observers, including participants, in a "by the way, did you know we did . . . " manner. The positive feedback is neceesary to keep your champions fueled.

The second error technical people make is not leaking information on success. Be careful to leak, not brag. Give credit to the plant and champions. Repeat business is dependent on word of mouth.

By now, you are probably curious as to what other actions are addressed and what are the results.

Using the techniques described, we have sold energy and maintenance to 57 of our plants around the world. We have champions in South America, Europe, etc., who are now totally in charge of selling . . . I mean, marketing . . . the programs in their countries. As for other actions, by observing good product, we could set attainable usage goals. By observing a missed goal and noting what happened (i.e. clogged steam trap), we were able to develop action plans for quick correction. We found more waste, in some cases, when the plant was down versus peak production. A hundred little, but very controllable things. The action plans, put into the hands of the 95% who showed up to do the right thing, made it work.

--- DEVELOP CHAMPIONS

--- TOP MANAGEMENT WILL GO ALONG ONCE A GROUND SWELL IS STARTED

--- KEEP IT QUIET IN THE MIDDLE

--- LEAK POSITIVE RESULTS

--- USE YESTERDAY'S VICTIM AS TOMORROW'S CHAMPION

FIGURE 4.

In summary, the marketing of energy management programs to top management is simple once the ground swell of champions have been established. Also, energy management is achievable.

Chapter 53

ENERGY MANAGEMENT FOR THE HOTEL INDUSTRY

B. A. Sher

In a market where guest comfort is the number one concern for the hotelier, it is still important to increase margins through a lowering of operating costs. The intent of this presentation will be to focus on reducing utility costs in the lodging industry by effective energy management without effecting guest comfort.

The methodology used is based primarily based upon my past experience as "Director of Engineering" for the Howard Johnson Company. The first step toward establishing an 'energy management action plan' is to determine the present energy level for a given property. This should be expressed in measurable energy terms, typically BTU's per square-foot. Once this has been done, a prioritization of energy measures is undertaken in order to reduce the overall energy level to a prescribed 'target' level.

Once the energy level for a hotel has been determined, specific recommendations for energy reductions should be made. Several "good" prospects for energy savings in the hotel industry include: (1) lighting retrofits; (2) programmable thermostats; (3) room controls; (4) heat recovery systems; & (5) cogeneration. Since the advent of "power line carrier" technology, room control systems are the most attractive method for producing energy savings in the hotel industry.

The front desk room control system allows control of all heating & cooling units from a central location (as depicted in Figure 1). Since guest comfort is the primary concern, the hotelier should consider a room control system that is transparent to the customer. The reason for this is that failure to induce a guest to return as a customer will negate any energy savings obtained from room control. A remote control unit is inserted inside the heating & cooling unit within a guest room and is therefore hidden from the guest's view.

The central master control system maintains control of energy use in public areas and guest rooms which are checked out by sending digital signals over power lines to the heating & cooling units to be controlled (via the Signal Insertion Unit). The guest rooms which are already checked in are controlled by individual guest room receiver control units unless overriden by the central system for special conditions such as peak demand.

Additional system features permit total override of all energy management functions from the front desk via power line carrier, demand control of guest rooms where demand rates are high, and control of high energy usage in public space areas. Also, with an optional RS-232 port interface, the central control system can automatically provide check in's and check out's through a property management system.

The success in generating energy savings is very dependent on the hotel operator's ability to properly use the system, and providing adequate monitoring of the system results. It is essential that the energy use per square foot is monitored for reduction, rather than the overall dollar amount for verifying paybacks. A power line carrier room control system normally provides less than a two year payback on investment when performing as designed.

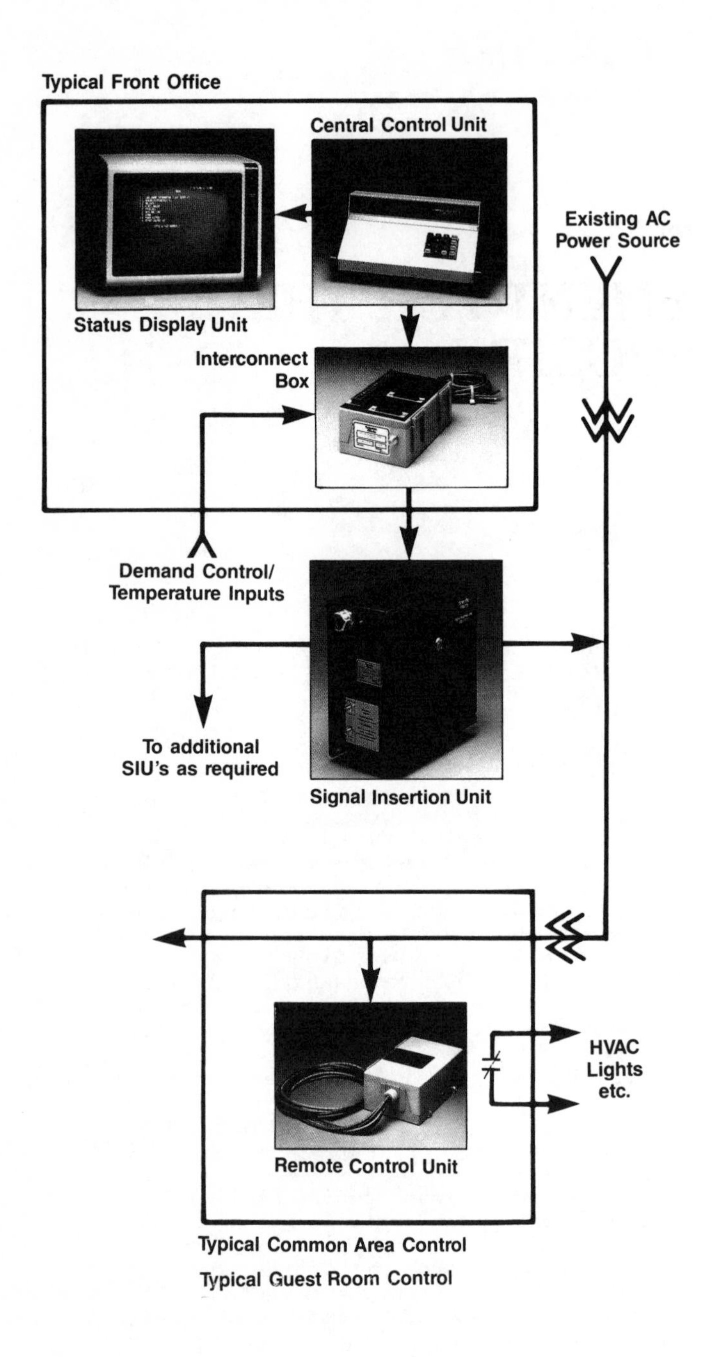
Typical Front Office
Central Control Unit
Status Display Unit
Interconnect Box
Existing AC Power Source
Demand Control/ Temperature Inputs
To additional SIU's as required
Signal Insertion Unit
HVAC Lights etc.
Remote Control Unit
Typical Common Area Control
Typical Guest Room Control

Figure 1

Chapter 54

A PREVENTIVE MAINTENANCE SYSTEM FOR OPTIMUM PHYSICAL PLANT PERFORMANCE

R. G. Paquette

INTRODUCTION

Any discussion about energy cost containment or an effective energy management program must, in due course, involve the issue of equipment or device maintenance. And, more often than not, the organization which can be characterized as an inefficient energy user will also provide, comparitively, less than average maintenance on its energy consuming devices.

In some organizations, this level of reduced maintenance is a short term response to economic conditions, where the maintenance effort has been required to share in the sacrifices common to all operating departments. In others, it is simply business as usual. Nevertheless, a strong correlation can be shown between excessive energy consumption (efficiency) and adequacy of maintenance effort.

Energy consultants and managers having experience with Technical Assistance energy audits under the federal energy grants program to schools and hospitals (National Conservation Policy Act) will agree that lack of coordinated and consistent building maintenance is frequently a significant factor in overall energy waste. How often have you heard of equipment operating continuously because the trip pins were loose or fell out of an electromechanical timer? Or, perhaps, the installing contractor, in the haste of completion, failed to remove a temporary electrical jumper wire purposely installed to override some important control.

These examples are not at all uncommon, and, without some program of regular inspection, testing, and/or servicing, may go unnoticed for many months. Further, they represent a failure to provide even relatively simple inspections; the absence of which can not be successfully argued as being the result of budgetary considerations. The resulting energy waste can be significant and easily avoided. The solution is an effective preventive maintenance program.

PREVENTIVE MAINTENANCE vs CORRECTIVE MAINTENANCE

In order to better understand the concept of preventive maintenance, it is helpful to review the definition of preventive maintenance and its counterpart, corrective maintenance.

Preventive Maintenance: (or proactive maintenance) The consistent application of an organized program of inspections, investigations, and coordinated repairs with the intent of minimizing equipment failures and unanticipated breakdowns.

Corrective Maintenance: (or reactive maintenance) Maintenance efforts which are characterized by uncoordinated long range work schedules and formulated in response to instantaneous equipment or building needs and directed at the resolution of identifiable operational problems. (Some have humorously linked this maintenance style with the person who represents the philosophy which espouses the familiar precept that "IF IT AIN'T BROKE, DON'T FIX IT!")

One method of visualizing the relationship between Proactive and Reactive maintenance is to consider both in their purest sense as occupying the extremes of a continuum. The extremes and the connecting line is referred to as the Preventive/Corrective Maintenance Mix Continuum. In this visualization, the extremes are limits, and are unachievable in their absolute sense. That is, no organization can consistently function in either a purely proactive (preventive) mode or in a totally corrective (reactive) sense. The position of every organization, then, can be found somewhere on the line between the two points, the actual position determined by the 'mix' of reactive and proactive maintenance practiced. Figure 1 illustrates the concept of the Preventive/Corrective Maintenance Mix Continuum.

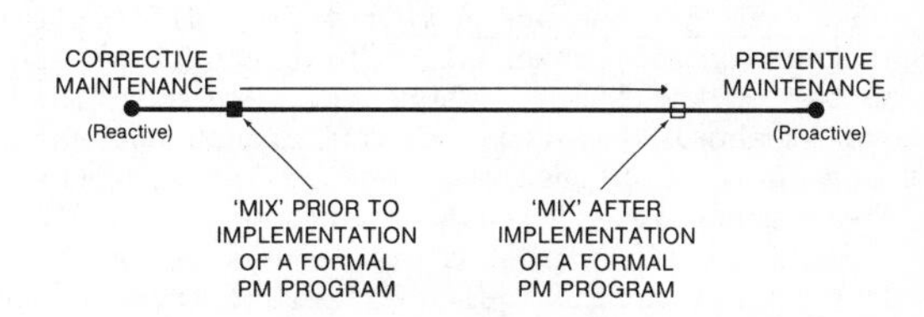

FIGURE 1. PREVENTIVE/CORRECTIVE MAINTENANCE MIX CONTINUUM.

Determining the 'Mix'

Where your organization lies on the Preventive/Corrective Maintenance Continuum of Fig. 1 will be the result of many factors. Among the most important are:

- Business type (i.e. manufacturing, transportation, institutional, etc.)
- Organization size
- Geographic location
- Complexity of technology
- Skill level and number of maintenance personnel (administrative and laborers)
- Financial strength of the organization
- Expected duration of operation
- Regulatory requirements (legal and voluntary)
- Insurance requirements and other risk considerations.

Some factors tend to move the organization towards a Proactive maintenance style while others will tend to increase the level of Reactive work. Some factors, such as the skill level of the maintenance personnel may be influenced by the organization, whereas others, like regulatory requirements, are not controllable by the organization. A more categorical definition of the controlling factors suggests that three general areas impact upon the Preventive/Corrective Maintenance Mix. They are:

I. Technical - Involves the complexity of the maintained equipment as well as the predictability and historical experience with the attendant technology, etc.

II. Environmental - Factors which involve the business operating climate, the legal and regulatory interference as well as geographical considerations, etc.

III. Economic - Organizational fiscal factors, industry wide economic conditions, competitive pressures, size of the organization, replacement value of equipment, etc.

Most factors affecting the Preventive/Corrective Maintenance Mix, including those listed earlier, will fall into one of the above broad categories.

Understanding the relationship between these factors and your organization may provide some interesting insight into why your maintenance system, and specifically the preventive maintenance efforts, may or may not be considered successful. Not surprisingly, many organizations will find that their 'Mix' is heavily influenced by factors and events well outside of normal maintenance department control, such as economic and environmental items; factors having little to do with the skills, size, and abilities of the maintenance personnel.

Considering the variety of factors affecting the Preventive/Corrective Maintenance Mix it is not difficult to see that there is no universally "best position" at which to be (on the line). Where your organization is, and where it should be, requires a thorough understanding of the factors influencing your business. For example the preventive maintenance performed by a JCAH (Joint Commission of Accreditation of Hospitals) accredited hospital will be quite different from an industrial plant such as an injection molding shop. In each case, the 'Mix', though different, may be optimal. One would expect that similar organizations within a common industry and comparable geography to be reasonably close together on the Mix line.

Determining where your organization lies on the Preventive/Corrective Maintenance Mix line should be more than an academic exploration. This concept will provide a tool to better understand the factors that influence your system of maintenance delivery and some of the difficulties which arise within that process. It will help you to locate and understand what combination of Corrective and Preventive maintenance is 'right' for your organization.

THE PERCEPTION/PRACTICE DISJUNCTION

Regardless of the organization, and irrespective of the opinions expressed within the organization, the Preventive/Corrective Maintenance Mix exists, and with some introspection, the mix can be evaluated and a position on the preventive/corrective maintenance continuum can be determined.

In many organizations, though, a problem exists in recognizing the existence of the mix and understanding its impact on the delivery of the overall maintenance effort. The maintenance performance is judged by others who possess performance expectations that cannot be reasonably provided by the mix. This situation reflects less upon the maintenance ability of the organization, but more upon the ability of the maintenance operation to effectively communicate the Preventive/Corrective Maintenance Mix, and the level of performance which the mix suggests, to those who rely upon it. Figure 2. illustrates the Perception/Practice Disjunction and how it may be visualized on the Preventive/Corrective Maintenance Mix line.

PREVENTIVE/CORRECTIVE DISJUNCTION

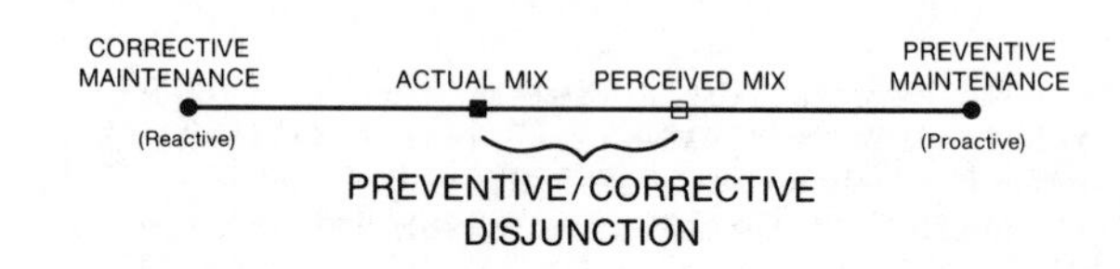

FIGURE 2. THE PERCEPTION/PRACTICE DISJUNCTION

Much of the organizational discord over maintenance can be avoided by simply providing a better measure of understanding between the groups rendering the maintenance and the parties receiving that maintenance. When the perception or expectation of the level of maintenance is close to the actual practice, many complaints will cease. That is not to say that the level of maintenance will improve, but that the expected level of maintenance will be more like that actually delivered.

CHANGING YOUR 'MIX'

The dynamic nature of any maintenance organization reflects in changes within the maintenance mix. The proportion of Corrective to Preventive maintenance will change throughout the year and follow changes in the causitive factors to the degree that a correlation exists. When management has control of a causitive factor, then the mix may be changed by design. Certainly, a new annual performance goal of implementing a formal computer based preventive maintenance system to replace an existing manual system would fall within this category. When the goal takes into consideration the existing conditions within the maintenance department, such as available man-hours, financial resources, computer equipment, etc., the mix can be changed. What must be avoided is simply stating the goal without providing the resources necessary to assure implementation

PROACTIVE SYSTEMS -DEFINED

Proactive, or preventive maintenance systems fall into two general classifications:

Formal Systems - Characterized by written policies and procedures directing a dynamic system of tasks and machine or equipment files created to schedule repetitive maintenance efforts. Formal systems come in two types:

Manual - based upon a 'hard copy' form which utilizes a filing scheme or written checklists.

Automated Systems - based upon an electronic data processing or computerized sorting routine with magnetic file storage.

Informal Systems - Characterized by the absence of substantial documentation and by strong individual direction. They are recognized most often by an 'effective' maintenance director or supervisor, and talented maintenance personnel. Long term maintenance planning is the result of, and resident in, the memory of the participating employees. The informal system commonly develops as the result of an extended on the job experience and is a naturally occuring evolutionary process reflecting the learning curve of employees.

As one would expect, formal systems tend to produce a more organized and reliable preventive maintenance program, although a conscientious maintenance group can provide a quality informal proactive maintenance program. Informal systems are, however, rarely optimal. This deficiency stems from their inability to produce documented work schedules and the almost total lack of administrative reports showing work production standards and incomplete or missed preventive maintenance tasks. It is possible for a highly developed informal system to evolve into a formal system as the degree and quality of documentation improves.

As a practical matter, any decision to install a formal PM system should include an examination of existing informal PM practice to glean valuable task and frequency data on which to base the formal system development. The past practices of an informal system can be very valuable to the formal system design.

DEFICIENCIES OF AN INFORMAL PREVENTIVE MAINTENANCE SYSTEM

Perhaps, the greatest deficiency of an informal preventive maintenance system lies in the fact that it is centered on the same skills, experiences and initiative of one or more individuals that make the system work! Most often, this person is the maintenance supervisor. Should this individual leave the organization, few, if any, records remain to document the nature and scope of the maintenance previously performed, as well as future needs. In effect, a new supervisor must either search out his/her predecessor's program through conversation, historical work order documents and records, or subordinate employee debriefings. Or, as in most cases, the new supervisor simply implements a new program based upon his/her own skills and experiences, and with little regard to past practice. That 'new' program will take time to implement and may not be as effective as the one utilized by the previous supervisor. Thus, the informal preventive maintenance system usually suffers a severe regression when the leadership changes.

In summary, informal preventive maintenance systems are:

1. Rarely documented, either in scheduling or in task execution, and the communication channel is nearly always verbal.
2. The success is highly dependent upon individual knowledge and performance.
3. Suffers a severe regression following changes in key personnel.
4. Improved or refined in response to specific maintenance problems, many of which are costly to the organization in terms of unscheduled down time or value of repairs.

The remainder of this paper will focus on formal preventive maintenance systems, and although directed towards computer based versions, is valid for either manual or automated programs.

ORGANIZATIONAL PREREQUISITES FOR A SUCCESSFUL PREVENTIVE MAINTENANCE SYSTEM

Understanding your MIX

First and foremost, you must understand your optimum Preventive/Corrective Maintenance Mix. This introspection must be made in conjunction with executive level personnel to assure that all factors in the mix are considered. In particular, it is important for superiors to understand the resources required and the synergism between their expectations and the technical, environmental, and economic factors which define the preventive maintenance potential of the organization.

For example, in a process industry where production equipment is in use around the clock and scheduled shut downs are rare, existing production schedules may not allow the necessary equipment down time for periodic in-depth preventive maintenance procedures. In this case, either the production schedule must be altered (with the concomitant effect on income) or the preventive maintenance expectations must be lowered (with a probable increase in corrective maintenance needs.)

Too often the maintenance group experiences a continued demand for improved preventive maintenance without being allowed the required access time. The expected level of preventive maintenance cannot be achieved, and frustration builds within the maintenance personnel.

Executive Support

Even the best preventive maintenance plan will fail to achieve its maximum benefit, and may fail altogether, if it is not vigorously supported by executive management. The earlier example of a continuous production process industry is an example of one business where executive management plays a very important role in assuring a viable PM program. If the production supervisor refuses to allow periodic process shutdowns for preventive maintenance, the maintenance program will fail. If executive management truly desires an effective proactive maintenance program, it has the responsibility of providing leadership in policy areas such as scheduled equipment downtime, and must certainly, consider the economic impact of such a production interruption during system pre-planning.

Proper Preliminary Planning

The experience of the author suggests that, of the operating preventive maintenance systems which he has reviewed, the single greatest area of deficiency involves the subject of Preliminary Planning. When pre-planning has occured it was rarely written or available for periodic review. When the facility is large, full system implementation may take many years to achieve. Here, program continuity demands a written plan, particularly when key personnel changes may occur prior to full system implementation. The value of a fully documented plan can not be understated.

Contents of the Preliminary Plan: The plan must contain a statement of the long term goal of the system and the method by which the goal will be achieved. In addition, and especially for large facilities, it should include an implementation timeline. First, however, the scope of the system must be determined. This involves two specific areas:

- Size of the system (number of machines included)

- Degree of comprehensiveness of the tasks.

The size of the system can be determined by the size of the facility and the number of devices, equipment, machines, etc. to be included in the preventive maintenance program. Further, a decision must be made as to how the machines will be identified. Several options exist. For example, on large complex machines with many motors, pumps, fans, controls, etc., the machine can be given a single identification (usually a number), or the subassemblies can each be given a unique identification. This decision will not affect the scope of the task descriptions, but it will determine the number of 'machine' or 'equipment' files necessary to handle the task descriptions. Clearly this will affect the size of the file cabinet or amount of computer storage needed to maintain the system.

The degree of comprehensiveness of the tasks will define the level of sophistication of the aggregrate system. Three 'degrees' of system implementation exist. Figure 3 illustrates the relationship between the three degrees of implementation and the relative number of work orders generated by each.

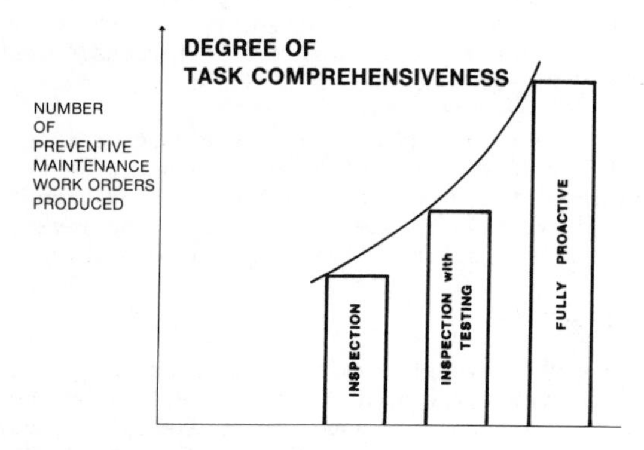

FIGURE 3. DEGREE OF TASK COMPREHENSIVENESS

The three basic implementation degrees are:

1. Inspection - Essentially a visual, audible, and olfactory inspection of the equipment to verify operation.
2. Inspection with Testing - Inspection with added testing of components, such as pressure testing, electrical leakage detection, resistance testing, rpm checks, vibration analysis, infrared inspections, etc.
3. Fully Proactive - Inspection, testing, simulation testing, nondestructive testing, disassembly and renewal of parts, and programmed part replacement.

Obviously, each of the above options will determine the number and complexity of task descriptions needed for implementation. Similarly, the costs in labor and materials will increase as the degree of implementation becomes more comprehensive. Each of the three options listed above have an impact upon the Preventive/Corrective Maintenance Mix. As the level of preventive maintenance increases, the expected level of corrective maintenance should decrease. Figure 4 illustrates the typical relationship between preventive and corrective maintenance by showing the relationship in numbers of work orders produced for each type of maintenance thru time. This example would apply to an existing organization without previous preventive maintenance activities.

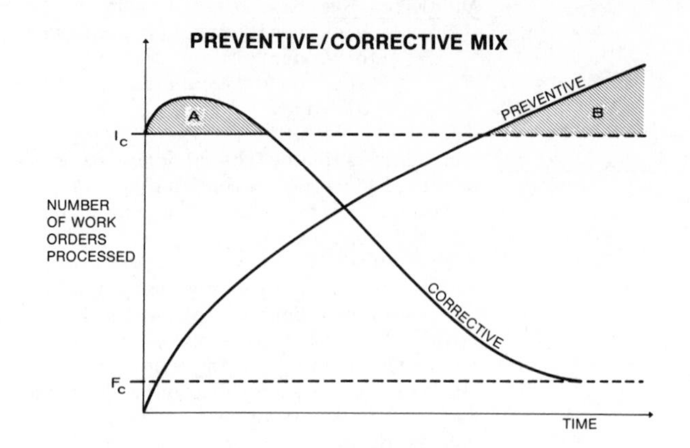

FIGURE 4. THE PREVENTIVE/CORRECTIVE MAINTENANCE MIX

We will return to Figure 4 later in this paper.

Evaluating the cost impact of the degree of implementation becomes more difficult. Two separate costs are affected. First, the direct and measurable costs associated with the preventive maintenance procedure: labor, parts and materials, cost of lost production, etc. Second, and most difficult to determine, are the avoided costs associated with improved maintenance. These are actually savings. This calculation should include the indirect costs of avoided downtime, and becomes somewhat speculative, as unscheduled downtime could include the labor costs of an entire production line which might be idle, yet paid.

The importance of these factors will differ depending upon the organization involved. A large unionized production facility might easily justify a fully proactive formal preventive maintenance system entirely on the basis of avoided costs of unscheduled breakdowns.

Adequate Resources and Cost Considerations

Not even the best system design can overcome the difficulty of inadequate organizational resources. The maintenance team must be provided with adequate tools and equipment as well as the labor hours needed to perform the required tasks. Depending upon the degree of task comprehensiveness, the needs will be different. The lower the degree (i.e. less comprehensive) the fewer labor hours will be required. With simpler tasks the amount and value of test equipment and tools will be comparitively lower.

One signal that a system is inadequately supported by organizational resources will be the occurence of large numbers of incomplete or missing PM work orders. This condition may also be the result of improper scheduling of workers, and an executive administrator reviewing a problem system should look to resource availability as a possible cause of consistently low system performance. Maintenance supervisors which have failed to "buy into the program" can, through worker scheduling, mimmic the effect of an overdesigned system by withholding the required amount of labor hours to complete the scheduled tasks.

System Costs

There are two separate cost categories in the operation of a preventive maintenance program. The first cost group is associated with the administrative and business aspects of the system operation. For a computer based system, these costs include:

- Clerical expenses
- Data Processing Costs
  - data entry labor expense
  - computer and peripheral use
  - paper, ribbons, binders, etc.
  - programming or software costs
- Printing costs for forms and manuals
- Management and administrative labor
  etc.

These costs are system support costs and, although somewhat difficult to evaluate a priori, are often underestimated in system preliminary planning. In particular, a large closed loop system, (explained later) will require large amounts of data entry labor.

The second category of costs are entirely related to the actual cost of labor and material required to perform the prescribed maintenance. Obviously, this cost will vary for each organization and the nature of the PM system application. The aggregation of the labor and material costs takes on more meaning when it is contrasted with the concurrent cost of providing corrective maintenance. Indeed, the comparison of preventive maintenance efforts to corrective maintenance efforts is the essence of why a PM system is implemented in the first place! Preventive maintenance costs are incurred to reduce the level of corrective maintenance, unanticipated downtime, reduce injuries, and severity of equipment failures when they do occur.

Figure 4 shows the typical ralationship between corrective and preventive maintenance work orders for a hypothetical organization with no previously working PM program. I_c is the initial level of corrective maintenance work orders. F_c is the final level of corrective maintenance work orders. The shaded area marked "A" represents an initial surge of corrective maintenance work orders which results from the actual on-site implementation effort and early scheduled inspections that detect existing equipment deficiencies. This phenomenon is a rarely recognized benefit of all formal PM system implementations and can result in very interesting and valuable findings. It represents a short term increase in corrective maintenance costs but often results in significant operational improvements and energy savings.

The shaded area of Figure 4 which is marked "B" illustrates how a fully implemented highly proactive maintenance system can generate considerably more work orders than the organization has been accustomed to in the corrective maintenance mode. It should be understood, however, that the typical monetary value of a preventive maintenance work order is measurably lower than an average corrective maintenance work order.

For purposes of illustrating the Total Cost of an implemented system, lets assume that the cost of a completed PM work order equals the cost of a completed corrective work order. To find the total cost of the system, and the optimum implementation level of a formal PM program, we add the two curves together. Figure 5 represents the total cost curve for the example in Figure 4. If we were to establish our final system implementation goal on the basis of total cost, we would try to build a PM program which, when fully installed, brings the total cost in at the minimum point of the total cost curve.

The purpose of this Total Cost example is to show that, even with a PM system, one must deal with the reality of marginal cost theory and the law of diminishing returns. In reality, the total cost must consider not only the cost of providing the preventive maintenance (as well as the corrective maintenance) but also the <u>utility</u> of providing better preventive maintenance. That <u>utility</u> function will be different for each organization. Consider the differences in preventive maintenance <u>utility</u> between a large department store and a nuclear power plant.

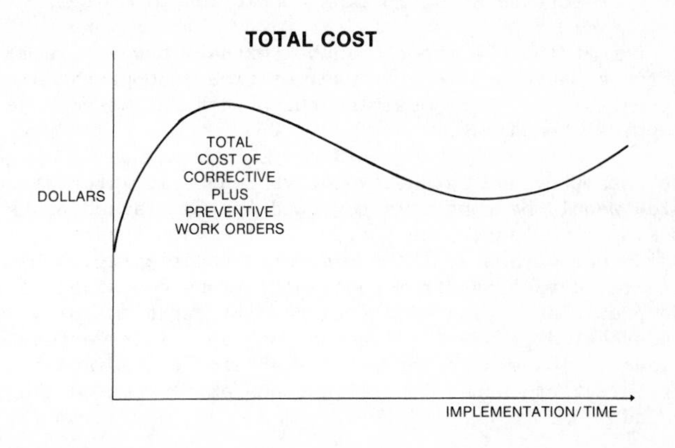

FIGURE 5. TOTAL COST

<u>Resources Beyond the Tradesperson</u>

Any properly designed and implemented preventive maintenance system will be a dynamic system. Frequent reviews, additions, deletions, and changes must occur to keep the system accurate and reflect the changing needs of a facility. Additional staff may be required to perform numerous support functions, such as producing the proper PM work orders for each period, maintaining information files, and performing data processing functions if the system is computer based. These clerical needs are equally as important as the technician or worker that performs the hands-on maintenance. In smaller organizations, this support work can be added to existing job descriptions with little or no adverse result. In larger organizations, the system support may require the addition of full time employees or a significant revision of existing job descriptions. These considerations must be included in the preliminary plan or the PM system startup will be plagued with labor problems.

<u>Periodic Executive Review</u>

A key element to the success of a proactive maintenance program is regular review by the executive level administration. The preliminary plan should define the frequency and content of required periodic synopsis reports which detail the system performance. If the user organization utilizes Management By Objective (MBO) then the performance of the PM system should be included in the annual goals and periodic MBO appraisal of the responsible manager. Without this motivation, it is very easy for the long term aspects of a preventive maintenance program to become subordinated to unrelated short term demands placed on the manager of the system.

<u>The Periodic Executive Report:</u> This document should be very concise and of a standard format. The principal areas of interest to most executives are:

1. Total number of machines, equipment, etc. being scheduled by the system.
2. Total number of PM work orders produced, by period, including most recent
3. Total number of PM work orders completed, by period, including last period.
4. Number of incomplete or missing work orders, by period.
5. Total labor hours expended for PM work, by period.
6. Total cost of materials used in completing PM work orders, by period.

7. Significant or notable deviations from the system implementation plan or timeline.
8. Significant problems encountered since the last report relating to task completion.

The format for the report can be textual, however, some of the comparisons lend themselves nicely to graphical presentation. When possible, the author recommends the graphical technique.

The data provided in the executive report is information which should be routinely reviewed and maintained by the PM system manager. The various performance figures are indicators of how well the system is functioning. Substantial deviations from the expectations contained in the preliminary plan will flag possible problems with resources, employee 'dedication' or supervisory effectiveness. Consistent deviations should be examined carefully for cause. Occasional deviations can be expected.

Administrative Requirements

As with any comprehensive program involving various employees, the administrative details of the system become important. Business related items include such things as flow charts, forms, job descriptions, report formats, performance indices, etc., and includes seemingly minor details such as the style and size of identification numbers to be applied to equipment, how workers will receive PM work orders, where and with whom to deposit completed work orders, etc. All of which must be effectively and routinely communicated to the employees that will be involved in making the program a success.

For the above reasons, employee inservices are a necessary part of any operating PM system. They should address all of the issues mentioned above. Further, the inservices should be used to convey to the workers the same performance indicators as are provided to the executive management. Informational inservices should occur about every 6 months. Technical inservices dealing with the PM tasks, like testing procedures, should occur as needed, and certainly as new employees become involved with the program. A general meeting should be held at least annually to review the entire system performance with all participating employees, including an executive staff representative.

CHARACTERISTICS OF A FORMAL PREVENTIVE MAINTENANCE SYSTEM

Open Loop vs Closed Loop Systems

There are two principal types of formal systems in use. The open loop system is primarily a work scheduler. It does not require or accept "feedback" from the completed work order. Therefore, an open loop system cannot generate work performed reports, missing work order reports or other summaries which require information from the completed work order. Open loop systems work best with simple, 'inspection only' preventive maintenance systems.

Closed loop systems allow (or require) the "posting" of completed work orders. This typically includes information like worker comments, task summary, labor hours, material costs, completion date, worker name, etc. A computer based closed loop PM system often provides extensive reports based upon the posted information or allows specific report algorithms to be provided by the user.

Closed loop systems will require considerably greater management effort compared to an open loop system. The additional time is primarily clerical or data entry, and must be considered in the preliminary planning phase of the system development. It is not generally prudent to require a maintenance supervisor to personally record the work order feedback, as lesser costly job descriptions can effectively handle the record keeping or data entry function.

Some closed loop systems will operate satisfactorily in an open loop mode, then, as the users needs or system sophistication increases, the closed loop features can be activated. In this manner, wholesale system replacement will not be necessary to improve PM program effectiveness if you choose to begin your PM efforts slowly.

Five Characteristics of Formal Systems

Five primary characteristics can be identified in most formal preventive maintenance systems. They are:

1. Equipment files - Equipment or machine details. Model numbers, serial numbers, date of purchase, manufacturer, location in users' facility, vendor, cost, etc.
2. Task files - Task descriptions to be used when performing preventive maintenance work.
3. History files - Chronological or other listing of services performed on equipment or machines scheduled by the PM system.
4. Reports and summaries - Various reports and performance indices used to ensure the effectiveness of the system implementation and accumulate costs associated with maintenance efforts. Includes missing work order reports, executive synopsis reports, work performed reports, etc. (Note: this item may not be found in an open loop system.)
5. Policies, procedures and instructions - Complete system documentation, including system goals, organization, responsibilities, etc., including technical instructions on how to 'operate' the system, whether it is manual or automated.

Two Types of Formal Systems

As was mentioned earlier, formal systems can be either of two types:

Manual Systems
or
Automated Systems

Manual Systems: These can be found in a great variety of operating designs, and their only common characteristic is that they are always based upon 'hard copy' information. That is, the files and task descriptions are maintained in written form, and certain "manual" operations by one or more individuals are required to prepare work requisitions for each equipment schedule within each maintenance period. Simple manual systems are typically the evolutionary result of a conscientious and tenured maintenance department, and can be very effective. Large manual systems are cumbersome and difficult to manage.

Automated Systems: Generally computer based, these systems utilize the speed of a computer or other mechanical device to sort equipment files for predetermined maintenance schedules. In computerized systems, the work schedules will be matched with the appropriate task and printed. This process is repeated for each maintenance period. Automated systems will include provisions for creating and supporting equipment and task files, as well as a report printing section. They may be either open loop or closed loop designs, and come in either personal computer or mainframe based configurations.

The recent growth in powerful and low cost personal

computers has provided an opportunity for many organizations, previously unable to afford an automated system, to implement a cost effective computer based system using commercially available programs. In fact, the current low cost of personal computers and inexpensive software make the use of an automated preventive maintenance system the best option available at this time.

Personal Computers vs Mainframe Computers

For large facilities where PM programs will have extensive task and equipment files, the single disadvantage of the personal computer based system versus the mainframe system involves the relatively slow printing speed of the typical character printer used on PC's. When compared to the mainframe's fast line printer, the PC based system is super slow. PM systems which produce 400 or more work orders per week will require several hours of printing time per week if produced by a character printer. This is often found to be unacceptably long. Moreover, if the personal computer printer is a relatively slow "letter quality" printer, you will be in for a horrendous wait!

If your organization is large and supports a mainframe computer installation, it may be possible to retain the convenience of a PC based preventive maintenance system and utilize the fast printing capabilities of the mainframe computer by uploading the work order printing information to the mainframe. You should consult with your systems engineer or programmer for the best method of providing this service.

IMPLEMENTATION

Implementation of an extensive PM system will require hundreds of labor hours. And, since effective implementation demands a technically skilled and experienced team, the PM program will, often, be in competition with a number of other priority projects for the total hours of technical time available within your organization. In this situation it is not difficult to understand why a large preventive maintenance program might require several years to fully implement, in addition to the normal time needed to keep the equipment and task information accurate. This 'available time' problem explains why poorly planned PM programs often fail in their infancy.

Where 'in-house' implementation is a problem, either due labor hour shortages or the lack of technically proficient staff, an alternative exists. The utilization of a contract consultant or technical service to implement a PM system has several advantages and disadvantages. First, the advantages:

1. The opportunity to implement large systems promptly without interfering with typical operational routines.
2. Familiarity with PM system design options and available software.
3. Large existing task libraries for commonly encountered PM procedures.
4. Objectivity in specifing procedures.

The disadvantages are:

1. Potentially high up-front cost of bringing the system on line.
2. Inadvertent creation of the "not invented here" syndrome within the users maintenance or engineering operation, and an attitude of indifference by operating personnel.
3. Possible unfamiliarity with highly technical or unusual processes or equipment.

Surprisingly, because of the technical expertise and efficiency a third party implementation, it may be less costly than an in-house program and render a better product. Certainly, this option should be considered during the preliminary planning stage, and especially if a rapid implementation timeline is desired.

The author's experience suggests that for large computer based systems involving conventional physical plant equipment (no production equipment), the technical time needed for the implementation of each piece of separately scheduled equipment will average about 1.0 hours. Clerical and other support will require an additional 0.5 hours per machine. These estimates should assist the prospective user in generating preliminary estimates of implementation time and costs. A busy maintenance supervisor might expect to allocate 3 or 4 hours per week to implement a PM program before seriously affecting other job responsibilities. It is not difficult, therefore, to understand why a fully implemented preventive maintenance system requires serious long range planning. Many years of implementation can be necessary.

Accurate Equipment Files and Effective Task Descriptions

The subject of accurate equipment file information cannot be understated. The fully implemented PM system can offer numerous advantages beyond the expected work scheduling. Accumulated equipment files can be extremely valuable resources for various statistics regarding plant equipment. Depending upon the system used, these files can become the central information location for equipment data and other important information, which, when combined with PM and corrective work histories, can assist in repair/replace decisions and reliability studies.

Effective task descriptions are the key to the end-result success of the PM application. Even the best administered program cannot provide quality results if the technical details of the task descriptions are inadequate. Qualified personnel should produce the needed task descriptions using manufacturer's recommendations, along with the personal experience and suggestions from knowledgeable maintenance staff.

This author wishes to emphasize the importance of the safety aspect of the actual text of the task description used. In today's increasingly litigious society, maintenance managers should recognize that a preventive maintenance (or corrective maintenance) work order is a written instruction detailing a specific job. In that regard, it is important that the written procedure meet all applicable safety requirements such as OSHA (or your state's equivalent) and NIOSH rules. The author of any task description should assume that the least competent maintenance worker could be assigned to perform the task. For example, when the author must write a procedure to thoroughly inspect a machine's drive train, the first requirement of the task will be to "disconnect, lock-out or tag-out the power source before performing the" required task. This extra statement may seem unnecessary to the skilled mechanic, but its absence could send a new or inexperienced worker to the hospital, or worse. One could expect a negligence suit stemming from any injury where the task description failed to warn the employee of a legally required (or even obvious) safety precaution or requirement. Do not overlook reminding the worker of requirements to wear additional or unusual protective apparatus.

SUMMARY

Developing and implementing a formal PM program is not

Chapter 55

SUBJECTIVE ANALYSIS OF ENERGY MANAGEMENT PROJECTS

R. J. Morris

Why do energy management savings calculations sometimes give an accurate prediction of savings, but more often than not the results are unexpected? Some results exceed our predictions and others fail. Can we identify and control this intangible?

Before implementation, every energy saving project is evaluated quantitatively. The common procedure includes a study of the energy consuming equipment and analysis of the energy history. Usually the payback and/or the return on investment is computed. This is adequate under laboratory conditions, but the real world is different. Energy management is a people business. Energy management is a state of mind. It involves change and people resist change.

John Naisbitt in his book "Megatrends" explains the high tech - high touch principle. He theorizes that technology will not work without close human interaction. Man will find ways to circumvent things he doesn't like or understand. Everyone has seen the locked thermostat cover with a hairpin protruding from the top. We as engineers spend a disproportionate amount of our time looking for and solving technical problems instead of psychological ones. Many times a pencil session with maintenance men is worth thousands of dollars in future savings. The people part of the energy management industry is far more challenging than the technical part. We cannot eliminate people from the equation. If you analyze the most successful energy conservation projects, you will always find someone behind the scene that fine-tuned the system. Gone are the days of the mysterious black box that hangs on the wall of the basement. Those are all overriden or bypassed.

How can this human interaction be predicted or measured? Engineers and scientists typically detest subjective analysis. Conclusions are only as good as the data used to formulate them. If you put garbage in - you get garbage out. Therefore a subjective analysis of predicted savings must be formulated by actual case histories. What are the characteristics of successful projects and what are the characteristics of the failures? If we ask the right questions before a project is designed, our savings forecast will improve.

Before we list examples there is one important concept needed to achieve a complete understanding of subjective analysis. That concept involves conversion of terms. For example, if we are designing a system for an office building, we must put cost and payback in terms of dollars per square foot. Office building owners, managers, and operators do not understand or care about kilowatt hours, BTUs or power factor. They do understand cost per square foot. Every decision they make relates to cost per square foot; so why don't we speak to them in their language instead of ours? The office building industry has other terms we must deal with, such as: pass-through, stops, common area, and leasable space. Each of these terms are critical to payback calculations. We cannot use standard out-of-the-textbook calculations for an accurate evaluation of energy management for office buildings. The same holds true for schools, churches, factories, etc.

The following are examples of subjective questions to pursue when evaluating an energy management project. These questions are structured so that numeric values can be plugged into computer programs. This can be viewed only as a sample. Each engineer should formulate his own variation and tailor those for each market sector he is involved in.

SUBJECTIVE ANALYSIS FOR OFFICE BUILDINGS

Note: Questions #2, 5, 9 are additive, add together for score of that question.

These questions are only a sample. They will supplement other load and weather calculations. However to ignore or take lightly the subjective analysis of a building will produce erratic savings predictions. Each question requires explanation so that the impact of the answers are accurate.

1. Is the person that is responsible for the utility budget also responsible for the energy management project?

   Yes +15, No 0

   Sometimes organizations become so large the right does not know what the left is doing. The design engineer must find out if the person responsible for energy costs is the same person responsible for the conservation project. Many times a project will be approved, designed, and installed without the knowledge of the people required to make it perform. Some projects are completed and the equipment is used to make everyone more comfortable or used to locate and correct main-a casual matter. Proper preliminary planning must occur to assure an achievable and operational end result. This planning phase should include considerations of available resources, both labor and monetary, as well as the technical proficiency of the maintenance organization that will be charged with the system operation and management.

A formal PM program is a long term investment, the benefits of which cannot be easily measured over the short term. It is a dynamic process which requires frequent progress measurements and periodic review and audit. Properly designed and implemented, a formal PM maintenance program will result in long term savings in operating downtime, energy consumption, and longer equipment lifetimes. Furthermore, a functioning system will become a framework of maintenance planning which transcends the void created by key personnel changes and vacancies.

Moreover, when implementation and operation is linked to a management by objective (MBO) program, the PM system can be expected to remain viable and provide a continuing proactive maintenance environment for many years ahead.

SECTION 18

ENERGY IN WESTERN EUROPE AND THE NETHERLANDS

Sponsored by the Netherlands Chapter of AEE

Chapter 56

ENERGY CONSERVATION IN WESTERN EUROPE

W. van Gool

ABSTRACT.

In the past decade energy conservation was one of the objectives of energy policy in many European countries. It is important to observe that energy conservation is often not a well defined and unique concept. There are differences between "energy conservation" and "the increase of energy productivity". These differences are not only time dependent, but they are also influenced by the energy resource and demand situation in the different nations. Furthermore, there is not a unique way to derive the progress in either energy conservation or in the energy productivity from the available statistical data.

Since the problems mentioned are not special for Western Europe alone, a more general analysis of the concept of energy conservation is given before some results are reported.

TRADE-OF BETWEEN ENERGY, ECONOMY AND ENVIRONMENT.

After World War II many countries in Western Europe had to rebuild their industrial structure from scrap. Coal was an important energy resource in that situation since the indigenous oil production was low. Somewhere around 1960 the recovery process was over and the influence of Western Europe in the international trade had become relevant.

Two developments in the field of energy supply are important for the next decades.

First, the internationally operating oil companies started to exploit the immense and inexpensive oil resources in the Middle East. This oil had to be transported to Japan, the United States and to Western Europe. In the transport to Europe the Suez Canal was an important and vulnerable link. Political difficulties around the Suez Canal and the increasing amounts of oil to be transported induced the construction of larger and larger oil tankers. When the Canal was closed (1967) there was enough tanker capacity to transport oil inexpensively along alternative routes. This gave one leg to support the increasing energy demand of the fast growing industrial production in the period of 1960 to 1973.

The second development of major importance for the industrial developments in the decades to come was the discovery of the large natural gas fields in the Northern part of the Netherlands in 1960. Since the high expectations about the possible growth of inexpensive nuclear energy at that time, it was decided to export the natural gas to other countries in Western Europe. In addition the gas distribution system in the Netherlands was expanded quickly. Both the electric utilities and the industry started to use the natural gas extensively.

The period from 1960 to 1973 can be characterized by its strong economic growth. The energy supply was secure and the price of energy decreased. The urge to participate in this growing economy and wealth was such that no time was left for other issues. It was recognized by analysts that such a growth could not be continued forever. The first blow came at the end of the period with respect to the environmental burden due to the waste of the industrial production and due to the use of the industrial products. Obviously, the environmental problems got special attention in countries with a high population density. The second blow came in 1973 when OPEC demonstrated its power to interrupt the energy supply and to demand prices of oil far above the production cost. Western Europe, depending heavily upon imported oil, saw its industrial growth endangered, just as many other countries without sufficient indigenous oil production.

It is obvious that in the period after 1973 the energy issues often dominated in policy and other activities. However, changing energy supply and demand is a time consuming activity and it was only after the second large increase of oil prices in 1979 and 1980 that the impact became large enough to change the picture considerably. Presently, the dominating position of OPEC has been undermined. At the same time, however, the environmental impact of the large energy use becomes dominating again: acid rain, dying woods and lakes are facts which can not be neglected.

This short summary of economic growth, energy supply and environmental pollution in the last decades show that the trade-off between these factors - among others- constitutes a major issue in the analysis of the industrial production in the next decades.

ENERGY POLICIES IN WESTERN EUROPE.

In connection with the analysis of energy policies in Western Europe it is important to specify where we are talking about: "Western Europe" seems an attractive concept when looking from the USA to Europe, but it is not a legal entity in which coherent energy policies can be developed.

First of all, the nations in Western Europe have national governments, national laws and national structures. Important with respect to energy is that the national resources are quite different.

Several nations have coal production (UK, West Germany, Belgium, France, Spain). Oil and gas are produced on the North Sea. This area is divided over the UK, Norway, Denmark, West Germany, and the Netherlands. The resources are not proportional to the surface "allocated" to each nation. According to the present knowledge the UK and Norway are the big winners. In the official statistics the reserves on the North Sea are added to other reserves which the involved nation might have on their territorium. There is still left a considerable amount of natural gas in the Northern part of the Netherlands.

Some statistical data of the reserve position of

Western Europe are reported in Tables 1 and 2. The data were taken or calculated from the BP Statistical Review of World Energy (1). Western Europe is used in the same way as defined in these Reviews. See Appendix 1 for a complete list of countries.

It is obvious from Table 1 that the oil reserves in Western Europe are dangerously low when compared with the consumption: 6 years of supply. The situation with respect to natural gas is much better, mainly due to the large reserves of Norway.

TABLE 1. WESTERN EUROPE OIL RESERVES 1984

(in million tonnes of oil)

	Reserves (R)	Production (P)	R/P (year)	Consumption (C)	R/C (year)
Norway	1100	35	32	8.3	133
U.K.	1800	126	14	89	20
Others	400	26	16	494	<1
Total	3300	186	18	591	6

TABLE 2. WESTERN EUROPE GAS RESERVES 1984

(in million tonnes of oil equivalent)

	Reserves (R)	Production (P)	R/P (year)	Consumption (C)	R/C (year)
Netherl.	1750	62	28	31	56
Norway	2270	26	87	-	-
U.K.	650	31	21	45	14
W.Germany	153	13	12	41	4
Others	446	20	22	73	6
Total	5270	152	35	190	28

In Table 3 the ratio between reserves and consumption (R/C) is reported for Western Europe, the USA and Japan. It shows that oil remains the weak point in the energy supply of the important IEA countries.

TABLE 3. RATIO OF RESERVES TO CONSUMPTION (YEAR)

	COAL	NATURAL GAS	OIL
WESTERN EUROPE	183	28	6
USA	293	11	6
JAPAN	64	.5	<.1

In addition to the national policies with respect to the energy issue several international cooperations exist which might have some influence. Two organizations are mentioned here. First the European Communities (EC), which includes many of the Western European Countries. (See Appendix 1) The EC has basically the power to override certain aspects of the national policies, but practically this power is constrained by the decision procedures in the EC. The EC has developed several community R and D programs in the field of energy.

Secondly, all West European Countries - except France- participate in the International Energy Agency. (For a list of all nations involved in the IEA see Appendix 1).The IEA has no legal power to override national policies, but their annual evaluations of national policies with respect to the objectives of the IEA are important to judge the credibility of the nations upon the intensity of their participation. The annual evaluation reports contain very valuable information which has been used for this paper. (2)

It is very important to recognize that energy policy after 1973 was influenced by three not completely exclusive but also not completely coherent objectives:

A. Decrease oil import from OPEC countries.

This approach dominated the IEA policy. Developing oil productions in non-OPEC countries (for example on the North Sea and in Alaska, Mexico) was supported, just as the increased use of coal (direct or by gasification), nuclear energy, solar energy, etc.. Improving the energy productivity was also accepted, but the decrease of demand by using less services, materials and commodities did not get an important push.

B. Decrease the use of all fossil fuels.

This view originated from long term resource and environmental considerations (carbon dioxide, nitrogen oxide, acid rain). Here nuclear energy, solar energy and other flow types energy, and increasing energy productivity were dominating. The reduction of the demand as such was not an objective as long as resource depletion and environmental damage would not enforce such a reduction, perhaps locally and temporarily.

C. The "small is beautiful" approach.(3)

Here basically all large plants and organizations are considered to be damaging. Local energy supply by solar and wind energy and the use of biomass are considered as acceptable options. The necessary decrease of the demand can only be obtained by important changes in the social structure in the developed nations.

National policies were never based exclusively upon one of these objectives. Objective A dominated in the practical fulfillment of the energy needs (nuclear energy, large scale oil exploiration and exploitation outside OPEC). The increase of the energy productivity was often stimulated by subsidies, tax reductions, etc.. In the mood of the past decade there were many actions in line with view C: car pooling, reducing the temperature in buildings and homes, using public transport in stead of cars. National policies and also the EC policy gave a lot of lip service to approach C, supported by R & D programs, but the real implementation is still very limited.

When the pressure was more or less of the energy kettle (1982- 1983), the idea of market conform operation became another objective of some national energy policies. One might ask whether or not this is still an energy policy at all.

Quite generally the policies were summarized with the descriptions "diversification" and "conservation", but it is obvious that the judgment of the success of the policies depends to a certain extend upon which objective A, B, or C dominates. As an illustration some data about the diversification are reported in Table 4.(conservation is discussed in the next section).

The Table shows that the move away from oil occurs in the sequence Japan --> Western Europe --> USA and that the compensation is mainly by nuclear power in Japan and Western Europe, less so in the USA. The USA has increased the share of coal. The limited changes in the USA supply is understandable with respect to its strong position with respect to coal, but for oil the reluctance to move to other resources can not be based upon the indigenous oil resources.

TABLE 4. DIVERSIFICATION PRIMARY FUELS IN %. 1975 - 1984

	WESTERN EUROPE		USA		JAPAN	
YEAR	75	84	75	84	75	84
OIL	55	47	44	40	72	59
COAL	22	20	19	24	18	18
NATURAL GAS	13	15	29	25	3	9
HYDROPOWER	8.1	8.6	4.6	5.3	5.9	5.5
NUCLEAR	2.1	8.4	2.6	5.0	1.6	8.5
	100	100	100	100	100	100
TOTAL FOSSIL %	90	83	93	90	93	86

Looking from the carbon dioxyde problem it seems that this has not any influence on the present policies: when fossil fuels are available or can be taken from the world market, they are preferred. It must be remarked, however, that the active use of solar energy is not (and can not be) reported in this type of statistics, since only commercially available fuels are reported. The sun is (still) free available.

ENERGY CONSERVATION.

Taking into account the different objectives of the energy policies mentioned in the former section, it is obvious that there are problems in defining energy conservation. In option A one could define the decrease of the imported oil (in the US, the EC, the IAE, etc.) as "conservation", independent of the question whether or not more nuclear energy, solar energy, etc. is used. Conservation in option B can be measured by considering the decrease of the total amount of fossil fuel used. Compare the former section: the concepts "diversification" and "conservation" tend to coincide in this approach. Option C has to be judged by the decrease of the use of all types of energy except the flow types. Note that the concept of "alternative energy" also depends upon the choice of the objective: nuclear energy is an alternative for options A and B, but not for C.

It is not amazing that one has tried to find measures to evaluate energy conservation independent of the objectives.

One method is to take the total primary energy requirement (TPER) per unit Gross Domestic Product (GDP). The difficulties of this method have been discussed in the literature: both the energy use and the GDP are highly aggregated quantities (4). Therefore, values quoted in Table 5 should be viewed more as a starting point for comparison than as a judgment of the energy intensity of the different nations.

It would require a lengthy paper to interpret these data. Here just a few special aspect are mentioned. Luxembourg, with about 80 000 inhabitants, is special due to its high level of electrification. Note the decrease of the energy intensity of the GDP in the period from 1973 to 1983 with the exception of Spain and Portugal. The energy intensity of the USA GDP is still high compared to the other industrialized nations. This fact induced many studies, since it was obvious that this high energy intensity did not necessarily lead to a higher quality of life and thus could indicate a waste of energy in the USA.

Another way is to evaluate the energy use for certain economic sectors or for special materials (steel, aluminum, PVC, etc.) or products (cars, milk, homes,

TABLE 5. TOTAL PRIMARY ENERGY REQUIREMENT PER UNIT GROSS NATIONAL PRODUCT. UNIT: TOE / 1000 $ 1975 DOLLARS AND EXCHANGE RATES.

	1973	1983
Belgium	.77	.50
Denmark	.51	.37
West Germany	.64	.51
Ireland	.96	.80
Italy	.69	.58
Japan	.70	.49
Luxembourg	1.94	1.18
Netherlands	.74	.59
Norway	.76	.69
Portugal	.53	.63
Spain	.57	.60
United Kingdom	.93	.74
United States	1.14	.91

etc.). When the resources, the products , and the production process remain basically unchanged, one can use the amount of energy per unit product to evaluate the progress of the energy conservation. However, this definition limits the conservation measures more or less to the good home-keeping actions. Larger effects can be obtained when in new facilities the process is optimized with respect to the higher energy prices or when completely new processes are installed. But the optimization with respect to the production factors belongs to the normal activities of industrial design and the corresponding increase of the energy productivity can hardly be qualified as a result of energy conservation. Taking into account that increased energy productivity often takes place by a shift from energy use to capital investment, it is clear that an input-output analysis is required , to evaluate the total effect in the economy. The I/O analysis is generally much later available than other statistical data. Its use is also limited due to the aggregation level of the published data.

An important factor in judging the difference between energy conservation and the increase of energy productivity is the time needed to establish equilibrium between the increased energy prices and the structure of capital investment. The lifetime of cars and many home appliances is rather short and adaptations can be reached in 5 to 10 years. Homes and buildings might require 50 to 100 years before they are replaced by modern structures. Accepting that an active energy policy will be pursued only between the moment on which a price shock disturbs the market until the time that the normal design process takes care of the changed costs of the production factors, it will be obvious that for many industrial productions conservation is diminishing in importance as a point of interest. However, conservation activities will have to be continued for a long time in connection with buildings and homes and with other changes with a long term perspective.

Generally, the official statistics of the different nations is not detailed enough to analyze conservation and increased energy productivity seperately: more detailed analysis of production sectors is required for a full analysis. Such an analysis has also to take into account that in a period of one or two decades the final products (such as cars) might be changed considerably. Although there is no possibility to report on the detailed results in different sectors in different nations in detail in this short survey, it is possible to summarize some general trends.

Decisions about activities to improve energy conservation or to increase energy productivity are taken every moment on many different levels and in thousands of different situations. The time horizon for these decisions is often a few years and the expectation of the -financial - rate of return is often dominant. In these decisions questions about the depletion of world resources, the environmental impact, the political indepence of nations, etc. are of minor importance. Consequently, the major results in energy conservation were obtained due to the increased energy prices. Government actions, such as subsidies or tax revenues, were more important in confirming intended decisions than to provoke completely different options.

THE FUTURE.

Now, in May 1986, it seems more than ever difficult to say anything about the future. Oil prices came down to a level that did not occur in any of the many models for predicting oil prices (5). The recent nuclear accident in Chernobyl opens a lot of questions about the Russian position with respect to the export of its oil and about the application of nuclear energy in general.

First the oil problem: obviously, when the large increase of oil prices in 1973 and 1980 were considered as damaging to the economic development of the oil importing countries, it can not be such that damage would be the only result of the decreasing oil prices. It is true that any unexpected large change in the oil prices - up or down- creates uncertainties about investments and it might decrease the profitability of investments in new energy resources or conservation.

In Europe and Japan the uncertainty is even larger since the exchange rate of the dollar into foreign currencies influences the local price. The exchange rate can be influenced by factors unrelated to the energy issue and the total effect can be dramatic when the oil price and the exchange rate change correspondingly. See Table 6.

TABLE 6. OIL PRICE AND EXCHANGE RATE.

	FUEL OIL $/METRIC TON	EXCHANGE RATE DFL/$	FUEL OIL DFL/METRIC TON
1985			
JANUARY	193	3.57	689
APRIL	173	3.49	603
JULY	143	3.28	469
OCTOBER	150	2.98	448
1986			
JANUARY	132	2.75	363
MARCH	91	2.57	233

HEATING OIL: 1% S - FOB CARGOES.

The decrease of the oil price is due to the fact that the world production capacity is presently larger than the demand. The oil producing countries -OPEC and non-OPEC- did not come to a proportional decrease of their productions. Saudi Arabia, with the largest oil reserves, could not take any longer the burden of a decreasing share of the oil market in order to maintain a price of 25$ per barrel or higher.

Note that the stabilizing oil demand - or at least a decreasing growth- was the objective of many policies in the past decade. Furthermore, the present price is the consequence of the fight for the market: it is not an indication of the resource situation in the future. This is to be illustrated with the continued oil production of England in the North Sea with a low rate of return, whereas it is known that the English production will start to decline within ten years. When England and some other oil producing countries decide to cut back the production, the oil prices could go to higher levels again. Once the production and the demand are in equilibrium, the speculative and sensitive oil market can swing up or down, depending upon accidents, wars, etc..

Concluding it can be remarked that although the low oil price might stimulate the economic activity in many countries, it remains threatening to the oil position of Europe, the USA, Japan, and many other countries. Basically, their posistion remains vulnerable and the low oil prices will not stimulate the development of alternative -with respect to oil-resources and conservation.

With respect to the Chernobyl nuclear accident in Russia it can be remarked that the loss of the primary cooling system is a well known danger. The question is more whether the initial failure is specific for the graphite type reactor used in Chernobyl or that this could occur also in the reactors used in Western Europe, the USA or Japan. When the failure is specific for the graphite reactor there is not much reason to change the existing programs for reactors which have a (second) containment building. When the Russian reactor should have had such an additional containment we might have not known about the accident for a long time. However, a change in the construction of the Russian graphite reactors might be expected. In addition to this technical approach to the problem there is the political reaction, which might be different in each nation.

The influence of the accident on the further development of nuclear energy is very relevant to the subjects discussed in this paper. It was demonstrated earlier that nuclear energy is presently the only option to decrease the contribution of fossil fuels to the energy supply system. The necessity for this decrease has been discussed already before.

REFERENCES.

1. The BP Statistical Review of World Energy is annually published by The British Petroleum Company. It contains very useful data which have been used extensively to prepare this paper.
2. The International Energy Agency publishes every year a Review of the Energy Policies and Programmes of IEA Countries. For every member the Key Energy Indicators and Data are published.
3. A.B.Lovins, Soft Energy Technologies, Ann. Rev. of Energy, 3, 1978, 477.
4. E. Thoresen and D. Philos, The Relation Between Standard of Living, Production and Energy Consumption, in W. van Gool and J. Bruggink (eds.), Energy and Time in Economic and Physical Sciences, North-Holland, 1985.
5. T. Randall Curlee, Forcasting World Oil Prices, Materials and Society, 9, 1985, 413.

APPENDIX 1. COUNTRIES IN WESTERN EUROPE, EC, AND IEA.

The following countries are members of the European Community: Belgium, Denmark, France, Greece, Republic of Ireland, Italy, Luxembourg, Netherlands, Portugal, Spain, United Kingdom, West Germany.

In the BP Statistics Western Europe includes the EC countries plus Austria, Finland, Iceland, Norway, Sweden, Switzerland, Turkey.

The following countries participate in the International Energy Agency: Australia, Austria, Belgium, Canada, Denmark, West Germany, Greece, Ireland, Italy, Japan, Luxembourg, Netherlands, New Zealand, Norway, Portugal, Spain, Sweden, Switzerland, Turkey, United Kingdom, United States.

Chapter 57

ENERGY CONSERVATION IN THE AGRO-INDUSTRIAL SECTOR, NETHERLANDS

E. Nieuwlaar

INTRODUCTION

This paper summarizes and discusses some results of a research project on efficient and sustainable energy use in the Northern Netherlands (1). The research was carried out at the Center for Energy and Environmental Studies (State University of Groningen, The Netherlands). Special attention for the northern part of The Netherlands is justified because of the unfavourable position this region has in terms of energy consumption per unit GNP and the unfavourable economic and labour situation relative to the rest of the country.
Ample possibilities exist for the improvement of energy efficiency many of which are already being carried out. More steps will be taken in the years to come aimed at increasing the energy productivity of production. In the long run new and more complex techniques will be available or will become more economic. Before showing the potentials for energy conservation in some selected end-use sectors a short overview of the nature of energy consumtion in the region will be given.

ENERGY DEMAND

Table 1 shows how the energy demand in the Northern Netherlands is distributed in terms of energy carriers and energy demand sectors. The table shows that electricity use is dominated by the industrial sector (56%). The demand for fuels is dominated by electricity generation (32%) and housing&buildings (45%). Natural gas is the far most important fuel which is not surprising, if one realises that large dutch gas reserves are located in this region. In this paper housing, buildings and electricity generation will not be discussed any further.

	Electricity (TWhe)	Natural gas (PJ)	Oil and other fuels (PJ)	Total (PJ)
housing	1.2	67		67
buildings	0.9	35		35
agriculture	0.3	5	2	7
industry	3.1	34	11	45
electricity generation		67	4	71[1]
total	5.5	208	17	225

1) includes 9 PJ for electricity exported.

TABLE 1. TOTAL ENERGY DEMAND IN THE NORTHERN NETHERLANDS. (1980; transport not included).

Agriculture

Almost 70% of the land area is in use for agricultural purposes. Together with the industrial processing of the products from agriculture this represents one of the main sources of economic activity. Estimates of the energy consumption in agriculture have been collected in table 2. It can be seen that dairy farms are important consumers of electricity and diesel oil. The electricity consumption in the dairy farms has risen strongly in the seventees due to the introduction of milk storage tanks. Milk cooling and the production of warm water for cleaning purposes have thus become important new factors in the energy consumption of dairy farms. Greenhouses are responsible for the bulk of natural gas consumption in agriculture. More than 50% of the greenhouse-activity is located near one city (Emmen). Plans are being carried out to use industrial waste heat in this area. Another project which is still in consideration uses a STAG-unit to be built by the electricity company which delivers heat to an other location near Emmen.

	Natural gas (TJ)	Diesel oil (TJ)	Electricity (GWhe)
dairy farms	348	1671	177
other cattle	848	-	32
greenhouses	3172	21	7
crop farms	90	747	3
total	4458	2439	219

TABLE 2. ENERGY DEMAND IN AGRICULTURE IN THE NORTHERN NETHERLANDS (1980)

Industry

Two groups of main importance can be distinguished in the industrial sector. The first group is related to the presence of salt deposits and natural gas reserves. They produce basic chemicals and metals. Their importance from an energy perspective can be seen from table 3. It is interesting to know that six of them account for more than half of the industrial energy consumption. The availability of cheap energy is crucial for this group. Natural gas planning and pricing policy however are not tools available for regional planners. Inasfar as these industries are subject to governmental planning they are more important from a national perspective than from a regional viewpoint. We will therefore concentrate on the second group which is agriculture related. Note that the paper industry formerly used straw as their primary input for paperboard production. Now most factories use secondary paper to do the same job. Together with the agricultural sector we will denote these industries by the term agro-industrial complex and we will use the rest of this paper for analysing and discussing this complex.

	natural gas (PJ)	fuel oil (PJ)	other fuel (PJ)	electricity (TWhe)
el. generation	24.7	1.5	0.1	
minerals & chemicals	14.4		9.5	2.06
food & paper	13.3	0.9		0.56
other	6.5	0.1		0.46
total	58.9	2.5	9.6	3.08
of which:				
dairy	3.7	0.1		0.10
beetsugar	1.3	0.7		0.007
potatoes	3.3			0.13
paper	0.3			0.14

TABLE 3. INDUSTRIAL ENERGY DEMAND IN THE NORTHERN NETHERLANDS (1980)

THE AGRO-INDUSTRIAL COMPLEX

The three most important sub-sectors in agricultural production and subsequent industrial processing are related to milk, beet-sugar and (factory)potatoes. An energy analysis has been carried out to assess the direct and indirect use of energy associated with the production and processing of these three products. Table 4 shows some results which demonstrate that a significant amount of energy use is 'hidden'. The most important indirect energy demands are associated with the use of power-fodder, fertilisers and pesticides. Most of these contributions to the indirect energy requirements take place outside the Northern Netherlands. An important consequence of the high indirect energy requirements is that energy price movements will have a greater impact on product-prices than what might have been expected from direct energy requirements only. About 25% of production cost at the dairy farm is direct and indirect energy cost. The direct energy costs of milk processing are about 12% of the total production costs in the dairy industry.

energy use	milk	beet-sugar	potato starch
direct	6.9	2.0	4.5
direct + indirect	24.8	3.6	6.4

TABLE 4. DIRECT AND INDIRECT USE OF ENERGY IN THE AGRO-INDUSTRIAL COMPLEX IN THE NORTHERN NETHERLANDS (PJ, 1980)

These figures illustrate the need for efficient use of the raw material milk in the dairy factories which might be equally important as the application of direct energy conservation measures in the dairy factory.

DAIRY FARMS

After the introduction of milk storage tanks, the electricity requirement on the dairy farms is largely determined by the use of cooling and milking equipment. Hot water is used for cleaning and is produced either in electric or in gas-fired boilers. The potential for four possible measures and combinations of these measures have been evaluated for all dairy farms in the Northern Netherlands. The measures evaluated are: precooling, heat pumps, wind-turbines and biogas. To simplify the calculations, the dairy farms have been classified into groups according to size and local average wind speed (table 5).

average farm size (cows)	average windspeed[1] I	II	III	IV	Total
	number of farms:				
59	275	805	504	120	1704
82	247	723	459	119	1548
117	116	318	210	58	702
168	27	73	34	3	137
219	10	27	12	1	50
284	3	9	3	0	15

[1]) Wind speed classes:
I : 5.1-5.5 m/s III : 6.1-6.5 m/s
II : 5.6-6.0 m/s IV : 6.6-7.0 m/s

TABLE 5. CLASSIFICATION OF DAIRY FARMS

Detailed demand patterns on an hourly basis for electricity and fuel demand were developed using information on an equipment level for each farm size. Patterns were generated for the reference case with no energy conservation measures implemented and also for the case of precooling and/or heat pumps installed. These patterns are especially useful for the evaluation of windturbines and the biogas reactors where time dependence places constraints on the accessible level of energy conservation. We will refer to precooling and heat pumps as _demand options_ for energy conservation as they directly influence the requirements for cooling and cleaning. The other options (wind, biogas) will be denoted as _supply options_ as they influence the external fuel and electricity requirements. First the demand options will be discussed seperately.

Demand options

Precooling. Precoolers are small plate heat exchangers which are used in dairy farms to reduce the milk temperature to 18-20°C before the milk enters the storage tank where a temperature of 4°C is maintained. Without precoolers the milk enters the storage tank at a temperature of about 35°C.
Heat pump. In the heat pump option the condenser heat of the milk cooling system is used to preheat the boiler supply water to 50-60°C.
Both options can be combined into a third

option in which the milk is precooled before entering the milk tank and the boiler feed water is heated with condenser heat from the cooling equipment. The energy conservation which can be reached in an installation with both options cannot be calculated by adding the results of the individual options. After precooling the cooling load is reduced and consequently a lower quantity of condenser heat will be available. All cases influence both electricity and fuel demand. To correct for the difference in energy quality electricity will be rated at 10 MJ/kWhe which represents the fuel requirements in public electricity generation including transmission losses. It is for this reason that the over-all amounts of energy conservation to be shown do not have direct sense to the individual farmer. It is however a useful measure for regional and national planning.

The results have been summarized in figure 1 as the reduction in over-all energy demand that can be reached when the (simple) pay out time as a measure of economic preference is chosen. The upper curve can be seen as the supply curve for energy conservation for the three options evaluated. The figure further shows how the reduction in energy demand is distributed between precoolers (PC), heat pumps (HP) and the combined heat pump/precooler option (PC+HP). The three options are competitive. Depending on the pay out time chosen, more or less of each option will be installed with precoolers. With a pay out time of one year only 25 TJ of energy conservation can be realised. When a pay out time of 5 years is chosen precoolers alone can realise 111 TJ reduction in over-all energy demand. When heat pumps are also considered as an option only 67 TJ energy demand reduction will be realised with precoolers. The heat pump option itself is then good for an extra 52 TJ and the option with precoolers and heat pumps combined another extra 74 TJ, giving a total of 192 TJ reduction in over-all energy demand at the dairy farms in the Northern Netherlands. Note that precooling is the preferred option at low pay out times but that they will be implemented only on the largest farms. The potential for precoolers increases with the pay out time but so do the other options which are capable of realising larger reductions in the energy demand and are therefore likely to be preferred. Going from lower to higher pay out times preferences shift from precooler via stand-alone heatpumps to the combined precooler and heatpump option.

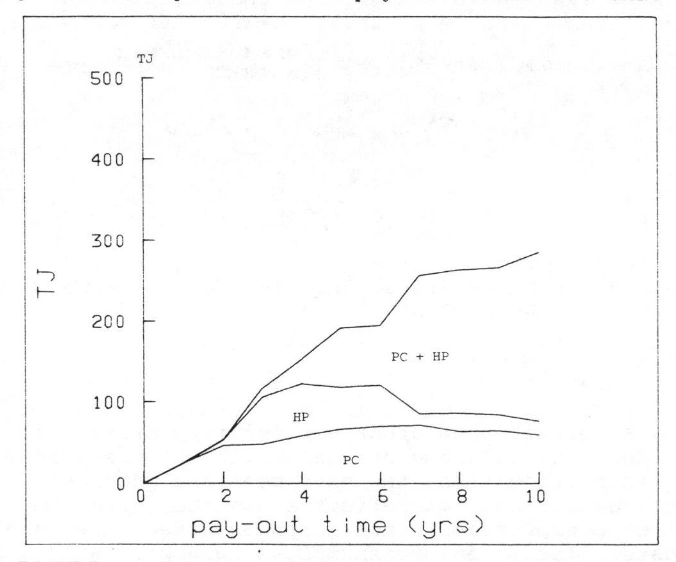

FIGURE 1. SUPPLY CURVE FOR ENERGY CONSERVATION WITH PRECOOLERS AND HEATPUMPS ON THE DAIRY FARMS IN THE NORTHERN NETHERLANDS.

Supply options

Windenergy. The application of newly developed windturbines in dairy farms is still uncertain at the moment. It is not clear yet when and how the cost of new windturbine types will decrease. Furthermore the recent energy price developments and the uncertainties about windturbine performance under local conditions prohibit rapid implementation of more windturbines. Two suitable windturbines (22 and 45 kW) have been selected for a detailed analysis. In the analysis hour by hour simulations have been carried out with both windturbines and for all dairy farm classes in table 5. Basic inputs for the simulations are the demand patterns for electricity and the supply patterns for wind energy. By carrying out the simulation on an hour by hour basis realistic estimates can be made of the amounts of electricity produced, the part that can be used within the dairy farm, the surplus which has to be sold to, and the deficit that has to be bought from the public electricity company. Of course a wind turbine is more profitable when a larger part of the electricity it produces replaces electricity that has to be bought otherwise (2).

Biogas: The fermentation of cow dung in biogas reactors is rather troublesome at the moment. Deceiving operational experiences with tank reactors resulted in installations with greater complexity, higher cost and hesitating farmers. Simulations with biogas reactors have however been carried out in which the biogas is used for electricity generation with a gasmotor CHP-installation. Gas storage is included in the system in order to optimize electricity consumption and production on the dairy farm (3).

Results: The supply curve for energy conservation for both supply options (wind and biogas) are given in figure 2. The curves apply to dairy farms with no demand options (heat pumps or precoolers) installed. For the largest farms biogas and windturbines are competitive, with windturbines taking the lions' share of the over-all reduction in energy demand. Calculations carried out seperately resulted in the conclusion that there is no cost-effective way of combining windturbines and biogas reactors on the same location as we did with precoolers and heat pumps before.

Discussion: These results demonstrate that windturbines and biogas reactors have to become cheaper through standardisation, serial production etc., will they ever play a substantial role in the regional energy system. One important point in the biogas and windturbine systems is that the systems are connected to the grid. When the reorganisation of the public gas and electricity distribution companies in the Netherlands is completed, a situation will probably emerge in which the distribution companies find a more vivid marketplace for electricity purchases: not only the large electricity production companies but also a diversity of decentral small electricity producers. The distribution companies can even stimulate this market through own investments or subsidies at locations where cost-effective small-scale electricity production is possible. Dairy farms are such locations and active participation by the electricity distributors can help the farmers overcome the idea that they are growing electricity instead of producing milk.

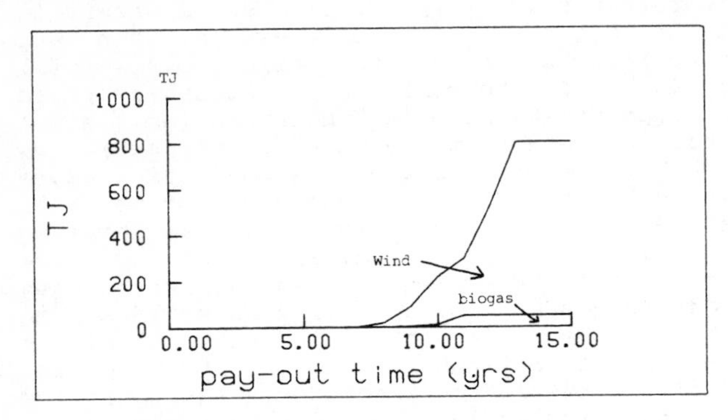

FIGURE 2. SUPPLY CURVES FOR ENERGY CONSERVATION WITH WINDTURBINES AND BIOGAS REACTORS IN THE DAIRY FARMS IN THE NORTHERN NETHERLANDS.

Demand and Supply Options

The windturbines and biogas reactors in the preceding section have been analysed for the cases with no demand options installed. Furthermore, local subsidies have not been accounted for. The results however indicate that the supply options should be analysed after the demand options have been implemented. Table 6 shows for one representative case how some of the characteristics of the 45 kW windturbine change.

demand option	el. demand (MWhe/yr)	utilisation (MWhe/yr)	pay out time[1] (yr)
none	35	16	7.7
precooler	30	14	7.9
heat pump	27	12	8.1
precooler+ heat pump	24	11	8.3

1) after subsidy.

TABLE 6. EFFECTS OF DEMAND OPTIONS ON THE 45 KW WINDTURBINE RESULTS ON A FARM WITH 125 COWS AND WITH AN AVERAGE WINDSPEED OF 6 M/S.

The lower electricity demand is accompanied by a lower utilisation of the electricity produced by the windturbine which results in a modest increase of the pay out time. Due to the fact that the demand options reduce the demand for boiler heat and/or electricity, the biogas option becomes much less attractive: sample calculations indicate pay out times exceeding 15 years in the best case.

Discussion: It must be emhasised again that despite the poor outcomes for the supply options, which also reflect current practice, the future is brighter than it seems to be. Solutions are available for the operational problems with biogas reactors. New biogas reactor types with shorter retention periods (through immobilisation of the micro-organisms), cheaper production methods and serial production should result in lower first cost for both options.

THE DAIRY INDUSTRY

The dairy industry processes milk and produces cheese, milkpowder, wheypowder and consumption milk products. More than 3 million metric tonnes of raw milk are processed annually, a figure that is stabilizing due to European Community policy. The scheme in figure 3 schows that most milk is used for cheese production and by-product wheypowder. The summer peak in the milk deliveries is always processed into milkpowder. The most important processes are evaporation an drying which require 70% of fuel consumption and 40% of electricity demand. Two options for energy conservation in the dairy factories have been studied more closely: more efficient evaporators and combined heat/power generation (CHP) with gasturbines and waste-heat boilers (4, 5).

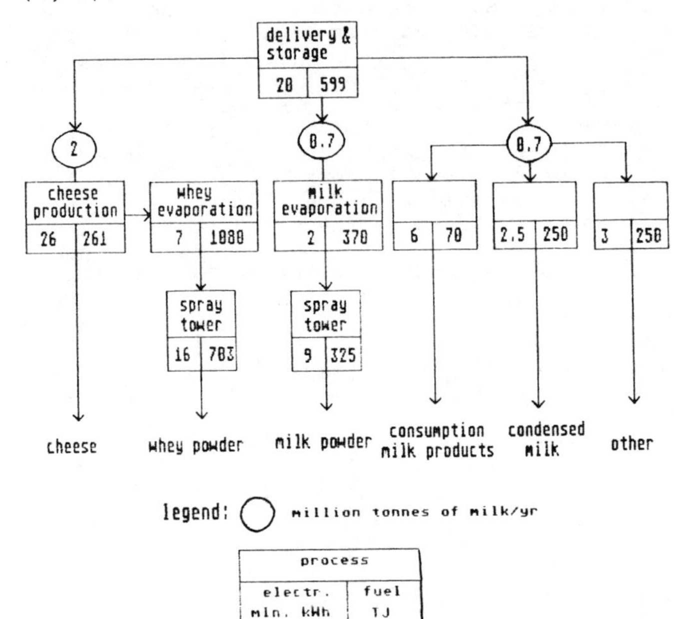

FIGURE 3. MILK PROCESSING IN THE NORTHERN NETHERLANDS.

Evaporators

First of all the potentials for more efficient water removal from whey and milk before the powder production step have been analysed. One decade ago multiple effect evaporators of the thermocompression type with 3 effects were used. The steam consumption then was about 0.25 kg per kg water removed (kg/kg). Current evaporators used in the dairy industry have 4 or 5 effects and a steam consumption of 0.15 kg/kg. The options considered now are evaporators with a larger number of effects (up to 7; steam demand: 0.09 kg/kg), and evaporators with mechanical recompression (steam demand: 0.01 kg/kg, which more than compensates for the extra electricity demand of 7.5 Wh/kg). For the largest factories these options have already been proven to be attractive and new installations are expected to be of these types. It was not clear however if the more efficient evaporators are cost effective in the medium sized factories (125-250 million tonnes of raw milk processed annually). Small gasturbine CHP-schemes could equally well prove to be an attractive option. To analyse these options time patterns for the steam and electricity demand of a selection of 6 medium size factories have been constructed using detailed information of the process equipment used, the production levels and the outside temperature. The resulting time patterns have been validated with measurements at one location. Replacing the data for the existing evaporators and associated equipment with the new data of more efficient evaporators, new time patterns have been constructed. These patterns have been used as the input for a computer simulation program that evaluates the performance of combined heat/power schemes in combination with process energy conservation measures.

Results: In figure 4 the results for evaporator replacement have been summarized as supply curves for energy conservation, this time in a slightly different way: the vertical axis presents the over-all energy demand of the six factories normalised with respect to the situation without improved evaporators.

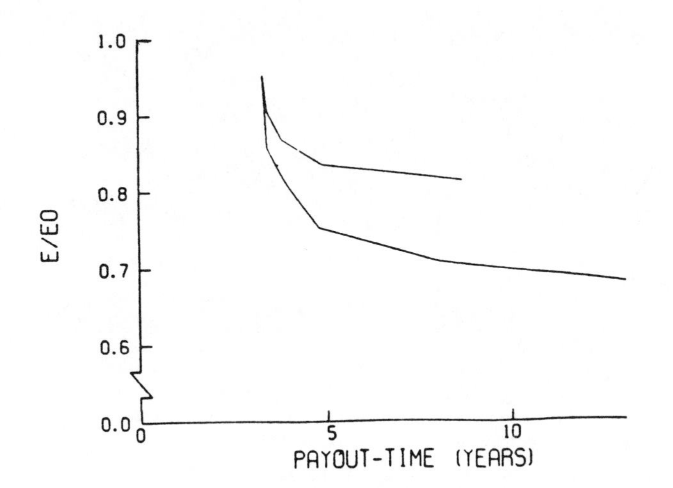

FIGURE 4. OVER-ALL REDUCTION IN ENERGY DEMAND IN SIX DAIRY FACTORIES IN THE NORTHERN NETHERLANDS THROUGH EVAPORATOR REPLACEMENT. (E_0=115 TJ). The upper curve applies to 7-effect thermocompression evaporators. The lower curve is for 3-effect mechanical compression evaporators.

It is found that
- evaporators with 7 effects instead of 4 reduce over-all energy demand wit 19%;
- replacing thermo-compression evaporators with mechanical compression evaporators reduce over-all energy demand by 32%;
- both options have comparable economic attractiveness;

These results are confirmed by recent developments in the dairy industry now that a demonstration project with a mechanical vapour compression unit has started. Another option which is likely to become more important in the future is reverse osmosis for preconcentration. This process no heat input and uses about 10 Whe per kg water removed.

Cogeneration

Two of the largest dairy factories generate about 60 GWh electricity per year with cogeneration plants. At present none of the six sites selected for further study have cogeneration facilities for steam and electric power production. The magnitude and patterns of the energy demand in these factories however indicate that the use of gasturbine CHP-schemes might be advantageous. Using the electricity and steam demand patterns described earlier, simulation calculations have been made with gasturbines and waste heat boilers of varying size. For convenience the results have been combined into two curves in figure 5, one for the current situation and one for the situation in which the existing evaporators have been replaced by mechanical compression evaporators. Both curves show the increasing potential for cogeneration (in terms of installed electric power) with increasing pay-out times. Furthermore this figure shows that cogeneration becomes less cost effective with ongoing energy conservation. At current energy prices and equipment cost the installation of efficient evaporators will not leave much room for cogeneration in this case. Changes in the gasturbine efficiency have only a moderate

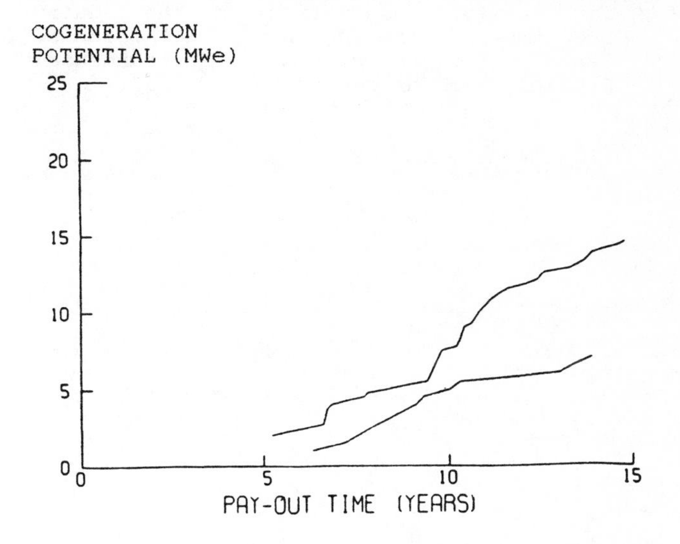

FIGURE 5. GASTURBINE COGENERATION POTENTIAL (IN MWe) FOR SIX DAIRY FACTORIES.
upper curve: no evaporators replaced
lower curve: after evaporator replacement

influence on the economic performance. The higher capital cost requirements of more efficient gasturbines is not compensated in this case by the increased efficiency.
Calculations carried out seperately showed that the economic attractiveness of cogeneration is severely sensitive to the

electricity/gas price ratio which showed a decreasing trend in the last decade. It is this trend that also stimulates the substitution of gas by electricity in industry, illustrated by the mechanical vapour recompression example earlier.

ACKNOWLEDGEMENT

The authour wishes to thank his colleagues at the Center for Energy and Environmental Studies (IVEM) at the Groningen State University for the permission to use research material from the project on energy planning in the Northern Netherlands which was supported in part by the Dutch Ministry of Public Housing, Physical Planning and Environmental protection.

REFERENCES

(1) B. de Vries et.al., Naar een doelmatige en duurzame energievoorziening in het noorden des lands. IVEM-rapport no. 8, 1985. (Netherlandish only).

(2) W. van Heemstra, B. de Vries, Windenergie in de Noord Nederlandse regio. IVEM-rapport no. 12, 1986. (Netherlandish only).

(3) H.P. Baars, J. Bijstra, E. Nieuwlaar, Rekenmodel voor anaerobe vergisting, simulatieberekeningen voor de melkvee-houderij. IVEM-rapport no. 6, 1985. (Netherlandish only)

(4) E. Nieuwlaar, B. de Vries, Energy conservation and cogeneration in the dairy industry. Heat Recovery Systems Vol. 4, No. 5, pp. 341-345, 1984.

(5) E. Nieuwlaar, B. de Vries, Supply curves for energy conservation in the dairy industry in the Northern Netherlands, Center for Energy and Environmental Studies, Working report no. 1, 1985.

SECTION 19
PROCESS ENERGY TECHNOLOGY

Chapter 58

PROCESS ENERGY COST REDUCTION – A METHODOLOGY

W. E. Lowthian, B. P. Richardson

Process modification or replacement is, in many cases, the most powerful tool available to reduce manufacturing energy costs. Yet, it is not widely used nor effectively applied. Many reasons account for the lack of use. This paper discusses the reasons for the reluctance, shows the benefits of change, and describes the methodology for implementing process change in a facility.

The focus of the paper is primarily on modification of existing processes. However, the methodology encourages the identification and initial evaluation of alternative processes.

In a sense, process changes require the same intellectual effort and care as a grass roots design. Modifying the heart of a $10 million facility is effectively a redesign of that facility. It is a time consuming effort in which the time cost of process development and engineering can sometimes equal of exceed the construction cost---a situation which is apt to be misuderstood by those unfamiliar with the work involved. But, as we will point out, the effort is usually repaid well.

ENERGY COST REDUCTION: 3 WAYS

We believe there are three fundamental types of changes which can be made to reduce the energy component of manufacturing costs:

- o reduction of energy purchase cost
- o conservation of released (flowing) energy
- o modification or replacement of the manufacturing process

It is not always easy to classify a particular operation or conversion according to the above types, but it helps to clarify the thought process to do so. To help distinguish among the three we will somewhat arbitrarily add the following descriptors:

- o Purchase cost - the purchased energy (eg. electricity, oil, wood, etc.)
- o Conservation - a utility function conserving (usually) a converted form of energy (eg. steam) or improving the conversion process (eg. fuel to steam)
- o Process - affecting the manufacture of the product itself

Reduction of the purchase cost can cover a wide range of changes including:

- o price reduction via market or competitive pressure or skillful negotiations
- o substitution of fuels
- o acceptance of interruptible service
- o controlling time of use (demand)
- o reducing demand related costs

Conservation typically includes items such as adding thermal insulation, using energy efficient motors and drives, improving lighting "efficiency" via high efficiency bulbs, day lighting, task lighting, improved reflectance, etc. Conservation measures can also take on a "process" tone. For example, upgrading boiler controls or replacing a low pressure steam boiler with a high pressure one capable of running a turbine-generator are, in a sense, altering the combustion process or the steam producing process. However, even though some of the same concepts apply, we prefer to retain the term process for the manufacturing operations.

Modification of the manufacturing process to save energy is more easily illustrated than described. It involves such things as changing the internals of a rotary dryer to transfer heat more efficiently, using a different catalyst to permit conversions at lower temperatures, using higher temperatures to increase conversion rate, controlling distillation via product analysis vs. temperature, etc. The list is virtually endless, determined only by the situation, imagination, technical capability, feasibility, and economics. In many ways the chemical engineering term "unit operations" (eg. distillation, drying, crystallization, filtering, size reduction, ion exchange, etc.) is a satisfactory way of defining the scope of "process" as we use it.

There is another class of process changes which is less daunting and occupies a point mid-way between utility conservation measures and process changes. An example would be the trimming of pump impellers to avoid unnecessary throttling, thereby saving electrical energy. Another example might be the use of turbo-expanders to let down high pressure gas streams to recover mechanical energy as electricity. Another would be the change of a fan wheel type and size to increase fan efficiency. And another would be the modification of a heat transfer surface to increase turbulence so that heat transfer efficiency is increased. Each of these examples have in common the transfer of energy (motive force, heat, or in some cases electrical or other) to the process.

BENEFITS OF PROCESS CHANGE

Most facilities/plants/processes are not optimum because:

- o new plant design is often under intense time constraints which prohibit optimization and encourage "conservative" design
- o new plant design often has inadequate data for close sizing
- o new plant design almost always misses some opportunities, or inadvertently creates them
- o predictive design (at its best) cannot cover all variables in all combinations
- o existing plant have grown in response (largely) to the need for increased production or better material conversions, often slighting energy
- o existing plant expansions tend to be
  - simple replications
  - add-ons which gradually complexify a system (particularly with regard to utility use, which is increasingly non-integrated)
  - inadequately designed, particularly if small projects, because of inadequate (and often relatively inexperienced) staff
  - inadequately designed because of intense time constraints
  - "old" technology
- o existing plants have "old" technology (unit operations, control methods, equipment "capability")
- o existing plants have evolved rules of thumb (conscious and unconscious) which may or may not make best use of equipment.

Methodical pursuit of process improvement and change can correct many of these short comings, reducing energy use.

In the most extreme form of process change, a new process is brought in to replace the old. If based on a different technology (eg. liquid separation by membrane operation vs. distillation) the energy savings may be drastic. However, this is not the typical outcome in the average facility. Instead, process modification achieves the energy cost reduction. Examples can only hint at the diversity of possibilities and benefits:

- o Redesigning the lifter configuration of a rotary dryer decreased energy use 10%, produced a drier product, and permitted through-put to be doubled. In plants with parallel trains, half the rotary units could be shut down.

- o A recent study showed that modification of a spray dryer and integration of associated process systems could reduce the plant energy use by 60%, resulting in savings of about $1.6 million per year on an investment of $4.0 million.

- o A process investigation discovered that combustion controls were permitting overfeeding of natural gas to a kiln resulting in an explosive atmosphere; control changes eliminated possible catastrophe while saving substantial fuel.

- o Stabilized control via product analysis and computer reduced distillation energy consumption about 25%, saving over $400,000 per year on a capital investment of $300,000.

A well-developed process change program will typically produce many benefits beyond simple reduction in energy cost. It's obvious why this is so: the process redesign requires an intimate knowledge of the process, allowing many other benefits to be built into the change. The intimate knowledge derives from careful intellectual modeling of the process using plant data, specifically designed plant tests, and the "oral history" provided by operators and others with a close working knowledge of the process and the systems which achieve the process. Additional benefits typically include:

- o higher through-put
- o better conversion and yields
- o reduced environmental impact
- o reduced worker exposure and discomfort

PROCESS CHANGE CAN BE DAUNTING

Despite the advantages, substantially modifying an industrial process is a daunting prospect for management. And, for good reasons as well as not so good. The list of real and perceived obstacles includes:

- o the "sanctity" of the process
- o the lack of technical competence to go inside the process
- o the risk of a possible failure and the substantial adverse consequences
- o the complexity of the methodology to make an effective, low-cost, low-risk change
- o the lack of a tangible (visible) change

Changing a process can be truly scary ground because it often is delivered from a company's research group shrouded in mystery (sometimes, actually, uncertainty) and absolutes (often reflecting limited runs in lab equipment). Or, the process has evolved over time with apparent understanding which, when the process is truly understood, has little to do with the actual process.

Changing a process is complex, time consuming, and often frustrating to management who see very little physical change, yet see thousands of hours being expended on testing and modeling and one-of-a-kind designs.

And, again, it's scary because a process failure involving loss of production, unsatisfactory product, or a safety failure can have a disastrous effect on cash flow and personnel well-being.

These, then, are the sorts of potential drawback fears which quickly stop "what if" process thinking early on. Yet, methodical and careful pursuit of process change can insure appropriate effort and success in reducing energy cost.

STRATEGIC ENERGY PLANNING

While some benefit can be derived by simply doing most energy projects, it is very easy to misplace effort and resources. For example, a recent study revealed that a good project which would provide heat to a facility was not only less attractive than a number of process projects, but that the heat required by the facility would be cut in half by the process changes. If the larger view study had not been performed several million dollars would have been committed to a larger than needed project which may not be really attractive for several years, depending on fuel prices.

Prudence demands that we think and plan before we do. Process changes are especially demanding on this point because a failure can mean much more than simply a waste of resources. While some projects may be obvious, our experience indicates that actually very little is obvious at the beginning. While most "obvious" projects retain their economics, others are discovered which are more attractive. A conscientious process investigation could end as easily with a recommendation to shut down the facility as to modify.

Because very little is truly obvious, we believe the first step in a major effort to look at process (or any other energy cost reduction approach) is to produce a Strategic Energy Plan. Ideally, a SEP "chapter" covers each of the corporate levels:

- o Company
- o Divisions
- o Plants
- o Facilities

The plan should be developed at least on the plant level. It is within this context that the process attack can be efficiently performed and managed.

The Strategic Energy Plan is the first round of the iterative process which ends with a detailed, step-by-step plan for implementing changes in the three cost reduction areas: reduced energy purchase cost, conservation, and process change.

The objectives of the Strategic Energy Plan are:

- o Develop corporate (or plant) energy goals
- o Describe the rationale and purpose of these goals
- o Identify potential areas of vulnerability
- o Identify the means to reduce vulnerability
- o Broadly inventory and characterize processes, systems, and building areas which use or produce energy
- o Determine broadly how processes, systems, and building areas might be integrated to achieve better energy usage and lower cost
- o Identify how (potentially) specific processes, systems, and building areas can be improved, altered, or replaced to improve energy usage and integration
- o Develop an overall logic matrix which can "hold" specific ideas or improvement suggestions such that the idea can be evaluated in relationship to others and the overall view
- o Identify the most effective energy accounting methods for the various business activities (e.g., production, transportation, etc.). Use these accounting bases to establish energy budgets, evaluate alternatives and increase progress
- o Create the management tools and resources for implementing, managing, and revising the Energy Management Program and the associated Strategic Energy Plan

The essential elements of strategic energy planning have the following general sequence:

- o Statement of Overall Corporate Goals Including Energy Goals
- o Situation Analysis
  - External factors (eg. fuel cost projections)
  - Internal Condition, Strengths, Weaknesses
- o Quantification and Definition of Energy Costs and Impacts
- o Identification of Energy Problems and Opportunities
- o Development of Objectives and Strategies
- o Development of Action Programs
- o Definition of Expected Results, Sensitivities, Risks, and Assumptions

The reality is that the planning process is iterative: later steps redefine earlier ones. Consequently, the program for developing the strategic plan should incorporate iterative rounds efficiently and the program should be designed to permit efficient periodic updating of the plan.

A program for developing the Strategic Energy Plan improves the planning process as well as the final plan. The program steps described below have several goals:

- o To identify all the possible important factors as early as possible in order to avoid a radical revision late in the planning process
- o To establish (describe and/or quantify) the relative worth of various factors, problems, and opportunities as soon as possible to permit evaluation
- o To sort the factors, problems, and opportunities as early as possible to reduce the amount of time required for evaluation.

The goal of strategic planning is not to predict the future; it is to assure that the company is in the best possible position to cope with a number of possible futures. Therefore, thoroughness in strategic planning is not a matter of getting it exactly right the first time. Instead, it is critical to identify all important factors, develop reasonable ways for assessing these factors, and periodically review how the plan matches the future as it unfolds.

It is, therefore, of paramount importance that the process of strategic planning be well managed according to rigorously developed guidelines, much in the same way that project construction cost control has been developed over the last two or three decades. Methods, checklists, evaluation techniques, etc. need to be incorporated into the program for developing the strategic plan so that errors and omissions are reduced to a minimum.

Once a well developed program exists, strategic planning and updating can be carried out efficiently with regularity. That process will effectively harness corporate judgment to serve the company's needs.

PROCESS ENERGY REDUCTION PROGRAM

The Strategic Energy Plan should provide a context for commencement of Process Energy Reduction Program. At the same time the program is in many ways a detailed extension of the Strategic Energy Plan, repeating in greater detail many of the SEP steps and methodology. The goals of the Process Energy Reduction Program include:

- o identification of problems
- o identification of objectives
- o identification of all possible attractive candidates
- o efficient, early elimination of unattractive candidates
- o effective sequencing of projects
- o development of sound projects

Figure 1, Energy Reduction Program summarizes the major program elements that the figure provides the framework for an overall energy study, but can be restricted to process. Normally, we believe the overall approach is best so that process candidates are developed within the larger context.

Step 1. Definition

A concerted effort is necessary to characterize the present situation and likely future situation regarding the operation of the facility and energy usage of the various process steps and support (eg. utility) functions. Figure 2, Step 1: Definition of Plant Operations and Energy Usage and Cost shows the activities required.

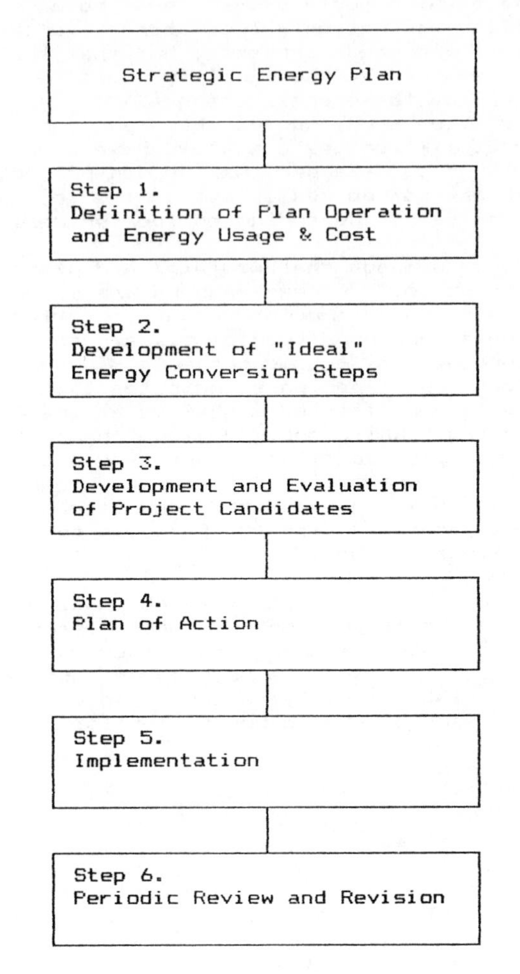

FIGURE 1. ENERGY REDUCTION PROGRAM

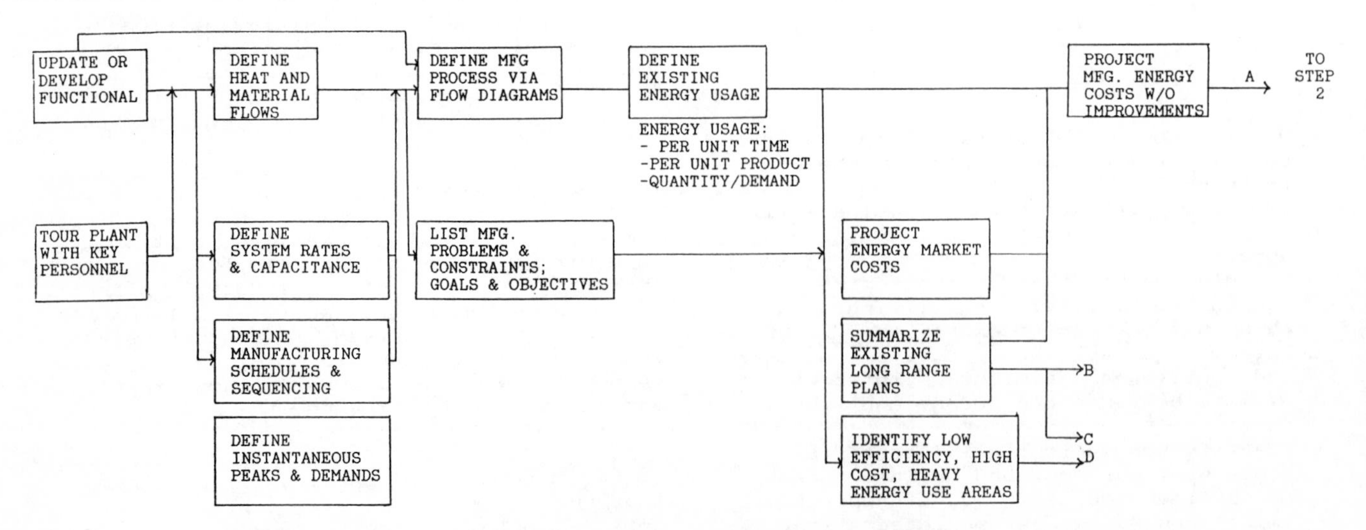

FIGURE 2. STEP 1: DEFINITION OF PLANT OPERATIONS AND ENERGY USAGE AND COST

Definition of Plant Operation: While it is probably obvious that it is useful, if not essential, to quantify energy usage for various steps, we feel it is equally necessary to characterize the manufacturing operation. The goals of these activities are:

- o identify inputs and outputs, exhaust and waste streams, disposal, resources
- o identify constraints on equipment or sub-facility scheduling
- o identify problems such as
  - inadequate capacity
  - low conversion or recovery factors
  - quality
  - low productivity
  - environmental impact
  - competitive pressures
- o describe manufacturing in functional terms
- o define process objectives
- o identify critical energy areas where instantaneous, short term or longer term (hours or days) outages are critical

Thermal Energy Usage: Thermal energy usage is largely a matter of how much is used in various process steps, and how it is converted into useful energy or a loss. For example, in a rotary drying operation the thermal energy "investment" was the following:

		MMBtu/hr
o drying "product"	(>20 mesh)	23.2
o drying "fines"	(<20 mesh)	4.1
o drying "dust"	(in exhaust)	5.2
o hot exhaust gas	(prod's of combstn)	3.0
o heat losses	-radiation and hot hood	0.2
	-hot seal gas leak	0.3
	-barrel	4.3
Subtotal		40.3
Less cooler recovery		(0.9)
Net total		39.4

(Note: We use the term "investment" to indicate the amount of fuel used to accomplish each function. This is different from a normal engineering approach which tags the various streams with the heat content. For example, the exhaust gas stream contains much more heat (in latent form) than indicated above. We have counted this latent heat as part of the function "drying product." The functional emphasis helps to understand the process in terms of its inherent constraints. On the other hand, the engineering heat flow diagram helps emphasize where heat is leaving the process, and where it might be recovered.)

The initial thermal investment calculations should determine the heat use and form of use (temperature, method of delivery - steam, how air, etc.) for each major process step or area. More detailed estimates should be made for high use steps or steps which may be candidates for integration for other processes. We have found it best to show the energy usage or investment figures diagramically on simplified flow diagrams. Later in the energy reduction study, candidate variations of the diagrams are also used to collect and display the thermal use information for quick comparison.

Electrical Energy Usage: Electrical use has the additional complicating factors of time of use and demand. As is well known, cost is dramatically affected by demand. While operating personnel usually have a good feel for the detailed scheduling of specific equipment, we have nonetheless found it useful to quantify electrical usage characteristics such as demand, load factor, scheduling, process capacitance (manufacturing storage) in order to search for candidate areas or process steps where electrical savings are possible.

Energy Costs Projection: Projection of energy costs is, as everyone knows, hazardous. We believe it is, nonetheless, necessary to develop projections in order to increase awareness of the possible changes and to develop, formally or informally a sensitivity analysis that demonstrates the economic sensitivity of the present and future energy mixes. Such an analysis may reveal vulnerability which can be dealt with quickly or may reveal a trigger point for opportunity in the future. Consequently, we are more interested in cost boundaries rather than "most likely" projections so that the energy mix can be chosen for maximum flexibility, safety, and economics rather than narrow economics alone.

Step 2. "Ideal" Energy Conversion Steps

We have found it very useful to develop "ideal" energy versions of the energy conversion and process steps. The usefulness lies less in creating a numerical target, though that's valuable, but more in conceptually developing the method of achieving the ideal and therefore the possible means of modifying the existing process.

"Ideal" turns out to be a very broad concept; there are many ideals depending on the criteria, boundaries, and definitions used. For example, the ideal "drying" energy for a pound of clay (dry) containing a pound of water might be:

- o 1500 Btu (ideal equipment conditions)
- o 970 Btu (theoretical heat to evaporate)
- o 800 Btu (with heat recovery)
- o 500 Btu (using a liquid absorption process)
- o 100 Btu (using an imaginary adsorption process)

Notice that the notion of "drying" shifts to "water removal" in the last two processes. Water removal is a "functional" concept whereas drying is a technique or method. The importance of functional definition is discussed in Step 3.

Step 3. Development of Project Candidates

Figure 3, Step 3: Development and Evaluation of Project Candidates, provides a general diagram of the following discussion.

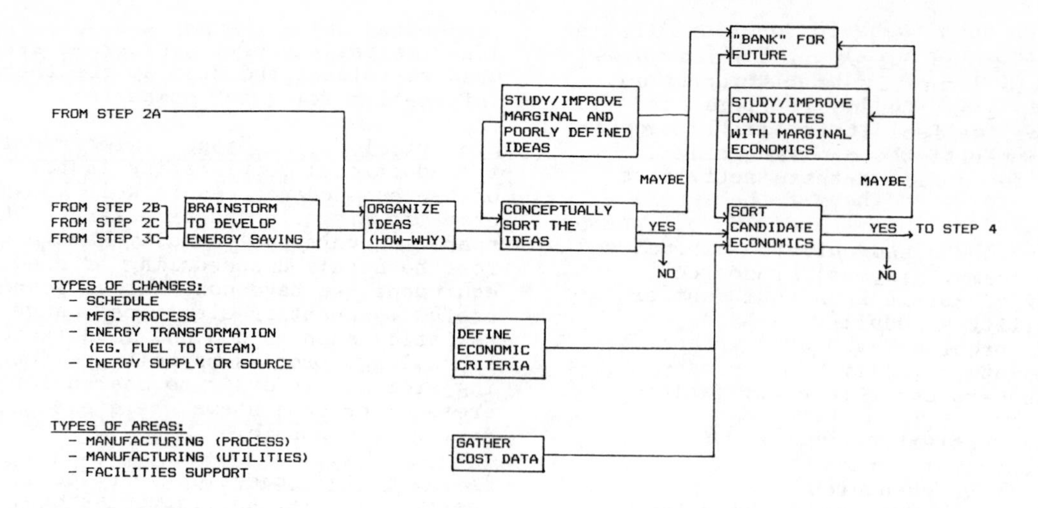

FIGURE 3. STEP 3: DEVELOPMENT AND EVALUATION OF PROJECT CANDIDATES

Up to this point most of the study effort has been directed toward establishing "what is" and "what will be." That is, the existing facility has been described as accurately as possible and the future, however hazy, has been projected within best judgment boundaries. We now turn to the games of "what if" and "what can be." The term game is deliberately used here, because much of the next phase should be a game, a time of fun and free thinking - but with rules.

We turn to techniques used in Value Engineering, a relatively new methodology for evaluating projects with purpose of reducing the construction cost. Reference 1 provides a fine introduction to value engineering as applied in the construction industry; the principles are applicable elsewhere. We have extended the methodology into the areas of energy source selection and energy use reduction (Ref. 2).

Problem and Objective Definition: As long as process change (or energy supply) is the objective, the opportunity exists to solve problems as well as achieve energy reduction. Effort should be placed on carefully identifying the basic problem or combination of problems and needs faced by a specific facility. Once the problem has been identified, it is important to write it down in order to clarify what exactly needs to be solved. This written definition of the problem can be used to obtain comment and then agreement from other cognizant managers so that there is consensus.

In order to achieve the necessary focus and management control of the study, we believe it is necessary to articulate and write down the objectives that a new system or energy source study is to achieve. For example, the objectives or purposes may include the best means of supplying future steam requirements considering the declining availability and increasing costs of fuel or "the most feasible means of increasing steam supply capacity" or "... of meeting air pollution regulations, etc." If it can be isolated, relate the objectives to a specific function. For examples, a foundry study might have as an objective, "the best means of melting scrap."

Structuring the Development Activity: Generally, we have found it necessary to structure the study and intellectual activity which follows so that only a few topics are being considered at a given time, as opposed to an unstructured grab bag of ferment. Normally, the use of process flow sheets is a good way to organize the activity. Without getting into too much detail, the flow sheet should show

- o blocks, representing major process steps or areas
- o flow arrows showing material and energy flows
- o important operating criteria such as system capacitance, scheduling of operation and energy input, energy investment, temperatures, flow rates

Following the flow sheet through encourages participants to focus, provides a convenient way to break meetings into segments, and allows selective participation of participants.

Another way to organize the activity is according to unit operations. For example, if a facility or company has a large number of distillation (or, more broadly, separation) operations, concentrating on the unit operation may be more effective. The same would be true for what we call unit processes (eg. boilers, pumps, air compressors, and the like).

This paper will assume that the flow sheet approach is used.

Functional Definition: While the foregoing is obvious to any thoughtful participant, functional definition may, at first, seem simply an abstract, academic exercise. To the contrary, we believe it to be one of the most important single activities for achieving the desired breakthrough that leads to substantial vs. mediocre savings.

Too often the ultimate function of energy is overlooked. It is important to simplify the whole search down to basic functions that an energy source must provide. For example, in a painting operation using steam as an energy supply medium, the one basic function is to dry paint, not to generate steam. By defining the function as drying paint, a greater scope of options for the best solution is revealed than if the function is limited to generating steam. The options can then include such alternatives as:

- o adding chemical to paint to accelerate drying without heat or changing to different paint which drys without heat
- o changing the product surface material so that it does not require paint
- o using fuel fired radiant heat
- o using waste heat sources

This abbreviated functional analysis and consequent list of options illustrates how energy source selection can be radically affected by the questions asked and objectives or functions identified.

Brainstorming: The next step in the value engineering technique is brainstorming. After you have defined the problem, identified the basic function, and have set your objectives and purpose, brainstorming can be used to identify all methods of performing the basic function. Brainstorming is best performed with a group of persons with varied backgrounds (some with expertise, some with only a broad background) who will generate innovative concepts to potential solutions. Figure 5 adapted from Reference 3 depicts rules for brainstorming. It is important to generate as many ideas of potential solutions to the problem and performance of the function as possible without judgment. Generation of spontaneous free-wheeling and "impractical" ideas is a key symptom of that a brainstorming session is "working." Out of this procedure comes creativity. A wild, impractical idea can be the source of an innovative solution.

Our experience indicates that working on functional definition (previously discussed) assists in idea generation. Working on areas, rather than the whole facility or plant seems to help by avoiding haphazard skipping around, but let ideas flow regardless. "Flip chart" sheets for each area should be taped to walls so that ideas can be written down immediately. Supplying participants with the simplified flow sheets generated earlier in Step 1, Definition, helps participants to focus, to muse, and to jot down ideas as they occur so that a fleeting glimpse is not lost. Removing "social constraints" by moving brainstorming sessions out of the normal office arena and outside of normal time constraints also aids the process. The willingness of more senior personnel to take the "risk" of stating "silly" ideas also loosens up the idea generation.

A facilitator who prompts the idea generation process can be key to making it a success. The facilitator has three jobs: to prompt (energize) participates, to eliminate inhibiting judgements and criticism, and to softly keep the group focused - but not too tightly. Many problems and ideas may be generated which are not energy-related, but are important to the well-being of the plant. The facilitator should ask questions which prompt such as:

- o Are we getting as much (functionally) out of each step as we could?
- o What functionally happens in this area? (Not how do we do it?)
- o How do we do it (the function) now?
- o How could we do it (the function)?
- o What problems do we have?
- o What are the high energy users?
- o Are we getting the conversion (recovery) we want?

Functional Analysis: The How-Why Diagram

Brainstorming yields a slew of ideas and concepts. The result can approach anarchy if there is no means to organize the output. Fortunately, a powerful organizational tool exists which we call the How-Why Diagram.

The How-Why Diagram is a slight modification of Function Analysis System Technique (FAST) Diagram presented in References 2 and 3. We have modified the original so that "time" and activity flows from left to right on the diagram following the convention of schedules, CPM's, flow sheets, and cause-effect.

Figure 4, Function Analysis System Techniques (FAST) Diagram Procedures, was adapted from Reference 3. It depicts the basic methodology of the diagram.

Figure 5, How/Why Logic Diagram of Rules for Brainstorming, adapted from Reference 3 applies the diagram technique for the specific goal of to "generate a wide variety of ideas."

Figure 6, How/Why Diagram for Fuel Selection for an Industrial Facility, illustrates the technique for a specific goal.

The power of the How-Why Diagram as an organizer is probably evident; it permits showing and relating a huge amount of information (some of our diagrams have grown to 3 feet square) and containing two hundred statement blocks. Not so evident is the fact that building the diagram forces one to think about the interrelationships of various approaches. It forces one to state the block objectives in unambiguous ways; if there is ambiguity, the diagram becomes confusing. And it helps build a solution sequence, making later planning less difficult.

However, we believe one of the most powerful aspects to the diagram is that you can start anywhere, with any statement and build the diagram forwards, backwards, up and down by repeatedly asking two questions of the block statement: "how" and "why". "How" obviously moves one toward a specific solution. "Why" moves one to a more functional description, a desirable effect since the goal is to create new solutions and new approaches, creative ones which have a substantial impact.

Several hints are useful for developing a How-Why Diagram:

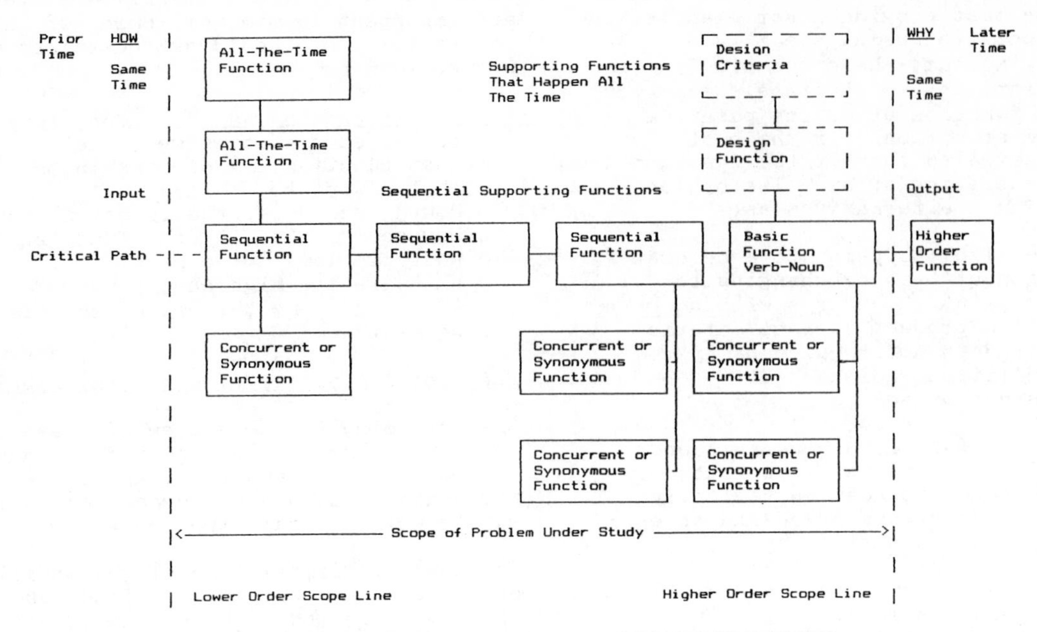

FIGURE 4 FUNCTION ANALYSIS SYSTEM TECHNIQUES (FAST) DIAGRAM PROCEDURES

(adapted with permission of Smith, Hinchman, & Grylls Associates, Inc.)

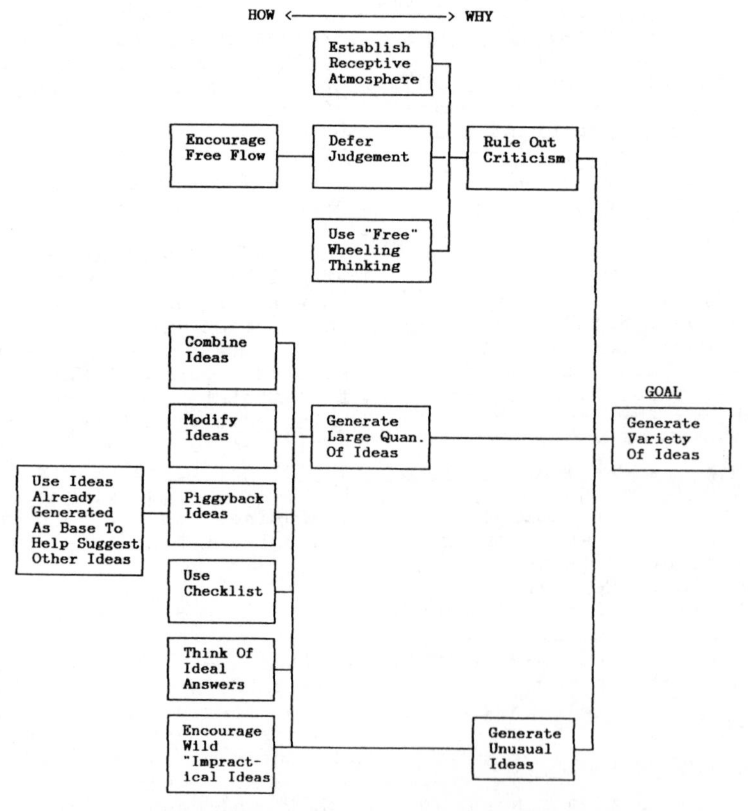

FIGURE 5 HOW/WHY LOGIC DIAGRAM OF RULES FOR BRAINSTORMING

(adapted with permission of Smith, Hinchman & Grylls Associates, Inc.)

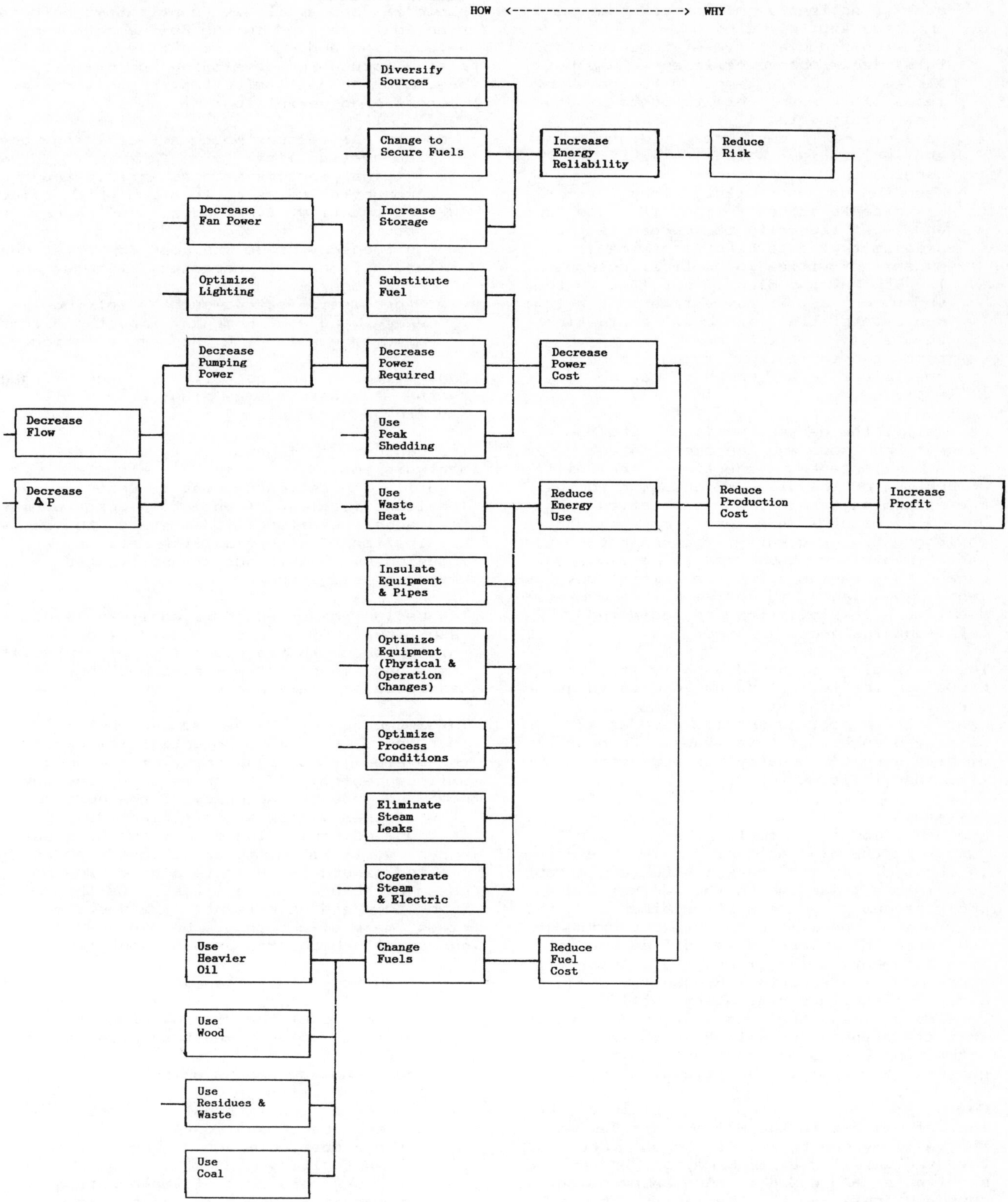

HOW <-------------------------> WHY

Diversify Sources

Change to Secure Fuels

Increase Energy Reliability

Reduce Risk

Decrease Fan Power

Increase Storage

Optimize Lighting

Substitute Fuel

Decrease Pumping Power

Decrease Power Required

Decrease Power Cost

Decrease Flow

Use Peak Shedding

Decrease ΔP

Use Waste Heat

Reduce Energy Use

Reduce Production Cost

Increase Profit

Insulate Equipment & Pipes

Optimize Equipment (Physical & Operation Changes)

Optimize Process Conditions

Eliminate Steam Leaks

Cogenerate Steam & Electric

Use Heavier Oil

Change Fuels

Reduce Fuel Cost

Use Wood

Use Residues & Waste

Use Coal

FIGURE 6 HOW/WHY DIAGRAM FOR FUEL SELECTION IN AN INDUSTRIAL FACILITY

- o Differentiate between a passive action such as "study" and an active action to "implement" or do. Generally, the passive actions permit or eliminate a proposed active action.
- o Use simple declarative statements: "do this" (eg. improve efficiency, use hot air, etc.) It is tempting to add a "by means of" phrase; this tends to hide a "how" statement
- o As a diagram grows, break it into smaller diagrams which are easier to handle
- o Keep the document mildly sloppy; it's unavoidable so don't fight it. Use "cut and tape" liberally to reorganize the diagram trying to keep some time (or phase) activities in vertical columns
- o The How-Why approach is not fast in the short run, but it saves time in the long run by assisting methodical evaluation
- o When a given action shows up more than once, the indication is that there is a possible interaction which can be explored.

Generally, the persons who build the How-Why Diagram are those who are carrying out the study for energy reduction. The initial production of the diagram can occur in the brainstorming session, but completion generally requires a quieter, more thoughtful environment. Frequently, the brainstorming participants are reconvened to review and expand the diagram after the initial development. The diagram is reviewed for completeness, more possibilities are added and relationships are clarified.

The final diagram should usually stay in its crude working form. Its purpose is to be used in succeeding steps as a source document. It is not, generally, used as a display document at this stage. To produce a display document usually requires more time than it is worth.

Refinement: Refinement takes many forms. On one hand, corporate goals (the ultimate "Whys" on the diagram) are carefully examined in terms of the corporate mission and as apt descriptors toward which the various energy projects and programs will be aimed. On the other hand, specific candidate projects are subjected to subjective as well as quantitative judgment in the effort to further define each candidate's worth. Rough order-of-magnitude evaluations will be developed. Many projects will be dropped at this stage and a few will have obvious attraction. However, most will hover in uncertainty requiring additional study.

One purpose of this step is to clean up the choices set out on the How-Why diagram so that a story can be clearly "read" from the diagram. The diagram may be redrawn and highlighted and coded to show an emerging consensus relative to alternative programs or projects. Often "families" of solutions or approaches emerge as more attractive than other families.

Tentative definition of specific programs or projects may be started. Specific limited studies may be initiated at this point to develop information about specific candidate projects.

Quantification: While order-of-magnitude estimates and available quantitative information would be used in the Refinement step to help define and rank alternatives, quantification focuses on developing the numerical basis for project selection. Four sorts of factors need definition:

- o External factors which affect energy cost and availability
- o Internal factors such as anticipated production rates or location which affect the quantity, type and cost of energy required
- o Unit energy usage and cost for existing and alternative processes, systems, and locations
- o Synergistic factors such as solving energy and environmental impact problems simultaneously with the same solution

Many of these factors will have been defined by the strategic energy plan; others will have to be developed.

The beginnings of sensitivity and risk analysis should occur in this step to identify and estimate areas of uncertainty. The identification of uncertain areas permits the targeting of additional study, the early elimination of high-risk alternatives, and focusing on an existing or anticipated high-risk situation.

The beginnings of economic analysis (e.g., cash flows, ROI's, etc.) should also occur in this phase so that a rough idea of financial needs and impact can be developed for candidate programs and projects.

This step can easily become overwhelming; there is so much potential information to develop. Good management of the program will concentrate first on ascertaining the need and required accuracy of the numbers. It will then manage the efficient development of those numbers. The object is not great accuracy, it is sufficient accuracy to aid in ranking candidate projects and developing a sense of future possibilities. As the importance and uncertainty of a decision rises, more effort should be expended to numerically bound the probable outcome.

The products of this step are:

- o An upgrade of the How-Why diagram
- o Refinement of documents started in the Refinement step
- o Additional documents which numerically define or estimate
  - external and internal factors
  - energy usage and costs
  - the probable impact of problems and opportunities
  - the probable cost of implementing alternative programs and projects

Sequencing and Timing: Once quantification is advanced sufficiently to have clarified alternatives, the next step is to develop several alternative program sequences which include specific programs and projects. Such sequencing might be guided by projected available capital. Or, it might be guided by a corporate directive which requires energy projects to be "self- financing" after an initial one-time capital outlay. Or, sequencing may depend on the need to prove out one part of a technology before proceeding to make other system changes.

Some candidate program sequences will involve parallel, non-duplicating efforts. Others will be competitive sequences, all but one to be eliminated from consideration.

Once sequencing is outlined, timing is investigated. Timing examines the interaction of a project sequence with external and internal factors for various schedules. For example, the external factor of a nuclear power plant coming on line and a concurrent rate increase in power rates may be the primary timing factor in a particular project sequence. Various program sequences and timings are looked at to eliminate the less desirable.

As with previous steps, the goal of this step is not to develop a definitive sequence, but to develop sufficient information to rank various sequence/timing alternatives so that some may be eliminated and others identified for a closer look. The goal is efficient, effective sorting, not final selection.

Step 4. Develop a Plant of Action

Two sorts of plans are required: an implementations plan and a management plan. Given the foregoing study and information, the various candidate projects and project sequences can be evaluated to determine those that best suit the company's or plant's needs. Depending on the company and project size, different information will be required to support a project or approach. Project selection and development of the implementation plan are relatively straight forward even if, occasionally, still burdened with uncertainty or contrary opinion.

Equally important is the management plan. The numerous specific tasks, studies, projects, and programs will require overall management to coordinate efforts, maintain schedules, and assure that the implementation plan assumptions reflect reality. Periodic reality checks are necessary. To do this efficiently requires that basic assumptions, criteria, and expected events and results are easily checked. A check list of items should be prepared for each project which allows managers to compare the program with expected results and with changing real-world conditions.

Step 5. Implementation

There is not much to be said about implementation that is not inherent in any project. Perhaps we have only one bit of advice concerning implementation: efficient process development requires that key assumptions be checked, even crudely, as early as possible to ascertain validity. Otherwise, a great deal of time and effort can be wasted.

Step 6. Periodic Review and Revision

While short-term projects require review to assure that actual results match those expected as a program unfolds, there is little revision unless a key process concept does not work out, financing falls through, or some other major factor occurs. Longer-term programs, however, may go through extensive revision over time. It is not unusual for us to develop 5-year plans starting with process changes and culminating with alternate fuel projects. Obviously conditions can change drastically during this time. Technology can change too although our observation is that in the energy area, particularly in thermal, changes are slower than anticipated. Nonetheless, a periodic planned review along the lines indicated in Step 4 is necessary to avoid inappropriate commitments.

SUMMARY

Process improvement and change is one of the major ways a process manufacturing facility can significantly reduce its energy consumption. However, many real and apparent factors hamper initiation and completion of improvement projects and programs. This paper has presented a view and methodology which greatly reduce the risk associated with process improvement while increasing the efficiency of such a program by methodically focusing the effort and increasing the likelihood of making truly significant improvements.

Four elements are necessary for a successful process improvement program:

- o thorough understanding of the situation
- o unfettered creativity in generating ideas
- o methodical selection of the best program
- o a well managed implementation plan

It is, admittedly, a time-consuming process, but the reward can be literally a re-make of the economic viability of a facility, plant, or company.

References

1. Dell'isola, Alphonse J., Value Engineering in the Construction Industry, Van Nostrand Reinhold Co., 1975.

2. Richardson, Brian P., "Industrial Energy Source Selection," 1979 Industrial Fuel Conference at Purdue University.

3. ACEC/AIA Value Engineering Workshop notebook, Smith, Hinchman, Grylls Associates, Inc., 1978.

SECTION 20

ENERGY EDUCATION

Sponsored by the
Energy Education Council of AEE

Chapter 59

ENERGY EDUCATION IN INDUSTRIAL AND SYSTEMS ENGINEERING AT THE UNIVERSITY OF FLORIDA

B. Capehart

ABSTRACT

A knowledge of energy conservation and energy management is important for all engineers in this time of uncertain energy cost and availability. Industrial and systems engineers have a critical need for education in this area due to their job requirements which place them in such roles as production cost analysts, production line supervisors and plant managers. In addition, more and more industrial engineers are being employed in service areas such as schools, hospitals, and local, state and federal government operations. Energy cost reduction and energy efficiency improvements are important in all of these areas, as well as many others. This paper describes the development of a course in industrial energy management which helps prepare industrial and systems engineering students to contribute solutions to these energy problems. Substantial effort was required to develop the teaching materials, case studies and projects to support the course. The author hopes that the information presented in this paper will aid other faculty and schools in developing their own courses in this area.

INTRODUCTION

Energy conservation and energy management are both topics of great importance in today's uncertain energy cost and availability climate. Dramatic increases in energy prices have provided incentive for all consumers to seek energy saving innovations as part of their overall effort to reduce energy costs. Industrial and systems engineers are often in the front line of attack on increased energy costs, particularly in the industrial and commercial sectors. Previously, energy costs accounted for an insignificant fraction of industrial production, and only a small part of total commercial operations costs. Now, however, energy costs are becoming significant enough that business and industry are hiring engineers with a specialty in energy management and conservation. Plant managers, who are often industrial or systems engineers, are increasingly being assigned energy cost reduction goals as part of their overall production tasks. In order to respond to this need for energy related education, the Department of Industrial and Systems Engineering at the University of Florida has developed a course titled "Industrial Energy Management". The purposes of the course are to give an overview of the present energy supply and demand picture, to analyze the various sectors of energy use, to investigate energy efficiency and conservation potentials and to formulate some basic principles of energy management. The course touches briefly on many other areas such as legislation governing energy conservation and use; energy auditing; waste heat recovery and cogeneration; and computerized energy management. Two very important features of the course are the use of guest speakers from consulting firms, utilities and industry, and field trips to several energy production and energy use facilities. The guest speakers and tours bring a real-world view of energy conservation and management to all of the students.

Energy education for industrial and systems engineers is critical because of the rapid technological concern for energy efficiency in our entire society. Our industrial productivity has dropped in recent years, and the efforts to create more energy efficient industrial processes will not only save dollars but could well improve our productivity, too. Entirely new industries have also developed due to the importance of energy management and conservation. These include service industries such as consultants in energy management and energy conservation, and manufacturing industries which produce devices such as energy monitors, energy controllers, high efficiency motors and high efficiency lights. For industrial and systems engineers, the energy management and energy conservation fields are wide open, with potential jobs in both service and manufacturing areas. A course such as the one described here, combined with standard industrial and systems engineering design courses, should help prepare students for challenging opportunities in energy management.

ORIGINATION OF THE COURSE

In order to meet the needs of this new technological area, the Industrial and Systems Engineering Department first offered a course in industrial energy management on an experimental, limited enrollment basis during the 1979 Fall Quarter, and then again during the Spring Quarter of 1981. Interest among the students was high because of the rapidly increasing industrial concern for energy efficiency and energy cost savings. However, teaching the course was difficult because no suitable textbook and only limited teaching materials were available. Selection of course content material was difficult due to the need to condense a large amount of new information into a cohesive course. Selection of class projects and suitable case studies was also a lengthy task. However, the development of this area was approached with great enthusiasm on the part of both faculty and students. The result has been a course that is in great demand and that addresses an area the students realize will be of importance after graduation. In 1982, the University of Florida converted to the Semester System, and the Energy Management course was expanded from a ten-week term to a fifteen-week term.

The major beneficiaries of the development of this course are the Industrial and Systems Engineering students who will be better prepared to assume their roles in running today's energy conscious industrial society. Because of the rapidly increasing demand for energy management tasks by industry, engineering graduates who have not received such training are likely to find themselves less able to perform competently in the real world. This course has been made an elective course for ISE students at the University of Florida and will thus have a specific impact on approximately 25-50 students per year. Additional enrollment from other engineering fields is anticipated since energy management positions are not limited to industrial engineers.

COURSE CONTENT

The industrial energy management course is presently designed around a fifteen week semester with weekly topics emphasized through lectures, projects, guest speakers and facility tours. The fundamentals of the course are presented through a series of weekly lectures augmented by related homework assignments. These lectures present the students with a variety of concepts and applications in energy management and a general picture of the present day energy climate. The following is a listing and brief discussion of some of the topics covered in the lectures.

(1) Introduction: This section deals with the basics of energy management and conservation. Topics discussed are the implications and need for an updated energy policy, energy and politics, load management programs, energy supply and demand data, energy use and distribution, and projections of the energy future. This part is designed to give the student a broad look at the total energy picture.

(2) Energy Economics: A major factor of any new system is the economics affecting its implementation. This is especially true for any attempt to conserve or mange energy effectively. This section looks at energy economics in the areas of economic decision criteria, energy pricing structures and conservation investment analysis. Topics include: the engineer's role in energy economics, energy uses and losses, identifying costs, calculating the energy content of a process, and the technique of life cycle costing. The goal is to convey the techniques in implementing a cost-saving energy management and conservation program.

(3) Energy Audits: Energy auditing is fast becoming an accepted and desired practice in residential, commercial, and industrial complexes. This part deals with the identification of energy use and conservation measures and the procedure used in performing an energy audit. Topics discussed are the energy used in given facilities, specific ways to save energy in different types of buildings, and the development of an energy audit program and testing procedure. Discussion of these topics is in preparation for an energy audit project to be performed later in the course.

(4) Energy Conservation and Use Legislation: Probably one of the greatest controversies of the decade is the development of a national energy policy. This section looks at some of the energy legislation of today and its impact on energy producers and energy consumers. Topics include the National Energy Act (NEA) of 1978, Public Utility Regulatory Policies Act (PURPA), the Power Plant and Industrial Fuel Use Act, and the National Energy Conservation Policy Act (NECPA). The legislation is discussed in terms of rate design standards, reporting requirements, wholesale provisions, cogeneration provisions, and financial planning.

(5) Energy Management Systems, Tools and Measures: The last part of the course presents some of the different types of energy management and conservation control systems. Application of a total energy management system can range from turning off a light to designing a microprocessor control system for energy cost optimization. Areas discussed are lighting, HVAC, demand leveling, monitoring and control, cost and load calculations, cogeneration, waste heat boilers, and computer control and optimization. Each area is considered for its application in energy management and its impact on conservation for cost minimization.

The "hands-on" concept of learning is very successful in terms of conveying some of the basic principles behind energy management and conservation. This is accomplished through group projects in which each group performs an energy audit on a building at the University of Florida or on a commercial building near the campus. The audit focuses on the identification and analysis of areas within the buildings that have the potential for energy and financial savings through conservation measures. The areas include lighting, air-handling, insulation, weather-stripping, and any other area which might be unique to a particular building.

To further supplement the audit project, a series of guest speakers and facility tours is presented. The guest speakers include a lighting design consultant, a utility energy conservation representative, and a phosphate industry energy manager, among others. In addition, the students typically tour a natural gas liquids plant, the university heat plant, the university energy management computer, and the university solar research park. The speakers and tours allow the students to hear and see some of the different energy management applications in use today.

CONCLUSION

The purpose of this paper has been to describe the development of a course in industrial energy management for Industrial and Systems engineers at the University of Florida. Substantial effort was required to design and structure the course as it presently exists, and additional effort is being applied to improve the course. It is hoped that the information presented here will be of help to other faculty and other schools in their development of similar courses.

APPENDIX I

INDUSTRIAL ENERGY MANAGEMENT

COURSE DESCRIPTION

Introduction to energy management and energy conservation. Discussion of energy supply and demand data, energy economics and investment analysis, and energy legislation affecting conservation and use. Overview of energy audit programs and principles of energy auditing. Discussion of energy management systems, commercial energy management and waste heat recovery. Applications to selected industrial facilities and plant tours.

COURSE OUTLINE

I. Introduction

A. Need for energy management and conservation
B. Energy supply and demand data
C. Projections of our energy future

II. Energy Economics

A. Economic decision criteria
B. Energy pricing structures
C. Energy conservation investment analysis

III. Energy Audits

A. NECPA and residential conservation service
B. Schools and hospitals audit program
C. Industrial audits

IV. Energy Conservation and Use Legislation

A. EPCA and ECPA
B. NEA 1978
1. Power Plant and Industrial Fuel Use Act
2. PURPA
3. Energy Tax Act

V. Energy Management Systems

A. Monitoring and control functions
B. Lighting, HVAC, demand leveling
C. Research in optimum scheduling for cost minimization

VI. Other Tools

A. Lighting and lighting design
B. Heating and cooling load calculations
C. Insulation cost and benefits

VII. Waste Heat Recovery

A. Waste heat boilers
B. Cogeneration
C. Topping and bottoming cycles
D. Total energy system case study

VIII. Commercial Energy Management

A. Energy use characteristics
B. Lighting, HVAC systems, boiler efficiency
C. Case studies - grocery store, fast food establishment

IX. Inspection Tours

A. Natural gas liquids plant
B. University heat plant
C. University energy management computer
D. University solar research park

X. Guest Speakers

A. Lighting design consultant
B. Utility energy conservation representative
C. Phosphate industry energy manager

APPENDIX II

COURSE SYLLABUS

INDUSTRIAL ENERGY MANAGEMENT EIN 4321 3 credits

GRADING:

Three Exams	20%, 25%, 25%
Audit Report and Case Study	20%
Homework Assignments	10%

TOPICS: Energy Supply and Demand; The National Energy Act; Energy Audits; Energy Conservation and Management: Residential, Commercial, Industrial,; Alternative Energy Sources; Investment Analysis; Energy Future;

FIRST EXAMINATION:

The first examination will cover Energy Future, Chapters 1 - 9. Exam will be closed book and will count 20%. Questions will be multiple choice, true-false, fill in the blank and short answer.

CATALOG DESCRIPTION:

Study of the objectives, design, implementation and management of energy conservation and management efforts. Scope includes energy conservation, choice of energy source, National Energy Act, contingency planning, and alternative energy sources. Application areas include homes, institutions, businesses, large buildings, and industry. Empahsis on energy conservation applications. Speakers from other departments and organizations.

PREREQUISTES: Junior Level Standing, Physics, Calculus, Knowledge of Engineering Economy and Thermodynamics

TEXT: Energy Future, Stobaugh and Yergin, Vintage Books, 1983
Energy Management, Kennedy and Turner, Prentice-Hall, 1984

OBJECTIVES:

To enable the student to understand the basic energy picture and where the world is heading.

To enable the student to review basic energy related sciences.

To enable the student to understand the methods of energy management in homes, institutions, businesses, large buildings and industry.

To enable the student to understand the realistic potential of renewable energy sources by listening to speakers, researching, and formulating their own opinions.

To enable the student to develop an overall energy awareness and a conservation ethic.

Chapter 60

SAN DIEGO S. U.'s ENERGY ENGINEERING INSTITUTE: PRODUCING A MORE VALUABLE HUMAN COMMODITY

H. M. Güven, D. H. Lark

ABSTRACT

In this paper, the organization of an institute in energy engineering at the San Diego State University is explained.

The described Institute is a joint University/ Industry/Government venture and its major objectives are:

- To provide education in energy engineering to the graduating engineers and to the local energy engineering community, and
- To coordinate and conduct applied/basic research projects (and studies) to solve the R&D problems of the local energy industry and energy engineering community.

Twelve energy engineering design/research projects are coordinated yearly by the Institute. The projects are drawn from the local industry. The majority of the projects are "applied" R&D studies and they provide solutions to the local R&D problems in energy engineering.

A Financial Committee with members from the local industry and the university was formed on December 2, 1985 to work on raising the necessary funds from the local/national companies and the state/local agencies. The Institute was officially activated on January 1, 1986.

INTRODUCTION

One of the most pressing problems in society today is the task of supplying energy efficiently and cost effectively to a populace of ever increasing demand. Nowhere is this more evident than in Southern California. With a growth rate that increases yearly, the acquisition of energy from outside sources, coupled with the output of the local power plants, fall short of the expectations. The problem becomes more complex and costly from year to year and, therefore, bears close scrutiny since it entails one of civilization's most basic needs. These facts necessitate:

- Development of new, novel and innovative approaches to provide short and long-term solutions to the local energy demand-supply problem;
- Creation and support of an energy engineering discipline in the local higher educational institutions in order to train new engineers as well as providing professional growth and development opportunities for practicing energy engineers and property managers in the fields of energy management, energy conservation, etc.
- Continued and enhanced research and development support and efforts in energy generation, energy management and energy conservation.

BACKGROUND

Responding to the challenge, in the recent years the local energy industry and energy engineering professionals in Southern California have undertaken several energy management and conservation projects as well as forming several successful professional organizations to facilitate information exchange. They have also sponsored/financed a number of successful educational/training activities and financial inducement programs. Some examples are:

- An energy professional development course (Certified Energy Manager (CEM) course offered by UCSD Extension),
- Thermal Energy Storage (TES) seminar sponsored by Southern California Energy Council, April 1985, Hyatt Islandia Hotel, San Diego,
- Southern California Energy Expo '84 and '85.
- SDG&E's Thermal Energy Storage inducement program,
- SDG&E's Energy Audit program.

Despite the seemingly high-level of activity, however, there has been no mechanism by which the local energy professionals could obtain solutions to their "applied" research/development problems. Furthermore, keeping abreast of and obtaining unbiased information on the fast changing energy engineering technologies has created sizable design/evaluation problems to the practicing energy engineers and property managers.

After coming to know about the problems and the needs of the energy engineering community during the Energy Expo '84, in January 1985 the SDSU Mechanical

Engineering Department has decided to study the nature of the needs and provide leadership in the R&D activities. Hence, the SDSU Mechanical Engineering Department started investigating meaningful ways to interact/cooperate with the local energy industry and the energy engineering community in order to address their problems. At the same time, the Department launched an effort to find out whether its curriculum in energy coverage was up-to-date, and whether the graduating engineers have had enough exposure to energy engineering during their formal education. During the period from January 1985 to December 1985, the Department engaged in a number of different activities which included:

- Energy-related senior projects are solicited from the industry under the Industry Sponsored Senior Projects (ISSP) program. (January 1985).
- A student chapter of AEE/ASHRAE was established. (April 1985).
- A technical elective course stressing thermal design entitled "Thermal Systems Analysis and Design" (ME 596) is developed and offered for the first time. (September 1985).
- SDSU-ME department invited 12 members of the energy engineering industry/community to the university and discussed the formation of an Energy Engineering Institute at the university. The guests also listened to several of the student senior project presentations. (December 1985).

As a result of this one-year investigation/study, the Department arrived at the following conclusions/observations:

Undergraduate-level

- After the 1973 energy crisis, there had been a concentrated effort in energy studies/research, conservation, etc. But after the governmental funding for such efforts dried up, energy education and R&D activities were considerably curtailed. The subsequent oil-glut has, of course, compounded the problem. The net effect of this has been reduced interest in energy research and education. It is found that our graduating mechanical engineering students were hardly exposed to the new trends in energy management, conservation, etc. Even though such topics were covered to a limited extend in senior-level technical elective courses, it was found that in such structured lecture courses exposure to fast changing energy engineering technology, optimum energy system design, etc., were quite limited. Moreover, enrollment and interest in energy-related technical elective courses were not as strong as before, therefore, fewer number of graduating seniors were receiving energy-related education/training.
- There were very few energy-related projects in the mechanical engineering design capcourse, ME 490 A/B Senior Design Projects. The reason for the poor representation of energy was, this time, economics. In the design capcourse, students were required to carry out a complete engineering study based on the analysis techniques they have learned in the previous semesters. As part of this effort, students were required to either design, build and test a system or work on projects that would provide hands-on experience with hardware (e.g., monitoring the performance of an existing, large engineering system for the purpose of evaluation, etc.). Available departmental funds consisted of $50/student project. Since thermal system components (e.g., pumps, compressors, heat exchangers, etc.) were inherently more expensive than mechanical system components (e.g., gears, shafts, etc.), most of the senior projects dealt with mechanical system design with an occasional energy-related project. In order to increase the energy representation in the senior design projects, industrial help must be sought.

Graduate-level

- Curtailed research funding in energy affected the graduate program as well. Limited funding reduced the number of graduate students working on energy-related thesis topics.

Industry

- Industry and energy engineering community is found to be fully cooperative with the university.
- The R&D needs of the local energy engineering community, energy industry, and property managers were found to be real and significant. Moreover, it is found that most of the local R&D needs can be satisfied by way of having undergraduate students work on these problems as senior projects. Thus, students get the desired exposure to energy engineering technology (applications and research) and, at the same time, this effort will increase the energy component of senior projects and provide a useful service to the energy engineering community.
- The projects that could not be tackled by an undergraduate project team can be turned over to a graduate student research team to be worked on as a thesis.
- The energy engineering community is in need of a database. It was observed that obtaining reliable information and literature in general was very difficult because of the rapid change and the fast-pace of the technology.

General

- The two local "Energy Centers", UCSD's Center for Energy and Combustion Research and SDSU's Center for Energy Studies, were not organized as centers to serve the special needs of the local community in the way of solving applied R&D problems, but rather they were set-up as "large-project-oriented energy centers" which could not, under their existing organizational structure, work on "small projects".
- The "Energy Centers" were established to address the needs that arouse after the 1973 energy crisis. As such, most of the projects undertaken by the centers were alternate energy studies rather than energy engineering projects. Being such, these centers have not yet made efforts to address R&D needs in the energy management, energy conservation, etc.

In the light of the above conclusions/observations, it was concluded that the San Diego State

University's energy engineering activities were responding to a very real need both from R&D and the educational standpoint. Furthermore, the curriculum of the Mechanical Engineering Department at SDSU was uniquely suited to respond to these needs quickly and effectively. Therefore, in order to sustain a high-level of activity and the desired leadership in energy engineering, to better serve the energy engineering community, and to ensure a quality and wholesome education to our students in all fields of science and technology, the department has decided to form an Institute to specifically address the educational and R&D needs in energy engineering.

It was decided to seek partnership with and funding from the local energy industry and community for the establishment and operation of the Institute which was to be named Energy Engineering Institute.

The objectives and scope of the Energy Engineering Institute are explained in the next section.

OBJECTIVES

1. Increasing the awareness of graduating mechanical engineering seniors to energy generation, energy management and conservation and to energy efficient system design through application-oriented projects.

2. Coordinating and conducting research and development activities in energy engineering to contribute to the body of knowledge in:

   (a) Energy generation, energy management and conservation, and
   (b) Computer-aided design/optimization of energy systems.

3. Serving the local energy engineering community by way of:

   (a) Solving their R&D problems,
   (b) Creating an energy engineering library and a database at the university for the use of the students and the energy engineering community,
   (c) Conducting educational short courses and seminars.

SCOPE/LIMITATIONS

The primary missions of the Institute are to provide education and service in energy engineering, and to conduct "applied" research/development projects (and studies) to support the R&D needs of the local energy industry and the energy engineering community.

The aforementioned R&D projects will be conducted by primarily undergraduate SDSU mechanical engineering students as part of a capcourse in the Mechanical Engineering curriculum, Senior Design Projects (ME490 A/B), which will earn them credit towards their graduation.

The Institute will provide funds through a "research seeding program" for two graduate research assistants to work on "basic" research problems in energy engineering as their thesis. The Institute's fixed operation budget, however, will not cover the cost of undertaking full-fledged basic research projects in energy engineering. As the name implies, the projects funded through the research seeding program are expected to develop into multi-year, full-fledged research projects funded by either a federal/state agency or a national grant. The initial funding provided in the form of a graduate research assistantship is therefore intended to help a faculty member develop a competitive research proposal to facilitate obtaining a national grant and hence help solve the basic research problems in energy engineering.

ORGANIZATION

The organizational chart for the Institute is shown in Figure 1.

Director: The director is a member of the Mechanical Engineering Faculty. The director will have expertise and background in energy engineering and he will be responsible for

- running the day-to-day business of the Institute,
- interfacing with the local energy engineering community,
- coming-up with project ideas,
- coordinating the project proposal solicitation,

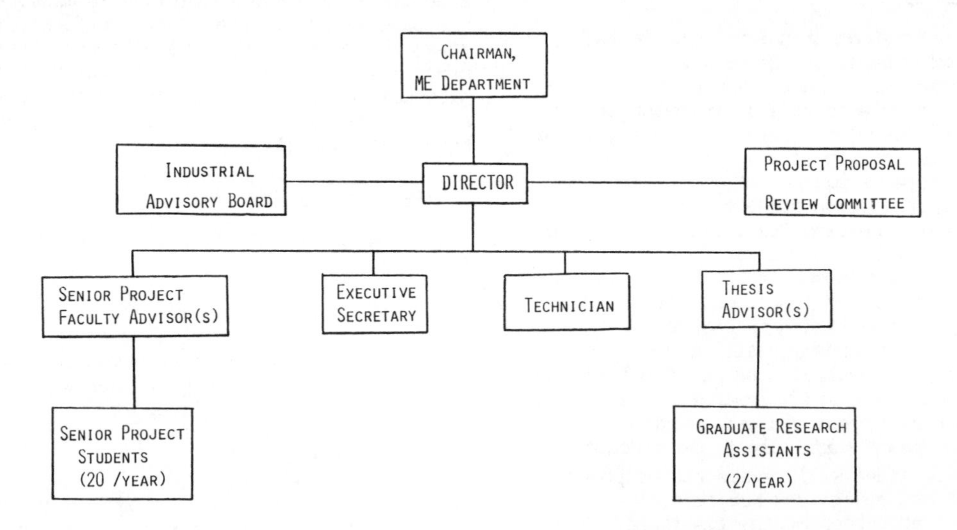

Figure 1. The organizational chart for the Energy Engineering Institute.

- overseeing the project progress/completion,
- serving as senior project faculty advisor (i.e., technical advisor) for a fixed number of senior projects,
- serving as the thesis advisor (technical advisor) of the two thesis students,
- preparing project proposals for external funding.

Project Proposal Review Committee: This committee will consist of the Institute director, representative(s) of the principal sponsor(s), and two prominent figures from the energy engineering community. The committee will meet twice a year (before the start of Fall and Spring semesters) to review the project proposals and select the projects to be funded by the Institute.

Industrial Advisory Board: The advisory board will consist of representatives from local energy-related professional organizations (e.g., AEE, ASHRAE, AIPE, APEM, etc.). This board will advise the director on the educational needs of the energy engineering community.

Executive Secretary: A half-time secretary will be responsible for administering the projects, purchasing, preparing and printing the Institute reports, publications, etc. The Institute will have a full-time secretary in its third year of operation.

Technician: A full-time technician will be utilized in the projects.

Senior Project Advisor and Thesis Advisor: These will be members of the Mechanical Engineering Faculty and they will supervise (and serve as technical consultants for) the senior projects and the graduate theses. The two graduate theses funded by the institute, however, will be directed by the Institute director.

Senior Project Students: These will be graduating Mechanical Engineering seniors enrolled in the Senior Design Projects course, ME 490 A/B.

Graduate Research Assistants: These will be graduate students enrolled in Graduate Research (ME 797) and Masters Thesis (ME 799) courses.

OPERATION GUIDELINES AND BENEFITS

Educational Activities

(a) The Industry Sponsored Senior Projects (ISSP) program of the Mechanical Engineering Department will be used as the primary vehicle to solicit relevant projects from the energy engineering community to be used as senior projects in Engineering Design Projects course (ME 490 A/B). The scope of the senior projects can vary from complete engineering feasibility studies to monitoring the performance of local energy projects. Sample senior project topics can be found in the next section. As shown in Figure 2, projects can be proposed by industrial concerns, institute sponsors as well as SDSU faculty. The principal sponsor of the institute will, however, have priority at proposing a set number of projects every year. The Project Proposal Review Committee will review the proposed projects and select the projects to be administered/funded by the Institute. The Institute will administer a minimum of 10

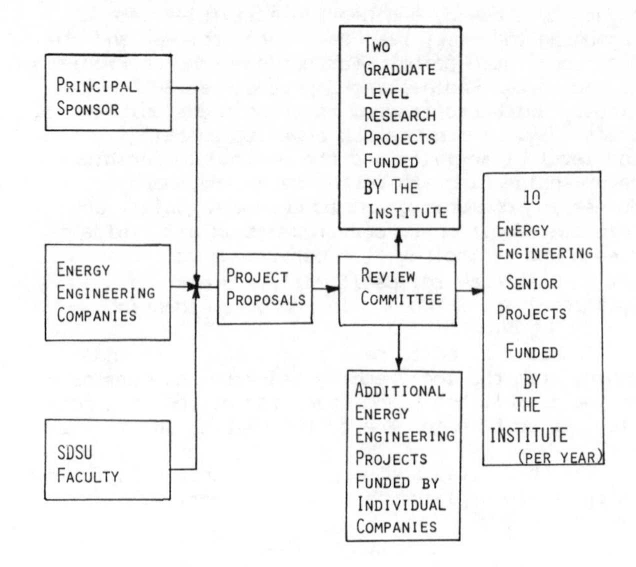

Figure 2. Project proposal solicitation and selection process.

energy-related projects per year. (This represents 20% of the total senior projects volume in the ME Department)

(b) At the graduate-level, it is anticipated that at least two masters thesis students will be funded by the Institute. The graduate-level projects will be administered under the guidelines of the Sponsored Advanced Study Program (SASP) of the Mechanical Engineering Department.

(c) The guidelines for seminars and short courses will be developed at a future date in cooperation with the Industrial Advisory Board.

Research and Development Activities

Initially, The R & D activities of the Institute will be confined to two research projects conducted by 2 Graduate Research Assistants as masters thesis under the supervision of the Institute director. These two research projects are funded under a "research seeding program". The Institute is expected to solicit national research grants for specific research projects at a future date. Potential funding agencies include NSF, DOE and EPRI.

Service Activities

The service activities of the Institute will include:

(a) Short courses and seminars as well as responding to the specified research needs of the local energy community. The format and frequency of short courses and seminars will be established by the help of the Industrial Advisory Board and the SDSU Extension.

(b) The Institute will be working to develop a database in energy engineering for the use of the SDSU students as well as the local energy engineering community. This database will evolve gradually as the R&D effort gets underway. The Institute will also maintain an up-to-date library in energy engineering. The copies of the old Institute reports as well as copies of the theses and the publications will also be kept.

(c) The Institute will publish a quarterly newsletter to inform its members and the energy engineering community in general about the activities of the Institute. The list of ongoing projects and feature articles on completed projects will be included in the quarterly.

SUGGESTED RESEARCH TOPICS

Some typical R & D projects that will be undertaken by the Institute are:

- Monitoring and evaluation of energy systems in San Diego county,
- Design of special instrumentation for computerized monitoring and control of energy systems,
- Projects on analysis of small cogeneration engine performance,
- Low-grade heat recovery, e.g., from hot water heaters and home central heating units.
- Energy management projects for residential applications,
- Projects on organic conversion to fuels (methane, alcohol, etc.),
- Projects on geothermal, photovoltaic, solar thermal, chemical power, wind power, etc.

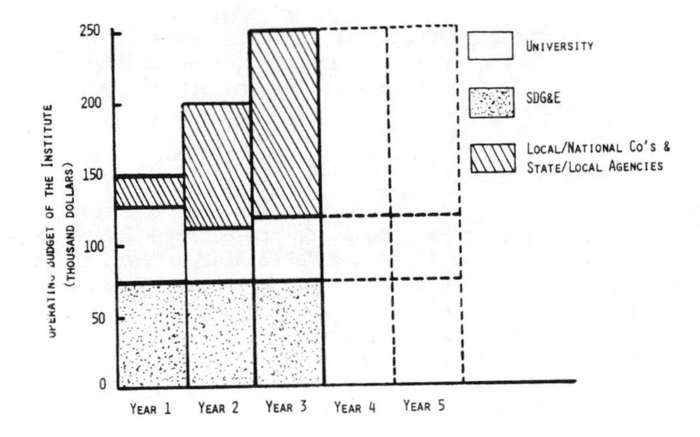

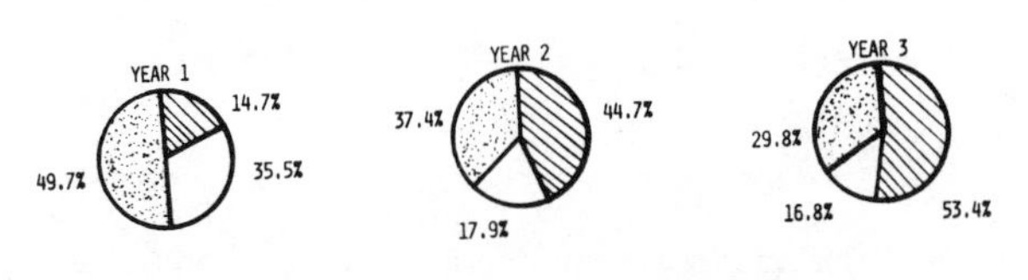

%'s refer to percentage of the total budget

Figure 3. Operating budget of the Energy Engineering Institute

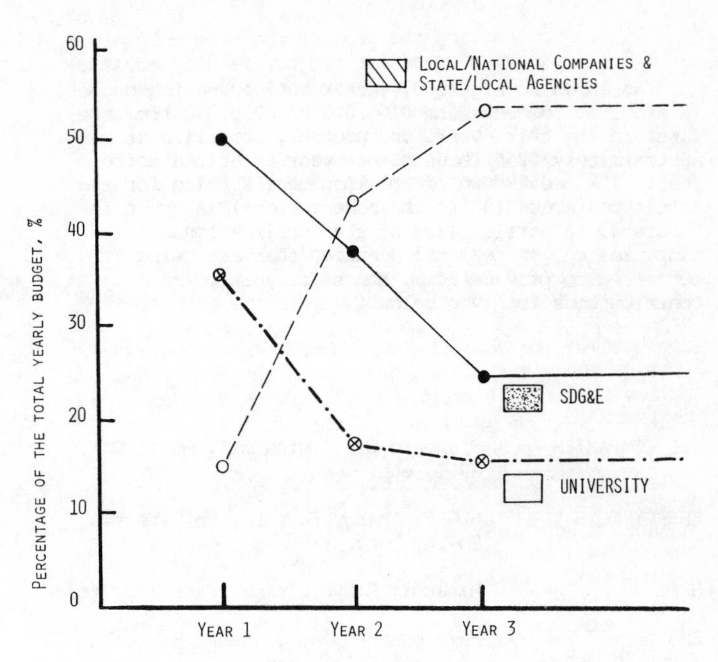

Figure 4. Long-term funding of the Energy Engineering Institute.

FUNDING

The Institute will be funded jointly by the University, the local industry and various state/local agencies (organizations). A three-year proposed budget for the Institute is shown in Table 1. As the leader of the energy industry in the San Diego area, it is anticipated that San Diego Gas & Electric Company (SDG&E) will play a pivotal role in getting the Institute started. It is proposed to SDG&E to make a three-year commitment to provide a fixed $75,000 yearly contribution to the Institute's budget. This will give SDG&E the 'principal industrial sponsor' status and hence priority in proposing a set number of projects every year. The performance, goals and the budget of the Institute will be reviewed/revised at the end of the third year.

TABLE 1
OPERATING BUDGET FOR THE INSTITUTE

	FUNDS		
	YEAR 1	YEAR 2	YEAR 3
University	$ 53,627	$ 35,878	$ 42,181
SDG&E	$ 75,000	$ 75,000	$ 75,000
Local Co.'s State/local Agencies	$ 22,338	$ 89,122	$ 134,418
TOTAL	$ 150,965	$ 200,420	$ 251,599

As shown in Figure 3, Institute's operating budget is expected to grow from $150,000 to $250,000 from the first to the third year, and probably stabilize at approximately $250 thousand per year after the third year. The break-down of the long-term funding for the Institute (according to the contributors) is shown in Figure 4. A partial list of the local/national companies and state/local agencies that are being contacted to provide commitments for yearly contributions is given below.

OIL COMPANIES	Standard Oil, Union Oil, Mobil Oil, ARCO, etc.
ENERGY CO'S	SDG&E, Energy Factors, University Energy, etc.
HVAC	Hitachi, Sanyo, Trane, Carrier, etc.
ENGINE MANUFACTURERS	Hawthorne Engine Systems, Waukesha Engines, Solar, etc.
LARGE ENGINEERING CO'S	Carter Engineering, Ebasco, Gold Coast Engineering, etc.
CONTRACTORS	General Dynamics, Rohr, Cubic, GA Technologies, etc.
COMPUTER CO.	Hewlett Packard, IBM, CDC, Harris, Intel, etc.
BANKS	Bank of America, Home Federal, Great American, etc.
AGENCIES	California Energy Commission, S.A.F.E. B.I.D.C.O., S.A.N.D.A.G., etc.
OTHER	General Electric, Union Tribune, McDonalds, Discflo, Kelco, etc.

CLOSURE

In this paper, a new approach to energy engineering education which brings together industry-university and government in assuming responsibility to provide adequate exposure and awareness to graduating engineers in rapid changing energy engineering technology is described. The institute has been successfully operating since January 1, 1986 and it achieved most of its financial objectives for the year.

Chapter 61

ENERGY MANAGEMENT EDUCATION AT LOUISIANA TECH UNIVERSITY

J. D. Lowther

Energy management education at Louisiana Tech University is a combination of formal course work at both the graduate and undergraduate level, directed independent study courses, graduate research, and the involvement of students as employees on the various externally funded projects of the College of Engineering related to energy management. This paper describes one aspect of energy management education in the College of Engineering at Louisiana Tech University: undergraduate course work in the Department of Mechanical and Industrial Engineering and externally funded energy management projects closely related to undergraduate education.

UNDERGRADUATE COURSES

Industrial Energy Conservation

Formal course work at the undergraduate level is centered around a course in industrial energy conservation taught in the Department of Mechanical and Industrial Engineering. The course evolved as a result of the College of Engineering's involvement in energy management and conservation in manufacturing and process industries and is closely tied to the Louisiana Tech Energy Analysis and Diagnostic Center program, which will be discussed later. The course is designed to provide students with knowledge and experience necessary to identify and analyze energy conservation opportunities in manufacturing and process industry plants. This course, entitled "Industrial Energy Conservation," is a three semester hour credit technical elective available to junior and senior engineering students. To date, the students enrolling in the course have been chemical engineering, mechanical engineering, and industrial engineering majors.

The course is unique among the technical electives available to the students in that, as a part of the course, each student visits an industrial plant and participates in the identification and analysis of energy conservation opportunities and the preparation of a report to the plant visited. The popularity of the course seems to be due in large part to this inclusion of "real world" experience.

Ten percent of the student's grade in the course is based on homework problems coordinated with the lecture material. Sixty percent is based on tests covering the lecture material, while the remaining thirty percent is based on the work done in connection with the plant visit.

Topics covered in the lecture portion of the course are:

- Energy Sources and Rate Structures
- Cost Estimating
- Economic Analysis
- Combustion
  - Analysis
  - Fired Equipment
  - Controls
- Waste Heat Recovery
- Steam Systems
- Electrical Equipment
  - Motors
  - Furnaces
  - Power Factor
  - Demand Control
- Compressed Air Systems
- Insulation
- Heating, Ventilating and Air Conditioning
- Lighting
- Cogeneration
- Energy Management Systems
- The Energy Conservation Survey
  - Energy Usage Analysis
  - Plant Survey
  - Data Gathering and Measurements
  - Analysis
  - Reporting

The lecture portion of the course has a distinct mechanical engineering orientation with less emphasis on management aspects such as the establishment of an energy management program in a plant. Homework problems are based on actual rate schedules and data collected by the instructor from actual plants.

Each student in the class participates in an energy survey or audit at a manufacturing plant. The class is divided into groups with each group making a one-day visit to the plant to perform the energy survey.

During the Winter Quarter of the 1985-86 school year, the course had an enrollment of 25 students. The class was divided into three groups, with each group performing an energy survey at a different plant. A prestressed concrete plant, a paper bag manufacturing firm, and a plant that manufactures rubber adhesives and molded rubber parts were visited.

Each student group analyzes twelve months of energy bills for their assigned plant prior to visiting the plant. At the plant, the students receive information on the plant operation and a tour of the plant provided by plant personnel. With the guidance of the instructor, the students compile a list of possible energy conservation opportunities based on their analysis of the plant energy bills and their observations during the tour of the plant. Each student is next assigned one or more of these energy conservation opportunities as his or her own.

Each student is responsible for collecting data needed for the analysis of his assigned energy conservation opportunities during the the plant visit. The remainder of the time spent at the plant is devoted to data collection by the students with guidance from the instructor. Students use instruments such as flue gas analyzers, anemometers, thermometers, and light meters to provide measurements of important parameters.

Upon returning from the plant visit, each student is responsible for completing an economic analysis of his energy conservation opportunities and preparing a written recommendation for each which becomes part of the report to the company visited. The written recommendation includes an estimate of the savings in energy and energy costs, an estimate of the cost required to implement the energy conservation opportunity, and the simple payback period.

Students are required to submit a one-page preliminary report on their assigned energy conservation opportunities soon after returning from the plant visit, a draft of their recommendations, and a final version of their recommendations. In addition, each student gives a short oral report on his recommendations to the entire class.

The course requires significantly more of the instructor's time than a typical three semester hour credit technical elective course, due to the added time required for the plant visits and the time which must be spent in individual consultation with the students while they are analyzing and writing the reports on the energy conservation opportunities that result from the plant visits.

The motivation and enthusiasm of the students more than compensates the instructor for the extra time spent on the course. The motivation and enthusiasm of the students seems to result solely from the fact that this course provides them with a rare opportunity to apply what they learn in the classroom immediately to real-world problems.

Two primary benefits of the course have been observed. One obvious benefit is that students who have taken the course are very aware of energy conservation and are quick to identify and analyze energy conservation opportunities on their first job after graduation. In addition, the plant visits have had a very positive influence on the image of the College of Engineering at Louisiana Tech University as perceived by the management of the plants visited. We get many favorable comments on the competence and attitude of the students.

Laboratory Courses

Senior students in Chemical Engineering and in Mechanical Engineering take courses in which the students design and carry out experimental solutions to engineering problems. During the past academic year, such topics as the determination of the effectiveness of polypropylene floats in reducing energy losses from the surface of heated liquids in open tanks and the development of a simple method of estimating the flow rate of steam leaks were studied in the senior laboratory courses.

Independent Study Courses

Many students choose to take an independent study course under the direction of a faculty member on a topic of mutual interest to the student and faculty member. Many of the topics result from faculty interest in energy management. Independent study course topics during the past year included:

- Average vs. Incremental Costs for Predicting Electrical Energy Savings
- Efficiency and Power Factor of Induction Motors at Part Load
- Computer Software for Economic Analysis of Energy Efficient Lighting
- Computer Software for Energy Cost Accounting.

EXTERNALLY-FUNDED ENERGY MANAGEMENT PROJECTS

Perhaps the greatest enhancement to energy management education at Louisiana Tech University has been brought about by externally funded programs designed to conserve energy by providing energy management expertise to both the private and public sector. These programs have increased faculty involvement and interest in energy management. In addition, these programs have provided employment opportunities for graduate and undergraduate students while attending college. These employment opportunities not only provide financial support for the students, but also valuable experience in energy management. During the past academic year, five faculty members, six graduate students, and fifteen undergraduate students have been employed on these projects.

Energy Analysis and Diagnostic Center

The Department of Mechanical and Industrial Engineering and the Department of Chemical Engineering jointly operate the Louisiana Tech Energy Analysis and Diagnostic Center (EADC). The Louisiana Tech EADC is one of ten such centers in the United States that operate under the management of the University City Science Center with funding provided by the U. S. Department of Energy. The purpose of the EADC program is to provide technical assistance in energy management and conservation to small- and medium-sized manufacturers who do not have in-house energy management expertise.

Under the EADC program, an EADC conducts an energy survey of a qualified plant, identifies energy conservation opportunities within the plant, and provides the manufacturer with a written report containing detailed analyses of the energy conservation opportunities recommended. At this time, the Louisiana Tech EADC has conducted energy surveys at over 80 manufacturing plants in four states.

As mentioned previously, the EADC program has close ties with the industrial energy conservation course, providing contacts with manufacturers in need of energy conservation surveys and making instruments and equipment available for use by students in the class.

Louisiana Department of Natural Resources Programs

During the past academic year, Louisiana Tech University has held contracts for two energy conservation programs funded through the Louisiana Department of Natural Resources. One of these, a joint effort between the Department of Mechanical and Industrial Engineering and the Department of Chemical Engineering, provided energy conservation surveys for industries in Louisiana outside the region served by the EADC program.

The other program, conducted by the Department of Mechanical and Industrial Engineering, provided building energy conservation surveys for 100 municipal buildings in cities and towns throughout Louisiana.

Chapter 62

DOE MODEL ENERGY MANAGEMENT COURSES

W. C. Turner

Recently the U. S. Department of Energy (Mr. Jim Demetrops) and Battelle Labs of Richland, Washington (Ms. Nancy Moore) agreed to support the development of two model energy management courses (one upper division undergraduate and one graduate course) for engineering schools. The development was conducted at Montana State University and a host of other engineering colleges across the country.

The final product is a "starter kit" available either from DOE Office of Industrial Programs, Battelle Labs or the author of this article. The rest of this article describes the starter kit.

INTRODUCTION

WHAT?

The kit is designed to help Engineering Educators develop and teach energy management courses. It allows significant variation from the model or complete adherence depending upon the professor's preference. Included in the kit are:

a) List and abstract of potential texts
b) Model curriculum for two courses (one at the junior or senior level and one at the graduate level) complete with discussion of objectives for each period and cross references to the potential texts and the list of references.
c) List of possible laboratory experiments and demonstrations complete with description of necessary equipment.
d) Sample Test Questions
e) Course outlines from other university programs.

College professors do not like to be told how to teach a course, but it is very difficult to organize a new course. This kit is only a suggestion as to how to teach the material. Probably, most professors will start pretty close to this model and deviate more as experience is gained.

There seems to be two types of energy management courses offered in colleges across the country. Interestingly, they never seem to appear together on one campus. This first is a policy oriented course that examines the global energy picture and a country's response. It concentrates on macro economics and large scale systems modeling. THIS KIT IS NOT DESIGNED FOR THAT KIND OF COURSE.

The second is designed to train the engineering student to be a good energy manager for some organization that must use energy to accomplish its objectives. The energy manager must then deal with site specific management and engineering techniques to optimally use the energy. This includes rate selection, fuel choice, waste heat recovery, demand leveling, employee motivation, and a host of other techniques. The courses described in the kit are designed to fill this need.

We anticipate the user will examine his/her course objectives and decide whether or not to use the model outline included herein. Then, the instructor will likely obtain copies of the potential texts, probably from the campus library, and decide on a text. They will likely use the other potential texts and the listed references to strengthen specific weaknesses in their chosen text.

The instructor will next likely design a course outline using the ones shown here as references or for suggestions. The sequence is, of course, quite flexible and can be modified to suit individual desires. The model curriculum can still be used to provide references to potential texts and other references.

Finally, the instructor will decide whether or not to use a laboratory. If possible, we recommend using labs to help the budding energy manager become familiar with the assorter equipment at his/her disposal and see how phenomenon such as power factor occur. Several labs are suggested, but remember each and every piece of analysis equipment (combustion analyzer, light meters, volt and current meters, etc.) is a potential lab experience. More lab experiences in the engineering education process are needed and these are courses where labs can be utilized.

In the syllabi, reference and page numbers are shown for the various topics. See the Annotated Bibliography in Section 5 for the detailed references.

ENERGY MANAGEMENT COURSE OUTLINE

The following outline is a possible design for a Junior to Senior level course requiring a good engineering science basis. It assumes 45 class periods with a laboratory exercise approximately every fourth period. For specific laboratory suggestions see the laboratory section of this kit. If no lab is used or if only a few sessions are used, the material can be expanded to cover more areas or more depth in each subject.

References are included when possible using reference numbers given on the REFERENCE LIST at the beginning of the kit. Sometimes the word "NOTES" is shown. This implies some good outside articles or other sources are available. At other times, specific suggestions are made, e.g. IES Publications - Illuminating Engineering Society and ASHRAE Publications - American Society of Heating, Refrigeration, and Air Conditioning Engineers-.

Course Title: Energy Management

Catalog Description:

Study of the objectives, design, implementation, and management of energy management programs. Scope includes energy conservation, choice of energy sources, safety and security of fuel storage, and contingency planning with emphasis on improving profits (reduce costs) through optimal energy management. Outside speakers and field trips may be utilized.

Prerequisites:

Engineering, Calculus, Heat Transfer, and Engineering Economy.

Text:

Instructor's choice.

Objectives:

To enable the student to understand the basic energy situation and present/future problems.

Understand profit improvement (cost reduction) potential of energy management.

Develop the necessary talents to design, implement, operate, and manage successful energy management programs.

Method of Instruction:

Mostly lecture with some laboratory exposure. Field trips may be utilized.

Grading: (One Possible Scenario)

Two Tests @ 20%	40%
Final Exam @ 25%	25%
Case Study or Research Paper @ 20%	20%
Homework and Special Assignments @ 15%	15%
	100%

Case Study/Research Paper:

The paper is to be an energy management study for some industry, office building, store, church, etc. of an in-depth probe into some appropriate subject. Subject must be approved.

Case Study/Research Paper:

If a case study, it should be a complete analysis (audit) of the energy profile with economic analysis and specific proposals for profit improvement. You will work in teams of two.

Research Papers must be approved before submission. You should thoroughly examine a topic somehow pushing the frontiers of knowledge concerning that subject. You might examine cogeneration potential for small industries or you might look at industrial uses of solar energy.

Case Study

Relations with Company	15 pts
Depth and Quality	45 pts
Report Structure	20 pts
Grammar, Spelling	20 pts
	100 pts

Term Paper

Choice of Subject	10 pts
Originality	10 pts
Depth and Quality	40 pts
References	10 pts
Report Structure	15 pts
Grammar, Spelling	15 pts
	100 pts

OUTLINE

Period	Topic	Ref #-Page
1	Introduction To Course Overview of Material	Syllabus
2	Energy Situation - Global and National Energy Picture and Predictions for the future	1-3, 2-1, 3-1 4-6, 6-5, 8-1
3, 4	Initiating, Organizing, and Managing E.M. Programs. How to design an E.M. organization and start it properly. How to monitor it.	1-7, 2-82, 5-2 6-395, 7-3, 8-7
4, 5	Energy Auditing - What is an energy audit? What do you look for? What equipment is needed? Checklists.	1-29, 2-86, 3-359 4-22, 5-7, 6-51 7-4, 8-25
7	Utility Bills - How is energy billed? How to read rate schedules. Calculating and checking bills.	1-67, 2-16, 3-249 5-33, 6-104, 7-64 8-678
8	Lab 1 - Auditing, Utility Rate Schedules	See above
9, 10, 11	Lighting - How to measure light levels. Different light sources, their advantages and disadvantages. Energy efficiency. Design of light systems.	1-90, 2-172, 3-212 5-172, 6-91, 7-82 8-399, 9-100
12	Lab 2 - Lighting Systems	See above

Period	Topic	Ref #-Page
13, 14, 15	Insulation - Why insulate? Calculation of heat loss and gain. Economics of heat loss and gain. Types of insulation. Properties of insulation types.	1-204, 2-362, 3-90 5-83, 6-392, 7-192 8-459
16	Lab 3 - Insulation Lab	See above
17, 18, 19	Electrical Energy Management - What can be done to reduce electricity costs? Energy management control systems, motors, power factor improvement, etc.	1-141, 2-269, 3-250 5-170, 6-80, 7-89 8-322, 9-3
20	Lab 4 - Electricity	See above
21, 22, 23	Heating, Ventilation, and Air Conditioning - Brief introduction to the different types of HVAC equipment. Economics, economizers, night setback, duty cycling, etc.	1-109, 2-352. 3-166 5-128, 6-237, 8-303
24	Lab 5 - HVAC - Velometer, Economizer	See above
25, 26, 27	Building Envelope - What can be done in the envelope itself? Building insulation, energy efficient glass, passive solar planning, infiltration, new facility design.	3-85, 5-129, 6-218 8-269
28	Lab 6 - Facility Design	1-257
29, 30, 31	Waste Heat Recovery - What is waste heat? Methods of waste heat recovery. Economics of waste heat recovery. Practical considerations.	1-163, 2-178, 3-38 4-132, 5-165, 6-113 7-106, 8-115
32	Lab 7	
33, 34, 35	Boilers and Fired Systems - Chemistry of combustion, heat losses, insulation, excess air control, boiler blowdown, economizers, recuperators.	1-138, 2-165, 3-148 5-97, 6-183, 7-58 8-10
36	Lab 8	
37-41	Steam-Condensate - Layout of typical steam system. Economics of insulation, flash steam recovery, steam traps and monitoring, condensate return.	1-170, 2-306, 3-112 5-113, 6-153, 7-86 8-164
42-45	Actually scattered through the course - Guest speakers, plant tours, tests, review sessions, etc.	

ADVANCED ENERGY MANAGEMENT COURSE OUTLINE

The following outline is a possible design for a Graduate level course in Energy Management. It assumes the student has taken the first Energy Management course and has a good basic understanding. No laboratories are used and the sequence is designed to be more flexible. Outside references and recent articles are much more important than in the first course.

References are included, when possible, using the same coding as before.

ADVANCED ENERGY MANAGEMENT COURSE SYLLABUS

Course Title: Advanced Energy Management

Catalog Description:

Advanced study of the design, implementation, and management of energy management programs. Concentration on areas more technologically or managerially complex than the basic energy management course. Covers topics such as cogeneration, alternative energy, energy reporting, and energy management control systems.

Text:

Instructor's choice.

Objectives:

To enable the student to become more adept in the more sophisticated areas of energy management.

To enable the student to become better managers by examining accounting-reporting measures and cost center metering.

To enable the student to learn more about management of technologically sophisticated areas of energy management.

Method of Instruction:

Lecture, some laboratory and field trip exposure
Outside lecturers used as appropriate

Grading: (One Possible Scenario)

Two tests @ 20%	40%
Final Exam @ 25%	25%
Research Paper @20%	20%
Homework, Special Assignments @ 15%	15%
	100%

OUTLINE

Period	Topic	Ref #-Page
1	Introduction to Course Review of Syllabus	
2-12	Energy Management Control Systems - What is an EMCS? What are the different types available? (Programmable controllers, mainframes, micros) Control Schemes (Duty Cycle, Demand Shed, Optimum Start-Stop, etc.)	1-177, 2-76, 3-171 5-77, 6-105, 7-89 8-356, 9-139

Other References

-Ottaviano, Victor B., Energy Management (USA:OTS Publication 1983)

-Owens, George R., "EMS Parts 1 and 2", Energy Management, March 1983

-------, "Reader Survey and Rating", Energy User News, New York, NY

-------, "Direct Digital Control", Technical Brief #6. Energy Extension Service of Georgia Tech., Atlanta, GA

-------, "Computer Based Energy Management", Technical Brief #3. Energy Extension Service of Georgia Tech., Atlanta, GA

21-22	Cogeneration - What is cogeneration? Why is it attractive? Industrial and institutional applications. Small scale cogeneration. Types of equipment. Economic analysis of cogeneration. Legal and regulatory aspects.	1-172, 2-189, 3-325 6-261, 8-203

Other References

-Pollmeros, George, Energy Cogeneration Handbook (USA: Industrial Press Inc. 1981)

-------, The Industrial Cogeneration Manual. (USA: The Regulatory Policy Institute, Washington, D.C. 1985)

-Kibert, Charles J. and Smith, W.A., "Analysis of Pressure Reducing Stations for Cogeneration". Energy Engineering. Dec.

-Various Manufacturers Literature

23-30	Alternative Energy Applications - What is an alternative energy source? Advantages and disadvantages of each. Economics of alternative energy sources. Solar, Wind, Refuse Derived fuels. Future of alternative energy.	1-243, 3-55, 5-206 6-291, 7-235, 8-499 9-295
30-34	Energy Reporting - Design of energy reporting-accounting procedures. Variance identification and quantification. Cost effective reporting mechanism.	1-16, 2-15, 3-359

Other References

-Turner, W.C., "Energy Accounting: A New Field Results", IIE Transactions, June 1984, page 135

-Shirley, James M., "Multiple Location Energy Accounting System: A Case Study", 1985 Annual International Industrial Engineering Conference Proceedings, Chicago 1985

35-37	Experimental Rate Schedules - Unique rate schedules offered to industries. Interruptable, curtailable, and standby schedules. What can they offer companies? Identifying potential applications.	
37-41	Miscellaneous topics not covered elsewhere. Maintenance for energy management, fleet management, other considerations.	
42-45	Actually scattered through course - Guest speakers, tests, plant tours, review sessions, etc.	

Research Paper

The research paper should be an in-depth analysis of some energy management subject. For example, it could analyze the advantages and disadvantages and pitfalls of energy management control systems or it could present a design for and economic analysis for a solar preheating system for an industrial process. The paper should be of research caliber and worthy of publication in an energy journal.

COURSES AT OTHER SCHOOLS

Montana State University and Oklahoma State University courses are embodied in the Model Curriculum given. The kit contains syllabi of courses at other universities. Some of these have the same basic philosophy as the two presented, but others have totally different approaches. The prospective teacher should look at all before deciding on their course.

Other universities represented include:

- University of Cincinnati
- Texas A&M University
- University of Utah
- Louisiana Tech University
- University of Kansas
- University of Florida
- California State Polytechnic University, Pomona
- University of Wisconsin
- Virginia Polytechnic Institute and State University

ENERGY MANAGEMENT LAB EXERCISES

As mentioned earlier, a strong emphasis is placed on labs in the Model Undergraduate Course. Numerous lab topics are discussed along with references. Any energy using device (boilers, lights, electric motors, etc.) or energy analysis equipment (combustion analyzers, light meters, power factor motors, etc.) are potential lab experiences.

One lab topic (electric rate schedules) is presented next. The full "starter kit" contains many others.

Title: Electric Rate Schedules

Objective:

To familiarize students with the complexities of utility rate structures not only in their home state, but also, in other states.

Discussion:

1) Discuss the purpose of rate schedules. Why so many?

2) Discuss the various types of rate schedules.

   a) Residential
   b) Commercial
   c) Industrial
   d) Experimental - Standby, Buy Back, Interruptable

3) Discuss Kilo-Watt-Hour and its measurement.

4) Discuss how utilities charge for KWH. Discuss declining rates, flat rates, and lifeline rates.

5) Discuss Kilo-Watts and how they are measured.

6) Discuss how and WHY utilities bill for peak demand. Ratchet Clauses, actual demand, billed demand, etc.

7) Discuss power factor and how it is measured. Discuss how and why utilities bill for power factor.

8) Discuss the Fuel Adjustment Factor.

9) Show students examples of how a total bill would be calculated for the same business on various rate schedules.

10) Give students some hypothetical electric usage profiles and have them calculate the total bill based on different rate schedules. Have them compare the total costs for the different rate schedules.

Equipment:

Various Rate Schedules
Example Electric Profiles

References: (See Reference Lits)

Ref #

1 Page 67
2 Page 16
3 Page 249
5 Page 33
6 Page 104
7 Page 64
8 Page 678

TEST QUESTIONS

The next section of the kit presents a sample of our 100 Test questions that could be used directly as an idea generator for other questions. One sample question is given below.

Electric Rate Schedule

1. You work for Ajax, manufacturer of adjustable wrenches. You are trying to understand the billing procedure and encounter the following. Calculate the bill for the month of November. Ignore any charges other than listed.

Rate Schedule
$5.00 per KW of billed demand
$0.03 per KWh of elec. consumption
Allowed KVAR (with no charge) = 70% billed demand
Excess KVARs billed at $0.75 per KVAR
Demand ratcheted 80% over last 12 months
Sales tax = 3%

Month of November
Actual demand = 1000 KW
Actual KVAR = 790 KVAR
Actual consumption = 300,000 KWh

Previous Demand
Dec. 1000 KW; Jan. 900 KW; Feb. 950 KW; March 960 KW; April 960 KW; May 1100 KW; June 1150 KW; July 1350 KW; Aug. 1150 KW; Sept. 1100 KW; Oct. 900 KW

SUMMARY, CONCLUSIONS

The kit is available at no cost from the author of the article and possibly from DOE or Battelle. The author has agreed to act as a clearing house of information. If anyone wishes a copy or wishes to add comments, lab exercises, test questions, etc. to the kit, they should send them to the address below.

Wayne C. Turner
Professor & Head
Industrial & Management Engineering
Montana State University
406-994-3971

SECTION 21
ENVIRONMENTAL STRATEGIES

Chapter 63

THE ENERGY MANAGER AND HAZARDOUS MATERIALS

R. C. Woehrle, Jr.

INTRODUCTION

"All substances are poisons; there is none which is not a poison. The right dose differentiates a poison and a remedy.

- Paracelsus (1493-1541)

Paracelsus was a swiss physician who founded iatochemistry (the art of combining medicine and chemistry). Long before he lived the Romans were suffering from lead poisoning because of the leaded dishes that they used. Recently, we celebrated the return of the Osprey to New England. The birds disappeared from that area due to our extensive use of DDT after World War II.

Since the oil embargo of 1973 the energy manager has worn many hats in his or her effort to conserve our natural resources. You've inspected and tested existing facilities. You've planned, designed, estimated, secured funds and coordinated the construction of many projects conserving energy. Today you are being called upon to help resolve a problem potentially more harmful than all the wars of the world combined - Hazardous Waste.

We Need You

The energy managers are the best equipped to solve the problem. You have spent the last thirteen years examining, in finest detail, mankinds use of energy. From the simplest processes to the most complex systems, the energy managers have searched for ways to minimize the use of energy while achieving the same or better results. It is fair to say that you are detail people with the experience to "see" where the problems are and how to fix them.

Common sense, trial-and-error, and curiosity have been your basic analysis tools. The energy manager has also relied heavily on the historical methods of our past generations. In particular you examined where resources and products were scarce. From site selection to process management, the energy manager has proven to be a valued member of business.

News Items

There has been much publicity involving hazardous materials. Highway accidents of tanker trucks carrying hazardous gases and liquids are commonplace in metropolitan areas. Asbestos removal projects in our schools bring concern and uncertainty for our childrens safety. In the District of Columbia large sums of money were spent to remove old lead paint from the Districts buildings. . . . To their suprise the new paint contained high levels of lead too.

The incineration of hazardous waste by ocean vessels is also in the news because they plan to use the ocean as the purification filter for the process. High levels of radioactive Radon gas were found along the Reading prong in Pennsylvania. Everywhere you turn hazardous materials exist.

Practical Resolution

But how can the energy manager help solve these problems? The Environmental Protection Agency's (EPA) primary objective is to protect human health and the environment. Key methods for achieving this objective are to identify the hazardous substances and to minimize their use. Once identified the general public is informed of the material and its proper handling. Safer substitutes are used whenever feasible. If it must be used, the hazardous material is used as long as possible in its original state. Secondary uses are sought for spent solutions and rejuvenation for reuse is also attempted.

Energy managers can be the eyes and hands for the identification and use of these hazardous materials. In your daily efforts you are exposed to many of the most serious hazardous materials in the work areas. As you begin to address the proper handling of these hazardous materials you begin to solve the problem and at the same time improve your credentials with your environmental experience.

In the early days as an energy manager you probably took a midnight walk through the business office. This revealed potential ways to save energy. You can also tune your senses to spot and implement potential ways to save our environment.

AREAS OF EXPERTISE

The activities of a particular energy manager can be as varied as there are companies on the earth. So a typical energy manager will be described in this paper. Each area that a typical energy manager would be responsible for will be analyzed with the intent to protect human health and the environment.

Location Selection

Many times the location of a facility is fixed. Sometimes the energy manager gets to participate in the selection of a location. A few areas you might look at are: the location, types and price of available energy sources, the distances from source and destination facilities, the weather conditions, the lay of the land, the neighbors and what they do. The environmental "eye" will look at: the historical use of the land, vegetation, quality of the roads between locations and quality of the available energy sources, as well as the items above.

The environmental manager is looking for things which can cause an unexpected cost for the employer or client when purchasing land or buildings. Pretreatment of potable water because of a neighbors smoke stack or removing the top eight inches of soil for decontamination of oil laced with polychlorinated biphenyl (PCB) are best identified before signing the contract.

No one wants to dig up underground storage tanks when excavating for a new building, especially when they have been leaking into an underground aquifer and they contain photographic wastes. Also, no one wants to build a chemical treatment plant to treat storm water runoff from a parking lot. These are real problems that can happen to you if you don't anticipate their possibility when selecting a site.

Building Construction

Once the land is purchased and the employee or client chooses to build a building, the energy manager will position the building to optimize the use of solar energy (sun, wind, and water) without violating a neighbors air space (when utilized or regulated). The environmentally aware manager will also consider what effect the building will have on its surroundings. Where will the storm water runoff go? How will the transport vehicles move about? What eyesores need screening? Will fleet maintenance be on-site? What solid waste materials will be generated for disposal in the building?

The energy manager evaluates the materials of construction. All parts of the building are scrutinized to take advantage of free energy and minimize the purchased energy. During this evaluation the manager can specify substitutes for unnecessary hazardous materials such as vinyl asbestos floor tiles, ureathane foam insulation, lead sound insulation, and formaldehyde based carpet glues. Paints and cleaning solvents can be evaluated to minimize risk as well.

Electrical Systems

New electrical systems should be studied by the energy manager for environmental impact. The legislative trend has been to minimize hazardous waste. Well, mineral oil is likely to be classified as a hazardous waste if it is contained in an electrical transformer. So where possible install air-cooled transformers. The same would be true for large liquid cooled power factor correcting capacitors. Where possible correct the power factor with small capacitors located at the motors which cause the phase shift. When using epoxy compounds on the electrical connections use all of the mixture on the joint rather then discarding any remainder. Solvents and cleaners should be used sparingly and application instructions should be followed carefully.

Mechanical Systems

These systems probably received the most scrutiny in the last decade due largely to the energy penalty paid for overdesign and the public demand for a fixed temperature and humidity throughout the work places. Simplicity of the design, economic placement of the equipment, ease of maintenance, load isolation, loss reduction, controlled ventilation, and remote control and monitoring of the systems are but a few of the energy managers interests. The environmental "eye" will also be observing the same things with a concern for the potential impact on the employees and the environment. Reliable ventilation controls, noise reduction, secondary containment for chemical feed systems, oil separators for parking lot drainage, and real time monitoring of an underground tanks integrity are additional points to consider.

Building Operation

When a building becomes occupied, there are additional areas of concern. The Occupational Safety and Health Administration (OSHA) has been very active in providing legislation which requires that certain employers identify, label, and train their employees about the hazardous chemicals in their work places. Several states have included all employers under their state requirements. As you tour an existing facility, look for unmarked containers. Find out what's in them, and don't be surprised if the employee responds with "I don't know but it's the best darned glue I've ever used".

Building Maintenance and Rearrangements

This is the area where the most environmentally hazardous substances are encountered. In the past, the use of certain hazardous materials like asbestos, polychlorinated biphenyl (PCB), mercury, and lead were the materials of choice (the most desired materials for the purpose).

Asbestos can be found everywhere. Several examples of where it has been used are: Roads, floor tiles, wallboard, concrete, water pipes, electric heaters, paper, roof shingles, wallpaper, duct insulation and ceiling insulation. The list is grossly incomplete but it provides the necessary impact to convince the last doubting energy manager that he or she is part of the problem.

You've probably replaced thousands of lights and light ballasts with newer higher efficiency lighting systems. Pre-1979 light ballasts usually contained capacitors which were saturated in PCB liquid. High temperature incineration of these light ballasts, in large amounts, is the only legal method of disposal.

Many indoor power transformers and large power factor correction capacitors also contained PCB liquid. Why? Because of it's flame resistance. It just won't burn! A byproduct of the incomplete combustion of PCB, however, is dioxin or "agent orange" which is a well know carcinogen.

Smoke detectors have radioactive substances in them. They are very good to have in the work place but you cannot legally throw them away in a landfill.

You've probably replaced major control systems with newer and better products. Most of the old systems used many mercury switches. Again in large amounts, it is illegal to just throw them away. The same is true with lead in paint, sound insulation, and cable coverings.

Demolition

Demolition is usually the worst time for human exposure to hazardous materials. This risk should be minimized by using proper respiratory equipment, using negative pressure ventilation systems which contain the airborne particles and restricting access to the work space. Material should be dampened before removal. Work area cleaning and personnel hygiene should be done at least daily. If large amounts of asbestos are present the isolation procedures and personnel hygiene are regulated by federal and state agencies.

General

Common sense and a knowledge of what to be looking for is an excellent start to managing hazardous materials. For example if you know that the brake shoes of a car contain asbestos, then you also know that it's unwise to blow the dust off a brake drum.

The high-technology industry has been using lithium batteries to retain the memories of computers, printers, and modems. These batteries, if opened to the air, can cause fires. Such materials are illegal for landfill disposal.

Every firm, large or small, should have an environmental management program suited to its size and the quantity of wastes it produces. It should include a written statement of policy from the Chief Operating Officer describing a commitment to protect human health and the environment. Someone in the company with the authority to allocate resources should oversee the environmental activities. Periodic, perhaps annually, your program should be reviewed for compliance with environmental regulations and risk minimization by an expert. Consultants or local regulatory agencies can be used for this purpose.

Today, not having a program, could be construed as negligence on the part of management. Criminal penalties range up to five (5) years imprisonment for such an offense. Personal civil penalties up to $250,000 and Corporate penalties up to $1,000,000 can also be assessed.

CONCLUSION

A quick mental review of the past thirteen years as a typical energy manager reveals many areas which would've been less hazardous if we had just known of their effect on the environment. In fact, several projects would not have been economically justifiable. If you already anticipate these problems I salute you as a pioneer in your field. Share your knowledge with your peers so your work will be a little less difficult.

The effort that will be required to guarantee a safe environment for our children seems formidable. The great country of ours is a world leader in every endeaver it undertakes. No one person is responsible for this. It is the combined efforts of each of us which makes such tasks achievable.

Chapter 64

ASBESTOS ASSESSMENT AND SURVEYS OF SCHOOL BUILDINGS

R. P. Villa

INTRODUCTION

Concern over the current regulations regarding the Friable Asbestos-Containing Materials in schools; Identification and Notification Rule (hereafter to be referred to as the Notification and Identification Rule), is a problem that should be addressed and analyzed. Local school administrators are facing daily financial, curriculum, maintenance, etc. problems, and the urgency to satisfy still another federal rule and regulation has proven to be a monumental task.

Asbestos in schools and all the meticulous details to fulfill, is an albatross that will not vanish on its own, and has a large impact on how a school system operates on a day-to-day basis. Parents, students, school board members, teachers, administrators, and maintenance personnel are all faced with the question of how to address asbestos in schools and where to turn for positive assistance in tackling the situation.

The experience and background I have gained with regard to the asbestos notification and identification rule have proven to be very useful to our clients. I hope to present some varied insight and approaches to the asbestos surveys, bulk samples procurement, assessment reports, phased implementation and design considerations for potential abatement and replacement that may also prove to be beneficial and informative.

GOALS AND OBJECTIVES

It is my intention to discuss the asbestos related rules, regulations and miscellaneous background and case history data in a concise and orderly manner. It is also my goal that this paper can be used by both school administrators, maintenance personnel, or any other (noninstitutional) management or maintenance personnel that has to continually deal with the every day concerns and sometimes confusing and often times misinterpreted aspects of asbestos.

In addition, I realize that many states and/or regions have initiated self-imposed restrictions and regulations regarding asbestos. This paper will focus primarily on the general rules and regulations and common occurrences regarding asbestos abatement so that it may hopefully be utilized to address one of your immediate needs.

REPORT FORMAT

This paper is divided into three (3) main sections, so that if any area is not of particular interest or pertain to your situation, it may, therefore, be omitted. In general, the following areas of asbestos related data to be covered, is as follows:

I. <u>Preliminary Investigation</u>

A. The need to review existing documents including: floor plans, architectural drawings, contract documents, and previously completed asbestos related reports and surveys.

B. Determine whether you will require the services of an outside consultant.

C. Procurement of bulk samples.

D. Laboratory analysis and selection of an experienced and reputable laboratory.

E. How to analyze laboratory results and determine the extent (if any) of asbestos containing material throughout your building(s).

F. If there is friable asbestos material in your building(s), discuss the regulations of the notification and identification rule.

II. <u>Determining a Course of Action</u>

A. Complying with the notification and identification rule. Assuring that the monitoring and maintenance requirements are also satisfied.

B. The need to determine quantities of asbestos material and cost estimates for potential removal

and replacement (or other appropriate abatement alternatives).

C. Potential development of phased implementation regarding asbestos abatement.

III. Case History(s)

A. A Consultant's perspective and actual involvement with Local Education Agencies.

B. Introduce the requirements of the asbestos notification and identification rule and misconceptions of the rule.

C. Involvement with school boards and administration.

D. Inform and work with the general public and assuring that public awareness is maintained.

E. Complete and submit an assessment survey report.

F. Discuss our involvement with E.P.A. inspections of school districts to assure compliance of the rule.

G. Present budget estimates.

H. Preliminary design contracts for potential abatement.

I. The development of Contract Documents and specifications.

J. Removal and replacement alternatives and identifying actual project related occurrences.

K. Closing out an asbestos abatement contract.

I. Preliminary Investigation

The initial phase in determining the existence or extent of asbestos material may seem trivial, but the initial approach becomes instrumental as the investigation continues. The most important aspect of any preliminary investigation, is gathering any information, documentation, or backup data regarding previous asbestos surveys, laboratory analyses, and reports. Contacting the person who used to be in your position or a maintenance/administrative position, (if applicable) is also a very positive starting point. Gather all the files, correspondence, and reports so that a determination may be made as to whether you wish to pursue the investigation with in-house personnel or seek the services of a consultant.

Numerous school districts have successfully completed the required surveys, laboratory analyses, assessment reports, recordkeeping, and notification requirements by utilizing their in-house expertise. The main consideration when using in-house personnel, is whether they fully understand the law and does the individual have the expertise and time to address all the aspects and ramifications involved with asbestos in school buildings.

Whether or not a school district wishes to complete this phase of the investigation on their own, it is still necessary to obtain the most current E.P.A. documents, which include the "purple" book. These and many other useful documents are easily obtainable by calling an E.P.A. regional office, or the Washington, D.C. office at 1-800-424-9065.

Special care, and thorough reading of the appropriate E.P.A. document(s) on procurement of bulk samples, is important in and becoming aware of the precautions required prior to taking samples. Selection of an experienced and proven analytical laboratory to analyze the bulk samples is also a requirement. The laboratory that submits a proposal should provide a list of clients and experience, as well as, procedures and the type of analysis that will be provided. The laboratory should utilize the polarized light microscopy method (PLM) when analyzing bulk samples. In addition, the analytical laboratory should be enrolled in the NIOSH Proficiency Analytical Testing (PAT) program for asbestos fiber counting.

After compilation of all the necessary background data regarding bulk samples and resultant analysis, it will be necessary to compile a complete asbestos assessment survey report. As you can see, the procedures to follow and areas to include in the report, may become complicated, which is why many schools (organizations) utilize the services of an outside (third part) consultant.

This survey report should include, among other items that may be appropriate to your situation, the following:

A. Identify the person responsible for and assuring that the rules are being satisfied.

B. Include bulk sample analyses and accompanying report(s).

C. Utilize as many floor plans/building sketches which will enhance the identification and location of the actual bulk samples.

Include as much additional information regarding square footage of material, lineal footage or actual locations of asbestos containing material. This could be identified on the sketches to improve clarity.

D. As stated in the E.P.A. rules, a school district is required to notify parents, teachers, custodians, maintenance personnel, etc. of the presence of friable asbestos containing material. Again, it will be important for you to review the E.P.A. documentation and recordkeeping information, which will provide further specifics regarding this portion of the rule.

E. A copy of the assessment survey report and all E.P.A. documents should be kept in the office of all school buildings as well as the administrative offices.

F. If there are any areas of immediate concern regarding friable asbestos or of asbestos that may potentially become airborne, school boards and administrators should make a decision whether to encapsulate, enclose, or remove the material.

Typically, the most common route selected by school boards and administrators is removal of the material so that the potential contamination can be eliminated from their facility. The rationale utilized in most cases for selecting removal versus any other approach is as follows:

1. The asbestos will be removed and there will not be any future concern over dealing the material.

2. Existing conditions (damage, occupancy, maintenance, etc.) often dictate the decision.

3. If any future building construction (renovation) is completed, then the asbestos (if encapsulated or enclosed) could be accidentally damaged, thus causing contamination. If this occurs, then the money originally "saved" by using an alternate approach is quickly lost.

G. As many of the administrators already know, there are no laws mandating removal of asbestos. School systems, are voluntarily removing asbestos containing material.

II. Determining A Course of Action

The majority of information contained in this section will be applicable to any school district or organization that wishes to undertake asbestos abatement activities. There are certain procedures and precautions that are highly recommended that would aid in assuring that any asbestos abatement activities are executed in a workmanlike and safe manner. In addition, states are gradually mandating various rules and regulations in an effort to assure that contractors are meeting their (each state's) training and certification requirements.

Throughout the context of this paper, I realize that the majority of the statements and recommendations are biased towards utilizing asbestos removal versus encapsulation. The removal projects that I have been involved with, and specified through our office, assure that potential hazards and contamination of any surrounding areas are essentially eliminated and contained within the work place. Our standard procedures with respect to developing Contract Documents and Specifications for asbestos abatement contractors is that they must be experienced, with submittals provided, regarding their background and include names and addresses of clients for whom they have previously completed asbestos abatement.

Another area where we are obviously biased, is that we believe that utilizing the services of a consultant such as ourselves, (Abonmarche Consultants, Inc. of Benton Harbor, Michigan), proves to be beneficial in many areas. The consultant that you work with must be experienced in completing on-site surveys, feasibility studies, assessments, analyzing situations and providing recommendations as well as budgets, and also most importantly developing Contract Documents and Specifications for the use in successfully soliciting competitive bids from Asbestos Abatement Contractors. Of course, a consultant does not always have analytical laboratory services on staff, therefore, in many instances a subconsultant would be required. It is very important to also realize that anytime a consulting engineering and architectural firm is working for a client, such as a school district, the number one goal is to assure that the safety and well-being of the client and the occupants are maintained which is obviously the part of the code of ethics for all engineers and architects.

We are not implying in any way that any other company that is involved in asbestos abatement is not also looking out for the interest of the client. A consultant assures that the various organizations working for a particular client are both experienced and have good references. There are many instances where emergency abatement may be required, but this still does not eliminate the need to competitively seek proposals from qualified contractors and associated air monitoring and analytical laboratory companies.

Typical procedures and chronological of events for selecting a Contractor for potential asbestos abatement are as follows:

1. Determine the extent of the project and the scope of the abatement work.

2. The need for asbestos abatement includes analyzing the existing condition of the material or future con-

cerns regarding deterioration, which would warrant the need for asbestos abatement.

3. Determine alternative approaches for resolving the presence of asbestos. The alternatives include, but are not limited to: encapsulation, enclosing, removal, or necessary monitoring to assure that the material maintains it's physical integrity.

4. The next step will be to provide both alternatives and budget estimates. Budgets include the cost for removal and replacement when required and laboratory and consulting fees. In some instances, a relocation of personnel or shutting down of facilities may be warranted which should also be included as part of the budget. Items to include in your budget are: replacement costs, air monitoring, disposal costs, mobilization, testing, contingencies, etc.

5. Select alternatives and develop a course of action. Schedule and prepare Contract Documents and receipt of bids.

6. Advertise in local publications (if required), plus the solicit known qualified asbestos abatement contractors in your area.

7. The specifications for asbestos abatement should be very specific and have provisions to the effect, that the contractor must satisfy all local, state and federal codes and laws.

8. After receipt of the proposals, if there is a contractor that you are not aware of their background, some extensive research would be mandatory. Our specifications ask for names, addresses, telephone numbers and contact persons of previous clients and projects of similar magnitude and type which would be either submitted prior to submitting a proposal or with the bid documents. Therefore, simply by making telephone calls and contacts to previous clients, and probably more importantly the Engineer/Architect on the job, and complete an investigation into background and work practices (the Engineer/Architect should be able to address this area) of a particular contractor could be made quite easily.

9. After award of a contract, a preconstruction meeting should be scheduled to discuss schedules, completion dates, set up requirements, air monitoring, etc. This is necessary to assure that the project is completed in a timely manner.

10. Air monitoring, as per any and all O.S.H.A. regulations, should be maintained throughout the preparation, removal, and post abatement process. In addition, on-site review by the consulting engineering/architectural firm is strongly recommended as a spot check with regard to procedures and work progress.

11. Final close out includes: on-site visit for required clean air checks, final area clean up requirements, receipt of air monitoring reports, Ten-Day Notice Form (should have been submitted at the preconstruction meeting), waste verification forms, landfill operator forms, and any other daily monitoring and posting throughout the work areas that were maintained throughout the abatement procedures.

III. Case Histories

As a consulting engineering and architectural firm, we have been involved in all aspects of asbestos identification and abatement as previously described in Sections I and II. The case histories that I will briefly discuss in this section are based on actual projects and depending on the different situation, I will discuss either feasibility studies, assessment surveys, or development of contract documents and specifications for asbestos abatement.

Throughout the context of each of the case histories, you will notice that I identify either the client or the school district as an initial or set of initials. This identification is for my convenience in order to remember the school district or company involved to better establish my outline of the chronological events.

Asbestos Assessment Survey and Report - School District CS:
We were initially contacted by CS to do a survey of all their buildings to determine the presence of asbestos material. The initial request was somewhat vague and based on our (the company's) experience it did not appear that we were being requested to provide the services that would satisfy their requirements.

After some discussions with administration, it was discovered that the request that was sent to our office was prompted by a flyer that they received from a company on the other side of the state. The organization was a laboratory that would provide the client with free on-site building survey services and only charge them for the analytical laboratory analysis. On the surface this does not appear to be a serious problem, but after we were shown the proposal from the laboratory, we were able to identify a few areas to the client that should be wary and take some precaution before engaging in a contract. A few of our observations were as follows:

1. The bulk sample analysis rate was nearly 2-1/2 times the average cost charged by local laboratories.

2. No reference was made in the proposal that they would follow any or all of the E.P.A. regulations.

3. In addition, there was no reference to the procuring of bulk samples per E.P.A. regulations, nor was a limit established for the number of samples they anticipated to procure.

   This was considered a problem area in that the laboratory could take as many samples as they wanted. In other words, they could take more samples than absolutely necessary, and in turn this "free" survey turns out to be a very costly assessment survey.

4. The proposal also identified the procurement of samples and laboratory analysis with no indication that the client would be provided the necessary paperwork, identification, notification, and recordkeeping criteria necessary to meet the identification/notification rule.

   Therefore, the laboratory could take numerous bulk samples, submit a analytical report with the client still not having the required report or assessment information.

5. If the client decided to work with the laboratory, it was established that this particular laboratory had no experience or background with regards to completing the reports as discussed above, nor did they have the personnel experienced in developing contract documents and specifications in the event that future asbestos abatement may be required.

6. The school district still pursued the services of this analytical laboratory and also received a proposal from our office and other local consulting engineering and architectural firms. Our office in turn submitted a detailed proposal of the services that we proposed to provide, along with the assurance that the identification/notification rule would be satisfied along with our utilizing an outside laboratory for our bulk sample analysis.

   In addition, our proposal identified many of the advantages discussed above, along with a list of our experience and background with regards to surveys, procurement of bulk samples, and development of contract documents and specifications. The school district awarded our firm the contract.

During the course of surveying the building for School District CS, and after the submittal of the assessment survey, several interesting misconceptions and omissions on the part of the School District were identified:

1. The original proposal only included buildings that the school district were currently utilizing. Their original list of buildings did not include a few buildings that were closed, the administration building, and buildings that were being leased.

   The assessment report did include a survey of all the above referenced facilities.

2. The presence of non-friable asbestos material was found in several of their facilities. The district perceived the rule that any time asbestos was found anywhere within the district, parents, teachers, staff, etc. all had to be notified. This was originally a problem, but was explained as a part of the survey report.

3. Many of the custodian and maintenance personnel were convinced that there was no asbestos material in their building. This misconception was brought on based upon the fact that they had previous laboratory analysis performed by the State of Michigan, Michigan Department of Public Health. The problem was, that the school did not realize that the original test results were performed utilizing X-ray diffraction versus the current acceptable Polarized Light Microscopy method.

4. During the course of the actual bulk sample procurement, I was keeping the district abreast of the laboratory reports prior to submitting a final report. Several areas were identified to contain asbestos, and school district administrators were very nervous with regard to not having enough money to remove all of the asbestos. Again, they were under the misconception that once asbestos was identified in their building, the federal government was mandating them to remove the material. Of course, this is not a true interpretation of the current federal rule.

5. In addition, during the initial phase of this on-site surveying, the district was attempting to utilize the local department of public health in order to save some money in survey costs and rule interpretation. The district soon found out that the health department was not as informed as they were lead to believe, and that the local health department was utilizing our firm as a basis for asbestos related information and education.

6. Several months after the assessment survey and report was submitted to the

district, I received a telephone call from an administrator saying that they were going to be inspected by the E.P.A. within the next several days. This E.P.A. inspection was completed a

few years ago as part of a random survey to assure school districts were complying with the identification/notification rule.

Needless to say, or else I would not be bringing up this survey performed by the E.P.A., the district received a very positive letter from the E.P.A. commending them on their thoroughness in completing the required information to satisfy the rule. In fact, the letter that was sent to the administrator of which we received a copy, made a statement to the fact that the E.P.A. would like to see more districts complete and satisfy the rules and regulations as thorough as the ones completed by Abonmarche Consultants, Inc. for school district CS. (To date, at least three (3) other local districts we worked with, have been inspected by the E.P.A. with the same positive results.)

Asbestos Abatement - School District SP:
Our firm completed an asbestos assessment survey similar to that described above for school district CS. The only difference was that this district (SP) had some previous laboratory analysis completed using the acceptable procedures which in turn was an aid when completing the survey and report. This case history, however, will focus upon the asbestos removal project that was completed a year or so after the assessment survey and report.

This asbestos abatement project entailed removing asbestos containing material from four boiler rooms and numerous riser pipes located throughout several hallways and classroom areas throughout the district. The project cost was not that large, but the set up and mobilization from building-to-building made it a project that required scheduling and coordination between the buildings, custodians, and principals.

It is our philosophy, whenever possible, to attempt to keep a building unoccupied during abatement activities. As you may or may not be aware, numerous precautions are taken so that it would feasible to have people working in the building during the actual removal, but as we suggest to attempt to alleviate future or potential liability of any type, it is suggested that you attempt to keep the building clear of any and all personnel.

In working with school districts, there is the advantage of having the flexibility of temporarily relocating a custodian or maintenance person and have them work in another building while abatement is being conducted in their particular building. This relocation is assuming that abatement will be completed during a summer recess or a holiday period.

For your review, the following are guidelines and suggestions, as well as actual occurrences that transpired during the course of this project that may be of use:

1. Assure that the contractor has adequate and the necessary workmen's compensation and liability insurance required to satisfy the scope of your project.

2. A preconstruction meeting was very helpful in this project because of the various buildings that the contractor had to visit. We were able to establish a schedule as well as a standard procedure to be followed for each and every building so that the contractor did not have to keep remembering what he needed to do when he got to any specific building. The procedures and requirements were kept uniform, therefore, the problems and misunderstandings were minimized.

3. A preliminary walk through of all the areas , which were to have abatement, were surveyed so that the existing conditions of the walls, windows, lights, etc. were noted prior to any abatement. This was important so that if any damages occurred, the problem of determining when the damages occurred and by whom, was minimized.

4. The contractor was required to contact our office at least twice a day (once in the morning and once in the afternoon), above and beyond any other discussions we had during the course of the day. This was particularily helpful in keeping track of the contractor so that if any questions or situations occurred during the course of the day, we would at all times know the status of work and whereabouts of the contractor.

5. During the course of this project, there was additional lineal footage of pipe that the school district decided to remove after the award of the contract. As a result of this situation from henceforth, we inserted a provision for all contractors who bid our projects to list a cost per lineal foot of removal, so that any future projects that may require additional removal will not result in any questions with regards to the amount the contractor would charge for any extra work.

Asbestos Assessment Survey, Report And Abatement - School District JS:
As you will notice by the title of this case history, the various phases of this project involved all of the potential aspects that we have been involved with re-

gard to asbestos related projects. One of the main reasons I wanted to further discuss this particular case history, is that

I was able to follow the evolvement of each particular phase.

The asbestos survey portion of this project did not have too many unusual or unique situations that were uncovered during the course of this survey. As is the case with all of our projects, we try to learn from the experience as well as attempting to document the various discussions and questions that are asked during any portion of the work.

Boards of education and administrators have different priorities and procedures that should be followed, therefore, each project is unique and must be handled with care. In addition, ample time must be allowed for proper education of the personnel involved with the project. An area which is a relative constant, is that the asbestos containing material found within a typical school building, is limited to distinct areas, therefore, the potential for omission with regard to identification of asbestos areas is minimized.

A chronological list of events, along with a few discussion items that were a part of the asbestos assessment survey and report are as follows:

1. An Administrator contacted our office to submit a proposal for surveying all the buildings throughout the district. We were not presented with any formal proposal or an outline of the scope of services.

   The verbal request that I received did, however, ask that our firm provide them with a survey report that included all buildings within their district. This was a positive aspect, in that they were aware that even though they were leasing or had buildings that were closed, they should still be made a part of the overall project. Even though it was not specifically requested, we provided a list of our previous clients and experience in the asbestos abatement area.

2. During the course of the actual procurement of bulk samples, we were notified by numerous people that we would not find any asbestos because a report was already completed and they could not understand why administration and the school board were wasting money redoing a previous report. This is an important point, in that we then made the administrators aware of these previous reports and the laboratory analyses were located.

   The previous laboratory analysis and correspondence indicated that the test procedure utilized was X-ray Diffraction. As we previously discussed in this paper, the X-ray Diffraction is not accepted as a viable method, with

   Polarized Light Microscopy method now being the accepted procedure.

3. All of the field notes, floor plans, sketches, and laboratory analysis, as well as, pertinent asbestos notification/identification criteria were submitted to the owner. In addition, we summarized all of the work and provided a list of guidelines to follow so that the district would be in compliance with the notification/identification rule.

The following information is a brief summary of the events that occurred during the abatement process:

1. A building maintenance man contacted me and requested a budget for removal of asbestos containing mechanical, acoustical and ceiling plaster from a middle school. Based upon some preliminary square foot areas of ceiling plaster and lineal footage of pipes that were anticipated to be removed, we developed a budget estimate for both removal, replacement, and corresponding consulting fees.

2. The next step was to provide a written proposal for scope of services which included but not limited to: on-site review of the project area, measurements of pipes, tanks and boilers, development of specifications for asbestos abatement, develop contract documents and specifications for the replacement of both ceiling plaster and mechanical equipment, and on-site project representation throughout the abatement process.

3. I will not go into detail with regard to the process that transpired with regard to the development of contracts and solicitation of proposals, in that we discussed this in detail in the above section. I want to mention that we did follow our standard operating procedures and had several contractors submit proposals, all of which were from reputable organizations.

4. A disturbing incident occurred (of course, it was very good news for the owner) in that the asbestos abatement costs were in essence 35-40% less than our budget estimate. The only logical reason we could attribute this to was the fact that at the time, asbestos contractors were not busy and were trying to schedule some work. In the meantime business improved and it would be difficult to determine whether the proposals would now be closer to our budget estimates. The estimates were based on were actual pro-

jects that were completed through our office over the past couple of years.

5. The preconstruction meeting, preparation of the work area, and abatement

   work was completed as per the schedule itemized in the contract documents and specifications. This project, I feel, went as well as it did, because, 1) we had a good contractor working on the project, and, 2) the specifications were very clear and specific with regards to necessary time frames and goals.

   In addition, I contacted several potential abatement contractors ahead of the actual completion date of the specifications and informed them of our time constraints so that they could start planning their work load and activities in preparation for this particular project.

6. An unusual situation occurred part of the way through this abatement project. I received a telephone call from an architect who was working for the district on a boiler replacement project and a conversion project (from steam to hot water) in other buildings. The interesting part of this situation is that the architect informed me that somehow they recently discovered that there are other buildings throughout the district that had asbestos containing material.

   It seems that a portion of the building principals and maintenance personnel thought their building was free of asbestos where others knew that there was asbestos present in their area. The report that we completed a year earlier did not seem to be circulated or on file. In addition, I discovered that many of the recommended procedures and notification/identifications rule were not followed.

SUMMARY

In the years that I have been involved with the many facets of asbestos related projects, it appears that the majority of problems occur with communications, awareness, and interpretation of the appropriate laws. The most difficult aspect of the entire asbestos related industry, with regards to school systems, is finding someone within the district who will take the responsibility and coordinate the required surveying, laboratory analysis, or abatement procedures.

Of course, we realize that throughout the context of this paper, experience show that utilizing a firm such as ourselves, or an experienced individual is in many times the avenue to pursue. The initative to confront the asbestos issue must come from within (administration, maintenance, etc.) and inherent concerns and problems of the tax payers and occupants of each building should be addressed and never taken lightly.

Chapter 65

ASBESTOS AND THE ENERGY MANAGER – FROM PROJECT EVALUATION TO A COMPUTERIZED DATABASE

P. J. Mulligan, J. A. Pollock

Energy Managers are called on to perform a variety of tasks. Initial design, building remodel, equipment replacement, and energy retrofit. We can expect to encounter asbestos during any one of these tasks and we need to be prepared to deal with it. Asbestos management has rapidly evolved into a sophisticated technology that need not be the cause of undue problems if we are informed and prepared.

The energy manager must always make a good faith effort to check for asbestos before starting a project. In the past many people have chosen to turn their backs on the asbestos problem. Avoiding the additional short term costs caused by asbestos abatement, and ignoring the long term costs of litigation.

Asbestos litigation is costly, it is important that asbestos containing materials are identified in your buildings. The problem must be dealt with in systematic manner that will protect all parties from future legal action and asbestos related diseases.

The situation varies, from the consultant who is looking at one job at a time, to the energy manager who has several projects under way covering many different types of building in different States.

We would like to present a brief outline of some practical approaches to the problem of asbestos abatement, that range from a simple project evaluation to a complete computerized database.

This would give a large corporate entity the ability to set up an asbestos management program that will allow them to identify all asbestos and estimate the abatement costs.

There are many ways an unsuspecting contractor can release deadly asbestos fibres into the atmosphere. In Los Angeles recently, a trash can was found to be full of loose asbestos after a plumbing contractor had demolished an old furnace and piping system. A jet-stream of asbestos fibres was hurled into the corridors of a hospital when duct-cleaning contractors used a vacuum cleaner to remove asbestos dust from the air-conditioning ducts. One building was found to seriously contaminated with asbestos after the contractor had installed new smoke detectors on the ceiling. The lobby of another building was seriously contaminated when unsuspecting contractors ground down the old asbestos vinyl floor during a remodelling project. A high school was contaminated both inside and outside when a painting contractor sand-blasted transite wall panels.

In every one of those cases, the building owners, building managers, engineers and the contractors involved were not aware that they were dealing with asbestos. However they would probably have been judged liable for the contamination had litigation been sought. Recent legislation passed in California, mandates that a person who owns, manages, contracts for, or supervises work in any building, must make a good faith effort to determine whether asbestos is contained in the building. Even if this is not mandated in your State, it would still be possible to establish liability if a person contracts an asbestos related disease. If there has been no work record of exposure to asbestos and the person is not a family member of an asbestos worker, that person or his surviving spouse's attorney may attempt to establish where there was exposure to asbestos. Should one of those locations be a property owned, or managed, by you the attorney may attempt to determine liability for the disease along the lines of that faced by the manufacturers of asbestos. These will include medical costs, pain and suffering, compensatory damages and punitive damages. Verdicts with the asbestos manufacturers are at present going as high as three million dollars. Even if it is proven that you are not responsible, the cost of litigation to demonstrate that, could prove costly. Already many attorneys are jumping on the litigation bandwagon and in a financial sense, you lose as soon as you enter into litigation.

WHAT IS ASBESTOS?

Asbestos is a general term used to describe a group of naturally occurring fibrous mineral silicates. The fibers are chemically inert, heat resistant, and cannot be destroyed easily. Asbestos has been widely used for the fireproofing of steel framed buildings, blown-on acoustic applications, and the insulation of mechanical systems and associated pipework. It has been used, to a lesser extent, in cement sheets and pipes, roofing felt and shingles, floor tiles, patching and taping compounds, insulating paper, protective cloth and electric wiring. Although banned for some applications, 200,000 tons of asbestos are mined or processed in the U.S. each year, from a peak of 800,000 tons in 1973. Two thirds of this asbestos is still used in the construction industry.

WHEN IS ASBESTOS DANGEROUS?

Asbestos that is soft and easily abraded is called "friable" which in it's normal state is usually not harmful. However if it is friable and it's integrity is disturbed and the fibres are allowed to float in the atmosphere, asbestos becomes extremely dangerous. The fibers are microscopic and mild currents of air in a building can keep them suspended almost indefinitely. Asbestos fibres are extremely small, about 0.4 micrometers in diameter, 2,500 would equal the diameter of a human hair.

Almost molecular in size, the fibres if inhaled or swallowed, remain in thelungs permanently. They can move from the lungs to almost all other parts of the body and can cause a number of serious asbestos related diseases.

ASBESTOS RELATED DISEASES

There are four major diseases that are directly related to asbestos exposure:

Asbestosis: The classic disease first described in 1907 and well known by 1931. This disease causes calcification and shrinkage of the lung with attendant loss of lung capacity, reducing the average effective life by about eight years.

Plural thickening or Plaques: This disease causes calcification of the diaphragm, impairing the ability of the lung to slide within the chest. Interfering with the respiratory system.

Mesothelioma: A deadly disease. A malignant fleshy tumor almost impossible to remove from the patient, doctors describe that removing it is like scooping jelly from a deep dish, you get a little on the spoon, most of it falls back in the hole and every where it lands it takes seed. A tumor so deadly that doctors rarely attempt to remove it. Death usually occurs within one year of diagnosis.

Lung Cancer: The fourth and most well known disease. This cancer can have other causes than asbestos exposure, although it is the most ominous of the asbestos diseases. The probability of death increases by about 80 times if the exposed person is also a cigarette smoker.

Up until about 12 to 15 years ago it was the common belief that only pure asbestos caused these asbestos related diseases. It has been demonstrated since, that asbestos containing material can cause these diseases and there has been no minimum levels for asbestos exposure yet established.

WHERE IS ASBESTOS USED?

Asbestos is an organic substance that is virtually indestructible. Ironically it is this toughness that causes the present day problems of removal and control. Prior to 1976 when asbestos spraying was banned by law, asbestos was used extensively in the construction industry. It was tossed into many materials to make things a little stronger or more resistant to wear. Caulking compounds, dry wall, taping compounds, acoustic ceiling spray, floor tiles, aluminum paint and cement pipe to name but a few.
Asbestos's most important function was as an insulator against heat and it's this function that we come across most often. Most buildings using structural steel were required by code to spray the exposed metal with fire-proofing. This was invariably asbestos based. The space between the roof and ceiling was then used for air-conditioning equipment, with the result that there are now thousands of buildings where loose asbestos fibres are in close proximity to air flowing into occupied spaces.

In the HVAC industry asbestos was used extensively for insulating boilers and piping, to protect against heat damage. Usually the piping is covered with asbestos, particularly at the elbows. Pump and boiler insulation is usually high percentage asbestos. Locations such as these are more prone to water damage, destroying the integrity of the asbestos bonding agent and allowing the fibres to become easily airborne. Unfortunately such mechanical equipment is very often located next to the air-handlers used for the air conditioning system, increasing the likelihood that asbestos fibres can circulate freely through a building.

WHAT SHOULD THE ENERGY MANAGER DO?

If you work on a building that contains asbestos you run the risk of contamination and subsequent liability if you don't identify the locations and stability of any possible asbestos. Asbestos will not go away. As the public becomes more and more educated the risks over legal action increase. Inspection and abatement is much cheaper and safer than litigation. If you should go into litigation, no matter what the outcome is you will still have to go to the expense of removing the asbestos.

The most important first step is to determine whether you have an asbestos problem and what the extent of that problem is. The following questions should be asked. Do you have asbestos? If you do have asbestos, where it is located? What is the potential hazard and how can it be controlled? How much will it cost to abate the problem?

IS IT ASBESTOS?

Careful bulk samples or air samples should be taken by an experienced asbestos abatement consultant and submitted for analysis. The determination of whether it is asbestos, what percentage, and what type of asbestos can only be made by microscopic analysis.

WHERE IS THE ASBESTOS?

A reputable asbestos abatement consultant can soon pinpoint the possible locations of suspected asbestos containing material in your building and take enough samples for confirmation.

WHAT IS THE RISK OF EXPOSURE?

The assessment of the risk of potential asbestos exposure is very difficult and very hard to quantify. A number of different factors are taken into account. These factors are quantified and entered into a mathematical formula known as an algorithm.

Baker Consultants, Inc. has developed an algorithm that can be adapted to suit most building applications. After an extensive survey a number of different iterations of the algorithm are run. The one that correlates closely to the written field comments is the one that is chosen for that particular survey. The final algorithm score is used to set priorities for remedial action in areas where friable asbestos is found. The score is computed from assessment factors that are determined in the field and in the laboratory.

Factors usually considered in the algorithm are:

F1	Physical Damage
F2	Water Damage
F3	Part of the Air Moving System
F4	Exposure
F5	Accessibility
F6	Activity
F7	Occupancy
F8	Integrity
F9	Type of Asbestos
F10	Percentage of Asbestos
F11	Releasability

ASBESTOS ABATEMENT

There are three basic recommended ways of controlling asbestos. Enclosure, encapsulation or removal.

Enclosure: The contractor surrounds the asbestos with an airtight structure that prevents contact and fibre loss. If the asbestos is reasonably stable, then this method is a fairly long term solution. It cannot be used where future access to the area is required, it will also have to be repeated when the bonding integrity of the asbestos eventually deteriorates allowing asbestos outside the enclosure. This method is not widely used.

Encapsulation: Here the asbestos is sprayed with an encapsulating material that will penetrate the asbestos and form a hard shell on the outside to prevent any fibre loss. The strength of the adhesion of the sub-strata is a big factor in determining whether encapsulation can be used. As in the previous method this is only a short term solution that will probably have to be repeated within five to ten years. The asbestos will still be present and a detailed operations and management program should be set up. Many States do not allow encapsulation of asbestos unless a removal date has been set.

Removal: The contractor removes the asbestos while using water or a wetting agent to minimize fibre release. Where practical this is by far the best solution. The problem is permanently solved and the possibilities of liability due to future maintenance work is eliminated. Usually removal is more expensive in the short term, but in general the medium to long term costs are much lower. However there are many factors to take into account during the evaluation of an asbestos abatement problem and sometimes complete removal is not possible.

COST OF ABATEMENT

Direct abatement costs, that is, the costs to remove the asbestos containing material, include:

1. Materials for setting up and sealing off the work area.
2. Disposable clothing and respirators.
3. Materials for containing and disposing of the asbestos waste.
4. Disposable air, water and personal filters.
5. Amended water.
6. Encapsulation material.

Other direct costs include:

1. Air Monitoring.
2. Industrial hygiene services.

Indirect costs include:

1. Medically certified and trained personnel
2. Training of employees.
3. Liability insurance.

Equipment and maintenance will include:

1. High efficiency filtered vacuum equipment and negative air pressure machines.
2. Decontamination trailers and setups.
3. Supplied air equipment.
4. Respirators.
5. High and low pressure sprayers.
6. Hazardous waste vehicles.
7. Scaffolding.
8. Portable lighting.
9. Replacement materials.

Costs incurred by the building owner or manager that are not paid to the contractor:

1. Operational costs: administrative costs, supervision, down-time costs, potential loss of income, etc.

2. Decontamination costs - Costs to decontaminate furniture and fixtures affected by the abatement area, and to remove and replace furniture and fixtures before and after abatement.

3. Management Costs

a) Setting up asbestos abatement contracts. This includes writing specifications, work procedures, scope of work, employee training, contractor pre-qualification interviews etc.

b) Project Management of Asbestos Abatement Contracts. This includes safety meetings, compliance inspections, air-monitoring etc.

A professional asbestos abatement company should be consulted in regard to controlling asbestos. Poor control techniques by an unqualified or reckless contractor can result in serious contamination of both the building and the surrounding areas.

The cost to abate the problem has to be based on a detailed analysis of the areas in questions. A measurement of the quantity of material and the selection of the abatement method preferred.

ASBESTOS ABATEMENT CONTRACTORS

The controlling of asbestos is a precise technique that should only be undertaken by professional asbestos abatement contractors. In all cases the area where the asbestos abatement is to take place is isolated in an airtight compartment usually constructed of heavy grade plastic sheeting. Access to the area is restricted by a series of air-locks that will prevent the escape of any airborne particles. Workmen entering the area through a clean room where they change into disposable protective clothing and respirator. They then go through a shower facility and into a disposal room before entering the work area. After completing a shift the worker goes back into the disposal room where they remove the disposable clothing, through the showers and into the clean room where they change into street clothes. Ensuring that no contaminated material or clothing passes to the outside, unless safely contained in double wrapped plastic bags. Some types of removal require the use of a compressor and air supplied respirators.

Qualified asbestos abatement contractors are obliged by law to ensure that their operatives are given regular training and medical examinations. They are also obliged to register as carcinogen users and as hazardous waste haulers. Before using an abatement contractor ask, to see his records and also call his previous customers for references. Mistakes made by unqualified contractors could be hazardous and much more costly in the long run.

A contractor removing asbestos should be registered as a carcinogen user. There are EPA and OSHA guidelines that govern the correct removal technique, the equipment required and the maximum airborne limits allowable. Both agencies must be notified by law before starting an asbestos removal project.

Any time there is maintenance, construction, repair, renovation or salvage activities where any materials containing asbestos are sanded, ground, abrasive blasted, sawed, cut, shovelled or otherwise handled in such a manner that asbestos dust would be raised, the project is subject to both OSHA and EPA regulations.

Penalties for not notifying the agency or for violating exposure limits or using dangerous removal techniques vary with the offense and the state, all of them involve large fines and possible jail sentences.

A PLAN FOR THE ENERGY MANAGER

In any management situation, the most important first step any manager can take is to determine whether there is a problem and what is the extent of the problem.

A professional survey of all property owned, managed or maintained by the manager must be made. The information should be collated in a manner that will make it easily accessible and easily maintained. Modern database technology and the increased use of micro-computers makes it fairly simple task to store the information on a computerized database.

Baker Consultants, inc. has created a compiled database program that will not only store the information but will also do a preliminary risk assessment, and cost analysis.

Data can be extracted in a number of ways that can be tailored to the needs of the different individuals using the database. The energy manager may want a report that lists all equipment, with an assessment of risk factors and costs of replacement of the asbestos. The administration manager may want to know which buildings that are occupied may have an asbestos problem. The general manager may want to know the total costs of abatement over the next five years, and which areas have the highest priority.

OPERATIONS AND MAINTENANCE

If you discover that you have an asbestos problem, it is not always practical or possible to remove it. You may be only able to afford to remove the serious problems, leaving other areas until budget constraints ease. You may choose to close down a building because it will be demolished or remodeled in the near future. You may choose the option of encapsulating the asbestos.

In all of the above situations the asbestos remains in place. It is important that occupants of the building and maintenance workers are aware of the location of any asbestos. A procedural operations and maintenance program should be formulated and followed to eliminate the problems associated with accidental exposure to asbestos.

CONCLUSIONS

Unfortunately asbestos will not go away. Public awareness of the problems associated with asbestos have increased dramatically over the past few years. A responsible approach to the problem should be attempted. Identify problem areas, assess the health and safety aspects of the asbestos and weigh them carefully against the costs of abatement and possible litigation. There are no hard and fast rules about asbestos, in many cases it is prudent to remove it. There are times when removal is impractical or cost prohibitive. Poor removal can cause a worse exposure than originally present. Asbestos abatement professionals should always be consulted in the event of a problem. It would be wise precaution to check the references of any asbestos abatement consultant you may hire.

Chapter 66

OPPORTUNITIES FOR ENERGY MANAGERS IN HAZARDOUS WASTE MANAGEMENT

W. C. Turner, J. Hansen, R. E. Webb, J. M. Shirley

INTRODUCTION

Now that industry is starting to understand the problems of energy management and is beginning to gain control, another iceberg is emerging whose tip leads us to believe it could be even worse than the energy crisis. That iceberg is the set of problems caused by hazardous materials, substances, and wastes and the regulations being developed.

New Right-To-Know laws mean any employer that uses hazardous materials must inform his/her employees and sometimes must inform the local community. RCRA reauthorization (Resource Conservation and Recovery Act) has brought an additional 150,000 (or so) firms under its regulation. The discussion could go on and on -- Congress is serious and has mandated fines and even felony convictions for violations.

Fortunately, much can be done to minimize the problems and in some cases eliminate them. Sheer economics of these regulations are making other alternatives highly profitable. For example, the authors have case studies showing resource recovery and/or material substitution with astounding paybacks.

Because of the energy manager's company wide perspective and similarity to energy problems, the energy manager is in a good position to make things happen.

This paper examines the problems of hazardous materials management. First, the paper explores (at a macro level) the regulations to set the stage. Then the emerging technologies for process modification, material substitution, and resource recovery are examined. Finally, case studies are presented to show the potential.

THE COST SAVING POTENTIAL

Hazardous waste management offers two areas of cost savings. The first is difficult to quantify and represents cost avoidance resulting from fines, civil suits, bad public exposure and other costly penalties associated with improper handling, storage and disposal of hazardous waste.

The second area of cost savings focuses on the reduction of the amount of waste generated and the degree of toxicity of that waste. This area represents quantifiable cost savings. Recent case studies show annual cost savings in excess of $315,000 for a oil well pump manufacturer with very fast payback on investment.

WHY ENERGY MANAGERS?

The similarity of hazardous material management to the early days of energy management is exceptionally strong. Early interest in both was generated mainly by environmentalists and those directly impacted. Energy management has gone through several stages of growth and has matured into a respected discipline. The authors maintain that hazardous material management is starting the same growth pattern. Obviously, energy managers know that pattern well.

Also, energy managers are accustomed to using the "economic systems" approach. Here economics is the basis of most rational decision making and a change can have a domino affect throughout the organization.

The big savings potential and the talents possessed by energy managers seem like a natural match. Energy Managers should "check out" the opportunities in hazardous materials management.

WHAT'S INVOLVED?

A user of hazardous materials and/or a generator of hazardous wastes is regulated by three separate government agencies: the Department of Transportation (DOT), the Environmental Protection Agency (EPA) and the Occupational Safety and Health Administration (OSHA). As illustrated in Figure 1, any time a hazardous material or hazardous waste is transported, DOT has numerous requirements concerning packaging, labeling, placarding and manifesting. These regulations are outlined in the Code of Federal Regulations (CFR) 49.

When a hazardous chemical or material is being used in the manufacturing work place, the OSHA Right-To-Know program requirements are in force. These requirements are summarized in 29 CFR Part 1910.

Finally, when a hazardous waste is produced and requires storage and disposal, the regulations enforced by EPA must be followed. These regulations are summarized in 40 CFR. In particular, the Generator requirements are shown in Part 262.

THE HAZARDOUS MATERIALS MANAGEMENT PROGRAM

The authors' experiences have led to the development of a hazardous material management program "life cycle". That cycle is presented in Figure 2 and is discussed below. The similarity between this program development and early writings on energy management is striking.

Actually, a company could start the program at just about any step but the discussion below starts with the audit.

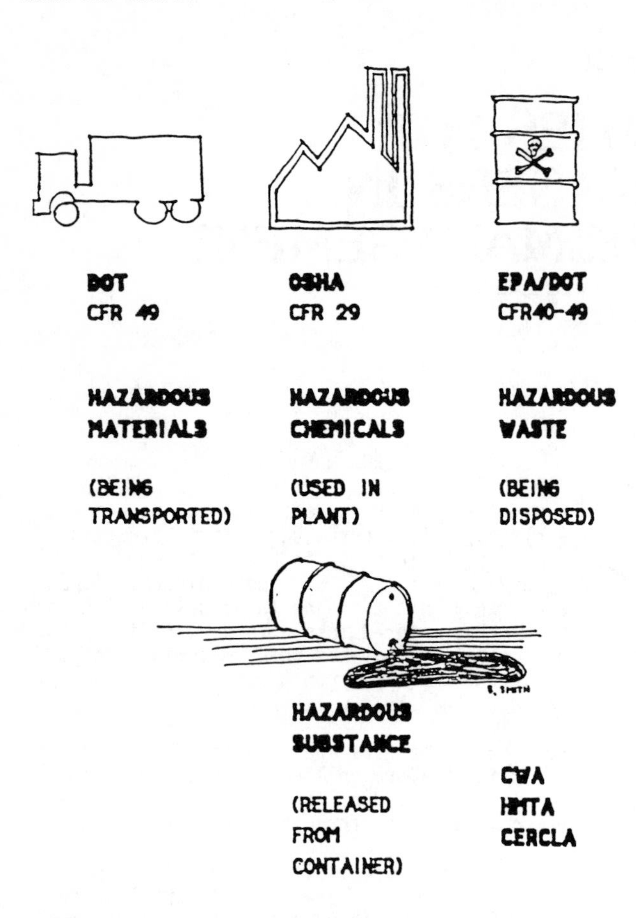

FIGURE 1. REGULATIONS IN HAZARDOUS MATERIAL MANAGEMENT

Step 1: Conduct Hazardous Waste Audit

An environmental audit is a process of reviewing the procedures, storage areas and recordkeeping systems used by the hazardous chemical and hazardous waste programs. The audit is required at the beginning of the program to evaluate the current practices and to assess the needs of the program. The audit should be conducted periodically, at least annually, to insure the program remains in compliance with changing regulations.

Step 2: Select Environmental Coordinator

An Environmental Coordinator must be selected to manage the program. This coordinator should be at a management level and must have the authority to commit the resources, both labor and capital, required to operate the program. The Coordinator should be an engineer with an understanding of the processes used in the company and have the ability to manage the recordkeeping systems required by each of the governmental agencies regulating the program. (An industrial engineer or energy manager is a natural for this position.)

Step 3: Develop On-Going Procedures

Policies and procedures for handling, storing and disposal of hazardous wastes must be developed and then used as a basis for employee training. Policies and

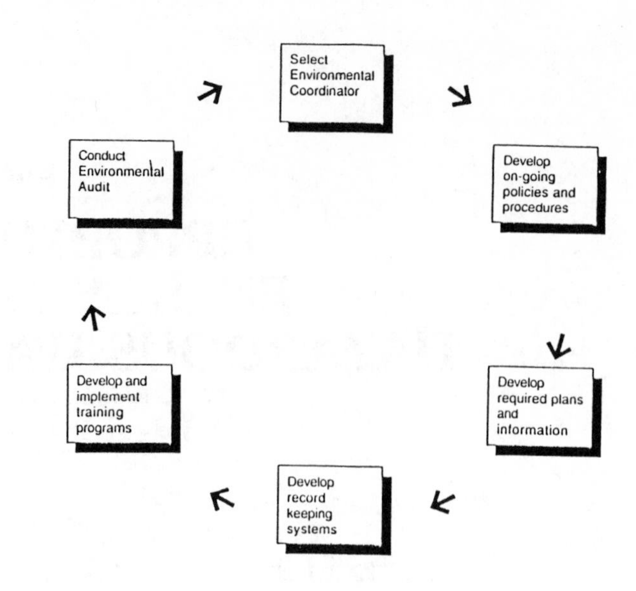

FIGURE 2. HAZARDOUS MATERIAL MANAGEMENT LIFE CYCLE

procedures should be developed for the following operations:

- Hazardous Waste Determination
- Waste Collection and Disposal
- Hazardous Waste Disposal
- Waste Container and Tank Inspection

Step 4: Develop Required Plans

Numerous plans are required by Federal, state and local agencies. The two most common are:

- Disposal Plan
- Contingency Plan

The disposal plan described the amount and type of hazardous waste generated each month and the proposed methods for disposal. Many states required these plans be approved by the state agency before waste can be transported for disposal. Some states require out-of-state companies transporting waste into their state file a plan before using the receiving state's facilities.

The contingency plan is an outline of the policies and procedures for responding to an emergency within the plant. The plan must describe the actions employees must take to respond to fires, explosions or any unplanned sudden or nonsudden release of hazardous waste or hazardous waste constituents to air, soil or surface water.

Step 5: Develop Recordkeeping Systems

The hazardous waste management program recordkeeping system is the most critical system of the overall program. The regulations require numerous pieces of information be documented and maintained on-site for at least three years. Generators must develop and maintain such records as are necessary to accurately reflect the types and quantities of controlled industrial wastes being produced, handled and disposed.

In the event of an inspection by state or Federal agencies, inspectors will often begin with the company's records. Records reflect the quality of the hazardous waste program.

Step 6: Develop Training Programs

Generators must develop and implement training programs for employees involved in the management of hazardous waste. Employees must receive training before performing tasks involving hazardous waste handling, storage or disposal. All affected employees must participate in an annual review of the initial training program.

COMMON MISTAKES

There are certain mistakes that seem to occur in many companies. Knowing these might help save some fines for companies, so they are repeated below. There are others but these ten seem to occur most frequently.

1. Containers of hazardous waste which are not marked or improperly marked and labeled.

2. No accumulation date shown on container.

3. No designated emergency coordinator.

4. No contingency plan or plan not filed with local emergency response organizations.

5. No emergency training or training not documented.

6. No recordkeeping systems to track waste generation and disposal.

7. Storage of hazardous waste for more than the specified number of days.

8. Shipping containers that do not meet DOT regulations.

9. Ignitable or reactive waste is stored within 50 feet of the property line.

10. Weekly or daily inspections of storage containers and tanks not performed or not documented.

HAZARDOUS MATERIAL MANAGEMENT

Proper hazardous material-waste management occurs in successive states as shown in Figure 3. The first 3 steps involve regulations and it is important that the company meet all regulations. Consequently, these 3 steps must be overcome before moving on to the more lucrative ones.

Next is "eliminate". Many companies are finding they can stop right there. After recognizing the "time cost" of hazardous materials, many companies find they can change design, processes, use, etc. and eliminate hazardous materials and wastes. All companies should be able to make some gains here.

To acquaint management with this "time cost" figure, the authors have developed a two cost model. The model includes:

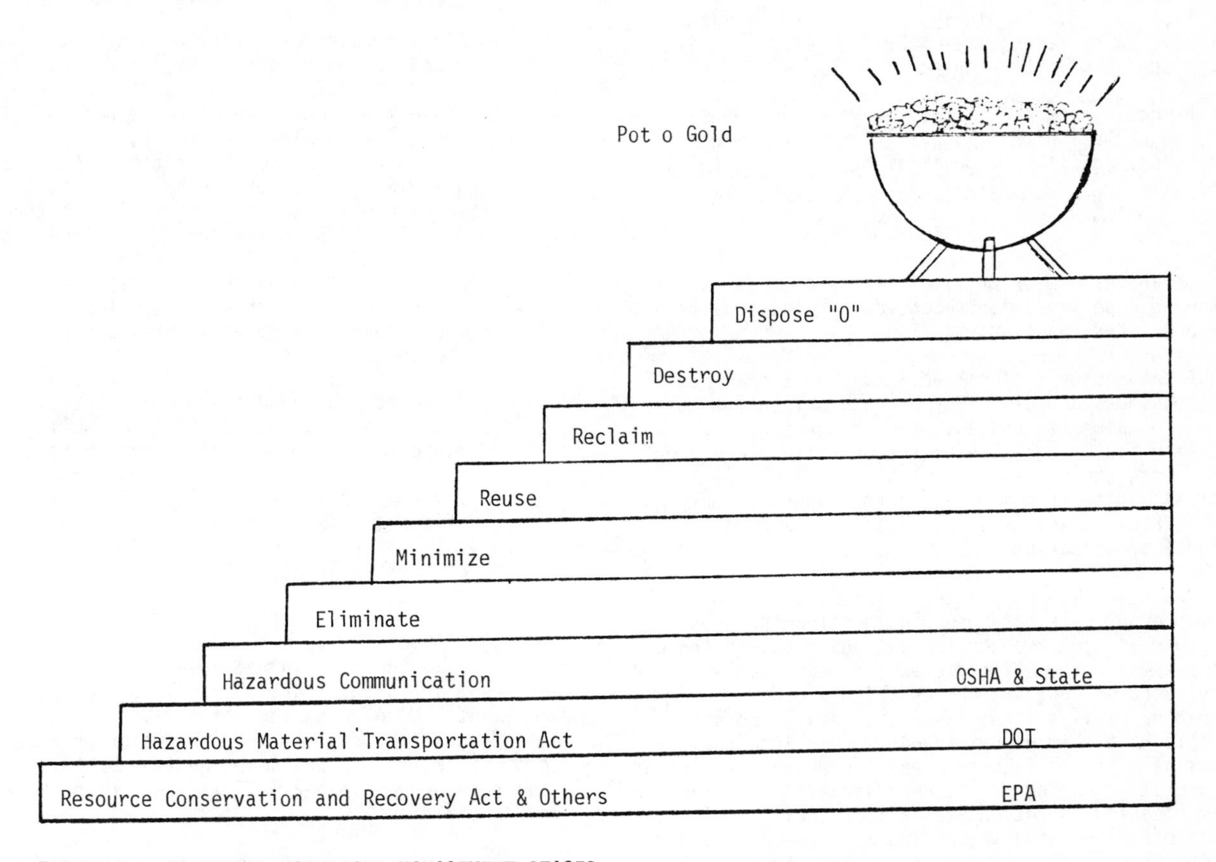

FIGURE 3. HAZARDOUS MATERIALS MANAGEMENT STAGES

- Initial chemical purchase price
- Waste disposal and shipping
- Waste disposal permitting fees
- Storage area costs
- Training program costs
- Emergency and first aid equipment
- Contingency plan development costs
- Updating cost for required plans
- Recordkeeping costs
- Manifesting and transportation
- Attorney fees
- Liability cost potential
- Special handling costs.

The total cost of generating a hazardous waste is usually four to seven times the cost of the initial chemical purchase price. The costs of "acutely" hazardous waste may be 10 times the purchase price.

Recognizing this high cost makes management more willing to work on the problem.

If all the hazardous material/waste can't be eliminated, then perhaps the company can tighten controls and minimize the volume or change chemicals to minimize the toxicity. Next the company should look at reuse (no reprocessing) or reclaim (filter, recycle, etc.).

The next step will become bigger as companies recognize the importance of destroying vs. disposal. On site treatment and incineration will become very big. However, permitting requirements for such on site work are presently very tight and expensive.

The last step -- disposal -- should only be used as a last resort. Hopefully, most hazardous waste will have to be taken care of by this step, but if not, disposal will be required.

Remember, you are liable for your hazardous waste regardless of how long it's been or how well you disposed of it. Disposal of hazardous waste will eventually be essentially zero in this country.

CASE STUDY

As an example of this multi-step procedure, the following case study is presented. The authors have numerous others available.

A manufacturer of oil well equipment has an unusual business aspect. They are the original manufacturer of equipment, and equipment returns continually for remanufacturing. Due to the operational environment of the equipment, some rather difficult cleaning problems manifest themselves in the returned equipment. This company is a multi-facility and multinational organization.

Due to a past corporate decision, only nonflammable solvents were used in the cleaning processes systemwide. Some product limitations required the use of a solvent with a high dielectric characteristic. A chlorinated solvent was chosen which was nonflammable. This solvent was recycled as much as possible, but some amount found its way into the waste stream of a steam cleaning operation which was part of the overall cleaning procedure. The effluent from the steam cleaning operation was collected with a minute amount of chlorinated waste, and hugh amounts of dirty water. Shop floor drains in the manufacturing facility also drained dirty mop water into this tank.

The tank was skimmed for solvent and oil, with the balance shipped to a landfill disposal site. As dumping requirements became more strict, additional effort was made to keep the contamination to a minimum. Finally, by January of 1985, the few disposal sites available stopped accepting chlorinated wastes, and arrangements were made to solidify the waste stream at a cost of approximately $22,000 per month. At this point, the need for change was obvious.

The following steps describe changes made in the operation to reduce the size of the waste stream and make the operation more economical:

1. Corporate management directed that the use of flammable solvents would again be permitted if applicable safety precautions were strictly adhered to. This change was not made in two manufacturing areas which required a higher dielectric than could be obtained with the flammable solvent.

   Eliminate -- Minimize

2. The two remaining chlorinated solvent operations were rethought. The equipment and methods were modified so that much less solvent was required and a closed system allowed better control of effluent. A stair-stepping arrangement was made so that the effluent from one process was scrubbed and used in the second process, further reducing solvent use. Total chlorinated solvent use dropped from 17,500 to 740 gallons per year.

   Minimize -- Reuse -- Reclaim

3. A waste water clarifier was installed to replace the holding tank with disposal of waste water directly into the sanitary sewer. This project was designed with the help of the EPA, state health department, sewer district, and storm water administration. Other requirements were met for handling equipment yard runoff water and processing it through the clarifier during the yard cleanup operation. This also offered protection against any spills leaving the property. Other impound areas were created to allow for safe drum storage of spent solvent and the bulk storage of new solvent.

4. A source was found to purchase the oily waste separated into the clarifier as well as the waste flammable solvent. Mixed with Bunker C Fuel oil, this became a new end product for powering ocean-going ships. The small amount of spent chlorinated solvent is drummed and sold for recycling since it is now a much cleaner effluent.

SUMMARY -- CONCLUSIONS

The opportunities in hazardous material waste management are significant -- rivaling those of energy management. Uncovering the potential requires skills in management, economics, and systems orientation (chemical skills would also be quite valuable). This means the energy manager is a logical person to absorb these activities.

The authors volunteer to help energy managers get started. Simply write or call. A list of references can be furnished at that time.

SECTION 22
RESOURCE RECOVERY
Sponsored by the
Energy Management Professionals Council

Chapter 67

RESOURCE RECOVERY: AN OVERVIEW OF INCINERATION

M. A. Mozzo, Jr.

Abstract:

Many localties and states are running into a serious problem, namely how to dispose of refuse, such as municipal solid waste (MSW), without harmful effects to our environment. There are potential solutions to this problem; however, emotional and financial aspects exist which hamper the development of these solutions to the problem. This paper, as a general overview to the topic at hand, will hopefully provide an introduction to the topic of Resources Recovery Application.

Introduction:

The United States generates millions of tons of solid waste annually. Disposal of such waste has become a serious problem in several parts of the country. Traditional methods of disposal such as landfill operations, uncontrolled incineration, and ocean burning are becoming either too expensive, nonexistent, or environmentally unacceptable. In New Jersey for example, it is estimated that there will not be any open landfills by 1987, and in fact, each county has been ordered to develop a plan to dispose of its solid waste within county lines by an environmentally acceptable method.

One potential for solid waste disposal is a waste-to-energy system more commonly known as incineration. This paper will discuss (1) waste-to-energy systems, (2) advantages and disadvantages of incinerator systems, (3) institutional problems with such systems, and (4) the economics of a typical large incinerator project.

Waste-to-Energy Systems:

According to a recent report by Frost & Sullivan, there are approximately 35,565 tons/day of waste-to-energy plant capacity. This figure is composed of three technologies -- mass burn, refuse derived fuel (RDF), and modular units. Discussion of RDF systems is outside the scope of this paper, though it should be pointed out that almost half of the waste-to-energy plant capacity is from this source.

Today there are 14,568 tons per day plant capacity at 19 mass burn units (average of about 765 tons/day), and 3,167 tons per day plant capacity at 31 modular units (average of about 100 tons/day). By the year 2000, it is estimated that an additional 65 new mass-burn plants with 129,200 tons/day capacity and 120 modular units with 14,950 tons/day capaity will be in operation. As can ben seen from the above data, the modular units are smaller on average than larger mass burn type units.

Figure one shows a simplified schematic of a typical waterwall boiler plant (referred to as mass burn previously) which can be used in a waste-to-energy project. Solid waste is transported to the plant site by truck and deposited into the storage pit. Hopefully, the waste has been somewhat segrated to remove non-combustibles or environmentally unacceptable materials. The storage pit's purpose is to provide a reservoir of "fuel" to compensate for the variability in deliveries by truck.

The waste is moved from the storage pit by a crane to the charging hopper as it is required. The charging hopper feeds the boiler where the waste is combusted and the heat released is converted to steam. The steam generated from the boiler can then become a cash stream for the project if a customer can be found to purchase the steam outright, or if it is used to generate electricity for resale.

Advantages and Disadvantages of Incineration Systems:

Ther are advantages and disadvantages of incinerator waste-to-energy systems, and even within the class of incinerators, there are advantages and disadvantages between large mass burn units and modular units. One of the greatest advantages of incinerators is the volume reduction which can be achieved through their use. Depending of course on the mix of the solid waste, a volume reduction of upwards to 95% can be achieved. The remaining ash can be disposed of in existing landfills, and with volume reduction, the useful life of the landfill will be extended. Another advantage for both systems is the marketability of the end product either in the form of steam or electricity, as long as it is competitively priced with other sources of supply.

Both types of equipment have high capital costs, though the larger mass burn units do have an advantage of economy of scale over modular units. Modular units in contrast, however, have an advantage in that total systems can be expanded incrementally, units can be regionally located instead of a central locations, and reliability due to a multitude of units (if present). Modular units though have some disadvantages from larger units, namely efficiency lossess, more pollution control points, and a need for auxilliary fuel (namely oil or gas) to operate the system.

Institutional Problems:

Anyone who has reviewed or read about incinerator installations are aware of several institutional problems which tend to frustrate, delay, and/or cancel such projects. These problems are identified as (1) informational, (2) jurisdictional, (3) implementation, and (4) marketing.

The informational problems revolve around a lack of adequate information and understanding at local levels to properly assess the technology required for their needs and to insure that systems are properly installed. Another informational problem is education of the public, which is definitely a key requirement.

Jurisidictional problems arise from the multitude of federal, state and local code requirements which tend to be overlapping. Further problems develop if the

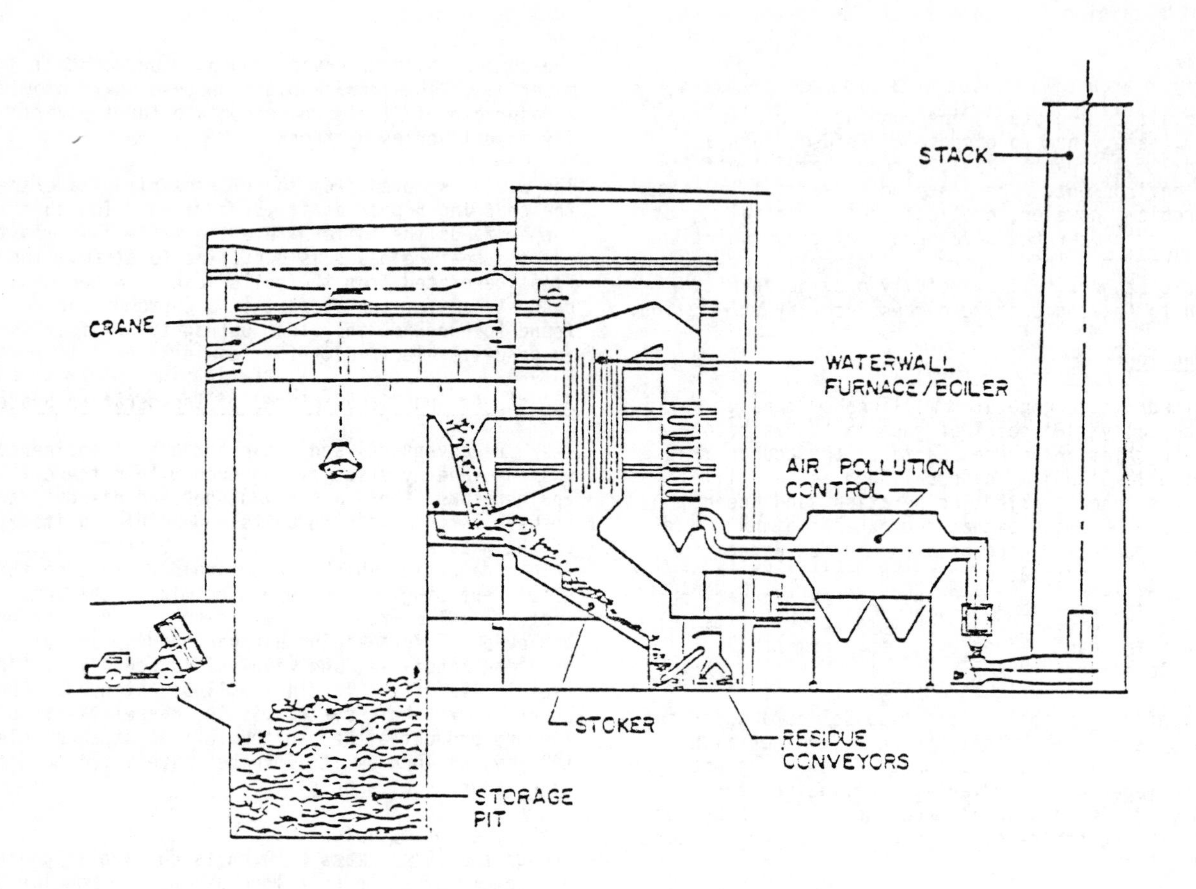

FIGURE ONE

TYPICAL WATERWALL BOILER PLANT

Source: Integrated Approach to Solid Waste Management In Mercer County

project requires cost sharing among many communities. Complicating jurisdictional matters is the potential roles of the public and private sector in the management of a solid waste problem.

Implementation problems center around two key areas. One is siting problems, obtaining permits, and overcoming adverse public reaction to locating the plants in populated area. The second problem area is in the area of obtaining financing to build the expensive plants.

The fourth area of institutional problems revolves around marketing, namely the requirement to obtain long-term contracts for solid waste as well as for the sale of the recovered energy. These contracts are needed to obtain funding and obviously are required to produce the necessary cash flow. Further complicating the situation is relatively "low" electric and/or steam prices which will tend to discourage long-term sales agreements for energy sales. It is important to recognize that these sales are necessary in order to pay off the high investment costs.

Economics of a Mass-Burn Facility:

As show previously, the average mass burn facility is about 765 tons/day. This section of the paper discussess relative economics of such a plant which emphasizes the economic problems facing such facilities. The example plant is a nominal 900 ton per day unit with an annual load of 250,000 tons/year, or about 76% of capacity. Estimated capital costs to install the facility is $120,000/ton, or $180,000,000 dollars. The efficiency of the unit allows for 450 KWH to be generated per ton of MSW. This means that there will be an annual electrical generation of 112,500,000 KWH assuming that there is a sales contract to purchase this electricity at 4.5 cent/KWH, an annual electrical sales revenue of $5,062,500 will be achieved.

Additional revenues will be gained from tipping fees and possibly a capacity or ready to serve charge. Assuming the operation is a non-profit organization, that is no return on investment is expected, a typical income sheet could look like this:

Revenues	
Electrical Sales	$ 5,062,500
Capacity Charge	900,000
Tipping Fees	12,737,500
Total Revenues	$18,700,000
Operating Expenses	
Debt Service @ 10 ½% (Prime +2% @ May 15)	$12,300,000
Operating & Maintenance	6,400,000
Total Operating Costs	$18,700,000

In order to generate zero operating income, a tipping fee of $50.95/ton must be realized.

While I have oversimplified the accounting treatment of such a project, I believe that the calculated tipping fee points out a serious economic flaw, in particular mass burn is too expensive to be competitive with traditional MSW disposal methods. Therefore, despite the institutional problems outlined previously, this economics problem could hamper overall acceptable of waste-to-energy projects.

Some Solutions:

Making what I would consider a valid assumption that these systems are needed, the following are some potential solutions which could assist in further development of waste-to-energy programs.

Probably first and foremost is an educational program to enlighten the public to this technology. The common perception that such systems are harmful are understandable and every effort to correct them should be made.

Efforts must be made by the public sector to adequately define roles of all sectors. This must be done to minimize overlapping (or underlapping) of responsibilities and to minimize permitting and siting delays.

It is also apparent that some economic subsidization must be done in order to allow the completion of the projects. Such sibsidization should not interfer with the competitive market place, but rather be used for the commercial development of this technology.

Summary:

Mass burn or incinerator waste-to-energy systems is a technology that is becoming more and more a necessity to this country. Certain institutional and economic problems must be overcome if the technology is to be adopted commerically. The public sector should take the lead in the encouragement of such projects.

Biobliography:

1. Intergarted Approach to Solid Waste Management In Mercer County, Mercer County Improvement Authority, Trenton, NJ, March 28, 1985.

2. Materials and Energy From Municipal Waste, A Report By the Office of Technology Assessment.

3. "Refuse-to-Energy Sales Seen Hitting $1.3 Billion/Year," Article Published in Engineering Times, April 1986.

4. "Solid Waste-to-Energy Overview and Status Report," A paper presented By Harvey W. Gershman, President Gershman, Brickner & Bratton, Inc., at the 12th Energy Technology Conference.

4. "Waste-to-Energy Project Update," A paper By Donald Marier, Published in Alternate Sources of Energy, April 1986.

SECTION 23
BIOMASS

Chapter 68

A WOOD CHIP COGENERATION PROJECT

E. F. Seboda

This paper traces the development of a large stationary power plant that produces steam for heating and cogenerating electricity for a 1,500-Bed Prison using wood chips as a primary fuel. The paper is divided into four sections: Section I. traces the history of the project and the barriers encountered in obtaining the funding for this project. Section II. describes the over-all project and the facility's power plant in detail. Section III. discusses the project economics based on life cycle costing, while Section IV. is a summary of the entire paper.

SECTION 1. HISTORY AND BARRIERS ENCOUNTERED IN DEVELOPING THE PROJECT

Maryland is an eastern state with a population of 4,200,000 people and a land area of approximately 9,837 square miles. Of that land surface, approximately 44%, or 2,798,000, acres are forested. The State is geographically divided into four major areas; Western Maryland, Central Maryland, Southern Maryland, and the Eastern Shore. Western Maryland is a mountainous area containing forest and farm areas. Central Maryland consists of urban and suburban areas stretching along the Philadelphia/Baltimore/Washington corridor. Southern Maryland, on the western shore of the Chesapeake Bay, is a region containing farm and forest areas. The Eastern Shore contains all the counties east of the Chesapeake Bay, and is primarily low-lying coastal plains, having farm and forest areas. The Eastern Correctional Facility is located on the coastal plains in the southernmost part of the Eastern Shore in Somerset County, a county whose principal industry is timber and timber-related industries.

Maryland's coastal plain is a low-lying area having a maximum elevation of less than 100 feet above sea level. It contains marshes with extensive rivers, creeks, and wetlands. On the lower Eastern Shore the primary timber that is grown is Loblolly Pine, a softwood that grows rapidly. In addition to the Loblolly Pine there are abundant hardwoods. However, because of the wet soil conditions, the hardwoods are considered to be a trash species which do not have much of a commercial value. In harvesting the Loblolly Pine, it is necessary to harvest and separate the hardwoods to reforest the Pine trees. The effort to find a commercial use for the hardwoods by-products became the driving force behind the project.

The original idea of developing a project whose primary souce of fuel was wood chips came from a Senate Joint Resolution passed by the 1978 Session of the Maryland General Assembly. In 1979 the State's Department of Natural Resources undertook a series of marketing studies to determine the uses for these hardwoods. The studies confirmed that these products were not being utilized. It was felt that this resource, if utilized for fuel, would generally provide economic growth in high unemployment areas in the State. The utilization of wood chips as fuel would ease our oil dependence by replacing oil with a renewable resource. The initial study focused on the conversion of a boiler at an Eastern Shore Mental Hospital. Later the study was expanded to review six additional sites in all sections of the State as candidates for burning wood chips. Three of these seven possible project sites were State-owned facilities, and four were privately owned. Of the seven projects in the study, four were economically feasible and consisted of heating and hot water at two State-owned mental hospitals and two privately-owned projects for generating process steam. Three of the feasible projects were on Maryland's Eastern Shore.

The two State facilities declined to use wood chips because of concerns on the reliability of the fuel source, concerns that the technology was experimental, and concerns with air quality standards. Discussions between the Department of Natural Resources, the Department of General Services, and the State Health Department were unable to convince the Health Department to move forward. The Department of Natural Resources discussed wood chip utilization with the private companies, but these projects did not develop because of capital concerns and a feeling that the technology was too experimental.

The lesson to be learned with all four of these projects was that the project should be controlled by the advocate. Even though the economics indicated that the projects were worthwhile, the fear of doing something different and being the first to utilize a new process tended to cause potential owners to reject using wood chips as a primary fuel. Because of this experience, it was decided that if wood chips were to be utilized, the project should: 1. Be on Maryland's Eastern Shore; and 2. Be a State-owned new construction, since new construction projects are totally under the control of the Department of

General Services, the principal advocate of this technology. The above criteria were then agreed to by the Department of Natural Resources.

In late 1982, it was recognized that a new prison would be needed to help ease overcrowding in Maryland's prison systems. Traditionally, prisons were one of the least desirable government facilities to be located in a political subdivision. Generally, politicians resisted, and in fact fought very hard to prevent prisons from being located within their subdivision.

Somerset County, on the lower Eastern Shore, was a County experiencing extreme unemployment problems. The unemployment rate was in excess of 20%. The County Commissioners of that County wrote to the Governor and indicated that they would consider having a prison in their County if it could be shown there would be economic benefits to the County, and a reduction in unemployment. The Governor accepted the offer and the State acquired land in Somerset County for the construction of the new facility. The Governor promised the Commissioners that reasonable economic initiatives would be considered as a major part of the project. In preparing the program for the facility, the Department of General Services specified that the Architect selected for the project would be required to undertake a life cycle cost study to determine the feasibility of utilizing wood chips at the facility.

As a result of the Architect's study, it was decided in the Winter of '84 - '85 that the most cost-effective approach would be to construct a cogeneration power plant, burning wood chips with fuel oil as a backup energy source. The study also showed that excess electricity could be sold to the local power company. Based on these understandings, it was decided to request an additional $4,500,000 for this innovative power plant. When this request was formally made to the General Assembly, the Legislature raised four issues. The Department of General Services responded to each as follows:

1. The plant is not necessary to operate the prison, and we would save $4,500,000 in capital cost by building an oil plant.

   This argument was offset by life cycle cost data that showed that the project was cost effective when the capital cost plus operating and maintenance costs were considered.

2. The project should not go forward because it is experimental technology.

   This argument was countered by demonstrating that the same equipment used in coal-burning plants, which still existed in the State, was similar to the equipment used for wood burning. It was also pointed out that man knew how to burn wood long before he discovered coal, oil, and other fossil fuels.

3. This plant required more manpower than a conventional oil powered plant. It was also more complex and thus beyond the capability of State employees.

   This argument was countered by showing that the facility was close to the Naval Base in Norfolk, Virginia, and that generation of steam at high pressures, along with generation of electricity was an activity that was routinely done on Naval ships. An active recruiting program targeted to retiring Naval personnel could attract the individuals to the area to man and work at this plant.

4. State salaries were lower than Federal salaries, and quality people may not be able to be employed.

   This argument was countered by stating that there were companies available who would operate the plant on a contractual basis and this would avoid the perceived problem of competitive salaries.

In addition to rebutting the concerns of the Legislature, the following points were made to reinforce the attractiveness of using wood chips as fuel:

1. The products of combustion were relatively clean compared to oil and coal.

2. There is an economic benefit of utilizing a product grown in the County which heretofore did not have a commercial value.

3. This fuel was a renewable resource, and the forestry in the area could support six plants of the size of the Somerset County facility.

After careful examination and extensive discussion, the appropriation was granted by the General Assembly, and Maryland's first wood chip fired, cogeneration facility was authorized for construction.

In analyzing the points raised by the opponents of the project during the Legislative debate, the major argument seemed to center on the experimental technology and whether it should be used in a facility as critical to the needs of the State as a prison. Although the appropriation was approved, there are a number of skeptics waiting for the plant to fail when it starts up. Prudently, the Department has recommended to the correctional officials that the power plant should be operated and maintained with contract personnel. At the time of the writing of this paper, a final decision had not been reached on the method of staffing the plant.

SECTION II. PROJECT DESCRIPTION

The Somerset County prison facility, or Eastern Correctional Institution as it is named, will cover approximately 140 acres and consists of 639,000 square feet of building space. There are 26 buildings in the project consisting of 8 separate buildings for housing prisoners, 8 guard towers, one County Detention Center, and 9 buildings providing administrative support, dietary and various program support for the facility.

Figure 1 is a site plan that shows the interrelationship of the buildings at the facility. The heating for the various buildings is by hot water generated in the central power plant.

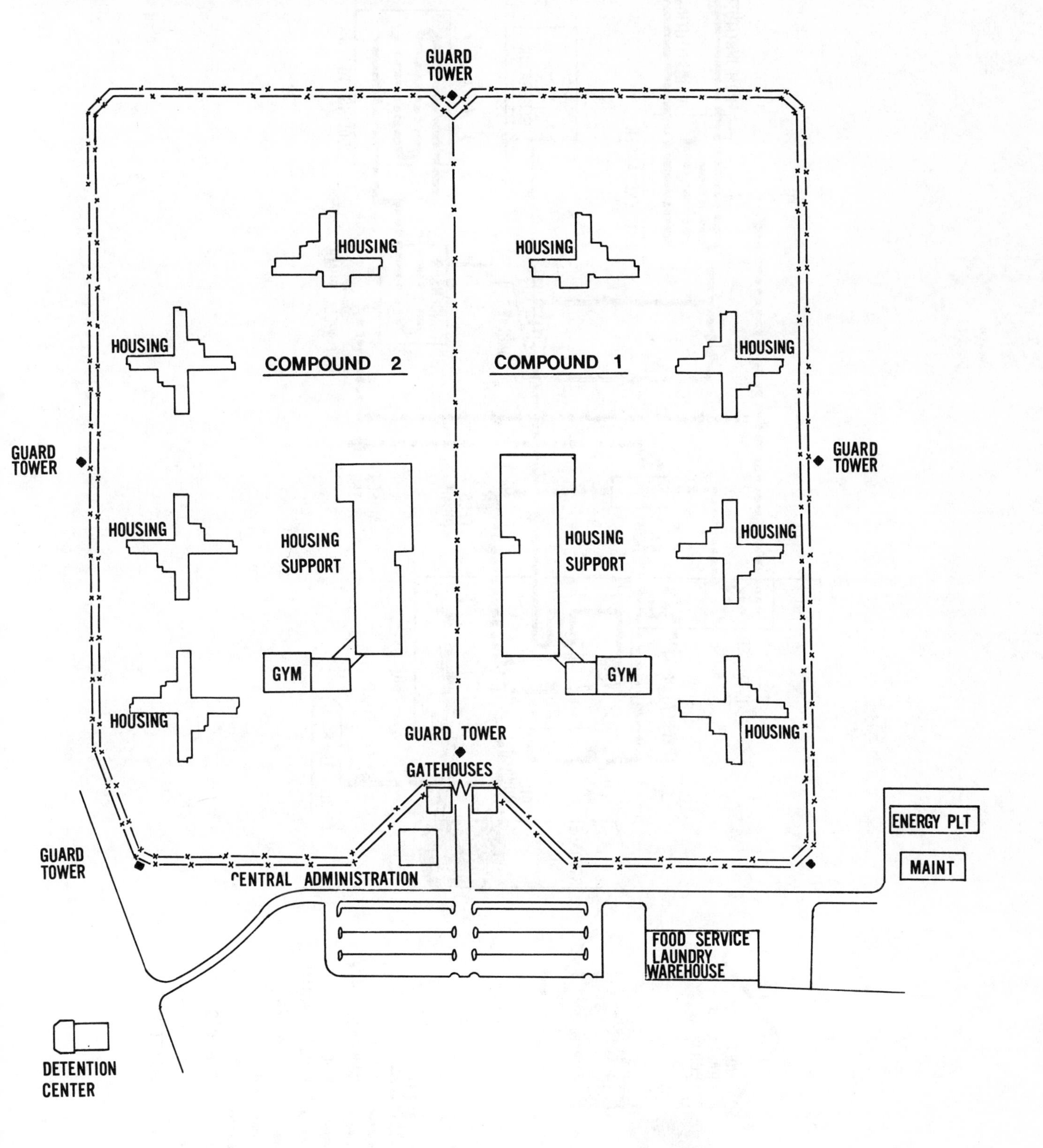

FIGURE 1 - SITE PLAN

EASTERN CORRECTIONAL INSTITUTION
SOMERSET COUNTY, MARYLAND

Figure 2 is a schematic drawing which indicates how the system works.

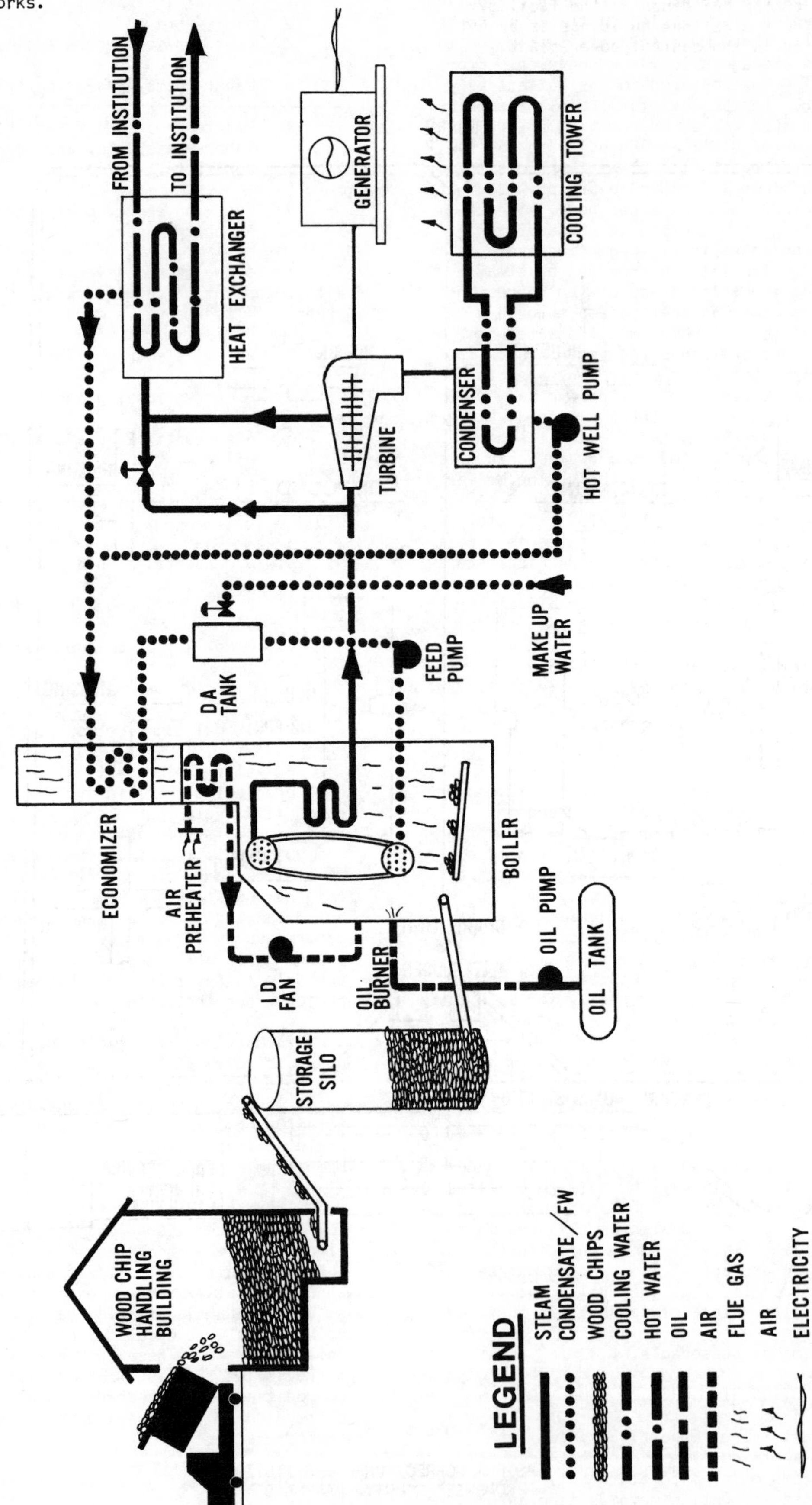

FIGURE 2 - SCHEMATIC DRAWING

Wood chips are stored in a wood-chip handling building in which trucks bring in the chips to be used for fuel. These materials are then moved to the wood-chip storage silo via a conveyer. From there the chips are conveyed to the boilers by a stoker feeder. The boilers for the plant consist of two, water tube boilers generating 25,000 pounds per hour of steam at 600 psi with 250 degrees of super heat. The steam then goes to two four-stage turbines which handle 600 psi steam at a flow rate of 20,000 pounds per hour. Steam, after exhausting from the fourth stage of the turbine, is condensed in a vacuum condenser. Heating for the facility is provided by steam extracted from the third stage of the four-stage turbine. This steam is then passed through a converter used to heat water and the water is pumped to various buildings requiring heat. The exhaust steam from the hot water converter then mixes with the condensate from the turbine condenser prior to passing through a feed water heater. The feed water after leaving the feed water heater is then heated in a heat exchanger by exhaust stack gases prior to entering the boiler to begin the process again. Air for the combustion process is also preheated prior to entering the boiler. The air is heated in a heat exchanger using exhaust stack gases. Final stack temperatures exhausting into the atmosphere are about 180 degrees F, which is a very efficient utilization of available energy.

This system also has the capability of augmenting steam to the hot water converter by the installation of a small boiler designed to burn solid waste.

Currently, a study is underway to see if the economics would be favorable to add this component to the system. There is a critical need in Somerset County to dispose of waste in other than sanitary landfills. Given favorable economics, the plant will burn the solid waste generated by the prison and also by the University of Maryland's Eastern Shore Campus, which is about five miles from the site of the prison. If this occurs, pressures on the local landfill will be reduced and more high-pressure steam will be available for generating electricity for sale to the power companies.

The wood chip equipment in the system is similar to the equipment used for burning coal and with slight modifications, the plant could also burn coal. The plant will come equipped with a secondary set of burners which will allow the plant to be fired with No. 2 oil. Thus, the power plant for the facililty will be able to be fired by either wood chips or fuel oil, and with slight modifications, coal could also be utilized in the plant. The flexibility of using three fuels allows the plant to adjust to changing market conditions associated with the fuel economy. Further, the alternate fuel capabililty then can be used as leverage to ensure that the cost of wood chips remains reasonable.

SECTION III. PROJECT ECONOMICS

The Department of General Services is required by law to do life cycle cost accounting on major systems going into State buildings. The life cycle cost accounting methods take into account five major elements that constitute the over-all cost of any project. Those elements are:

1. Capital investment.
2. Debt service, where applicable.
3. Labor costs, including fringe benefits.
4. Maintenance costs, including both direct labor, materials, and necessary service contracts.
5. Fuel and energy costs where the system is an energy user.

In making the decision to burn wood chips with cogeneration, nine separate systems were studied. These systems were:

1. An all electric plant.
2. A conventional plant burning wood chips.
3. A conventional plant burning No. 2 fuel oil.
4. A conventional plant burning No. 6 fuel oil.
5. A conventional plant burning coal.
6. A wood chip cogeneration plant.
7. A No. 2 fuel oil cogeneration plant.
8. A No. 6 fuel oil cogeneration plant.
9. A coal cogeneration plant.

All of the nine systems' economics were developed using the life cycle cost analysis. In doing life cycle cost one must escalate the items that are subject to inflation, and in this analysis fuel, labor, and maintenance would be escalated yearly over the life of the study. The original capital investment and debt service are not escalated. The capital investment was determined by fixed price construction cost. The financing is a fixed price and the repayment schedule is determined at the beginning of the project when the bonds are sold.

In Maryland life cycle costs are normally conducted over a 15-year period, the life span of the bonds that finance the projects. If the life cycle cost studies were extended to cover the actual useful life of the equipment, the econmics would shift placing a greater emphasis on operating expenses as opposed to capital cost.

In determining a life cycle cost, the following escalations were assumed: purchased electricity was escalated at a 5.7% annual inflation rate, fuel oil was escalated at a 6.8% annual inflation rate, wood chips were escalated at a 4.6% annual inflation rate, and labor and maintenance were escalated at a 5.2% annual inflation rate. These escalations were determined by reviewing the past 13-year history of these commodities on the Eastern Shore of Maryland. The costs assumed in comparing the various energy sources were:

1. Electricity - 5.6¢/Kilowatt Hour (This is the average cost paid by State facilities serviced by the Delmarva Power and Light Company)

2. Wood Chips - $16.00/Ton (Projected)

3. No. 2 Fuel Oil - 95¢/Gal. - (Based on State Contracts in 1985)

4. No. 6 Fuel Oil - 74¢/Gal. - (Based on State Contracts on the Eastern Shore in 1985)

5. Coal - $60/Ton - (Based on State Contracts in 1985)

Plant Alternative	Capital Investment	Annual Debt Service	Net 1st Year Annual Fuel Cost	1st Year Annual Labor Cost	1st Year Maintenance Cost
1. Electric	$2,988,000	$ 359,800	$2,533,800	$127,000	$ 63,000
2. Wood Chips	9,680,000	1,165,700	1,488,800	298,000	238,800
3. No. 2 Fuel Oil	6,870,000	827,300	1,985,500	280,000	151,700
4. No. 6 Fuel Oil	6,907,000	831,700	1,796,400	280,000	152,700
5. Coal	9,716,000	1,170,000	1,529,200	298,000	260,300
6. Wood Chips/ Cogeneration	11,775,000	1,418,000	857,600	421,000	304,300
7. No. 2 Fuel Oil/ Cogeneration	9,150,000	1,101,800	3,020,000	403,000	217,200
8. No. 6 Fuel Oil/ Cogeneration	9,187,000	1,106,300	2,227,000	403,000	218,200
9. Coal/Cogener- ation	11,811,000	1,422,300	1,063,500	421,000	315,000

TABLE III

Table III details the first year annual cost for maintenance, fuel, debt service and labor, plus the total capital investment.

Plant Alternatives	Capital Investment	15-Year Debt Service	15-Year Fuel Future Value	15-Year Labor Future Value	15-Year Maintenance Future Value	Total Life Cycle Cost
1. Electric	$2,988,000	$5,397,200	$57,603,400	$2,780,000	$1,379,000	$70,147,600
2. Wood Chips	9,680,000	17,485,000	33,459,800	6,523,200	5,227,300	72,375,300
3. No. 2 Fuel Oil	6,870,000	12,409,300	46,666,000	6,129,200	3,320,700	75,395,200
4. No. 6 Fuel Oil	6,907,000	12,476,100	41,696,200	6,129,200	3,342,600	70,551,100
5. Coal	9,716,000	17,550,000	33,955,400	6,523,200	5,698,000	73,442,600
6. Wood Chips/ Cogeneration	11,775,000	21,269,200	15,656,600	9,215,700	6,661,100	64,577,600
7. No. 2 Fuel Oil/ Cogeneration	9,150,000	16,527,700	72,833,100	8,821,700	4,754,500	112,087,000
8. No. 6 Fuel Oil/ Cogeneration	9,187,000	16,594,500	51,974,900	8,821,700	4,776,400	91,354,500
9. Coal/ Cogeneration	11,811,000	21,334,200	18,512,300	9,215,700	6,895,400	67,768,600

TABLE IV

Table IV lists the 15-year debt service, capital investment plus the assumed 15-year cost for fuel, labor, and maintenance escalated at the rates previously discussed over the entire 15-year period. When the five items are added, the total life cycle cost is determined. The studies indicated the most cost effective system to be wood chips with cogeneration, followed by coal with cogeneration.

The significant item in this study is the impact that fuel cost has on Energy Plant Life Cycle Cost studies. A wood chip/cogeneration plant which is capital intensive saves almost $6,000,000 over the 15-year period, versus electricity, which minimizes capital investment. In the Spring of 1985, the cost of wood chips was approximately one-third of the cost of electricity as a fuel. Thus, as you go into longer studies the capitalization impact is reduced as a factor in your life cycle cost and your annual operating expense, particularly fuel cost, becomes a major factor.

The Eastern Shore of Maryland historically has been one of the State's most costly public utility areas. You can also see from Table IV that higher cost fuels eliminate cogeneration as being cost effective. This point is demonstrated with No. 2 fuel oil in which cogeneration increases costs rather than reduces costs.

From the above analysis it can be seen that the life cycle cost technique allows you to make decisions in which increased capitalization cost can be offset by reduced operational costs over the life of the project.

In analyzing an energy plant, major factors surround the cost and availability of different types of fuels. Sharp swings in energy prices can have a significant effect on these calculations.

SECTION IV - SUMMARY

In advocating a project, such as the Eastern Correctional Institution's energy plant, the saleable points can be summarized as:

1. It is a clean fuel.
2. It is a renewable resource that allows us to be independent from foreign supplies.
3. It is an economical fuel.
4. On a life cycle cost basis the project is justified.
5. The cogeneration component assists utility companies in reducing their capitalization since a facility that is not air-conditioned, such as a prison, has more excess capacity in the summer when generally electric demand is at its peak.
6. A market is developed for a wasted resource.

The problems which make a wood plant with cogeneration difficult are:

1. More people are required than at a conventional plant.
2. The amount of equipment required is increased, thus increased maintenance is required.
3. Ash from the wood must be disposed of, however, the ash is less than that generated from a coal plant. Wood ash may have a commercial value.

In initially selling the project, the greatest problem encountered was the charge that it is experimental technology. Once this was overcome and when coupled with guaranteed sources of supplies plus good cost figures, the project is very saleable. In Maryland this wood chip project will become a "blue chip" experiment.

Chapter 69

EMERGENCY USE OF SIMPLE INEXPENSIVE GASIFIERS

H. La Fontaine

EUROPEAN BEGINNINGS

Gas produced from the reduction of coal, charcoal and peat was used for heat production as early as 1940. Aside from industrial heat production, the reports of using air-gas to fuel gas engines are found in England in about 1884.

The first engines were at least on a par with steam engines of the same relative power in terms of economy and efficiency. In addition they could be run on small grained fuels which caused difficulties in the furnaces of steam boilers. They could also consume reject materials, such as plant fiber, cotton bolls, rice and wheat chaff, etc., along with their normal diet of coal and coke. The handier liquid fuels, however, quickly gained acceptance in the growing gas vehicle industry, and air-gas fueled units remained stationary despite their economy and efficiency.

Europeans were always somewhat uneasy about their dependence upon foreign petroleum --a situation unfamiliar to oil-rich Americans. When war brought the anticipated shortages to reality, European manufacturers were able to come forth with mechanical alternatives which the populations were psychologically ready to accept.

It has been estimated that well over a million Gas-generators were built and operated in Europe from 1939-1945. Sweden alone built 75,000 units, and the people learned some significant facts. Trucks and buses fueled by Gas-generators turned out to be very efficient, especially when they were used in long distance hauling requiring few stops.

America lags far behind Europe in experience or readiness to employ these devices in a crisis. Until other dramatic and radical technological devices provide us with ultimately efficient fuels for our vehicles, we need to know more about the Gas-generators.

RUSSIA

Since World War II the Soviet Union has researched and used Biomass Gasification. The latest development indicates the breakthrough in using green wood with up to 100% moisture (dry basis) as fuel for tractors and portable Electrical Power Stations.

The ZNIIME-17 Producer (Fig. 35) is intended for operation on freshly cut split fuel wood, about 20 inches long, from 2.75 in. to 3.6 in. thick, or on round wood from 1.2 in. to 3.6 in. in diameter.

The upper bunker (Fig. 35-a) is of rectangular cross section, with sides of 21.5 in. X 15.0 in.. The total capacity of the upper and lower bunkers is 8.8 cu. feet. This suffices for the engine's continuous operation, at it's maximum capacity, for an hour, without additional fueling of the producer.

In the gasification zone the air is used for fuel gasification and for partial combustion of wood fuel. The heat produced in wood combustion facilitates wood drying in the bunker and water evaporation, while the steam goes out through the escape pipe (K), equipped with a damper (L), in the upper part of the bunker.

In the upper part of the fuel chamber is a removable cast iron diaphragm (M) with an opening of 6.2 ins. The diaphragm facilitates decomposition of tar and other products of dry distillation, which, along with producer gas, get into the gasification zone. The gas passes over the grate between the wall of the inner bunker and the producer shell and is sucked in by the engine through the pipe. (N).

At the same time, the producer gas, while it is cooling, is heating the walls of the bunker, thereby, eliminating the condensation of the products of dry distillation. Because of this, the inner walls of the bunker stay free of tar and the fuelwood does not stick to them, so that the wood settles down uniformally into the gasification zone.

Such a design is far ahead of any wood-gasifier known in the "Free World", and the technology of operating on green wood, with over 100% moisture (dry basis) could increase the production of hydrogen component of the Producer Gas, which alone merits further research and verification.

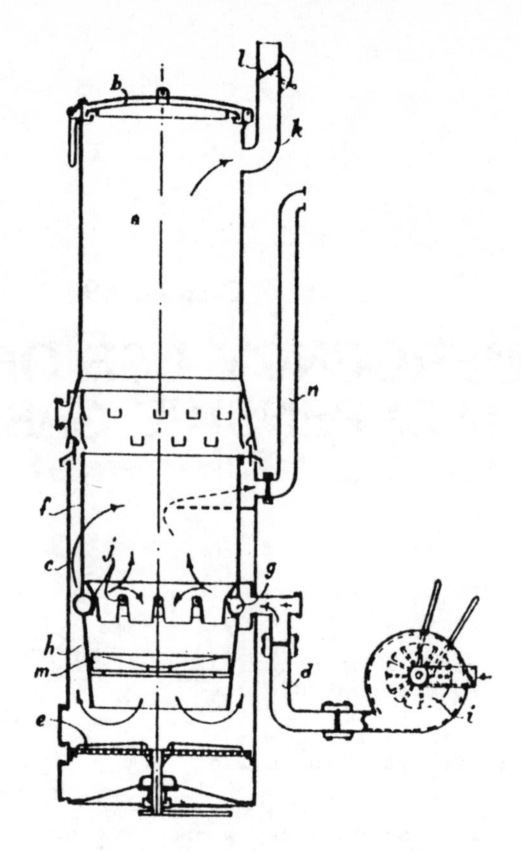

Fig. 35. Gas producer ZBIIME-17, operating on green fuelwood, for powering skidding tractor KT-12. a-Upper bunker; b-cover; c-case; d-air pipe; e-sectional grate; f-lower bunker; g-air main; h-fuel chamber; i-fan; j-short pipes from air main to gasification zone; k-steam escape pipe; l-damper; m-diaphragm; n-gas pipe to engine.

Fig. 11. Portable electric power station PES-12 for operating motor saws and other small logging machinery, with ZNIIME-18 gas producer, using green fuelwood of 1.2-in. - 3.5-in. X 20-in. (34) (Appeox.)

STRATIFIED DOWNDRAFT GASIFIER DESIGN

Fuel: inch chips
Rate: 10 kg/hr
Power:50 kW

```
Unburned ------->                DIMENSIONS
fuel zone                         Optional
Flaming pyr- --->                 7 cm
olysis zone
Reacting
Char zone ------>
Reacting ------->                 11 cm
Char zone
Non-reacting --->                 optional
char zone
Grate --->
Ash ------>                  --> gas
Insulated -->
Shell
                 |<  15 cm  >|
```

Dimensions of a 50 kW stratified downdraft gasifier predicted from model.

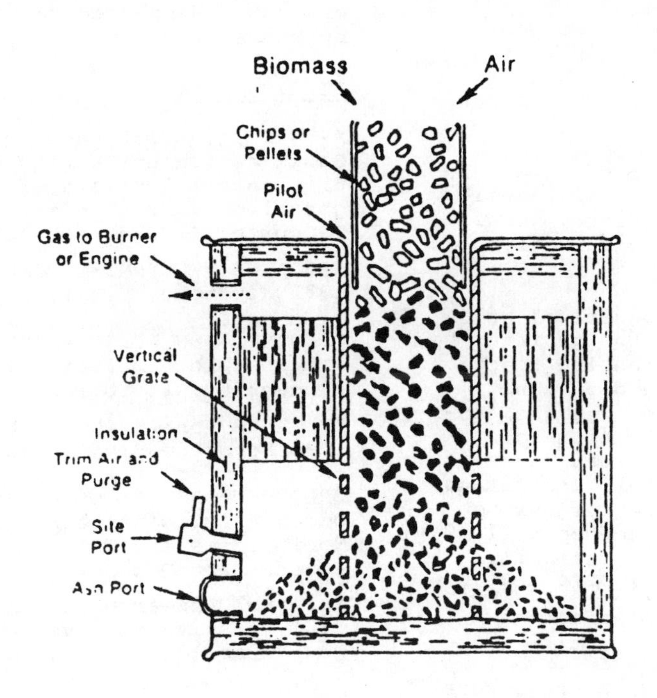

Figure 5. 10 hp stratified downdraft air gasifier built in a 5-gal. solvent can.

UNITED STATES OF AMERICA

The research and development of portable or stationary low B.T.U. Producer Gas units in the United States are far behind the rest of the World.

R and D on huge, stationary gasification units are well financed in the Unites States and proceding ahead of other countries, but our Government agencies may still be suffering from the "gasahol" intoxification, and the costly "synfuel" syndrome. Thereby, showing very little interest in how to transport and produce food to sustain our people in case of a severe emergency, caused by Civil upheaval, war or natural disaster.

Many individuals and United States firms have, since the 2nd fuel crisis in 1978, given up their project on low B.T.U. gasifiers, because of the lack of interest and funds from responsible U. S. agencies, and the bureaucratic delay in any dealing with them.

In spite of such disinterest by our Government, many private or semi-private organizations and individuals have tried to bring the United States up to par with the rest of the World on this technology.

One os the recent break-throughs in low B.T.U. gasification has been formulated by Dr. Thomas Reed, a Senior Scientist with S.E.R.I. in Golden, Colorado.

STRATIFIED DOWNDRAFT GASIFICATION

After working with many low B.T.U. gasification units all over the World in the last 45 years, we are convinced that Dr. Reed's stratified concept is a major breakthrough.

The technical and chemical formula was, in 1984, revealed in detail at several Seminars around the world. Therefore, we will only discuss our mechanical utilization of this project.

The "stratified, downdraft gasifier" in which air enters the top of the gasifier bed and passes down through successive reaction strata as shown in Figs. 4 and 5. The stratified downdraft gasifier has the advantage of simplicity and the open top permits a continuous flow of feed stock, also measurement of temperature and gas composition at all points in the bed during operation. The gasifier is conceptually simple and easy to model mathematically.

A simple 10 hp gasifier, built in a 5 gallon can, using these principles as shown in Figure 5.

In the last 12 months we have built several units based on Dr. Reed's theory, and have brought to this seminar, for demonstration, a standard, mass produced 7½ kw "ONAN" generator, 110/220 ac combustion-engine operated. We have equipped this unit with one of our simple, inexpensive, "stratified downdraft" gasification units.

CONCLUSION

The only known solution for operating food and transport equipment, when liquid fuel is not available, has in the last 100 years been simple, inexpensive, portable Producer Gas units. No other solution is available or being considered, anywhere in the World.

Our Country has never experienced a total fuel emergency crisis, with a breakdown of food production, transportation and electric power production. Therefore, it seems impossible to convince the different United States agencies that our civilian population should be informed, like people are in other countries on the only way known to avoid mass starvation in times of Civil upheaval, war or natural disaster.

As always if Government fails to respond to the needs of their people, private enterprise and our Science Community must try and solve the problem with their own money, on their own time;THIS IS NOW BEING DONE.

When private enterprise, participating universities, etc. have such simple, inexpensive gas units developed to the point where small local inductry, gas stations, farm shops, shade-tree mechanics, etc., can assemble, in a short time, from ordinary hardware and plumbing supplies, the millions of gasifiers needed to get the food from the farm and sea to the table, then how can we get it to our people?

The distribution services, boatyards and citizens interested can only be undertaken by respective Governmental agencies.

BIBLIOGRAPHY

"PEGASUS", a 136 page book on World War II Gasification units with schematic and pictures on the lost art of Driving Without gasoline by Prof. Niels Skow and Mark L. Papworth, $12.95, postage included.

"PEGASUS PUBLISHING COMPANY"
1995 Keystone, Miami, FL 33181

"PEGASUS" BUILDING PLANS, on construction with complete material list and operating precedure, $24.50 including postage,

"PEGASUS PUBLISHING COMPANY"
1995 Keystone Blvd., Miami, FL 33181

PRODUCER GAS: Another Fuel For Motor Transport, a 100 page book assembled by: Dr. Noel Vietmeyer, The National Board on Science and Technology.

National Research Counsil (3H-2170)
2101 Constitution Avenue
Washington, D. C. 20418

Generator Gas - The Swedish Experience from 1939-1945, $24.50

NTSI--U.S. Dept. of Commerce, Dept. TMEN
5285 Port Royal Road
Springfield, VA 22161

Chapter 70

SECONDARY TAR CRACKING IN THE PYROLYSIS OF BIOMASS

L. Chang

ABSTRACT

The pyrolysis reactions of two wood samples (western hemlock and pine bark) were studied with a rapid-heating batch reactor. With the 1000°C/s heating rate, the effects of the peak reaction temperature (300 to 1200°C), the holding period of the reaction temperature (0 to 5 sec.) and the particle size (60 to 250 μm) on the yield and the rate of formation of volitiles and char were studied. When the peak temperatures were between 300 and 700°C, the longer the peak temperature was held, the more volitiles were produced. Under the same reaction condition, the yields of volitiles of the larger wood particle were less than those of the smaller wood particle. Secondary tar cracking reactions were observed for pyrolyzing larger wood particles and for the sample which was pyrolyzed with a longer heating period. A single-step first-order reaction model were applied to the experimental results of char, tar and volitiles. The predictions of the yields of products with this model were satisfactory.

INTRODUCTION

Previous studies (1-3, 14-15) indicated that the renewable biomass has a great potential to become an energy source and to replace the petroleum-based products as a chemical feedstock. A great deal of work has been done on the subject of the pyrolysis of wood or related materials. But, the compex process of this kind reaction is not yet fully understood. There are some uncertainties in the detailed nature of the reaction, such as the effects of the sample size, the heating rate, the peak reaction temperature, the residence time of the volatiles in the hot zone etc.. Earlier kinetics studies (4-6, 8-10) have been conducted under a variety of experimental conditions resulting in a wide range of kinetic parameters. Only few of the previous studies (12,14) have shown the kinetics data of the individual products, most of them (8-16) concerned the overall weight loss or total volitile production of the biomass pyrolysis. The object of this work is to study the effects of the wood particle size, the reaction temperature and the residence time of the products in the hot zone on the kinetics of the individual product of the wood pyrolysis. The kinetic data of the wood pyrolysis with a high-heating rate in helium were reported. The overall volitiles production, char and tar formation processes have been discussed elsewhere (14-15). In this study, the activation energies and rate constants were reported for each gas products and total volitiles. The yields of each kind of volitiles of these two wood samples (hemlock and pine bark) have been compared with each other. This comparison shown the effects of the wood composition on the pyrolysis process.

EXPERIMENTAL EQUIPMENTS AND PROCEDURES

Material

For western hemlock only one kind of particle (63-70 μm) was used, but, for pine bark both 63-70 μm and 125-250 μm particles were used. The wood samples were pre-dried and then stored in a glass desiccator for eliminating the humidity effect.

Pyrolysis Equipments

Instead of using the convensional TGA reactor, an electric grid rapid-heating batch reactor was used (Fig-1). It consists of 1) the reactor, 2) the electric grid system which controls the temperature-time history, and 3) the temperature recording system. The wood sample was held between two brass electrodes by a folded strip of stainless screen. Each run was carried out with a new screen. The

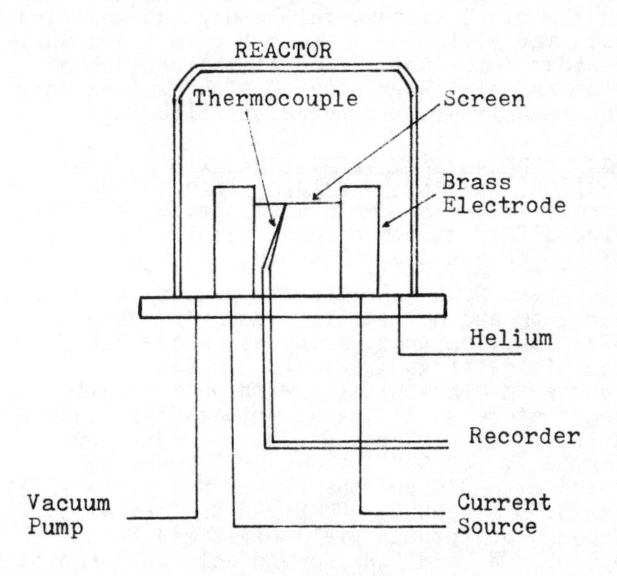

FIGURE I. SCHEMATIC OF APPERATUS

chromel-alumel thermocouple was inserted into the folded screen. The temperature-time history was recorded with a fast response strip chart recorder.

Experimental Procedure

Approximately 20 mg of wood powder was spread, in a layer one or two particles deep, on a preweighed screen which was streatched between the brass electrodes. The thermocouple was then inserted into the screen. The reactor had to be evacuated several times and flushed with helium. Then, the reactor was brought to the atmospheric pressure with helium and was ready for the experiment. The sample was then heated at desired heating rates. When the peak temperature was reached, it was either maintained for an extra holding time or the circuit was immediately broken.

When the reaction completion was reached, the pyrolysis gases were mixed by a fan and then withdrawn for analyzing by the gas chromatography. A slow vacuum was then applied to the reactor. Tar was collected on the filter paper and dissolved in methylene chloride. The solvent was evaporated and finally tar was weighed gravimetrically. The char remaining in the screen was also measured gravimetrically.

RESULTS AND DISCUSSIONS

Char, gases and tar were the major products of the wood pyrolysis reactions. In the previous studies (14,15), with the heating rate 1000°C/s, the author found that for hemlock, the yield of the total volatiles reached 90% as the peak reaction temperature was above 700°C. However, for pine bark, only 75-78% was reached when the peak temperature was above 750°C. The yields of tar from fine wood particles reached 20% to 26% when the peak reaction temperature was above 700°C. But, for larger wood particles, the final yield of tar was lower than that of the smaller wood particles. For further understanding the effect of the particle size on the yield of tar, this study has analyzed both the yields of gaseous products and tar. Besides this, the effect of the residence time has also been studied with hemlock only. The results are presented as following:

Gas, Char and Tar Formations with 1000°C/s Heating Rate and No Holding Time. The pyrolysis gas products consisted of at least five different components, namely CO, CO_2, CH_4, C_2H_4 and C_2H_6. The C_3H_6 and C_3H_8 also have been found in this study, but their yields were low and not easily measured. When the peak reaction temperature was above 280°C, the yields of gas products of hemlock increased monotonically with peak reaction temperature until the asymptotes were reached at fixed peak reaction temperatures. CO_2 formed at 300°C, it shown an increasing trend at 650°C and the asymptotic yield of it was 3.5% at 760°C. CO began to form at 500°C and the asymptotic yield of it was 10% at 850°C. CH_4 and C_2H_4 formed only when the peak temperature was about 670°C and the asymptotic yields were obtained at 850°C as 0.75% and

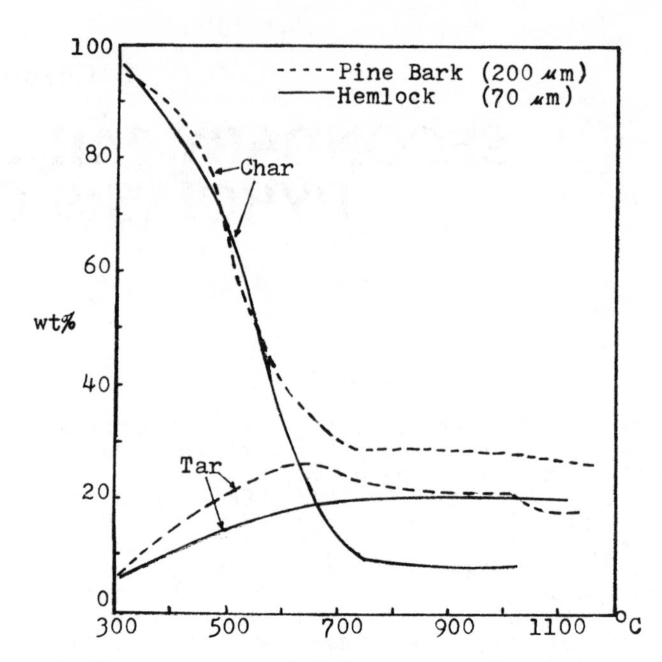

FIGURE 2. wt% VARIATIONS WITH TEMPERATURE (YIELDS OF TAR AND CHAR)

0.34%, respectively; C_2H_6 appeared only when temperature was above 750°C and the maximum yield of it was 0.11% at 850°C. The final char formation was 8% when temperature was higher than 850°C. The yield of tar started at temperature 320°C and increased smoothly until it reached the asymptote, 20%, at 675°C. Figs-(2) to (4) show the experimental results.

For pine bark (~200 μm), CO began to form at 420°C which is about 100°C lower than other

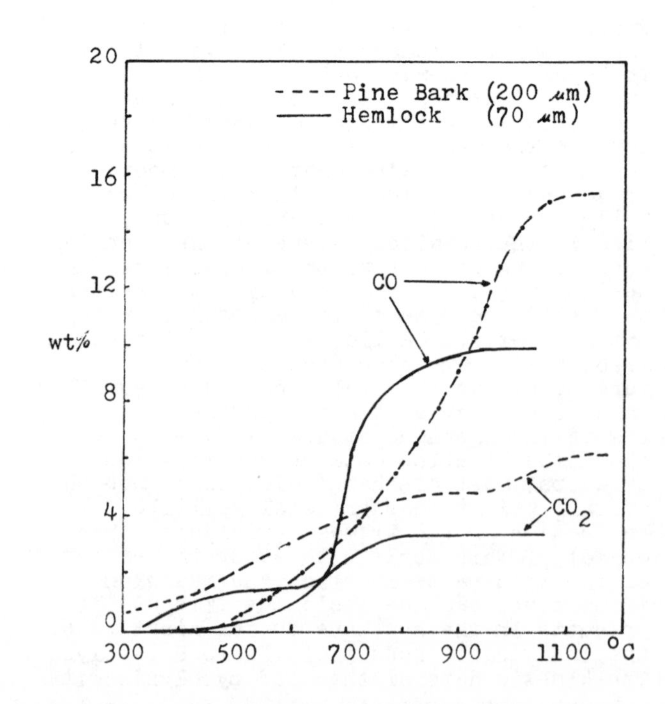

FIGURE 3. wt% VARIATIONS WITH TEMPERATURE (YIELDS OF CO AND CO_2)

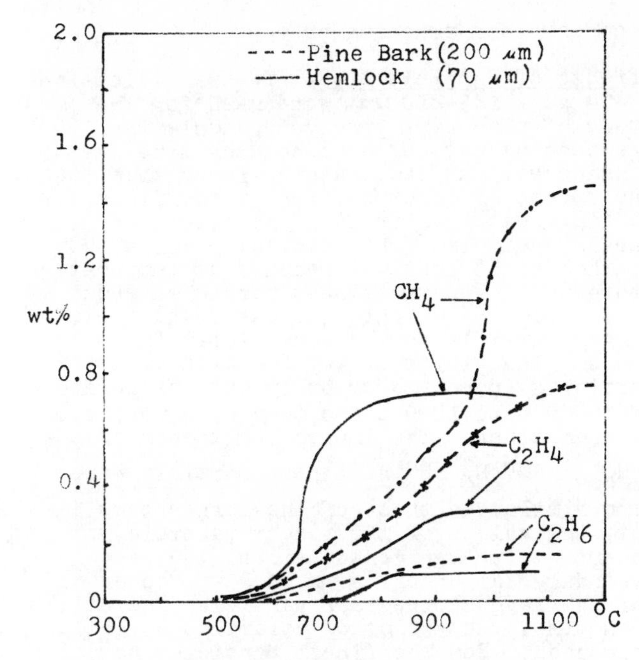

FIGURE 4. wt% VARIATIONS WITH TEMPERATURE (YIELDS OF TAR AND CHAR)

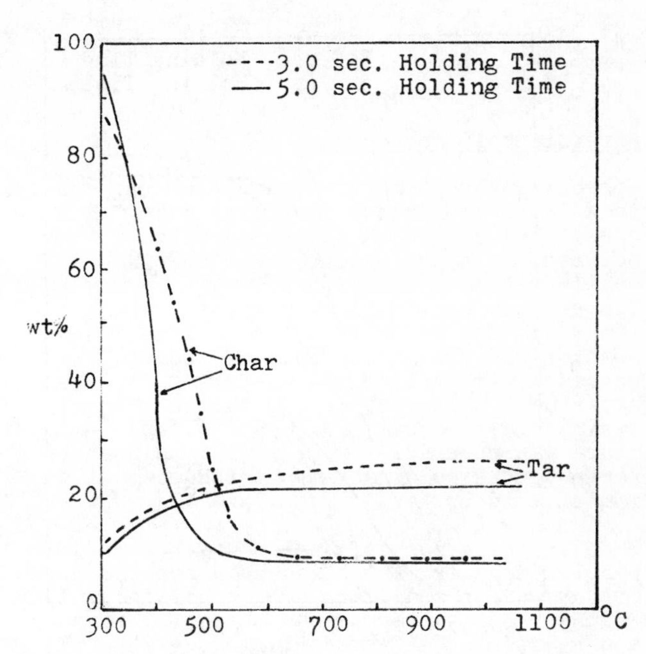

FIGURE 5. wt% VARIATIONS WITH TEMPERATURE (HEMLOCK)

two wood samples. It also shown a steep rise at 600-700°C. Its asymptotic yield was 11% when the temperature was above 1000°C. For CO_2, CH_4 and C_2H_4, they appeared at similar reaction temperatures as those of the western hemlock, however, their asymptotic yields were different: for CO_2, it was 5.5% at 870°C, for CH_4 and C_2H_4, they were 0.75% and 0.5%, respectively at 900°C. C_2H_6 came out at 700°C and its maximum yield was 0.06% at 900°C. The final yield of char was 22% when reaction temperature was above 850°C. Tar began to form as the temperature was higher than 340°C. Its asympototic yield was around 20% at 710°C which is similar as that of hemlock. Figs-(2) to (4) also show the results of pine bark.

The following diagram shows our suggested reaction scheme for the rapid-pyrolysis of wood particle. Our results indicated that the reaction pathway-(3) was important for pine bark (especially when the reaction temperature was high), however, for western hemlock, the reaction pathway-(1)&(2) were the dominated reaction routes. Our results also shown that pine bark produced less liquid products than other two samples did. We believed that those differences of the pyrolysis results between pine bark and western hemlock are because the differences of the structure and the composition between them.

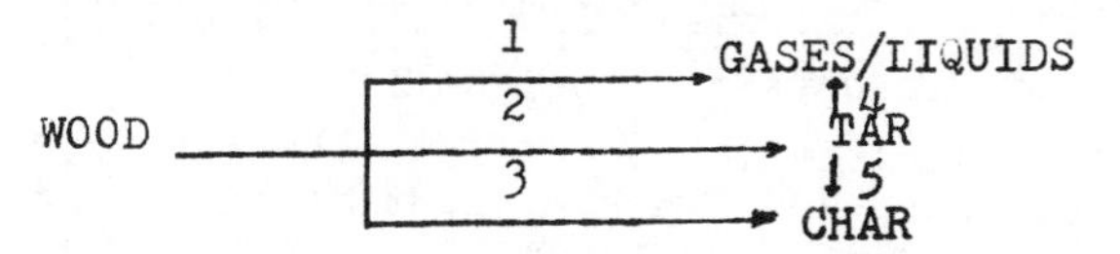

<u>Effect of Residence Time</u>: Residence time is defined as the total period including heat up time and the holding time for which the solid sample is maintained at a desired peak reaction temperature before letting it cool down. The example of the effects of holding time (0.0, 3.0 and 5.0 sec.) at the 1000°C/s heating rate on the extent of decomposition of western hemlock can be seen in Figs-(5) to (7).

For western hemlock, with 1000°C/s heating rate and no holding time at the peak reaction temperature, we noticed that the asymptotic yields of total volatiles was 92% at 800°C, of char was 7.8% at 820°C and of tar was 20.8% at 730°C. However, with 5 seconds

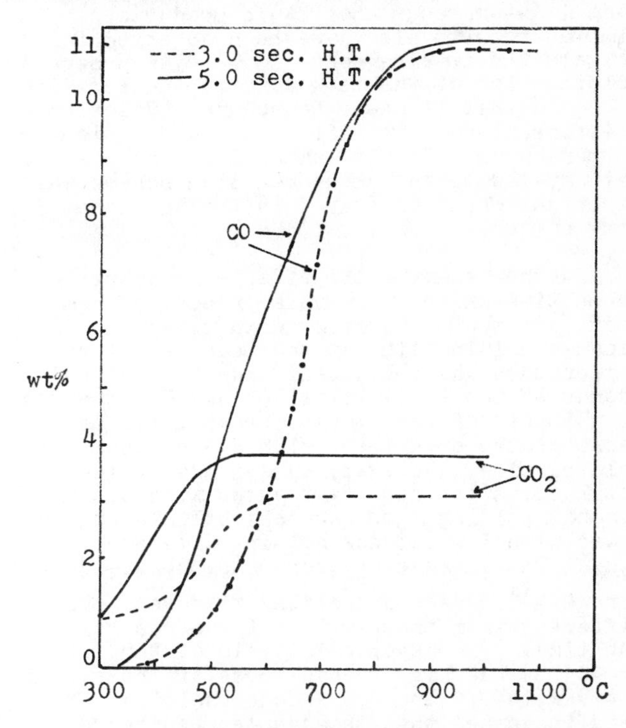

FIGURE 6. wt% VARIATIONS WITH TEMPERATURE (HEMLOCK)

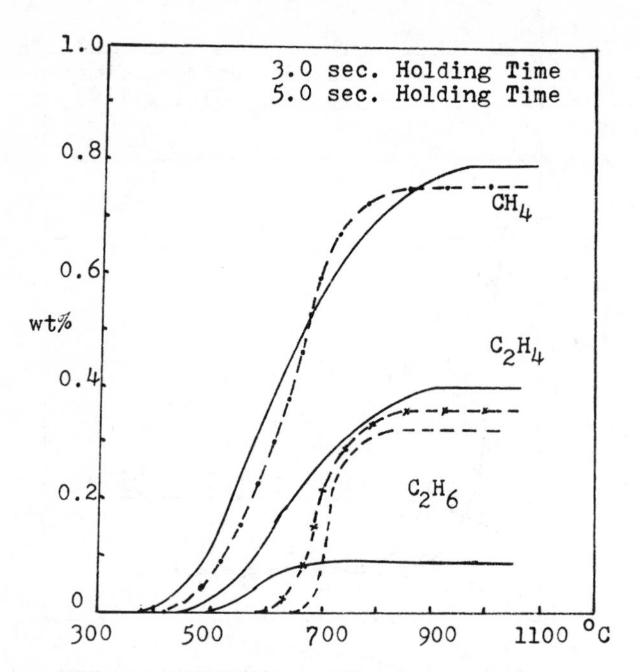

FIGURE 7. wt% VARIATIONS WITH TEMPERATURE (HEMLOCK)

holding time of the peak reaction temperature, the yield of the total volatiles increased fastly at low peak reaction temperature, a steep rise of it at 440°C was observed, 90% of the yield of the total volatiles was reached at about 520°C; and the yield of tar reached an asymptote, 22.4%, at about 630°C. The decreasing of the yield of tar (21% at 950°C) and the increasing of the total volatiles (asymptotic yield was 92.5%) of the reaction with 5 seconds holding time indicated that there was a secondary tar cracking process to form light gaseous and liquid products. Similar results also have been observed for Dougals fir at elsewhere (16). With 5 seconds holding time of the peak reaction temperature, we found that it has a pronounced effect on the formation of volatiles at low reaction temperatures. It also shown that the reaction pathway-(4) of the above reaction scheme was important when tar stayed in the hot zone long enough.

For further examing the effect of the residence time on the pyrolysis process of hemlock, a set of experiment with 2.5-3.0 seconds holding time at the peak reaction temperature was conducted. The increasing trends of the total volatiles and light gases of this set of experiment were similar as those of the experiment with 5.0 seconds holding time. However, the yields of the total volatiles and light gases with 3.0 seconds holding time were slightly lower than those with 5.0 seconds holding time except C_2H_6. The increasing trend and the yield of tar with 3.0 seconds holding time were also different from those with 5.0 seconds holding time. The asymptotic yield of tar (26% at 905°C) was higher than those of the experiments with 0.0 and 5.0 seconds holding time. This indicated that the shorter residence time just helped the reaction to reach completion. However, the longer residence time possibly provided the opportunity of the secondary tar cracking process.

Effects of Particle Size: Two particle sizes, 63-74 μm & 125-250 μm, were used for the study of pine bark pyrolysis. Only the 1000° C/s heating rate with no holding time was considered. At temperatures lower than 500°C, the extent of decomposition of the finest particle was greater than the extent of larger particle. The asymptotic value, 78%, of the weight loss was reached at temperatures above 850°C for the finest particle. But, only about 75% weight loss was found for the larger particle in the same temperature range. The yields of CO_2 for both sizes of particles increased smoothly with temperature from 400°C to 1000°C and they were very close to each other. The increasing trends of CH_4, C_2H_4 and C_2H_6 of the finest particle were also similar to those of the larger particle, but, the values of the finest particle were lower. As we mentioned before (14), a secondary tar cracking process was observed for the larger pine bark particles and at the mean time, the yields of volatiles slightly increased. For the finest particle, no secondary tar cracking process was observed.

Single Step First-Order Reaction Model: Suuberg et al. (12), Peters (2) and Bengali (7) have adapted a simplified first-order model to correlate their experimental results. It proved to be useful for those data of the rapid pyrolysis of coal and cellulose. In the present study, this model was applied to the wood pyrolyses. In the simplest version of this analysis, it is assumed that the cellulosic materials decompose directly to yield given reaction products i by single independent reaction pathways also designated by i:

$$\text{Cellulosic Material} \xrightarrow{k_i} \text{Product } i$$

the assumed first-order reaction rate equation, written in the Arrhenius form, is given by

$$dv_i/dt = k_{oi}(v_i^* - v_i)\exp(-E_i/RT) \quad \text{----- (1)}$$

where, E_i is the activation energy for reaction i, k_{oi} is the pre-exponential factor, v_i is the amount of product i which is produced during time t, v_i^* is the amount of product i which could be produced potentially, T is the absolute temperature and R is the universal gas constant.

Kinetic Parameters: The kinetic parameter, activation energy (E), pre-exponential factor (k_o) and the potential weight loss at infinite time (v^*), can be determined by fitting the data and temperature-time history to the first-order reaction model. For the total volatiles of western hemlock (at different reaction holding periods) and of pine bark (125-250 μm), the kinetic parameters were obtained and listed in Table-(1).

The predicted weight fractions of each

TABLE 1. KINETIC PARAMETERS OF WESTERN HEMLOCK AND PINE BARK

Heating Rate: 1000°C/s

Wood Sample	Holding Time, sec.	E, kcal/mole	k_o, sec.$^{-1}$	v^*, wt%
Western Hemlock	0.0	12.51	3.04×10^3	92.32
Western Hemlock	3.0	11.77	1.25×10^3	92.24
Western Hemlock	5.0	15.26	1.80×10^4	92.18
Pine Bark (125-250 μm)	0.0	15.50	2.70×10^4	77.26
Individual Product Samples	**Holding Time, sec.**	**E, kcal/mole**	**k_o, sec.$^{-1}$**	**v^*, wt%**
Pine Bark				
CO	0.0	17.24	5.50×10^3	15.51
Tar	0.0	10.20	2.10×10^3	22.54
Western Hemlock				
CO	0.0	35.89	5.33×10^8	9.37
Tar	0.0	19.22	5.95×10^6	18.09

product and of total volatiles can be calculated by using the kinetic parameters. Several examples of the comparison of the calculated values with the experimental results are shown in Fig-(8). The best fit is the 45° line.

CONCLUSION

The pyrolyses of two different kinds of wood were studied by a rapid heating system in helium. We have found that the reaction temperature, heating rate, particle size and the sample structure have significant influences on the pyrolysis process. The experimental results indicated that:

(1) The peak reaction temperature and the holding time of it are the most important reaction parameters in determining the rapid heating decomposition behavior of wood samples.

(2) The effect of the residence time of the wood sample in the hot zone was more pronounced at lower reaction temperature than at higher temperature. The yields of gas products increased when the residence time was increased at lower peak reaction temperature.

(3) By comparing the yields of total volatiles of the western hemlock (92%) and of the pine bark (75-78%), we found that the difference between them is mainly because the structure and the composition of the pine bark is different from those of western hemlock.

(4) For pine bark, at a fixed peak reaction temperature, the yield of the total volatiles of the larger particles (125-250 μm) was less than that of the smaller particles (63-74 μm). The influence of the particle size on the completeness of the reaction is obvious.

(5) For larger pine bark particles (125-250 μm), three asymptotes of the yield of tar were observed at the peak reaction temperatures 580°C (26%), 870°C (22%) and 1050°C (16%). This phenomenon indicated that the secondary tar cracking reaction exists in the large wood particles.

(6) From results of the pyrolyses of western hemlock with different residence times, we found that a shorter residence time helped the reaction to reach completion, but, the longer residence time provided the opportunity for secondary tar cracking process.

(7) A single-step first-order reaction model was successfully used to predict the yields of volatiles, tar and char of western hemlock and pine bark. It can also be used for some other kinds of cellulosic materials at similar reaction situation.

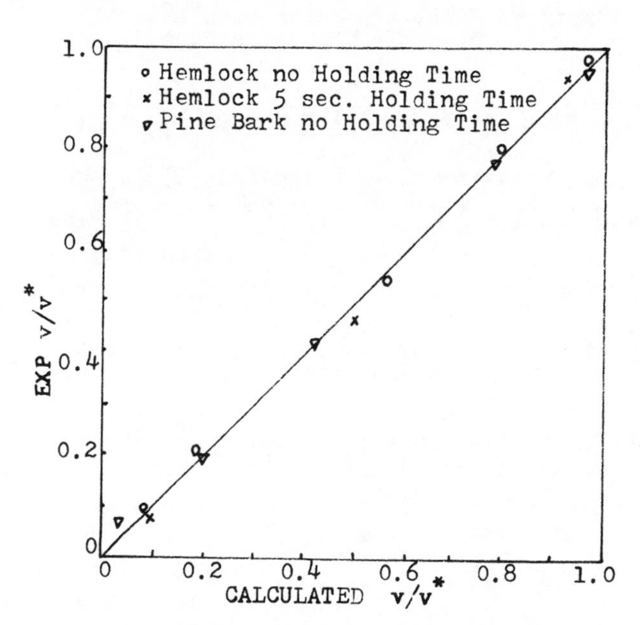

FIGURE 8. COMPARISON OF THE EXPERIMENTAL v/v^* AND THE CALCULATED v/v^* OF THE TOTAL VOLATILES.

REFERENCES

1. Klass, D. L., presented at Energy from Biomass and Wastes V, Florida, 1981.

2. Peters, W. A., M. R. Hajaligol, J. B. Howard and J.P. Longwell, Procedings, Specialists' Workshop on Fast Pyrolysis of Biomass, Copper Montain, Colorado, 1980.

3. Roberts, A. F., Combustion and Flame, 14, pp. 261-272, 1970.

4. Tran, D. O., and C. Rai, Fuel, Vol. 57, pp. 293-298, 1977.

5. Kanury, A., Murty A., Combustion and Flame, 18, pp. 75-83, 1972.

6. Zaror, C. A., I. S. Hutchings, D. L. Pyle, H. N. Stiles and R. Kandiyoti, Fuel, 64, pp. 990, 1985.

7. Bengali, S., M. S. Thesis, Oregon State University, Corvallis, Oregon, 1981.

8. Antal, M. J., Jr. H. L. Friedman and F. E. Rogers, Comb, Sci. and Tech., 21, pp.141, 1980.

9. Maa, P. S. and R. C. Bailie, AICHE 84th National Meeting, 1978.

10. Chatterjee, P.K. and C.M. Conard, Textile Res. J., 36, No. 6, pp. 487-493, 1966.

11. Shafizadeh, F., Applied Polymer Symp., 28, pp. 153-174, 1975.

12. Suuberg, E., Ph.D. Dissertation, MIT, Cambridge, Mass., 1977.

13. Min, Kun, Combustion and Flame, 30, pp. 285-294, 1977.

14. Chang, L. Y., M. S. Thesis, Oregon State University, Corvallis, OR, 1981.

15. Chang, L. Y., and F. Kyihan, 7th Miami International Conference on Alternative Energy Sources, Florida, 1985.

16. Chang, L. Y., Kinetics of Volatiles Formation Process of Wood Pyrolysis (in preparation).

SECTION 24
BREAKTHROUGHS IN LIGHTING

Chapter 71

EFFECTIVE LIGHTING ENERGY MANAGEMENT: RECENT EXPERIENCES WITH LIGHTING CONTROLS

J. L. Fetters

INTRODUCTION

In the past several years the Energy Manager has been provided many tools for effectively controlling his lighting load. Indeed, we are witnessing a revolution in lighting system components. At the AT&T Network Systems factory and offices in Columbus, Ohio, many of these new components have been employed in the past few years with varying degrees of success. This experience should prove valuable to others considering the application of lighting controls.

HISTORY

In the early days of our profession, lighting was highlighted for energy reductions, probably because it is so visible. Many attempted to reduce lighting levels below those needed to do quality work. This was especially true for those situations where there were older workers who need more - not less - light. Areas were selectively delamped as a commendable energy conservation practice, but this practice soon proved self-defeating and ineffective. Mature energy managers finally realized that the penalties of lost time and lower quality were more detrimental to a company's well being than the incremental cost of the electrical energy powering the lighting.

LIGHTING ENERGY MANAGEMENT

Sufficient light must be provided for every task in order for workers to be productive. The old energy conservation practice of arbitrarily reducing light levels to achieve an energy management goal is now past history and a whole array of equipment can now be employed for lighting energy management.

The goal of lighting energy management is to put the right amount of light on the task - where it is needed and when it is needed.

The 'right' amount of light for the task is sometimes debated, but here the designer must not be stingy and get a reputation with the users that may end up being self-defeating. When the 'where' part of this goal is examined, one thinks of positioning existing luminaires or selecting new luminaires and light sources to provide the required pattern of light for the task. By concentrating on the 'when' part of the control strategy, one begins to think in terms of time control and scheduling.

ENERGY CODES AND STANDARDS

In an attempt to limit energy for lighting, several energy conservation lighting design standards have been developed. Although a savings in energy can be achieved by reducing either the amount of power consumed (watts), or by reducing the time the power is used (hours), most codes and practices have focused only on power limits.

The ANSI/ASHRAE/IES Standard 90, first published in 1975 is by far the most popular code. This standard has been attacked for being too simplistic by prescribing power limits (UPD), while completely ignoring the time factor of the electrical energy equation: energy = power X time. The effect was to penalize the designer who employed state-of-the-art lighting controls to reduce the system operating time and essentially branded this design approach as ineffective by code standards.

Now, there is the proposed Standard 90.1P that attempts to rectify these shortcomings by recognizing that lighting controls are an effective means of providing lighting energy management by permitting more flexible and efficient use of lighting energy. It appears to the author that this is a case where the code is chasing actual practice and attempting to codify a fast changing technology.

UNIFORM POWER DENSITY (UPD)

The UPD is a lengthy, time-consuming procedure that has been established for use with new and existing buildings to determine an upper power limit for a building's lighting system. The power limit is for the total building and the sum of power budgets for each individual space in the building is allowed. The IES Lighting Handbook - Application Vol, Section 4 outlines the procedure for those who need this information.

REDUCING LIGHTING POWER - PERMANENTLY

A fast payback from lighting power reductions can be realized by the substitution of energy saving lamps for standard lamps. Fluorescent lamps have been improved to provide both acceptable color rendering qualities and reduced wattage. The user should be aware that when making this substitution, apparent increased ballast replacements may be experienced. This is due to the increased voltage rise across the ballast capacitor. This will occur more frequently with ballasts that are near their end-of-life. Fluorescent lamps can now be obtained with a watt-reducing feature that disconnects the cathodes to further reduce the power required.

A recent development that has found application in some office task lighting are the compact, twin-tube, U-shaped fluorescent lamps that are small in size, have long life and high efficacy. They are commercially available in 5-, 7-, 9-, and 13 watt sizes and require a ballast-socket adapter when used as replacements for incandescents. The units we are now installing are an integrally ballasted in the lighting fixture which is designed to mount under a desk unit shelf. It uses two 13 W lamps, rated at 890 lumens with 10,000 hours life.

Energy saving ballasts, primarily designed for use on energy saving F40 lamps are specified for all our new lighting installations and for maintenance replacements. They are a cost-effective way of limiting lighting power, recovering the additional expense in 3 to 5 years. Because of the poor performance of electronic ballasts experienced by others, we have not rushed to use them.

Early versions of energy saving incandescent lamps used krypton to provide a few watts reduction. Some recent advances have been made with incandescent replacements that not only have lower wattage with good lumen output but are also rated for longer life. We are just beginning to use these lamps, so we have not accumulated much experience with it.

LIGHTING ECONOMICS

The highest cost of operating a lighting system is the electrical energy cost. The next highest operating cost is the labor for lamp replacements and maintenance. This cost makes lamp life and the high cost of replacing short life lamps a consideration when calculating the economics for lamp replacements. The obvious savings from air-conditioning load reductions should also be credited in the evaluation. For those who have high electric demand charges, it is appropriate to calculate the savings in the same way that they purchase their electricity and include the demand reduction in their calculations.

For some applications, power reducing units are appropriate. One lighting installation, in a computer room that turned out overlighted due to higher than expected surface reflectances, was solved by using fluorescent lighting adjusters in the 277 volt power feed to the lighting circuits and adjusting both the lighting level and the power level to 60% of the original. This was a cost-effective solution compared to the labor cost of removing lighting fixtures. One advantage realized from the use of this type of equipment is that after the lamps begin to experience their normal lumen depreciation, the ambient level can be adjusted to restore the original preset lighting level.

In a similar situation, a computer entry area had been converted from key-punch machines to small green CRT's. This caused a problem for the operators who saw the veiling reflections in their screens. This problem was solved by adding a small power reducing device at each fixture. Both the power and light levels were more suitable for the application and the operators were satisfied after the retrofit was complete.

A recent use was made for incandescent dimmers in an atrium walkway to preset the maximum light level. The dimmers were located in the electrical closet so that the user was not aware of their presence, but the lighting designer had the flexibility of providing the task with the right amount of light, resulting in a tailor-made solution. Adjustments can easily be made if a change is required. Both lighting energy and light level are controlled, and the lamp life has been extended.

SCHEDULE CONTROL - TURNING LIGHTS OFF

Several years ago, our office building lighting was equipped with low-voltage relay control. Switches for each large area were located near each breaker box. A shutoff system was designed to shutoff all building lights sometime after quitting time. Each evening, the shutoff control would turn off all the lights at hourly intervals. Those working overtime could turn their area lighting back on as needed. This was appropriate for large open office areas. As many of these areas are now being converted to smaller offices, the control is being sub-divided for individual room control with a master turnoff from the building energy management system.

Low voltage control is the simplest and easiest scheduling control to use and administer. Because of the recent warnings of two major manufacturers of metal halide lamps and their recommendation to periodically shut off lighting systems, we are currently planning a control system that will both turn on and off selected zones and permit manual overide. The turn on feature will allow newly refurbished factory areas to be readied for work without workers having to wait for the characteristically long strike time of the metal halide lamps. A recently announced system that allows the user to overide the schedule program to turn selected lights on by using a telephone appeals to us.

Time clocks are still an effective way to control lighting loads, but the user should be aware of some of the drawbacks. Our main reason for converting many of the timeclock functions to an energy management function was to eliminate the labor to maintain the clock schedules when there was a power outage, or bi-annual change to and from daylight savings time and because of the increased flexibility that is provided with energy management schedules. Simple as they are, we have found 7-day timeclocks that were not only the wrong hour but on the wrong day! This can be a problem, especially if they are set with a skip day function that is expected to handle weekend days and is skipping Fridays or Mondays instead. In addition, timeclocks, unless they are the more recent electronic vintage cannot skip holidays and there is a loss of savings due to this limitation.

A new, electronic version of the old astronomical timeclock is now available for outdoor lighting loads. It is programmable and requires that the current day sunrise and sunset times be entered as well as the location latitude. once programmed, the timer will track the correct sunrise and sunset times for the location programmed and has auxiliary contacts that can be programmed on a separate schedule. With battery backup and a high load capability this timeclock is finding use in our outdoor lighting control applications. It is an electronic control, though and is susceptible to electromagnetic interference when used with some contactor coils. The use of MOV varistors is recommended to reduce this problem.

This new timer control has now replaced photocells and is expected to provide higher levels of reliability and lower maintenance costs than the photocells did. Photocells deteriorate and malfunction after several years in service and unless scheduled maintenance is performed to replace them they can be responsible for whole groups of lamp failures if the PC fails to latch and begins to cycle the lamps.

VARIABLE CONTROL-TURNING LIGHTS DOWN

Electronic lighting control equipment can also be used where it is desired to reduce the light level in response to an event or to provide a supplemental control in response to daylight levels. Two types have been applied, all from the same manufacturer. They both work in the same way to reduce the fluorescent light level and consequently the power level. The minimum level can be preset at the control unit. One operates as a three level control in response to a combination of inputs from an energy management schedule program and a demand shedding signal. The second operates to maintain a constant ambient level in an atrium supplemental daylighting control. The rate of change is very well controlled and and has not been noticeable by the occupants.

Another type of variable control has been used in conference rooms where room control is required for sales presentations or when using visual aids. These controls allow the user to remotely control the light levels of each zone as well as turn them on and off. Some of these are equipped with wireless control, providing an added degree of flexibility for the user. The designer must keep the needs of the user in mind when designing these controls, and be able to easily change the controls once the room is in use and the user discovers what they really need!

A COMBINED CONTROL - DOES IT ALL

A new control, combining many of the previously described features of separate components are integrated into one unit. The application is a cafeteria lighting retrofit with many zones of various sources on individual schedules and three-lamp fixtures in the dining area that will be controlled in response to photocells to supplement the available daylight from the large windows on two sides of the area. Other photocells in the peripheral soffit will switch off the peripheral lighting when the daylight level indicates that these lights are not required. This unit is expected to provide the flexibility required of the remodeled space. Lighting levels can be easily preset and programmed as needs change. Considerable savings are also expected, since the original lighting system did not even have light switches!

OCCUPANCY CONTROLLED LIGHTING

Conference rooms, small offices, and small toilet rooms are not occupied 100% of the time. This makes them prime candidates for a lighting control that uses some means to detect the presence of people in the room and turn the lights on when people enter and turn the lights off when people leave. This is a sophisticated, high-tech approach to lighting controls that works and is cost effective if applied correctly. We chose a simple, easy to apply, infrared system, with no adjustable controls. (If the user has access to controls, he will adjust them!) Lessons learned from our applications include: Provide an overide switch, located away from the entry door, to allow the occupant to turn off the room lights for showing projected visuals; Follow the installation instructions, especially concerning the placement, range and sensitivity pattern of the sensor(s); Watch out for electromagnetic interference with these electronic units when using relays or contactors (MOV varistors help here, too). After these controls were used in manager's offices, we discovered that there was a signalling system, based on the office lights being on that meant the manager was in that day, but temporarily out. With room occupancy controls, once the delay time that controls the off time after the occupant leaves the room expires, the lights go out and the old signal has no meaning. Retraining is now in progress to modify the old communications system!

SUMMARY

This paper has presented an array of lighting controls and lighting energy management strategies that will provide the lighting designer and energy manager with a variety of solutions to reduce the electrical cost of their lighting installations.

Chapter 72

STRATEGIC LIGHTING MAINTENANCE: MANAGEMENT'S NEW COST-SAVING TOOL

H. Chappell, Jr.

Building managers and owners from all across the country are rapidly realizing the value of an emerging services industry specializing in the strategic maintenance and management of lighting systems. Until the last decade, management saw little value of such services, usually delegating the routine repairs of lighting systems to a janitorial staff with no real training in the procedures required for proper maintenance. A few building owners and managers with larger properties might even have a staff electrician who performed the routine maintenance procedures, but with rare exceptions little need was seen for outside services or assistance.

In the early 1970s, with the oil embargo, a new awareness of the cost of lighting began to emerge. Many governmental bodies began to legislate outdoor and decorative lighting. The trend prior to 1970 was simple--"More is better." Lighting systems were over-designed to compensate for what engineers and architects knew in advance: Most lighting systems would lose 30% to 40% of their efficiency during the first three to five years of life because of inadequate on-going maintenance, creating excessive costs, from design to daily energy consumption. The lamp manufacturers responded with energy saving lamps at the same time that many managers and owners turned to some sort of "black box" for energy conservation. But most owners continued to fail to make any significant strides in managing the cost of lighting, even though lighting would account for nearly one-half of total energy consumption in many commercial buildings.

An array of specialty product manufacturers has sprung up since the mid 1970s in an attempt to answer the conservation needs facing building owners. This has only added confusion to a problem that most owners have yet to bring into clear focus; but because of pressing needs for energy conservation in the marketplace, technology advanced in spite of the lighting industry's fragmentation. In the lighting industry, that is estimated to have annual sales in excess of $10 billion (domestically), most commercial and industrial lighting users have continued to give their lighting system no more attention than they would a window. The system comes with the building: when it's broken, fix it; when it's dirty, wash it. There are exceptions of course, but there are vast amounts of money spent in pursuit of cost containment, improved environment, and employee productivity.

Owners of buildings no more than two years old can experience large savings in energy costs and increases in productivity by having the newest lighting systems designed and installed: more dramatic yet, many buildings can benefit from modernization (retrofit) of their existing lighting system the day that they are completed. Developers, not perceiving lighting as a selling feature to tenants, spend construction dollars on other building features and allow their tenants to pay monthly dollars that are saved front-end in construction.

Although improved employee productivity, enhanced environment, and greatly reduced energy consumption are apparent benefits from proper lighting management technics, research reveals that there is little awareness of any supplier of services that can bring all of the needed services together for a complete package to the industrial and commercial users of lighting. Research does reveal that prospective users for lighting management are now beginning to realize (when prompted) that lighting is a system that must be conceived, designed, engineered, built, installed and maintained. This is the first indication that owners and managers are coming to the realization that such an industry even exists.

Two factors that are helping focus attention on the lighting industry can be found in legislative actions and the rising cost of electricity.

Many states are now governing the watts allowed per square foot. California and New York have led the way with this legislation, allowing only two watts per square foot for new buildings. Now legislation is being seen that also places limits on existing buildings. California has recently passed such legislation giving building owners definite limits on power consumption and a timetable to meet those limits.

A great deal of lighting awareness is being created because power rates are expected to rise at five to 10 times the rate of inflation, and because many utility companies are involved in programs to reduce demand for power. Many utility companies across the country are now offering rebates to building owners that reduce power consumption of their lighting system. This effort was pioneered by Pacific Gas & Electric of California, which was soon followed by Texas and Florida power companies. These utilities help fund the installation of such items as energy saving lamps and ballasts, watt reducers, and reflectors.

As a result of their efforts to curb energy demand, many building owners are left with upgraded lighting systems that no longer afford the owner the ability to perform maintenance as an afterthought, or to follow the practice of "just fix it when it's broken." The need for professional lighting maintenance is showing itself mainly because a lighting system can no longer contain the excess that once was apparent in system design.

As a consequence of these developments, the traditional reliance on a local electrical contractor as the source of lighting services has been steadily supplanted by growing use of qualified professional lighting systems managers, whose skills and resources involve a far more extensive range of services.

Qualified lighting system contractors can advise the building owner or manager how to meet the demands of new legislation, and how to take advantage of a rebate program offered by the utility companies. These experts can provide valuable insights about which products are applicable for a specific installation--and provide for the installation of these products. Practitioners of the lighting system management discipline can produce the answers to the questions of on-going preventative maintenance, which becomes a critical issue as excessive light levels are reduced.

The emergence of this discipline depended, naturally, on its ability to demonstrate clearly to the building owner the benefits of a properly maintained lighting system. This it was able to do, both after the fact on a retrofit basis, and as part of the building design.

Retrofit of lighting systems can often pay for itself from energy savings in less than one year. Many lighting contractors are now performing work on a shared savings basis or a pay from savings basis, methods which allow a building owner to go ahead with needed design and lighting changes without the investment of as much vital capital. Savings are often times so dramatic that many owners are astonished at the effect that lighting retrofit can have on the bottom line.

The lighting maintenance professional contractor is also aware of the balance that must be struck between savings and efficiency; when, as important as the amount of light needed within a given space, is the quality of that light. Many work spaces designed prior to the use of such office tools as CRTs now present unique lighting problems. Any reduction in energy use of that lighting system, without regard to the resulting light level or quality of that light, may bring disastrous results. Many owners are using the retrofit energy savings to incorporate designs that will better provide for the quality of light desired to perform specific tasks.

R.J. Reynolds Tobacco Company is an excellent study in the application of lighting maintenance techniques, both on a retrofit and a design basis. It is a case study, also, that demonstrates how valuable the cooperation between building owner and lighting maintenance management contractor can be.

Until 1973 Reynolds Tobacco, headquartered in Winston-Salem, N.C., took a very high output-type fixture approach in lighting its tobacco manufacturing facilities, the "making and packing" areas where tobacco is turned into the company's cigarette products. Company policy--then and now--is that the illumination in these critical production areas is never to drop below 100 footcandles.

To guarantee that, the company had typically lighted these areas with a system of 1500 milliamp fluorescent lamps, mounted in hooded industrial fixtures of average aperture, suspended by rods at 10-to-12 foot heights from 13-to-18 foot high ceilings. The fixtures, set end-to-end in parallel rows and running the length of a facility, each drew 445 watts. The lamp lumen depreciation of these at 70% of rated life was 42%, but this decrease was compounded (as much as 30% more) by the accumulation of dirt and tobacco that collected on the reflectors and lamps.

It was the procedure at that time to replace burned out lamps one at a time, on a spot basis, and there was no formal program to guarantee that the reflectors got cleaned at the time of replacement. To maintain the 100 footcandle standard, the facilities had to be overlighted initially, as high as 150 footcandles at installation.

The energy crunch that dominated the mid-1970s led the company to apply energy conservation techniques to all its operations, particularly the lighting program which comprised 10% of the company's annual electricity budget.

The first step was to analyze alternatives offered by energy-saving lamps then on the market, specifically the 800 milliamp fluorescents. Drawing only 225 watts, as replacements they would virtually halve the connected load. They also showed only 23% lamp lumen depreciation at the 70% life.

Calculations by Reynolds Tobacco engineers indicated that a group relamping program tied to a 70% life changeout timetable could greatly reduce energy and labor costs. A test at one of the making and packing areas showed that the combination of lower wattage, energy-efficient ballasts, and fewer but cleaner fixtures, could indeed meet the minimum illumination standards--and with fewer fixtures.

By 1980 the company was retrofitting the 800 milliamp fixtures into all its manufacturing facilities--one in downtown Winston-Salem, and a second at its showcase Whitaker Park facility on the outskirts of the city - and was also putting its office buildings on group relamping. That produces energy and labor costs savings each year of between $250,000 and $350,000.

The source of those savings lies in the efficiencies that a group maintenance program offers over spot relamping. Energy saving opportunities are present in facilities like Whitaker Park, where fewer fixtures or lower wattage lamps become possible. Labor savings dominate in office buildings, where the cost per individual changed fixture drops dramatically. Both situations benefit from savings that are possible with volume purchasing. Simply put, it is cheaper to buy a thousand lamps when relamping than to keep a dozen sitting around in a closet at all times.

Such savings increase when group maintenance is designed into a facility, as is the case with the company's Tobaccoville manufacturing plant that is scheduled to begin full operations in 1987.

The huge plant will be lighted by 2,200 sealed, recessed metal halide fixtures, suspended at 20-foot heights over production areas. The wattage of the lamps (rated at 400 watts) was basically determined by that height; the number of fixtures was not.

The engineers calculated how many fixtures would be required to maintain the 100 footcandle minimum, given the traditional parameters--reflectance of the walls, ceiling and floor, for example, but they also calculated the effect of a strategic lighting maintenance program. On a spot relamping basis the new facility would have to be designed with 2,900 fixtures. With group relamping assumed, that dropped to only 2,200 fixtures.

Informed of this, management committed to a group relamping program for Tobaccoville, and the building was designed with 700 fewer fixtures. This approach saved some $250,000 in capital costs (materials and labor) and it will save about $35,000 in annual operating costs as well.

All of Reynolds Tobacco's facilities and office buildings on group maintenance are now tied into a computer prompting system: Months before a plant's changeout, Engineering is alerted by a computer print-out, and the plant manager is advised to arrange with IllumElex to schedule the relamping. Contracting offers Reynolds Tobacco several advantages: It is less expensive. It lets them accomplish the task during the limited time afforded by yearly shutdowns--for example the Christmas week--which is important for a task that takes up so much time. The 1,600-plus fixtures at the Whitaker Park facility, for example, take an eight-man crew upwards of three days to relamp and clean. It is more sensible for their maintenance personnel to be free during that time for changing, for example, motor control centers and process controllers on the production floor, not changing lamps.

The overall effect of group lighting maintenance at R.J. Reynolds Tobacco has been to cut energy consumption for lighting in half and increase light levels, through a program that more than pays for itself. That record, and the short payback period that was involved (six months to two years depending on the particular facility) explains why interest in strategic lighting maintenance is growing.

Our company's experience is that approximately half our new customers in 1986 are interested in retrofit group relamping programs. We also get about a dozen inquiries a month about group relamping for new installations, and that doesn't seem to be tied to a particular state or industry.

Lessons which this case study hold should be encouraging to everyone concerned with the best use of our energy resources. Lighting is considered by many to be the most misused and abused facet of American business today. It is the Professional Lighting System Manager who can help American business correct that, whether it be a simple cleaning that can increase lighting levels by as much as 40%, or a complete relamping of an existing system. And it is the lighting systems management firm that brings under one umbrella the wide assortment of energy savings products and services available to properly address these problems, that provides the best possible lighting solutions to building owners. From consulting services to implementation, this emerging industry has become management's new cost saving tool.

SECTION 25
STEAM SYSTEMS

Chapter 73

COST SAVINGS THROUGH PROPER TEMPERATURE CONTROL AND CONDENSATE RECOVERY IN STEAM SYSTEMS

D. D. Dugan

Despite recent drops in fuel prices, controlling costs related to energy remains a top priority in the effort to stay competitive. The wise steam user has found that properly selecting and applying temperature controls and correctly utilizing condensate recovery systems will maximize efficiency in steam plants and result in substantial cost savings. By following steam from the boiler through the mains to the end process and back through the condensate recovery system to the boiler, typical applications will be found to illustrate these savings.

To ensure maximum efficiency in a steam system requires as much heat as possible to be delivered to the point of use with minimum losses along the way. This is done by generating high quality, dry steam which is transmitted through insulated piping to efficient heat exchange equipment which is automatically controlled, and then returning the hot condensate.

Operating the boiler at its highest rated pressure will generate the maximum quality of steam with minimum carryover of water. Since this pressure is usually higher than needed at the plant, pressure reducing valves can lower the pressure at the point of use. Thus, the steam can be distributed at high pressure in relatively small insulated mains.

All boilers, barring those with superheaters, produce steam with some entrained moisture. Since this moisture can lead to problems with waterhammer, corrosion and reduced efficiency of heat exchangers, steam separators and trap sets must be installed to remove it. Proper installation of this equipment will improve steam quality to approximately 97% or 98% dryness fraction. At this point, we are able to focus on the further efficiencies to be realized through the proper control of temperature and through the return of condensate.

TEMPERATURE CONTROL OF STORAGE TANKS

One of the most common applications is the temperature control of bulk storage tanks. For example, oil fired boilers are fed from storage tanks. Products, such as chemical feed stocks, milk or hydrocarbons are stored in tanks while awaiting shipment or movement to the next step in the process. Some tanks are filled with just plain water. These tanks are heated for many different reasons. Oil tanks are heated to lower the viscosity for pumping. A tank filled with milk is heated to inhibit bacterial growth. Water tanks are heated to prevent freezing. Whatever the reason, proper control of the heating is essential. The installation of the correct temperature control to the heating coil should be considered a necessity rather than a luxury. Apart from the difficulty which may be experienced in handling the fluid at the wrong temperature, heat losses (and energy costs) mount steadily as the temperature rises. Storage tanks should therefore never be heated above the minimum acceptable temperature. For example, even a relatively small insulated tank 6 feet in diameter and 15 feet long running only 10°F above the required minimum temperature would waste approximately 15,000 pounds of steam a year. How do we control temperature in a storage tank?

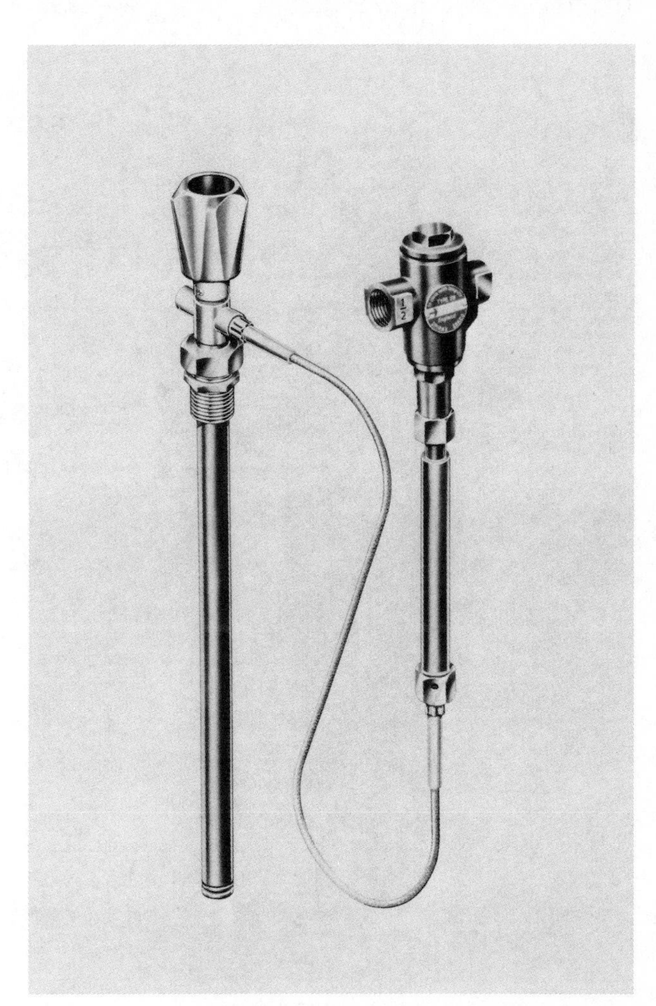

FIGURE 1. SELF-ACTING TEMPERATURE CONTROL

A self-acting temperature control (Fig. 1) requiring no external source of power, involving no fire risk, requiring no weather protection and the minimum of maintenance, is ideally suited for this job and would pay for itself in a very short time. This type of control draws its operating power from the temperature rise of the fluid in which the sensor bulb is immersed. It provides closed loop proportional control with feedback. It gives smooth, close control due to the fully modulating movement available through the valve and control system. The self-acting temperature control is perfect for remote, hard to reach applications since you can set it and forget it. For applications requiring higher capacity, pilot operated temperature controls are also available. These are driven by temperature pilots which are, in effect, very low capacity self-acting controls.

A typical self-acting temperature control consists of two parts: A thermal system and a valve. The thermal system has a sensor bulb with a tamper proof adjustment knob calibrated in degrees F, a capillary and an actuator. The adjustment knob could also be on the actuator or at some convenient location between the sensor and the actuator. The entire thermal system is filled with a high grade mineral oil. As the sensor bulb is heated, this oil expands and pushes through the capillary to the actuator where it compresses a bellows and drives the valve stem. Also located in the sensor bulb is a gas filled bellows which provides protection against temperature overrun.

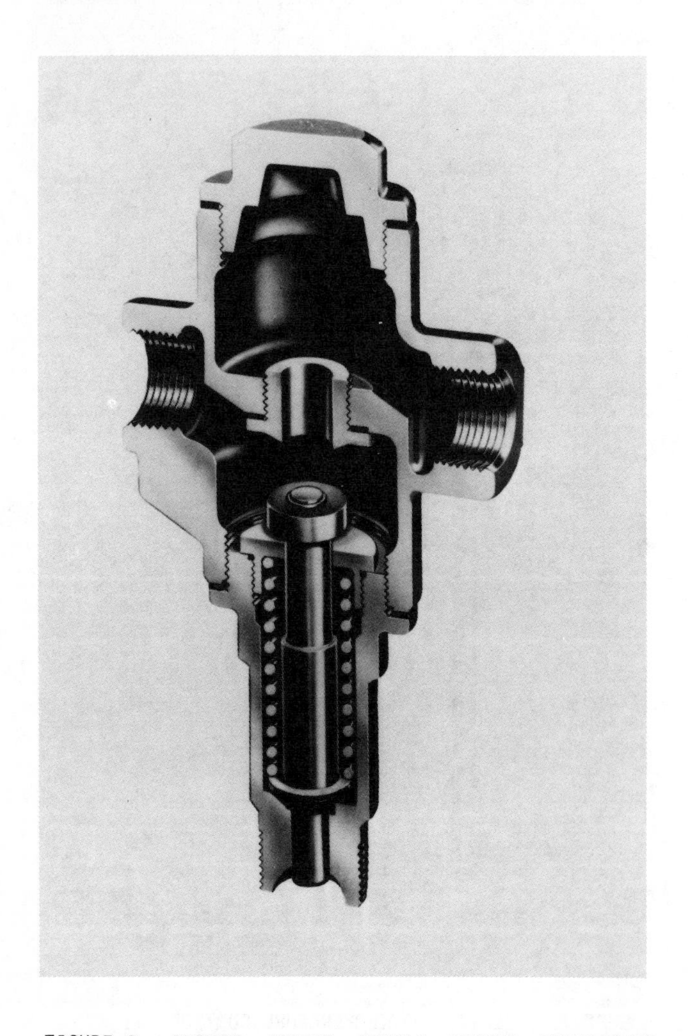

FIGURE 2. DIRECT ACTING SINGLE SEATED UNBALANCED VALVE

The other part of the self-acting temperature control is the valve. For heating applications, the valve would be a direct acting, normally open type. As the temperature rises and the bellows in the actuator compresses, the valve plug moves toward the seat ring, reducing the flow of steam. As the temperature drops, and the mineral oil contracts, the return spring pulls the plug from the seat ring, increasing steam flow. Figure 2 shows a single seated, unbalanced valve. Also available are double seated and bellows balanced single seated valves. With the bellows balanced type, it is possible to achieve tight shut-off against pressure drops of 200 psi or more in valve sizes up to 2 inch. This is more than sufficient for most applications.

Now, let's see how a self-acting temperature control can be applied to a fuel oil storage tank. Generally, fuel oil must be heated in order to lower its viscosity so that it can be readily pumped. The temperature required will, of course, depend on the actual viscosity which should be obtained from the supplier. Whether or not the oil will be stored at this temperature will depend on the method of heating employed. The oil can be heated, prior to pumping, in two ways. The entire tank can be maintained at the pumping temperature (bulk heating) or an "outflow" heater can be used to heat the oil as it leaves the tank, while the bulk of the oil is kept at a lower temperature (outflow heating). In a typical installation for bulk heating, the steam coil is below the level of the oil outlet and the sensor is installed roughly half-way between the two. When the oil is delivered to a storage tank, it is already at or above the minimum pumping temperature. Bulk heating should therefore only require the addition of sufficient heat to offset the losses from the surface of the tank. Since these losses occur from the entire exposed surface, the tank should generally be insulated if the losses are not to be excessive. The control valve should be selected to suit the running load. Where it is necessary to bring the oil up from cold, this warming up load should be handled by a manual bypass or a separate warming up coil and valve. This will ensure that the control valve does not spend the greater part of its life in the almost closed position, causing erratic temperature control and possibly suffering eventual wiredrawing of the seating surfaces.

The other method of heating oil for pumping is outflow heating. When an outflow heater is installed, the contents of the tank are not maintained at pumping temperature. The amount of steam used, therefore, is only the minimum required. The heater protrudes from the suction connection into the oil space and only the oil in the immediate vicinity of the suction is heated to the pumping temperature. Heat is thus only demanded when the oil is being drawn off and, since the tank surface temperature is lowered, insulation can sometimes be dispensed with.

The heating element of an outflow heater is normally encased in a shroud to prevent the loss of oil over the element. The outlet is arranged so that the heater is always flooded and baffles have been installed to improve the efficiency of heat transfer. Thermostatic control is essential due to the very high ratio of heating surface to oil volume within the heater. A suitable temperature control for this application must be capable of giving a tight shut-off when no oil is flowing, since even a slight leak can cause overheating. The position of the sensor requires some thought since it must sense the temperature of the oil, whether it is flowing or not. It should not be placed in a stagnant corner of the heater where the oil temperature will be different from that of the oil flowing through the center, since this will give incorrect outflow temperatures. Likewise, it should not be installed outside the heater in the pump suction line, since it will not be aware of any overheating in the heater body when the oil is not flowing. It is also essential that the whole of the sensor bulb should protrude into the pipe line so that it is in contact with the oil. Unless this is done, the response to changes in oil temperature will be sluggish.

Particularly with the heavier grades of oil, a combination of bulk heating and outflow heating is often employed. A steam coil in the tank provides "background" heat, facilitating the flow of oil into the outflow heater where the temperature is boosted to full pumping temperature. This retains the advantage of the lowered tank surface temperature, while keeping the outflow heater to a reasonable size. The choice of method will depend on the number and situation of the tanks, the frequency and rate of fuel usage, and the local delivery conditions. It is always advisable to consult the company supplying the oil before making a final decision.

Although most fuels today are thermally stable within normal limits, high pressure or highly superheated steam should not be used in oil heating as this could lead to oil "caking" on the heating surfaces and reducing heat transmission. Moreover, the lower the steam pressure, the greater is the quantity of latent heat per pound of steam. For all steam applications, the most economical pressure is the lowest at which the plant can be operated and this has the added advantage that it is easier to control than high pressure steam. The saturation temperature of the steam must, of course, be sufficiently far above the desired oil temperature to give a reasonable "temperature head" and keep the heating surface within practical limits. Something in the region of 20 to 30 psi is generally right. Let's see how significant steam savings can be realized by reducing steam pressure as low as possible, in existing as well as new installations, with a pressure reducing valve.

PROPER SELECTION OF STEAM PRESSURE

There are two forms of heat energy available in steam. "Sensible heat", that which elevates its temperature to the boiling point and "latent heat", that energy which changes the liquid water into steam vapor. The latent heat is what is given up by steam when it is condensed in an application. This change of state occurs at the "saturated steam temperature" which is constant for every steam pressure.

TABLE I

PROPERTIES OF SATURATED STEAM

Steam Pressure		Steam Temperature		Heat in BTU's per Lb.	
PSIG	Bar	°F	°C	Sensible	Latent
0	0	212	100	180	971
10	.69	239	115	208	953
20	1.38	259	126	228	940
50	3.45	298	148	267	912
75	5.2	320	160	290	896
100	6.9	338	170	309	882
125	8.6	353	178	325	869
150	10.3	366	186	339	858
200	13.8	388	198	362	838
300	20.7	421	216	399	805

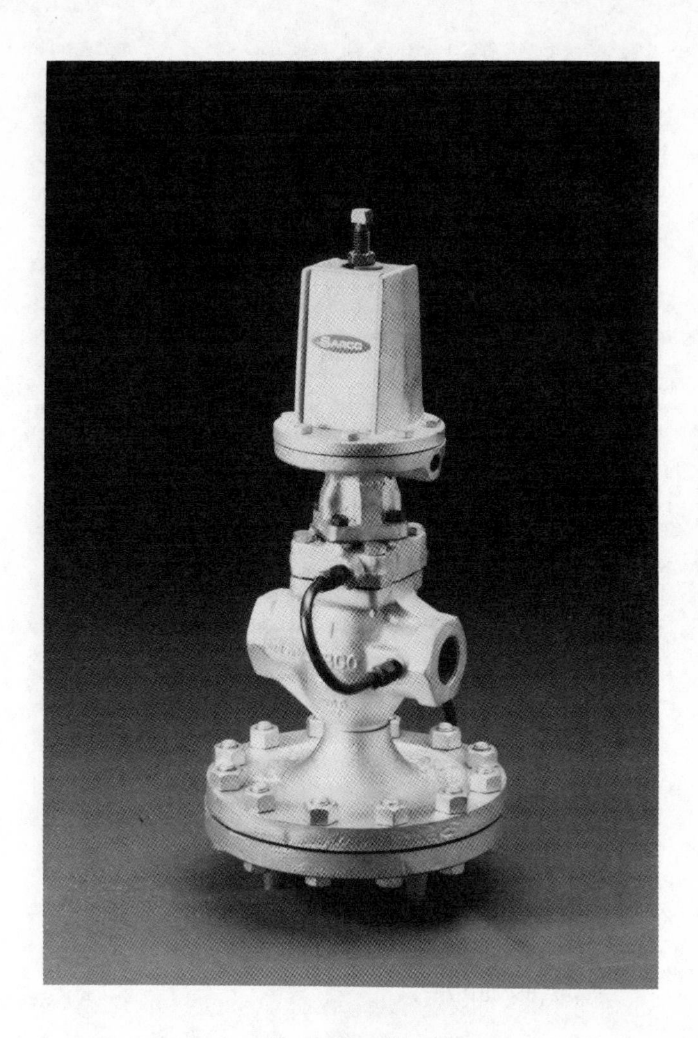

FIGURE 3. PRESSURE REDUCING VALVE

The Steam Properties Chart shows how proper selection of steam pressure for most economical operation is made by understanding these two points:

1. High pressure steam has a higher temperature and is most economical to distribute through steam mains by requiring smaller size piping.

2. Lower pressure steam contains more latent heat per pound and thereby provides the most economical operation.

As a general rule, steam is most economically generated and distributed at high pressure and should be reduced just before it is used to the lowest pressure that will satisfy the temperature requirement of the installation.

TABLE II

STEAM SAVED BY REDUCING PRESSURE

Original Pressure Reduced Pressure	125 psig	150 psig % Steam Savings	200 psig
100 psig	2.1%	3.6%	6.8%
75 psig	4.4%	5.9%	9.0%
50 psig	7.2%	8.6%	11.6%
20 psig	11.5%	13.0%	15.8%
10 psig	13.7%	15.0%	17.8%

The Steam Savings Chart gives the percentage savings realized when a 125 psig to 200 psig original steam pressure is reduced and all non-flashed condensate is collected and returned to the boiler.

The steam savings by reducing any pressure condition for any application can be calculated from the total BTU/Hr. heat required and the BTU/Hr. flash steam loss at that pressure. The % flash steam for any pressure reduced to 0 psig is:

$$\% \text{ Flash loss} = \frac{H_f - 180}{971} \times 100$$

Where H_f = sensible heat at steam pressure

Example: Steam consumption of a 20 GPM heat exchanger which heats water from 50°F to 150°F (1 GPM = 500 Lb./Hr.)

BTU/Hr. required = Lbs. water/Hr. x temperature rise
= 20 GPM x 500 x (150°F - 50°F)
= 1,000,000 BTU/Hr.

A. Original pressure of 125 psig (latent heat = 869 BTU/Lb.)

BTU/Hr. flash loss =

$$\frac{1{,}000{,}000 \text{ BTU/Hr.}}{869 \text{ BTU/Lb.}} \times 14.8\% \text{ flash loss} \times 1{,}150 \text{ BTU/Lb.}$$

= 195,857 BTU/Hr.

B. Reduced pressure of 20 psig (*available heat = 965 BTU/Lb.)

BTU/Hr. flash loss =

$$\frac{1{,}000{,}000 \text{ BTU/Hr.}}{965 \text{ BTU/Lb.}} \times 4.9\% \text{ flash loss} \times 1{,}150 \text{ BTU/Lb.} =$$

= 58,394 BTU/Hr.

Heat savings = (195,857 - 58,394) = 137,463 BTU/Hr.

$$\% \text{ heat savings} = \frac{137{,}463 \text{ BTU/Hr.}}{1{,}195{,}857 \text{ BTU/Hr.}} \times 100 = 11.5\%$$

*Available heat assumes constant enthalpy process for the 125 to 20 psig pressure reduction.

Reducing the operating pressure from 125 psig to 20 psig results in a 137,463 BTU/Hr. savings or 11.5% steam savings. When operated 14 hours per day, this gives an annual savings of $5,268 where steam costs $7.50 per 1,000,000 BTU. (approximately 1,000 Lbs.)

Existing installations must have sufficient heat exchange surface area to achieve their rated output at the lower pressure but this can be easily allowed for when designing a new installation.

It is clear that properly controlling temperature in storage tanks can result in significant savings.

Overheating tanks can waste thousands of pounds of steam every year. Using too high a steam pressure can result in "caking" of the coil, which then becomes inefficient and requires more and more steam to provide the same amount of heating. Selecting too large a control valve can cause erratic temperatures, waste of steam, and shortened life of the valve itself through wiredrawing. The costs of these problems can be considerable.

CONTROLLING FUEL OIL LINE HEATERS

Let's look at some other temperature control applications involved with fuel oil. Line heaters are used to raise oil from pumping temperature to burning temperature. For pressure-jet burners the oil is heated under pressure to a temperature which will reduce its viscosity to approximately 15 to 25 centistokes. This temperature, of course, varies with the grade of fuel. Rough guides to the heating required can be obtained, but optimum conditions can only be obtained by trial and error. The type of plant as well as the grade of fuel will have a bearing on the temperature required. Line heaters are highly rated and contain a large amount of heating surface compared with the volume of oil. A temperature control is therefore essential to prevent temperature overrun and should be capable of giving a tight shut-off on no-load. The sensor is placed within the heater body, across the oil flow as it leaves the heater so as to sense the oil temperature whether the oil is flowing or not. Difficulties arise when the heater capacity is out of all proportion to the demand.

Firstly, it is common practice on a multi-boiler layout to use one heater to serve several boilers. However, when one or more boilers is off-load, the heater and its temperature control become grossly oversized for the reduced duty. Where possible, therefore, individual heaters should be used for each boiler or, in large boiler houses, for each pair of boilers. Secondly, for commercial reasons, the capacity range of oil heaters is limited, it being usual to take for any one job the nearest stock size above the requirements. This often leads to heaters being provided having a capacity considerably in excess of the maximum demand. At the same time, the heater must be designed for the very worst conditions, and therefore for the majority of the year it is well oversized.

As a result of these various factors, the temperature control valve is likely to be oversized for the greater part of the time resulting in erratic control and wiredrawing of the valve which is working too close to its seat. The best way to make the heater more controllable is to reduce the steam pressure which, in turn, reduces the output of the heater and the effective capacity of the control valve. This use of a pressure reducing valve will not only enhance proper control of temperature but, as we have already seen, can result in substantial steam savings.

Heating is carried out in either single or multi-stage units depending upon the load. Where the steam flow through a multi-stage unit is in parallel and the oil flow is in series, it is essential that each stage is individually trapped. Group trapping can cause waterlogging of the primary stages and result in uneven temperatures. The steam traps must be capable of getting rid of condensate immediately as it is formed and should be able to vent air freely since a pocket of air in the steam space could halve the efficiency of the heater. Float and thermostatic traps, which prevent waterlogging and can vent air freely, are always the best choice in a process application. It is also important to install a drip trap in front of the control valve. This ensures only high quality steam reaches the valve, thus reducing the possibility of wiredrawing. The installation of an air eliminator on the oil heater outlet ensures that any air or gas which may have been liberated during heating is disbursed. In many instances flame fading on fuel oil burners has been traced to an accumulation of air and gas in the supply pipes. Automatic float control valves installed at the high points will release any accumulation of gas or air.

Where large amounts of oil are being recirculated from pressure-jet burners to the pump suction, trouble is sometimes experienced due to hot oil gassing at the pump suction. If this occurs, an emergency line can be laid to return recirculated oil to the storage tank when the plant is operating on maximum turndown. The oil flow through this emergency line can be automatically controlled by a three-way valve installed with the sensor in the pump suction. This will allow the hotter recirculated oil to mix with cooler oil from the storage tank, thus eliminating the gassing.

We have concentrated on fuel oil storage heating applications, but let us not forget that similar problems and similar opportunities to save energy can be found with heating any other type of fluid in a storage tank. Be sure that every tank has the proper temperature control regardless of the fluid being heated.

PROPER CONTROL OF STEAM TRACING

There is another very common heating application that cries out for proper temperature control: Steam tracing. If not looked after, improper steam tracing can result in serious problems.

In many industrial processes, particulary those in the refinery and chemical fields, it is often necessary to maintain the temperature of liquids during transit in pipelines. This is done most commonly by jacketed lines or lines to which a separate "tracer" line carrying some heating medium such as steam has been attached. The actual duty of these heating or tracing arrangements is varied. There are a number of typical needs for steam tracing. Steam tracing is sometimes required to prevent freezing, particulary in the colder parts of the world where freezing of the product can take place. It is used to prevent denaturing or a change in state by chemical or physical reaction due to temperature. Steam tracing is used to maintain desired product viscosity in order to simplify pumping or where variations in viscosity before passing through a flow meter or other instrumentation would upset the accuracy. Steam tracing is also used to prevent condensing in gas lines.

In looking at steam tracing for freeze protection, whether it is to prevent water from freezing and bursting a pipe or asphalt from turning into a solid cylinder that is very difficult to pump, there are two things that are of greatest importance to us. First, we need a temperature control we can rely on. Second, we need a control that saves energy. A self-acting tracer temperature control answers both these needs. (Fig. 4) This control is normally installed outdoors. The sun shielded ambient sensing bulb is filled with an oil that expands as the surrounding air temperature rises. This expansion pushes the valve plug toward the seat and, at set point, shuts off tightly. As the ambient temperature drops, the oil contracts and the return spring lifts the plug from the seat. Should the thermal system fail, the valve opens providing fail-safe freeze protection. This control also provides a savings of energy that is twofold. First, as a self-acting temperature control, it draws its power from the heat of the air surrounding it and requires no external power source. Second, it saves steam by shutting off the tracer lines when it is not needed, just like turning off the lights when you leave the room. In an area with a five month winter, for example, and approximately 1,800 hours of ambient temperature below 40°F steam savings would approach 50% on tracing lines by using self-acting temperature controls. In addition to this major point, the need for manual control of steam to tracers will be eliminated, saving maintenance man hours for higher priority work.

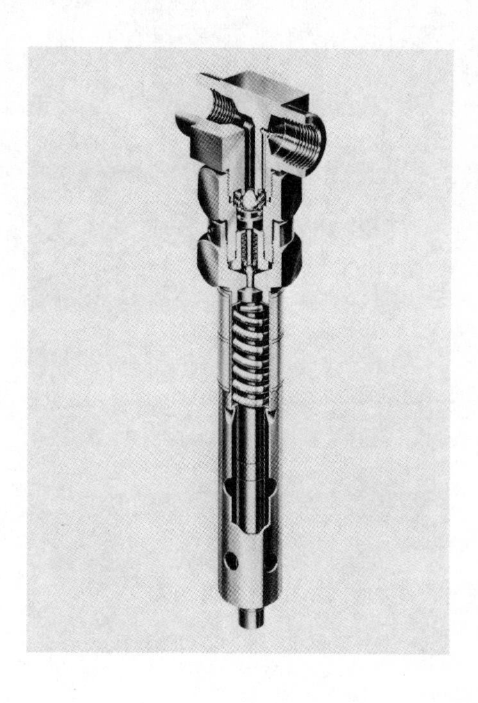

FIGURE 4. SELF-ACTING TRACER TEMPERATURE CONTROL

Tracer line temperature controls are also available which control the steam flow based on the temperature of the product in the pipe. With this control, the sensor is strapped tightly to the pipe so that it can accurately measure the temperature. The pipe and the sensor must then be properly insulated. If required, the stainless steel sensor could also be inserted through the pipe wall into the product. In fact, direct insertion is the recommended method of installation on critical tracing applications. This type of control should be easily field adjustable as well as compact and light weight for installation on small diameter tracing lines.

FIGURE 5. THERMOSTATIC STEAM TRAP

SUBCOOLING CONDENSATE

Additional savings can be realized on steam tracing lines by subcooling the steam condensate. This is achieved by using the proper type of steam trap at the end of the tracing line. (Fig. 5) Many steam tracing applications have a process temperature less than that of hot condensate and can absorb the sensible heat it contains. Using subcooled discharge, steam traps on these applications will result in increased thermal efficiency, especially at higher operating pressures which have a greater sensible heat content. The percent of steam saved by a subcooled discharge trap compared to a trap operating at steam temperature, both discharging to atmosphere, can be calculated using the following formula:

$$\% \text{ Steam Savings} = \left(1 - \frac{L_1}{L_1 + T_1 - T_2}\right) \times 100$$

Where L_1 = Latent heat of steam at operating pressure

T_1 = Steam temperature at operating pressure

T_2 = Subcooled discharge temperature

Steam savings on a continuously operating 100 psi product line below 190°F, with a condensate load of 60 pounds per hour, will be:

$$\% \text{ steam savings} = \left(1 - \frac{882}{882 + 338 - 190}\right) \times 100$$

$$= (1 - 0.856) \times 100$$

$$= 14.4\%$$

Monthly savings per trap, based on an average steam cost of $7.50 per 1,000 pounds of steam generated, will be:

$$\text{Cost Savings} = 14.4\% \times \frac{\$7.50}{1{,}000 \text{ Lb.}} \times \frac{60 \text{ Lb.}}{\text{Hr.}} \times \frac{720 \text{ Hr.}}{\text{Month}}$$

$$= \$46.66 \text{ per month}$$

Similar cost savings per trap may be determined by substituting other operation conditions in the formula above using the percent steam savings realized at any given operating pressure. The following table illustrates some typical examples.

TABLE III

STEAM SAVED BY UTILIZING SENSIBLE HEAT IN CONDENSATE

Operating Pressure	Steam Savings @ 190°F Operation
300 psig	22.4%
200 psig	19.1%
100 psig	14.4%
50 psig	10.6%
25 psig	7.6%
10 psig	5.1%

Cooling condensate accumulates in the piping ahead of the trap as its sensible heat content is absorbed by the system. A successful application must be designed to prevent waterlogged equipment and waterhammer problems from developing. Steam main drips do not utilize any sensible heat gain and using subcooled discharge traps provide only reduced discharge of flash steam as a benefit.

CONDENSATE RECOVERY

When all the temperature controls have been properly selected and installed, when the steam pressure has been reduced to the most efficient level, and when the sensible heat of the condensate has been used on non-critical applications, there are still substantial savings to be realized from recovering and reusing the condensate. In fact, returning all condensate to the boiler instead of dumping it down the sewer provides three-way energy savings. It reduces your water and sewage costs, saves on water treatment chemicals, and most importantly eliminates the cost of steam used to pre-heat cold boiler make-up water. Returning all condensate also provides environmental savings where regulations prohit the dumping of hot condensate into a sewage system without first sub-cooling it. It eliminates the use of cooling water equal to 80% of the condensate load. Returning condensate puts fuel costs back into the system instead of down the drain.

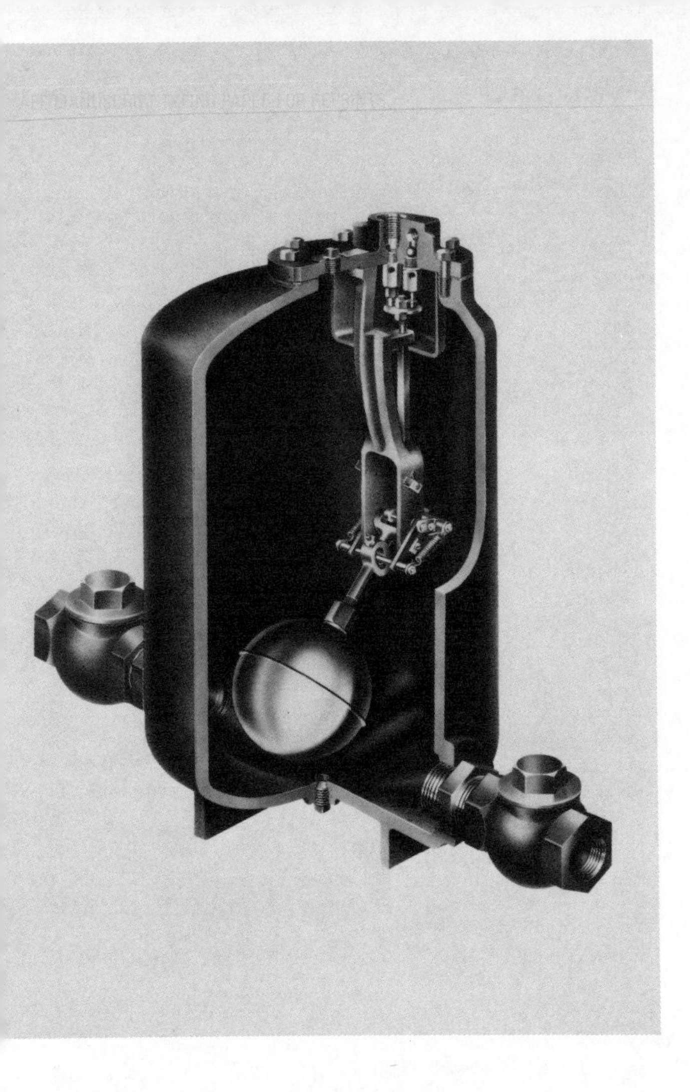

FIGURE 6. PRESSURE-POWERED PUMP

Although condensate can be lifted by the steam pressure at the trap outlet, it should really be allowed to flow away by gravity. Such an arrangement is essential if the pressure at the trap outlet is low or the equipment is temperature controlled. Unfortunately, it is rarely possible to return condensate by gravity back to the boiler feed tank. For this reason, it is usual to run condensate to a collecting point from which it can be pumped back to the boilerhouse. Electric pumps are capable of working against a high resistance. Thus, small return lines can be used when condensate has to be pumped over a long distance. The reduction in line size will produce a corresponding reduction in heat losses, resulting in condensate reaching the boiler feed tank at a higher temperature. In many cases, however, a pressure-powered pump (Fig. 6) is more advantageous to use than conventional electrically powered pumps. This is especially true in remote areas, where electrical service is not readily available, or where explosive atmospheres prohibit the use of electrical power. It offers a more economical installation than electric pumps, especially for those special applications which require expensive electric panels, starters and accessories. When maintenance is required, it can be easily handled by only one craft.

For sizing purposes, the electric "pump load" is usually three times the actual load to ensure that the motors do not run constantly and burn out in a short time. This makes them higher horsepower and more expensive than necessary. A pressure-powered pump is sized for the actual load and can therefore handle the same load as a larger and most costly electric pump.

Operating costs are reduced by choosing a pressure-powered pump over an electrical pump. When vented to atmosphere, the pressure-powered pump uses only 3 pounds of steam for every 1,000 pounds of liquid pumped. When the exhaust is vented back in a closed system, the steam is recovered and the cost of operation is negligible.

The dollars saved annually be returning condensate are calculated by determining the cost of the water, chemicals and BTU's of fuel saved. The following example shows the annual savings realized by returning a load of 5,000 pounds of condensate per hour.

DOLLARS SAVED ANNUALLY BY RETURNING 5,000 LBS. PER HOUR OF CONDENSATE WITH A PRESSURE-POWERED PUMP

Operating Conditions and Energy Costs

A. Condensate load - 5,000 Lb. per hour

B. Annual hours of operating - 8,760 hours per year

C. Water cost

-Water and sewage cost - \$0.0006 per gallon
-Water treatment chemicals - \$0.0020 per gallon
-Total water cost (sum of above) - \$0.0026 per gallon

D. Temperature rise

-Condensate return temperature - 180°F
-Cold make-up water temperature - 50°F
-Make-up water temperature rise (difference of above) - 130°F

E. #6 fuel oil cost - \$0.70 per gallon

F. At 75% boiler efficiency contains net 115,200 BTU per gallon.

G. Steam cost - \$8.00 per 1,000 pounds

Water and chemical savings by returning condensate (multiplied by 0.9 to adjust for flash steam loss)

$$\text{Annual Water Savings} = \frac{0.9 \times \text{condensate load} \times \text{Annual hours of operation} \times \text{Total Water cost}}{8.33\ \text{Lb. per gallon}}$$

$$= \frac{0.9 \times 5000 \times 8760 \times 0.0026}{8.33}$$

$$= \$12,304.00$$

Oil savings by eliminating preheating of make-up water (multiplied by 0.9 to adjust for flash steam loss)

$$\text{Annual Oil Savings} = \frac{0.9 \times \text{condensate load} \times \text{annual hours of operation} \times \text{make-up water temp. rise} \times \text{oil cost}}{\text{Net oil BTU per gallon}}$$

$$= \frac{0.9 \times 5000 \times 8760 \times 130 \times 0.70}{115{,}200}$$

$$= \$31{,}139.00$$

Cost of steam to operate a pressure-powered pump (vented to atmosphere)

$$\text{Annual Operating Cost} = \frac{\text{Steam Consumption} \times \text{Steam cost} \times \text{Condensate load} \times \text{Annual Hours of Operation}}{1000 \times 1000}$$

$$= \frac{3 \times 8.00 \times 5000 \times 8760}{1{,}000{,}000}$$

$$= \$1{,}051.00$$

For total savings:

Add, annual water savings	+$12,304.00
Add, annual oil savings	+$31,139.00
Subtract, annual operating cost	-$ 1,051.00

Total dollars saved annually = $42,392.00

Clearly then, systems with only a few traps can waste a great deal of money and will see a fast payback of capital costs by returning all condensate.

We have seen the importance of proper temperature control in several common applications in a steam system. The potential cost savings through reduced energy usage have been demonstrated. By controlling storage tank temperature at the minimum required, we have shown that even with a small tank, we can save 15,000 pounds of steam a year. Larger tanks, or groups of tanks, could obviously save hundreds of thousands of pounds of steam each year, which means dollars saved in fuel costs. Reducing steam pressure also saves energy. The lowest steam pressure which gives the required product temperature should always be chosen. Excessively high pressures cause much waste and should only be used where a high product temperature is essential. Using the sensible heat in condensate on non-critical applications will increase thermal efficiency resulting in further savings. Finally, returning all condensate will afford significant savings in both energy and water costs.

In summary, the proper application of proven technology will result in significant cost savings and rapid payback.

Chapter 74

STEAM TRAPS: A VITAL LINK TO ENERGY CONTROL

K. Giovanetto

Trap Flak

In recent years steam traps have taken alot of flak. One reason might be their looks. Steam traps are rather unattractive. Of course, their looks shouldn't have anything to do with their acceptance, but this is the '80's. We live in the high tech age. During the low tech age, steam traps faired well, but now the old cast iron traps seem out of place. It's true that some efforts have been made to dress traps up a bit. Stainless steel traps, for instance, look almost contemporary. But industry yearns for a replacement--perhaps something you can attach a control wire to...

I once envisioned an electronic trap with a camera-shutter orifice that opened and closed based on fluctuations in condensate load. Think of it. Steam loss would be virtually eliminated. The shutter mechanism would be made of stainless steel so it wouldn't wear out, and the electronic control wouldn't fail because it was electronic. Of course, there could still be a problem getting rid of air in the system, but the electronic control would take care of that--somehow.

Who knows. Maybe I'll event that trap yet, but in the meantime I would like to share a few thoughts on conventional --somewhat ugly-- steam traps. Why are steam traps used? How are they supposed to work? How can you tell if they're working the way they're supposed to? Is the time and effort required to make sure they're working really worth it?

Why Are Steam Traps Used?

Two types of heat are present in steam--sensible and latent. Sensible heat is heat that can be sensed with a thermometer. Latent heat cannot be sensed, but is still present and is given off when steam condenses. The steam trap stops or traps the steam until it gives up its latent heat and condenses. The steam trap then allows the condensate to discharge and return to the boiler where it is reheated into steam. This cycle is illustrated below:

Steam Cycle

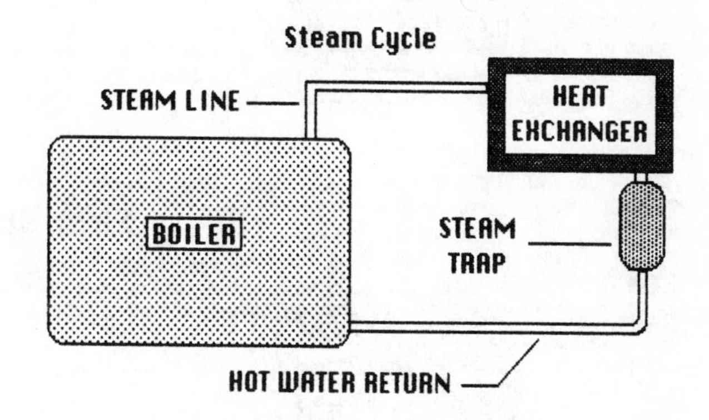

Without the steam trap, the steam would not give off its latent heat, and the efficiency of the heat transfer in the heat exchanger would be greatly reduced. This reduction in efficiency can be translated into increased energy costs, and avoiding these increased costs is the primary reason steam traps are used.

Steam traps are also used to remove air and dirt from steam systems. Trapped air is especially dangerous in steam systems because oxygen in the air can oxidize steam lines. Over an extended period of time this oxidation process will eat through the steam pipes and create severe steam leaks.

How Are Steam Traps Supposed To Work?

All traps are designed to distinguish between steam and condensate. To be effective, steam must stop (or trap) steam and release condensate. The variety of differences between the physical properties of steam and condensate has led to a variety of approaches in steam trap design. Some traps, for instance, are designed to distinguish between the difference in density between steam and condensate. Other traps are designed to distinguish between the difference in temperature between steam and condensate, and still others recognize pressure differences between steam and condensate.

The best way to understand the different methods of trap operation is to see the traps in action. Since that cannot be accomplished on paper, however, the following illustrations depict the inner workings of several of the most common steam traps currently on the market.

Float and Thermostatic (F&T) Trap

The F & T trap is a mechanical trap that operates on the difference in density between steam and condensate. The illustrations below show the start-up and subsequuent stages of operation for the F & T trap:

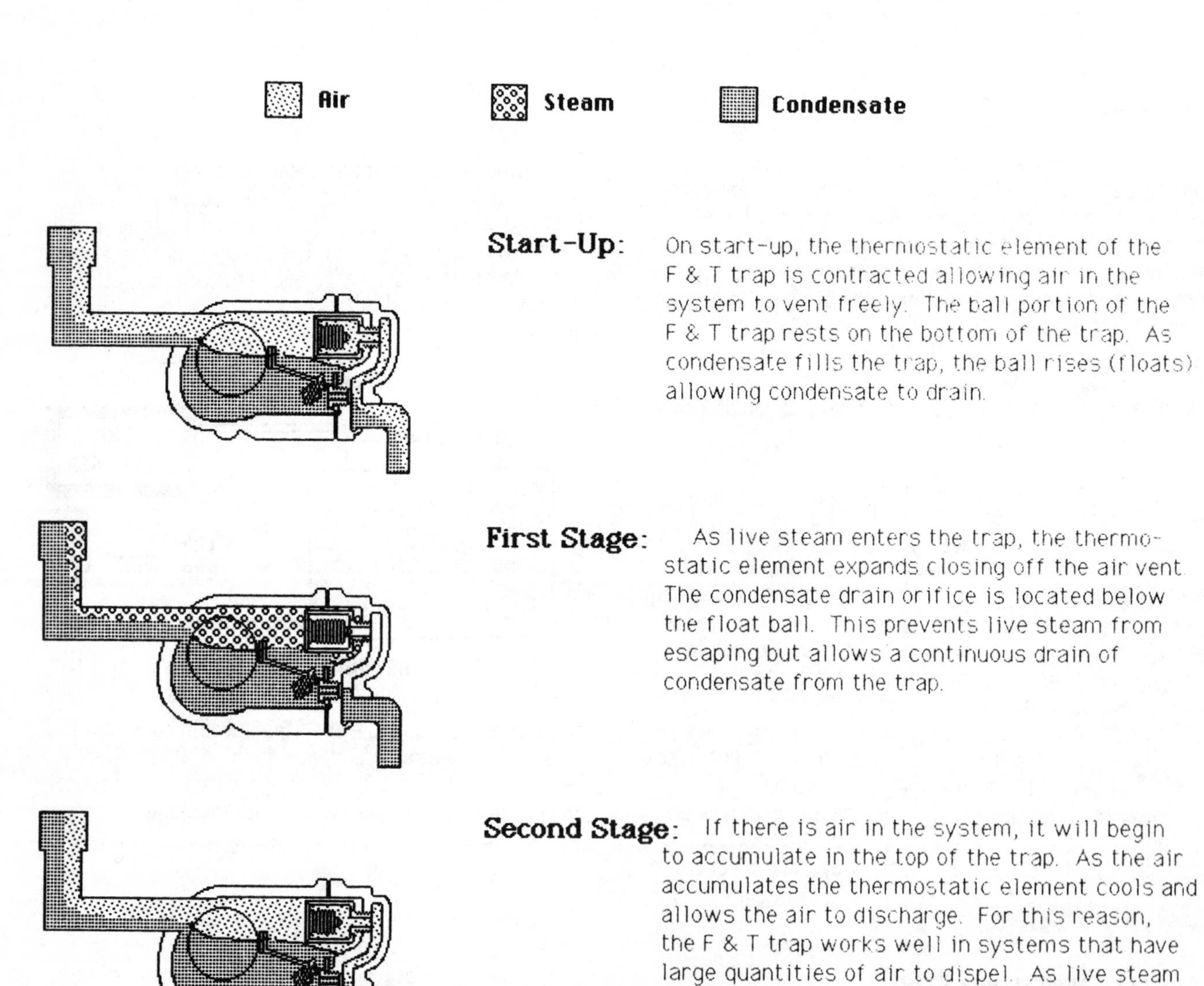

Start-Up: On start-up, the thermostatic element of the F & T trap is contracted allowing air in the system to vent freely. The ball portion of the F & T trap rests on the bottom of the trap. As condensate fills the trap, the ball rises (floats) allowing condensate to drain.

First Stage: As live steam enters the trap, the thermostatic element expands closing off the air vent. The condensate drain orifice is located below the float ball. This prevents live steam from escaping but allows a continuous drain of condensate from the trap.

Second Stage: If there is air in the system, it will begin to accumulate in the top of the trap. As the air accumulates the thermostatic element cools and allows the air to discharge. For this reason, the F & T trap works well in systems that have large quantities of air to dispel. As live steam displaces the air, the thermostatic element expands and closes off the air vent again.

Thermostatic (Bellows) Trap

The thermostatic trap operates on the difference in temperature between steam and condensate. On start-up, the thermostatic element is contracted and allows air and condensate to discharge. As live steam enters the trap, the thermostatic element expands and closes the orifice. The open and closed positions of a typical thermostatic trap are illustrated below:

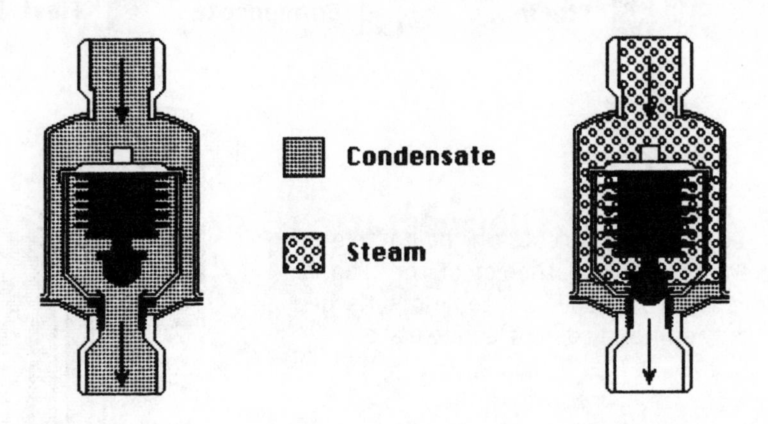

Disk Trap

The disc trap operates on the thermodynamic principle of available energy. On start-up, the initial pressure in the steam lines lifts the disc and allows air and condensate to discharge. As steam fills the trap, pressure builds up on the back of the disc forcing it closed. When the steam condenses, the pressure on the back of the disc is eliminated, and the condensate again lifts the disc. This cycle is repeated frequently in a normally operating disc trap. The figure below illustrates the steam/condensate movement through the trap:

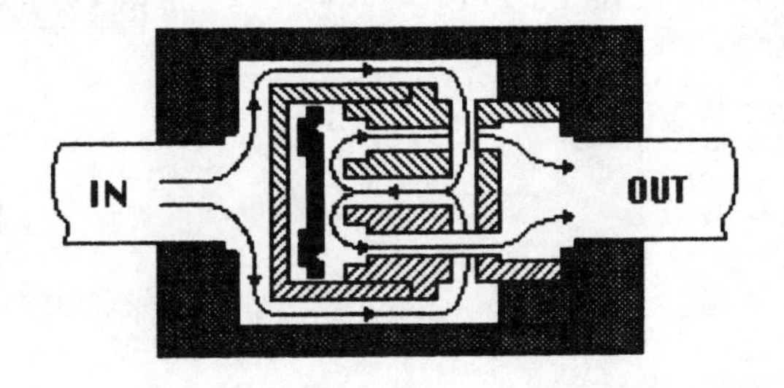

Fixed Orifice Trap

The orifice alone accomplishes condensate removal in a fixed orifice trap. The size of the orifice is carefully engineered for a specific steam pressure and condensate load. The orifice is engineered to be small enough to keep steam from escaping but large enough to keep condensate from backing up. The drawing below illustrates:

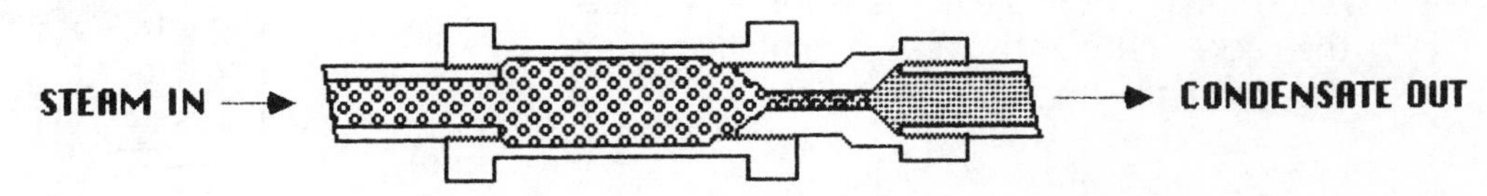

Inverted Bucket (IB) Trap Operation

The inverted bucket trap is a mechanical trap that operates on the difference in density between steam and condensate. The illustrations below show the start-up and subsequuent stages of operation for the inverted bucket trap:

Air Steam Condensate Flash Steam

Start-Up: On start-up, the bucket rests on the bottom of the trap and the valve at the top of the trap is open. This allows trapped air to be discharged along with the initial rush of condensate.

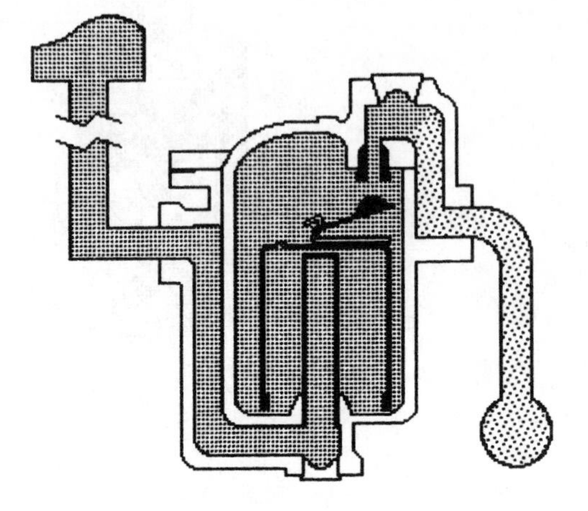

First Stage: During start-up, the initial rush of condensate entering the trap creates a water seal around the bottom of the bucket. As live steam enters the trap, the bucket rises and closes the orifice at the top of the trap. This prevents steam from escaping.

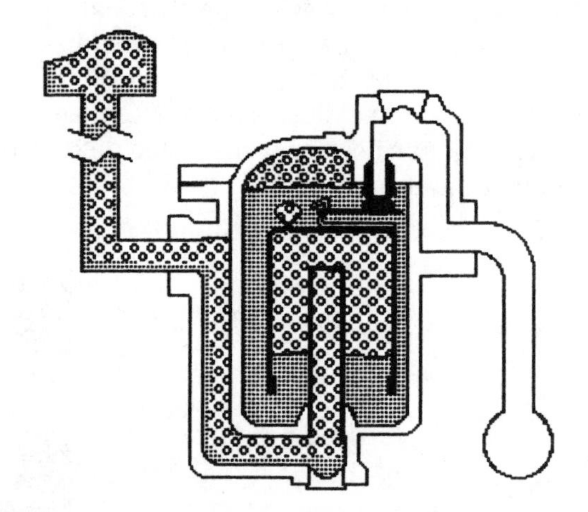

Second Stage: A tiny hole in the top of the bucket portion of the trap allows condensate to enter the trap slowly. As the bucket fills with condensate, it becomes heavier and sinks to the bottom of the trap allowing condensate and any accumulated air to be discharged through the orifice at the top of the trap. The condensate is at steam temperature and flashes as it is released to the lower pressure return line. After the condensate is released, the bucket fills with steam again and rises to the top of the trap closing the orifice.

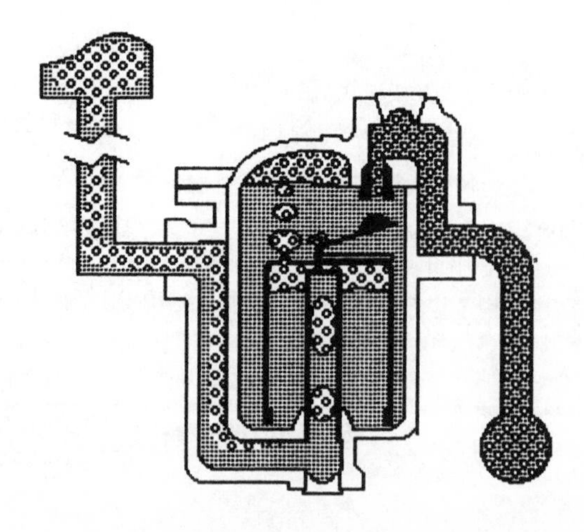

How Can You Tell If Steam Traps Are Working The Way They're Supposed To?

Theoretically, steam traps work as previously described. Mechanical traps allow only condensate to flow out. Thermostatic traps expand in the presence of steam and contract in the presence of condensate with efficient regularity. Thermodynamic traps understand the physical laws of the universe and operate according to plan. Fixed orifice traps are engineered so exactly that they remove condensate consistently at a constant rate and never fail...

Of course, that's only theoretically. Actually, mechanical traps have delicate linkages that wear with time, float balls that cease to float, buckets that lose their prime. Thermostatic traps have elements that expand and contract for awhile and then get tired, or they have delicate balls filled with distilled water that expand and contract until a flood of water (water hammer) smashes them. Thermodynamic traps have tiny discs that hop up and down until they wear away their seating surfaces. And fixed orifice traps encounter situations they were never designed to encounter, and since they were not designed to cope with changes, they continue to operate on their original-now-erroneous premises.

In point of fact, most steam traps have a relatively short life. At times minor surgery (also referred to as steam trap repair) may add a few years to their lives, but steam traps cannot be installed and forgotten. They need to be checked on a regular basis to make sure they are still functioning properly. <u>Every trap in a facility should be checked at least once per year</u>.

But how should steam traps be checked? Three different methods are promoted as good ways to test traps. They are:

<u>Visual Method</u>: The visual method consists of opening a blowoff valve on the return side of a steam trap and observing the discharge. If a trap has failed open, the percentage of steam will outweigh the percentage of condensate in the discharge.

<u>Temperature Method</u>: The temperature method is based on the assumption that the temperature of the condensate discharge side of a steam trap that has failed open approaches the temperature of the steam supply side of the defective trap.

<u>Listening Method</u>: The listening method consists of learning to recognize the sounds steam traps make under various operating conditions.

Each method has proponents as well as opponents. The most vocal supporters of either side are often manufacturers. Makers of delicate infrared heat sensing devices strongly advocate the temperature method of steam trap testing while makers of sonic sounding sensors insist that the listening method is most useful. In many cases, therefore, the best method of steam trap testing is determined by the best marketing sales pitch.

But putting sales pitches and marketing considerations aside, which method is really best? The answer can be summed up in two words: It Depends. The visual method works well when a blowoff valve is positioned on the return side immediately following a steam trap. The visual method combined with a knowledge of the inner workings of various traps is probably the surest way to determine if a steam trap is operating properly. The problem is that most steam traps don't have blowoff valves on their return side.

Then the trap tester must rely on either the temperature method or the listening method of steam trap testing, and neither of these methods is as straightforward as the visual method. The temperature method, for instance, might allow quick identification of traps that have failed closed. The temperature of the return side of the trap will be substantially lower than normal. However, in the case where a trap has failed open, the temperature method of testing often yields questionable results. Why? Because live steam at zero pounds pressure is approximately 212° F, and discharged condensate which flashes into steam at zero pounds pressure is also 212° F.

In the same way, the listening method can be used with varying degrees of success. In testing a bucket trap, which has an intermittent discharge and makes a distinct sound, the listening method can be used successfully by most hearing people. The F & T trap, however, has a continuous discharge, and the only difference in sound between a properly operating F & T and an F & T that has failed open is a variation in the pitch of the hissing discharge. A well-trained trap tester with a good ear might be able to hear this rather ambiguous difference, but most part time trap testers would simply have to guess with F & T traps.

Even so, I tend to favor the visual and listening methods of trap testing because they are based on the actual operating characteristics of widely different traps. The table below gives guidelines for using the listening method of testing on most common steam traps.

Steam Trap Testing: A Sound Method

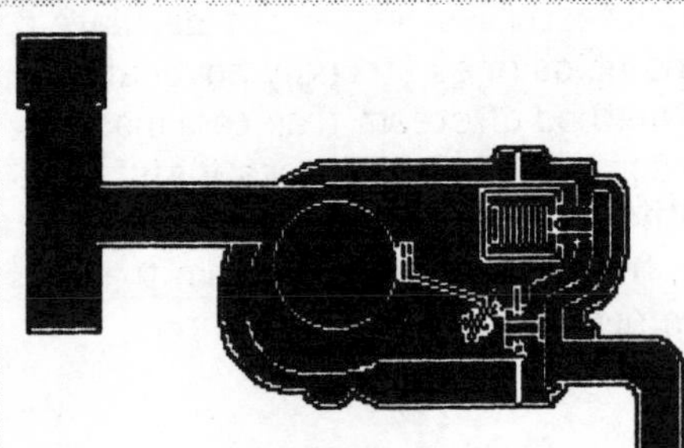

F & T Trap

Discharges: Continuously

Fails: Closed Or Open

Sounds: The continuous discharge of a properly operating F & T trap makes a soft, continuous, low-pitched hissing sound. A trap that has failed open makes a loud, continuous, high-pitched hissing sound.

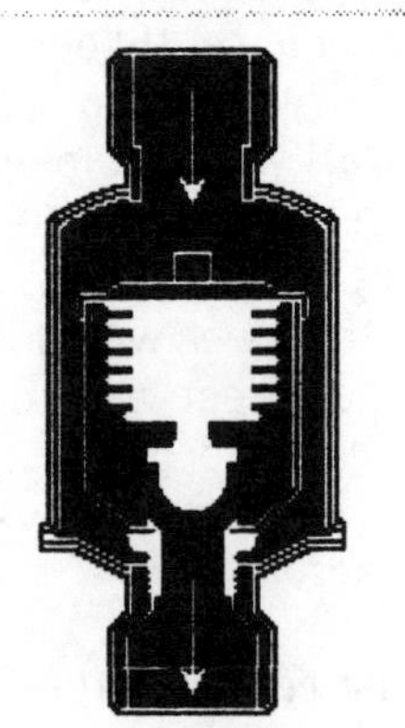

Thermostatic Trap

Discharges: Intermittently

Fails: Normally Closed

Sounds: To test a thermostatic trap using the listening method, the steam supply to the trap must be shut off temporarily. Often a check valve preceding the trap can be closed for a few minutes to simulate a shut down. When the valve is opened, steam will hiss through the trap for a moment until the thermostatic element expands and closes off the flow of steam. Steam sound will then stop.

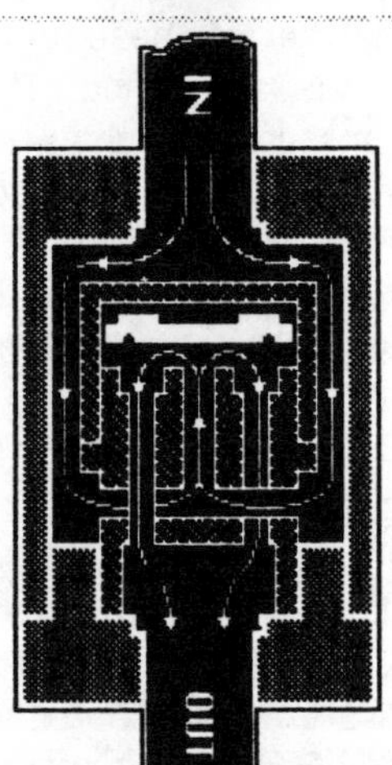

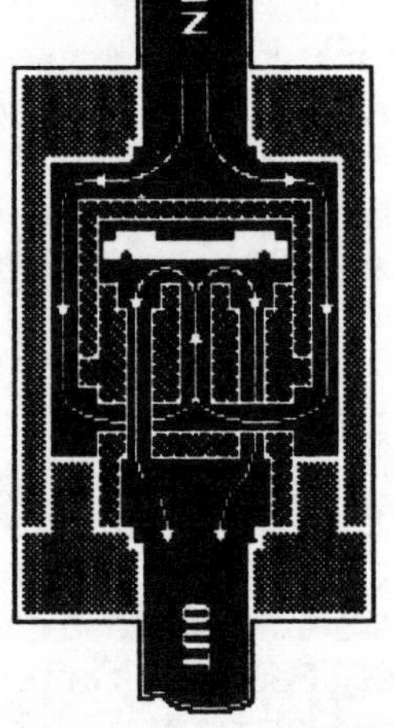

Disc Trap

Discharges: Intermittently

Fails: Normally open

Sounds: The intermittent condensate discharge (whooshing sound) followed by a clicking as the disc seats is the distinctive sound of the disc trap. If the trap has failed, there will be a continuous clicking as the disc rattles loosely in the trap.

I B Trap

Discharges: Intermittently

Fails: Normally open

Sounds: The intermittent rush of discharge as the bucket sinks to the bottom of the trap and opens the drain orifice indicates a properly operating bucket trap. A continuous hissing sound indicates the trap has failed open, and a continuous clanking (bucket dance) indicates the trap has failed to get its prime.

Is The Time And Effort Required To Make Sure Steam Traps Are Working Worth It?

The answer to this last question has largely been taken for granted by those involved with steam. Most industrial and commercial maintenance personnel have seen steam loss calculations that suggest thousands of dollars in needless energy costs will haunt those facilities that neglect their steam traps. Calculations of this type are based on a steam loss table similar to the following:

STEAM LEAK RATE THROUGH HOLES

Orifice Diam"	Steam Pressure (psig)				
	5	15	75	125	200
1/16"	2.0	3.4	10.3	16.1	18.9
1/8"	7.9	13.7	41.3	64.3	75.8
5/32"	12.3	21.3	64.5	100.0	118.0
1/4"	31.6	54.7	165.0	257.0	303.0
3/8"	71.0	123.0	371.0	578.0	682.0
1/2"	126.0	219.0	660.0	1028.0	1212.0

If the orifice size and steam pressure are known, the table above may be used to determine the steam loss in pounds per hour. An example of the standard method of calculating steam loss and cost is given below:

What is the steam pressure?	**125 psig**
What is the orifice size?	**5/32 "**
How many hours per year is the steam system used?	**2000 hr/yr**
What is the cost of steam?	**$5.00/1000#**

The table indicates that a 5/32" hole at 125# steam pressure blows 100 lbs/hr which means the steam loss cost in this calculation would be:

100 lbs/hr x 2000 hrs/yr x $5.00/1000#
= $1,000 per year.

The standard method indicates that the potential cost of one faulty trap in this instance would be $1,000 per year. This figure is then multiplied by assuming that a certain percentage of the traps in a facility are blowing steam. For instance, if there are 100 such traps in a facility and 15% (sometimes the estimate is much higher) are blowing steam, then the facility is losing 15 traps x $1,000/yr = $15,000 per year in steam.

A steam trap survey for such a facility would probably cost in the neighborhood of $1500 -- only a fraction of the total cost of the calculated steam loss. In this instance, a steam trap survey would appear to be a worthwhile investment. Trap repairs or replacements would also be justified.

And, for the most part, I think trap maintenance is justified. There are, however, a few problems with the standard method of calculating steam loss. Currently steam loss calculations for steam traps are based on tables which give the rate of steam leaks through holes. The tables were developed not in reference to conventional steam traps but in reference to conventional holes -- the type you might find venting to atmosphere from a steam line.

A steam trap, however, is not a hole, and even if a trap has failed open, its physical characteristics make it substantially different from a hole. Another point to consider is that the steam is not dry. A specific condensate load is present in the steam, and that condensate forms at any point where the steam flow is impeded. The steam trap orifice slows the steam flow, and condensate is formed and discharged along with blowing steam.

If, for example, the steam trap orifice was sized with a 3:1 safety factor, then 1/3 of the discharge through the orifice should be condensate and 2/3's of the discharge steam. In the previous calculation, therefore, the cost of blowing steam would only be 2/3's of the original estimate or $667 per trap. And even this figure may not represent the actual steam cost, because it is based on the assumption that the condensate and steam never mix. But condensate and steam do mix, and when they do, the steam loss is reduced even further.

A new means of calculating steam loss through steam trap orifices is needed, but at this time I cannot offer one. I can only offer my intuitive opinion on the matter until the results of further testing are available. My opinion is that 25% - 50% of the figures normally used would represent a more realistic range to use when figuring the cost of blowing steam through steam traps. Instead of the $1,000 savings indicated in the previous calculation, I would estimate the actual savings would be between $250 and $500 per trap.

Even so, steam trap maintenance and repair appear to be a vital link to energy control.

K.G.

STEAM'S FUTURE: An Interview With An Expert

The following interview was conducted on May 20, 1986, with John A. Kremers. John is currently the Manager of Application Engineering for Armstrong Machine Works. He graduated from the University of Wisconsin in 1950 with a B.S. in Mechanical Engineering. Since that time, John has been registered as a P.E. in Wisconsin and Michigan. He has worked in steam and steam trap engineering since 1962 and has a vast wealth of knowledge on the subject. John's willingness to share his experience makes him the living embodiment of Armstrong's slogan: *Knowledge Not Shared Is Energy Wasted.*

GIOVANETTO: What do you see as the future of steam use?

KREMERS: I think steam's future is in industrial process applications. The close temperature control required in many processes is accomplished easily with steam. Control the pressure of steam, and you control the temperature. Steam at 15# pressure condenses at 250° and is then replaced by more steam at 250°. The control temperature remains constant. Steam is currently used effectively in chemical plants, paper mills and refineries. Steam is also used effectively in heat tracing applications for freeze protection. In fact, more steam traps are probably used in heat tracing applications than in any other single application.

GIOVANETTO: In reference to steam traps, do you see any major innovations in trap design coming in the near future?

KREMERS: No, I really don't. I think the inverted bucket trap and the F&T (float and thermostatic) trap will continue to meet the majority of needs in the area of condensate removal. They both work on the difference in density between steam and condensate. Little steam is lost and large quantities of condensate can be effectively removed.

There has been some interest in the "engineered hole" concept of condensate removal, but this is not a new concept. Basically, this is merely the resurrection of the fixed orifice trap, and I think the interest will be short lived. Fixed orifice traps can be used effectively on Navy ships where the purity of the water supply is strictly monitored, but in most applications several problems result from their use. For instance, since the orifice is sized for a specific steam pressure and condensate load, when either the steam pressure or condensate varies, so does the effectiveness of the orifice. Excessive steam losses occur under higher steam pressures or reduced condensate loads, and condensate backs up under lower steam pressures or increased condensate loads. Our experience also indicates that fixed orifice traps tend to plug easily unless the orifice is oversized.

GIOVANETTO: John, I've appreciated your comments. Do you have anything else you'd like to share regarding steam or steam trap use?

KREMERS: Yes, there has been a growing interest in subcooling condensate. My opinion is that condensate should be dumped at steam temperature in heat exchanger applications. Subcooling condensate can lead to the following problems:

1. Condensate cooler than saturation temperature dissolves noncondensibles such as CO_2 and O_2 producing a corrosive mix.
2. Subcooling can result in condensate back-up in a heat exchanger and reduce the heat exchanger's capacity.
3. The back-up of condensate in heat exchangers can also create situations where water hammer is likely to occur.
4. Subcooling of condensate from outdoor air heaters allows condensate back-up in the outdoor coil resulting in freeze damage.

Waste heat recovery is an important part of energy management, but in the case of subcooling condensate I think the potential problems outweigh the potential benefits.

Chapter 75

AUGMENTED HEAT TRANSFER RATES IN STEAM CONDENSERS

R. M. Desmond, R. F. Amberger, J. A. DeFrees

ABSTRACT

Tests were conducted to quantify the heat transfer enhancement that occurs when a fluoroplastic strip is applied longitudinally along the bottoms of the tubes of a steam condenser operating under conditions typical of those found at turbine exhausts.

The fluoroplastic used to coat the tubes is a solvent-resistant, durable, resin-bonded PTFE low friction coating. In the present study, the fluoroplastic was applied over an arc of approximately 38 degrees on 19.05mm (0.75 in) diameter, admiralty brass condenser tubes. Eighty tubes, each 6.10m (20 ft) long, were assembled into a condenser bundle. The condenser was a shell-and-tube design having two water-side passes. An identical, untreated tube bundle was constructed to serve as a control.

Both bundles were tested under the same conditions which approximate those found at the exhausts of condensing turbines (4.81 Kpa, ABS [28.5 in hg vacuum]). The water-side velocity was varied from 0.62 to 2.13 mps (2.0 - 7.0fps). In this application, the findings were that the modified tube bundle exhibited an enhancement of the overall heat transfer coefficient of from 40% to 50% above that of the untreated tube bundle.

NOMENCLATURE

A_o	=	outside surface area of condenser tube
C	=	specific heat of water
LMTD	=	log mean temperature difference
$\dot{m}$	=	mass rate of flow of cooling water
Q	=	overall heat transfer
T_{in}	=	temperature of water at condenser inlet
T_{out}	=	temperature of water at condenser outlet
U_o	=	overall heat transfer coefficient based on A_o
V	=	tube water velocity

INTRODUCTION

Over the years many attempts have been made to produce more efficient heat exchange equipment. As noted by Bergles, Webb, and Junkhan [1], the goal of such efforts may vary from attempting to reduce the size of a heat exchanger for a given heat transfer rate, to increasing the capacity of an existing unit, or to decreasing the temperature differentials of the heat transfer fluids required for a given application. In terms of condensers, an increase in the total heat transfer to a set of condenser tubes will increase the overall capacity of the condenser to which they belong. Consequently, many attempts have been made to enhance the heat transfer to condenser tubes.

In their studies, various investigators have examined both filmwise and dropwise modes of condensation. In filmwise condensation, the vapor condenses into a continuous film covering the entire surface of the tube. The film grows thicker toward the tube bottom where the water collects until the gravatational force becomes greater than the surface tension force holding the water to the tube, at which point the water runs off. In dropwise condensation, the vapor condenses into small droplets of various sizes which run down the side of the tube and fall off when inertia and gravitational forces exceed those due to surface tension. It is desirable to maintain dropwise condensation because its heat transfer coefficient is many times that of filmwise condensation. However, in practice, either may be found alone or, as usually is the case, in a combination of the two. Filmwise condensation is dominant in utility steam condensers and it is its enhancement which will be considered here.

Enhancement of Filmwise Condensation

The study reported here concerns itself with the problem of enhancing the heat transfer in large utility condensers. Such a condenser may have more than ten miles of condenser tubing and have a tube bundle 3.05m (10 ft) by 3.05m (10 ft) and be more than 12.19m (40 ft) long. It is easy to see where reducing the quantity of tubes saves both space and condenser manufacturing cost.

It is possible to manipulate the variables in filmwise condensation to improve the heat transfer rate by:

1) decreasing film thickness;
2) changing the surface configuration; and
3) changing the thermal conductivity of the condenser tubes.

Of the options given above for improving the heat transfer in filmwise condensation, the first option of decreasing the film thickness was pursued. It was felt that the thermal conductivity of the condenser tube was not a free variable since the type of tubing used depends upon the cooling water available at the site, and upon the need for high-integrity condensers in modern power plants. Often new units are built with stainless steel or titanium tubes, depending upon the location and type of power plant. The possibility of changing the external surface configuration of the tube by adding fins was not considered since the high condensation film coefficient makes finning undesirable. The possibility of changing the internal configuration is an option which has received much attention [1] and will continue to receive attention in the future. In a large utility condenser, pumping costs are a prime concern since changes in the internal configuration of the condenser tubing cause increased pressure drop. Consequently, the decision was made not to explore changing the internal configuration of the condenser tube.

Having decided to attempt to reduce the film thickness, it was necessary to select a practical method. All the suggested means for promoting dropwise condensation have the effect of reducing condensation film thickness. As a starting point, these techniques were reviewed in hopes of finding an approach which might prove workable. Davies, Mojyeheki, and Ponter [2] give the four main methods of promoting dropwise condensation as:

a) Injection of a promoter into the steam, e.g., straight chain primary amines;
b) Use of chemically-adhering promotors, e.g., fatty acids;
c) Use of physically-adhering promoters, e.g., Teflon; and
d) Plating noble metals onto the surface.

Briefly, all of these means of enhancement have drawbacks. Garg [3] points out that method (a) is short term, lasting only several hours before additional injection is needed and has the side effect of contaminating the condensate. Blackman, Dewar, and Hampson found a number of chemically-adhering promoters that lasted up to 3500 hours before being washed away. Such time periods are impractical when considering the utility condenser where lifetimes are measured in decades, not hours. The use of noble metals [5,6,7] has received much attention and shows good results but is very expensive, and in time, the metal wears off. Butcher and Honour [8] claim that it is more difficult to promote dropwise condensation with gold plating than with fluoropolymers. It should also be noted that fluoropolymers (physically-adhering promoters) also wear off with time.

In reviewing the information about the four main methods of promoting dropwise condensation as an indicator of what might be done to reduce film thickness, it was decided to further investigate physically-adhering promoters. This choice was based on a consideration of expense, purity of the condensate, and of recent advances made in the development of more durable fluoroplastics.

Edwards and Doolittle [9] used .889m (35 in) long heat transfer tubes 21mm (0.84 in) O.D., 19mm (0.75 in) I.D. coated with .025mm (0.001 in) of Teflon(TM) and found that the overall heat transfer coefficient for the coated tubes was from 16 to 30 percent greater than that for a similar uncoated tube. This was encouraging since the Teflon(TM) coat had added additional conductive resistance. Glichman, Mikic, and Snow [10] noted that since the layer of fluid condensate on the outside of a horizontal tube is teardrop in shape (thicker at the bottom of the tube and very thin at the top), if the film could be interrupted and allowed to reform below the point of interruption, then the overall film thickness would be reduced and the heat transfer increased. They used a non-wetting tape to interrupt the film. Five different locations for attaching tape were examined and it was found that the use of tape along the bottom of the tube gave the greatest incremental increase in heat transfer.

Desmond and Karlekar [11] reported the results of single tube condensing steam at atmospheric pressure with water velocities ranging from 1.7 to 2.4 mps (5.6 to 7.9 fps). They attached a 9.5mm (.37 in) wide and 0.025mm (.001 in) thick strip of the non-wetting fluoroplastic Emralon 330(TM) and reported approximately a 20 percent increase in the overall heat transfer coefficient.

Based on these findings, it was decided to develop an experimental program to quantify the heat transfer enhancement that occurs when an Emralon 330(TM) strip is applied longitudinally along the bottom of the tubes of a steam condenser operating under conditions typical of those found at turbine exhausts.

EXPERIMENTAL APPARATUS

What follows is a description of the components of the experimental apparatus.

Condenser

Since the purpose of this test program was to test a condenser having design characteristics similar to utility condensers, an industrial-type condenser was selected as a test vehicle. The condenser was a T.E.M.A. Model No. CVL 12-240 BET H-2 3/4-18 having 29.17m^2 (314 ft^2) of effective surface area. The tubes were 19.05mm (0.75 in) O.D. with 18 BWG (1.24mm [0.49 in]) wall thickness. The tube material was admiralty (SB 111 Alloy 443) brass. There were 80 tubes (40 tubes per pass) each 6.1m (20 ft) long arranged in a 23.8mm (15/16 in) triangular pitch. There were two tube-side passes. The tubes were straight with a floating return-end waterbox. The condenser shell was steel with an outside diameter of 40.64cm (16 in). It had a perforated, air-venting tube located in the center of the tube bundle and running axially its entire length. The tube support plates were of the NESTS(TM) type. The NESTS(TM) tube support plate is a design of Ecolaire Heat Transfer, Inc. and is a built-up tube support system consisting of formed stainless steel strips which are laid in place after each successive row of tubes is inserted. This type of support plate was selected to minimize abrasive damage to the treated tubes during the assembly of the tube bundle. Two tube bundles were furnished, one having untreated tubes (control bundle) and the other having tubes treated with the enhancing material (test bundle). In the case of the modified tube bundle, Emralon 330(TM) was applied over an arc of approximately 30 degrees longitudinally along the bottom of the tubes. During the early part of the test program, it was determined that the surface area of the condenser was too great for the capacity of the steam boiler. At that time, it was decided to reduce the effective surface area of each bundle by plugging tubes. Accordingly, fourteen tubes per pass were plugged reducing the area by 35 percent. Figure 1 indicates which tubes were plugged.

Steam System

Steam was generated in a Weil-McLain Model P-686 gas-fired, cast-iron boiler rated at 418kW (1.428 MHB) burner capacity. The boiler was located adjacent to the condenser and connected to it by a 20.3cm (8 in) delivery pipe. The condensate was returned to the boiler through a gravity return line. For this purpose, the condenser was mounted on a steel support structure which raised the condensate discharge connection of the condenser approximately 30.48cm (12 in) above the normal water level in the boiler. The boiler was filled with de-ionized water supplied by Beebe Station of Rochester Gas and Electric Corporation. Prior to start-up the boiler was skimmed and washed out using procedures recommended by the manufacturer (Figure 2).

Cooling Water System

Cooling water was drawn from a 37,583 liter (10,000 gal) capacity tank by a centrifugal pump. The pump delivered the water to the condenser through a 0.10m (4 in) pipe fitted with valves which were used to regulate the water flow. The temperature of the cooling water was regulated by using a three-way regulating valve to return a certain amount of heated water to the pump inlet where it was mixed with water coming from the reservoir. Warm water was delivered to a direct-contact cooling tower rated at 341.3kW (1.0 MBH) from which it was returned by gravity to the reservoir (Figure 3).

Air Removal System

Air was removed from the condenser using a Nash Model MT-34, two-stage, liquid ring vacuum pump. The vacuum pump was rated at 0.95 L/S (15 CFM) inlet capacity at 3.4kPa (1.0 in Hg) absolute inlet pressure. The vacuum pump was directly connected to the air offtake connection of the condenser (Figure 2).

Instrumentation

The steam inlet, condensate outlet, cooling water inlet, and cooling water outlet temperatures were monitored with type-K thermocouples. Temperatures were indicated by a digital temperature indicator having a resolution of 0.055°K (0.1°F). The cooling water flow was measured using an ultrasonic flow meter. It has an intrinsic accuracy of 1 to 3 percent and a linearity of 0.00305m/s (0.01 ft/sec). The flow measuring section was located on the discharge side of the condenser in a long, straight section of 0.10m (4 in) line.

TEST METHOD

The schematic diagrams of the steam and cooling water systems are shown in Figures 2 and 3. Testing periods were of several hours duration. A test was initiated by first starting the cooling water system (circulating pump and cooling tower) and then the vacuum pump. The vacuum pump was allowed to operate for a period of approximately 15 minutes to evacuate air from the condenser and boiler before the boiler was started. After a sufficient vacuum had been achieved, the boiler was fired. As the boiler was heating, the water flow rate for the test was established using the hand valves to regulate the flow. As the boiler started steaming, the cooling water recirculating valve was adjusted to maintain an inlet cooling water temperature of 300 $\pm$ 0.44°K (80 $\pm$ 1°F). The firing rate of the boiler was adjusted to achieve a saturated steam temperature of 313.3 $\pm$ 0.22°K (104 $\pm$ 0.5°F) at the condenser inlet. This steam temperature, which corresponds to a saturation pressure of 7.4kPa (2.18 in hg abs), was maintained for the entire testing program on both bundles. The equipment was operated for a period of up to one hour to ensure that equilibrium was achieved.

When equilibrium had been achieved as indicated by the instruments, test data were taken. Data were taken at ten minute intervals to ensure that the flow meter had a sufficient integration period to yield an accurate reading and to see if it was necessary to correct a drifting trend. An effort was made to take at least four data readings at each flow rate. Data points were repeated several times to ensure that the data were repeatable. Also, because of scatter in the data, data points were repeated to obtain sufficient data for a statistical analysis of the results.

TEST RESULTS

The rate of heat transfer for a condenser can be calculated as:

$$\circ \quad Q = \dot{m}\, C\, (T_{out} - T_{in}) \qquad (1)$$

or by:

$$\circ \quad Q = U_o A_o \,\mathrm{LMTD} \qquad (2)$$

The overall heat transfer coefficient can be found by equating the heat transfer rate in the preceding equations and solving for the overall heat transfer coefficient:

$$\circ \quad U_o = \frac{\dot{m}\, C\, (T_{out} - T_{in})}{A_o \,\mathrm{LMTD}} \qquad (3)$$

Values of the overall heat transfer coefficient were calculated for each data reading. Mass flow rates were converted to equivalent tube velocities. The method of least squares was used to define the relationship between cooling water tube velocity and overall heat transfer coefficient for the results of each bundle.

A least squares fit on the data for the plain bundle gives the following relation:

$$\circ \quad U_o = 1129.38 \cdot V + 545.12 \ \frac{W}{m^2 \cdot K} \qquad (4a)$$

$$\circ \quad U_o = 60.62 \cdot V + 96 \ \frac{Btu}{hr\ ft^2 \cdot F} \qquad (4b)$$

where

U_o = Overall heat transfer coefficient,

$$\frac{W}{m^2 \cdot K} \left(\frac{Btu}{hr\ ft^2 \cdot F}\right)$$

V = Water velocity, m/sec (ft/sec)

The confidence interval for U of this function is approximately $\pm$ 62.46 $\frac{W}{m^2 \cdot K}$ (11 $\frac{Btu}{hr\ ft^2 \cdot F}$) at the 95 percent probability level (Figure 4).

Similarly, a least squares fit on the data for the modified tube bundle gives the relations:

$$\circ \quad U_o = 1642.09 \cdot V + 955.94 \ \frac{W}{m^2 \cdot K} \qquad (5a)$$

$$\circ \quad U_o = 88.14 \cdot V + 168.35 \ \frac{Btu}{hr\ ft^2 \cdot F} \qquad (5b)$$

with a confidence interval for U of $\pm$ 170 $\frac{W}{m^2 \cdot K}$

(30 $\frac{Btu}{hr\ ft^2 \cdot F}$) at the 95 percent probability level (Figure 4). The wider confidence interval for the modified tube bundle is due to the smaller temperature differences occurring in the terms of the LMTD for the modified tube bundle.

The test data showed some scatter (Figures 5 and 6) due to the lack of instrument repeatability and uncontrolable fluctuations in flows and temperatures. In spite of these random effects, the overall heat transfer coefficient of the modified bundle always exceeded that of the plain bundle. The average increase in the overall heat transfer coefficient for the modified tubes over the plain tubes was 50 percent for cooling water velocities between 1.22 and 1.83mps (4 and 6 fps).

The extent of the enhancement is substantially more than the 15-20 percent increase in overall heat transfer coefficient anticipated by Desmond and Karlekar [11], but is in agreement with results predicted by Glicksman, Mikic, and Snow [10], who obtained a 100 percent increase in steam-side film coefficient when testing with a non-wetting Teflon(TM) strip applied to the bottom of a tube. A 100 percent increase in the steamside film coefficient corresponds to approximately a 50 percent increase in the overall heat transfer coefficient assuming no change in the tube-side film coefficient.

Marto [13] has summarized the various representations which can be used to model the flow of condensate within condenser tube bundles. It is our speculation that the non-wetting strip is effective because its net effect is to cause a thinning of the condensate film on the tube by causing a break in the continuity of the film. A further effect may be attributable to a more rapid release of condensate from the non-wetting strip itself. The presence of the non-wetting strip may also affect the side-flow by redirecting this flow in such a way that it reduces inundation of the lower tubes.

We conclude that the modified tube bundle shows a marked improvement over the plain bundle, and that the method of enhancement using Emralon 330(TM) holds considerable promise for utility, shipboard, and other types of steam condensers.

REFERENCES

1. Bergles, A.E., Webb, R.L., and Junkhan, G.H., "Energy Conservation via Heat Transfer Enhancement", Energy-The International Journal, Vol. 4, No. 2, April 1979, p. 193.

2. Davies, G.A., Mojyehedi, W., and Ponter, A.B., "Measurement of Contact Angles Under Condensation Conditions; The Prediction of Dropwise-Filmwise Transition", Int. J. of Heat and Mass Transfer, Vol. 14, 1971, pp. 709-713.

3. Garg, S.C., "The Effect of Coatings and Surfaces on Dropwise Condensation", Naval Civil Engineering Lab, Port Hueneme, California, Report Number NCEL-TN-1041, July 1969.

4. Blackman, L.C.F., Dewar, M.J.S., and Hampson, H., "An Investigation of Compounds Promoting the Dropwise Condensation of Steam", J. Appl. Chem., Vol. 7, April 1967, pp. 160-171.

5. Griffith, P. and Lee, M.S., "Effects of Surface Thermal Properties and Finish on Dropwise Condensation", Int. J. Heat and Mass Transfer, Vol. 10, 1967, pp. 697-707.

6. Baudin, D., and Lespinas, B., "Improvement in Heat Transfer Coefficient During Water Vapor Condensation on Horizontal Tubes Coated with Gold Deposits in Strips of Continuously", (in French), Comptes Rendus, Series B. 270, 1970, p. 133.

7. Baudin, C., and Lespinas, B., "Improvement in Heat Transfer Coefficient by Water Vapor Condensation on Horizontal Tubes Equipped with Devices to Strip Condensate Film", (in French), Compotes Rendus, Series B. 270, 1970, p. 1081.

8. Butcher, D.W., and Honour, C.W., "Tetrafluoroethylene Coatings on Condenser Tubes", Int. J. Heat and Mass Transfer, Vol. 9, 1966, p. 835.

9. Edwards, J.A., and Doolittle, J.A., "Tetrafluoroethylene Promoted Dropwise Condensation", Int. J. Heat and Mass Transfer, Vol. 8, 1965, p. 633.

10. Glicksman, L.R., Mikic, B.B., and Snow, D.F., "Augmentation of Film Condensation on Outside of Horizontal Tubes", AIChE Journal, Vol. 19, 1973, pp. 636-637.

11. Desmond, R.M., and Karlekar, B.V., "Experimental Observations of a Modified Condenser Tube Design to Enhance Heat Transfer in a Steam Condenser", Paper No. 80-HT-53, Joint ASME/AIChE National Heat Transfer Conference, Orlando, FL, July 27-30, 1980.

12. Wolberg, J.R., "Prediction Analysis", D. Van Nostrand Co., Inc., Princeton, NJ, 1967.

13. Marto, P.J., "Improving the Thermal Performance of Large Condenser Tube Bundles", EPRI Symposium on State-of-the-Art Condenser Technology, Orlando, FL, 1983.

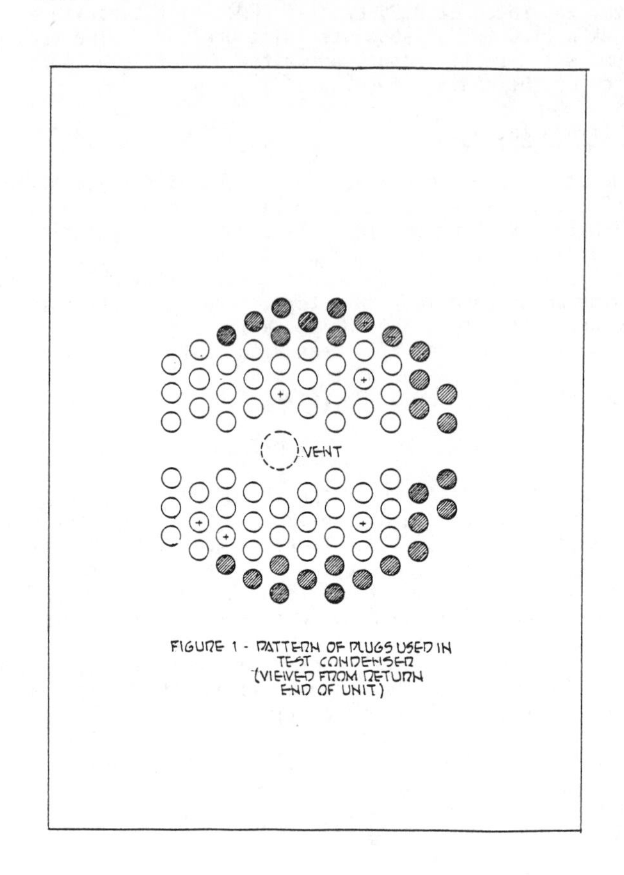

FIGURE 1 - PATTERN OF PLUGS USED IN TEST CONDENSER (VIEWED FROM RETURN END OF UNIT)

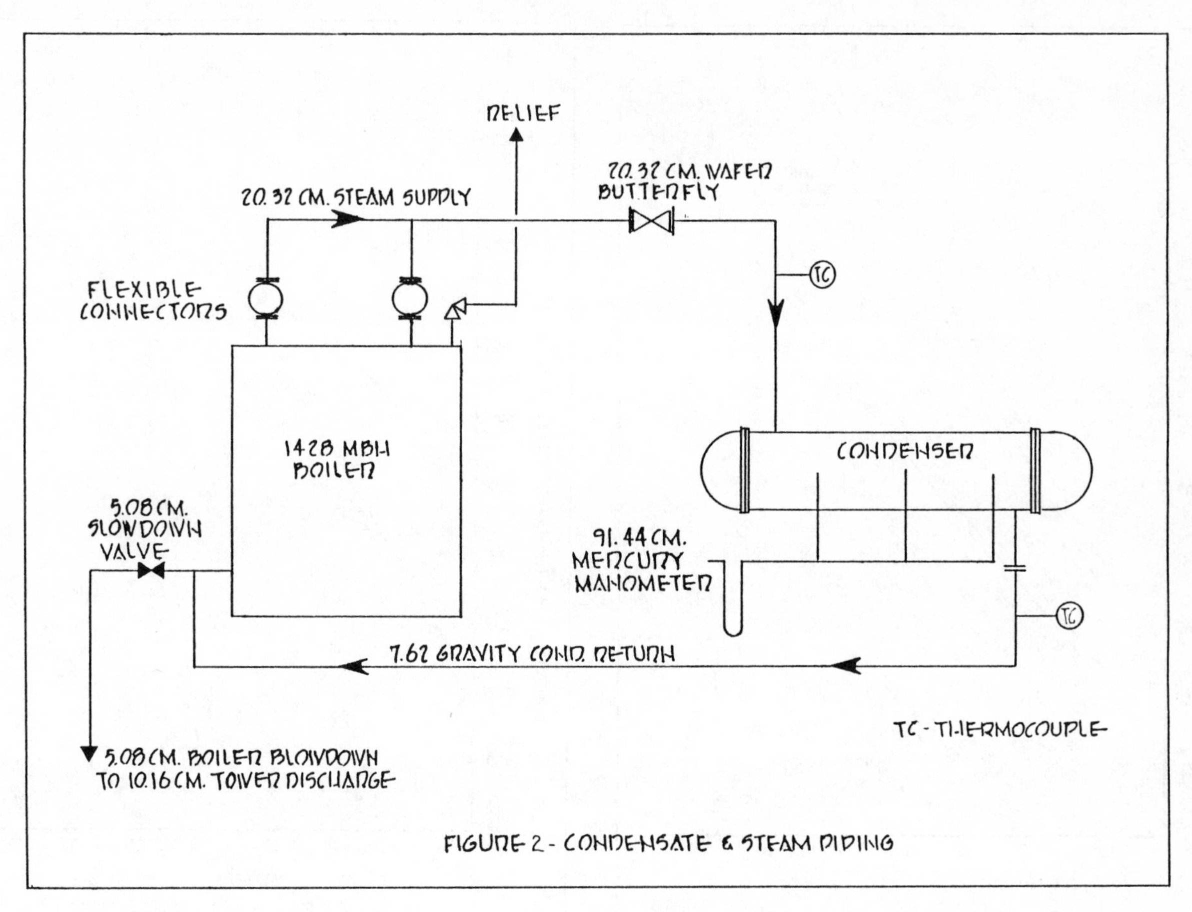

FIGURE 2 - CONDENSATE & STEAM PIPING

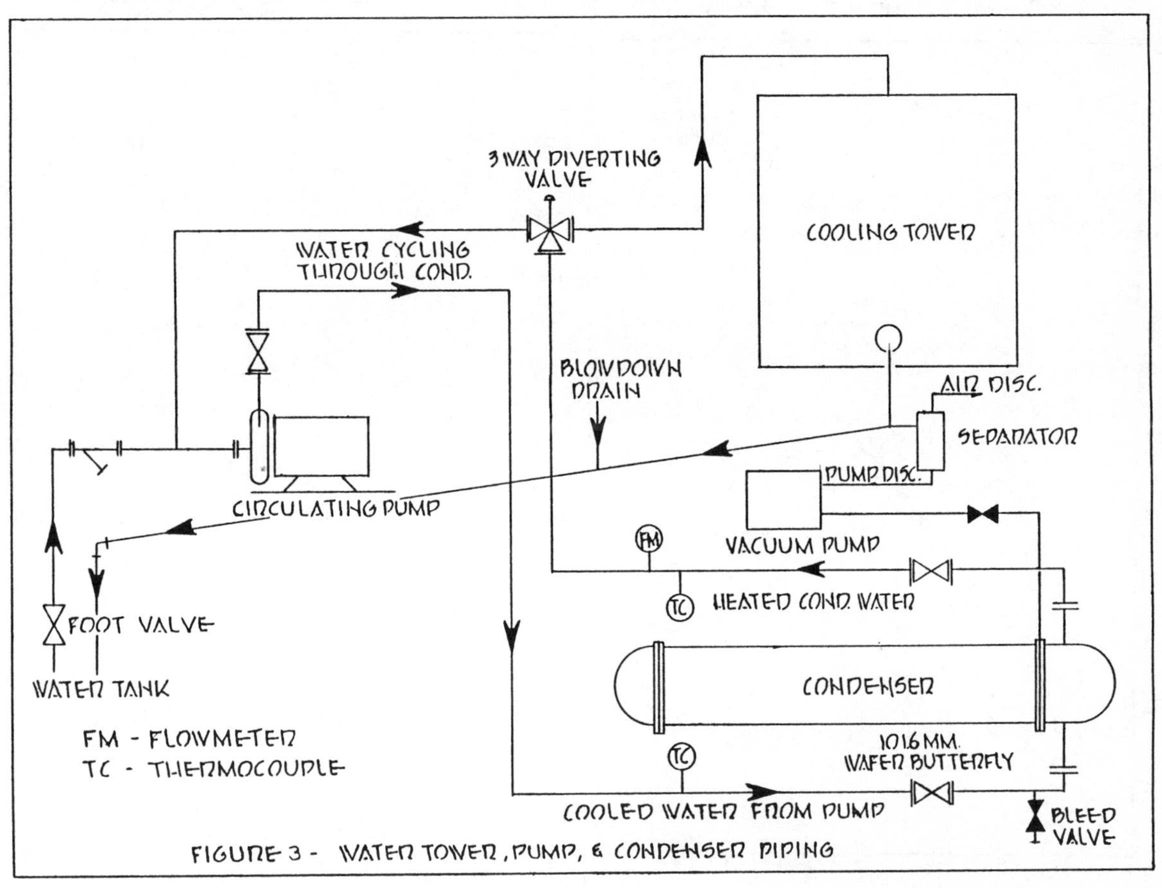

FIGURE 3 - WATER TOWER, PUMP, & CONDENSER PIPING

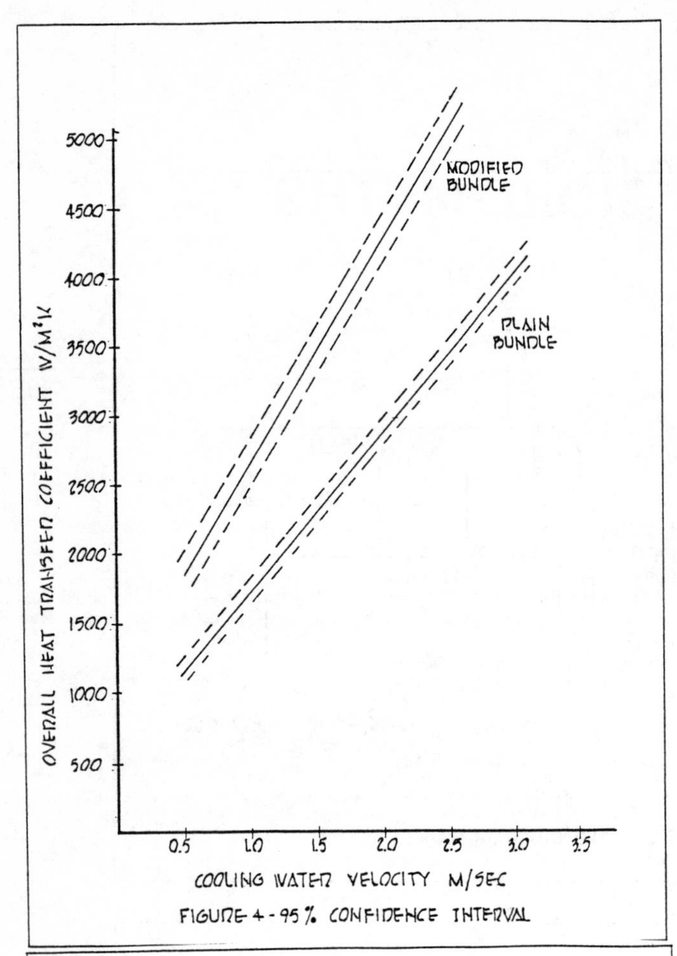

FIGURE 4 - 95% CONFIDENCE INTERVAL

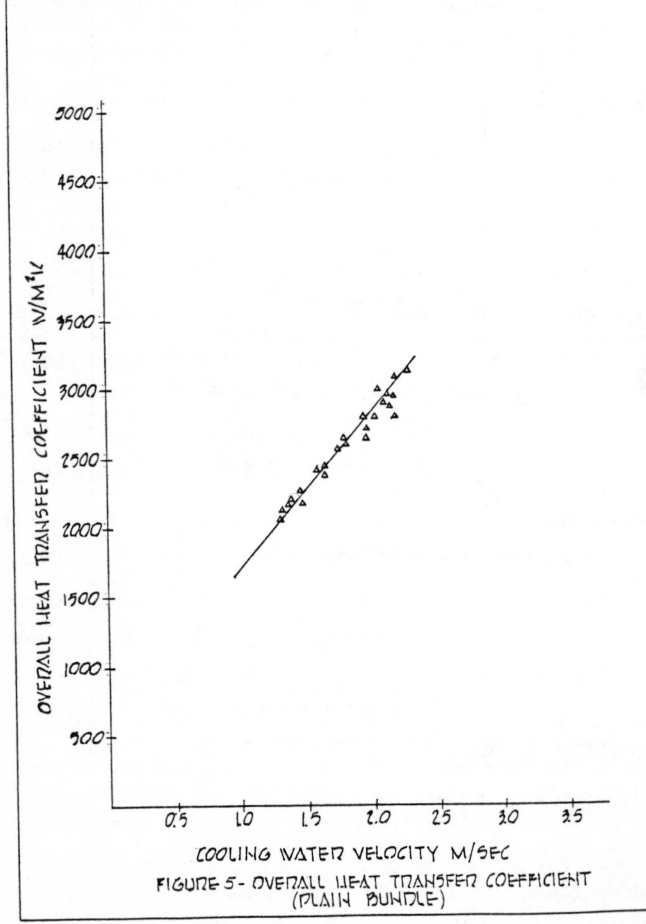

FIGURE 5 - OVERALL HEAT TRANSFER COEFFICIENT (PLAIN BUNDLE)

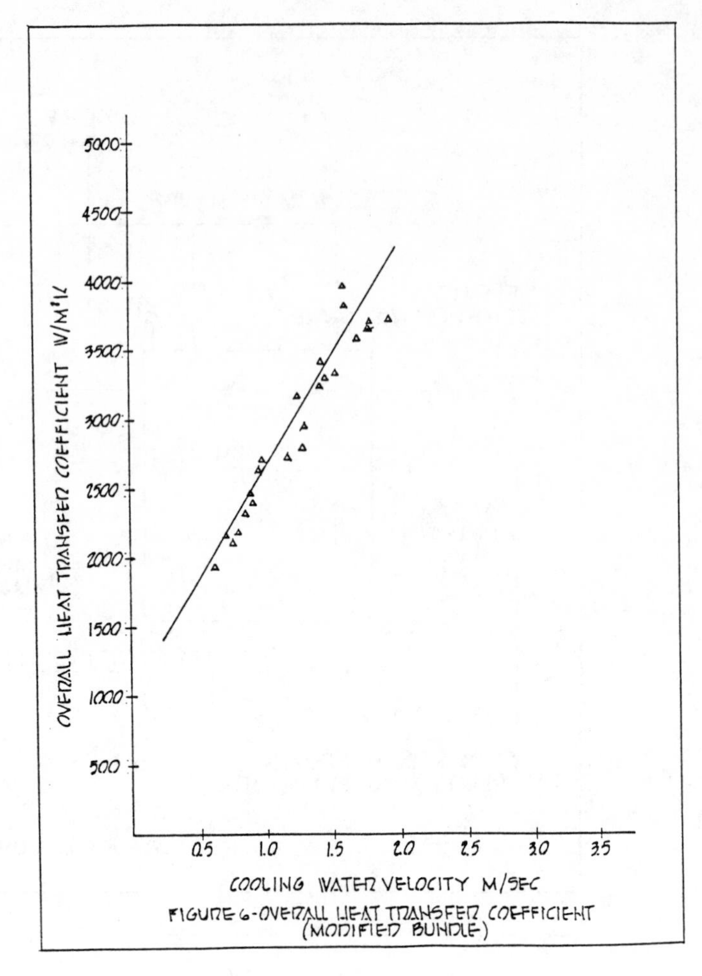

FIGURE 6 - OVERALL HEAT TRANSFER COEFFICIENT (MODIFIED BUNDLE)

Chapter 76

STEAM TRAPS – MORE MYTHS

F. Dickman

ABSTRACT

Turn of the century concepts of steam trapping are being abandoned by leading industrial corporations.

This technical paper examines in detail, some new concepts concerning the specialized field of multiphase choked flow physics, and how these concepts are being successfully applied to resolve the problems of steam trapping.

INTRODUCTION

Industrial Age concepts of steam trapping are being re-examined by leaders in the petrochemical, commercial, industrial and nuclear energy fields.

This technical paper is the third in a series presented before the AEE World Energy Engineering Congress. In less than three years time, a Third Wave of technical development has crested to engulf one hundred and fifty years of engineering stagnation in the steam trap industry.

The first technical paper, "The Elimination of Steam Traps," traced the historical development of the technology and documented some of the perpetual difficulties of maintaining steam traps. A solution was offered based on eight years of domestic and international experience."[1]

The second technical paper, "Exploding the Myths", confronted some of the misconceptions pervasive throughout the steam trap industry and provided an inside look at the economic motivation behind the myths.[2]

This third technical paper, "More of Exploding the Myths," concisely restates the problems, and details a solution which has provided substantial results for clients like Polaroid, Rockwell, Goodyear, Crouse-Hinds, Abbott Laboratories, SASOL, Exxon, Cargill, Minnesota Mining & Manufacturing, General Motors, the U.S. Navy, Los Alamos National Laboratories, and several facilities of the U.S. Department of Energy.

THE PROBLEMS WITH STEAM TRAPS

Steam traps are essentially mechanical devices used to remove condensate from steam lines, while retarding the loss of live steam. They are typically inexpensive to purchase and highly unreliable in operation. The best traps have a failure rate of about 20% per year. Recent studies document that the percentage of malfunctioning traps in a typical facility will be 42%.[3]

At this level of reliability, steam losses for every 1000 installed traps can exceed $200,000 a year.[4] Planned maintenance can cut losses by 50% or more, but maintenance is expensive and continuous. The typical expense will be $120,000 per 1000 traps.[5] With the best planned maintenance program, trap failures may still average 12-24% per year - depending on the severity of service - and losses will never really be eliminated.[6] In terms of payback, one of the maintenance service companies considers $50,000 spent quarterly to achieve a $200,000 annual savings to be a 12 month payback. This arrangement has very limited economic appeal, when continuous maintenance is required.

One source of the problem is that the design basis for mechanical steam traps dates as far back as 1824, when the float trap was already in use. The inverted bucket trap, one of the better mechanical designs, was patented in 1911 but the design has remained essentially unchanged since that time.[7] An examination of steam trap engineering concepts reveals an industry that has not made substantial advances since the days of the Wright Brothers.

A major contributor to the problem is that the steam trap industry is dependent upon the status quo. There are six major manufacturers and 30-60 smaller manufacturers. The sale of spare parts, replacements, and service is the larger and much more profitable side of the industry. The relatively short and unreliable life of the equipment guarantees continued business even in the face of reduced new construction.[8] Worldwide sales of steam traps is estimated at $500 million dollars a year.

INNOVATION: RE-EXAMINING THE STATUS QUO

When frustration is widespread, an opportunity exists. To capitalize on that opportunity, it is necessary to examine the problem in depth, determine the extent and cause of the problem, postulate all the possible solutions and concentrate on the one best solution. It is essential to ask one question along the way. It is the question of a child.

The question is, "Why?"

Why do we have steam traps? Why are there so many trap manufacturers? Why do traps fail? Why do we maintain them? Why are there so many trap maintenance companies? Why are there no advances in the technology. Why?

Condensate removal methods were originally intended to completely remove condensate, as it forms in the steam system, while retarding the loss of live steam. A small drain hole or partially open valve was first used to perform this function, and was quite effective. (In the petrochemical industry it was the most common method in use up to the 1960's.)[9] But toward the end of the 19th century, the crudeness of steam generating equipment, poor quality of steam produced, erratic operation, primitive materials and lack of precise sizing ability combined to make this method ineffective for most facilities.[10]

Steam traps were developed to perform this function in a haphazard environment. But, at best, they only approximate the original requirements. Traps are mechanical devices with moving parts. None respond instantaneously and none will remove condensate completely or continuously as it forms. Because the mechanical parts are subject to wear and failure, traps are also ineffective in fulfilling the second requirement, the retardation of steam loss.

All of this was quite acceptable performance in an era when energy was less than 10¢ per million Btu's. Energy cost and available technology has changed substantially in recent times and one source of possible solutions is a re-examination of the original design basis. According to one of the last Renaissance men in Europe, that is where the answer is often found.

> "Everything has been thought of before, but the problem is to think of it again."
>
> \- Goethe

All innovation begins with frustration over the status quo, followed by struggle, followed by a conceptual solution. In documenting the advantages of a refined solution, this technical paper also defines the process of innovation itself.

A SOLUTION

Saturated steam and condensate co-exist at the same temperature and pressure, but they have substantially different densities. This density differential offers a clue in providing a separation of the two fluids.

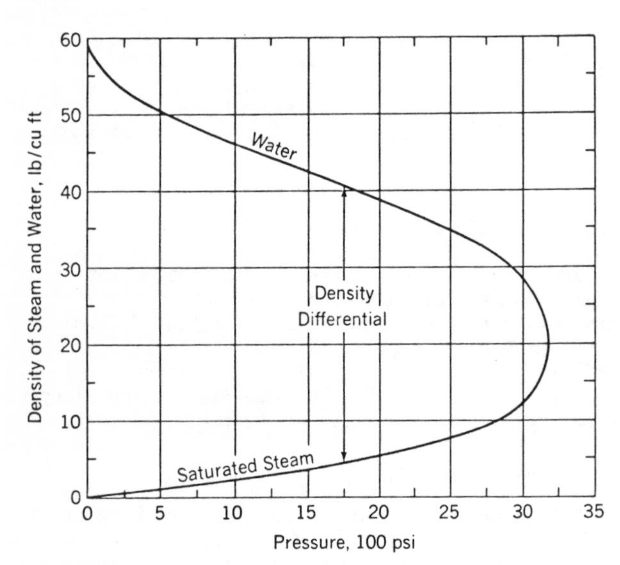

Fig. 1 DENSITIES OF STEAM AND WATER AT SATURATED STEAM TEMPERATURE FOR PRESSURES FROM ATMOSPHERIC TO CRITICAL.
SOURCE: BABCOCK & WILCOX[11]

With this in mind, let's take a fresh look at how a simple orifice functions, and how it might fulfill our requirements.

Assume that a simple orifice is used as a drain. Consult the formulas and engineering tables listed in the sources. Then, for various pressures, compare the flow rates of steam versus condensate through a specific orifice diameter.[12]

You will discover that an orifice is essentially a volumetric device which will pass a large mass of condensate or a relatively small mass of steam at any given pressure and temperature.

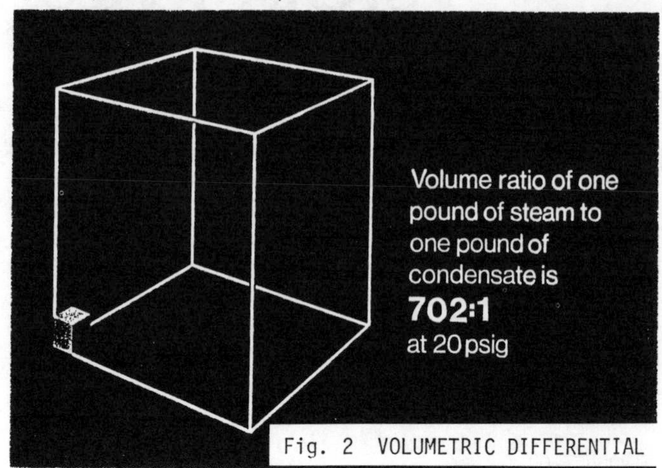

Volume ratio of one pound of steam to one pound of condensate is
702:1
at 20 psig

Fig. 2 VOLUMETRIC DIFFERENTIAL

To observe an example of this simple principle, you may construct an experiment. A child's balloon with a cork and small tube may be alternately filled with air, or water plus air. Water is 62.39 lbs/cu. ft. Standard air is .075 lbs/cu.ft. A large 15" balloon will hold about one cubic foot of air. The equivalent amount of water would be a little more than one fluid ounce (1.15 oz.) Hold the balloon upright and time its discharge. One ounce of water can be drained in a very short time. Draining the air will take 33 times as long. Shaking the balloon, to simulate a varying load, will produce very little effect. To get the air out, the water must first be drained.

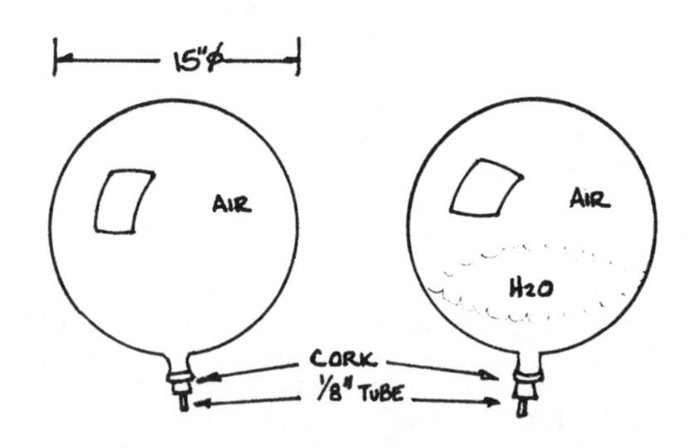

Fig. 3 A SIMPLE EXPERIMENT

If you graph this relationship, you will find that even such a simple device, with no moving parts, is remarkably effective in separating the fluids according to density.

A simple orifice can be used at 50 psig to drain one hundred pounds per hour of water or four pounds per hour of steam (worth about 2¢ @ $5.00/1000 lbs.) This is equivalent to the performance of many steam traps and better than some. The device cannot fail open, like a trap mechanism, and is incapable of losing several hundred pounds of steam an hour as might a steam trap.

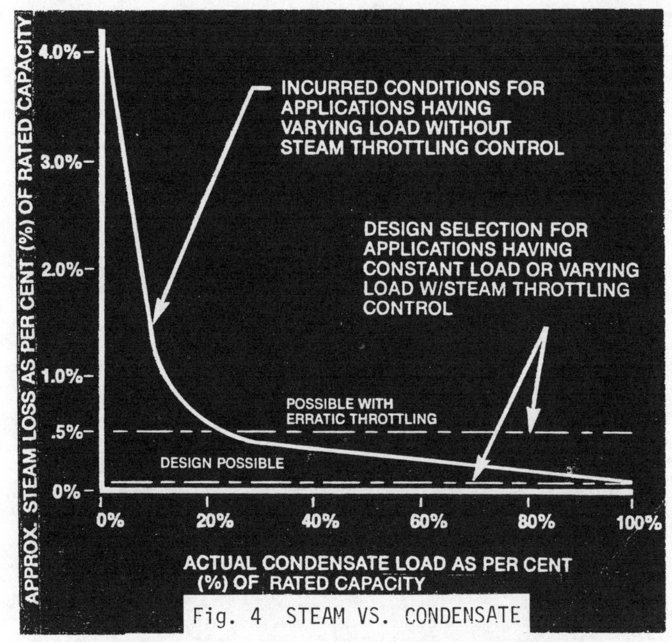

Fig. 4 STEAM VS. CONDENSATE

Such a simple device might be used on the majority of steam distribution lines and tracing applications. These represent the bulk of all steam trap applications. On most tracing and drip applications, loads are on the order of 3-10 pounds per hour with variations of 4 or 5:1 during start-up.

In such service, a simple device could remove condensate continuously and completely while retarding the loss of live steam as shown in Figure 4.

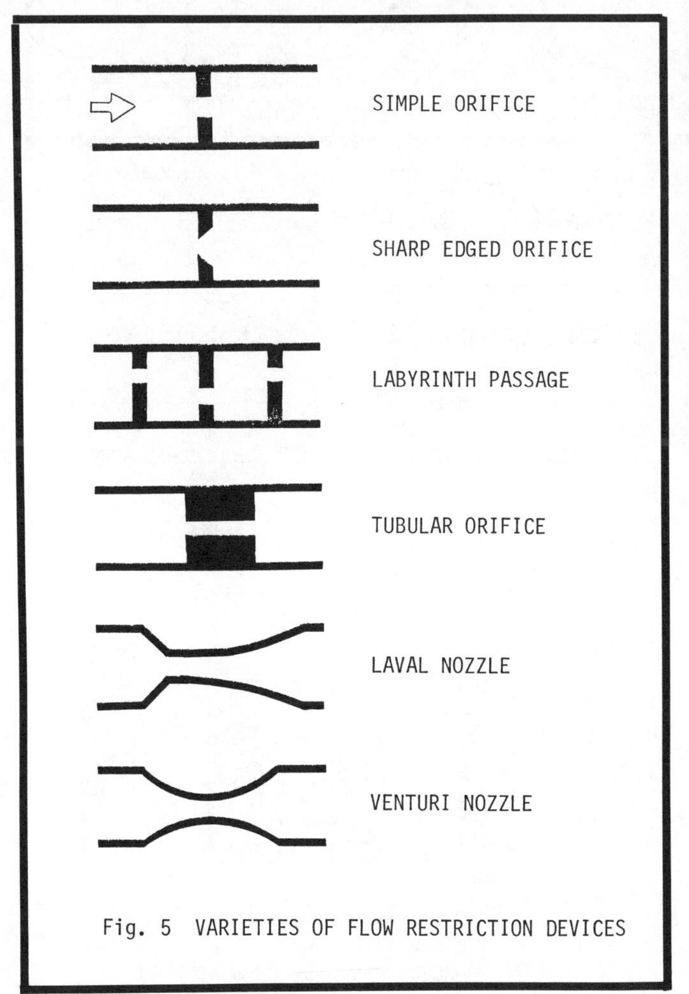

Fig. 5 VARIETIES OF FLOW RESTRICTION DEVICES

These are interesting results, but is it possible to provide even better performance? One advantage is provided by considering geometric configurations other than the simple orifice. These are: the sharp edged orifice; the labyrinth passage; the tubular orifice; the laval nozzle; and the venturi nozzle shown in Figure 5.

Each of these arrangements offers advantages, disadvantages, and complication in commercial application. In returning to our original design objective, however, it is clear that one design may be most favorable. That is a design which will offer the least restrictions to condensate flow while offering a superior restriction to the flow of steam.

The preferred arrangement is the modified venturi nozzle. The throat of the modified venturi nozzle is long necked to offer a substantial wear surface area. The nozzle has four sharp convergent and divergent stages arranged to enhance turbulence through a single passage. This staging also provides a high resistance to plugging. A patented example of the modified venturi nozzle is shown in Figure 6.

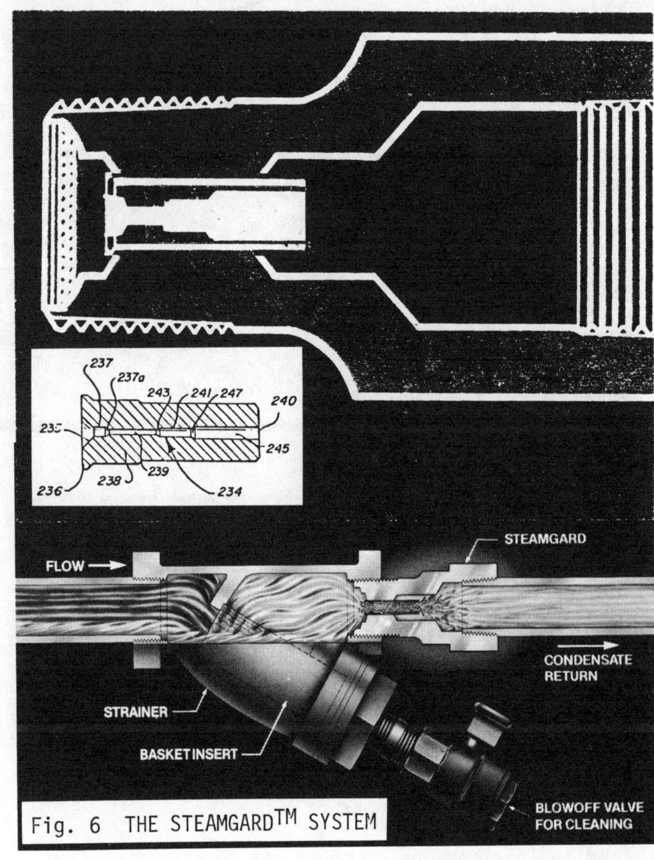

Fig. 6 THE STEAMGARD™ SYSTEM

VARYING LOAD

The advantages of the modified venturi nozzle are further enhanced by an examination of the performance characteristics under varying load conditions. Based upon data provided by Brookhaven National Laboratories for Advanced Physics Research, graphs of performance characteristics for various models were developed.

The upper curve, with the magnified steam scale, shows that when a two phase flow condition exists, the potential for steam loss is dramatically reduced.

This two phase flow condition is the most common occurance in steam nozzles. Single phase dry steam flow is virtually a theoretical condition for saturated steam systems. There is always some water present, and

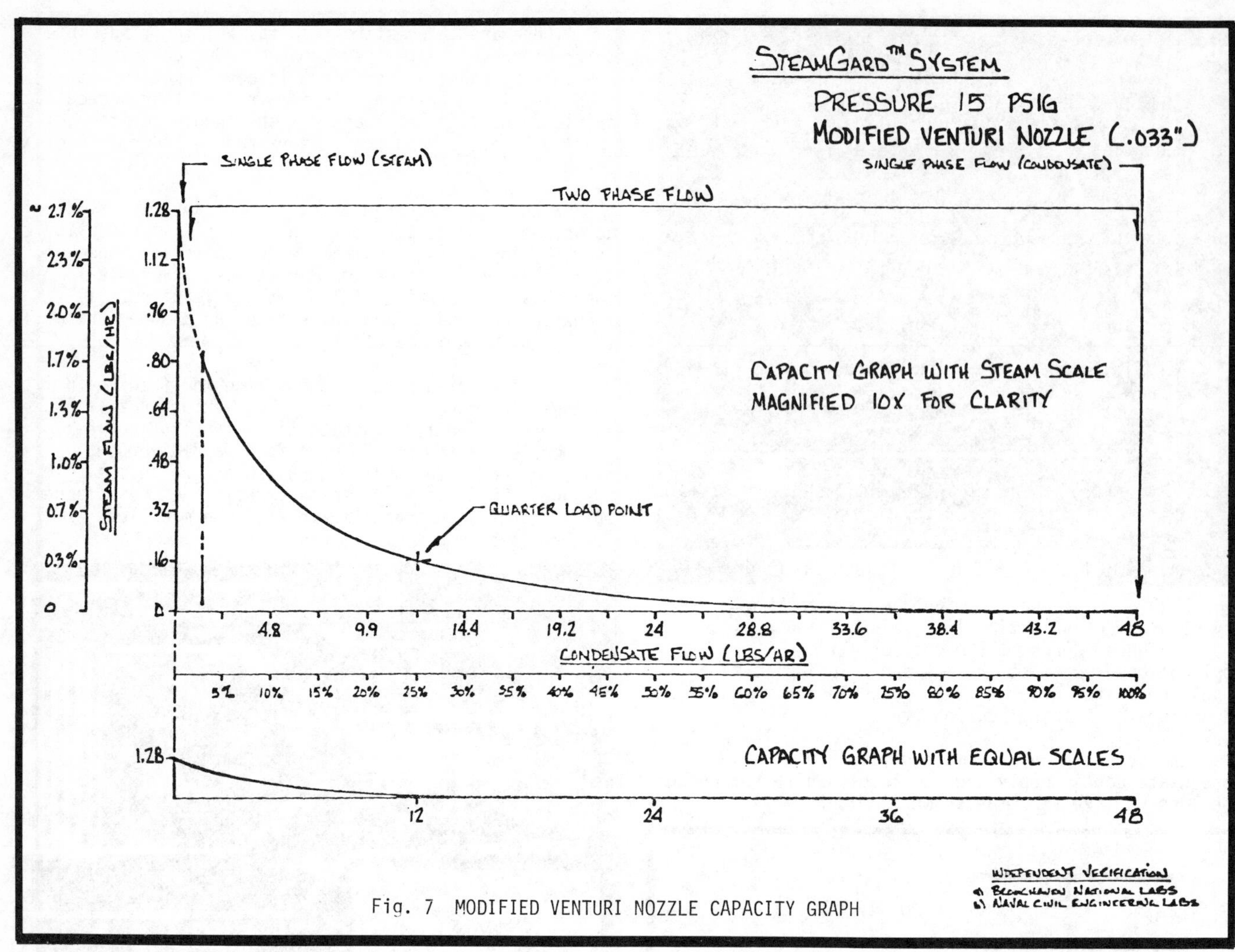

Fig. 7 MODIFIED VENTURI NOZZLE CAPACITY GRAPH

the presence of water significantly impedes steam flow. For details of the regimes of two phase flow in pipes, see Figure 8. Nozzle flow regimes are similar.[14]

Steam, which is lighter than air, is attempting to pass through the throat of the nozzle at a speed approaching Mach I (roughly 760 mph) but the steam is impeded by any condensate present. Condensate, being much denser, wants to travel at speeds of 25-30 miles per hour. Basically, the presence of condensate slows down the steam and more or less gets in its way. The throat of the nozzle is essentially choked by condensate, which impedes the steam flow, while pressure thrusts the condensate ahead.[13]

In the performance graph it can be seen that the presence of a condensate flow equal to 25% of the full condensate capacity will reduce the potential for steam loss by 87.5% below the theoretical maximum, the single phase steam capacity.

In many cases, this is below the limit detectable by simple experimental methods.

A SIMPLE CONCEPT APPLIED

The most rigorous tests are provided in the real world. To examine the function on a genuine application with varying loads, let us consider an example:

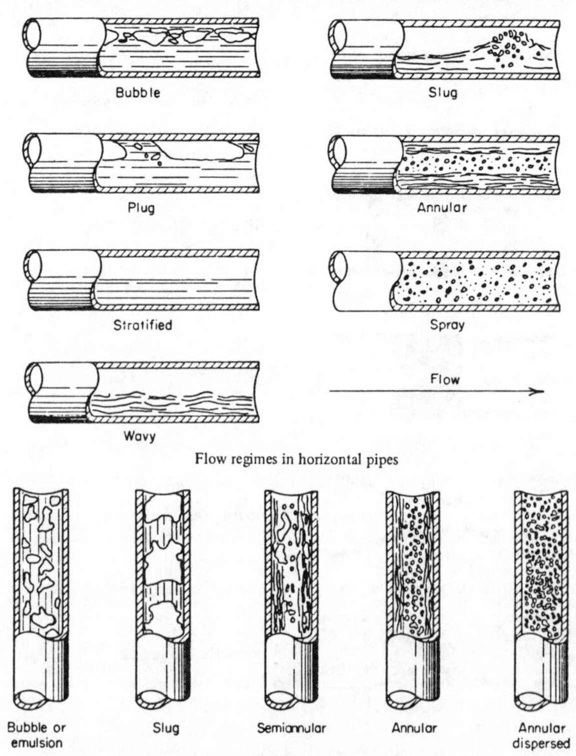

Fig. 8 TWO PHASE FLOW REGIMES
SOURCE: HANDBOOK OF HEAT TRANSFER

Consider the example of a main distribution line:

Application:	Main distribution line
Location:	Boiler House 70°F Indoor
Diameter:	6 inches (152.4 mm)
Length:	100 feet (30.48 meters)
Type:	Schedule 40
Pressure:	15 psig (1.02 bar.)
Insulation:	1" glass fiber
Warmup:	Daily, one hour
Existing Trap:	3/4" NPT Inverted Bucket (3/16) orifice

By referring to basic heat transfer equations, rather than the safety factored tables published by trap manufacturers, you will determine that:

Normal load will be:	12 Lbs/Hour
Warmup load will be:	40 Lbs/Hour

This example would be best handled by the modified venturi nozzle shown in Figure 7.

An examination of the performance characteristics will reveal that:

a) During warmup the potential for steam loss is essentially zero, and warmup time may actually be reduced by about ten minutes due to excess capacity of the nozzle.

b) At normal load the potential for steam loss is about 0.16 lbs/hr. (for a sixty hour work week with steam valued at $5.00/1000 pounds, that amounts to about 5¢ a week.)

c) At zero load the worst case potential for steam loss is roughly 1.28 lbs/hr. (about half a penny per hour.) It should be understood that zero load is a momentary condition at best. In order to produce zero load for a full hour, it is necessary to suspend the laws of heat transfer for that length of time.

This is easier to understand by examining the load fluctuation for various applications as a function of time, shown in Figure 9. By comparing Figures 7 and 9 it is clear that when sizing is performed by bracketing the load characteristics, continuous variations of load can be handled with performance better than the equivalent steam trap.

This performance can be further demonstrated by considering what would happen if we arbitrarily moved this main distribution line outdoors in winter at 20° below zero. Warmup would now take 1 hour and fifteen minutes, but normal load would only be 19 lbs/hr., well within the design limits. Potential for steam loss would be even less than in the previous example.

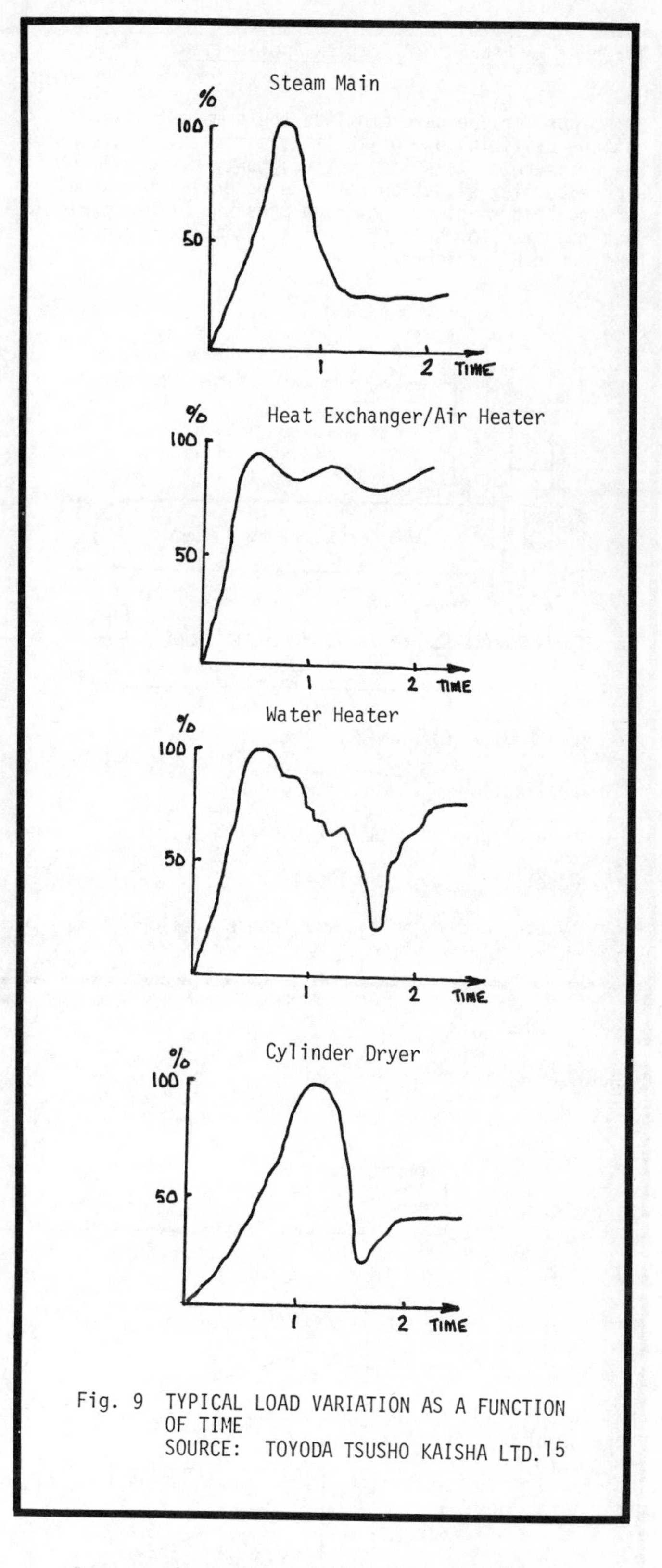

Fig. 9 TYPICAL LOAD VARIATION AS A FUNCTION OF TIME
SOURCE: TOYODA TSUSHO KAISHA LTD.[15]

In comparison, the existing steam trap has a capacity of 600 lbs. per hour and is grossly oversized, even though it is the smallest model available.[16] Because it is only called upon to handle a tiny percentage of its total capacity through a 3/16 inch orifice it has the potential to consume 18 pounds of steam when new, and lose 40 pounds per hour when failed. (at a cost of $12 per week, rather than 38¢ per week.)

THE HEAT EXCHANGER: A Complex Application

Thus far, we have examined the simplest of applications utilizing one of the smallest nozzle sizes at low pressure. It is instructive, however, to examine a more complex situation with the potential for widely varying load conditions at high pressure. The nozzle size required for such an application might approach half an inch in diameter.

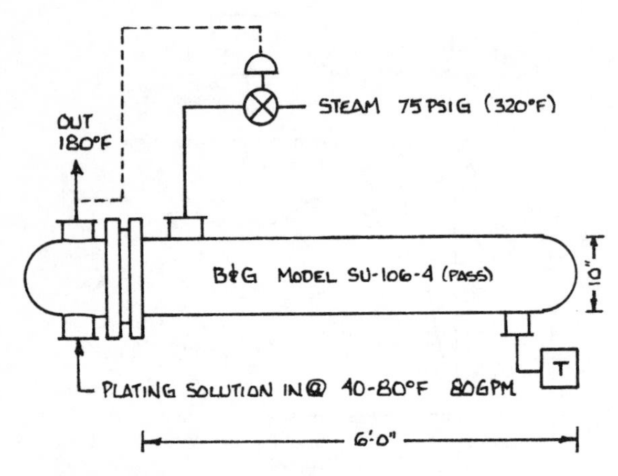

FIG. 10 HEAT EXCHANGER

Application:	Heat Exchanger
Manufacturer:	Bell & Gossett
Model:	SU-106-4
Type:	4 Pass, Tube & Shell
Dimension:	10" Diameter, 6 feet long
Media:	Plating Solution
GPM:	80 (4 ft./min.)
Temp In:	40^oF
Temp Out:	180^oF
Fouling Factor:	1.88 (Mississippi River)
Supply Pressure:	75 psig
Back Pressure:	Zero
Control Valve:	Masoneilan

At max capacity, the condensate load at 75 psig may be determined by:

$$Q = \dot{m}\ Cp\ \ T$$

$$= (80 \text{ gal/min.})\ (8.34 \text{ lbs/gal})\ (60 \text{ min/hr})\ (1 \text{ Btu/lb-}^oF)\ (180^oF-40^oF)$$

$$= 5{,}604{,}480 \text{ Btu/hr.}$$

$$\text{Load} = \frac{\dot{Q}}{H_{75}} = \frac{5{,}604{,}480 \text{ Btu/hr}}{895 \text{ Btu/lb}} =$$

6262 lbs/hr. of condensate.

The nozzle selected for this application would have a throat diameter of roughly 5/16 of an inch (0.312".)

On applications like heat exchangers, air handling coils or steam absorption chillers, a flow control valve

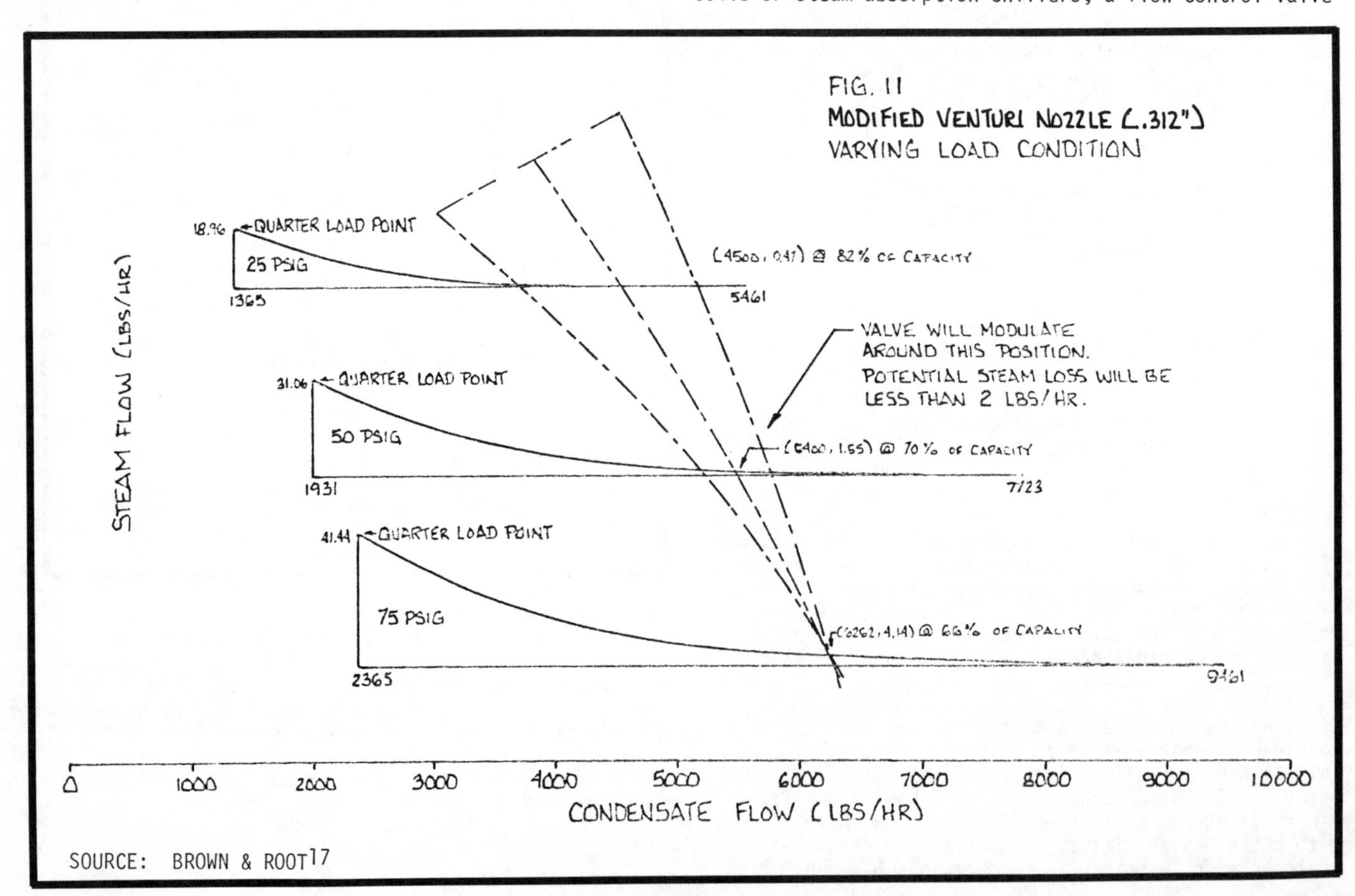

is used to maintain a set temperature. The valve adjusts the steam flow to the requirements of the equipment and the process.

The capacity curve for this nozzle, and all others, is pressure dependent. The capacity decreases with decreasing pressure. The curve shifts to the right on increasing pressure.

Normally, the pressure drop through a control valve is small, but steam is unlike most other media. When steam gives up its heat, it collapses to form water, a much denser fluid that occupies less space. This can create a lower pressure in the equipment. When the valve pinches off, condensate load will drop (there is less heat transfer) and pressure will drop as well. The modified venturi nozzle's capacity will be reduced on the lower pressure/lower capacity as demonstrated in Figure 11. The potential steam loss will average less than 2 pounds per hour.

The capacity of a nozzle is pressure dependent. In this manner, the device will actually track even minute fluctuations of the control valve. The modified venturi nozzle acts in concert with the control valve and the control loop. It acts as a tiny bleed on the system. Tests have shown this action provides superior temperature control and reduces control valve swings and other excursions.

Steam traps cannot act in concert with the control valve. They are outside the control loop and are closed except in the presence of condensate sufficient to activate them. They dump condensate at that point and contribute to the loss of temperature control.

The equivalent trap on this application would have a 3/4" orifice and a capacity of 19,000 lbs/hr. of condensate.[18] It would be grossly oversized for the service required. When it fails, it will lose more than 259 pounds of steam per hour valued at $9,324 for a 7200 hour year. This assumes a full load is available to help choke the steam flow. Otherwise, the loss could be increased by 800%.

SUBSTANTIAL RESULTS

All of this is fascinating theory, but what does it mean in the real world of dollars and cents? In nine years of real life applications, the system has provided substantial results. Those results are demonstrated by case history documentation in the following examples.

Fig. 12 THE ELIMINATION OF STEAM TRAPS

Case History Documentation

1. Zenith Radio Corporation's Rauland Picture Tube Division in Melrose Park, IL, converted one 700-trap manufacturing plant for $65,000 in 1981, and realized fuel savings of $120,000 in the first year. Savings provided by the new system have actually escalated in succeeding years because of increasing fuel costs. A previous eight-man trap maintenance crew was reassigned to production duties when their trap responsibilities were curtailed three years ago.

2. Chicago & Northwestern Railroad converted its 130-trap locomotive repair facility west of downtown Chicago for $16,000 in 1983. A savings of $35,000 was predicted for the first year, so the railroad was pleasantly surprised when they actually saved $65,000 within six months.

3. One high rise medical center, the 20-story Rehabilitation Institute of Chicago, realized a payback of one month after conversion to the new system five years ago. A record steam savings of 54 percent prompted their steam supplier to check the meter. No malfunction was found and the center is quite happy with the results. Accumulated savings to date are in excess of $200,000. Maintenance of the system amounts to about $100 per year.

4. Lakeside Medical Center, a Veterans Administration Hospital in Chicago, IL, concludes that its conversion to the new system is saving $770 a day in steam and 700 gallons a day in make-up water and boiler chemicals during the heating season.

5. A petrochemical facility, Powell-Duffryn Terminal, Inc., of Lemont, IL, also realized a payback of two months, and a fuel savings of 42 percent. Savings there averaged a staggering $37,000 a month for a population of 310 traps.

6. Other substantive users of the system currently include Ford Motor Company, Johnson & Johnson, Prudential, Alcoa, Minnesota Mining & Manufacturing, Martin Marietta, Hitachi, Shell Oil, and Abbott Laboratories.

SOURCE: ENERGY MANAGEMENT TECHNOLOGY NOVEMBER, 1984

This system has been demonstrated to function on virtually every type of application, including 54"Ø distribution lines, superheated distribution lines, dirty steam systems, powerhouse pressures of 2400 psig, vacuum return systems, condensate lifts, 150,000 CFM banks of air handling coils, petrochemical reboilers, every variety of tracing systems, and in every industry from aerospace to woodworking.[19]

The company responsible for the development of the system, Engineering Resources, Inc., has doubled annually in size, sales and personnel for the last nine years. Success of this nature is the market's way of saying you are doing something right in providing substantial benefits to the end user.

Objections to the viability of the system, largely raised by steam trap manufacturers a dozen years ago, are persuasively countered by a nine year record of success. Previous arguments centered mainly on the possible effects of varying load, a projected high potential for plugging, excessive wear, air venting, and other imagined disorders. In light of the system's effective results, these arguments are now difficult to support. Other convoluted technical objections, like those once directed toward the horseless carriage and manned space flight, become frivolous once the impossible has been achieved.

The system is performance warranteed for a minimum of three years. Full refund is offered in the first year.

SUMMARY

No one can afford to turn their back on the kind of economics this system provides. And no one can shut out the future. The old arguments just don't hold any water.

In the South Pacific it is still possible to find stone age technologies. And twenty years from now there will still be someone, somewhere, who is buying steam traps and living with the frustration of maintaining them.

There are always proponents who will argue that things should remain as they are or as they have been.

Fortunately, there are always managers capable of the vision and leadership necessary to keep pace with the requirements of an expanding technology. Their desire for greater efficiency, higher yields, improved production and increased profit have always succeeded in overcoming the objections to new or untried methods. It is the actions of these leaders that provide the benchmarks of industrial growth.

SOURCES & REFERENCES

1. The Elimination of Steam Traps, Proceedings of the 7th World Energy Engineering Congress, F. Dickman, Chapter 51, November, 1984, published by The Association of Energy Engineers, Atlanta, Georgia. Hardcover ISBN 0915586-87-8 @ $45.

2. Steam Traps: Exploding the Myths, Proceedings of the 8th World Energy Engineering Congress, F. Dickman, Chapter 79, October, 1985, published by The Association of Energy Engineers, Atlanta, Georgia. Hardcover ISBN 9 88173-008-3 @ $45.

3. Industry Week, May 14, 1984, page 74C.

4. Plant Engineering, December 22, 1983, page 15.

5. Maintenance Management Technology in Steam Distribution Systems, IETC - Houston, June 19, 1986, Yarway Tech/Serv.

6. Plant Engineering, July 11, 1985, page 97.

7. Steam Boiler Operation, J. Jackson, Prentice-Hall, 1980.

8. What to Watch in Steam Traps, J. Bachetti, CPI Purchasing, July, 1985.

9. Interviews, Exxon & Shell Oil, 1985.

10. Steam Traps vs. Second Generation Fixed Orifices, C.N. Stavropoulos, 1979.

11. Steam - Its Generation and Use, 37th & 38th Editions, Babcock & Wilcox, 1972.

12. ASME Flow Measurement Report, Chapter 4, Part 5.
Design Handbook, Flexitallic Gasket Co., Bulletin 474-SL-176-10M.
Nomograms for Steam Generation & Utilization, V. Ganapathy, Fairmont Press, 1985.
Phaseout of High Pressure Steam Traps, L. Guzick, Naval Engineers Journal, April, 1973.

13. Energy Management Technology, Editors, November, 1984

14. Handbook of Heat Transfer, W. Rohsenow & J. Hartnett, McGraw-Hill, 1973.

15. Handbook of Steam Trapping, Toyoda Tsusho Kaisha Ltd., 1981.

16. Steam Trap Catalog, Armstrong Machine Works, Catalog 107-C 50M 7/820. (See also: Plant Engr, Aug-85, pg 49)

17. Performance of Steam Heat Exchangers, J. Mather, Brown & Root, Chemical Engineering, September 3, 1973.

18. Steam Conservation Guidelines for Condensate Drainage, Armstrong Machine Works. Design Manual, Bulletin M101 50M 12/81-0.
Steam Trap Catalog, Armstrong Machine Works, Catalog 107-C 50M 7/820.

19. SASOL II, Great Plains Coal Gasification Plant, Prudential, Ohio Edison, Daley Civic Center, Exxon, Rockwell & Baldwin Piano.

ABOUT THE AUTHOR

Born in Chicago in 1949, Frank Dickman is a graduate of the Illinois Institute of Technology, with a Bachelor of Science Degree in Mechanical and Aerospace Engineering. Widely traveled, Mr. Dickman has fourteen years of experience in design, construction and technical assistance in the power, steel and petrochemical industries. He is currently Product Engineering Manager of Engineering Resources, Inc., in Chicago.

SECTION 26
WASTE HEAT RECOVERY

Chapter 77

WASTE HEAT RECOVERY FROM STACKS USING DIRECT-CONTACT CONDENSING HEAT EXCHANGE

W. F. Thorn

ABSTRACT

Flue gases exiting the stack of a boiler create thermal losses normally amounting to 15 to 20% of the high heating value of the fuel fired. By capturing and using this lost energy using condensing heat recovery, the overall effiency of the system can be raised to over 95%.

This paper reviews the origins of stack heat losses, direct contact condensing heat recovery processes, the Rocket Research Company CON-X condensing recuperator equipment and systems, site specific case studies and fuels and condensate acidity. A detailed example of the determination of the magnitude of stack heat losses is presented along with a methodology for the reader to make a preliminary heat recovery evaluation.

BACKGROUND

Boiler System Losses

When a fuel is burned, as in a boiler, approximately 80 to 85% of its high heating value (HHV) is transferred to the product steam and the remaining heat is lost up the stack and through the walls of the boiler to the atmosphere. The radiative/convective loss from the boiler hardware is on the order of 1% of the HHV. Thus, by far, the largest losses are in the residual heat carried out of the stack by the flue gases and can amount to 15 to 20% of the HHV depending on the fuel burned and the boilers efficiency of transferring heat. Similar stack losses are incurred in fuel-fired furnaces and dryers as well.

In the flue gases, heat is carried in both sensible and latent form. The sensible heat loss is determined by the temperature of the flue gas and the combined heat capacities of its constituents. The latent heat loss portion is determined by the amount of water present in the flue gas in vapor form. The water vapor is present principally as a result of the combustion of hydrogen contained in the fuel. A small part of the water enters the process through humidity of the combustion air and other water can enter as a part of the fuel itself.

The proportion of the heat loss carried by the water vapor in the flue gases is in the range from 55 to 75% of the total stack loss for natural gas fired systems, depending on the stack temperature and excess air being fired. With other fuels, the percentage may fall outside this range: lower with dry fuels having higher carbon/hydrogen ratios than natural gas, e.g. fuel oil, or higher with high fuel-borne water content such as with certain solid fuels.

Recovery and use of these sensible and latent heat losses can yield significant increases in boiler system efficiency and corresponding reductions in fuel costs. Figure 1 illustrates this general potential for heat recovery. Sensible heat recovery down to the dew point can yield 2 to 5% overall system efficiency improvement. Cooling below this level increases the rate of recovery by capturing the latent heat losses as well and can yield 11 to 15% or more improvement typically. Figure 2 illustrates, again in a general way, the variation in efficiency improvement potential with variation of the inlet temperature to the heat recovery equipment, assuming a fixed exhaust temperature from the recovery equipment. Note the higher improvement potential in natural gas fired systems.

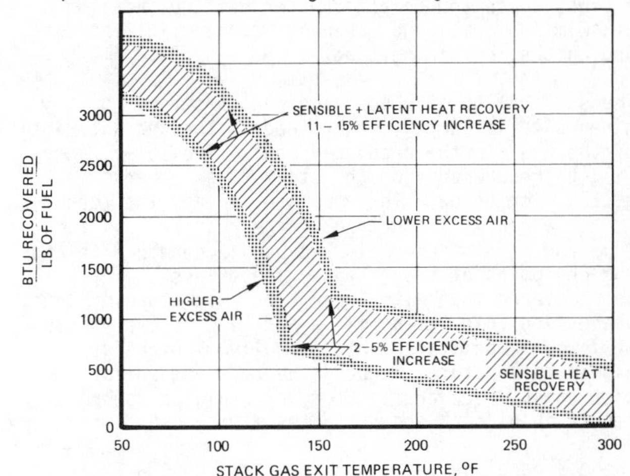

FIGURE 1. HEAT RECOVERY POTENTIAL (NATURAL GAS FIRED BOILER)

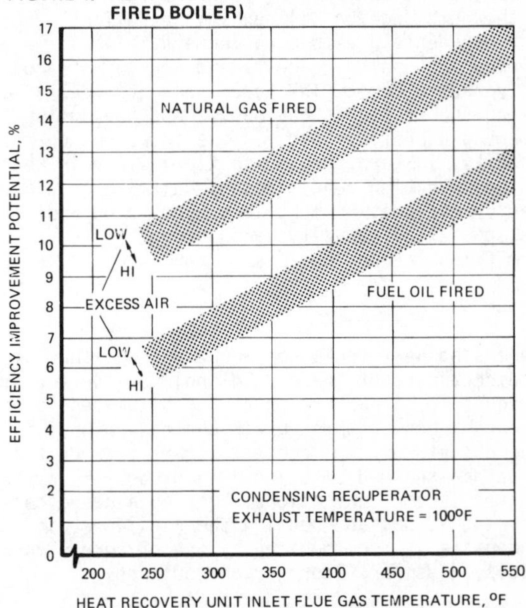

FIGURE 2. EFFICIENCY VARIATION WITH HEAT RECOVERY UNIT INLET FLUE GAS TEMPERATURE

Appendix A presents an example of the derivation of these boiler stack losses and their recovery potential using methane as a fuel for simplicity of illustration. Since methane is the primary constituent of natural gas, these results are representative of a natural gas fired boiler system as well. Appendix A also includes several basic curves of data for water vapor and natural gas to permit the reader to make a preliminary evaluation of any boiler using the same methodology.

Recovered Energy Use

Heat recovery from flue gases, for example with conventional economizers and air heaters, has traditionally been in the sensible, noncondensing heat range. While adding several percent to overall boiler efficiency (reference Figure 1), a large amount of unrecovered heat remains in the exhaust gases downstream of these devices. By recovering and using the considerable latent heat available at temperatures below the flue gas dew point, boiler efficiencies as a percent of the HHV can be increased to over 95%. To achieve such high levels of efficiency through flue-gas heat recovery, a low-temperature use (heat sink) for the recovered energy must be available and condensing heat recovery must be used. Typical low-temperature uses include preheating of boiler feed water or process fluids, space and domestic water heating, heating of swimming pools and greenhouses, heavy oil heating, and combustion air heating.

The suitability of condensing heat recovery for any given site is largely determined by the characteristics of the use for the recovered heat. Typically, energy will be recovered from the stack at a temperature of 135°F or below. The amount of energy that can be recovered is a function of the required use temperature and rate of use. If the use temperature is near the dew point of the exhaust gases, less energy will be recovered than with lower use temperatures. Thus, preheating cold water will yield high recovery rates at lower temperatures whereas delivering energy at higher temperatures reduces the total amount of energy that can be recovered. Of course, higher use rates result in higher recovery rates at any use temperature.

Where a good user heat sink exists, the CON-X direct-contact condensing heat recovery system discussed in the next section will exhibit excellent payback and represents a simple, quick and reliable means of reducing operating costs and improving margins for years to come. The hedge thus afforded against rising fuel costs is obvious. Less obvious but also lowering operating costs is the increased operating capacity, in turn, providing flexibility in seasonal margin-operating conditions by delaying or avoiding startup of additional boilers, providing additional peak operating capacity, and through energy recovery from fired standby boilers.

Recovery Processes

Condensing heat exchange can be accomplished by indirect or direct contact means. In indirect contact systems, a liquid (e.g. water) or air to be heated is directed through tubes or through air channels placed in the flue gas stream. No contact occurs between the flue gases and the medium being heated, and the system behaves like a conventional heat exchanger, cooling the exhaust gas and heating the liquid or air. Acidic condensate is accommodated by use of corrosion resistant alloys, glass or fluorocarbon coatings.

With a direct-contact system, water is introduced into the hot gas stream in counter-flow directly and intimately using spray nozzles. The flue gas in turn is cooled adiabatically, i.e., by evaporation. When sufficient water is thus introduced, the flue gases will be cooled below their adiabatic saturation temperature and subsequently below the dew point of the entering gases. The flue gases exit the direct-contact process saturated at low temperatures while the water leaves in a heated condition. Acidic condensate is handled in this system through use of ordinary stainless steel, PVC and cast iron owing to the high level of dilution with the water sprays.

As a seeming paradox, the saturated, low-temperature flue gases are exhausted from the direct-contact heat recovery process with a lower water vapor content than the hot entering gases, even though a water spray was used to effect the process. Figure 3 illustrates this process of adiabatic cooling and condensation of natural gas combustion products using the background of a psychrometric chart. The humidification and cooling of the gases follows a line of constant enthalpy (roughly the wet bulb temperature line) from the entering point, assumed here at 400°F, left to the saturation line. The temperature at the intersection with the saturation line is the adiabatic saturation temperature.

Up to this point in the process, no energy has been removed from the system since all energy given up by the gases has gone into vaporizing the water and is carried in latent form by the water vapor/humidity of the now-saturated gases. Continued cooling results in the condensation of moisture from the gases (dehumidification) yielding the latent heat of the water vapor. The end point of the process will be determined by the availability of the user heat sink, i.e., the temperature and flowrate of water coming to the recovery system for heating and, thereby, its ability to remove heat.

CON-X EQUIPMENT

CON-X Recuperator and Tank

The Rocket Research Company (RRC) CON-X recuperator is a direct-contact, condensing heat recovery system well proven in many presently operating systems in Europe and England. RRC has licensed this technology from L'Industrielle de Chauffage of France, a mechanical engineering and equipment firm, and a leading designer of these systems in Europe under the trade name "ICCO". Now available throughout the U.S. and Canada, this patented system is offered in a variety of configurations and sizes to suit any installation. (Reference Table 1.). Basic performance of the CON-X system is shown in the nomograph of Figure 4.

Figures 5 and 6 illustrate the basic CON-X hardware comprised of the recuperator and auxilliary tank. The recuperator is a "baffle-tower" type fabricated from 316L stainless steel, with internal diversion devices that cause the flue gas to cross a number of water curtains in its upward course from the inlet. The spray water enters at the top through nozzles and cascades downward across the baffles forming the water curtains. The heated water accumulates in the bottom of the recuperator and exits by gravity flow to the auxilliary tank.

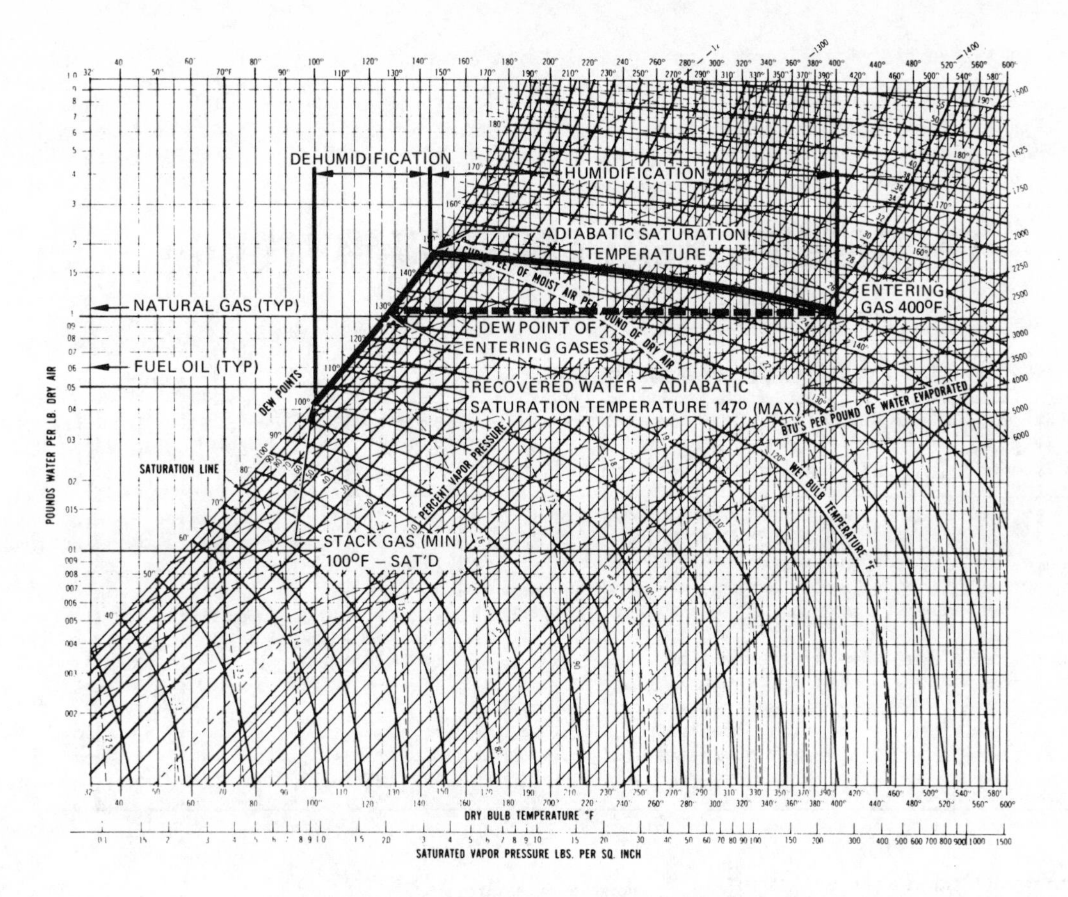

FIGURE 3. DIRECT CONTACT HEAT EXCHANGER PERFORMANCE

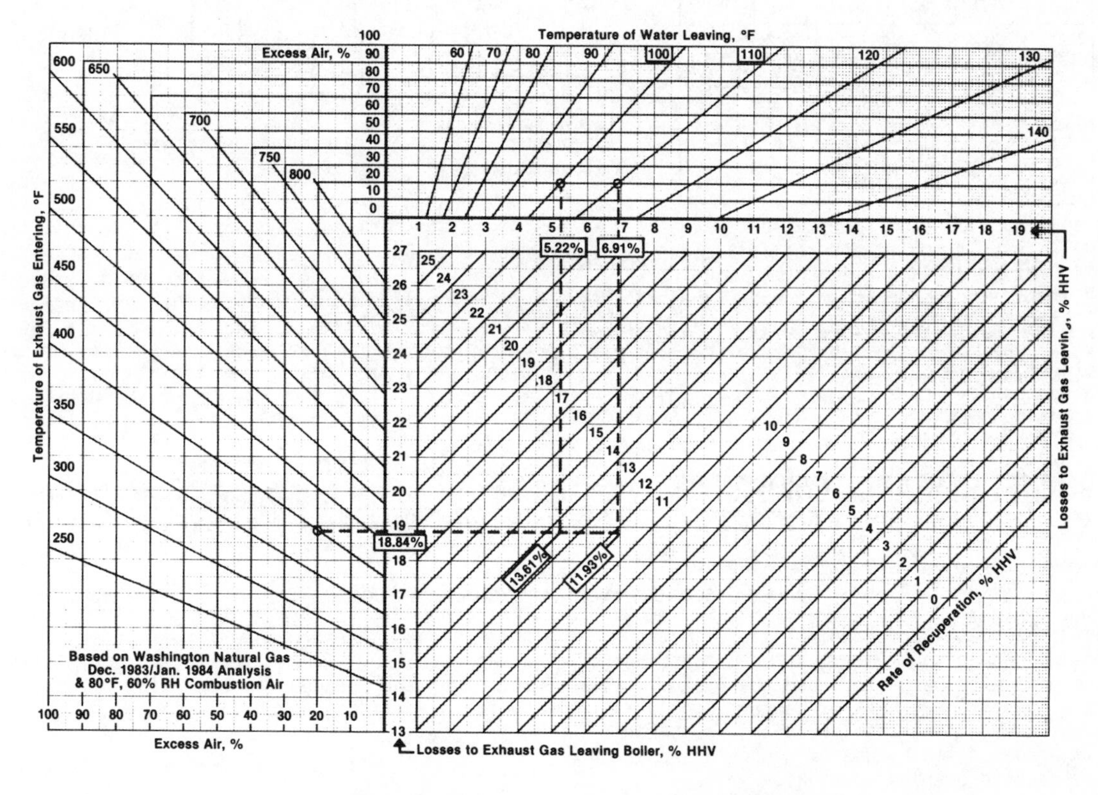

FIGURE 4. CON-X RECUPERATOR PERFORMANCE WITH NATURAL GAS-FIRED BOILER

CONDENSING HEAT EXCHANGER - CON-X

STANDARD RECUPERATOR SIZES

Series	Max. Flue Gas Flow (scfm)	Nominal Boiler Power		Water Flow (gpm)	Approximate Dimensions								Approx. Dry Weight (lbs)
		10^6 Btu/hr	HP		D (in.)	H (in.)	A (in.)	B (in.)	C (in.)	G (in.)	W1 (in.)	W2 (in.)	
300	210	0.87	26	15	11.75	120.00	10.25	5.00	21.75	34.75	1.5	2.0	130
450	470	1.98	59	35	17.75	120.50	15.25	7.75	22.25	37.50	2.0	2.5	245
600	860	3.57	107	60	23.75	132.50	20.50	10.25	22.75	40.50	2.5	3.0	320
750	1,360	5.56	166	95	29.50	145.25	25.50	13.00	24.50	44.75	3.0	5.0	440
900	1,880	7.94	237	130	35.50	164.00	29.50	16.25	29.50	52.50	3.0	5.0	615
1050	2,560	10.71	320	175	41.25	173.25	35.50	18.50	30.75	55.25	3.5	5.0	925
1200	3,360	13.89	415	230	47.25	189.00	39.50	21.75	42.25	69.75	3.5	5.0	1,215
1350	4,270	17.86	533	295	53.25	189.00	43.25	25.25	35.75	65.25	5.0	6.0	1,585
1500	5,240	21.82	652	360	59.50	198.00	47.25	28.50	36.50	69.25	5.0	6.0	1,765
1650	6,360	26.59	794	440	65.00	208.75	51.25	32.00	42.50	78.25	6.0	8.0	2,005
1800	7,560	31.74	948	530	71.00	216.50	59.00	33.00	45.25	79.50	6.0	8.0	2,625
1950	8,710	35.71	1,067	595	76.75	223.50	63.00	34.75	46.50	83.75	6.0	10.0	2,930

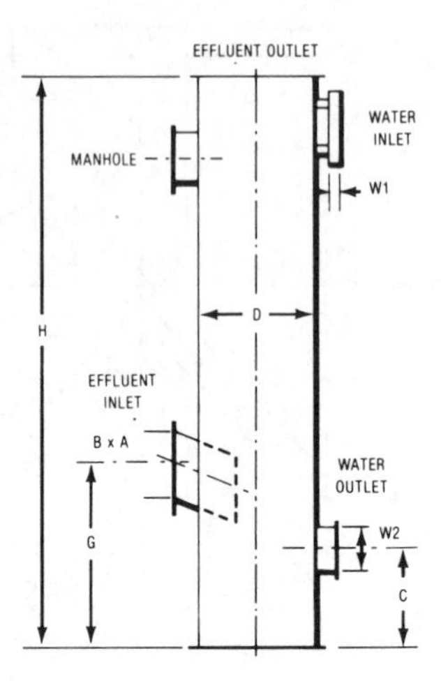

STANDARD TANKS ■ 3-COMPARTMENT, SINGLE RECUPERATOR CONNECTION

Series	Water Flow Rate (gpm)	Approximate Dimensions			Approx. Dry Weight (lbs)
		A (in.)	B (in.)	H (in.)	
14	62	23.75	35.50	26.75	210
21	92	35.50	35.50	27.50	355
40	176	39.50	39.50	33.50	465
60	264	39.50	39.50	45.25	530
82	360	39.50	49.25	39.50	550
100	440	41.25	49.25	47.25	750
120	528	49.25	49.25	50.00	885
160	704	63.00	49.25	51.25	1,015
210	924	63.00	49.25	60.00	1,190

NOTE: COVER ROTATED 90° FOR ILLUSTRATION

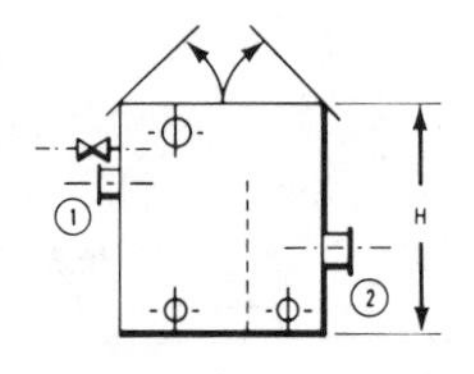

TANK TUBING POSITIONS AS REQUESTED:

(1) CON-X unit → Tank

(2) Tank → Service use

RETURN COMPARTMENT

MULTIPLE UNIT RETURN OPTION:

(3) Service use → Tank

(4) Tank → CON-X units

AVAILABLE OPTIONS:

- Effluent inlet through the bottom
- Horizontal effluent outlet
- Shorter recuperator cylinder — larger diameter
- Larger sizes
- Reinforcement for stack support
- Multiple section construction
- Tank with "return" compartment
- Special dimension tank

TUBING ORIENTATIONS:

- W1 & W2 may be located anywhere on the 1/2 circumference opposite the inspection port or effluent inlet

ROCKET RESEARCH COMPANY
A DIVISION OF ROCKCOR

For more information contact:
Marketing Department
ROCKET RESEARCH COMPANY
11441 Willows Road ■ Redmond, WA 98052-1012 ■ (206) 885-5000

TABLE 1. CONDENSING HEAT EXCHANGER — CON-X

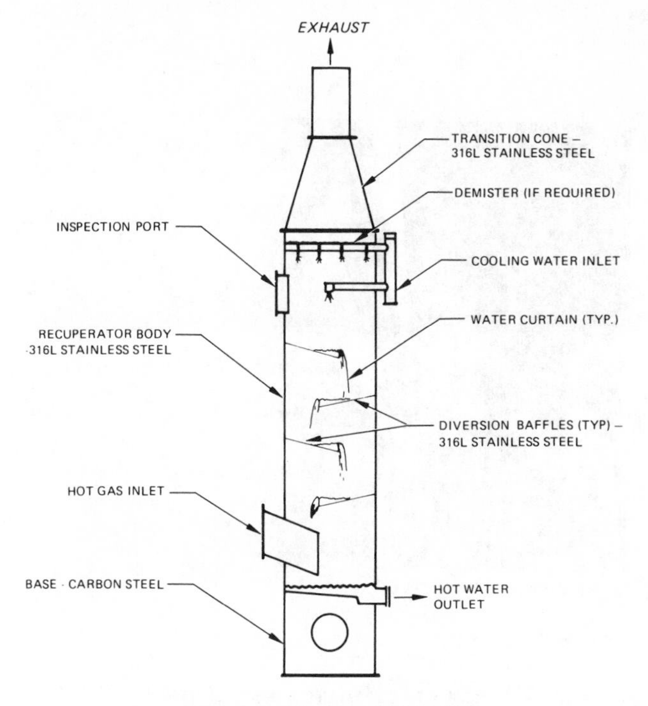

FIGURE 5. CON-X RECUPERATOR

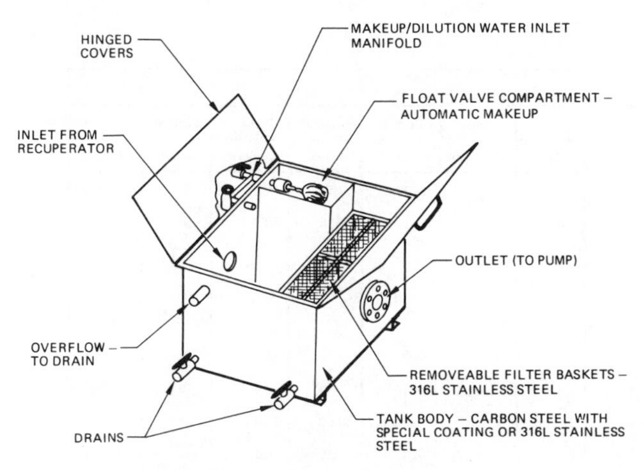

FIGURE 6. CON-X AUXILIARY TANK

The tank is divided into several compartments including the water entry area, the float valve compartment and the filter baskets. Water coming from the recuperator flows over a wier through the stainless steel filter baskets to the outlet leading to the spray circuit pump. The float valve will provide automatic makeup to the spray water circuit any time there is evaporative loss from varying boiler operating conditions. Normally, due to condensation, there is a gain of water in this circuit and a continuous overflow to the drain. The tank is either fabricated from 316L stainless steel or from carbon steel with an acid-resistant interior coating and epoxy enamel exterior. The filter baskets are removable to permit their periodic cleaning by hosing out the dust/carbon sludge accumulation captured by the spray water.

Figure 7 shows the CON-X equipment in final assembly just prior to startup at the first U.S. installation at the Oregon State Hospital in Salem, Oregon. For reference, the recuperator is a Series 900 size and the tank is a Series 40. The equipment is now installed and operating. Two new 400 Hp Cleaver Brooks boilers are connected to the recuperator via isolation dampers in their stacks. The installation, completed in mid-1985, was designed to heat 25 gpm of water from 80°F to 120°F (minimum) with either boiler at 50% firing rate and above, thus recovering and supplying 500,000 BTU/hr (minimum) (Reference Figure 8). At present, 37 gpm of water are being heated from 64°F to 115°F for a total heat recovery of 8-900,000 BTU/hr at mid-fire and above. Table 2 shows the startup data for the system with a range of uncertainty on total heat recovery due to inaccuracies inherent in the type of temperature gauges used. Based on the installed equipment cost and a natural gas cost of $5.00 per million BTU, the original simple payback for this system was 2.1 years. As presently operated, simple payback is estimated at approximately 1.5 years.

CON-X System

The basic building blocks of a complete CON-X system are shown in Figure 8. This figure is completed for each installation to characterize the design-point sizing requirements and performance based on a system analysis using the aforementioned input data sheets.

The system can be configured in a variety of ways to suit the needs of the user facility. Normally, installation will be made using a pump and secondary plate heat exchanger to isolate the spray water circuit and to deliver the recovered heat to a treated or potable user water stream. In Europe, a number of direct-coupled installations have been made without the secondary heat exchanger where the user water (e.g., from a swimming pool) is heated directly in the recuperator. The direct installation, where usable, will provide a slightly higher output temperature and several percent higher recovery rate since no allowance is needed for Δ t in the secondary heat exchanger.

When the user heat sink is air for space heating or combustion, an air coil is used in lieu of the plate heat exchanger. If outside air below the freezing point of water is to be heated, both types of exchanger may be used with a glycol antifreeze solution in the loop to the air coil.

When a low flow of water is to be heated and/or a high temperature is required, a variant of this basic approach is used as illustrated in Figure 9. In this case, an air coil is installed between the heat source (boiler) and the recuperator. The user-circuit water enters the plate heat exchanger and is then routed to the air coil where its temperature is raised to the final delivery level (170-180°F typically). Circuit interconnections permit balancing the flows in accommodating variations in boiler flue gas output. By this tactic, and uniquely associated with low user water flows and high waste heat availability, condensation can be achieved where otherwise not possible, the temperature supplied and the amount of energy recovered are elevated simultaneously, and the CON-X exhaust temperature is reduced.

a. FLUE GAS ENTRY

c. HEATED WATER OUTLET

b. AUXILIARY TANK & HEAT TRANSFER EQUIPMENT

FIGURE 7. CON-X RECUPERATOR INSTALLATION AT OREGON STATE HOSPITAL, SALEM, OREGON

Item	Units	Test Results						Estimated Design Point Performance (50% Firing Rate)					
		Low Fire		Mid Fire		Hi Fire		Boiler	Original	Original	Present	Present	Present (2)
		Meas	Calc	Meas	Calc	Meas	Calc	Heat Sink	Original	Present	Original	Present	Present
1. Gas consumption	CFM	37.5*	38.46	(150.1)	154.2	262.7*	271.2		135.6	135.6	135.6	135.6	135.6
2. Firing level	%	—	14.27*	—	57.14	—	100.00*		50	50	50	50	50
3. O_2*	%	8.0	—	4.0	—	4.0	—		3.0	3.0	4.0	4.0	4.0
4. Excess Air	%	—	56*	—	22	—	22*		16	16	22	22	22
5. Boiler stack temp.*	°F	325	—	340	—	360	—		—	—	—	—	—
6. Boiler stack temp.	°F	290	—	350	—	365	—		405	405	338	338	338
7. Recuperator stack temp.	°F	89	—	116	—	117	—		121.8	115.4	118.5	112.3	107.6
8. Recovered water temp.	°F	90.5	—	123.5	—	123	—		132.3	124.3	128.1	120.4	114.4
9. Recuperator return temp.	°F	85.5	85.7	113	111.7	113	110.4		123.4	112.3	120.0	109.4	101.7
10. Spray water flow rate	gpm	137.4	—	137.4	—	137.4	—		137.4	137.4	137.4	137.4	137.4
11. Domestic water inlet temp.	°F	64	—	64	—	64	—		80	64	80	64	64
12. Domestic water outlet temp.	°F	86	81.8	115.5	107.2	115	110.1		128.6	108.0	124.7	104.2	110.7
13. Domestic water flow rate	gpm	37.0	—	37.5	—	37.5	—		25	37.5	25	37.5	37.5
14. Energy recovered (1)	10^6 Btu/hr	0.344 to 0.407	0.330	0.722 to 0.966	0.811	0.688 to 0.957	0.865		0.609	0.827	0.559	0.755	0.877
15. Δt_{LM}	°F	10.87	14.25	22.62	29.24	22.62	26.22		16.12	29.49	14.94	28.34	14.68
16. Condensate flow	gpm	—	0.33	—	0.47	—	0.49		0.08	0.44	0.20	0.53	0.73
17. Basic boiler efficiency	%	—	81.03	—	80.92	—	80.54		79.89	79.89	81.23	81.23	81.23
18. Efficiency w/recuperator	%	—	95.0	—	89.50	—	89.64		87.15	89.75	88.01	90.39	91.88
19. Dew point	°F	—	124.4	—	132.2	—	132.2		133.8	133.8	132.2	132.2	132.2

(1) The lower value in the measured column is derived from the spray circuit data and the higher value from the domestic water data.

(2) Uses larger heat exchanger

*From Boiler Test Data

TABLE 2. OREGON STATE HOSPITAL STARTUP DATE

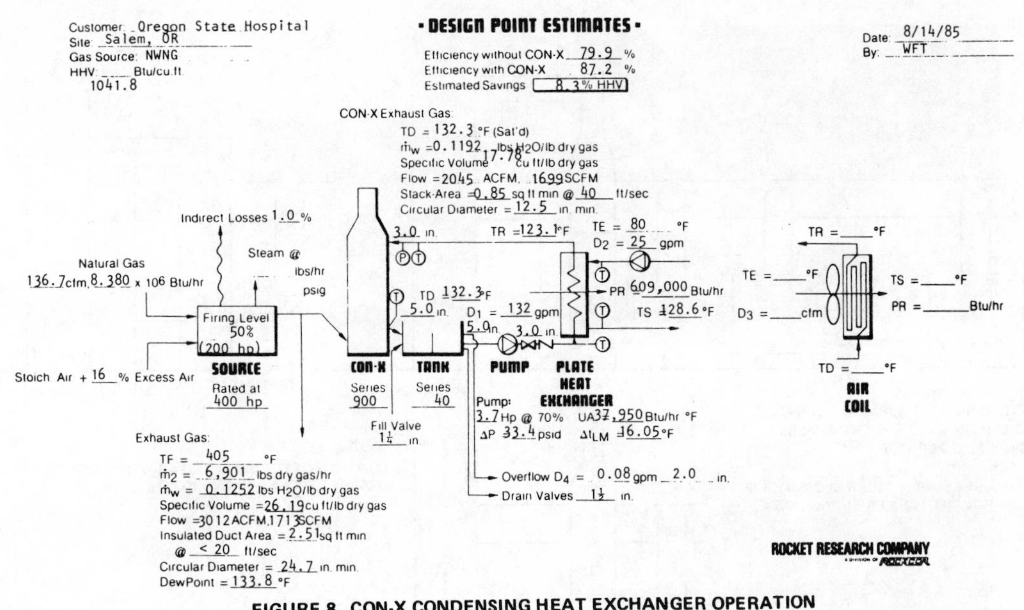

FIGURE 8. CON-X CONDENSING HEAT EXCHANGER OPERATION

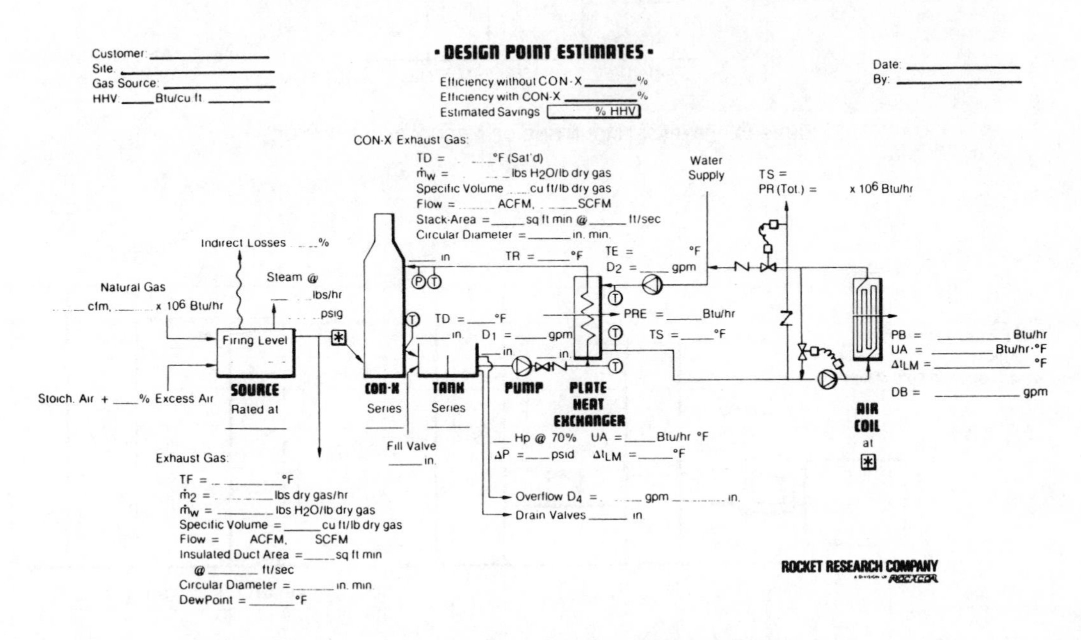

FIGURE 9. CON-X CONDENSING HEAT EXCHANGER OPERATION

CON-X Installation

In considering multiple boiler installations, the CON-X recuperator may be interfaced in several optional ways as shown on Figures 10 and 11. The "bypass" method of mounting of Figure 10 results from a limited ability to use the recovered energy and allows an economic installation using a recuperator size matched to the use. Where the use permits, two boilers can be connected to a single recuperator as shown in Figure 11 in "either-or" mode with the recuperator sized to handle the full output of one boiler. Other variations are possible as well to suit the needs of any installation.

Similarly, the recuperator can be interfaced with the auxilliary tank, heat exchanger and boiler controls in a variety of ways. Several recuperators, individually installed on separate boilers, can be serviced by a single auxilliary tank which may be supplied with an extra "return" compartment for this purpose. The spray water flow to individual recuperators may be controlled by starting and stopping individual pumps to each or by solenoid valves at the recuperator using a single pump. If appropriate to the installation, separate secondary heat exchangers can be set up for individual uses and a hot water storage tank can be utilized to buffer a varying user load.

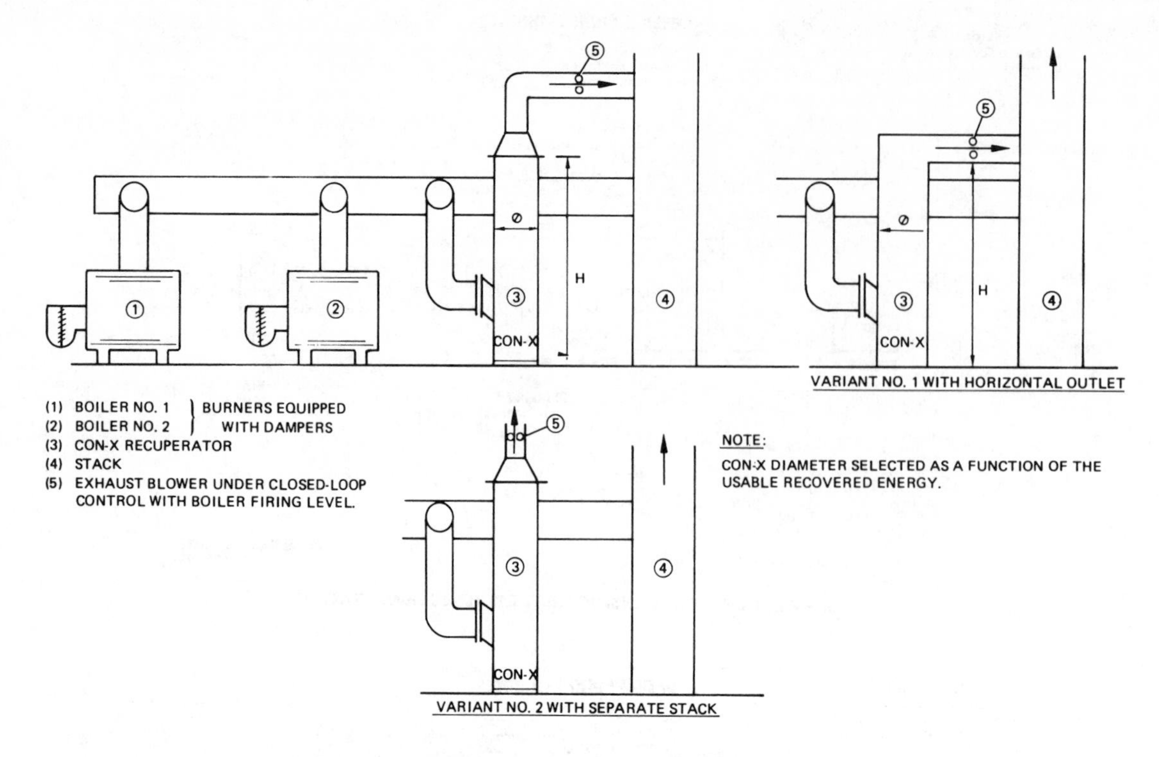

FIGURE 10. "BYPASS" MOUNTING OF A CON-X RECUPERATOR

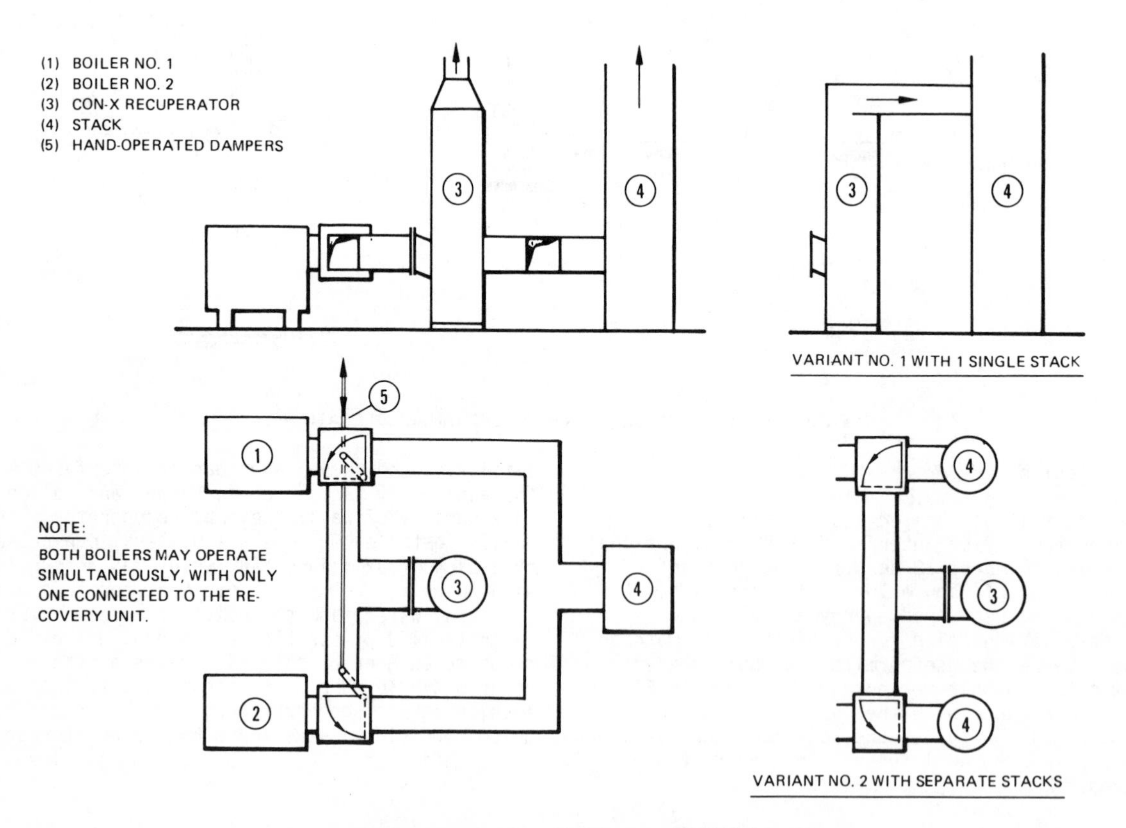

FIGURE 11. MOUNTING OF A CON-X RECUPERATOR ON TWO BOILERS (ALTERNATE BOILER OPERATION WITH CON-X)

Certain installations, particularly those set up in "bypass" mode, may require the use of an induced draft fan in the outlet of the recuperator. Either axial-flow or centrifugal-type standard industrial fans may be used. The pressure-drop requirement for the fan is only approximately 1 inch WC (varies $\pm$ 0.25 inch WC depending on the size of the unit) when used, and this fact coupled with the cool location of the fan yields low operating horsepowers (equivalent to approximately 0.5% of the recovered energy).

Figures 12 and 13 show several representative existing installations in France. The equipment of Figure 12 is located at the airport at Marignane, France. Figure 13 shows a unit installed on a wool dryer in Albine, France. Note the axial flow fan unit located in the recuperator exhaust stack.

CON-X Benefits

The benefits of the direct-contact condensing heat recovery system include:

- Increased system efficiency (typically to 92 to 95% HHV)
- Low first cost
- Operating cost savings (typicaly 12 to 16%)
- Short system payback (typically 9 to 24 months)
- Easy installation
- Simple low maintenance
- Reduced water vapor emissions
- Reduced particulate and noxious gas emissions
- Reduced noise emission from the stack
- Low back pressure (approximately 1.0 in W.C.)
- Increased system operating flexibility & improved capacity

FIGURE 12. WAREHOUSE SPACE HEATING AT AIRPORT IN MARIGNANE, FRANCE

Increased system efficiency is a function of the ability to use the recovered energy. The magnitude of the efficiency gain that is possible in the system is usually determined by the magnitude of the available heat sink, as noted previously. Often, the available waste heat will exceed the uses for it which permits generation of water at higher temperatures with limited total BTU recovery. Where a large heat sink is available, its temperature may only be elevated 15 to 30°F (i.e., preheated) but the total BTU recovery will be maximized.

Low first cost, simple installation and low maintenance lead to short system paybacks. Depending on the extent of recovery attempted, systems examined to date are able to show paybacks between 9 and 24 months in the U.S., and between 12 and 30 months in Canada, the latter times reflecting generally lower natural gas prices.

As has been illustrated, water vapor emissions from the boiler stack are reduced by condensing heat recovery. Particulate and soluable noxious gas emissions are similarly reduced by the scrubbing action of the direct contact water spray, and the spray also acts as a muffler to reduce noise emissions from the stack.

Low back pressure results directly from the open, baffle-tower design of the CON-X unit.

A FINAL WORD ABOUT FUELS AND ACIDITY

Up to this time, the CON-X and its European progenitor the "ICCO", have been applied primarily on natural gas fired systems for two main reasons. First, as illustrated in Figure 2, the recovery potential with natural gas is considerably better than with fuel oil due to its higher hydrogen content. Secondly, except for trace quantities of mercaptan odorants, natural gas is free of sulfur which, when burned, creates sulfur dioxide and sulfur trioxide gases, in turn giving rise to sulfuric acid when these gases absorb into water (e.g., condensate and/or spray water). Fuel oils all contain sulfur.

FIGURE 13. HEAT RECOVERY FROM AN INDUSTRIAL WOOD DRYER IN ALBINE, FRANCE

Solid fuels generally show lower recovery potential and, in the case of coals, contain sulfur as well. Wood fuels have high fuel-borne moisture content and low/no sulfur but, as with coal, produce an ash. Incompletely combusted fuel may produce a tar as well. Solid fuels are also less expensive than natural gas or fuel oil which, when combined with lower recovery rates and increased maintenance, extends the payback for heat recovery equipment for these fuels.

In Appendix A, the basic combustion process is shown to produce carbon dioxide and water. Combustion with air, normally with excess air, introduces both oxygen and large quantities of nitrogen in the flue gas. In the high temperature flame zone, nitrogen oxides can form in small quantities.

These nitrogen oxides and carbon dioxide both are present in the flue gases of all fuels and, when dissolved in water, create carbonic acid and small amounts of nitric acid.

In brief then, this is the origin of the acidity in the condensate from flue gases and the primary reason for avoiding condensation in stacks with earlier heat recovery equipment, e.g., air heaters and economizers.

In the CON-X system, this acidity is controlled by the dilution effect of the moisture condensed from the flue gas, by the deluge of spray water introduced, and by the choice of 316L stainless steel, PVC and the use of a Plasite coating as materials of construction for wetted parts. When operation of the system is in the normal condensing range with overflow from the tank, pH of the spray circuit water will typically be in the range of 5.5 to above 6.0. If the boiler operation increases relative to a fixed user heat recovery load or if the user load decreases, the spray water temperature returning to the recuperator increases, the recovery rate decreases, and the system may drift temporarily into the noncondensing regime. In this case, water is evaporated from the spray circuit, there is a continuous automatic influx of makeup water through the float valve, and the pH will remain between 6.0 and 7.0. When the boiler and user load conditions are such as to cause the system to operate in the neighborhood of the dew point, condensation is minimized and no makeup water is admitted. Under these conditions, pH of the spray circuit water can fall into the range of 3.0 to 5.0.

Since the boiler and recovered heat load are seldom constant, periodic check of the pH must be made by test kit, hand held meter or continuous meter with readout, so that a low pH condition does not continue for an extended period. When a low pH condition (pH < 5.5) is observed, it is corrected by the simple expedient of dilution using an auxilliary makeup water valve which is a part of the inlet manifold on the tank. Experience indicates that such checks should be made approximately once each week in a natural gas fired system.

Operation of a CON-X heat recovery system on a boiler fired by #2 fuel oil especially low sulfur oil, should be straightforward although not demonstrated to date. The anticipated special needs are the addition of a small tank and metering pump for the low-level addition of a neutralizing chemical in the auxilliary tank, and, most likely, more frequent cleaning of the tank filters due to the increased particulate load.

If such a boiler is already equipped with a scrubber, heat recovery from the saturated scrubber exhaust using the CON-X system may be economically accomplished with somewhat reduced total recovery. The need for neutralization in the CON-X tank will be determined in this case by the scrubber efficiency in removing sulfur.

Although overall heat recovery rates will be lower with fuel oil, and both initial cost and maintenance expense will increase slightly, substantial amounts of heat can be recovered in such a system. RRC estimates reasonable paybacks can be achieved (i.e., in the range of 18 to 36 months) at present fuel oil prices with the CON-X system.

APPENDIX A

AN EXAMPLE OF FLUE GAS HEAT LOSSES AND THEIR RECOVERY POTENTIAL USING METHANE AS A FUEL

Combustion (oxidation) of carbon and hydrogen produces carbon dioxide and water vapor respectively, according to:

$$C + O_2 \longrightarrow CO_2 \qquad (1)$$

$$2H_2 + O_2 \longrightarrow 2H_2O \qquad (2)$$

Similarly, when methane, the principal constituent of natural gas is burned, its products of combustion are carbon dioxide and water vapor:

$$CH_4 + 2O_2 \longrightarrow CO_2 + 2H_2O \qquad (3)$$

Since the oxygen for combustion in a boiler comes from air, a large percentage of inert nitrogen passes through the system unreacted and absorbing heat. The ratio of nitrogen to oxygen in air (including the rare gases as nitrogen) is:

$$\text{Air} = \frac{0.7901\ N_2}{0.2099\ O_2} = 3.764\ \frac{N_2}{O_2}$$

In other words, every unit volume of oxygen from combustion air carries with it 3.764 unit volumes of nitrogen. This can be reflected in equation (3) as follows:

$$CH_4 + 2\ (O_2 + 3.764\ N_2) \longrightarrow CO_2 + 2\ H_2O + 7.528\ N_2 \quad (3a)$$

Equation (3a) describes the stoichiometric combustion of methane with air, i.e., with an amount of air just sufficient for the complete combustion of the fuel. Real systems operate with an excess of air to assure that, in particular, the combustion of carbon goes all the way to carbon dioxide (CO_2) and does not stop at carbon monoxide (CO) thus not releasing all of its available heat. If equation (3a) is modified to include, for this example, 20% excess air, it now appears as:

$$CH_4 + (1.2)(2)(O_2 + 3.764\ N_2) \longrightarrow CO_2 + 2H_2O + 7.528\ N_2 + (0.2)(2)(O_2 + 3.764\ N_2)$$

This can be simplified to:

$$CH_4 + 2.4\ O_2 + 9.034\ N_2 \longrightarrow CO_2 + 2\ H_2O + 0.4\ O_2 + 9.034\ N_2 \quad (3b)$$

This then describes the real-world combustion of methane with 20% excess dry air and provides the basis for analysis of this example system. The numbers appearing in front of each constituent are the "mols" or volumes of each that are used (left side of the equation) or produced (right side of the equation). This same process is used for actual natural gas combustion analysis including a similar accounting for the other hydrocarbon constituents of natural gas (i.e., ethane, propane, normal and iso-butane, normal and iso-pentane, hexane and higher molecules) as well as fuel-borne oxygen, hydrogen, nitrogen and carbon dioxide. For a fuel oil the total carbon, total hydrogen, sulfur and other constitutents are used. Since combustion air normally has some level of humidity, this correction is also made.

Continuing with the simplified methane example, Table A-1 can be constructed using equation (3b).

Item	Fuel	Combustion Air		Flue Gases				
	CH_4	O_2	N_2	CO_2	H_2O	O_2 (Ex)	N_2 + Ex	Total
Mols/volumes	1	2.4	9.034	1	2	0.4	9.034	12.434 moist 10.434 dry
Vol % (moist FG)				8.04	16.09	3.22	72.66	100
Vol % (dry FG)				9.58	—	3.83	86.58	100
Molecular Weights	16	32	28	44	18	32	28	
Weights, lbs	16.00	76.80	252.95	44.00	36.00	12.8	252.95	345.75 moist 309.75 dry
Weight % (moist FG)				12.73	10.41	3.70	73.16	100
Weight % (dry FG)				14.21	—	4.13	81.66	100
Weight per lb fuel	1	4.80	15.81	2.75	**2.25**	0.80	15.81	21.61 moist **19.35 dry**

TABLE A-1. EQUATION (3b) RESULTS

This broad data is mainly for general interest and to illustrate the analysis methodology. Two key parameters from Table A-1 are needed for a heat recovery analysis. First is the weight of water vapor in the flue gas per unit weight of fuel burned and the second is the weight of dry flue gas per unit weight of fuel burned. These are highlighted in Table A-1. With these parameters the weight of water vapor per unit weight of dry flue gas is determined:

$$\frac{2.25\ \dfrac{\text{lbs } H_2O \text{ Vap}}{\text{lb Fuel}}}{19.36\ \dfrac{\text{lbs Dry Flue Gas}}{\text{lb Fuel}}} = 0.1162\ \frac{\text{lbs } H_2O \text{ Vapor}}{\text{lb Dry Flue Gas}}$$

Using this ratio and tables for the enthalpy (heat content) of dry flue gas/air and for the water vapor (superheated steam), the heat carried away by flue gas of a given temperature can be determined based on unit fuel consumption, i.e., for any size boiler, and the corresponding overall boiler efficiencies and recovery percentages can be determined as well, as illustrated below.*

*As an aid to the reader to make an independent assessment of a natural gas fired boiler, three curves (Figures A-1 through A-3) are attached which, for first-cut accuracy, permit the determination of the same type data as presented in Table A-2. Knowing the firing rate in ft^3 fuel/hr, lbs fuel/hr or Btu/hr will then permit determination of the actual losses in Btu/hr and the annual savings potential by following the attached guide.

For this example, a 400°F original stack temperature has been assumed and the recoveries possible with a conventional economizer and a direct-contact condensing heat exchanger/recuperator and compared. It is assumed that the flue gas temperatures are reduced to 275°F by the economizer (sensible heat recovery only) and to 100°F by the recuperator (sensible and latent heat recovery). The HHV of the methane fuel is 1,012 Btu/ft^3 fuel or 22,707 Btu/lb fuel. This yields an energy entering the boiler of:

$$\frac{22{,}707\ \dfrac{\text{Btu}}{\text{lb Fuel}}}{19.36\ \dfrac{\text{lb Dry Flue Gas}}{\text{lb Fuel}}} = 1172.9\ \text{Btu/lb Dry Flue Gas}$$

Enthalpy of the water vapor is determined from:

$$\text{Enthalpy of Water Vapor, } \frac{\text{Btu}}{\text{lb } H_2O} \times$$

$$\text{Water Content } \frac{\text{lbs } H_2O}{\text{lb Dry Flue Gas}} =$$

$$\text{Enthalpy } \frac{\text{Btu}}{\text{lb Dry Flue Gas}}$$

Loss percentages are determined by:

$$\left(\frac{\text{Total Loss, Btu/lb Dry Flue Gas}}{1172.9\ \dfrac{\text{Btu Entering}}{\text{lb Dry Flue Gas}}} \right) (100) = \text{Loss, \%}$$

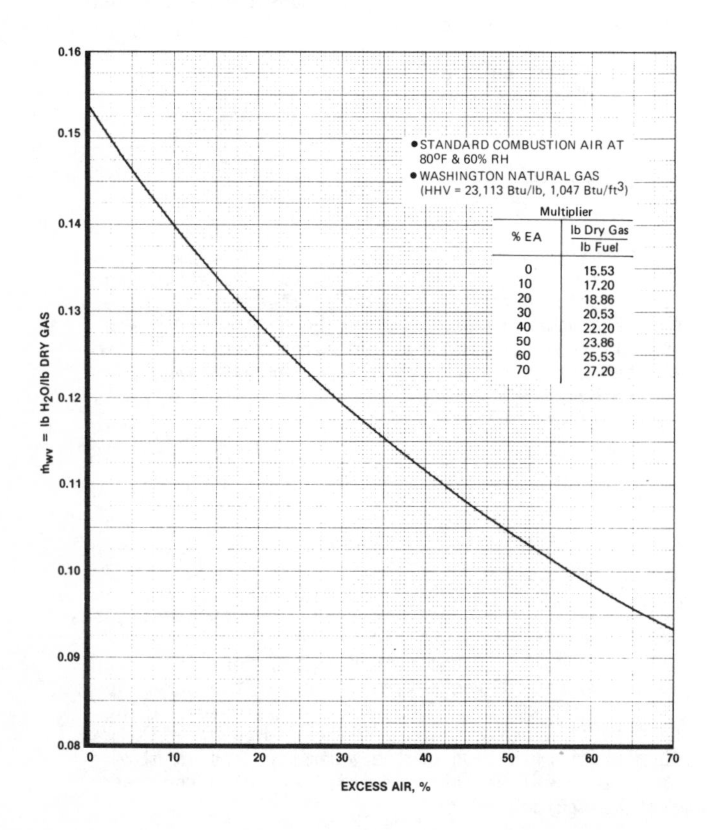

FIGURE A-1. WEIGHT OF WATER PER POUND OF DRY FLUE GAS FROM NATURAL GAS COMBUSTION

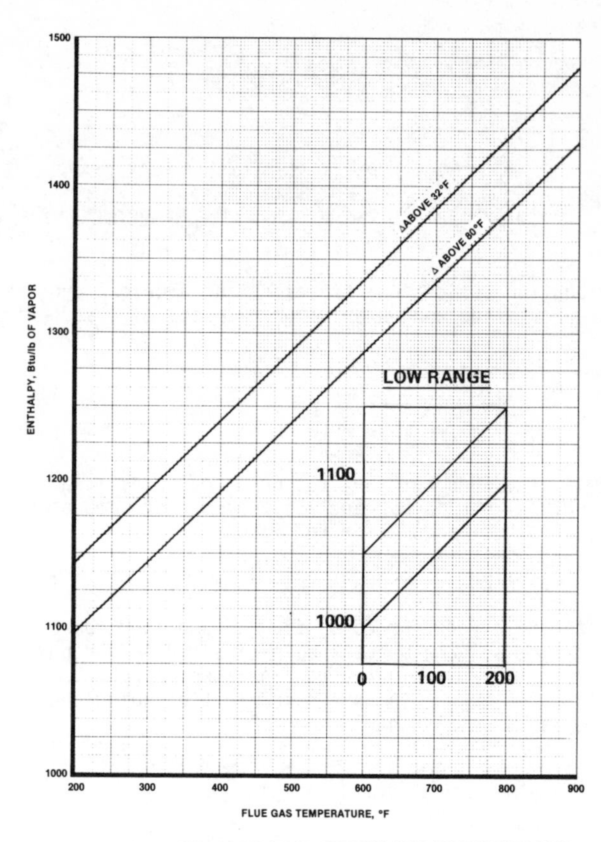

FIGURE A-2. ENTHALPY OF WATER VAPOR (SUPERHEATED STEAM) AT 1 ATM/14.696 PSIA

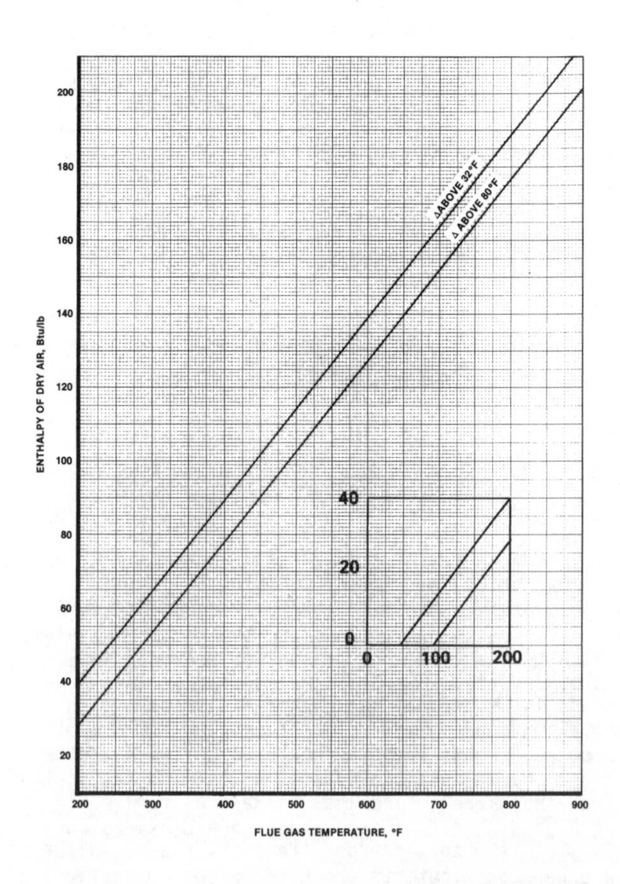

FIGURE A-3. ENTHALPY OF DRY AIR AT 1 ATM/14.696 PSIA

Ignoring the relatively small radiation/convection losses which apply to all cases, the results of this heat recovery analysis are summarized in Table A-2.

Item	Flue Gas Temperature		
	Original (400°F)	Economizer (275°F)	Recuperator (100°F)
Water content (lbs/lb dry flue gas)	0.1162	0.1162	0.0432
Enthalpy (Btu/lb dry flue gas)			
Of water vapor	144.0	137.2	47.7
Of dry flue gas	88.9	58.5	16.3
Total loss	232.9	195.7	64.0
Recovered from original loss	—	37.2	168.9
Percent enthalpy			
In water vapor	61.8	70.1	74.5
In dry flue gas	38.2	29.9	25.5
Percent recovered from original loss			
From water vapor	—	4.7	66.9
From dry flue gas	—	34.2	81.7
From original loss	—	16.0	72.5
Boiler loss, % of entering energy (HHV)	19.9	16.7	5.5
Boiler overall efficiency, % HHV	80.1	83.3	94.5
Improvement from original, % HHV	—	3.2	14.4
Fuel cost savings, %	—	4.0	18.0

NOTE: Based on HHV of methane = 22,707 Btu/lbm

$19.36 \frac{\text{lb dry flue gas}}{\text{lb fuel}}$ and $1172.9 \frac{\text{Btu entering}}{\text{lb dry flue gas}}$

TABLE A-2. HEAT RECOVERY FROM METHANE COMBUSTION

From the data of Table A-2, it may be seen that a large percentage (over 60 percent) of the heat lost in the flue gases is contained in their water vapor content. Through direct-contact condensing heat recovery, it may also be seen that much of this heat loss (over 70 percent) can be recovered resulting in significant cost savings.

As a final comment, it should be noted that the effects of excess air are to increase losses and decrease the dew point of the gases entering the recovery equipment. As excess air increases, boiler efficiencies are thus reduced and energy recovery, while more necessary, is also more difficult. It is simply good economics to maintain boiler operation at a minimum of excess air in the primary operating regimes and to assure the best efficiency possible before/in conjunction with implementation of a heat recovery project.

GUIDE SHEET FOR PRELIMINARY ESTIMATION OF STACK LOSSES AND ANNUAL SAVINGS THROUGH THEIR RECOVERY USING THE CON-X RECUPERATOR

Given:

1. Firing Rate = Btu/hr, Lbs/hr or Ft^3/hr
2. Excess Air
3. Stack Temperature - present level and with recuperator (80^0F to 120^0F)

Find:

Step

1. $$\frac{\text{Firing Rate, } \frac{\text{Btu}}{\text{Hr}}}{\text{HHV, } \frac{\text{Btu}}{\text{lb Fuel}}} = \text{lbs Fuel/hr}$$ or, 1b. $$\frac{\text{Firing Rate, Ft}^3\text{/hr} \left(\frac{\text{HHV, Btu}}{\text{Ft}^3}\right)}{\text{HHV, Btu/lb Fuel}} = \text{lbs Fuel/hr}$$

2. $$\left(\frac{\text{lbs Fuel}}{\text{hr}}\right)\left(\frac{\text{lbs Dry Gas}}{\text{lb Fuel}} \text{ @ Given Excess Air*}\right)\left(\frac{\text{Total Loss, Btu}}{\text{lb Dry Gas}}\right)^{**} = \frac{\text{Total Loss, Btu}}{\text{hr}}$$

Note: Perform Step 2 for present conditions to estimate present loss. Repeat to determine residual loss with recuperator and subtract the two to find recovery rate in Btu/hr.

3. $$\frac{\left(\frac{\text{Btu Recovered}}{\text{hr}}\right)\left(\frac{\text{Fuel Cost, \$}}{10^6 \text{ Btu}}\right)\left(\text{Hrs. of Operation}\right)}{\text{Original Boiler Efficiency}} = \text{Gross Annual Savings, \$}$$

*Refer to table on Figure A-1.

**From Table A-2 or derive Total Loss using Figures A-1 through A-3 instead of Step 2 as follows:

Using Figure A-1: (lbs H_2O/lb Dry Gas***) (lb Dry Gas/lb Fuel) (lbs Fuel/hr) = lbs H_2O Vapor/hr.

Using Figure A-2: (lbs H_2O Vapor/hr) (Enthalpy, Btu/lb Vapor) = Btu/hr in H_2O Vapor.

Using Figure A-3: (Enthalpy, Btu/lb Gas) (lbs Dry Gas/lbs Fuel) (lbs Fuel/hr) = Btu/hr in Dry Flue Gas.

Add results from A-2 and A-3 to get total loss in Btu/hr. Process assumes enthalpies of dry air and dry flue gas are the same.

***From Figure A-1 or estimate from Figure 3 for flue gas from boiler. Estimate from Figure 3 for recuperator exhaust in a temperature range between 80^0F and 20^0F.

Chapter 78

VOC EMISSIONS CONTROL AND HEAT RECOVERY FOR WEBB OFFSET PRINTING FACILITIES

E. Napp, R. M. Desmond, M. C. Lints

ABSTRACT

The Graphic Park facility of Case-Hoyt/Rochester Corporation houses six large, web offset printing presses, each of which has a natural gas-fired, high-velocity, hot air dryer. On the average, 73% percent of the fuel energy input is rejected from the dryers as solvent-laden exhaust with volatile organic compounds (VOC) emissions of approximately 670,270 lbs./year.

An emissions control and heat recovery system was designed to accomplish three things: 1) reduce gas consumption by the dryers, 2) minimize VOC emissions to the atmosphere in the most efficient manner possible, and 3) recover energy from the exhaust to heat part of the building during the winter months.

To reduce dryer gas consumption, a unique Lower Flammability Limit (LFL) control system was installed at each press. These systems modulate the exhaust flow of each dryer based on solvent concentration. A central catalytic oxidizer was installed to reduce VOC emissions to the atmosphere and to provide preheated make-up air to the building through the use of a secondary heat exchanger.

System energy consumption was monitored for one year and compared to previous energy usage.

All system components have proven to function quite well. Depending on the dryer type, dryer gas consumption dropped between 7% and 63%. Approximately 90 percent of the 1984/85 heating requirement for the bindery was provided by recovered heat, and emissions tests revealed a VOC destruction of approximately 95 percent.

THE WEB OFFSET PRINTING PROCESS

Web offset is a specialized form of lithographic printing. It is a relatively high speed process; ink impressions are made on a continuous roll of paper traveling at between 600 and 1,600 feet per minute, depending on the particular job and the maximum capacity of the press.

The lithographic process is based on the mutual repellence of water and ink. Printing plates are chemically treated so that image areas accept ink and repel water, and non-image areas accept water and repel ink. The term offset relates to the transfer of the image to the web by means of an intermediate roll called a blanket cylinder. A schematic of a four color blanket-to-blanket press is shown in Figure 1.

Dampening solution, a mixture of water and isopropyl alcohol, is applied to the plate to make the non-image areas retain their hydrophilic characteristics. A portion of the isopropanol and most of the solvents in the heat-set are vaporized in the drying process and emitted from the dryer with the exhaust stream. The web is cooled in the chill stand section after leaving the dryer to fully set the ink and to prevent web breakage during folding.

Natural gas fired, high-velocity hot air dryers are the most common type of dryers used for web offset printing. Although there are significantly different designs among the many available type of hot air dryers, the fundamental operation is the same. Heated air is impinged upon the web surface via air bars which are located above and below the web. Although the volume of air remains essentially constant, the temperature can be varied depending upon the web speed and the ink coverage to obtain proper drying.

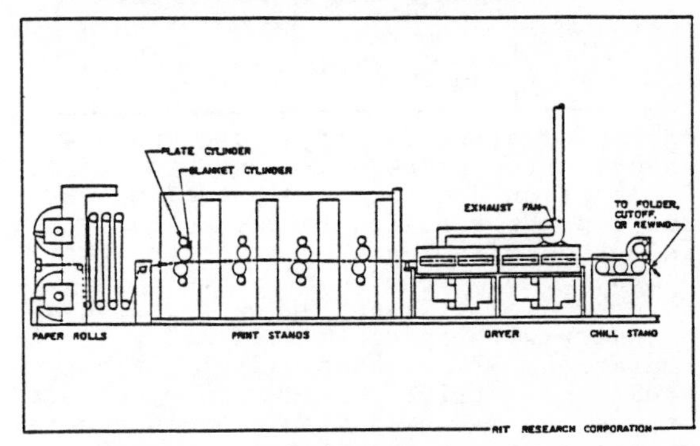

FIGURE 1. SCHEMATIC OF FOUR COLOR WEB OFFSET PRINTING PRESS

* Robert M. Desmond is Dean, College of Graphic Arts and Photography, Rochester Institute of Technology

THE EMISSIONS CONTROL PROCESS

The two basic ways to reduce hydrocarbon emissions from the drying process are fume incineration and solvent recovery. Fume incineration is the most commonly used alternative and has become very popular because of its simplicity and high efficiency. These systems are relatively small, require little maintenance, and operate at low pressure differentials. Process heat recovery can easily be combined with fume incinerators, thus creating a good return on investment (ROI) in many cases.

The two common fume incineration combustion systems used are thermal and catalytic oxidation, whose advantages and disadvantages are compared in Table 1. Careful consideration is required to determine which type of system is most suitable for a given situation, and the feasibility of using individual emissions control systems vs. central systems, when more than one process dryer is present.

Table 1 : COMPARISON OF ADVANTAGES AND DISADVANTAGES OF THERMAL AND CATALYTIC OXIDATION SYSTEMS

	ADVANTAGES	DISADVANTAGES
Thermal Oxidizers	Wide range of applications; can handle multiple solvent mixtures. Insensitive to concentration variations. Can incinerate some particulates. Steam-generating and heat recovery capabilities. Can operate with as high as 40 % LFL solvent concentration with adequate monitoring.	High operating costs; high fuel consumption if no heat recovery is used. Requires relatively frequent maintenance inspections. High operating temp. may limit refractory life in some applications.
Catalytic Oxidizers	Can handle multiple solvent mixtures. Relatively low operating expenses. Low maintenance. Small, lightweight systems feasible. Steam-generating and heat recovery capabilities.	Limited applications; halogens and metals may poison catalyst. Maximum operating level normally is 25% LFL solvent. Catalyst must be cleaned or replaced periodically.

When incinerating the organic compounds present in the process exhaust, the products of combustion are carbon dioxide and water vapor and the reaction is exothermic. For this method of solvent destruction, the EPA and state codes require a hydrocarbon destruction of at least 90 percent, which might vary with specific solvent formulations. The major difference between thermal and catalytic oxidation processes is that the thermal oxidation process generally requires a higher temperature for VOC destruction (typically 1,200 - 1,800°F) in comparison to the catalytic oxidation process (500 - 900°F). When used in conjunction with a recuperative heat exchanger, catalyst oxidation requires little or no fuel except for unit startup.

An alternative to fume incineration is solvent recovery. The viability of recovering solvent as a VOC emissions control alternative is mainly dependent on the concentration and the recovery value of the solvent emissions. The three basic technologies available for solvent recovery are:

1) Granular carbon with direct steam regeneration
   and
2) Granular carbon with regeneration by vacuum and indirect steaming.
   and
3) Granular carbon with regeneration by vacuum and indirect steaming.

When evaluating incineration and solvent recovery alternatives, the most cost-effective approach, over the lift cycle of the process, should be selected to solve an emissions problem.

HEAT RECOVERY OPTIONS

Heat recovery is applicable only to the fume incineration process, and it is typically achieved by installing one or more heat exchangers downstream from the oxidizer. Some options to recover process waste heat are steam generation, liquid heating, direct air recirculation, building or process makeup air preheating, and exhaust preheat. The best method of heat recovery is determined by the plant's specific need.

Installing a fume incineration system with process heat recovery or a solvent recovery system can be economically attractive. This is particularly true where utilization of process equipment is at a high level and inlet air from the drying process is at a high temperature. The pay back varies from installation to installation, but generally an acceptable ROI can be expected.

Consumption rates prior to LFL control installation and with the LFL controls installed are compared in Figure 2.

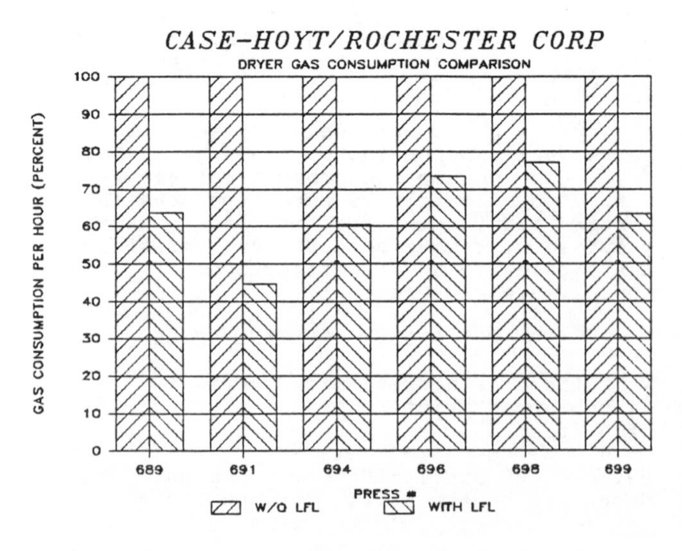

FIGURE 2. COMPARISON OF GAS CONSUMPTION RATES

To minimize VOC emissions to the atmosphere, a central catalytic oxidizer was selected and installed. This system was designed, built, and installed by Tec Systems, who guarantees a ninety percent (90%) reduction of VOC during a warranted catalyzer life of five (5) years and an estimated catalyzer life of seven (7) years.

A secondary heat exchanger provides heat transfer from the process exhaust flow to the building makeup air flow when the thermostat inside the building calls for heat. This feature drastically reduces natural gas consumption for space heating during the heating season. The possibility exists to further increase energy savings by adding an absorption water chilling system.

CASE HISTORY - CATALYTIC OXIDATION AND BUILDING MAKEUP AIR PREHEATING

The Graphic Park of Case-Hoyt/Rochester Corporation houses six large web offset printing presses, each of which has a natural gas fired, high-velocity hot air dryer. These dryers are not all of the same design, but their fundamental operations are similar to the earlier description.

On the average, seventy-three percent (73%) of the fuel energy input is rejected from the dryers as solvent laden exhaust, twenty-two percent (22%) is retained by the webs, and five percent (5%) is transferred to the pressroom by radiation and convection. Prior to the installation of the emissions control and heat recovery system, the annual emissions of volatile organic compounds (VOC) to the atmosphere from all presses were estimated to be 670,220 lbs per year.

Various heat recovery systems and utilization schemes were evaluated prior to implementing this project. Catalytic and thermal oxidation equipment were investigated in conjunction with dryer LFL control and heat recovery via air recirculation, absorption cooling, or building space heating. A central catalytic oxidizer with dryer LFL control and space heating appeared to have the best return-on-investment possibilities given the economic conditions at Case-Hoyt/Rochester Corporation.

The emissions control and heat recovery system was designed to accomplish three things: 1) reduce gas consumption on the dryers by modulating exhaust flow based on solvent concentration, 2) minimize volatile organic compound emissions in the most efficient manner possible, and 3) recover energy from the exhaust to heat the building during the winter months.

To reduce the dryer gas consumption by modulating the exhaust flow based on solvent concentration, Tec Systems, DePere, Wisconsin, has developed a unique Lower Flammability Limit (LFL) control system for the web offset printing industry. This system, which has been field tested by Case-Hoyt/Rochester Corporation, modulates the dryer exhaust flow rate to achieve a preset LFL and/or a minimum exhaust stack pressure. These fully automatic LFL control systems were installed on all six web offset printing presses at the Case-Hoyt printing facility. Depending on press speed and ink coverages, most dryers in the printing industry operate well below the maximum allowable LFL of 25% (typically between 5% and 15%). Several overriding safety features ensure safety for each dryer. When using this type of LFL monitoring and control system, the National Fire Code (NFC) allows an LFL of up to fifty percent.

Figure 3 shows a schematic of the basic system, including the make up air preheat and LFL control system.

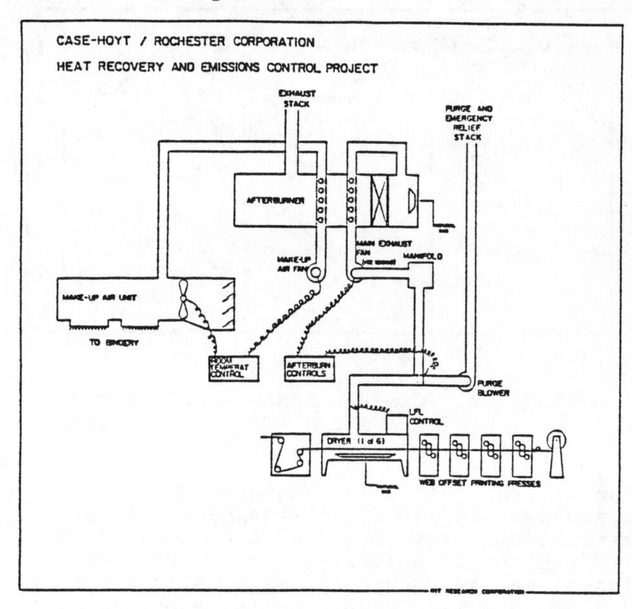

FIGURE 3. EMISSIONS CONTROL, HEAT RECOVERY, AND LFL CONTROL SYSTEM

The control package for the entire system was designed by Tec Systems based on specifications from Cast-Hoyt/Rochester Corporation and RIT Research Corporation.

Basically, the dryers are purged using the individual dryer fans upon start-up. When the dryer burner is turned on, the tee damper will switch position and direct the exhaust to the afterburner (oxidizer). To prevent any downtime, each press control console has a manual override which will exhaust dryer fumes directly to the atmosphere via the individual exhaust fan.

The exhaust flow to the afterburner is modulated by a variable speed afterburner exhaust fan depending on the number of presses which are on-line. In other words, fan speed varies to maintain a constant negative pressure in the main exhaust duct. As presses come on-line the main exhaust duct pressure will drop, causing the fan to speed up, and vice versa as presses go off-line. The entire system is balanced with manual flow dampers at maximum flow so that each dryer is properly exhausted.

The makeup air isolation damper on the afterburner will be opened when the building calls for heat. Once the damper is fully open, it will trip a limit switch which turns on the makeup air fan. If the afterburner is unable to maintain proper temperature in the building, the existing makeup air heating unit will be activated to supplement the afterburner heat.

Figure 4 shows the general arrangement of the oxidation and heat recovery equipment.

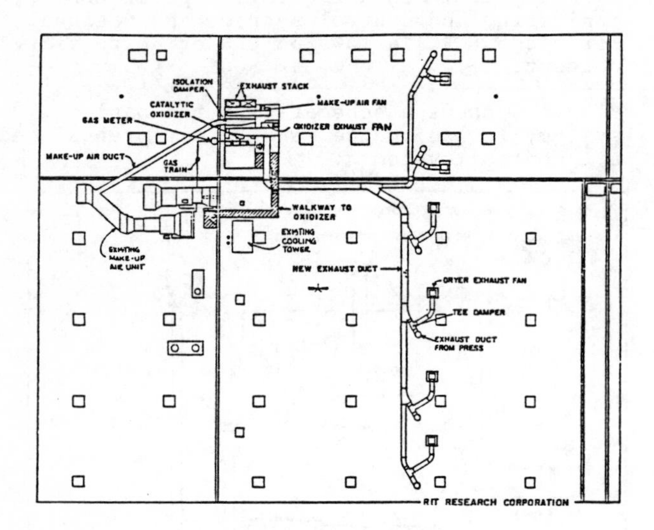

FIGURE 4. GENERAL ARRANGEMENT OF THE OXIDATION AND HEAT RECOVERY EQUIPMENT

The gas savings where estimated to be approximately 120,000 therms/year with an estimated yearly increase in electrical consumption of approximately 90,000 KWH. Annual maintenance costs were estimated to be $3,000, and maintenance costs associated with replacing the catalyst were estimated to be $36,000 for every seven (7) years. With an economic life expectancy of fifteen (15) years and by using the Accelerated Cost Recovery System (ACRS) depreciation method, the pay back period for the entire installation was estimated to be roughly six (6) years.

SECTION 27
COMBUSTION

Chapter 79

A NEW ACOUSTO OPTIC SOLID STATE COMBUSTION GAS ANALYZER

R. L. Nelson

ABSTRACT

A recent breakthrough in the growth of excellent quality single crystal thallium arsenic selenide (TAS) on a production basis has made it possible to build an electronically controlled acousto optic tunable filter (AOTF) capable of operating in the infrared. Such a filter with integral ultrasonic transducer can be used in place of mechanical filter wheels, spinning gas cells, moving mirrors, diffraction gratings and mechanical light choppers. The TAS AOTF produces an electronically controllable narrow band infrared filter capable of being tuned to any infrared frequency desired. It provides a chopped and tuned IR source that can be directed across the stack on any combustion process to measure the concentrations of CO, CO_2, SO_2, NH_3, CH_4, NO, NO_2, H_2O, etc. simultaneously.

INTRODUCTION

Measurement of flue gas content from combustion processes has become an essential requirement for industrial and utility applications. Control of fuel-air ratio, evaluating burner performance, and monitoring emissions for EPA compliance have become more important as energy costs rise and environmental regulations become tighter. Reliable measurement, with a minimum of maintenance cost, is a prime requirement for stack gas measurement equipment.

Extractive or sampling gas analyzers were the first continuous gas measuring systems. Many of these extractive systems used modified ambient air analyzers or laboratory analyzers assisted by sample conditioning systems.

Extraction of a gas sample from a stack requires a number of actions. The sample must be conditioned by filtering particulate matter, condensing water vapor, and in some cases removing specific gases that interfere with the measurement system. Sometimes a single sample conditioning system is used to supply a number of single gas analyzers so the sample conditioning system must be well maintained if reliable operation is to be achieved.

In addition, the added complexity and cost of an efficient sampling system must be added to the basic analyzer when making a competitive evaluation.

In the last decade major reliability improvements were achieved in stack gas measurement by the use of in situ analyzers. In situ analysis is performed on the gas as it exists in the stack. These analyzers are installed either across a stack (cross-stack) or employ a probe inserted into the flue gas stream. In each case the analyzer does not extract or modify the flue gas.

In 1972, the in situ zirconium oxide oxygen analyzer began a revolution in combustion control. The ability to measure the excess oxygen content of combustion flue gases, on line, and with high reliability, made it possible to control the fuel-air ratio by measuring the net result of the combustion process. Previously it was necessary to measure the fuel and air flow supplied to the burner with high accuracy over a wide range in order to infer combustion conditions.

Zirconium oxide was the first solid electrolyte measuring cell to be applied to in situ stack gas analysis. It could be operated at high temperature so that water vapor condensation problems were eliminated and the ability to operate within the flue eliminated the need for sample flows, with the attendant line plugging, caused by particulates and condensation. In addition, the solid electrolyte cell provides an exponential output response, with respect to gas concentration, so that accuracy as a percent of reading remains constant even at low concentrations.

Two years ago a second high temperature solid electrolyte analyzer was commercially introduced. A potassium sulfate solid electrolyte combined with a zirconium oxide cell made high accuracy in situ measurement of sulfur dioxide possible. SO_2 and O_2 measurements provide the means for monitoring sulfur dioxide, corrected for excess air, as required by EPA regulations.

Unfortunately, high temperature solid electrolytes are not yet available for many of the other stack gases of interest.

ABSORPTION SPECTROMETERS

A second measurement method used for flue gas analysis involves absorption spectroscopy. This technique uses infrared or ultraviolet radiation and determines gas concentrations by measuring the absorption of radiation by gases of interest.

The most common extraction absorption spectrometer is the nondispersive type. In this type the source radiation is not dispersed by a prism, diffraction grating, or other means in order to separate out the wavelength of interest.

Figure 1 is a simplified schematic diagram of a nondispersive infrared extractive analyzer. Infrared light from an IR source passes through two gas cells, a reference cell and a sample cell. The reference cell generally contains dry nitrogen gas, which does not absorb light at the wavelength of interest. As light passes through the sample cell, stack gas molecules will absorb some of the infrared light. As a result, when the light emerges from the end of the sample cell, it will have less intensity than when it entered. It also will have less intensity than the light emerging from the reference cell. The intensity difference is then sensed by some type of detector or detector/filter pair that is sensitive to the particular infrared frequency of interest.

The detector is often a microphone type, filled with gases of the species being measured, or a semi conductor type coupled with a broad band-pass infrared filter centered at an absorption peak of the flue gas molecule of interest.

Absorption of light follows the Beer-Lambert law. This law states that the transmittance, T, of light through a medium that absorbs light is decreased exponentially by the product of the attenuation coefficient, "a," the concentration of the gas, "c," and the distance the light beam travels through the gas, "l."

$$T = I/I_o = e^{-acl}$$

where I = intensity of light leaving the gas
I_o = intensity of light entering the gas

The attenuation coefficient, "a," is dependent upon the wavelength of the radiation and the properties of the gas molecule.

The coefficient tells how much light energy a molecule will absorb at a given wavelength. If no absorption occurs, "a" will be zero, and the transmittance would equal one (1) or 100 percent. If the gas absorbs energy at some wavelength, "a" will be greater than zero, and the reduction of light energy across the path, "l," will depend upon the gas concentration, "c," and the original intensity, I_o, of the light beam.

In the case where the reference cell is filled with dry nitrogen the attenuation coefficient, a_{ref}, equals zero and the detector reading for the reference cell is:

$$I_{ref} = I_o e^0 = I_o \quad (1)$$

The ratio between I_{sample} and I_{ref} then becomes:

$$I_{sample}/I_{ref} = I_o e^{-acl}/I_o = e^{-acl} \quad (2)$$

Solve equation (2) for the concentration, "c" by taking the logarithm of both sides.

$$\ln [I_{sample}/I_{ref}] = -acl \quad (3)$$

$$c = \ln [I_{sample}/I_{ref}]/al \quad (4)$$

where l = known length of path.
a = known value or instrument calibrated to account for the value
I_{sample}/I_{ref} = ratio of intensities detected by the detector.

The "a," for the gas being measured, is that for the absorption band center of the gas of interest. Typical infrared band centers for gases found in stack emissions are shown in Table I.

TABLE I

INFRARED BAND CENTERS FOR SOME STACK GASES

Gas	Micrometers	Gas	Micrometers
CH_4	3.3	CO_2	2.7, 4.2
NO	5.25, 6.1	H_2O	2.7
NO_2	3.4	CO	4.5, 4.7
SO_2	4.0	C_2H_6	3.4
NH_3	3.0	H_2S	3.7, 4.2

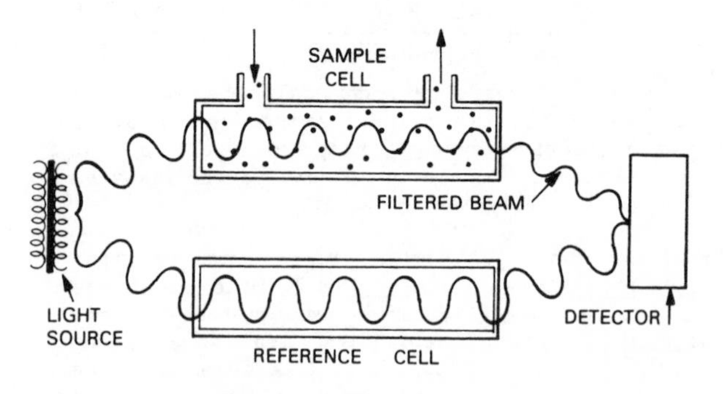

Figure 1. SIMPLIFIED SCHEMATIC DIAGRAM OF A NONDISPERSIVE INFRARED ANALYZER

CURRENT IN SITU SPECTROMETERS

In situ spectrometers do not compare absorptions using a reference cell. Instead they measure the degree of absorption by one of three techniques: differential absorption, gas filter correlation, or second derivative spectroscopy.

In situ measurement is accomplished by means of (1) a cross-stack analyzer which measures the gas of interest across the stack diameter or a major portion of the diameter or (2) by an in-stack analyzer that measures over a limited sample path length using a probe. In either case the analyzer consists of a radiation source, a means for directing that radiation through some of the stack gases as they flow through the stack, a mechanical light chopper to convert the DC radiation of the source to an AC light variation in order to make the signal easier to detect and amplify, and one or more detectors to measure the radiation not absorbed by the stack gas.

Differential Absorption Spectroscopy

Differential absorption spectroscopy measures absorption at a wavelength in the absorption band of the molecule of interest and compares it against the absorption at a reference wavelength in a region where the gas of interest has minimal absorption. The particular wavelengths of interest are selected by a dispersive device like a diffraction grating or by selected narrow band optical filters. The ratio of the absorptions produces a signal that is related to the pollutant concentration similar to that seen earlier for the case with a sample cell and a reference cell.

When using the differential absorption technique, particulates in the flue gas will attenuate the amount of light energy passing through the optical path. If the light attenuation is the same for the light energy at the measuring wavelength and at the reference wavelength, each intensity would be reduced by a constant factor. Interference caused by broad-band absorption of water vapor or other molecular species should similarly cancel out if the measuring and reference wavelengths do not differ too greatly.

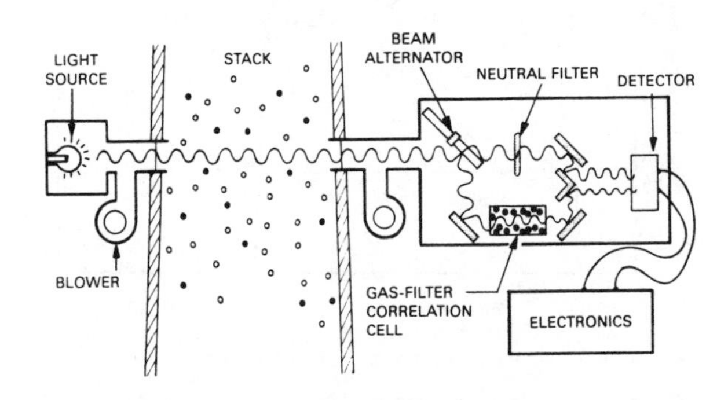

Figure 2. GAS-FILTER CORRELATION SPECTROMETER

Gas Filter Correlation Spectroscopy

Gas filter correlation spectroscopy uses a filter made from a cell filled with some of the gas of interest. In its simplest form, referring to Figure 2, an infrared source radiates light through the stack to the detector assembly where the beam is alternated between a neutral filter and a gas filter correlation cell. When there is no pollutant gas in the stack this cell contains enough of the gas being analyzed so that most of the energy contained in the individual absorption lines of the gas will be removed. Light of wavelengths not absorbed by correlation cell gas is not removed and passes on to the detector. This results in a reduction in light energy after the beam traverses the correlation cell.

The neutral density filter in turn reduces the energy from all of the wavelengths in the beam before it reaches the detector. The gas filter cell only cuts out energy at the absorption wavelengths. With the proper choice of a neutral density filter and gas concentration in the correlation cell, the amount of energy reaching the detector from each beam is the same and the system is said to be balanced. See Figure 3 (a).

When there is pollutant gas in the stack the molecules absorb light energy at wavelengths corresponding to their absorption spectra. Since the gas-filter correlation cell was chosen to absorb energy at these same wavelengths, the absorption is already complete in the correlation cell beam, and the detector will see the same signal as it did when the stack was clean. The beam passing through the neutral density filter, however, will have less energy than previously, since light was selectively absorbed by the pollutant gas in the stack. The difference in energy between the two beams can be related to the pollutant concentration and is monitored at the detector. See Figure 3 (b).

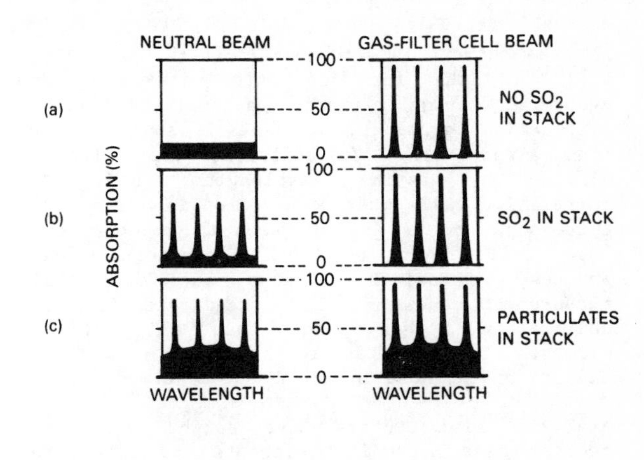

Figure 3. ABSORPTION PRINCIPLES OF A GAS-FILTER CORRELATION ANALYZER

Particulates will reduce the intensity equally in each of the beams. If the two signals are ratioed, the effect of particulate matter will cancel out. Note that particulate interference is equal in both graphs of Figure 3 (c). Molecules with spectral patterns near that of the pollutant molecule being measured will not affect the measurement if they do not correlate or overlap with the pollutant spectral pattern. If there is some overlap, some interference will result.

Second Derivative Spectroscopy

Second derivative spectroscopy differs from differential absorption spectroscopy in that instead of just sitting on a specific wavelength the scanner or moving slit of a diffraction grating scans back and forth across the central wavelength. The scanner modulates the light at wavelengths across the width of the absorption peak. Maxima will appear at the detector signal at double the frequency of the scanner. By tuning in on a frequency which is double that of the frequency of movement of the scanner, strong signals indicate strong absorption.

The amplitude of of the detector signal at twice the frequency is proportional to the second derivative of the absorption with respect to wavelength. The analyzer output is generated by dividing the second derivative output of the detector by the instantaneous absorption value so that variations in source intensity, optical misalignment, and broad-band absorption from other gases or particulates are avoided. This results because a change in absorption by a constant percentage will induce an identical percentage change in the second derivative detector output and the ratio of the two values cancels out the effects. [1]

ACOUSTO OPTIC TUNABLE FILTER SPECTROMETER

Background

All the current in situ spectrometers use moving parts in the form of motor driven light choppers, moving mirrors, gas filter wheels, diffraction gratings, sequential shutters or beam alternators. In addition, the filters, diffraction grating wavelengths, and gas correlation cells must be selected in advance to correspond to the gas or gases to be measured. Some units even use dual detectors, dual sources, or dual light paths, one for normal measurement and one for standardization or calibration. This means that all optical elements in the standardization mode must be made to match those in the measurement mode.

Analyzer manufacturers have sought means to reduce these mechanical elements and eliminate the need for multiple paths to accommodate operating and check modes. Some modern units have made some progress in this direction.

Recent developments in single crystal materials have opened the door to the development of a solid state, multi gas spectrometer for stack gas analysis. This is the result of many years of research into birefringent optical materials. Such materials exhibit different light velocities depending on the direction of propagation within the medium. As a result when light passes through such a material it splits into two refracted paths. One of these follows the ordinary laws of refraction and is called the ordinary ray (o-ray) while the other deviates somewhat and is called the extraordinary ray (e-ray). These two beams are plane-polarized at right angles to each other.

Certain birefringent materials which are termed acousto-optic materials can be used as a filter in a spectrum analyzer. In such acousto-optic materials, a light beam propagating as a polarized e-ray can under certain conditions be converted into an o-ray and in addition be spacially separated from the original e-ray by interaction with, and diffraction from, an acoustic wave propagating thru the same medium. This phenomenon has been used in fabricating narrow band optical filters, the peak transmission wavelength of which can be selected by properly choosing the frequency of the acoustic wave. Such filters are known as acousto optic tunable filters (AOTF). [2]

Recently Westinghouse invented a new efficient infrared transmissive acousto-optic material called thallium-arsenic-selenide, TAS, that has been proved to provide excellent operation as an acousto optical tunable filter over the near to mid infrared spectrum from about 1 micrometer to about 16 micrometers wavelength. See Figure 4. TAS (Tl_3AsSe_3) is a stoichiometric crystal, i.e., the crystal composition is the ideal composition expressed by the formula. It has a melting point of 311°C, and a density of $7.83 g/cm^3$.

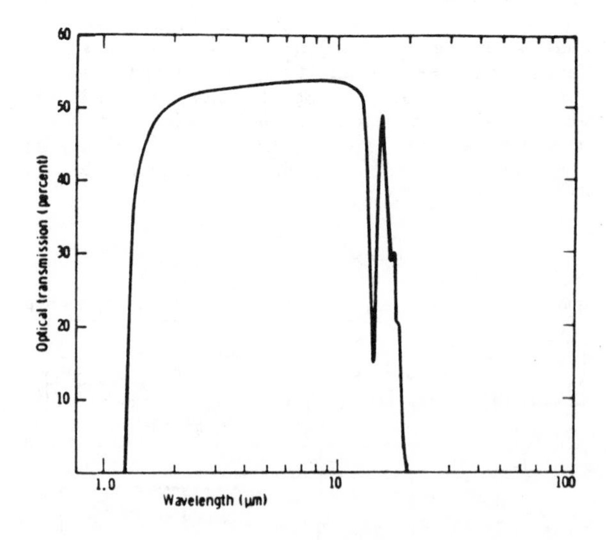

Figure 4. OPTICAL TRANSMISSION OF $Tl_3A_sSe_3$

Even more recently, a break through in the growth of excellent quality single crystal, TAS, on a production basis has made it possible to build an AOTF on a commercial basis for operation over the 2 to 5.5 micron band. Such a filter with integral ultrasonic transducer can be used in place of mechanical filter wheels, spinning gas cells, moving mirrors, diffraction gratings and mechanical light choppers. The TAS AOTF produces an electronically controllable narrow band infrared filter capable of being tuned to any infrared frequency desired. See Figure 5 and 6. It provides a chopped and tuned IR source that can be directed across the stack on any combustion process to measure the concentrations of CO, CO_2, SO_2, CH_4, NO, NO_2, H_2O, etc. simultaneously.

Advantages

The AOTF is ideally suited to a form of differential absorption spectroscopy. Instead of being limited to two absorption frequencies by the use of selected narrow band optical filters or mechanically driven diffraction gratings, the AOTF can be tuned to any selected frequency in a matter of milliseconds.

This means that many of the mechanical and optical elements that are necessary when multiple filters and beam splitters are used can be eliminated. It also means that more complex gas concentration algorithms can be implemented with ease and a single optical train can perform all calibration and standardization procedures without introducing multiple sources, detectors or multiple light paths. In addition, elimination of optical elements such as beam splitters and mirrors minimizes the long term degradation of optical elements.

The AOTF is ideally suited for the design of "smart" real time spectroscopic sensors and has four outstanding characteristics.

1. The aperture times the acceptance angle (etendue) for the AOTF can be extremely large. This large light throughput permits design of an extremely fast optical sensor. The large optical speed permits real time optical monitoring with excellent signal to noise.

2. The AOTF can operate with random spectral access since changing the acoustic drive frequency changes the center passband of the device. Access time to any given frequency is limited only by the acoustic transit time through the crystal which is a few microseconds in actual devices. This may be lengthened to a millisecond in order to allow acoustic wave reflections to die out before reexcitation unless the wave is absorbed or deflected. Random spectral access together with high optical speed permits sequential monitoring, under computer control, of an optimal set of infrared wavelengths thereby analyzing multiple gas contents of a stream.

3. The optical speed of the AOTF is independent of the optical resolution of the device. The resolution is primarily determined by the length of the acousto optic interaction, i.e., the length of the crystal. This characteristic contrasts with conventional monochromators where slit width controls both bandwidth and aperture. Thus resolution can be selected without compromising optical speed in an AOTF based sensor.

4. The AOTF is a small, rugged, solid-state device and thus offers great potential for field applications even in harsh environments. It is insensitive to mechanical

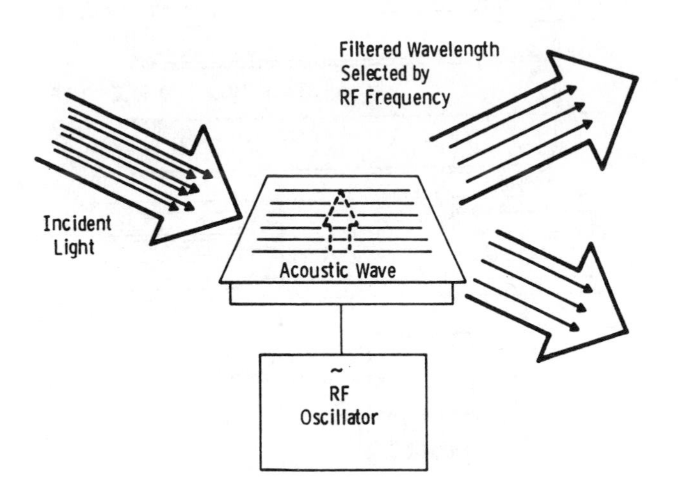

Figure 5. THE AOTF AS A TUNABLE SOURCE OF INFRARED RADIATION

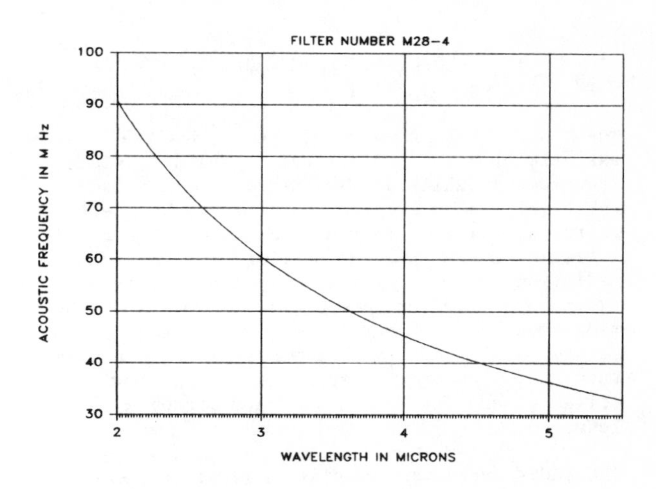

Figure 6. IR WAVELENGTH SELECTED VERSUS ACOUSTIC DRIVE FREQUENCY

vibration and can be easily maintained at constant temperature. Remote control is readily achieved since only one cable supplying RF power is required. [3]

THE OPTAN PROJECT

In a development program, code named OPTAN for Optical Analyzer, a commercial multi stack gas analyzer is under development using the TAS AOTF technology. Facilities for the growth of single crystal TAS have been built and are in commercial operation. A stack gas analyzer was designed to incorporate the AOTF and its associated electronics into a suitable package for stack mounting including the appropriate stack interface.

The AOTF filter can operate in either of two modes: as a source of tunable infrared radiation with a detector whose operating range covers the spectral region of interest or as a tuned-detector with a broadband source covering the required spectral range. In the OPTAN development, a tuned-source technique is being used since the AOTF can then also serve as a solid state light chopper and the DC background stack radiation will not mask the chopped source signal.

The overall stack gas analyzer design is shown in Figure 7. It consists of three major functional systems: an optical system, stack mounted electronics system and control room electronics system. The optical portion houses the infrared source, the AOTF, the detector, three infrared lenses and the source and detector assembly air lenses. The stack mounted electronics includes both the source and detector electronics. A single twisted pair serial bus interconnects the stack electronics to the control room electronics. The control room electronics provides microcomputer control of gas concentration algorithms, operator displays and printed logs.

OPTICAL SUB SYSTEM

The optical portion of the analyzer is essentially an infrared solid state spectrometer which is designed to operate over a relatively wide spectral range. A heated infrared source provides a broad band of infrared radiation. A portion of the output radiation is collected and focused on the AOTF by a lens. After passing thru the AOTF the radiation is collected and collimated by a second lens. The collimated beam then passes thru the process stream or stack and is collected and focused on the detector by a third lens.

The AOTF provides spacial separation between unfiltered and filtered beams. Although the diffracted filtered beam is also switched to an orthogonal polarization, no use of this polarization shift is made in this stack analyzer. The unfiltered beam goes off at a 9° angle so is not collected by the detector lens, whereas, the filtered beam of narrow band infrared light is directed across the stack so as to be focused on the detector. Relatively long focal length lenses were selected to insure that the AOTF's acceptance angle is not exceeded.

Use of spacial separation eliminates the need for input and output polarizers and their attendant losses. The simple in line optics with a single source and single detector is possible because of the extensive flexibility built into the AOTF. The ability to select rapidly any number of infrared wavelengths for analysis provides the means to measure all infrared absorbing gases in the range of interest, eliminate interactive effects by proper algorithm design and provide zero and range checks without beam splitters or moving elements.

All the optical elements shown in Figure 7 are prealigned and mounted in a metal cylinder at fixed positions. The AOTF is factory aligned in

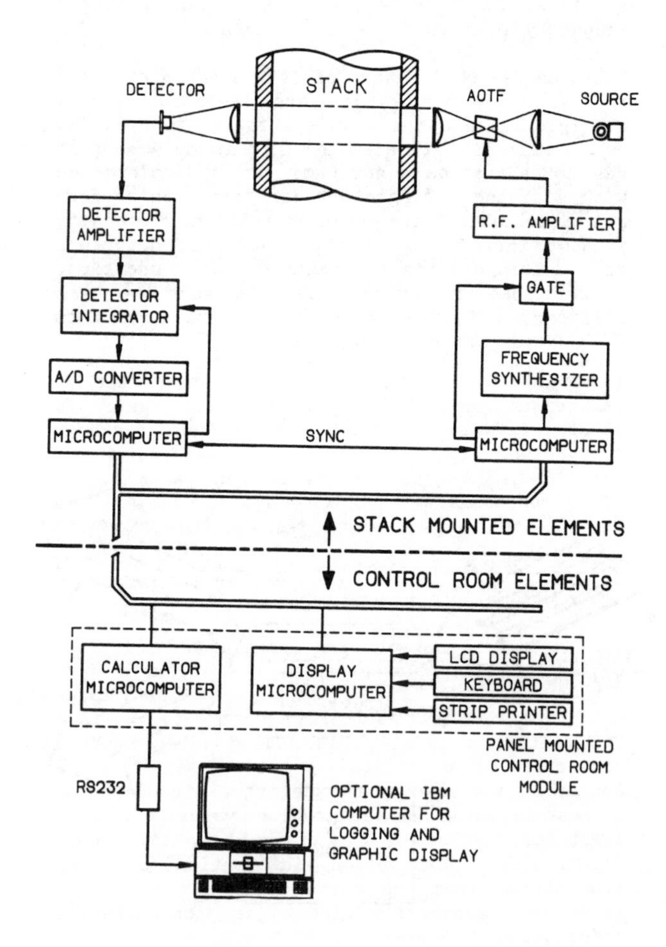

Figure 7. OVERALL GAS ANALYZER SYSTEM

a cylindrical holder which mounts at a fixed position within the cylinder. This means no internal optical adjustments are necessary in the field to assure alignment between source, lenses, or the AOTF. The AOTF is designed so that the light exiting the filter is coaxial with the light entering.

The interface to the stack is achieved by means of a spherical joint, to provide for alignment across the stack, and an air lens to prevent the flue gas from coming in contact with any of the optical elements.

If the air for the air lens should fail, a check valve closes to prevent flue gas from flowing backward thru the air lens and a differential pressure switch notifies the appropriate stack computer of the failure. A manual operated shutter between the optical assembly and the air lens allows for the removal or replacement of the optical assembly while maintaining the air lens purge.

STACK MOUNTED ELECTRONICS

The stack mounted electronics interfaces with the optical subsystem at the detector and at the AOTF. It is the purpose of the stack electronics to impress selected frequency RF drive power on the AOTF in such a way that the optically filtered infrared signals detected can be used by the detector microcomputer to determine the absorption resulting from the presence of selected gases in the process stream.

The source microcomputer, through appropriate interface, controls the output frequency and amplitude from a frequency synthesizer, much the way a quartz tuner selects a television channel. Since the detector requires chopped radiation in order to eliminate the effect of background radiation, an electronic gate is located between the lower power output frequency synthesizer and the higher output power RF amplifier. The gate assures that RF pulses, 7 to 10 microseconds wide, are applied to the AOTF at about a one percent duty cycle. Thus the AOTF is functioning, not only as a rapidly tunable narrow band infrared filter, but as a solid state optical chopper as well.

The detector output is integrated over the period of time during which the acoustic wave passes thru the filter so as to measure the radiation received during the entire period that the filter is open. This analog value is then converted to a digital value by an A to D converter for use by the detector microcomputer in establishing an absorption value for each frequency selected by the control room electronics. Absorption information is then transmitted over the serial bus to the control room for conversion into gas concentration information.

Under software control the system is made to operate as an automated analyzer system. The control room microcomputer acts as the system master to determine the IR frequencies to be evaluated and to perform the computations required to convert the absorption information received from the stack electronics into gas concentrations. Since the relationship between the drive frequency and the AOTF pass band is known (See Figure 6) for a given filter, the control room microcomputer can be programmed to cause the AOTF to first transmit the infrared radiation in a spectral band where there is known to be no absorption and then to transmit the infrared radiation in a spectral band where a gas of interest is known to absorb. After sampling each wavelength a prescribed number of times, and averaging the results, the stack electronics can provide absorption information to the control room electronics for conversion into gas concentrations.

CONTROL ROOM ELECTRONICS

Although the simple algorithm described illustrates the classic differential absorption technique, more complex algorithms reside in the control room microcomputer so that special interference conditions can be accounted for. Additional gases or different gases can be addressed by simply developing new software for those new gases.

While the normal mode of operation is to test only those infrared wavelengths necessary to determine the specific gases of interest on a real time basis it is also possible to program a scan mode of operation where the frequency synthesizer will increment thru a range of frequencies, a step at a time, to produce a plot of absorption versus frequency. Figure 8 illustrates a typical scan made plot for methane. The time required to perform such a

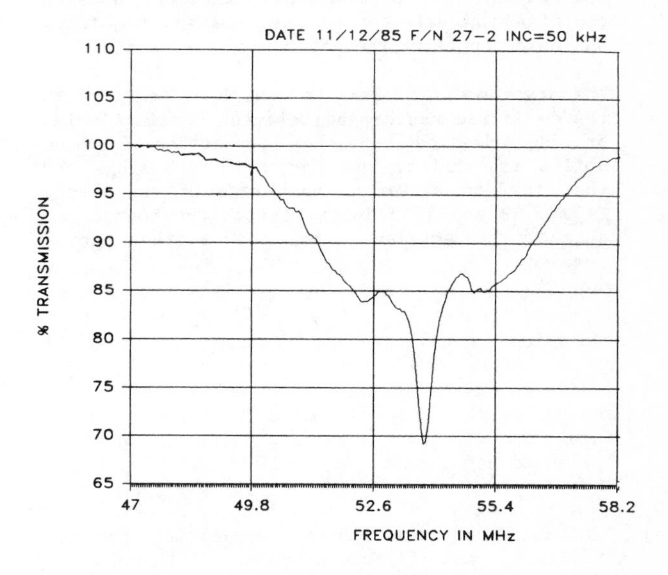

Figure 8. SCAN MODE PLOT FOR METHANE

scan will depend on the frequency range to be scanned and the size of the frequency steps desired. Such a scan mode allows one to easily study the absorption spectrum of a given process. This is particularly useful in developing new software for new gases, studying interference effects between gases or studying the changes in absorption at various gas temperatures or pressures.

The control room electronics may take several forms. Since the twisted pair cable connecting the stack electronics to the control room uses standard Intel BITBUS™ communication protocol, a BITBUS™ to RS232 interface allows a standard IBM-PC to be connected to serve as the master station. This should make the analyzer system of interest to those who want to develop their own analyzer algorithms.

Additional BITBUS™ compatible cards will be available for a panel board LCD display, multiple gas analog outputs, and a gas computation board for use when no IBM-PC is available.

SOURCE AND DETECTOR ASSEMBLY PACKAGING

The source assembly, shown in Figure 9, consists of a cylindrical housing, containing the optical elements, mounted to the air lens assembly. Directly below the air lens mounting flange is the air lens blower used to maintain an air flow into the stack when positive stack pressures exist. Power supplies and source electronics are housed in the enclosures below the source cylindrical housing.

The detector assembly, shown in Figure 10, consists of a cylindrical housing containing the detector and a test gas chamber where test gases may be introduced into the light path. The box mounted on the end of the cylindrical housing contains the detector electronics and the fined box below contains the power supply elements.

The stack mounted elements have been designed to reside inside source and detector housings which provide additional weather protection for the optics assemblies, the electronics housings and the air lens blower on each side of the stack. Figures 9 and 10 illustrate both the source and detector assemblies with the weather cover removed.

SUMMARY AND CONCLUSIONS

Measurement of flue gas content for emissions monitoring and evaluation or control of combustion by in situ measurement methods has expanded rapidly over the last decade. High temperature solid electrolytes for oxygen and SO_2 are now widely used while infrared and ultraviolet spectrometers have moved out of the laboratory into industrial and utility combustion applications. These units successfully use differential absorption, gas filter correlation, and second derivative spectroscopy. A new technology built around the acousto-optic tunable filter is expected to bring major new advancements to the in situ combustion analyzer field.

The recent breakthrough in the growth of excellent quality single crystal thallium arsenic selenide, on a production basis, has made it possible to built an electronically controlled acousto optic tunable filter capable of operating in the infrared.

Development of a solid state multi stack-gas analyzer without mechanical filter wheels, spinning gas cells, moving mirrors, or diffraction gratings, and mechanical light choppers indicates the AOTF will produce a major revolution in optical, in situ, combustion sensor development.

The ability to measure virtually all combustion gases with a single solid state, in situ, analyzer could easily add a new dimension to the development of future combustion control systems.

REFERENCES

1. United States Environmental Protection Agency Handbook, "Continuous Air Pollution Source Monitoring Systems."

2. Ryan, F.M., "A New Method of Measuring Stack Emissions," Westinghouse 1985 Electric Utility Engineering Conference.

3. Wolga, G.J., "Combustion Control With Smart Sensors," Unsolicited Proposal Submitted to the Department of Energy by Cornell University, Ithaca, New York.

Figure 9. Stack Gas Analyzer Source Assembly

Figure 10. Stack Gas Analyzer Detector Assembly

Chapter 80

DESIGNING, COMMISSIONING AND MAINTAINING LINEARITY – THE KEY TO EFFECTIVE CONTROL

K. E. Heselton

A DEFINITION

A control system satisfies the requirements for linearity when a change in the output signal of each final controller produces a proportional change in the process flow within the normal operating range.

FLOW IS CONTROLLED

In applying linearity to control system operation, one should accept the fact that flow and only flow is controlled. A controller can not regulate pressure, temperature, level, mix, etc. Regulation of those variables is achieved solely by regulating flow. The process measurement used to generate a controller output is a function of the controlled flow.

Most control systems regulate the flow of fluids (liquids and gases) and this discussion is restricted to a discussion of those systems. The proccesses for linear control of other systems may be extrapolated from the application of linearity to fluid systems.

In evaluating linearity of a control system, the change in process flow is compared to the change in the output of the controller regulating that flow.

THE IMPORTANCE OF LINEARITY

With the exception of the new microprocessor based controls, a controller has but one gain adjustment. The controller responds to a difference between the measured process variable and set point by changing its output proportional to that difference. The error (difference between actual and desired signal values) is multiplied by the controller gain to determine the change in output. If the change in the process flow rate is not proportional to the change in the controller ouput signal, the process variable will not return to the desired setpoint value requiring the controller to change the output again.

The lack of linearity is normally corrected by the controller, but at the expense of excursions in the value of the process variable.

Consider, for example, the control loop with a flow to output characteristic as indicated by the curve of figure 1. If the controller gain is adjusted at high loads, the process variable will overshoot dramatically at low loads. If the controller gain is adjusted at low loads, the process variable will return to setpoint very slowly at high loads.

There is always one point in a non-linear system where it will respond well, that being at the load where the controller gain was last adjusted.

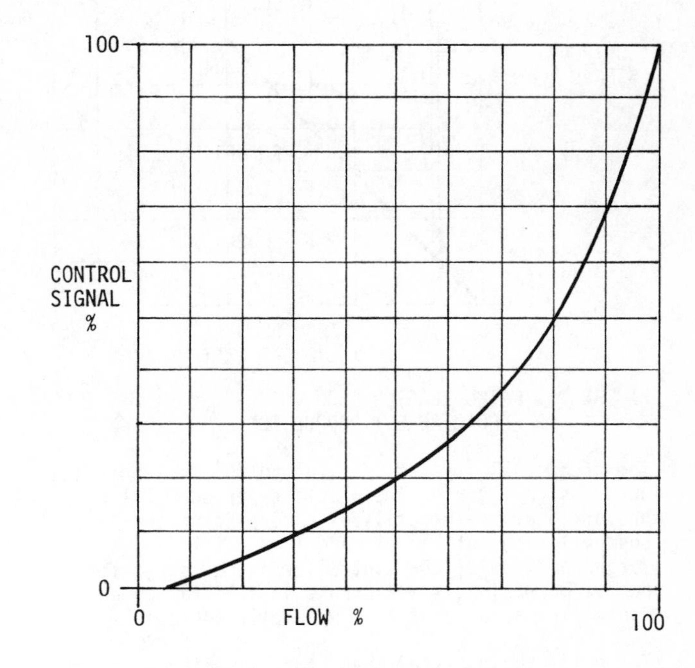

FIGURE 1. A NON-LINEAR SYSTEM

PROPORTIONAL SYSTEMS COMPARED TO PREDICTABLE SYSTEMS

Most control systems should have complete proportionality, where the flow should change proportional to each control signal change. Such systems are identified as proportional systems. Certain processes require linear control only within a portion of their capacity. These are described as predictable systems. As an example, consider a batch process where the contents of a reactor must be heated to a certain temperature then held at that temperature for the reaction period. The process could permit a rapid increase in temperature but require precise temperature control once the reaction temperature is achieved. For a reactor heated with steam, the control system operation would provide better performance with an output control that is linear within a narrow range and predictable than a completely proportional system. The two systems are shown in figure 2.

On starting the process up, both systems will heat the reactor at the same rate because the steam valve will be wide open. The difference between the two system curves indicates the predictable system will permit more precise control of the reaction temperature during the critical reaction period. It will also limit overshoot of the reaction temperature when the reaction temperature is achieved.

When the process reaches the reaction temperature, the predictable system will reduce steam flow to the reaction range rapidly. The proportional system must ramp through 80% of the controller's output range before steam flow is reduced to the normal flow range.

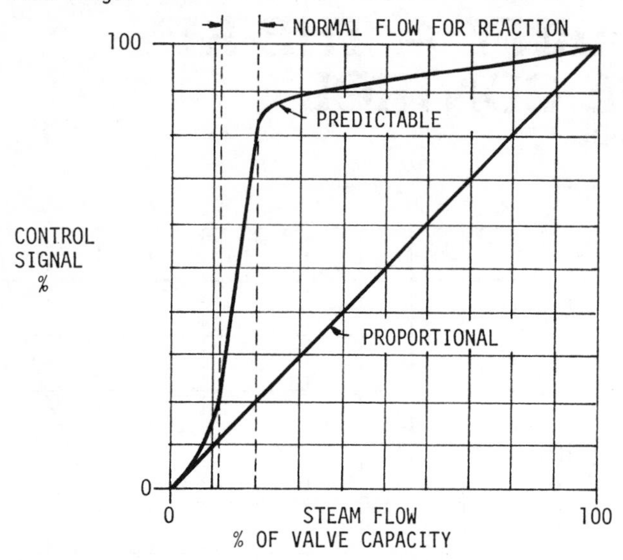

FIGURE 2. BATCH REACTOR FLOW CURVES PREDICTABLE / PROPORTIONAL.

The predictable system utilizes 60% of the controller output signal during the reaction period. The proportional system utilizes a mere 8% of the controller output signal range. By utilizing a larger portion of the controller output range for normal operation, small errors in calibration and controller adjustment will be amplified less.

The predictable system meets the linearity definition because it is linear in the "normal operating range."

Application of the design, establishing and maintaining linearity that follow describe only proportional systems. The same approaches can be applied to predictable systems by carefully defining the normal operating range.

DESIGNING FOR LINEARITY

The following descriptions for designing to achieve linearity consist, primarily, of quick graphic analysis. A more refined and accurate analysis would, normally, be unproductive. The designer need only provide a system that can be linearized by the startup personnel. The design exercise also serves as a check of system performance.

Developing a throttling curve

Whenever possible, the first step in designing a system with linearity is to develop a throttling curve. This should be done before the equipment is ordered. The exercise of plotting the curve may demonstrate need for an equipment change if the flow cannot be controlled over the desired operating range.

Figure 3 is an example of the development of a throttling curve. The system resistance curve (S) is determined without the pressure drop through the control valve or damper and is plotted on the pump or blower curve (P/B) or a similar curve that represents the pressure available at some source. The throttling curve (T) is plotted using the flow axis and the difference between the S and P/B curves.

It is not necessary to calculate each point on the system resistance curve. Simply plot the differential pressure at zero flow and design flow and use the difference to plot other points. To locate any point, divide the value of flow by the design flow, square the result (multiply it by itself), multiply that result by the difference between system differential (pressure drop) at zero and design flow, and add the zero differential value to obtain the differential at the selected flow.

To plot the throttling curve: at each value of flow, transfer the distance between the S and P/B curves to a distance from zero differential. Use dividers (as shown), or any convenient transfer method.

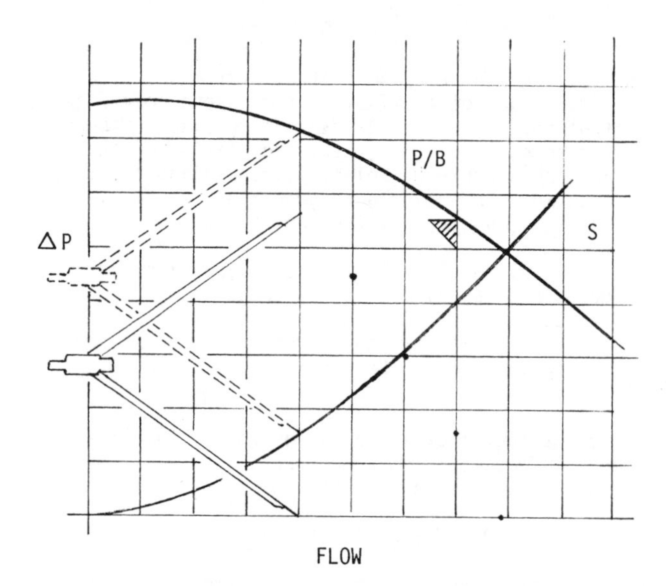

FIGURE 3. PLOTTING A THROTTLING CURVE.

Care should be tanken to ensure the P/B curve covers the desired operating range. Occasionally, manufacturers will not display characteristics below a given flow to permit display of more detail and accuracy around the design point.

Figure 4 is a group of examples of different system types. Be certain that you have selected the correct zero and full load differential pressures. 4(a) is controllable, but the same pump/blower design conditions for the system in 4(b) is uncontrollable below 50% of design flow.

It has been said that a centrifugal pump or blower will surge if operated to the left of the peak in its P/B curve where the slope is positive. The difference between the 4(a) and 4(b) curves demonstrates when the devices will surge - when the slope of the throttling curve is positive. It is the match of pump or blower and system that determine when, and if, a system will surge. Even the unique P/B curve of a forward curved fan (figure 4(d)) does not present a problem in a suitable system. If the slope of a throttling curve is positive (slopes up as flow is increased), control at those flows is impossible.

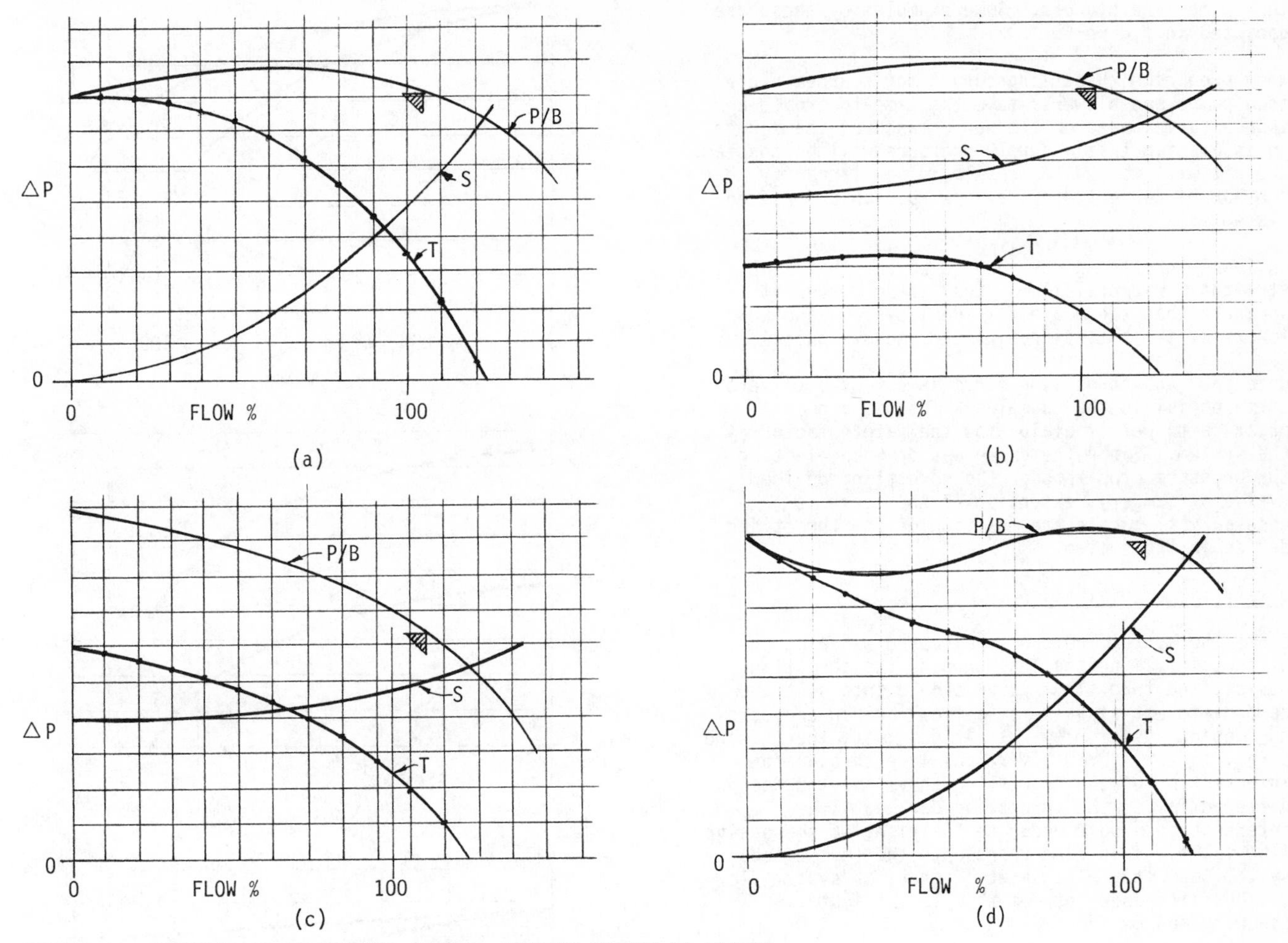

FIGURE 4. EXAMPLES OF THROTTLING CURVES, PUMP OR BLOWER AS SOURCE

Return flow systems

Where required to maintain fluid temperatures or for positive displacement blowers or pumps, the throttling curve is plotted as the difference between the system pressure and return line (R) differential curves as shown in figure 5.

When the system is served by a positive displacement pump or blower, the 100% flow value used is at the intersection of the system pressure and P/B curves, not at the design flow. System pressure is plotted for decreasing flow (reversed) in the analysis. This is important when system pressure must vary with load as shown in figure 5(b). Note that system pressure cannot be less than the pressure drop at the maximum flow through the return line.

Allow for pressure drop that may occur between the location where pressure is sensed for control and in supply piping to the connection of the return line.

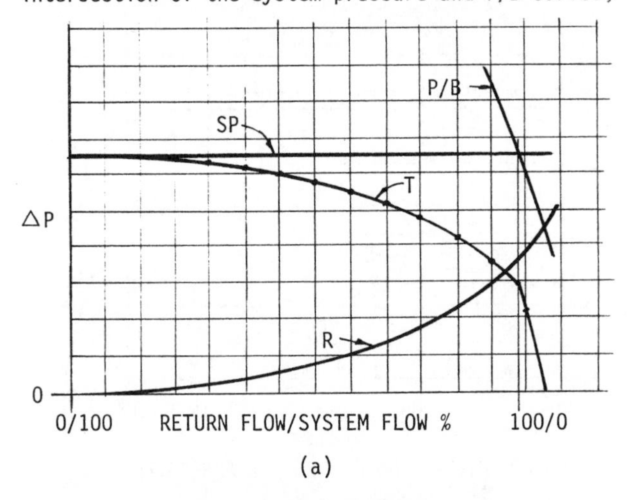

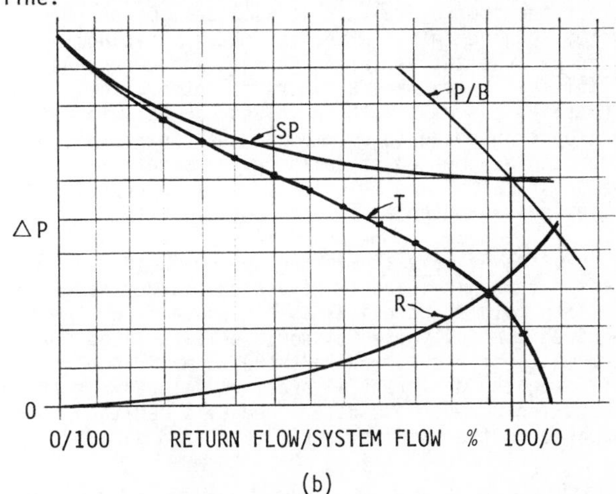

FIGURE 5. RETURN SYSTEM THROTTLING CURVES

There are sources of pressure that generate flow other than pumps and blowers. Some examples of these are depicted in figure 6.

When preparing throttling curves for sources other than pumps and blowers, take the time to create a source curve based on the performance of the source. An assumption that a supply pressure will be constant when it will not be can result in non-linearity that can not be corrected or, even worse, an undersized system.

An ideal throttling curve would be one that is a straight horizontal line. From these curves it is apparent that there are few ideal systems and how important it is to linearize the ones we have.

Note that the throttling curve is extended to zero differential in the examples. This is a good practice to permit evaluating the safety factor of the system. Since the curve was drawn neglecting the pressure drop through the throttling device (valve or damper), extension of the curve is necessary to locate the position of the throttling device in the system.

Safety factor evaluation

Since the system (return line) curve was plotted without including the loss through the throttling device, the throttling curve should intersect the zero differential value at a flow rate in excess of the design system flow. If it does not, there is no safety factor. Draw a vertical line through the intersection of the throttling curve and the design differential of the throttling device. The intersection should occur to the right of the design flow value. This line represents the (estimated) system capacity. The safety factor for system flow is the difference between the flow at system capacity and design.

Note the relationship between the safety factor and the difference between system capacity and the intersection of the throttling curve and zero differential. If the safety factor is the smaller of the two, the safety factor should be re-evaluated.

Matching valve curves

Control valve manufacturers provide information that can be used to determine how a valve will perform in a system. Utilizing that data, the designer can select the control valve that will best match the system requirements. A perfect match is seldom found because the variety of throttling curves is limitless. Valve manufacturers do not provide throttling curves for their valves so the information must be transposed to accomodate the control valve manufacturers method of defining characteristics. The "best match" can be determined using one of the following two methods.

Calculating Cv values: If the system fluid is exposed to sonic velocity, flashing, large changes in specific volume, or exists as two phase flow, the required control valve Cv should be calculated for increments of flow throughout the normal range utilizing the differential pressure values from the throttling curve. The determined Cv's can then be compared to the manufacturer's tabulated data.

Creating a valve curve: Convert the throttling curve data to create a required valve characteristic curve.

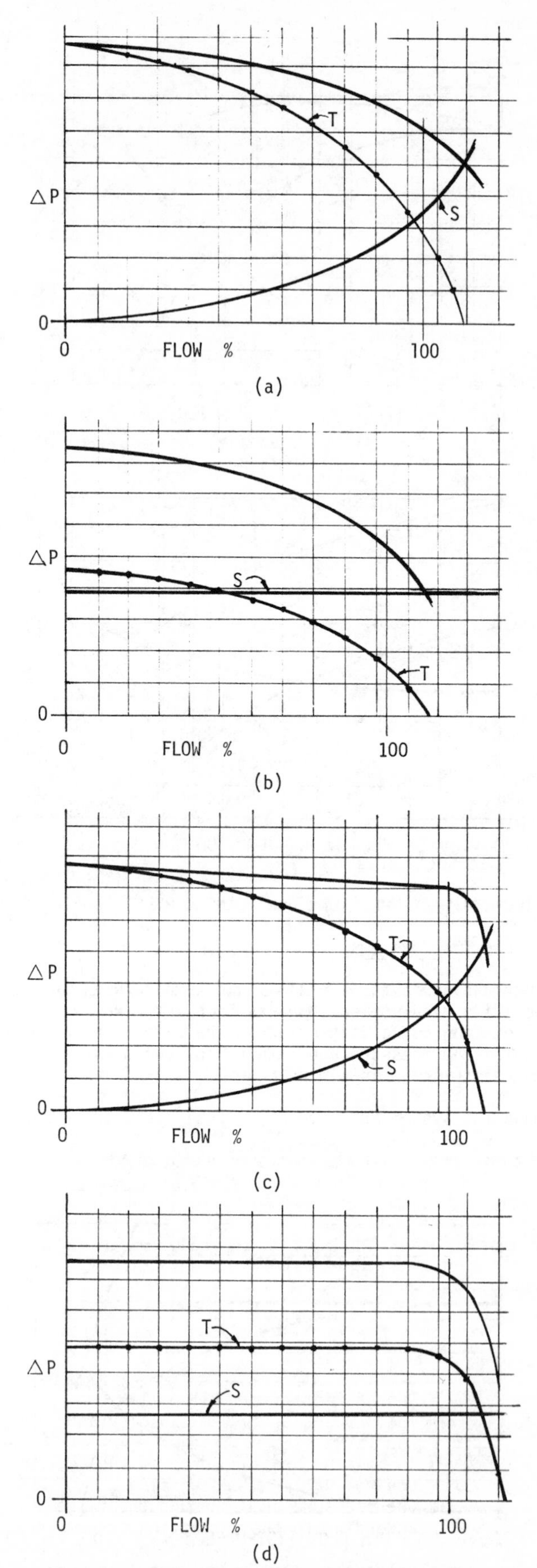

FIGURE 6. THROTTLING CURVES - EXAMPLES FOR MISCELLANEOUS SOURCES

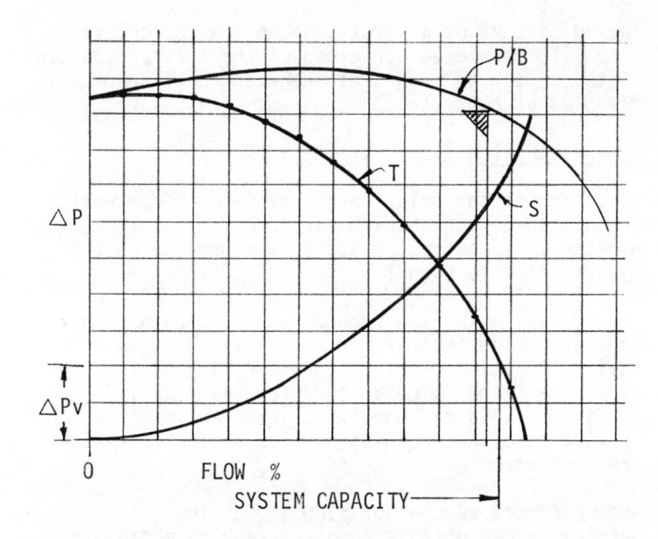

FIGURE 7. SYSTEM CAPACITY DETERMINATION.

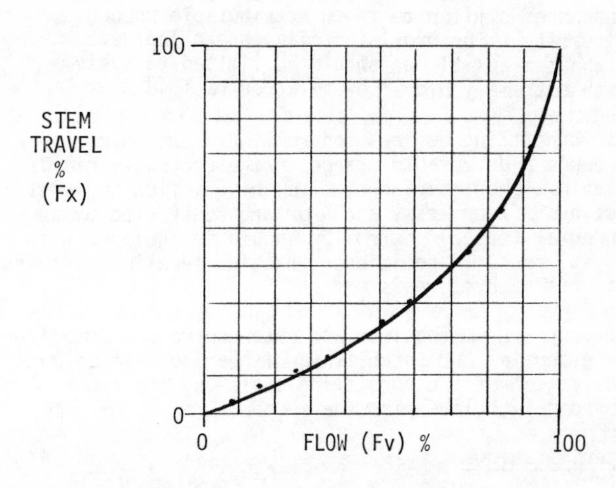

FIGURE 8. REQUIRED VALVE CHARACTERISTIC CURVE FOR THE SYSTEM IN FIGURE 7.

Most valve manufacturers have printed valve characteristic curves which indicate the flow through their valve relative to stem position at a constant pressure differential accross the valve. The curves are usually referred to as (1) linear, (2) equal percentage and (3) quick opening. In addition to these three basic types, some manufacturers have identified other characteristics which match system requirements for which a valve design has been produced.

The throttling curves described above can be utilized to generate a required valve characteristic curve for incorporation with purchase specifications or comparison with the valve manufacturer's valve characteristic curves.

To convert a throttling curve to a valve characteristic curve, the flows at the required pressure drop through the valve are converted to the flow at a constant pressure drop. In calculating and plotting a required valve characteristic curve the author converts all engineering units to percentages. This permits plotting the required characteristic on prepared 0 to 100% graph paper. Also, the valve manufacturers utilize the same scales in describing the characteristics of their valves.

The stem travel index of the valve characteristic curve will be equated to the percent of system capacity to produce a required valve characteristic that will pass a flow proportional to stem position for linear lift. The flow on the required valve characteristic curve is calculated using the formula:

$$Fv = \sqrt{\frac{\triangle Pv \times Fx^2}{\triangle Px}}$$

Where: Fv = The characteristic valve flow.
Fx = The percent of system capacity and the valve stem position.
$\triangle$Pv = The design pressure drop of the control valve at design flow.
$\triangle$Px = The pressure drop through the valve according to the throttling curve at Fx

Figure 8 is a valve characteristic curve developed from the throttling curve of figure 7.

If your calculator does not have a square root key, the square root can be determined using the differential flow graph paper of figure 9. Draw a diagonal line from the bottom left corner to the top right corner of the graph. A line drawn horizontally from the value on the left index to the diagonal and then vertically down to the bottom intersects the bottom index at the square root of the value.

Dampers

Dampers are seldom designed with special performance characteristics and their performance is highly dependent upon their relationship to system pressure drop. For application of dampers, the author strongly recommends you obtain a reprint of Edward J. Brown's article "How to select multiple-leaf dampers for proper air flow control" published in the April 1960 issue of "Heating, Piping and Air Conditioning."

Fans with variable inlet vanes

A fan or blower equipped with variable inlet vanes is a flow source integrated with a throttling device and does not permit development of a throttling curve. These tend to produce a flow characteristic similar to figure 1. Correction of the non-linearity can be accomplished with linkage adjustments, but a positioner will permit better adjustment. A flow characteristic can be plotted using the fan or blower curves to determine the best cam selection for a positioner for this equipment.

Hysteresis and positioners

Hysteresis in an output loop is due to the friction in or lost motion in linkage connected to the throttling device or a combination of the two. It requires some change in output signal to overcome the friction and / or displace the slack in the linkage before changing the flow. The difference between static and dynamic friction and / or the altering of slack by dynamic forces imposed on the throttling device by the flow of fluid can produce changes in flow that exceed that required to correct the error between process and set point. If the throttling device is not equipped with a positioner, hysteresis can produce control system responses similar to those attributable to non-linearity. The provision of a throttling device without a positioner should be limited to systems with extremely high flow to error ratios.

All throttling devices controlling flows which produce a detectable change in the process variable within a short period of time, have a flow to error ratio of 5% or less, and / or are controlled by an integral (reset) controller should be equipped with positioners. A positioner practically eliminates the effects of hysteresis.

If your system requires accurate control, a positioner is essential for establishing linearity. It permits adjustment of the throttling device by startup personnel to linearize the system.

Specifications

Having completed the analysis to determine the proper application requirements for a throttling device, it is important to ensure that it is provided to meet those requirements. The purchasing specifications for control valves, dampers, positioners, transmitters, etc. should detail the requirements for the operating flow range. If the device specifications are limited to a description of the design capacity conditions, vendors will furnish equipment that is selected for that operating point alone. Operation at other flows may be totally unacceptable.

Whenever you expend the time to create it, include a required valve characteristic curve with requests for control valves.

Drawings

If instrumentation is not included to indicate the flow in a system, ensure that the drawings provide for pressure connections or other means to permit the startup personnel to measure flow relative to the controller output.

Startup instructions

Prepare a startup directive for the system. Selecting the right equipment and determining the requirements for linearity does not guarantee that it will operate as designed after installation. This is especially true when a predictable system like that shown in figure 2 is required. The investment in time that a designer spends communicating the system control requirements to the personnel that put the system in service will produce a substantial return in reduced startup time.

ESTABLISHING LINEARITY

If each output loop of a control system is linearized, or adjusted for predictable performance as specified by the design engineer, a startup will take less time and callbacks for adjustment will be reduced. Frequent callbacks for problems with a control loop dictate a check for linearity.

The service (startup) personnel should be equipped with the necessary instruments to measure flow at each control loop. It is not necessary to know the precise flow values unless the system requires a predictable control. Totally proportional systems can, and should, be linearized from zero or minimum to the maximum flow attainable.

The adjustment of a throttling device to achieve linearity should be performed on the initial startup of the system and repeated whenever non-linearity is detected or suspected.

Determining the flow characteristic

To determine the relationship of flow to controller output, an output characteristic curve should be plotted to identify the actual performance of the system (flow to signal).

For systems with flow recorders or indicators that provide a flow indication, the serviceman can utilize that information. However, if there is no flow indication, a means to determine flow is required. This can consist of test equipment which provides a direct reading of flow or a differential pressure reading.

When a direct reading of flow is obtained, the serviceman can utilize regular graph paper to plot flow as a function of the controller output signal. For determining flow with a differential pressure reading alone, Power and Combustion developed the differential flow graph paper in figure 9. With either graphing method, the plot should produce a straight diagonal line with positive slope when the output characteristic is linear.

For simplicity in preparing a plot of the output characteristic, the maximum (normal) flow should be achieved first and used as a base to plot other values. This makes full use of a zero to one (0 to 100%) graph. Each successive value is divided by the maximum value to obtain a unit fraction of the maximum value. Multiply the result by 100 for percent of maximum flow. Our graph paper includes indices for the common 3 to 15 psig. and 4 to 20 ma signal ranges. The differential index (for flow) is arranged for unit fractions, but the actual differential could be plotted if desired.

By plotting the flow or differential on the graph paper, the startup personnel can determine if the system is linear. If the plot is not a straight line, they can then make adjustments to obtain linearity and repeat the plot or accept the curve as adequately linear.

Adjusting the characteristic

A typical non-linearity discovered on startup is shown in figure 1. The curve is typical of the combustion air flow / air controller signal characteristic curve. Normally, these can be linearized by adjusting a positioner cam on the forced draft damper or inlet vane positioner. If the fan positioner does not have a cam or the cam is not readily adjustable, the fan linkage can be arranged to obtain something close to linear air flow.

Linkage adjustment

Linearizing by adjustment of damper linkage is normally the only method available on small boilers and air conditioning systems. The length of the linkage arms must be adjusted to stroke the damper (to produce a 90° damper movement with the full stroke of the drive). This can, and frequently does, inject a non-linearity due to differences in the stroke of the damper and drive. The radial position of the linkage arms can be altered to adjust for non-linearity.

POWER and COMBUSTION
INCORPORATED
Baltimore, Maryland

JOB NAME ______________________ JOB NUMBER __________

SYSTEM ______________________ PRESSURE ________ TEMP. ________

SERVICEMAN ______________________ DATE ___ / ___ / ___

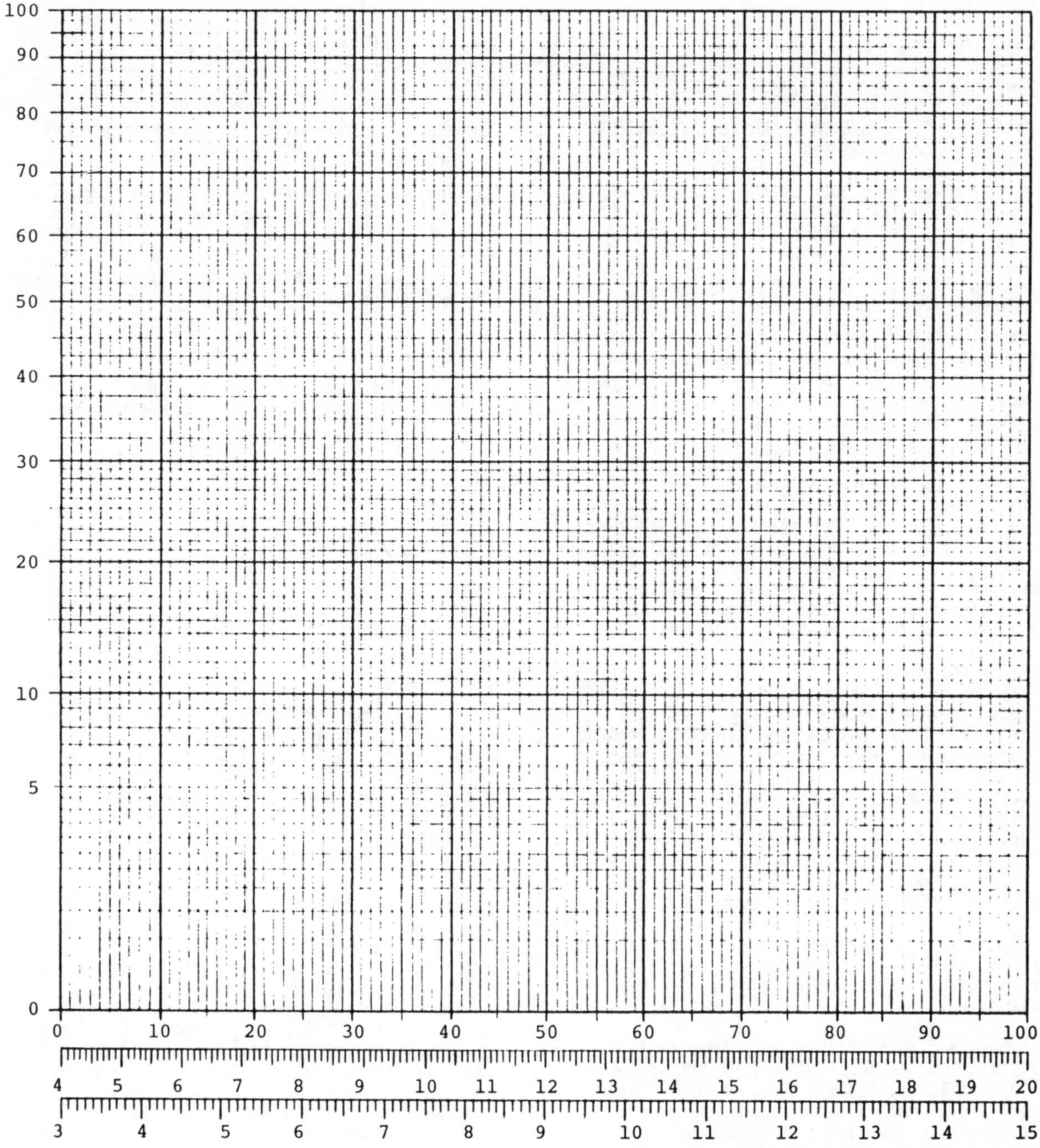

FIGURE 9. DIFFERENTIAL FLOW CHARACTERISTIC GRAPH

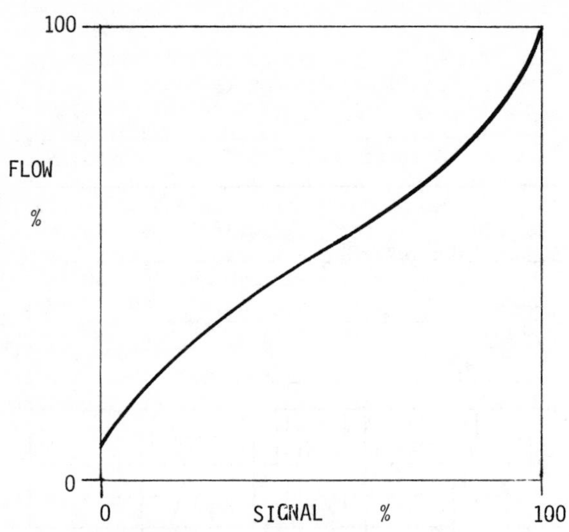

FIGURE 10. EXAMPLE OF SYSTEM CHARACTERISTIC AFTER LINKAGE ADJUSTMENT.

When the only means of adjusting the system to achieve linearity is adjustment of damper or valve linkage, a plot similar to that of figure 10 might represent the best that can be established.

Positioner adjustment

When a throttling device is equipped with a positioner, the graph of the flow characteristic can be utilized to determine the required changes in the positioner cam to achieve linearity. Draw a diagonal line on the signal to flow graph to represent the desired (linear) characteristic and correlate desired and actual flow values as shown in figure 11. Select calibration points, usually at each unit value of signal (psi / ma). From the calibration value (A), draw a vertical line to intercept the diagonal line (A-B). Draw a horizontal line to intercept the actual flow curve (B-C). From that intercept, draw another vertical line (C-D) to intercept the signal index at the bottom of the graph. Tabulate the calibration (A) and intercept (D) values for cutting the cam.

Figure 11 is identical to figure 1 in values. The indices are reversed. Graphs with the flow plotted as the left index facilitate their use for actual alignment in the field while graphs plotting flow as the bottom index are common practice for engineers.

It is not necessary to draw the diagonal line to zero if zero flow cannot be, or should not be, established. Simply draw the diagonal from the 100% corner to the value for minimum flow. For multiple burner boilers where air flow should not be less than 25%, the minimum differential pressure should be at 6¼%.

The tabulated values are used to lay out the cam. The desired flowrate (A) is established by cutting the cam to its height at the position where that flow existed (D).

The system should be shut down while the cam is marked, removed, cut, and replaced. When a system contains several output loops, attempt to acquire the ouput characteristic of each loop while operating on manual to minimize the number of times start up and shutdown are required.

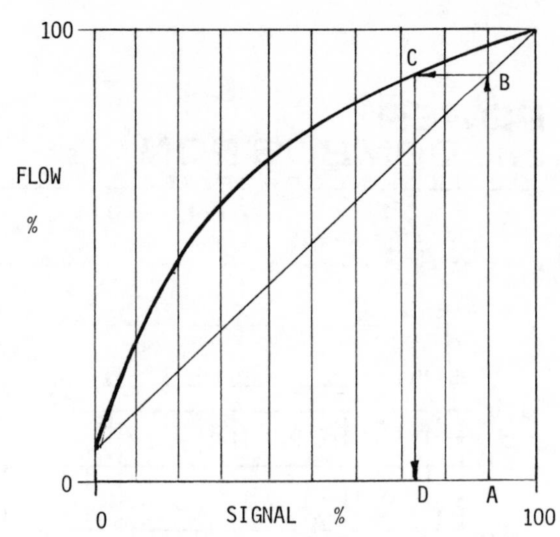

FIGURE 11. DETERMINING CAM HEIGHT TO ACHIEVE INEARITY.

Marking the cam: With the system shut down, or the throttling device bypassed, mark the existing cam at each of the tabulated points utilizing a means of referencing the required height (at D) to the cam position for calibration (A). Figure 12 represents one method of marking a cam.

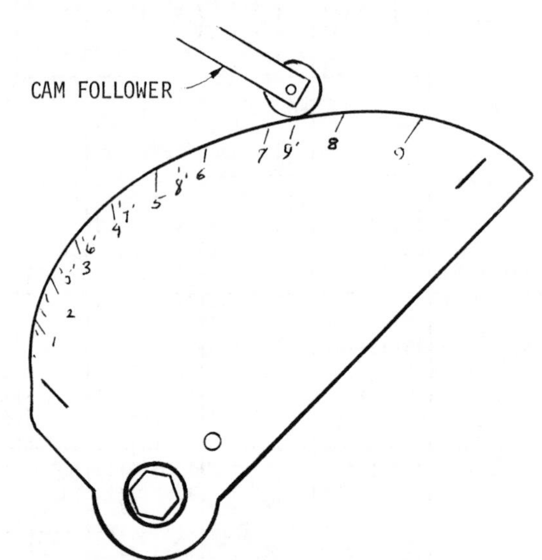

FIGURE 12. MARKING CAM POSITIONS

Cutting a new cam: If the found characteristic curve falls to the right of the diagonal line on the system characteristic curve, a new piece of cam material or a blank cam will be required to produce the linear cam. Remove the marked cam from the positioner and lay out the cam to achieve the desired linear characteristic by locating the cam height at each calibration point (A) equal to the height at the cam position for the signal value of the D intercept. The height should be determined as the distance from the center of rotation of the cam. If the center of rotation is not evident when the cam is removed, scribe an equidistant line on the cam as it is rotated while marking it. Cut the cam to a smooth curve through the plotted points and reinstall it in the positioner, making sure the

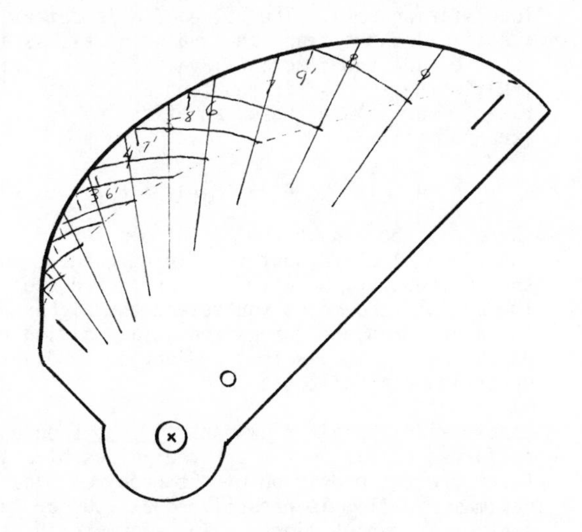

FIGURE 13. PLOTTING THE NEW CAM

cam is returned to the calibrated position.

After a cam has been cut to linearize the output, repeat the cata collection to check for linearity. The final output characteristic curve should be retained for future reference along with a detail sketch of the cam. Copies of the graphs and cam sketches should be given to the owner for his record.

DETECTING NON-LINEARITY

When the operator says "It doesn't work on automatic!"; "It worked fine all summer (winter)!"; or "It worked fine until they...!"; look for non-linearity. These quotes are so common that we tend to ignore them. However, they come from the source most familiar with the day to day operation of the system. It is imperative to recognize that a control system can perform well when the boss or serviceman observes operation. They are usually there when the system is operating at the load it was tuned. The serviceman may adjust the controller response for the current load to eliminate the controller instability and leave without solving the problem.

If we listen to the operator and cease to ignore these common complaints, we will find non-linearity.

Non-linearity is evident when controller response is excellent at one load and responds sluggishly and / or overreacts at other loads.

MAINTAINING LINEARITY

To maintain linearity: (1) Maintain startup and service records, (2) Review the importance of maintaining linearity with maintenance personnel, recommending they record every turn of a nut, linkage position, etc. before working on control valves and dampers so they will not alter system linearity, (3) Have a serviceman check the linearity when dampers, positioners, or control valves are overhauled or replaced. Retain removed material until the linearity is established, it may be valuable to the serviceman in adjusting the system. (4) Give the serviceman enough time to linearize a system.

Service personnel

The initial alignment of a control system and the control system maintenance are the two most important factors in the safe and efficient operation of a control system. Qualified and trained personnel that start up and service systems are expensive. However, the harm that can be done by people that do not understand all the requirements for control systems, including linearity, may generate hidden costs in frequent calls and systems that are inoperative, unsafe, or inefficient. Power and Combustion's service personnel must complete a five year apprenticeship program and are equipped with an inventory of service and test equipment with a value that far exceeds the price of the vehicles they drive. Good service personnel represent a substantial investment and that is why service rates are what they are.

The serviceman that places a control system into initial operation or seeks to correct a problem with a controller should demonstrate a concern for the linearity of the output by collecting data to identify the system ouput characteristic first.

Usually the serviceman is pressed to complete the startup or get the system back in operation. The pressure is either obvious or implicit by virtue of the number of people looking over his shoulder. If he feels he does not have time to check the system linearity, he may skip it or take some shortcuts which leave non-linear loops in place to haunt the operators later.

VARIABLE EXCESS AIR IS ESTABLISHED WITH LINEAR SYSTEMS

If you are familiar with fired equipment, you know that excess air must increase as the firing rate is decreased and it is not a linear (straight line) function. The typical excess air (EA) curve of figure 14 is not linear. The required excess air curve is developed by the serviceman on startup by reducing the excess air at intervals in load until incomplete combustion is detected. The curve is plotted as the minimum amount of excess air for each load that will permit complete combustion.

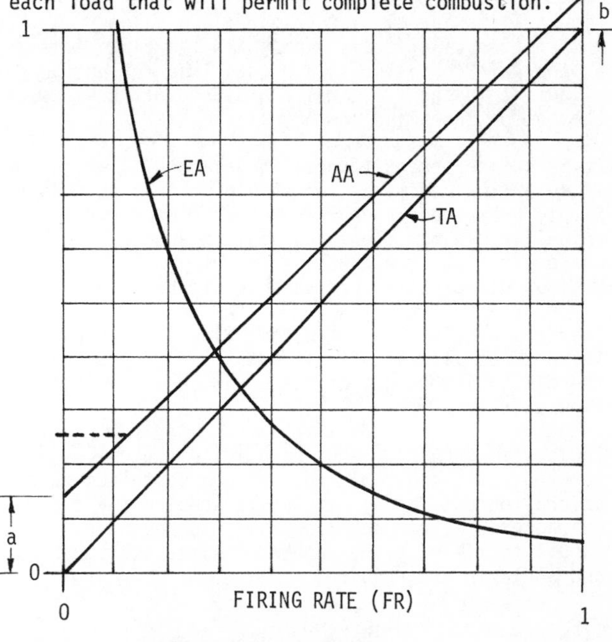

FIGURE 14. COMBUSTION AIR CURVES

Excess air is that volume of air that exceeds the theoretical air required to completely burn the fuel. It is normally identified as a percentage of the theoretical air. Figure 14 has theoretical air (TA) and actual air (AA) curves plotted along with the EA curve. The EA curve is the corresponding excess air as a percentage of theoretical air for the actual air values plotted. Note that both TA and AA are linear values. The dotted line indicates the NFPA 85 Code requirement for 25% of full load air flow as the minimum permissible air flow for multiple burner boilers.

The excess air quantities of figure 14 are higher than we would expect to obtain in a modern burner installation. The values depicted do, however, improve clarity of the figure and represent many of the burners still in service. A new low excess air burner will normally plot with the value of a less than the value of b.

The definition of the non-linear function for excess air as a function of the actual air flow permits determination of the requirements for actual linear air flow to achieve the required excess air. The equation is derived as follows:

Values are expressed as unit fractions. Multiply the values by 100 to obtain percent and divide percentages by 100 to obtain the formula value.

$$EA \text{ (excess air)} = (AA - TA) / TA \quad (1)$$

The theoretical air (TA) and actual air (AA) can be defined as functions of the firing rate (FR) where:

$$TA = FR \quad (2)$$

$$AA = a + FR * (1 + b - a) \quad (3)$$

Substituting (2) and (3) in the excess air equation (1) and reducing, we have:

$$EA = b - a + a/FR \quad (4)$$

The value of b is readily determined as the fractional excess air required at the maximum (full load) firing rate. The value of a is determined by substituting the fractional value of excess air (EA), b, and the fractional value of the firing rate (FR) in the excess air equation at several firing rates. For this purpose, equation (4) is re-arranged as:

$$a = \left[(EA + b) * FR\right] / \left[1 + FR\right] \quad (5)$$

There will be a number of solutions for a, using equation (5) throughout the firing range. They should, however, be within a narrow range of values. The author recommends you select the highest value to ensure complete combustion at all firing rates; excepting any values that are obviously due to an error in data collection.

Linearizing the air flow control loop should be performed utilizing the derived values of a and b to ensure the provision of the required excess air. Maximum air flow is established at 100% of the controller output signal. To determine the air flow at zero output signal, substitute the derived values of a and b in equation (3) along with the minimum firing rate as the unit fraction FR. Correct for the excess air at maximum by multiplying the result by 1 + b.

When calibrating an air flow transmitter for a full metering combustion control system, the signal should be offset to produce the required actual air flow. The transmitter output should be at 100/(1+b) percent at 100% air flow and at zero at 100a/(1+b) percent air flow. Adjusting the transmitter output to 100a/(1+b) percent of the signal range below a live zero at zero air flow will produce a matching transmitter output.

Chapter 81

ENERGY SAVINGS OF A BOILER FEEDWATER STACK GAS ECONOMIZER

A. G. Hamp

INTRODUCTION

For maximum savings and practical efficient use, it is important to change water into steam as quickly and cheaply as possible in any boiler system. A well designed, clean, boiler operating at optimum combustion conditions with proper water treatment and blowdown considerations coupled with conscientious maintenance and inspections will give many years of practical efficient service. However, every effort should be made to keep the heat losses from the boiler and steam system to and from the loads to a minimum and maximize the use of heat losses wherever it is possible and practical to do so. One particular case, presented in this paper, ;is to heat the deaerated, preheated feed water from 210°F to a higher practical temperature prior to going into the boiler by the use of stack gas heat going to the atmosphere.

Heat exchangers or economizers have been utilized within the design of boilers for many years and are certainly not new to the industry. However, the modification of an existing heating system in which a heat exchanger is placed in an existing stack design is relatively new and has been proposed by several companies since l973, the beginning of the energy crunch. This is a report of the initiation, justification, financing, installation, operation and energy savings of such an economizer.

Initiation

Contacts were made with different economizer manufacturers as early as l977 for practical data and description of their product for use in a four (4) foot diameter vertical stack. This stack came from a 40,000 lb/hr Keeler water tube boiler fired by a Coen burner for natural gas and No 2 oil to create l00 psi steam. The information supplied by the manufacturers and a simple analysis of the heat transferred to the water, coupled with natural fuel costs, indicated an energy savings of 4% to 7% was possible with a simple payback of 1.2 years. With fuel bills constantly rising, and natural gas bills approaching $60,000 per month savings which was worth striving for. In addition, the stack of number 3 boiler rose directly vertical from the floor and offered a perfect installation of a vertical economizer in the stack or part of the stack with minimum amount of physical and mechanical changes. This was particularly true because the feed water lines to the boiler and Fisher flow regulating value, isolation valves, and the stack were close to each other on the same side of the boiler.

Financing

Initial cost estimates of the economizer was estimated to be $20,000 for owner installation to $45,000 for contracted installation. Cost estimate of the economizer itself was $10,000 to $15,000. Armed with this information, the Utah Energy Office was contacted for financial support. The possibilities of money came from two sources, the State of Utah Energy Office, and a grant from the federal government which was also handled through the Utah Energy Office. In both cases an energy audit was required and performed. A "Technical Assistance Report, Heating Plant Building No. 18 at Weber State College", Ogden, Utah was submitted for a federal grant June, 1983. The U.S. Department of Energy, Institutional Conservation Program approved grant No. DEFG4883R807549 an Energy Conservation Measures grant in October, 1983.

Financial payback was based on simple basic calculations on the following data. The boiler operates 4380 hours with an initial feed water temperature of 210°F, a differential temperature of 60°F at a flow rate of 80 gpm which would give an energy savings of 7,658 Dth. This savings compared with the total energy used in 1983 of 162,944 Dth, indicated a yearly savings of 4.7%. At the natural gas cost of $3.00 per Dth, a savings of $23,035 per year was possible.

On the basis of the savings, the Federal grant would cover 65% of the expected installed cost of $25,263 with Weber State College installing it in house. There was a possibility that additional funds would be made possible from the State of Utah Energy Office fund for educational buildings. This, in fact, was the case. After the economizer was installed, $14,768 was contributed by the State of Utah Energy Office to help cover a $37,500 total installation charge by a contractor.

Obtaining and Installation

After the financial arrangements were made, a specification was written for the economizer and giving the engineering data and drawings of the heating plant. The specification was written based on previous information given by economizer manufacturers, a study of economizers, and on-site evaluation of existing operating economizers. A bid package was submitted and an analysis and evaluation of the resulting bids for four different designs of the economizers were performed.

The analysis included the physical characteristics, and machanical interfacing of existing plant equipment as well as the operating and savings characteristics. The operating and energy saving characteristics are shown in Figures 1, 2, and 3. These depict the tube side differential temperature, the energy savings in decatherms, and the economizer shell output stack gas temperature as a function of boiler steam flow output. It is clearly evident that the Kentube economizer design was superior in performance and efficiency. The contract was submitted and delivery of economizer was made in five (5) weeks by the manufacturer in July, 1984.

Installation of the economizer was started in September and completed by September 26, 1984. Pictures submitted show the economizer in the stack and the heating plant. The boiler was rebalanced by Coen Company the latter part of October, 1984 for both oil and natural gas, and put in service November 1, 1984. It was in operation through the winter to the end of February, 1985 and again in June, July and August of 1985. It was placed in service in June, 1986 for the summer months.

Complete data was taken before and after the installation of the economizer in the stack to compare the results with predicted and what was obtained. Early data prior to the installation of the economizer is submitted in Table 1 for different steam flows. Data to show the operating and energy savings are shown in tables for each curve of characteristics of Figure 1, 2, and 3, respectively. It is to be noted that boiler combustion efficiency both before and after the installation of the economizer was 81 to 82 percent, the oxygen was 1.5 to 3.5 percent with peaks up to 4.6 to 5.3 percent. Carbon dioxide ran from 8.7 to 10.5 percent with peaks up to 11 percent in oscillations. The data presented is steady state as far as boilers go. However, with as large a steam system that we have with two miles of condensate return lines and twenty-two (22) buildings on line, the boiler will hunt. Hunting can be exaggerated depending on the sensitivity of recording equipment. It is also noted that a MC Products Model 50 Combustion Efficiency Analyzer was used to measure the stack gas temperature, carbon dioxide, oxygen and efficiency. It should be noted that there is a considerable difference in the stack temperature from the gauge listed at the top of the data sheet. Checks were made using a Bachrack instrument which was in agreement with the MC Model 50.

Energy Savings

Energy savings of the economizer is compared with actual operating data of the boiler for a full twenty four hour period for comparable months with and without

Fig 1. FeedWater Temp. Gain vs Steam Flow

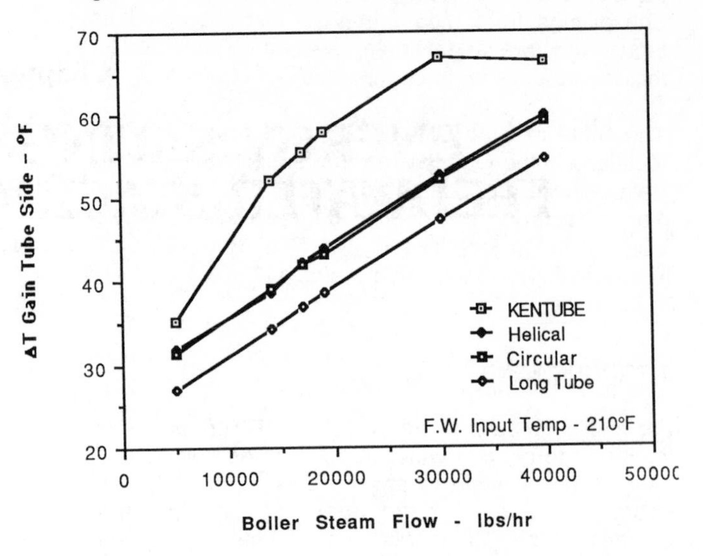

Fig 2. Energy Saving vs Steam Flow

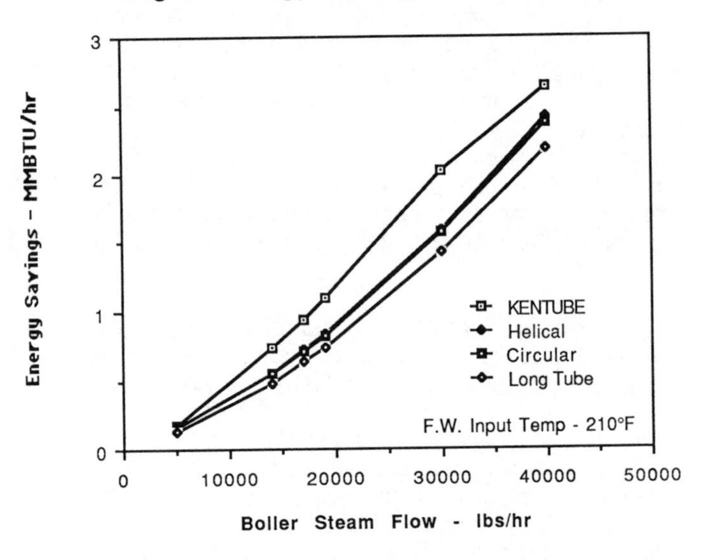

Econ. Shell Output Temp. vs Steam Flow

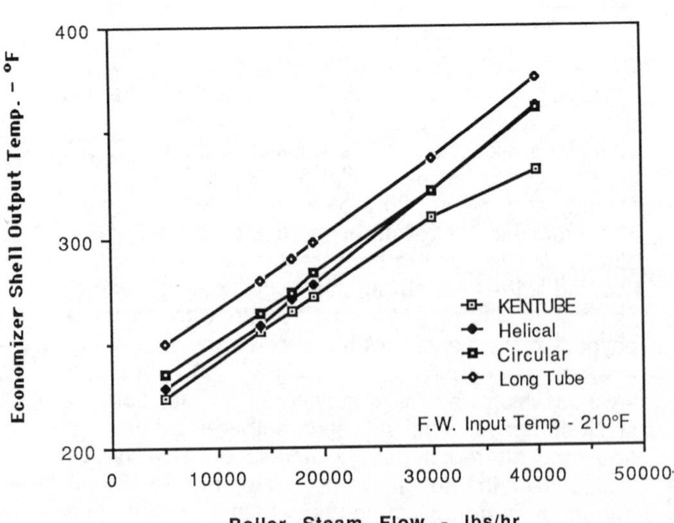

the economizer. This occurred for July 1984 without the economizer and July 1985 with the economizer. The billings from Mountain Fuel are submitted as Figure 4. However, this data needs to be corrected for the degree-days for each month.

The State of Utah Climatology Data report lists two locations in the Ogden area that supplies climatology data. These are located at Pioneer Plant and at the Sugar Factory. The cooling degree days (CDD) for each of these locations is 341 CDD and 303 CDD respectively for July, 1984, and 441 CDD and 415 CDD respectively for July, 1985.

Pioneer Plant is four miles from Weber State College and is on the bench of the Wasatch Mountains and so is WSC. Date from this location shall be used as required.

It should be noted that July represents cooling degree days and is small in number. Because there would be so much questionable error in the cooling degree days, the cooling degree correction is not used and the data stands uncorrected. If the 100 cooling degrees were corrected, a tremendous savings could be realized. Thus, for July comparison a savings of energy 23,740 - 19,536 or 4,204 decatherms is realized and at a cost of $3.30 per decatherms a $13,873 savings is realized over the previous year for the month of July.

An analysis of data for January, 1985 realized a savings of $5,923 and for February, 1985 when the unit was operating, a savings of $7,683 was realized. The final cost of the economizer completely installed was #37,500 and with a savings of $27,479 in three months, the economizer will have paid for itself in less than six months of operation, with a profit to spare.

It was also noted in taking data that the economizer saved 5,000 lbs per hour of steam at an outside temperature of 100°F during the July period for the same temperature the year before.

Conclusion

An economizer can be designed very efficiently to save energy from normally wasted stack gas going up the chimney. To obtain an efficient economizer, one must study existing economizers, obtain good data from your facility, write a tight specification, including the data, request computer program data of each economizer manufacturer as part of the specification, and have a good installation. Accurate instrumentation is necessary to evaluate the results. Data must be taken before and after installation of the economizer.

Fig 4. FeedWater Temp. Gain vs Steam Flow

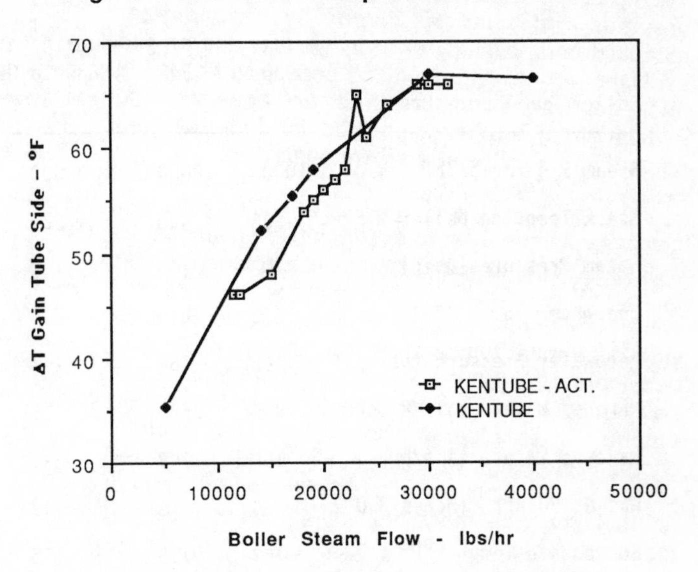

Fig 5. Energy Saving vs Steam Flow

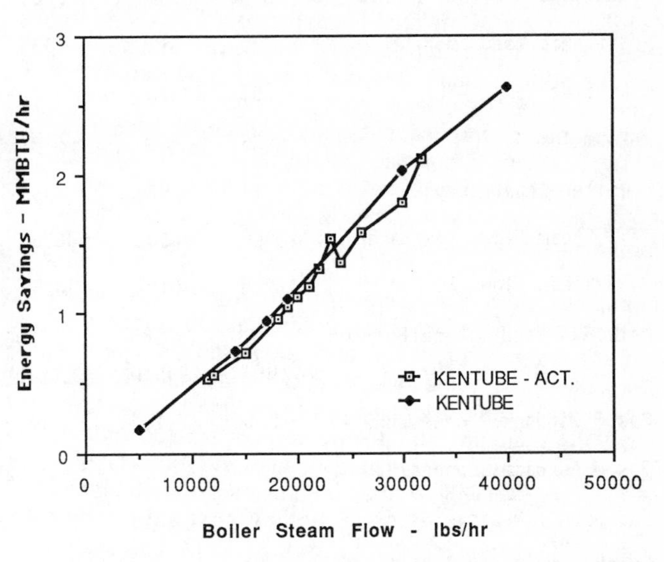

Fig 6. Econ. Shell Output Temp. vs Steam Flow

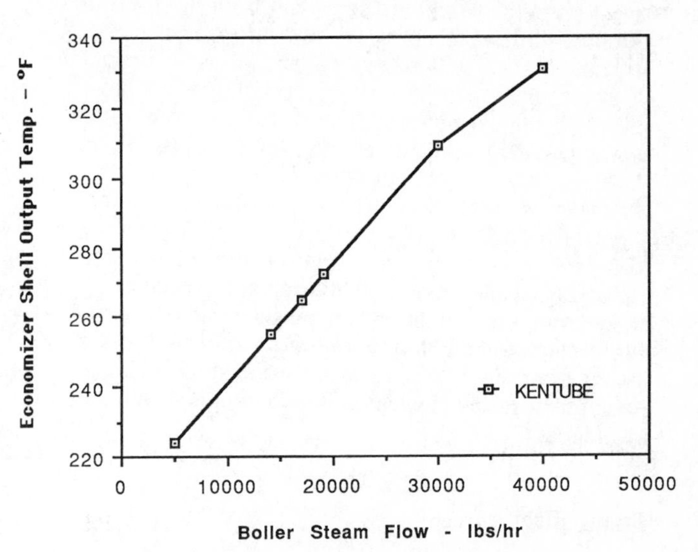

Boiler #3

Date	9/4/83	9/9/83	9/16/83	9/16/83	9/19/83	9/23/83	10/6/83
Time	0920	1545	0800 to 0945	1200 to 1210	1550 to 1545	1345	1000 a.m.
Boiler Run Time - Hrs			3466.8	3470.3	3510.95	3597.5	3873.55
Steam Flow - lbs/hr	10000	19000	32000	21000	5000	20000	7500
Stack Temp. on Boiler °F	365	420	520	422	336	423	350
Steam Pressure (psig)	100	100	100	100	100	100	100
Feedwater Temp "°F"	212	213	211	211	210	212	213
Feedwater Pressure (psig)	166	164	144	151	165	162	167
Make-up Water gals/24 hrs	2390	3580		3430	2220	3730	
Make-up Water gals/hr	100	149		143	93	155	
Gas at Burner Inches/H_2O	30	18	42	19	0	17.2	0
Condensate Temp "°F"	162	195	195	195	161	196	160
Nat. Gas Used MCF/8 hrs	628	2500	2600	2658	729	1990	249
Nat. Gas Used MCF/hr	79	313	325	332	91	250	32
Outside Temp "°F"	55	70	72	84	72	75	63
Room Temp "°F"	85	86	87	86	85	93	85
Boiler Input Temp	91	92	93	94	91	100	84
Steam Flow lbs/24 hr	389400	504450	246300	64600	50000	62500	163850
Steam Flow lbs/hr	16225	21019	10263	2692	2083	2604	6827
Nat. Gas Used Decatherm/Hr	74	294	306	313	86	236	30
BTU/hr	$74x10^6$	$294x10^6$	$306x10^6$	$313x10^6$	$86x10^6$	$236x10^6$	$30x10^6$
Gas @ Windbox Inches/H_2O	1.0	1.4	2.25	1.4	.8	1.4	1.00
Gas @ Furnace Inches/H_2O	0.3	.2	.25	.2	.3	2.5	.T5
Gas Supply Press. psig	9.9	10	9.95	9.95	9.9	9.95	9.9
Stack Temp(Meter) °F	310-318			363-381	292-286	356	
Oxygen %	4.5-3.5			2.3-.9	4.6-5.3	1.5	
Efficiency %	82			82	83	82	
CO_2 %	9.4-9.2			10.5-11.5	9.1-8.7	11	
O_2 Air Standard %	20.6			20.8	20.9	20.8	
CO Evaluated %							
Excess Air Eval. %	24.6			9.5	28	6.9	
Stack Temp. Eval. %	315			360	285	350	
Steam Upper Tank °F	98	115	180	105	102	98	112
Steam Upper Hx Outlet °F	85	98		83	85	83	97
Steam Hx Inlet °F	72	72	72	72	72	72	73
Heating Plant current amps		166,176,206			87,165,174	87,171,177	
Elect. Power KW/Hr		76			55	56	

MOUNTAIN FUEL Supply Company

WEBER STATE COLLEGE
3800 HARRISON BLVD
OGDEN UTAH 84403

YOUR ACCOUNT NUMBER	RATE	SERVICE PERIOD FROM	SERVICE PERIOD TO	CURRENT SERVICE PAST DUE AFTER
212 0001 2924A	I-2	12-31	01-31	02-27-84

BILLING CODE	METER NUMBER	METER READING PRESENT	METER READING PREVIOUS	DIAL DIFFERENCE	VOL. ADJ. FACTOR	MCF	HEAT VALUE MULTIPLIER	DECATHERMS
	152 00020	92109	88248	3861				
TOTAL				3861	4.8397	18686	.9484	17722

CURRENT BILLING
CURRENT GAS SERVICE $ 60,133.61
OGDEN CITY TAX 6% $ 3,608.02
CURRENT SERVICE AMOUNT $ 63,741.63

PREVIOUS BALANCE $ 58,722.94
PAST DUE BALANCE pd $ 58,722.94

17113

3508-552

David M. Mafson

PAY THIS AMOUNT $ 122,464.57

WEBER STATE COLLEGE
3800 HARRISON BLVD
OGDEN UTAH 84403

YOUR ACCOUNT NUMBER	RATE	SERVICE PERIOD FROM	SERVICE PERIOD TO	CURRENT SERVICE PAST DUE AFTER
212 0001 2924A	I-2	01-31	02-29	03-27-84

BILLING CODE	METER NUMBER	METER READING PRESENT	METER READING PREVIOUS	DIAL DIFFERENCE	VOL. ADJ. FACTOR	MCF	HEAT VALUE MULTIPLIER	DECATHERMS
	152 00020	95713	92109	3604				
TOTAL				3604	4.8910	17627	.9476	16703

CURRENT BILLING
CURRENT GAS SERVICE $ 58,389.22
CUSTOMER METER CHARGE $ 124.25
OGDEN CITY TAX 6% $ 3,510.81
CURRENT SERVICE AMOUNT $ 62,024.28

PREVIOUS BALANCE $ 122,464.57
PAYMENTS $ 63,741.63CR
PAST DUE BALANCE $ 58,722.94

pd Chk 65267 01-12-84

David M. Mafson

PAY THIS AMOUNT $ 120,747.22

* GAS SERVICE CHARGES REMAINING UNPAID AT THE END OF THE 2ND BILLING PERIOD (APPROXIMATELY 30 DAYS ...

MOUNTAIN FUEL Supply Company

WEBER STATE COLLEGE
3800 HARRISON BLVD
OGDEN UTAH 84403

YOUR ACCOUNT NUMBER	RATE	SERVICE PERIOD FROM	SERVICE PERIOD TO	CURRENT SERVICE PAST DUE AFTER
212 0001 2924A	I-2	06-30	07-31	08-27-84

BILLING CODE	METER NUMBER	METER READING PRESENT	METER READING PREVIOUS	DIAL DIFFERENCE	VOL. ADJ. FACTOR	MCF	HEAT VALUE MULTIPLIER	DECATHERMS
	152 00020	16526	10338	6188				
TOTAL				6188	3.5438	21929	1.0826	23740

CURRENT BILLING
CURRENT GAS SERVICE $ 76,769.17
CUSTOMER METER CHARGE $ 124.25
OGDEN CITY TAX 6% $ 4,613.61
CURRENT SERVICE AMOUNT $ 81,507.03

PREVIOUS BALANCE $ [illegible]
PAYMENTS $ 60,686.67CR

17113

3508-552

David M. Mafson

PAY THIS AMOUNT $ 81,507.03

* GAS SERVICE CHARGES REMAINING UNPAID AT THE END OF THE 2ND BILLING PERIOD (APPROXIMATELY 30 DAYS ...

MOUNTAIN FUEL Supply Company

WEBER STATE COLLEGE
3800 HARRISON BLVD
OGDEN UTAH 84403 00

YOUR ACCOUNT NUMBER	RATE	SERVICE PERIOD FROM	SERVICE PERIOD TO	CURRENT SERVICE PAST DUE AFTER
212 0010 3488A	I-2	12-31	01-31	02-25-85

BILLING CODE	METER NUMBER	METER READING PRESENT	METER READING PREVIOUS	DIAL DIFFERENCE	VOL. ADJ. FACTOR	MCF	HEAT VALUE MULTIPLIER	DECATHERMS
	152 00020	40852	36962	3890				
TOTAL				3890	4.2185	16410	1.0806	17733

CURRENT BILLING
CURRENT GAS SERVICE $ 65,220.25
CUSTOMER METER CHARGE $ 124.25
OGDEN CITY TAX 6% $ 3,920.67
CURRENT SERVICE AMOUNT $ 69,265.17

PREVIOUS BALANCE $ 65,157.72
PAYMENTS $ 65,157.72CR

17113

3508-552

David M. Mafson

PAY THIS AMOUNT $ 69,265.17

MOUNTAIN FUEL Supply Company

WEBER STATE COLLEGE
3800 HARRISON BLVD
OGDEN UTAH 84403 00

YOUR ACCOUNT NUMBER	RATE	SERVICE PERIOD FROM	SERVICE PERIOD TO	CURRENT SERVICE PAST DUE AFTER
212 0010 3488A	I-2	01-31	02-28	03-27-85

BILLING CODE	METER NUMBER	METER READING PRESENT	METER READING PREVIOUS	DIAL DIFFERENCE	VOL. ADJ. FACTOR	MCF	HEAT VALUE MULTIPLIER	DECATHERMS
	152 00020	44348	40852	3496				
TOTAL				3496	4.2411	14827	1.0736	15918

CURRENT BILLING
CURRENT GAS SERVICE $ 53,326.04
CUSTOMER METER CHARGE $ 124.25
OGDEN CITY TAX 6% $ 3,207.02
CURRENT SERVICE AMOUNT $ 56,657.31

PREVIOUS BALANCE $ 69,265.17
PAYMENTS $ 69,265.17CR

David M. Mafson

3508-552

RECEIVED
MAR 13 1985
WEBER STATE COLLEGE
CONTROLLER'S OFFICE

PAY THIS AMOUNT $ 56,657.31

* GAS SERVICE CHARGES REMAINING UNPAID AT THE END OF THE 2ND BILLING PERIOD (APPROXIMATELY 30 DAYS FROM THE PAST DUE DATE) WILL BE CHARGED INTEREST AT 1 1/2% PER MONTH 18% PER ANNUM.

MOUNTAIN FUEL Supply Company

WEBER STATE COLLEGE
3800 HARRISON BLVD
OGDEN UTAH 84403 00

YOUR ACCOUNT NUMBER	RATE	SERVICE PERIOD FROM	SERVICE PERIOD TO	CURRENT SERVICE PAST DUE AFTER
212 0010 3488A	I-2	06-30	07-31	08-27-85

BILLING CODE	METER NUMBER	METER READING PRESENT	METER READING PREVIOUS	DIAL DIFFERENCE	VOL. ADJ. FACTOR	MCF	HEAT VALUE MULTIPLIER	DECATHERMS
	152 00018	63000	58104	4896				
TOTAL				4896	3.7371	18297	1.0677	19536

CURRENT BILLING
CURRENT GAS SERVICE $ 60,674.73
CUSTOMER METER CHARGE $ 124.25
OGDEN CITY TAX 6% $ 3,647.94
CURRENT SERVICE AMOUNT $ 64,446.92

PREVIOUS BALANCE $ 62,630.42
PAYMENTS $ 62,630.42CR

17113

3508-552

David M. Mafson

PAY THIS AMOUNT $ 64,446.92

* GAS SERVICE CHARGES REMAINING UNPAID AT THE END OF THE 2ND BILLING PERIOD (APPROXIMATELY 30 DAYS ...

SECTION 28
HEAT PUMPS

Chapter 82

INDUSTRIAL AND COMMERCIAL HEAT PUMP APPLICATIONS

R. C. Niess

ABSTRACT

The energy crisis of 1973 accelerated the development of large-scale heat pumps in the United States. Since that time, the commercial, institutional, and industrial applications of heat pumps for waste heat recovery have expanded.

This paper reviews the trends in heat pump cycle developments and discusses both the closed vapor compression cycle and refrigerants most commonly used and the open-cycle mechanical vapor compression heat pumps. Waste heat sources, heat loads served by heat pumps--and typical applications using heat pumps for large-scale space heating, domestic water heating, and industrial process water heating-- are discussed.

Typical installations include commercial applications in hotels, high-rise apartments and condominiums, and office buildings. Institutional installations discussed include hospitals, universities, wastewater treatment plants, and airport terminals. Industrial applications largely center on food processing industries, feedwater heating, metal fabricating, and other industries. Reference is also made to other applications and alternative energy sources now gaining acceptance, including groundwater/geothermal water.

INTRODUCTION

The large-scale application of heat pumps in the United States had its beginning with the first known installation of an air-to-air heat pump in Reading, Pennsylvania, in 1932. Since that time, the air-to-air heat pump market has gradually grown until it now represents a significant portion of the year-round air-conditioning installations in residential and small commercial projects. A major consumer attraction is the heat pump's ability to supply both cooling and heating at a relatively small installed cost addition over cooling-only systems and slightly more over forced-air heating systems, which are predominant in the United States.

No market for "heating only" heat pumps existed prior to 1973. Also, few large heat pumps of any type were installed, since the price of energy (electric, gas, and oil) was too low to encourage owner investment.

Then came the oil/gas crisis of 1973, spearheaded by the oil embargo and completely revolutionizing the energy pricing and availability structure. One major effect was the development of interest in waste heat recovery and heat pumping, which could conserve energy. At the same time, solar and geothermal resources were studied, and heat pumping emerged as a better way to use these alternative energy sources.

Since 1973, major heat pump developments in the United States have occurred and have been commercialized on a large scale. This paper will cover heat pump applications in large commercial, institutional, and industrial projects principally using the nonreversible water-to-water closed vapor compression cycle and open-cycle mechanical vapor compression. Air-to-air, air-to-water, and water-to-air heat pump developments and their applications (largely residential) are beyond the scope of this discussion.

HEAT PUMP CYCLE DEVELOPMENT

Basic developments have largely centered on four cycle types (1). Mechanical vapor recompression, as shown in Figure 1, is one cycle. The most common use is steam compression in industrial facilities, where owning and operating costs make it attractive to use low-pressure waste steam or flash hot condensate return to subatmospheric steam and compress it for reuse in the plant. Economics are often favorable when low compression ratios are involved.

A second cycle, as shown in Figure 2, using the addition of an evaporator, finds use in petrochemical applications, particularly for distillation columns with close proximity of bottom reboilers and overhead condensers. This can be an alternative to multiple-effect evaporators and evaporation of fluids having a low boiling-point elevation.

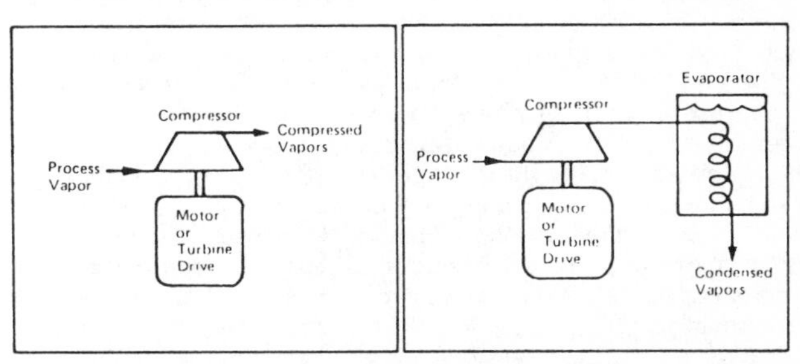

Figure 1. Open Vapor Recompression Cycle

Figure 2. Vapor Recompression Cycle with Evaporator

A third cycle, as shown in Figure 3, is the waste heat-driven Rankine cycle. This application is not yet widely used, largely due to high capital cost and some difficulties in matching heat source, heat sink, and compressed vapor needs.

The fourth cycle developed, as shown in Figure 4, is the closed vapor compression cycle. Using readily available fluorocarbon refrigerants as the heat pump working fluid, this cycle is commonly used because of its wide application opportunities.

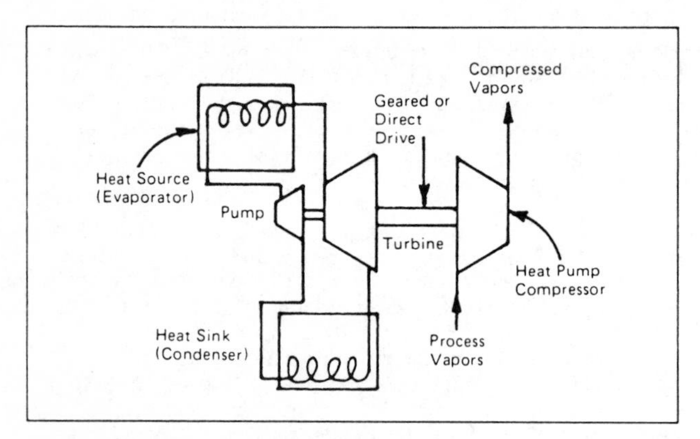

Figure 3. Waste Heat Driven Rankine Cycle

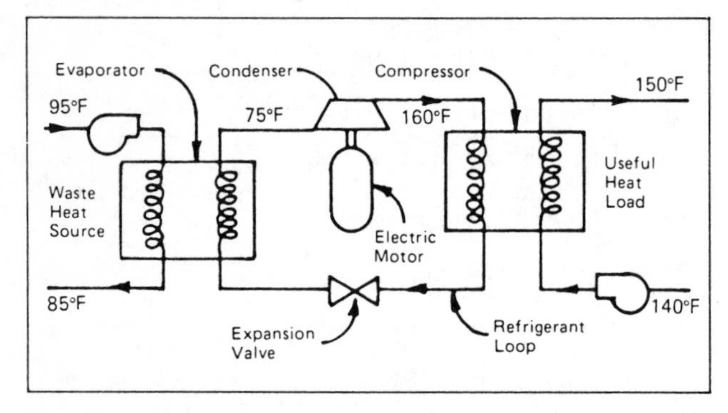

Figure 4. Closed Vapor Compression Cycle

CLOSED VAPOR COMPRESSION CYCLE

Typically, these heat pumps transfer energy from a waste heat fluid source, usually water, in a closed vapor compression cycle (2). Low-temperature energy is recovered by evaporating the heat pump working fluid. These vapors are then compressed to a condensing temperature corresponding to pressure slightly higher than the delivery temperature. The process water stream then picks up this higher temperature energy in the heat pump's condenser, returning the condensed liquid working fluid through the pressure-reducing (expansion) valve to the evaporator. By increasing the heat of compression, more heat is delivered than is recovered from the waste heat source.

Commercially available in the United States, these closed-cycle heat pumps use reciprocating, screw, and centrifugal compressor-electric motor drives, usually hermetic. They are currently being applied up to 20-million-Btu/hr output capacities in a single unit. Due to the high cost of job-site labor and the requirement for high reliability, most units are factory assembled and tested prior to shipment.

The most commonly used heat pump working fluids in a reciprocating compressor are Refrigerant-22 up to 125°F, Refrigerant-500 up to 140°F, Refrigerant-12 up to 160°F, and Refrigerant-114 up to 220°F. In centrifugal machines with slightly lower upper temperatures, the most commonly used heat pump working fluids are Refrigerant-12 and Refrigerant-114. Refrigerant-113 is also used by some manufacturers.

The typical coefficients of performance (COP's) for large centrifugal compressor heat pumps are shown in Figure 5. These curves are based on leaving source water temperature from the evaporator and leaving hot water temperature from the heat pump condenser. These two temperatures, coupled with average delta temperatures found in the evaporator and condenser, determine the overall temperature lift. This, in turn, can be translated to power inputs and the COP by the formulas:

$$COP = F \left[\frac{T_u + 460}{T_u - T_s} \right] \quad (1)$$

where:

$$COP = \frac{kW_t \text{ thermal output}}{kW_p \text{ power input}} \quad (2)$$

F = heat pump performance factor

T_u = cycle condensing temperature °F

T_s = cycle evaporating temperature °F

460 = conversion to °R.

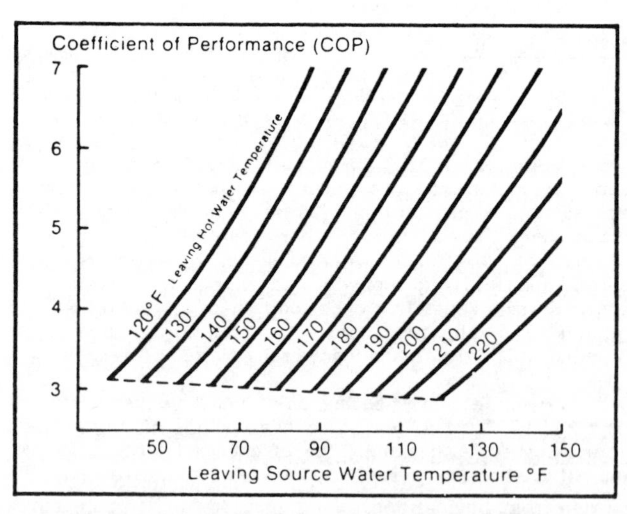

Figure 5. Typical Coefficients of Performance of Centrifugal Compressor Heat Pump

In applying large-capacity centrifugal compressor heat pumps, the maximum temperature lift in a single unit is about 90°F. When a higher temperature lift is required, a two-stage cascade system, as shown in Figure 6, is normally used. This is done for several reasons--to take advantage of the better thermal characteristics of Refrigerant-12 at output temperatures of 140°F and below, and of Refrigerant-114 above 140°F; to avoid operation at a vacuum at any point in the cycle; and to permit side loads to be handled at the intermediary loop temperature. This approach has proven to be more viable than multi-stage compression. Cascade systems have been installed in a number of projects, with significant success in performance and economics.

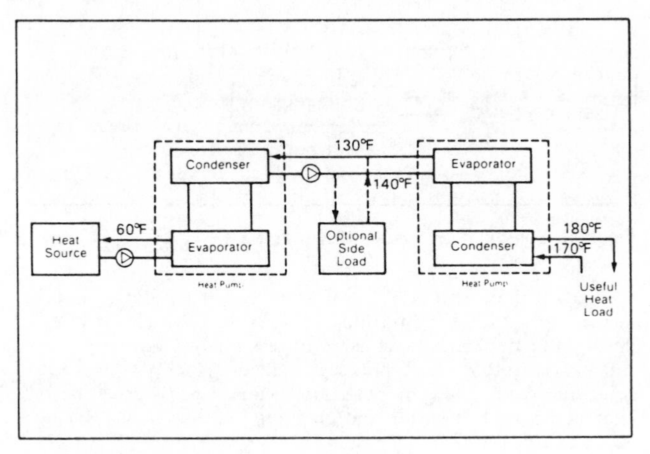

Figure 6. Cascade System

On smaller capacity installations, from about 15 kilowatts to about 100 kilowatts of power input, heat pumps using reciprocating compressors have generally been used.

WASTE HEAT SOURCES

The principal water heat source is water sent to a cooling tower which, in turn, rejects the heat energy to the atmosphere. Increasingly, this heat energy is being recovered and, through heat pumping, reused for space heating, service (domestic) water heating, and boiler feedwater and industrial process heating.

The waste heat can come from the condensers of refrigeration systems on air-conditioning systems for buildings or plants, low-level process heat from annealing and heat-treating furnaces, quench tanks, electric seam welders, air compressors, extruders, injection molders, pasteurizers, steam, and process condensers. Other sources that have been used include exhaust air streams and effluents from sewerage treatment plants and from manufacturing processes, such as those in textile, pulp, and paper mills.

More recently, where these sources are not available, there have been numerous installations using well water, groundwater, or low-temperature geothermal water from liquid-filled solar collectors and from earth-coupled heat pumps using buried pipes or downhole heat exchangers.

HEATING LOADS SERVED

Hot water from the heat pump condenser has been used for space heating, domestic water heating, makeup and reheat air heating, feedwater heating, parts washing and rinsing, degreasing systems, and general manufacturing processes that require process hot water.

Installations have been used in new construction and for retrofitting existing projects for increased energy efficiency. Percentage wise, they have been split about 50-50, with new construction seeming to be on the increase due largely to lower capital cost and increasing design attention to the "balanced heat recovery" concept by consulting engineers, architects, and owners.

TYPICAL COMMERCIAL INSTALLATIONS

In the United States, commercial installations include hotels, high-rise apartments and condominiums, and office buildings.

The principal need in hotels, apartments, and condominiums has been for the domestic hot water heating load. One example is the large Hershey Hotel in Philadelphia, Pennsylvania, which reclaimed heat from the air-conditioning system serving interior cooling loads in the lobby, restaurant, disco, meeting, and ball rooms. By using this waste heat, they--along with many other hotels--have heated most or all of the hot water needed for room, kitchen, and laundry use. In this case, the installation paid for itself in slightly over 1 year, operating at a 4.7 COP.

For intermittent hot water applications, such as domestic hot water, a storage tank is used. Typically, the storage tank is designed to serve one-half the peak hour demand, and the heat pump is sized to do the other half. Water is continuously circulated from the tank bottom, through the heat pump condenser and directly to the system or back to the tank, depending on the demand flow, as shown in Figure 7.

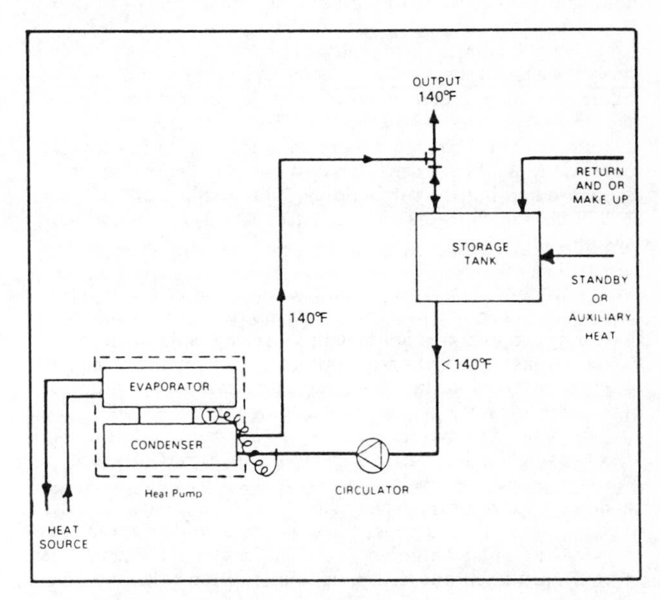

Figure 7. Domestic Hot Water Schematic

There have been numerous office building installations, typically in those that have a large internal cooling load year-round due to people, lights, computers, or any other heat-producing devices.

Such applications have ranged from a retrofit heat pump for domestic hot water and/or space heating to a multi-use installation typical of that used in several Bell Telephone Company buildings, as shown in Figure 8 (3).

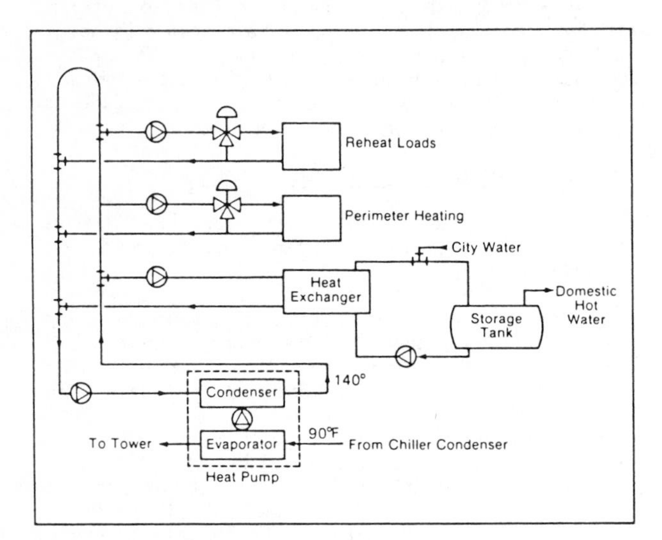

Figure 8. Typical Telephone Building Schematic

The waste heat from the chillers serving the year-round cooling load in the switch-gear areas is reclaimed and used to serve the perimeter heating load, reheat loads for humidity control and, through a heat exchanger, the building's domestic hot water needs. Three large centrifugal heat pumps--located on a mid-floor of the 20-story, 750,000-square-foot Indiana Bell Telephone Company headquarters--have split water head condensers. Half of the hot water flow is piped to the upper floors, and the other half is pumped to the lower floors. This reduced the design water working pressure on the system that would otherwise have been required had the equipment been located in the sub-basement. The efficiency of this system is demonstrated by the fact that after 2 years of operation, a third identical unit was added to serve a second adjoining, newer building that was retrofitted for 150°F baseboard radiation from a constant-volume, all-air system.

Another rapidly emerging office building and hotel heat pump application uses a combination of multiple, unitary water-to-air heat pumps serving individual perimeter areas and cooling-only units serving interior zones, plus a water-to-water heat pump, as shown in Figure 9. The interconnecting loop is maintained between 60°F and 90°F. When the majority of the unitary heat pumps are in the heating cycle, the loop temperature gradually drops. When the loop temperature reaches 60°F, heat must be added. Conversely, when the units are predominantly cooling, the loop temperature rises. When it reaches 90°F, heat must be rejected. Within this range, heat is transferred back and forth via the loop for balanced heat recovery.

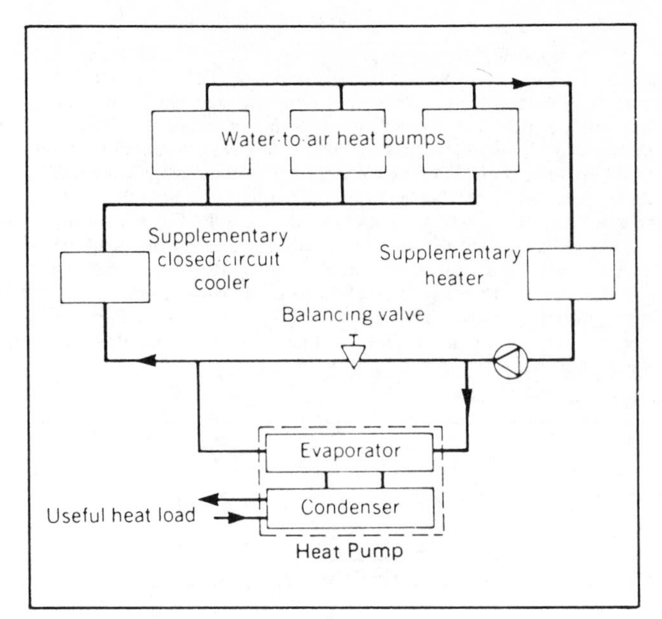

Figure 9. Combination System Schematic

Experience has shown that in many buildings, even in northern climates, the loop temperature in winter rises during the day, and heat is rejected. To effectively use this heat, a loop heat pump is added prior to the heat rejection device to generate hot water. Hotels use this to heat domestic hot water and/or makeup air.

Office buildings are storing this heat in a hot water tank, gradually heated to as high as 180°F during the day. In the 60,000-square-foot Philadelphia Life Insurance building built in 1980, a 15,000-gallon water tank is heated during the day whenever the loop temperature rises. When the automatic control system senses the loop temperature dropping, the heat pump is stopped, and the hot water from the tank is bled back into the loop to maintain its temperature above the minimum. This is shown schematically in Figure 10.

Only when the entire loop and tank system reaches 60°F is the water heating boiler turned on, and purchased energy used, to provide the building heat needed.

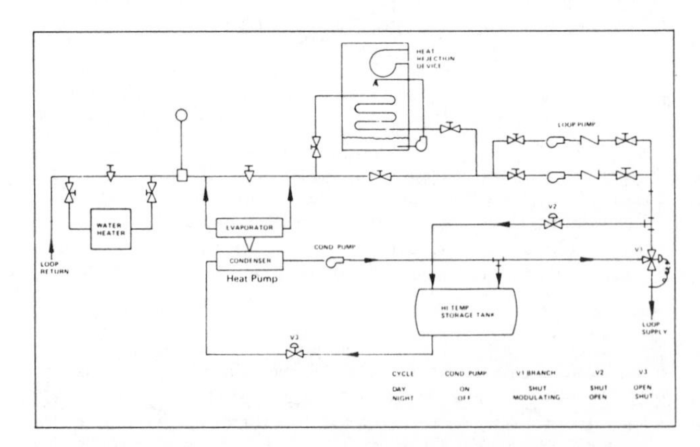

Figure 10. Combination System with High Temperature Storage

TYPICAL INSTITUTIONAL INSTALLATIONS

Hospitals have been a principal user of large-capacity heat pumps, primarily due to their need for hot water and the availability of waste heat. Hot water heating for hospital laundries consumes much of the thermal energy used. Waste heat is readily available from their chiller condenser and from the 75°F exhaust air. Heat pump reclaim from either of these sources is usually more than enough to provide the hot water needs. In some cases, both service water and space heating can be economically provided.

For example, Crozer Medical Center in Chester, Pennsylvania, uses 20,000 gallons/day of hot water in its laundry, which processes 5 million pounds of linens a year (4). Incoming city water is first preheated to 75°F using a heat exchanger, supplied with 90°F water from a chiller condenser. This same waste heat source also serves the heat pump. During the laundry cycle, a 10,000-gallon tank is emptied twice a day. After refilling with the preheated 70°F city water, the heat pump gradually heats the tank to 150°F final temperature. The mean COP for tank recovery over about 7 hours was 4.15, and the payback on the heat recovery investment was about 1½ years.

Universities, schools, laboratories, and museums have also used heat pumping effectively to reduce energy costs for space heating and domestic hot water heating. One example is Johns Hopkins University, which installed four large heat pumps over 6 years ago. The first installation of a centrifugal heat pump in August 1978 heats two buildings, totalling 160,000 square feet, and provides domestic hot water to five similar buildings, including two cafeterias (5). Supply water temperature is reset based on outdoor temperature, from 120°F in warm weather (service water heating only) up to 160°F in very cold weather. During the first year of operation, fuel oil consumption was reduced by 40,000 gallons. Subsequent installations also proved equally attractive.

Another widespread heat pump application is providing space and service water heating in sewage treatment plants (6). Prior to 1973, these plants used the gas byproduct from the digesters to provide heating. Designs today largely use this gas to fuel engine-driven pumps and generators. To meet these space heating needs, large heat pumps use the heat available in the plant's effluent and provide hot water to serve their heating needs.

Other institutional major-scale installations include buildings such as the large airport terminal complex at Orlando, Florida. The entire complex is both heated and cooled by a combination of water chillers and heat pumps. Standby heat has only been used when the cooling towers were shut down for routine maintenance or emergency repairs. Libraries, prisons, and government buildings are other institutional applications of closed-cycle heat pump heat recovery systems.

TYPICAL INDUSTRIAL INSTALLATIONS

Low-temperature heating within the output temperature range of current technology heat pumps has been used in a variety of industrial applications. Food processing industries use large quantities of hot water in the temperature ranges shown in Table 1.

TABLE 1

Food Processing Hot Water Uses

Process Use	Temperature °F
Cleaning and washdown	120 to 150
Bottle washing	120 to 140
Pasteurization (beer, milk, etc.)	140 to 190
Sterilization	150 to 185
Cooking oil preheat	165 to 180

The waste heat source in food industries usually comes from condenser heat rejection of the refrigeration system (7, 8). Because this use of evaporative condensers is common in the United States, the installation usually includes adding a water-cooled refrigerant condenser piped in parallel with the evaporative condenser. The source heat needed is derived from this water and is piped to the heat pump. One alternative is a heat pump directly condensing the plant's refrigerant in the heat pump's evaporator, with the heat pump condenser delivering heated water. Principal installations to date have been in meat packing, dairy, brewery, poultry, and frozen food processing plants.

Many industrial plants use steam boilers having a relatively high boiler feedwater heating load. This occurs where steam is sent to the plant and is sparged into the process, becoming contaminated, or condensate is not returned for other reasons. A combination of heat exchanger/heat pump is then used to preheat incoming feedwater at 50°F to about 160°F, thus offloading the boiler from this low-temperature heating load.

Other industrial applications in which heat pumps have been commercially applied are parts washing, degreasing and rinsing in metal fabricating industries, plastic molding plants, electroplating and recovery operations, and glass fabricating plants.

In the past several years, a number of dehumidification heat pumps have been installed for drying furniture-grade lumber. The slow buildup of heat in the kiln results in reduced warping, splitting, and checking of the product, while reducing operating costs. Dehumidification heat pumps are also now being used as fish dryers and for indoor swimming pools.

ALTERNATIVE ENERGY SOURCES

A number of solar collector and groundwater/geothermal water well installations are currently in use in combination with large water-to-water heat pumps. In both cases, a sizeable reduction in the number of solar collectors or well water flow and/or temperature has been made possible by combining the alternative source with heat pumping.

Many of the large solar installations designed to produce hot water involved government financing or tax incentives, since the solar energy economics do not yet deliver an acceptable return on investment. One improvement in reducing the installed first costs has been coupling lower cost, liquid solar collectors with heat pumps.

As the solar heat collected can be well below the end-use temperature required, fewer and lower cost collectors can be used. The resultant first cost is then substantially lowered, with only a small penalty in operating cost.

One example of this concept is the solar heat pump installation at Mercy Hospital in Pittsburgh, Pennsylvania (9). The solar system was originally intended to only meet the hospital's service hot water needs. The bids on this design came in at $980,000--which was well above available funding, even with the government grant.

The project was redesigned using a heat pump combined with fiberglass-covered polypropylene absorber collectors. With this system design, the bids were $504,000, and the project proceeded. One interesting and unanticipated benefit of the system was the ability to collect enough heat at night during the spring and fall to meet the lower nighttime hot water demand.

Groundwater and Geothermal Water Sources.

The application of water-to-water and water-to-air heat pumps to extract energy from groundwater and surface water and from well water is becoming increasingly popular in the United States (10, 11). Since groundwater and well water have temperatures ranging from 40°F to 80°F throughout most of the continental area, heat pumps are being used effectively for both heating and combination heating and cooling purposes.

In smaller capacities, the combination systems use refrigerant-reversing valves. In larger sizes, the water flow is reversed.

A unique application of a water-to-water heat pump is the Ephrata, Washington, geothermal energy project. The municipal water system is supplied from 84°F wells. A centrifugal heat pump extracts 13°F from the water, which is then returned to the city main, and supplies up to 130°F hot water to heat the municipal office buildings. In addition to the economic savings, the heat pump lowers the water temperature, which is too warm for domestic consumption.

In Europe, district heat systems are using heat pumps to reclaim heat from well and lake water or wastewater treatment plant effluent, in sizes up to 400-million-Btu/hr output.

OPEN-CYCLE (MECHANICAL VAPOR RECOMPRESSION) HEAT PUMPS

Unlike closed-cycle heat pumps, the open-cycle applications are all in industrial processes, where large quantities of energy are rejected in the form of low-pressure waste steam or low-grade waste heat (Figures 1 and 2). Economic heat recovery is possible, despite the low temperature levels and the possible contamination of the steam, vapor, or fluid. Table 2 lists some of the many applications where open-cycle heat pumps can be used to recover waste heat, conserve energy, and reduce energy costs.

TABLE 2

Typical Open-Cycle Heat Pump Applications

- Pulp and Paper
  - Neutral sulphite semi-chemical (NSSC) pulping evaporators.
  - Kraft pulping digester blowoff steam recovery, black liquor evaporators.
  - Thermomechanical pulping refinement of steam recovery.
  - Paper-drying, flash steam recovery.
- Chemical and Pharmaceutical Manufacturing
  - Evaporation, concentration, and crystallization processes.
  - Distillation and stripping.
  - Drying and heating.
- Food Products
  - Contaminated steam recovery.
  - Evaporation, concentration, and crystallization processes.
  - Food drying.
  - Rendering.
  - Steam cooking.
- Petroleum Refining
  - Low-pressure waste steam recovery.
  - Distillation.
  - Stripping and extraction.
- Miscellaneous
  - Solvent recovery.
  - Waste concentration.
  - Excess steam recompression.
  - Desalination.
  - Hot water flashing.
  - Boiler feedwater preheating.

Through the open cycle, waste heat can be converted to low- or subatmospheric-pressure steam, then mechanically compressed to a useful pressure, or the steam or vapor can be directly compressed to the needed process level.

OPEN-CYCLE COMPRESSORS

Open-cycle heat pump developments have primarily involved improvements in the design of screw, mixed-flow and centrifugal steam, and vapor compressors. The cycles are often referred to as mechanical vapor compression (MVC) or recompression (MVR) cycles. The selection of the compressor type is largely a function of the compression ratio (CR) required and the actual cubic feet per minute (ACFM) of inlet steam or vapor flow.

The compression ratio is defined as:

$$CR = \frac{\text{outlet psia}}{\text{inlet psia}} = \frac{\text{outlet psig} + 14.7}{\text{inlet psig} + 14.7} \quad (3)$$

And the actual flow in cubic feet per minute is defined as:

$$ACFM = \frac{\text{lb/hr steam flow x cu ft/lb at inlet pressure}}{60 \text{ min/hr}} \quad (4)$$

In the open-cycle compression process, several different thermodynamic paths may be followed (12):

- Direct compression of two-phase inlet mixture to desired conditions.
- Direct compression of dry steam to desired pressure, followed by liquid injection to desired temperature.
- Multistage compression of initially dry steam with interstage liquid injection.

The compressor COP, when compression takes place along these three paths, is shown in Figure 11.

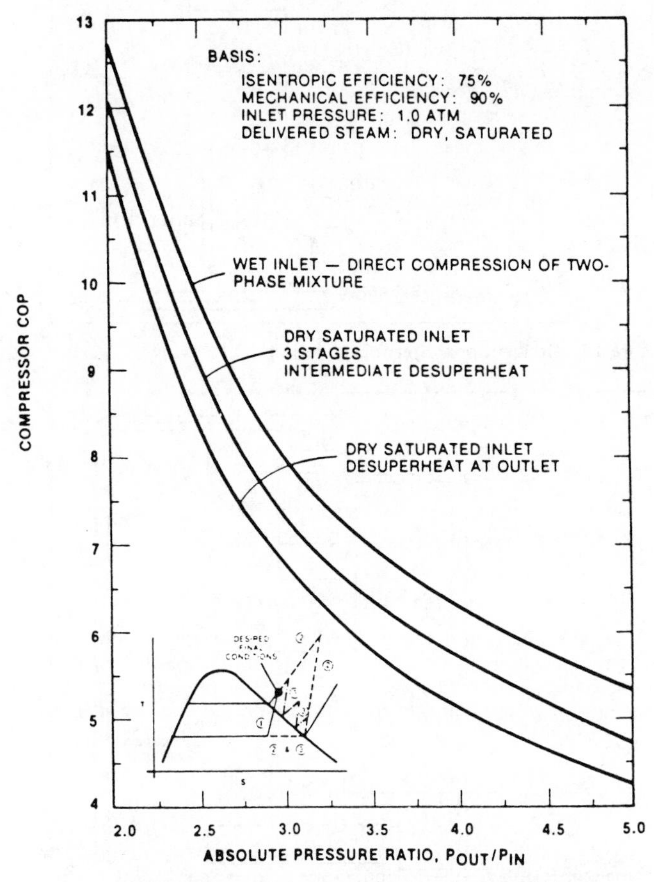

Figure 11. Compressor Coefficient-of-Performance at Various Compression Paths

The first method follows the most efficient compression path because the vapor is continuously cooled by evaporation of the entrained liquid droplets. This is practical with a screw compressor. Paths 2 and 3 are generally used with single-stage and multistage centrifugal compressors. To ensure that the steam is dry at the compressor inlet, about 10 percent of the superheated outlet vapor is recycled back to the inlet. This represents an additional equivalent percentage reduction in COP over the values shown in the figure.

In general, the positive screw compressor is used for up to five compression ratios and in sizes from 1,200 to 20,000 ACFM in a single unit. For steam compression, it has the advantage of being able to use direct water injection in the compressor itself for steam desuperheating.

Mixed flow and conventional centrifugal compressors are available in single-stage design. Compression ratios are usually limited to two per stage, with desuperheating done externally to each state. Sizes start at about 2,000 ACFM, and range up to 75,000 ACFM for mixed flow and to over 200,000 ACFM for centrifugal machinery.

For rough estimating purposes, the compressor horsepower requirements can be approximated by the formula:

$$HP = \frac{15\,(CR)(\text{lb/hr steam flow})}{1{,}000} \qquad (5)$$

More precise figures can be obtained by actual calculation of the adiabatic head at design conditions and by using compressor and driver efficiencies obtained from the manufacturer.

The decision to use open-cycle versus closed-cycle heat pumps is usually a function of the process involved and the inlet conditions. Compressor costs are approximately linear to the ACFM. From the previously cited formula for ACFM, it can be seen that the ACFM will vary directly with the inlet cubic feet per pound (4). Below about 160°F, the cubic feet per pound starts rising very rapidly by making the open cycle increasingly costly. Therefore, open-cycle steam compression is usually only considered above 150°F inlet conditions. Closed-cycle heat pump evaporation is economical for concentration of solutions that require low processing temperatures, down to 60°F.

EVAPORATOR TECHNOLOGY

Improvements have been made in the design and application of evaporators with the open-cycle heat pump (13).

Evaporation is a technology suitable for a broad range of processing applications in the food, pulp and paper, and chemical industries:

- Concentration of products.
- Chemical recovery.
- Concentration for incineration and heat recovery.
- Waste concentration.
- Crystallization.

Evaporators come in many configurations. The workhorse is the falling film evaporator, available in energy-conserving designs, incorporating multiple-effect configurations as well as mechanical vapor compression. Forced circulation evaporators and distillation columns complete the array of evaporation technology.

FALLING FILM EVAPORATORS

Falling film evaporators provide high heat transfer coefficients and maximize available temperature differences to reduce heat transfer surface requirements, allowing compact design. These evaporators may be made with the heat transfer surfaces either horizontally or vertically oriented.

Rising fuel costs have had a major impact on the economics of evaporator design. The first conservation measure was to link two or more evaporators in a series, so that heat resources could be used more efficiently. These multiple-effect units have gone to ever-larger numbers of evaporator bodies, as fuel costs made larger investment costs more practical. Mechanical vapor compression, coupled with these evaporators, can eliminate or substantially reduce steam requirements.

VAPOR COMPRESSION EVAPORATION

Mechanical vapor compression is ideally suited to handle fluids with low boiling-point elevation and provide the lowest energy consumption of any evaporative process--typically about 40 Btu/lb of water evaporated. This process is similar to multiple-effect evaporation, except that vapor is compressed and returned to the same module instead of flowing to additional effects (Figure 12). The vapor condenses on the inside of the heating tubes, providing the heat for vaporizing part of the recirculating fluid. Vapor compression evaporators are often added to increase the capacity and to reduce the energy consumption of existing systems.

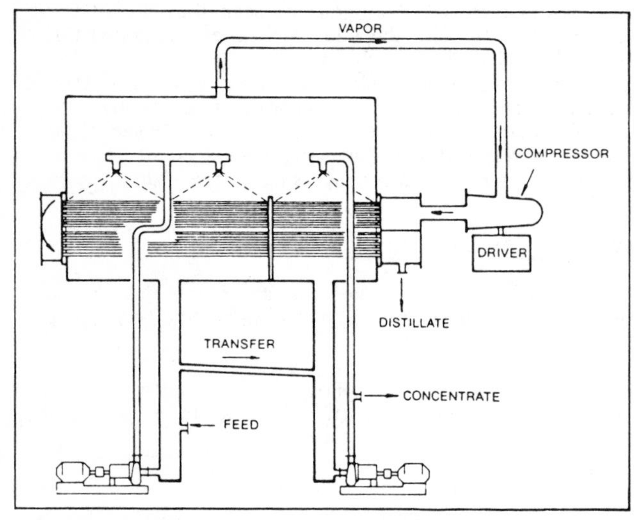

Figure 12. Low-Energy Vapor Compression System

DISTILLATION

Distillation is the separation of two or more components on the basis of the difference in their boiling points or volatility. This is accomplished by partial vaporization and subsequent condensation of the lower boiling-point components from those having a higher boiling point. Distillation systems are used for separation and enrichment of aqueous organic feed streams such as dilute ethanol or methanol, glycol, and solvents. Mechanical vapor compression is employed to reduce energy required for distillation by substituting mechanical energy for boiler steam to provide the heat of vaporization, as shown in Figure 13. As fossil fuel prices escalate, this technique will generate greater and greater operating cost savings, providing rapid capital cost payback.

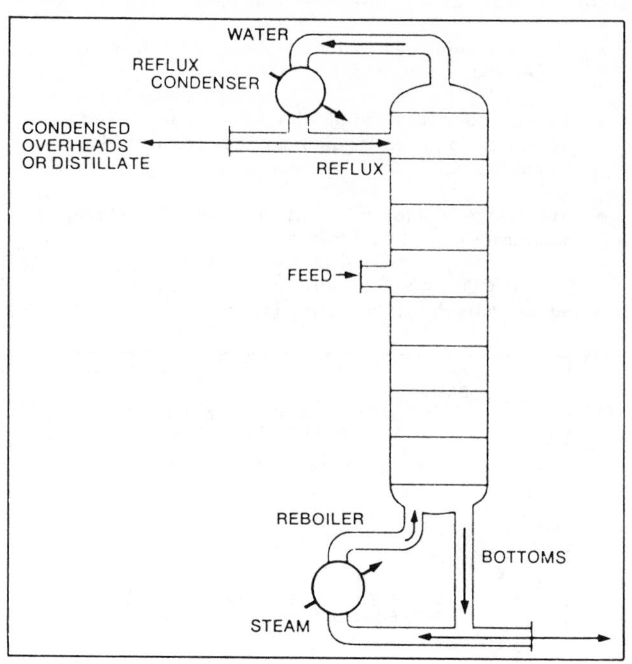

Figure 13a. Conventional Steam Distillation

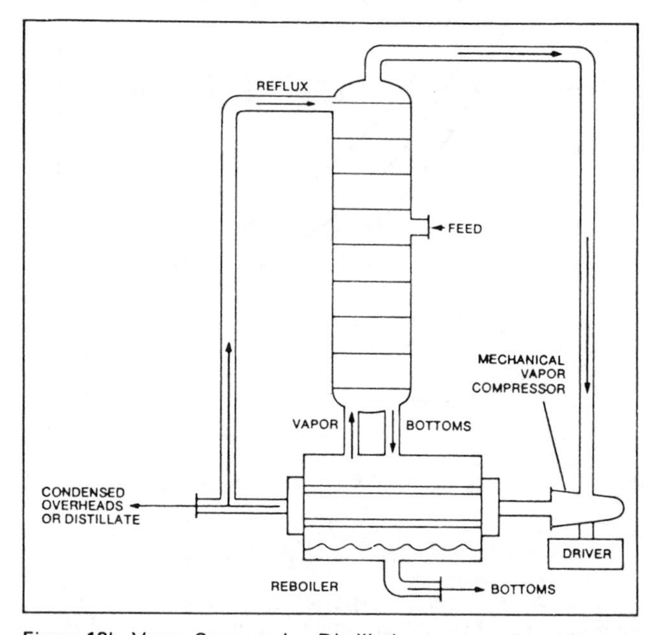

Figure 13b. Vapor Compression Distillation

Distillation equipment can also be integrated with evaporators to provide complete processing systems for such applications as agriculturally produced alcohols.

OPEN-CYCLE OPERATING ECONOMY

The operating economy of a multiple-effect evaporator system, compared to an open-cycle MVR heat pump system, depends on several factors.

- Number of effects--In general, about 0.85 pounds of water will be evaporated per pound of steam used. Therefore, the greater the number of effects, the better the economy.

- Total temperature difference--The temperature difference between the supply steam and the condenser cooling water is the driving force for the multiple-effect evaporator. This difference must be divided between the effects. As each effect must have a reasonable temperature difference between vapor and product to cause heat transfer, there is a limit to the number of effects.

- Boiling-point rise--Pure water boils at 212°F at atmospheric pressure. When the water contains soluables, depending on their nature and the amount in solution, it will boil at a higher temperature--this difference being the boiling-point rise, or elevation.

- Temperature difference across mechanical vapor compressor--This is a direct function of the compression ratio. The lower the temperature rise (therefore, compression ratio) across the compressor, the better the operating economy.

- Cost of energy--This is the cost of steam (for the multiple-effect evaporator) compared to the cost of power (for the MVR heat pump).

TYPICAL ENERGY COST ANALYSIS

One example of such an analysis would be a pulp mill that wants to examine the cost of energy for concentrating a sulphite liquor from 10 to 60 percent by weight of total solids, comparing a five-effect evaporator to an MVR heat pump. At the boiler's net steam to production efficiency and current fossil fuel cost, the 25 psig steam costs $6.00 per million Btu and has a latent heat of 934 Btu/lb; electric power costs are $0.04 per kilowatt-hour.

FIVE-EFFECT EVAPORATOR

Typically, evaporation processes will operate at 0.80 to 0.90 pounds of water evaporated per effect per pound of steam used. For this analysis, 0.85 was used. The cost per 1,000 pounds of water evaporated is:

0.85 lbs water/lb steam · effect x 5 effects =
4.25 lbs water evaporated/lb steam

$$\frac{934 \text{ Btu/lb steam}}{4.25 \text{ lbs. water/lb steam}} = 220 \text{ Btu/lb water evaporated}$$

$$\frac{\$6.00}{1 \text{ mill. Btu}} \times 1{,}000 \text{ lb water} \times 220 \text{ Btu/lb} = \$1.32/1{,}000 \text{ lbs}$$

This energy cost of $1.32 per 1,000 pounds of water evaporated will be compared to the cost of the process using a MVR heat pump.

MVR HEAT PUMP

Steam compressors will typically require 0.6 to 0.65 kilowatt input per degree F delta T per 1,000 lb/hr vapor flow for centrifugal design and 0.67 to 0.71 kW/F x 1,000 pph for screw compressors.

Considering the boiling-point rise of the sulphite liquor and a reasonable heat transfer temperature difference of a multiple-body spray film evaporator, the delta T saturated was determined to be 16.5°F.

The operating economy of the MVR heat pump is then:

0.65 kWh/°F · 1,000 lb x 16.5°F = 10.7 kWh/1,000 lb water.

The energy cost of the MVR heat pump is then:

10.7 kWh/1,000 lb water x $0.04/kWh = $0.43/1,000 lb.

This represents an energy cost savings of:

$1.32 - $0.43 = $0.89/1,000 lb water evaporated.

The capital cost difference between these systems will typically result in a simple payback of under 2 years.

CONCLUSION

The increasing need in the United States to conserve energy and to reduce dependence on oil and gas has resulted in the use of a variety of heat recovery products. The use of heat pumps--which have been applied in many different industrial process heating, institutional, and commercial facilities--is prominent. New heat pump products and applications are limited only by the imagination of the engineer.

In the near term, it is expected that heat pumps will be applied to serve multiple-building, central heating and district heating projects. Source heat from low-temperature geothermal resources, and possibly from electric power plant waste heat, is the most likely to be used. Vapor recompression cycle developments will increase the applications for production and use of steam and in various distillation and evaporation processes.

Heat pumps are expected to continue their market growth, as energy prices increase faster than general inflation and economics dictate their consideration as an alternative to fossil fuels.

REFERENCES

(1) J. S. Gilbert, "Industrial Heat Pumps," Plant Engineering, November 23, 1983.

(2) "Applied Heat Pump Systems," ASHRAE Handbook, Systems Volume.

(3) P. Norelli, "Industrial Heat Pumps," Plant Engineering, August 21 and September 18, 1980.

(4) "Hospital Heat Recovery System Saves a Bundle," Commercial Remodeling, August 1981.

(5) A. Stucki, "Heat Pump Cuts Oil Use," Contractors Electrical Equipment, November 1979.

(6) R. C. Niess, "Effluents and Energy Economics," Water/Engineering and Management, August 1981.

(7) J. Forwalter, "Waste Heat from Refrigeration System Provides Energy for Hot Water," Food Processing, December 1979.

(8) D. Woods and R. F. Ellis, "Waste Heat Recovery System," Food Processing, August 1983.

(9) A. Weinstein, et al. "Solar Assisted Domestic Hot Water Heat Pump System," proceedings of the American Section of the International Solar Energy Society, May 1981.

(10) G. W. Lund, "Low-Temperature Geothermal Development," Geothermal Resources Council Bulletin, March 1984.

(11) R. C. Niess, "Geothermal Heat Pump Systems," Geothermal Resources Council Bulletin, December 1982.

(12) F. E. Becker and A. L. Zakak, "Mechanical Vapor Recompression for Waste Energy Recovery," proceedings of the National Petroleum Refiners Association Annual Meeting, March 1985.

(13) Aqua-Chem, Inc. bulletin WT-447-R1.

Chapter 83

IMPACT OF HEAT PUMP WATER HEATERS ON UTILITY COMPANIES AND HOME OWNERS

D. P. Mehta, D. J. Rocke, D. C. Zietlow

ABSTRACT

The objective of the work reported in this paper was to evaluate the benefits, if any, from the use of Heat Pump Water Heaters (HPWH) for domestic hot water. The purpose of the evaluation was to provide information to the home owners for making purchase decisions and to recommend the level of involvement of the utility in the marketing of HPWH.

The objectives of the project were accomplished by installing, instrumenting, and monitoring two different kinds of HPWH viz; Add-on type (AHPWH) and Integral type (IHPWH) at two different residences in Peoria, IL. The measured performance of HPWH was compared with the performance of an Electric Water Heater (EWH), Natural Gas Water Heater (GWH), and Liquid Propane Water Heater (LPWH). The technical comparison was used to carry out an economic analysis. The results of the analysis are presented in this paper.

INTRODUCTION

Generally, utility planners can make use of five general strategies available for changing load shapes. The first three are classic load management techniques for improving utility load curves by smoothing out the peaks and valleys of customer demand. Peak clipping reduces system peak loads, valley filling builds off-peak loads, and load shifting moves demand from on-peak to off-peak periods. Another possibility, strategic conservation, reduces total energy use without necessarily reducing peak demand. In choosing this objective, the utility planner takes into account the conservation actions that would occur naturally and then evaluates the cost-effectiveness of utility programs to stimulate or accelerate those actions. The fifth possibility for changing a utility's load profile is strategic load growth, which means an increase in beneficial sales. In the last two cases the strategic aspect is selectivity. The potential impacts need to be quantified by evaluating the performance of electricity consuming products for optimal selection of strategies.

The purpose of the research reported in this paper was to quantify the impact of an electricity consuming product viz., Heat Pump Water Heater (HPWH), both on the utility and on the home owner. Two different kinds of heat pump water heaters viz., Add-on type and Integral type were installed and instrumented at two different residences in Peoria, IL. The method of obtaining and analyzing test data for systems evaluation consisted of several test sensors, and a programmable data acquisition system, and analysis software developed for use with an IBM Personal Computer.

The residences were also equipped with electric water heaters (EWH). The HPWH mode and EWH mode were switched manually on a weekly basis. Energy in, energy out and standby losses were measured. Data were taken to calculate the heating penalties, air-conditioning savings, and dehumidification savings in the HPWH mode of operation. The performance of the HPWH was also compared with natural gas and liquid propane water heaters. An economic analysis was carried out for the home owners. The level of involvement of the utility company in marketing HPWHs was determined. The details of the data analysis and the results obtained are reported in this paper.

DATA ANALYSIS

A computer program was developed which could read the collected data from the diskettes directly and could calculate the energy transfers, stand by losses, energy savings, coefficients of performance, demands, load factors, heating penalties, air-conditioning/dehumidification savings, and other parameters necessary to quantify the impacts of HPWH. The information so obtained was used to run economic analyses both for the home owner and for the utility.

Data Analysis for the Home Owner

The following assumptions and input data were used in doing an economic analysis for the home owner:

1. The first costs of different kinds of domestic hot water heaters were determined by calling several vendors and the data used are:

Electric Water Heater (EWH):	$365
Add-On Heat Pump Water Heater(AHPWH):	$800
Integral Heat Pump Water Heater(IHPWH):	$865
Liquid Propane Water Heater (LPWH):	$365
Natural Gas Water Heater (GWH):	$365

   It is assumed that the costs of LPWH and GWH include the cost of a small flue.

2. The life of the AHPWH is equal to the life of any other water heater and is equal to ten years. It is recognized that this assumption applies only to the situations of new construction or where the customers are ready to retrofit. However, this assumption is made to eliminate the differences in the time value of involved costs if water heaters to which AHPWHs are added are replaced at different times, which are difficult to estimate, during the life of AHPWH.

3. The energy costs used in the analysis were derived from the current rate structure of the local utility company and are as follows:

   Electricity- --9.10¢/KWH in summer (5/7-9/5)
   --4.16¢/KWH in winter (9/6-5/6)

Natural Gas: 53.4¢/Therm

Liquid Propane: 76.0¢/Gallon

The price of liquid propane is based on the information collected by calling several vendors.

4. Energy content of fuels used were based upon the values used by the Department of Energy and are

   Natural Gas: 100,000 Btu/Therm

   Liquid Propane: 93,000 Btu/Gallon

5. It was assumed that a typical family of four members used 450 gallons of hot water per week. This data is based upon the studies done by the Department of Energy and is also used by the manufacturers to prepare 'Energy Guide' for water heaters. This data on hot water consumption was further supported by the results of a study done on solar water heaters.

6. It was assumed that a typical family heats water to 120 degress F and on the average the cold water temperature is 59 degrees F. This information is based on field data.

7. It was assumed that there are no tax advantages to the home owner because of installing and operating HPWH.

8. It was assumed that there is no salvage value on retirement of water heaters. Several plumbers were asked if they would buy a retired water heater. The answer was 'No.'

9. It was assumed that the fuel prices increase at the rate of general inflation rate. This is supported by the past historical trend.

10. The impact of the heat pump water heater upon the heating, cooling, and dehumidification equipment was determined based on the following assumptions

    a) The unit is installed in a space that requires dehumidification.

    b) The unit is located in a basement which is heated with electric heat and cooled by a central air-conditioner.

11. Natural gas water heaters and liquid propane gas water heaters were assumed to be 50% efficient for calculating costs and savings. This assumption is supported by the field tests and includes the stand-by losses.

12. No water heater blankets were assumed to be covering the water heaters and the stand-by losses used were based on the actual field data.

Data Analysis for the Utility

The assumptions made for the home owner data analysis and described above apply to the data analysis for the utility also. In addition, the data analysis for the utility was based on marginal costs and revenues. For the purpose of this analysis, marginal costs are the average annual investments incurred by the utility when a home owner installs a water heater. The analysis for the utility assumed that there will be no need to build additional generation or transmission facilities in the next ten years.

The marginal revenues were based on the current rate structure of the local utility company. The revenues used were net revenues which excluded any expenses such as taxes and fuel costs.

RESULTS

Home Owner Costs and Benefits

Using the assumptions described previously, annual operating costs and savings for different kinds of water heaters were calculated and are shown in Tables 1-2 and in Figures 1-2. The savings shown in Table 2 and Figure 2 include heating penalties, and air-conditioning/dehumidification savings in addition to operating cost differences.

Table 1. Annual Operating Costs for Different Types of Water Heaters

Add-On HPWH	Integral HPWH	Electric Water Heater	Natural GWH	Liquid Propane Water Heater
$142.72	$159.89	$337.07	$109.33	$167.18

Table 2. Annual Savings due to the use of Add-On HPWH

Vs Integral HPWH	Vs Electric Water Heater	Vs Natural GWH	Vs Liquid Propane Water Heater
$17.16	$260.48	$32.74	$90.56

The performance of the add-on HPWH was compared with the performances of integral HPWH, EWH, GWH, and a LPWH by applying an economic analysis model. The add-on HPWH was found to have an economic advantage over all other water heaters. For a typical home owner with a family of four members, the payback period (P.B.) and rates of return (R.O.R.) on an investment in an add-on HPWH are shown in Table 3 and in Figure 3.

FIG. 1 – ANNUAL OPERATING COSTS OF DIFFERENT TYPES OF WATER HEATERS

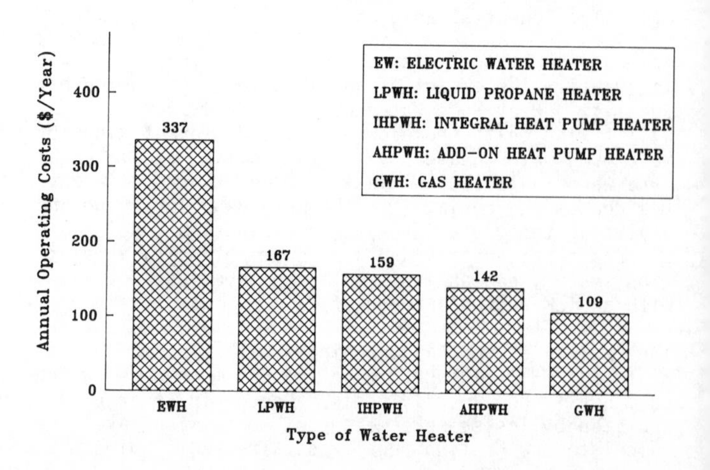

FIG. 2 – ANNUAL SAVINGS BY USING ADD-ON HEAT PUMP WATER HEATER VS. OTHER WATER HEATERS

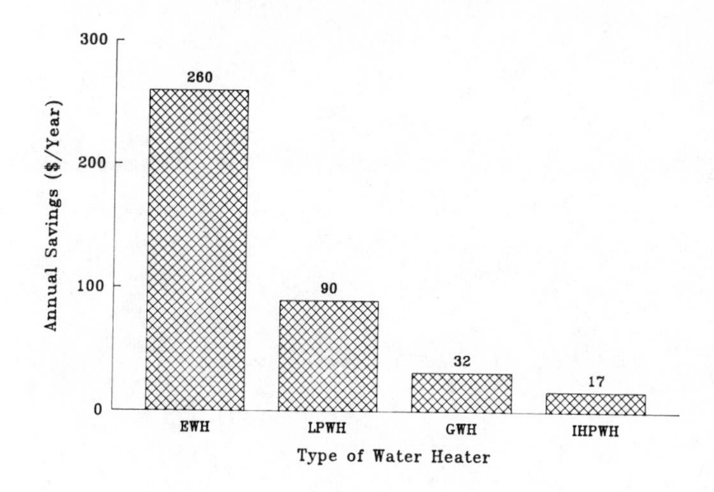

Table 3. Economic Analysis for an Investment in Add-On HPWH.

Economic Parameter	Vs Electric WH	Vs Integral HPWH	Vs Nat. gas WH	Vs Liquid Propane WH
R.O.R	30%	< 0.25%	< 0.25%	2%
P.B.	3 years	17 years	24 years	9 years

FIG. 3 – ECONOMIC ANALYSIS

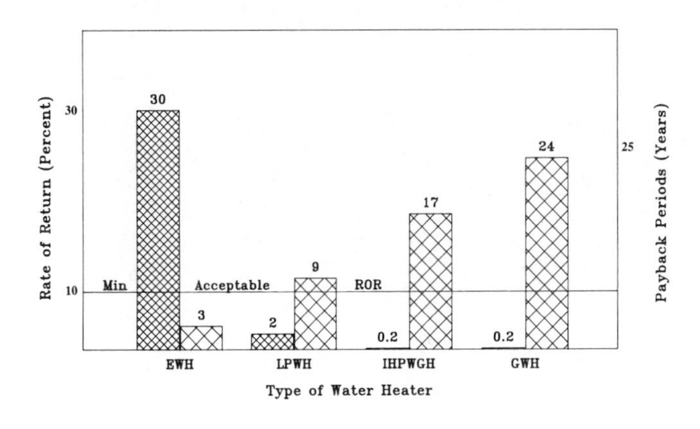

In the case of the integral HPWH, GWH, and the LPWH where the R.O.R. and P.B. are not attractive for the home owner, a sensitivity analysis was done. In this analysis, required variations in the first costs, hot water used, fuel prices or variations in efficiencies were determined which will ensure at least 10% rate of return for the homeowner. These variations are summarized in Table 4.

Table 4. Sensitivity Analysis for a 10% R.O.R. from an Investment in an Add-On HPWH

Type of Water Heater	For a Typical Home Owner			
	Reqd. Reduction in First Cost of Add-On HPWH	Required Increase in Hot Water Use	Required Increase in Fuel Cost	Required C.O.P.
Integral HP	$695	2.8 times	SR=25.4¢/KWH WR=11.6¢/KWH	3.30
Natural Gas	$599	1.9 times	$1.00/Therm	2.24
Liquid Propane	$244	1.5 times	$1.03/Gallon	1.77
Natural Gas with Rebate	$363	1.5 times	$ .81/Therm	1.77

The possible impact of a one time rebate was also investigated. The rebate program could work for the owners of GWHs if variations shown in Table 4 (see entry for natural gas water heater with rebate) take place as they would ensure a 10% R.O.R. for the home owner. The owners of LPWH's can expect a R.O.R. of about 14% from an investment of an AHPWH under the rebate program.

Utility Benefits

Several types of domestic hot water heaters were evaluated to determine what benefits, if any, would be available to the utility company. Table 5 shows the input data on energy consumption and demands which was used in an economic model for calculating the utility benefits. The energy consumptions and demands shown in Table 5 were calculated using the actual field data and by applying the assumptions stated previously. The outputs of the economic model showed that the utility company is most benefited if domestic hot water is heated by an electric resistance water heater.

Table 5. Input Data for Economic Analysis of Utility Benefits

Type of Data	Add-On HPWH	Integral HPWH	Electric Water Data	Natural Gas Water Heater	Liquid Propane Water Heater
Energy Consumption					
@ Summer Rates	847 KWHS	884 KWHS	1921KWHS		
@ Winter Rates	1693 KWHS	1768 KWHS	3842 KWHS		
Annual	2540 KWHS	2652 KWHS	5763 KWHS	205 Therms	220 Gal.
Customer Peak Demand	1.4 KW	2.34 KW	2.44 KW		

The outputs of the model were also useful to the utility company to determine its level of involvement in the marketing of different types of domestic water heaters.

CONCLUSIONS

The performance of heat pump water heaters has been evaluated and compared with the performance of several other types of domestic hot water heaters. The benefits of add-on type heat pump water heater over the other heaters, if any, were evaluated both for the home owner and for the utility company.

For the home owner, it was determined that an investment in an add-on HPWH is economically attractive with a R.O.R. of 30% if it is added to an existing electric water heater. Adding this water heater to natural gas or liquid propane water heater does produce some savings. However, the R.O.R. is not attractive. The home owner with a natural gas water heater can expect a 10% R.O.R. from an investment in AHPWH if the hot water usage is about 850 gallons per week or if the price of natural gas increases to about $1.00 per Therm or if the first cost of the AHPWH drops down to $200.

For the utility company, the highest profits are when domestic hot water is heated by pure electric resistance heater. The utility company can get involved with the marketing of AHPWH for those customers who own liquid propane water heaters. The utility company can also get involved with the marketing of AHPWH to natural gas water heater owners if the price of natural gas increases to $0.81/Therm or when AHPWH with a seasonal COP of at least 1.8 are available.

ACKNOWLEDGEMENTS

Financial support from the Central Illinois Light Co. to carry out the research work reported in this paper is gratefully acknowledged. Special thanks are due to Mr. Frank Rossi, a graduate from the Mechanical Engineering Department of Bradley University, for his assistance. Appreciation is also extended to Mrs. Gayle Deynzer for her interest and efforts in typing this paper.

Chapter 84

VARIABLE SPEED DRIVE HEAT PUMP PERFORMANCE

S. M. Jeter, W. J. Wepfer, G. M. Fadel, N. E. Cowden
A. A. Dymek

ABSTRACT

Development of a simulation model for variable speed heat pumps is described and representative results are presented. The system under consideration employs a hermetic compressor driven by an integral three-phase induction motor. Compressor speed can be modulated by varying the frequency of the current synthesized by an inverter which supplies power to the system. A modular simulation system is used wherein an executive program manages the input and output of data and coordinates the numerical simulation procedure. The executive program calls various subroutines which model the system components, evaluate thermodynamic properties, and perform numerical tasks. Simulation results demonstrate that the variable speed heat pump has an improved COP at reduced frequency, desirable for enhancing energy conservation under part load conditions, and higher heating rates at high frequency, a useful feature for reducing supplementary resistance heat. The simulation program is used to generate performance data over a range of ambient conditions. This data is then used as the basis for seasonal energy consumption calculations performed using a temperature bin format.

INTRODUCTION

A modular simulation program for studying the performance of variable speed drive heat pumps relative to conventional constant speed heat pumps has been developed and successfully implemented. A simple variable speed heat pump is modeled using a polytropic compressor module, a constant coefficient flow control valve, and simplified heat exchanger modules. Seasonal performance is computed via a temperature bin analysis. Results indicate that the variable speed unit requires on the order of 6 to 10% less electrical energy than a comparable constant speed unit operating in the heating mode. These results do not penalize the conventional unit for cycling losses which can be significant.

Modular simulation allows a system to be analyzed in terms of well defined components. The system can then be simulated by integrating the components into an encompassing model. The relatively complicated component modules interact following simple rules to simulate the behavior of the system as a whole. At least four component modules are necessary to model a heat pump in the heating mode: compressor, flow control device, condenser, and evaporator.

HEAT PUMP SIMULATION PROGRAM

Compressor Module

The compressor module was designed to simulate the operation of a variable-speed positive-displacement compressor. The module inputs include the exit state of the evaporator, the condenser pressure, and the frequency of the electrical power supplied to the compressor motor. Several other pertinent parameters are also required. Using this data, the module calculates the mass flow rate of the refrigerant, the electrical power required to compress the refrigerant, and the state at the outlet of the compressor.

During the course of this project two different modules were written. Both of the modules were developed assuming the compressor to be adiabatic. The first is a simple model that bases its calculations on the isentropic efficiency concept. This simple module was used as a prototype for the later more complicated module. The later module uses the concept of polytropic compression to calculate the needed quantities. It is more detailed in that it takes into account:

1. Heating of the refrigerant as it passes over the electric motor (assuming a hermetic compressor).

2. Pressure drops in the inlet and outlet valves.

3. Mechanical efficiency of the compressor.

4. Electrical efficiency of the motor.

5. Calculation of volumetric efficiency based on the clearance volume.

Flow Control Device

The flow control device maintains a pressure differential between the condenser and evaporator. Conventional heat pumps rely on one of several practical devices for this function. The simplest component is a fixed restriction, normally a small diameter tubing or capillary. Controlled valves are typical in more contemporary applications. Both constant pressure and, most commonly, thermostatically controlled expansion valves are used.

In the current simulation program the expansion device is modeled as a simple capillary tube. This was done to make the initial simulation model as simple as possible while remaining physically realistic. Extension to a thermostatic expansion valve which would operate to maintain a set degree of superheat at the evaporator exhaust is straightforward and would entail the addition of a feedback control loop in the system. Since the control function would only serve to adjust the restriction between the condenser and evaporator, the development of a fixed-resistance capillary model was a necessary precursor. Various control strategies can be assessed once this extra complexity is included in the system. The possibility of direct digital control of the expansion valve by a microprocessor included in the heat pump's control system provides the opportunity to achieve optimal control of the pressure ratio to maximize the cycle COP or to help meet extreme loads.

The flow through a fixed expansion valve should be well into the hydraulically rough regime and, consequently, Reynolds number independent. This situation implies that the conventional valve coefficient model should be adequate. Using this formalism, the pressure drop is given by:

$$P_{cnd} - P_{evp} = (V_f/C_v)^2$$

where V_f is the volumetric flow and C_v is the valve coefficient. The valve coefficient should be reasonably constant for a given device and refrigerant or even similar refrigerants. When the program advances to model controlled valves, the coefficient, C_v, will become a function of the valve opening.

Simple Heat Exchanger Modules

Two modules were developed to implement simple models of the condenser and evaporator. These modules have several uses including:

1. Expediting the development of the simulation system.

2. Providing preliminary results.

3. Serving as a system-level check on simulations that employ more complicated modules.

4. Acting as prototypes for more complicated modules.

In present form both modules consider only a single flow geometry, cross flow with the air side unmixed and the refrigerant side mixed. In their current form both modules appear to be reasonably accurate and numerically stable, but this level of performance has been attained only after considerable testing and development.

Initial attempts to employ an effectiveness-NTU model by iteration on the unknown refrigerant heat capacity rate was unsuccessful. Some improvement was obtained by a switch to iteration on the refrigerant temperature change; however, in view of the sensitivities of such a model to phase changes, a more direct approach was required.

The successful solution to the convergence problem was the implementation of a more deterministic heat exchanger model that does not require iteration or unduly accurate determination of the change in the thermodynamic state. The basic analyses for both the condenser and the evaporator are similar. The exchanger is analyzed as a series of (50 or 100) elements. For cross flow, an element receives the entire refrigerant flow but only a fraction of the air flow; consequently, the air is sure to be the so-called "minimum fluid" for each element. The number of transfer units (NTU) for an element can be calculated directly as:

$$NTU = UA_j/C_{aj}$$

where UA_j is the conductance for element j and C_{aj} is the air flow across element j. Since the refrigerant heat capacity rate greatly exceeds that for the air, the simple formula (valid for C_{min}/C_{max} approaching 0) is applicable so that:

$$\epsilon_j = 1 - \exp(-NTU)$$

The heat rate for an element is given by:

$$Q_j = \epsilon_j C_{aj}(T_{a,in} - T_{r,in})$$

where the two temperatures are the inlet air temperature and inlet refrigerant temperature (from the preceding element) because the maximum temperature difference must be between the fluids entering the element.

The overall heat rate is determined by accumulating the elemental rates, and the overall effectiveness can be computed from the definition:

$$\epsilon = Q/Q_{max}$$

where the fundamentally limiting heat rate is given by:

$$Q_{max} = C_{min}(T_h - T_c)$$

where T_h and T_c are either the refrigerant or air temperature entering the heat exchanger, depending on whether the condenser or the evaporator is being modeled. Since the heat rate would have already been evaluated deterministically, the minimum fluid can be selected and the effectiveness computed directly.

In addition to the heat exchange analysis, the evaporator module must compute a new value for the evaporating pressure. Steady-state operation requires that the heat burden on the evaporator (the condenser heat less the compressor work), equal the evaporator heat rate. The evaporator module includes an additional algorithm to adjust the evaporating pressure to a higher or lower value as needed to balance the heat burden with the heat rate.

The heat exchange calculations are the most important and troublesome computations; however, it is also necessary to consider the air side fan dynamics. The fan laws are used to adjust the flow rate and hydraulic power for off-design conditions. Typically, a fan driven by an induction motor will operate within a few (2 to 5) percent of synchronous speed regardless of the load. It can be assumed then that the fan speed is a fixed fraction (near unity) of the synchronous speed. The flow rate at off-peak electrical frequency is given by:

$$V = V_d N/N_d$$

where V_d is the design volumetric flow and N_d is the design synchronous speed (e.g. 1200, 1800, or 3600 RPM) while V and N are the prevailing flow and speed. The synchronous speed is determined by the electrical design of the motor and the electrical frequency. Typically the indoor coil is provided with a centrifugal blower powered by a nominal 1/3 horsepower six pole motor (1200 RPM synchronous speed) and the outside coil is ventilated by an axial fan with a four pole motor (1800 RPM) of around 1/4 horsepower.

The hydraulic power of the fan (rate of flow work done on the air) varies with the cube of the speed ratio according to the appropriate fan law:

$$W = W_d(N/N_d)^3$$

Design pressure drops are typically 0.3 inch (water gage) for the outdoor coil and about 0.8 inch for the indoor fan which serves a deeper coil and must accommodate the frictional resistance of the ductwork as well.

The electrical power consumed is typically much greater than the hydraulic power on account of the necessarily low efficiency of the small fans. This power is given by:

$$W_e = W/n_f$$

In heat pump applications the fans are typically mounted downstream to provide a favorable pressure gradient across and thereby a more uniform flow through the coils. The leaving air enthalpy is increased by the amount of electrical power consumed all of which can be assumed to be dissipated in the air stream. This configuration dictates that the indoor fan power augments the heating effect and reduces the cooling effect of the indoor coil. All power from the outdoor motor is dissipated to the environment in such a configuration.

The fan efficiency surely varies with operating conditions, especially speed, but due to paucity of reliable data a fixed value of 50% was used.

SIMULATION PROCEDURE

The simulation system includes a main program, four component modules, and several utility programs. The main program manages the input of data, the output of results, and oversees the cycle convergence procedure. The component modules treat each of the four heat pump system components: the compressor, condenser, flow controller, and evaporator. The utility programs implement convergence procedures, compute thermodynamic properties, and perform numerical operations such as interpolation.

The primary function of the main program is supervision of the sequential and iterative cycle analysis. The block diagram shown in Figure 1 illustrates the flow of information in the simulation system. If one choses, as was done in this analysis, to begin the simulation sequence at the compressor inlet, guesses or initial estimates are needed for three quantities to allow the completion of the cycle analysis. These quantities are two properties of the refrigerant to fix its thermodynamic state and a guess of the condenser or high-side pressure which will allow the calculation of the refrigerant flow rate. Since guesses of three unknown quantities are required, iteration will be required until the guesses converge on calculated values. The information flow diagram (IFD) clearly illustrates the three information recycle loops that were used to analyze the heat pump system. Data supplied to a module are referred to as "inputs" and the results returned by a module are referred to as "outputs". These logical inputs and outputs frequently, but not always, correspond to the physical inlet (or intake) and outlet (or exhaust) quantities such as material flows and properties, heat rates, or control signals.

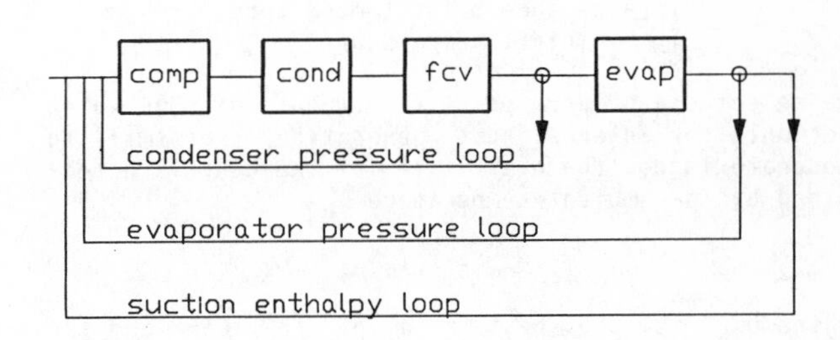

FIGURE 1. INFORMATION FLOW DIAGRAM (IFD) FOR THE HEAT PUMP SIMULATION SYSTEM

The compressor module requires values for the state of the inlet refrigerant (e.g. evaporator pressure, P, and suction enthalpy, h) and a value for the condenser pressure. These values cannot be known initially so reasonable guesses must be generated. With these inputs, the mass flow rate and outlet state can be computed as output variables. The condenser module requires the refrigerant mass flow and inlet state, the condensing or high-side pressure, and air properties. The inlet air properties are known from specification of the operating conditions. In the simple model, the fan laws are used to compute the air flow rate and fan power from rated conditions and a specification of the fan efficiency. Values for the refrigerant flow and state come from the compressor module. The condenser is followed by the flow control valve (FCV). The module representing the flow control valve computes a new value for the high-side pressure from the condenser outlet state and the evaporator pressure. Since the FCV output includes the recalculated value of a previously guessed value, this point in the IFD is a critical decision node for the innermost recycle loop. The convergence routine must compare the computed value with the guessed value and provide a new guess if the agreement is unsatisfactory.

The output of the evaporator module is a decision node for two recycle loops. One for the evaporator pressure and an outer loop for the suction enthalpy. In practice several iterations are usually required to obtain a convergent evaporator pressure whereas convergence for the suction enthalpy is quicker since the evaporator pressure has been adjusted to make the evaporator heat rate approximately match the heat burden.

ANNUAL BIN CALCULATIONS

In order to compare the annual performance of the variable speed heat pump (VSHP) and the constant speed heat pump (CSHP), a simple method using temperature bins is used. Basically, a file contains the number of hours per year the ambient conditions are within temperature intervals or bins (the average temperature is used out of an interval of 5°F). This file is used in conjunction with steady-state runs of the CSHP and the VSHP at these ambient conditions.

The hourly heat rate required is:

$$Q_b = UA\ [T_r - T_a]$$

where Q_b = Heat rate of the CSHP
UA = Building conductance
T_r = Balance point temperature
T_a = Ambient temperature.

We selected a balance point temperature of 65°F which accounts for internal heat generation. For small to moderate loads, the heat rate of the CSHP is determined by the ambient temperature T_a:

$$Q_{cs} = f(T_a)$$

where Q_{cs} is the heat rate of the CSHP and the portion of the hour it runs is given by:

$$t = Q_b/Q_{cs}$$

The CSHP will consume electric energy for this bin in the amount:

$$W_c = Q_b(1\ \text{hour})/COP_{cs}$$

If $Q_b > Q_{cs}$, resistance heat has to be added:

$$W_r = (Q_b - Q_{cs})\ 1\ \text{hour}$$

And the total electric energy consumed by the CSHP is:

$$W_{cs} = W_c + W_r$$

For moderate loads, the VSHP will run the entire hour but at a lower speed and presumably a higher COP to just meet the load:

$$Q_b = Q_{vs}$$

where Q_{vs} is a function of ambient temperature and electrical frequency. The VSHP will consume a smaller amount of electrical power given by:

$$W_{vs} = Q_b(1\ \text{hour})/COP_{vs}$$

Note that at very light loads, the VSHP cannot run the whole hour since minimum speed constraints will restrict the operation of the machine. A minimum frequency is imposed on the machine and if the heat load supplied by the VSHP is still too large for the house load, the VSHP will cycle on/off like the CSHP, but at a slower rate. At high loads, a maximum frequency limit is imposed on the VSHP; if the VSHP cannot meet the load when running at that maximum frequency, resistance heat is added as done for the CSHP. Also, only heating loads are considered; consequently, bins above 65°F have been disregarded.

RESULTS

To exercise the model and develop the performance characteristics needed for the annual calculations, a series of simulations were run with the ambient temperature ranging from 10°F to 70°F and the indoor temperature maintained at 70°F. Figure 2 shows the heating COP of the fixed speed heat pump over this range of ambient temperatures. Also shown is the COP for the variable speed unit running at a fixed electrical frequency of 60 Hz. The only difference is a 10% loss due to inverter inefficiencies.

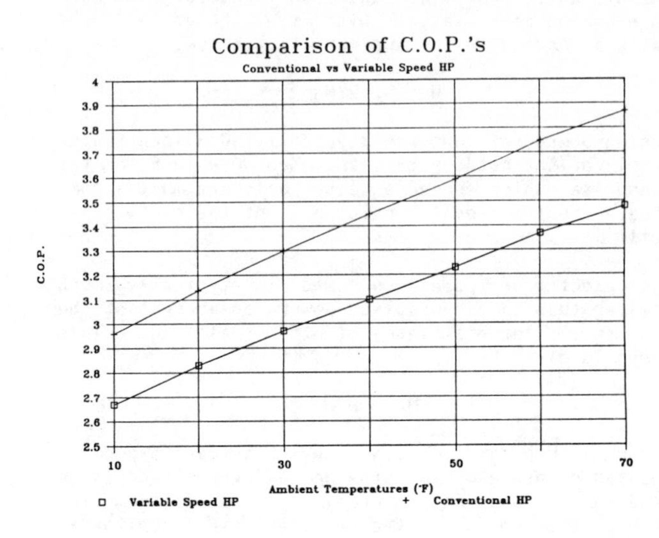

FIGURE 2. HEATING COP OF THE HEAT PUMPS AS A FUNCTION OF THE AMBIENT TEMPERATURE

COP's for the variable speed unit will vary with frequency as well as ambient temperature. This behavior is illustrated in Figure 3 which shows the heating COP of a variable speed unit at various electrical frequencies and ambient temperatures. In this case the fans are operated at line frequency with no inverter loss. Notice that the COP's tend to a maximum in the neighborhood of 30 to 40 Hz. Efficiencies deteriorate at higher frequencies because the heat exchangers are more heavily loaded requiring the condenser to operate at a higher temperature and pressure and similarly forcing the evaporator to a lower pressure. As a consequence of this higher pressure ratio, the work to compress a unit mass of refrigerant is increased and the COP decreased. Improvement in the COP does not however continue unabated to the lowest frequencies as the COP tends to decrease below 30 to 40 Hz. At these low speeds the relatively fixed component of the irreversible compressor work dependent on mechanical friction tends to be a larger fraction of the total work resulting in a drop off in the compressor's mechanical efficiency. This loss in mechanical efficiency increases the compressor work at lower frequencies enough to overcome the advantage of the lower pressure ratios.

Figure 4 shows the performance of a variable speed unit with fans powered from the inverter. Above 60 Hz the fan power increases dramatically because of its third degree dependence on speed. Since this increased power consumption is not accompanied by commensurately improved performance, the fan frequencies have been assumed to be limited to 60 Hz for the

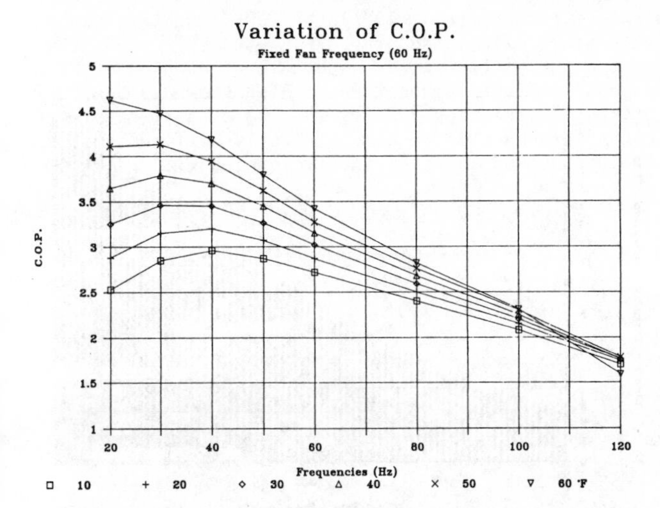

FIGURE 3. HEATING COP OF THE VARIABLE SPEED HEAT PUMP WITH FIXED FAN FREQUENCY AS A FUNCTION OF FREQUENCY. PARAMETRIC CURVES ARE PLOTTED FOR SPECIFIED AMBIENT TEMPERATURES.

higher compressor frequencies. For higher frequencies the unit with variable fan speeds has the lower COP. This is primarily because of the increased inverter loss. At lower frequencies the results are mixed. For the higher heat rates when the ambient temperature is high, the fixed fan speed gives higher heat exchanger effectiveness hence closer temperature approaches and a lower pressure ratio. This situation improves the performance of the system. At low ambient temperature the heat rates are necessarily low and the added power consumption with fixed fan speeds degrades the COP.

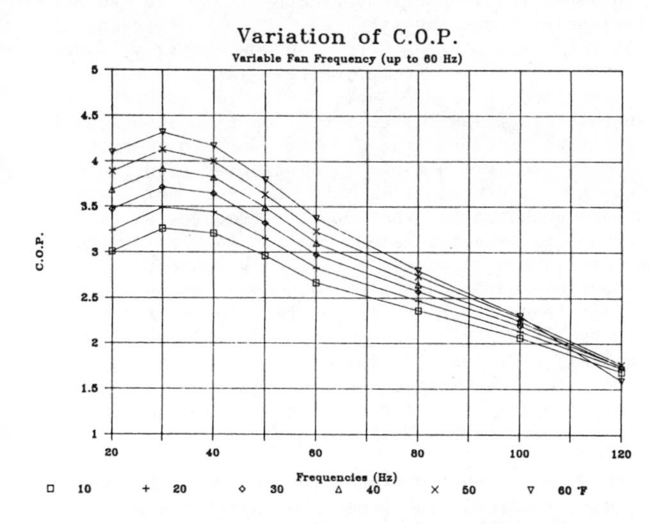

FIGURE 4. HEATING COP OF THE VARIABLE SPEED HEAT PUMP WITH VARIABLE FAN FREQUNECY AS A FUNCTION OF FREQUENCY. PARAMETRIC CURVES ARE PLOTTED FOR SPECIFIED TEMPERATURES.

The improvement in COP when the frequency is reduced is but one advantageous feature in variable speed heat pump operation. Another principal advantage is the capability to meet severe load conditions at lower ambient temperatures by overspeeding the system. The loss of capacity by a conventional heat pump at low outside temperatures is a significant detriment since such periods correspond to higher heating loads. Considerable resistance heat is required to meet such conditions, and resistance heat is, of course, delivered at a "COP" of only unity. Figure 5 shows representative effects of frequency increase on heat rate. The heat rate has a nearly linear increase with frequency. At the highest frequencies, above 100 Hz, the drop in compressor mechanical efficiency is so great that it may be suboptimal to design for such high speeds; however, the ability of the variable speed unit to adapt to severe loads is a major benefit of the concept.

While the trends observed in the results discussed above are probably realistic, some reservations are held concerning the precise quantitative results. For example, the current simplified model has not accounted for the effect of air flow rate on the air side convection coefficient. This effect would further degrade performance at lower fan speeds. Additionally, the fan laws are used to deduce fan performance, both air flow and power consumption, at off design conditions. These simple relations are not so accurate as detailed analyses of the air system dynamics. More detailed models now under development will account for these and other details.

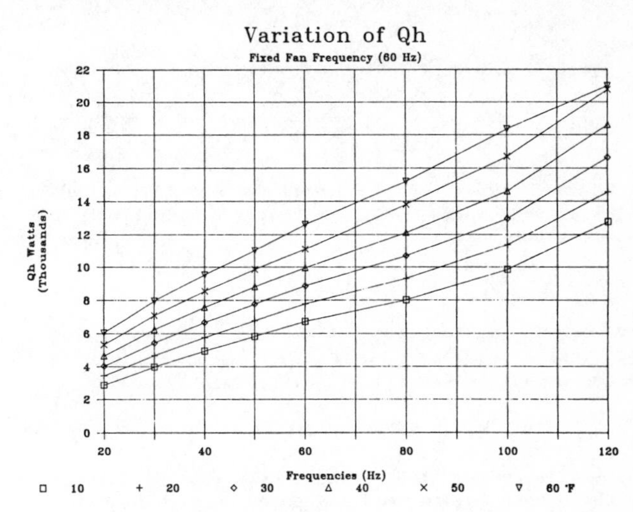

FIGURE 5. CAPACITY VARIATION OF THE VARIABLE SPEED HEAT PUMP AT FIXED FAN FREQUENCY AS A FUNCTION OF FREQUENCY. PARAMETRIC CURVES ARE PLOTTED FOR SPECIFIED AMBIENT TEMPERATURES.

The simulations outlined above provide the necessary input data for seasonal calculations of the heating performance using the bin format. Figure 6 shows the seasonal energy requirement for the variable speed heat pump in comparison with a conventional unit. The annual consumption comprises energy to drive the heat pump and supplementary electric resistance heat to meet the load when the ambient temperature is low. The net energy consumption and resistance heat requirement vary with the magnitude of the load. One extreme application would be to install the nominal 3 USRT heat pump to serve a load so small that the system alone can meet even the extreme heating load. In this case the peak heat load equals the peak heat rate, and this situation corresponds to the left edge of Figure 6. Larger loads are to the right on the plot. For any larger loads the conventional heat pump will require some resistance heat but the variable speed unit can run at higher speeds to help meet extreme loads. The energy component for resistance heat is also plotted separately. Note that no resistance heat is required with the variable speed unit unless much larger loads are served. The variable speed unit thus has two advantages, improved COP at part load and higher capacity for extreme conditions. The variable speed unit outperforms the fixed speed heat pump with either fan control scheme (fixed or variable speed). Our calculations predict an improvement of 8 to 10 percent with the line powered fan and 6 to 8 percent with variable fan speed. The variable speed unit has improved performance both because of its better COP's at part load operation but as well because of its ability to overspeed and provide a higher heating capacity at low ambient temperatures. This higher heating capacity at lower speeds reduces the resistance heating required to meet extreme loads and improves the overall electricity to heating COP.

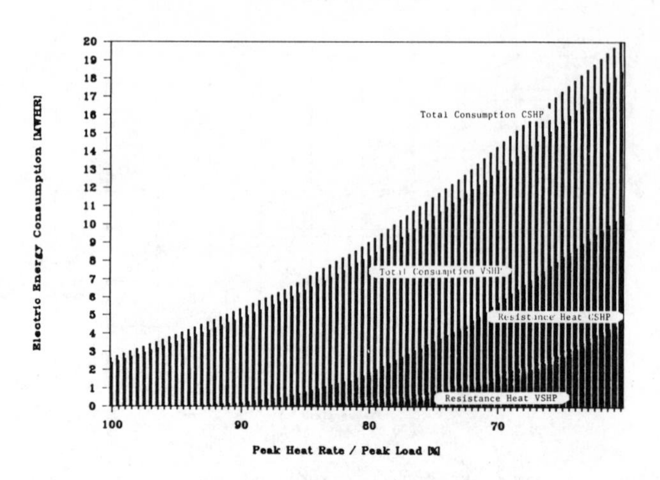

FIGURE 6. COMPARATIVE ENERGY CONSUMPTION RATES FOR THE VARIABLE SPEED AND CONSTANT SPEED HEAT PUMPS

ACKNOWLEDGEMENT

This work was performed under the sponsorship of the Georgia Power Company. We wish to thank Mr. Gary Birdwell and Mr. Ed Houtz for their support and encouragement over the course of the project.

SECTION 29
MICROCOMPUTERS

Chapter 85

USING AN INDUSTRIAL PERSONAL COMPUTER FOR ENERGY MONITORING

W. L. Stebbins

ABSTRACT

The advent of the personal computer has permitted a quantum leap forward in the ability to manage large amounts of data which is then assimilated into a variety of formats for revenue billing, trend analysis, and for assurance of compliance to stringent contractual requirements.

An investment in PC hardware, software, and I/O equipment valued at less than $25,000 now provides capabilities which, until just recently, were available only in large minicomputer systems.

Details examined include equipment and software selection and system design considerations. Start-up experiences and suggested techniques to employ along with pitfalls to avoid are discussed.

All dollar values are approximate, and are based on 1986 equipment and energy costs in the Southeast. Specific brand names and equipment suppliers are included to present an accurate picture of the installation.

There are currently over half a dozen manufacturers of PC units capable of performing the required tasks outlined below. At the time of the evaluation only IBM offered a version designed especially for the industrial atmospheres.

There are a variety of firms with the capabilities to supply staisfactory software and I/O equipment. Megasystems (1) was chosen for this specific application based on their previous experience in power plants and the marine industry.

Application of this hardware and software for these specific requirements should not be construed as a general endorsement by either Celanese or by the Author. It is important to note that a variety of brands and suppliers should be evaluated by anyone considering a similar application.

Values given for flows, temperatures, pressures, unit energy costs and contractual requirements approximate actual numerical quantities and are used to illustrate the methodology employed in the author's plant.

INTRODUCTION

Background

The purchase by a third party of a production unit resulted in a contractual agreement to provide various utility streams and waste treatment of various sewers on a fee basis. The nature of the contract required a metering and data collection system capable of measuring, recording, reporting, billing, and trending the twenty variables shown in Figure 1. Functional design parameters called for an automatic system that was user friendly, reliable, easy to maintain and calibrate, which could run for extended periods of time with little or no operator input.

Monitoring Requirements

Brief consideration was given to conventional metering devices such as circular or strip chart recorders and digital data loggers. These were deemed unsuitable due in part to cost and excessive manhours required to interpret the data and translate into a billing format.

For example, the contract requirement for metering of 150 lb. steam called for the ability to monitor the following:

1. Flow, which was expected to average 8,765 pphr, not to exceed 9,876 pphr maximum peak demand during any 8 (not necessarily adjacent) hours in a 24 hour period from midnight to midnight. (These simulated quantities are only for illustration purposes).

2. Temperature, which was to range within 340°F minimum to 460°F maximum.

3. Pressure, which was to range within 130 PSIG minimum to 150 PSIG maximum.

If the flow rate was exceeded, then the temperature and pressure requirements no longer held. Similar parameters were established for the other utility streams shown in Figure 1. A trending capability for plotting up to four variables to show interacting effects (e.g. flow vs temperature vs pressure of 150 pound stream) was an additional requirement.

Equipment Selection

The cost-effective, state-of-the-art system chosen is shown in the block diagram, Figure 2. The system consists of an intelligent I/O front end along with menu-driven software both supplied by Megasystems (1). This is coupled to an IBM Industrial Computer System designed especially for the industrial atmosphere where conditions are more physically demanding than those in the typical office environment. See Appendix A for a detailed description of hardware.

COMPUTER SYSTEM DESIGN

Hardware

The PC/XT was chosen over the PC/AT because of cost, and the fact that the industrial version of the AT was not available in a desk type model.

A total of 4 systems were ultimately purchased. The first and second for energy monitoring, the third for use in the utilities department and the fourth as an off-line development system. The PC/XT was judged most suitable overall for these four applications.

Service, pricing, and delivery were factors considered in selecting a PC products distributor (2).

The final hardware configuration consisted of the following:

1. 5531-021 with 256K and 360KB Drive.
2. AST.SPK064 Real time clock with 64K and RS-232 port.
3. Five 64K modules with AST card.
4. Persyst stretch memory card with 256K.
5. IBM 10MB Hard disk drive.
6. 8087 Math Co-processor.
7. 5532 Industrial Color Display.
8. 5533 Industrial Graphics Printer.
9. Parallel cable for printer.

Software

Megasystems' MULTI-TASKING INTEGRATED DATA ACQUISITION SOFTWARE (MIDAS) configures the IBM PC into a general purpose data acquisition, monitoring, display, and control host station. The multi-tasking software allows users to run their own programs under TOPVIEW or concurrent DOS.

Appendix B details specific features of the various software packages included in this system.

Appendix C outlines a typical user-written set of instructions used by the utility operators responsible for system operation.

SYSTEM OPERATION

Each of the 20 inputs is scanned by the intelligent Signal Processor Unit, and the values averaged over 1-minute's time. Thirty of these one-minute intervals are then added together, synchronized to the hour and half hour. The average for this 30 minute demand interval is then stored on disc until needed for a report or trend plot. See Appendix C for details.

Unit energy costs are revised inputs each year to reflect the cost of energy and waste treatment. These unit costs multiplied times the consumption yields a billing document for the specific time period: a day, week, month, etc. See the example at the end of Appendix B.

FLOW INSTRUMENTATION DESIGN

Utility Stream Metering

Vortex shedding meters were chosen for metering of all utility streams, based on satisfactory operation within the plant in other applications (3).

Vortex meters rely on creating designed turbulence in a pipeline (vortex shedding) and relate this effect to the fluid velocity. A specially-shaped strut is placed in the fluid flow resulting in small eddies or vortices which are shed alternately behind each side of the obstruction. The frequency at which they are shed is proportional to the velocity of the fluid and its attendant flow rate. Vortex meters apply equally well to all relatively clean, non-corrosive liquids or gases because calibration is dependent only upon the size and shape of the strut. Vortex meters also have good rangeability, long term repeatability, and offer the advantage of good metering accuracy with no moving parts. Additional data on vortex meters are available in references 4, 5, 6, 7 and 8.

All meters were installed in a pipe rack, shown in the left side of Figure 3. For ease of installation and future calibration checks, a metering platform was constructed, Figure 4. Installation, wiring, checkout, and calibration was facilitated by use of Loop Sheet drawings, a sample of which is shown in Figure 5 for loop number 107, 100 PSI Instrument Air. This same general P & ID drawing format is used in graphical screen presentation of data, Figure 6.

Sewer Flow Metering

A flow based on measuring height of liquid in a Palmer Bowlus flume was used in the 4 sewers. A Drexelbrook (9) system was chosen based on past experiences by the design engineering firm.

Figure 7 illustrates a typical sewer Loop Sheet drawing, with the graphical screen presentation shown in Figure 8.

Both Utility stream and sewer flow data are backed up with wall-mounted integrators, Figure 9. These FQI's (Flow Quantity Integrator) hold the accumulated flow data during power interruptions and any computer outages.

A summary display log, Figure 10, is also available on the screen. The complete hardware system is shown in Figure 11.

PROJECT EXPECTATIONS

This project was brought on-line on schedule, under budget, and worked correctly. Checkout and debugging were more involved than expected. It was soon recognized that the success of any computer - related project depends a great deal on proper documentation of specifications and expectations on the part of all parties.

The problems experienced during this project reinforce the problems inherent in any software application: expectation for system versus functionality obtained. Unless a system has been observed, tested and fulled scrutinized, then problems of this type will surely arise. This fact emphasizes the need to prepare detailed specifications and document and obtain written confirmation for any modifications requested.

The specifications should explicitly state what the system is required to do, how the system should perform the functions required, who is responsible for programming or updating, and when equipment delivery may be expected.

RESOURCE MATERIAL

A fundamental law of energy system engineering states, "If you can't meter it, you can't manage it." (10) The advent of the PC has greatly aided the plant engineer in the task of minimizing energy use.

Articles frequently appear in a variety of publications which serve to update the capabilities of PC's for industrial systems (11), (12), (13), (14).

It is hoped that information presented will whet the appetites of those involved in the measurement and use of energy, to do further investigation into the exciting applications of PC's.

REFERENCES

1. Megasystems, 1075 Broken Sound Parkway NW, Boca Raton, Florida 33431.

2. Mill Power Technologies, 9801-C Southern Pine Blvd., Charlotte, NC 28210.

3. Yokogawa Corp. of America, 2 Dart Road, Shenandoah, Georgia 30265.

4. Charles M. Flora,"Flow Measurement/Flowmeter Selection," Proceedings of ISA SECON '81 CONFERENCE AND EXHIBIT; Greenville, SC, April, 1981.

5. Technical Data Sheet 3031, Fundamentals of Flow Metering, Rosemount, Inc. P.O. Box 35129, Minneapolis, Minnesota 55435.

6. Guide To Flow Measurement, Fischer and Porter, Warminster, Pennsylvania 18974.

7. Charles M. Flora, "Process Measurement For Energy Management", Proceedings of ISA SECON '78 Conference and Exhibit, Gatlinburg, Tennessee, May, 1978.

8. Fisher Controls, P.O. Box 190, Marshalltown, Iowa 50158.

9. Drexelbrook Engineering Co., 205 Keith Valley Road, Horsham, PA. 19044

10. Wayne L. Stebbins, "New Concepts In Electrical Metering For Energy Management", IEEE Transactions On Industry Applications, Volumn IA-22, Number 2, March/April 1986, Pages 382-388.

11. Shirley Housch and John Mathis, "Video Displays Enhance Control System Information", Plant Engineering Magazine, Technical Publishing, Barrington, IL November 14, 1985, Pages 44-47, File 8501.

12. William H. Evers, "Main Frame, Mini, and Personal Computers In The Plant", Plant Engineering Magazine, Technical Publishing, Barrington, IL November 14, 1985, Pages 60-63, File 9020.

13. Marilyn A. Harris, "IBM: Trying To Put All The Pieces Together", Business Week, McGraw-Hill, New York, NY April 21, 1986, Pages 62-63.

14. Jeanine Katzel, "An Exclusive Survey Report, Putting Personal Computers To Work In The Plant", Plant Engineering Magazine, Technical Publishing, Barrington, IL April 24, 1986, Pages 40-45, File 9020.

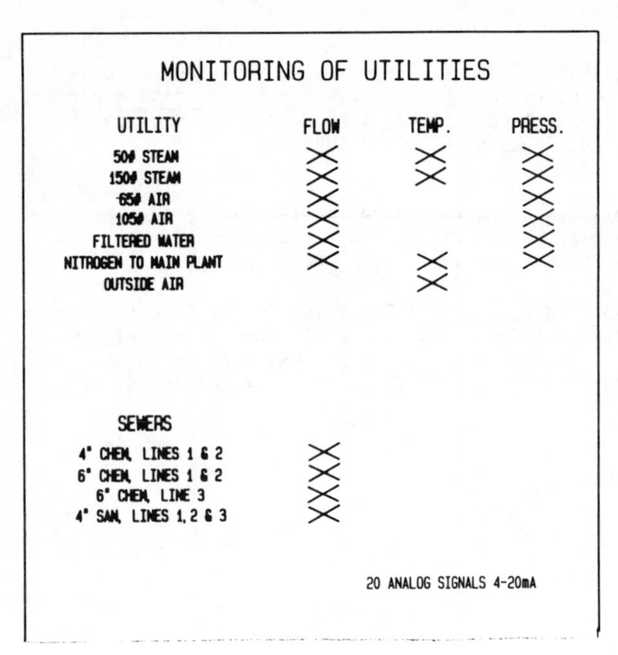

FIGURE 1
UTILITY STREAMS BEING MONITORED

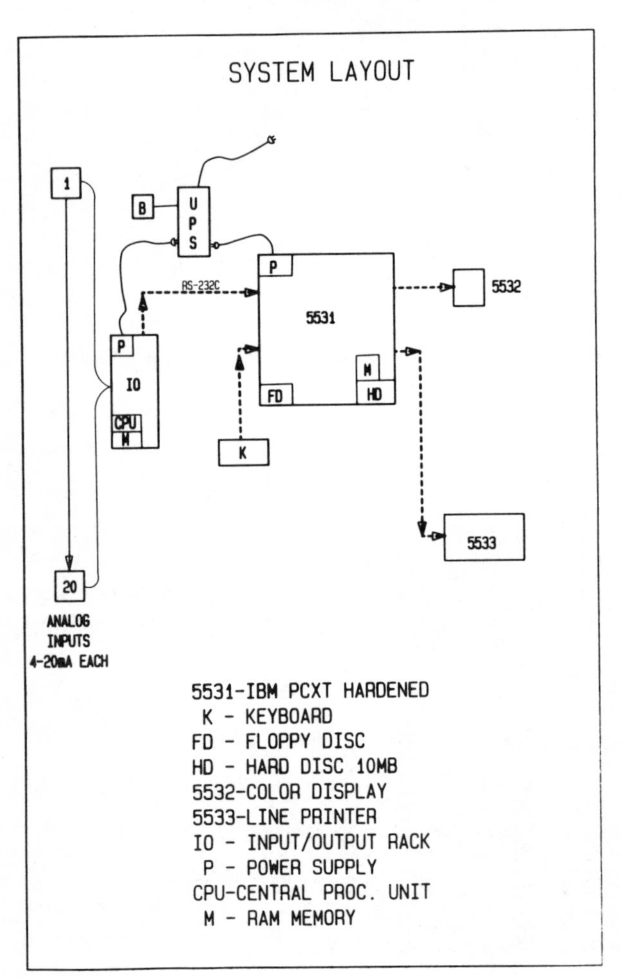

FIGURE 2
BLOCK DIAGRAM OF SYSTEM

FIGURE 3
METERING INSTALLATION IN PIPE RACK,
LEFT HAND SIDE

FIGURE 4
METERING PLATFORM FOR EASE OF
CALIBRATION CHECKS

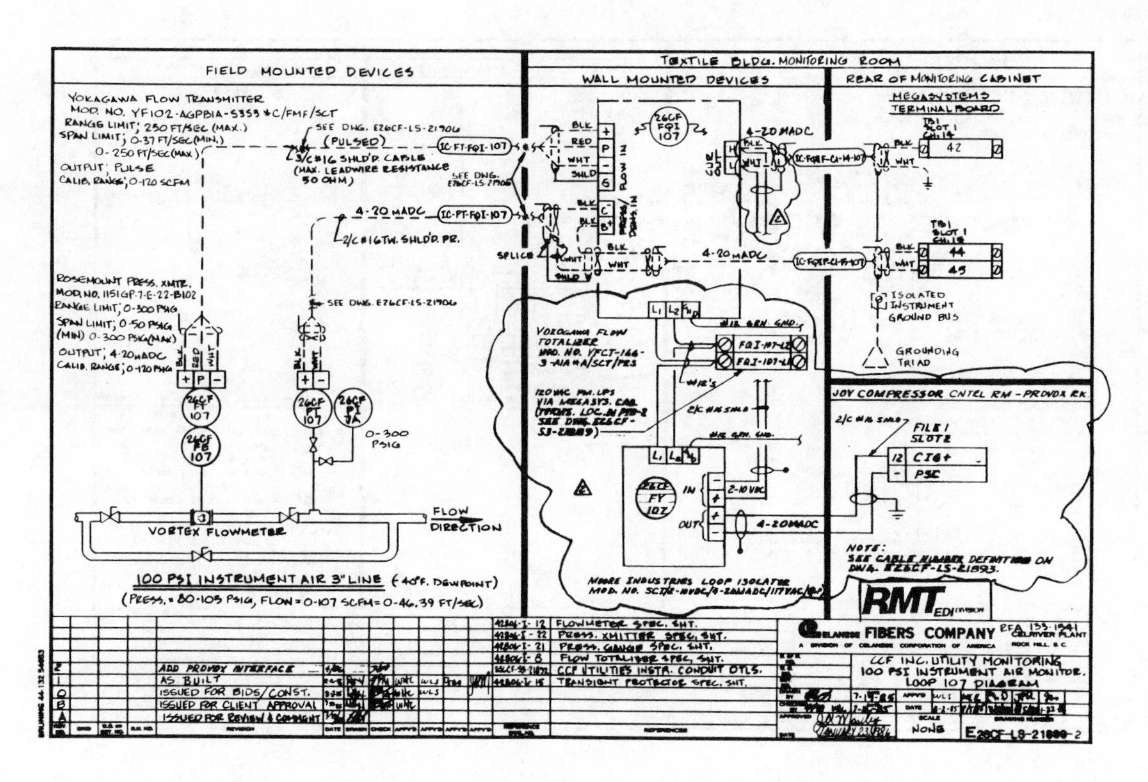

FIGURE 5
TYPICAL LOOP SHEET FOR INSTALLATION OF AIR FLOW METERING

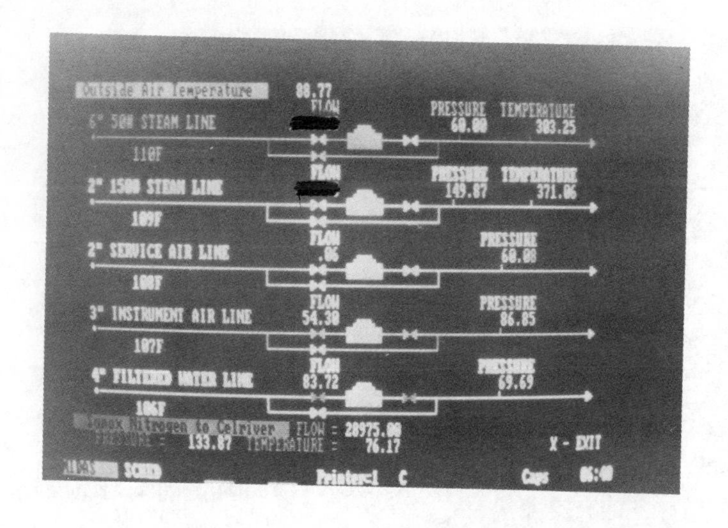

FIGURE 6
SCREEN DISPLAY OF UTILITY STREAMS BEING MONITORED

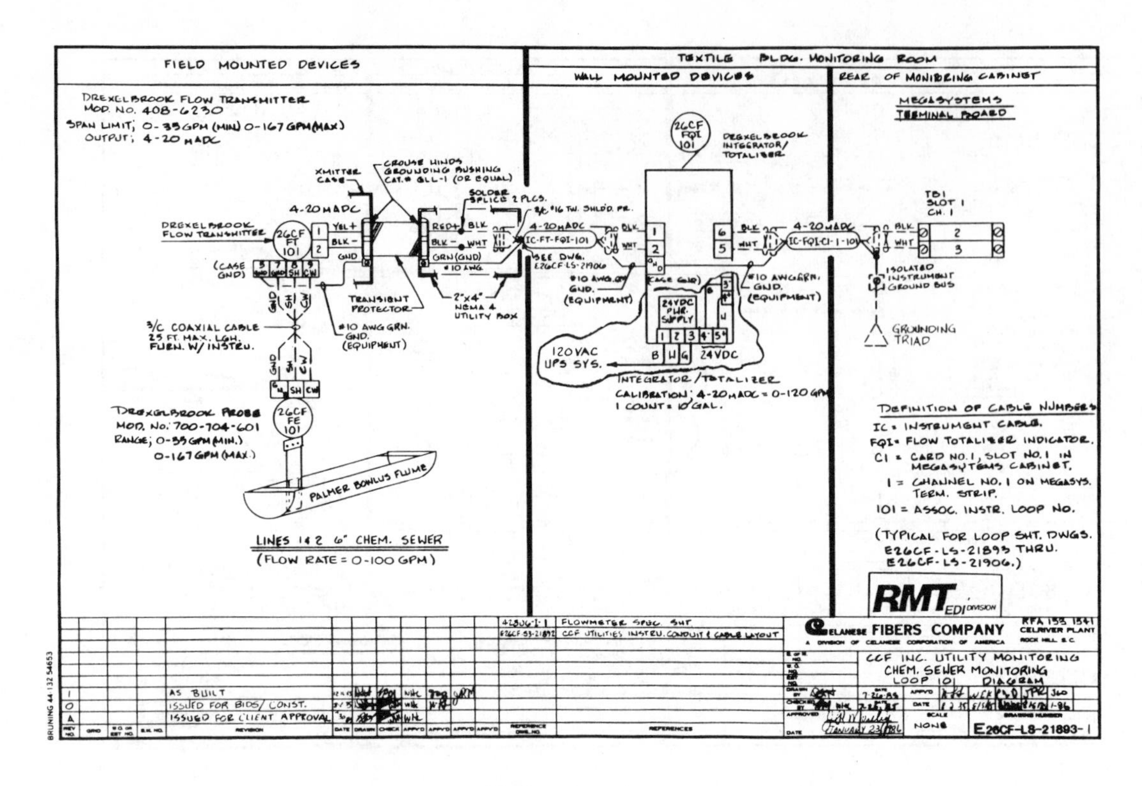

FIGURE 7
TYPICAL LOOP SHEET FOR INSTALLATION OF SEWER FLOW METERING

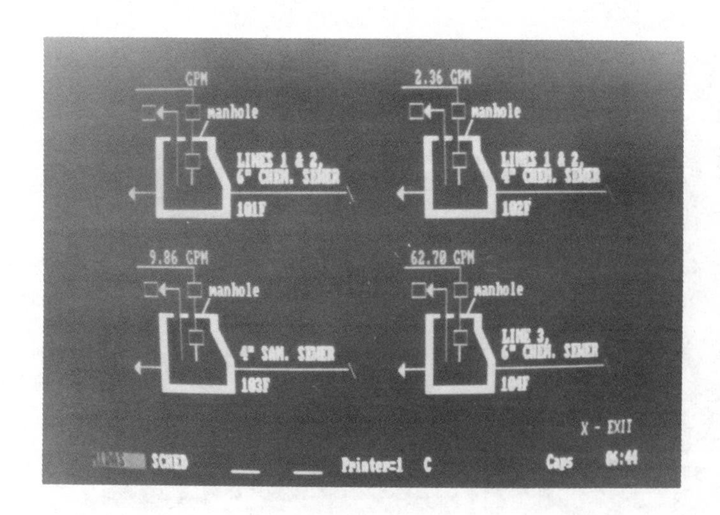

FIGURE 8
SCREEN DISPLAY OF SEWER FLOW MONITORING

FIGURE 9
WALL-MOUNTED FLOW INTEGRATORS

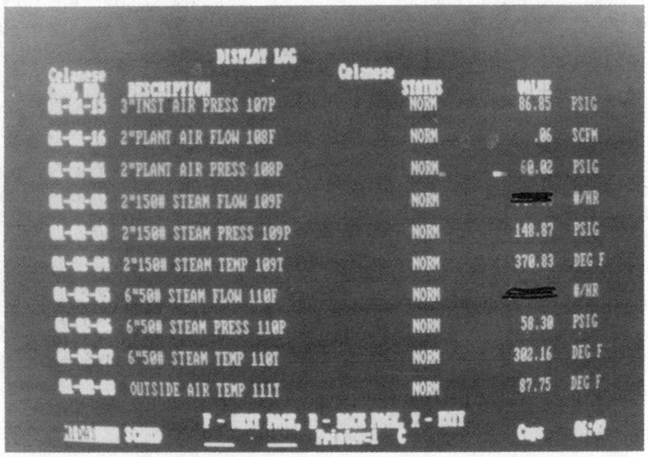

DISPLAY LOG

Celanese COMP. NO.	DESCRIPTION	Celanese STATUS	VALUE	
01-01-15	3"INST AIR PRESS 107P	NORM	86.85	PSIG
01-01-16	2"PLANT AIR FLOW 108F	NORM	.06	SCFM
01-02-01	2"PLANT AIR PRESS 108P	NORM	60.02	PSIG
01-02-02	2"150# STEAM FLOW 109F	NORM	[illegible]	#/HR
01-02-03	2"150# STEAM PRESS 109P	NORM	140.87	PSIG
01-02-04	2"150# STEAM TEMP 109T	NORM	370.83	DEG F
01-02-05	6"50# STEAM FLOW 110F	NORM	[illegible]	#/HR
01-02-06	6"50# STEAM PRESS 110P	NORM	58.30	PSIG
01-02-07	6"50# STEAM TEMP 110T	NORM	302.16	DEG F
01-02-08	OUTSIDE AIR TEMP 111T	NORM	87.75	DEG F

[illegible] SCHED F - NEXT PAGE, B - BACK PAGE, X - EXIT Printer=I C Caps 05:07

FIGURE 10
SUMMARY DISPLAY LOG WITH ALARM STATUS

FIGURE 11
IBM PC/XT INDUSTRIAL COMPUTER HARDWARE

APPENDIX A

The IBM Industrial Computer system is designed especially for the factory floor where conditions are more physically demanding than those of the typical office environment. The system consists of the following:

- 5531 Industrial Computer, which offers full Personal Computer XT function and software compatibility.
- 5532 Industrial Color Display.
- 5533 Industrial Graphics Printer.

The operating environment includes areas where there may be extended temperatures, vibration and shock, power and voltage fluctuations, contaminants and particulates.

In addition to industrially hardened covers, each unit contains a cooling fan and a replaceable filter to prevent particulates from entering the unit.

The 5531 Industial Computer comes with a keyboard that has been designed with a sealed membrane; either 128KB or 256KB or memory installed on the system board; a 360KB diskette drive and Diskette Adapter; a 10MB fixed disk and Fixed Disk Adapter; a Color/Graphics Display Adapter; and a special Combination Adapter.

The Combination Adapter card offers a fully programmable asynchronous communications port, parallel printer interface port, a battery-backed realtime clock, and a thermal sensor interface.

For security, an optional keylock can be installed on the 5531's drive cover door to restrict access to the diskette and fixed disk drives.

In addition to its other features, the 5531 has been designed with a retaining bracket that holds the adapter cards securely in place.

The 5532 Industrial Color Display, has a shatter-resistant, tinted screen cover that reduces glare. An optional clear screen cover is available.

The 5533 Industrial Graphics Printer is bi-directional and prints 120 characters per second.

The 5533's control panel contains a protective shield to prevent contaminants and particulates from entering the unit.

Highlights

Standard features of the IBM 5531 Industrial Computer:

- Intel 8088 Microprocessor.
- 128KB or 256KB of memory.
- Keyboard attachment and keyboard.
- Dual-sided diskette drive.
- Diskette Adapter.
- 10MB of fixed disk storage.
- Combination Adapter:
  - Asychronous communication port.
  - Parallel interface port.
  - Battery backed clock.
  - Thermal sensor.
- Color/Graphics Display Adapter.
- Eight system expansion slots.
- BASIC language interpreter in read-only memory (ROM) built into every system unit.
- Automatic power-on self-test to system components.
- Full 128-character ASCII character set plus many special graphics and control characters for a total of 256 characters.
- Built-in speaker.
- Drive cover fits over disk/diskette system unit area.
- User-installable key lock option for drive cover door.

Keyboard

- IBM Personal Computer keyboard designed with membrane technology.
- Detached with adjustable angle.
- 83 keys with full function for data processing and text processing.
- Ten-key keypad for numeric entry and cursor control.
- Buffered input.
- Automatic repeating feature on all non-control keys.
- Print screen key transfers display image to printed page.
- Access to all 256 characters via the Alt key.
- Ten program supported function keys for a total of 40 possible functions using keyboard shift keys.
- Insert and delete modes.

Specifications

- Intel 8088 Microprocessor.
  - 4.77 MHz clock speed.
- 40KB read only memory (ROM).
- 128KM or 256KB of memory on system board.
- 250 ns memory access time.
- 410 ns memory cycle time.
- Memory parity checking.
- Eight feature slots (six full feature, two smaller slots) with retainer bar to secure adapter cards.
- 130 watt power supply.
- Electrical:
  - AC operating voltages; 104 minimum to 127 maximum, 57 Hz to 63 Hz.
  - Transients, such as lightning strike, 2500V maximum with 16 microsecond nominal pulse width.

Highlights

Standard features of the IBM 5532 Industrial Color Display:

- Industrialized design of the IBM personal Computer Color Display.
- 13-inch (diagonal) monitor.
- 640 x 200 addressability.
- Black mask contrast.
- 16 colors.
- Brightness and contrast controls.
- Six foot power cable.
- Five foot signal cable.
- Cooling fan and filter.

Highlights

Standard features of the IBM 5533 Industrial Graphics Printer:

- Cooling fan and filter.
- Control panel with protective shield.
- Bidirectional printing.
- 120 characters per second.

- Line buffering for performance.
- 12 character modes.
- Standard, compressed, and emphasized modes with double strike, subscript, superscript, and underline. Standard and double width combinations, 36 modes in all.
- 9 x 9 character dot matrix.
- Character set consisting of:
  - Standard characters.
  - Accented alphabetics.
  - Box drawing.
  - Greytone.
  - Block.
  - Greek characters.
  - Mathematical symbols.
- Four line lengths (40, 66, 80, 132 characters per line).
- Multipart forms.
- Friction-feed and pin-feed.
- Single feed, or continuous forms - from 114.3mm (4.5 in.) up to 254mm (10.0 in.) wide.
- Variable form length.
- Skip to top of next page (manual or programmed).
- Variable vertical spacing.
- Horizontal tab stops.
- Printer self-test.
- Replaceable cartridge ribbon.

<u>Specifications</u>

- Print method: Impact dot matrix.
- Print speed: 120 CPS (nominal).
- Print direction: bidirectional with logic seek.
- Character set:
  - 96 ASCII characters.
  - 64 graphics characters.
  - Special European characters and symbols.
  - Certain Greek and mathematical symbols.
- Character font: 9 x 9 dot matrix.
- Character size:
  - 2.1mm (0.08 in.) wide.
  - 3.2mm (0.12 in.) high.
- Paper feed: adjustable pin-feed tractors, or friction-feed.
- Paper: single sheet, or continuous form.
- Paper width: from 114.3mm (4.5 in.) to 254mm (10.0 in.).
- Copies: one original with two carbon copies.
- Line spacing: 4.23mm (0.77 in.) 3.174mm (0.13 in.), or programmable.
- Maximum number of characters per line:
  - 80 (standard size).
  - 40 (double-width size).
  - 132 (compressed size).
  - 66 (compressed double-width size).
- Characters per inch:
  - 10 (standard size).
  - 5 (double-width size).
  - 16.5 (compressed).
  - 8.25 (compressed, double-width size).
- Electrical:
  - 180 watt power supply.
  - AC operating voltages: 104 minimum to 127 maximum, 57 Hz to 63 Hz.
  - Power line lightning surges of ±2500 volts.
- Temperature:
  - System on: 4° to 46.1°C (39.2° to 115°F).
  - System off: 4° to 51.7°C (39.2° to 125°F).
- Humidity: 8% to 80% non-condensing.
- Shock: 0.5G at 10 millisecond duration.
- Particulates contaminants filtering.
- Vibration: 5-7 Hz at 0.005 inches double amplitude displacement:
  - 17-200 Hz at 0.07G peak.
  - 200-500 Hz at 0.036G peak.

Temperature Protection - Airflow

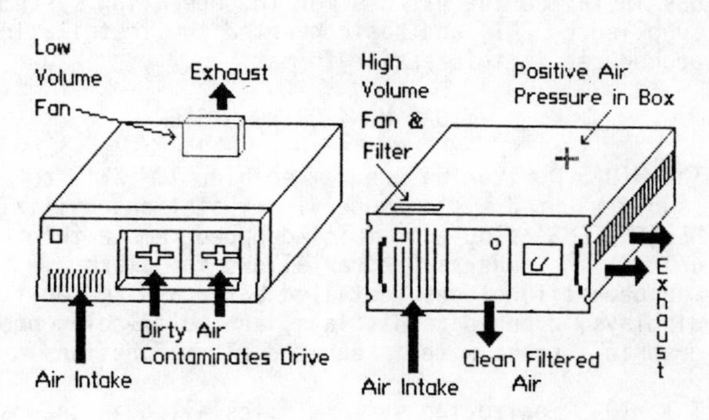

Internal Component Temperatures

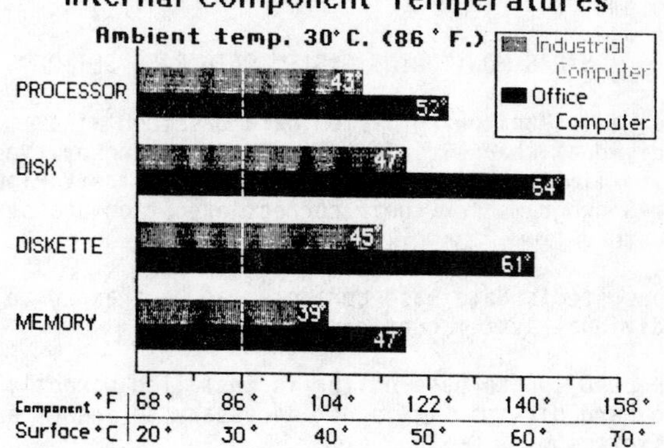

Reliability Summary

Abusive Environment	Typical Office Computer	IBM Industrial Computer	Reliability Benefit
Particulates	150 Micrograms per cubic meter	500 Micrograms per cubic meter	Protection is 3 times greater
Electical Surge	± 750 volt Surge	± 2500 volt Surge	Protection is 3 times greater
Shock & Vibration	150 -500 Hz @ .25 G's	200 -500 Hz @ .70 G's	Protection is 3 times greater
Temperature	15-32 C. 60-90 F.	0-50 C. 32-122 F.	MTBF 10MB Disk 3 times greater

APPENDIX B

SYSTEM SOFTWARE INSTALLATION

The following is for use to install MIDAS and CCPM on a customer's system. PLEASE NOTE: The version of CCPM being installed is a copy of the customer's licensed system from Digital Research. Megasystems has installed the patches for the operating system supplied by DRI, and has converted the installation procedures to this easier format.

MIDAS MONITORING SYSTEM

The MIDAS Monitoring program enables IBM XT's to act as distributed system/supervisory stations utilizing MEGASYSTEMS' single or multi-dropped remote front-end units. The general program allows for alarm management functions, detailed bar graph (meter type) displays, group data displays, and multi-color process graphic screens with integrated alarm functions.

The MIDAS monitoring system is installed in the hard disk of the IBM PC. The program will access automatically upon power-up, however, to return to the MIDAS program from another program section when operating under con-current PC-DOS,

press: CTRL 1

and the system will return to the MIDAS monitoring system.

MIDAS MONITORING SYSTEM DATA BASE SET UP

The Midas Monitoring System Data Base contains individual channel information such as sensor type, alarm limits, etc. This is utilized by the various MIDAS programs for their correct execution and screen update.

The system's data base contents can be changed to suit individual system configurations.

The LOAD 1 data base editor is installed directly into the hard disk, so it is not necessary to insert any diskettes.

To change contents in the data base,

enter: LOADDB and (return)
LOAD1 and (return)

PROCESS GRAPHICS SYSTEM OVERVIEW

The MIDAS Process Graphics Editor gives the user the ability to easily create and update 16 dynamic mimic displays for his own physical installation and application needs. The Editor allows the user to map the current value and status of up to 16 channels on each screen. The label size for each channel is limited only by the screen area available while the status message can be up to 12 characters. Up to 128 different foreground/background color combinations, each with or without foreground blink, are user-configurable per channel display. The graphics character set and color combination charts can be viewed using the built-in pop-up help menus. Text can also be placed on the screen using the full color pallet.

Through the use of the on-line help screen and pop-up menus, the user can quickly start building useful mimics for his own applications.

TRENDLINE GRAPHICS MANUAL

Megasystems' Trendline Graphics programs (TREND and REPLAY) enable the user to select specific points in the MIDAS monitoring system and display, magnify, and printout the historical trends of that data. Separate plots for up to four points can be displayed and printed on a single page as well as combined into one plot., Information for these plots is taken from megasystems' Scheduler program, which sets up the files for the Trendline Graphics as well as for generating reports. The TREND program automatically scales and graphs the plots on the display. The user can magnify the plots up to four times or down to one fourth the original size and easily view specific sections of the plots through the Zoom function. Printout is readily available using the REPLAY program, which enables the user to specify the size and resolution of each hard copy plot.

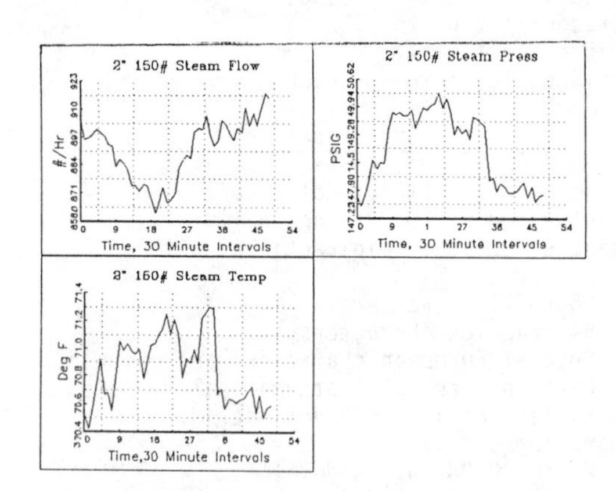

INDIVIDUAL PLOTS OF 150# STEAM FLOWS, PRESSURE, AND TEMPERATURE

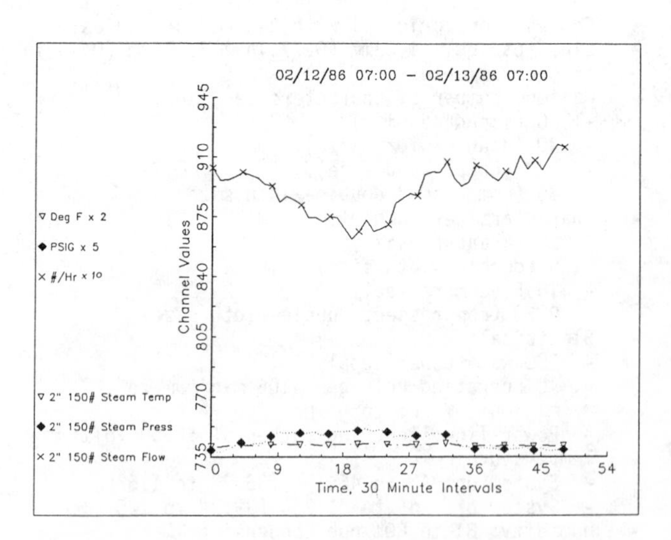

COMBINED PLOT OF 150# STEAM PARAMETERS

MANUAL AND FUTURE EVENT CONTROL PROGRAM

Megasystems' Manual and Future Event Control program enables the user to view and change both manually set and time activated outputs for analog and digital channels through an easy-to-use, fill-in-the-blank display. It communicates with Megasystems' Super/Processor units, using the GM MAP standard message format. The Event Control program consists of a fixed display of headings and labels with fields for variables in the display. The user calls up a channel by entering the channel number in the appropriate field. Current information on that channel is then displayed, including the current reading, the channel type, and the last assigned values of the manual and the time activated outputs. The user can change any of these values simply by entering the desired field and changing the value. Hard copy output is available through the Event log file. The Manual and Future Event Control program runs on the IBM, PC, XT, AT, or 100% IBM compatibles and can be used to control outputs in any size system--large or small. The program can provide on/off control for an air conditioning system, along with control of pumps, valves, lights and numerous other actuators.

SCHEDULER

Megasystems' Scheduler program gives the user the ability to organize and select information from MIDAS that he needs for reports, graphing trendlines, and statistical analyses. Scheduler enables the user to specify which channels in the monitoring system he needs data from, how often then are read and averaged, and to what file type they are written. Scheduler is easy to use--after the parameters are entered on the command line, Scheduler begins collecting data at the specified intervals. Because it is synchronized with a real-time battery backed-up clock, the information is collected at the exact intervals specified. Scheduler collects this data while the MIDAS system is on line, so no information from the monitored system is lost.

REPORT GENERATION

This Report Generation Section describes the custom designed dBase III reporting software package. It uses a menu-driven format to generate the reports and receives the information from the Scheduler option. Note that the format and information presented on the reports is specified by the user and can be changed to fit virtually any application. The reports used as examples are from specific systems.

The following is a typical set of menu-driven reports generated using dBase III while operating con-currently with MIDAS. The report generation section of the system is used when reports are required for billing functions or usage statistics. Typical reports are on: Total Flow; Peak Demand; Peak Demand Block (1-24 hour time period); and Temperature and Pressure. These reports will only be generated for the channels marked "T" on the editing data base.

To enter into the Report Generation section from MIDAS, the display must be changed from window 1 (Midas Monitoring System) to window 3 (Report Generation). To do so,

press: CTRL and 3 (from the numeric keypad)

simultaneously, and the MAIN MENU WILL DISPLAY:

- - - - - Main Menu - - - - -

1. Select a reporting interval.
2. Calculate Total Flow Report.
3. Calculate Peak Demand Report.
4. Calculate Peak Demand Block Report.
5. Calculate Temperature & Pressure Report.
6. Exit.

Selection, please?

TYPICAL PEAK FLOW DEMAND REPORT

STARTING 10/22/86 07:00
ENDING 10/23/86 07:00

Tag Number	Channel Description	Total Quantity	Cost $	Average Flow	Peak Flow	Peak Set Date	Time
110	6" 50# Steam	29,616#	$ 148	1,234 #/hr	2,345	10/22	12:00
109	2" 150# Steam	136,272#	$1,090	5,678 #/hr	6,789	10/22	12:30
108	2" Plant Air	177,120 SCF	$ 35	123 SCFM	234	10/23	06:00
107	3" Instrmt Air	656,640 SCF	$ 131	456 SCFM	567	10/23	01:00
106	4" Filtered Water	1,136,160 Gal	$ 341	789 GPM	890	10/22	14:30
105	3" Nitrogen	59,232 SCF	$ 118	2,468 SCFH	3,579	10/23	07:00
104	6" Chem Sewer 1	17,280 Gal	$ 9	12 GPM	23	10/22	14:30
103	4" San Sewer	48,960 Gal	$ 24	34 GPM	45	10/22	13:00
102	4" Chem Sewer 2	80,640 Gal	$ 40	56 GPM	67	10/22	15:00
101	6" Chem Sewer 3	112,320 Gal	$ 56	78 GPM	89	10/22	14:30

APPENDIX C

MEGASYSTEMS DOCUMENTATION

These instructions are intended for use by utility operators using the IBM PC/XT based monitoring system.

WINDOWS

Several programs run at once and can be looked at individually. There are 4 windows through which to look at these programs. Holding down the "CRTL" key (pronounced "control") while striking one of the number keys 1 through 4 on the right-hand keypad (not the upper row of number keys) will switch to the appropriate window 1, 2, 3, or 4. The lower left-hand corner of the screen has 4 blocks which show which programs are running in the 4 windows. Normally they will show "MIDAS" and "SCHED" in windows 1 and 2 respectively while window 3 will show "LOGEX" if a report is being generated. The block will be blank if no program is running in that window. Window 4 usually has nothing running in it.

MIDAS - WINDOW 1

MIDAS (Multi-tasking Integrated Data Acquisition Software) is the program that receives data from all the meters, produces alarms and produces the displays that are used for normal process monitoring. The main menu of MIDAS looks like:

1. Alarms
2. Word Table
3. Log Display
4. Graphics Alarm Display
5. Load Display File
6. Bar Graph
7. Exit

To choose from this menu enter the appropriate number and "return". You should always have a display with "live" data in it when you leave the computer, otherwise MIDAS is not updating its meters, and the reports that the computer can print will be wrong. Menu selections 1, 3, 4 and 6 produce such "live" data.

1. <u>Alarm</u>: This display will show any alarm conditions that exist in the system. meters above their upper limit, etc. are alarms. Hitting the " " key acknowledges alarms within MIDAS, but the external alarm box must be acknowledged also. The external alarm box will also alarm if MIDAS is shut down, or otherwise not scanning the meters, or if the entire computer is down. To get a printout of an alarm display, hold one of the shift keys (big up arrows) and hit the "PrtSc" key (print screen). This causes a "screen dump" to the printer and will work on any display in any window except when "Picture" displays are on the screen (choice 4 below). This is an easy way to create a record of any computer information that is important.

2. <u>Word Table</u>: This choice is meaningless to us users. Do not use it.

3. <u>Log Display</u>: This is the most often used display for process monitoring. You must type 3 (return), 1 (return), 1 (return), before getting to the meaningful displays. All channels set-up in the system can then be shown in channel order. There is more than one page that can be accessed by hitting "F" to go forward or "B" to go back. Make sure that the system is set to use all capital letters if things do not work right. An indicator in the lower right hand corner should say "Caps"; if it does not, hit the "Caps Lock" key.

4. <u>Graphics Alarm Display</u>: This allows you to look at whatever "Picture" type display has been loaded by menu choice 5 below. What this means is that you use the choice 5 to load a type of display from the disk into memory, and anytime later you can look at it by using choice 4. You will find that you will rarely want to use step 5 since the most useful display will usually be in memory already.

5. <u>Load Display File</u>: This will ask you to enter a display number 1-16 for the display to load into memory for use by choice 4 above. At present only 1 or 2 displays have been built and numbers for non-existant displays will give you an error message.

6. <u>Bar Graph</u>: This allows you to produce a bar type indication of the value of up to 7 channels on the system. It will ask you to enter the channel number; and if you strike (return) instead, no channel is used.

7. <u>Exit</u>: This choice does nothing, however, you do not ever want to exit MIDAS anyway. It must always run. If you want to do something else with the computer outside of MIDAS change windows and leave MIDAS running.

SCHED - WINDOW 2

This program should always be running in window 2. There is no way to talk to it, but it should show a list of when it writes records and files. What it is doing is taking the data that MIDAS gets from the meters and averaging it every half hour. The half hour averages are stored on the fixed disk for use by the reporting program. Each set of half hour averages is called a record and a whole day's records is called a file. Every morning at about 4:00 AM the previous day's file is copied from the hard disk to the floppy disk.

LOG - WINDOW 3

This program is only run when you want it. Just type "LOG" (return), and answer the questions. It will take a few seconds for the screen to turn blue, and it will then display a suggested time and date for the report. (The suggestion is for the production day that ended this morning). If you want to change the beginning or ending time or date, enter the number of the choice 1-4, and the computer will prompt you. You will have to enter the time or date in exactly the format shown by the computer, for example, the date 01/07/86 is OK, but 1/7/86 will not work. After all the beginning and ending times and dates have been set to what you want, just hit return. The computer will then ask you which type of report you want. Hit the appropriate number, and the program will start reading the half hour averages stored by SCHED and doing its calculations. You can then change windows, and you will notice that the border is blue until the report is completed. This way you can tell if a report is in progress from any window.

The report will take anywhere from 5 minutes to several hours to print out depending on the data requested. The more data you request the longer it will take.

A typical daily report of TOTALS and AVERAGES will take about 15 minutes. The program can handle missing data, but that will slow it down too.

Data can be lost if the program SCHED has been shut down for a program change, a hardware failure, etc. When this happens, the report program realizes that it has not got enough half hour averages, and it has to fill in the blanks with the reading immediately before the shut down.

If for some some reason you need to abort a report that is doing its calculations from window 3, hold down "Alt" and strike "C"; then answer the question that comes up with "Q". This will leave the border blue, but you can request another report.

WINDOW 4

Nothing is usually run in this window. It can be used to run miscellaneous programs such as copy, type, dir, etc.

DISKS - HARD AND FLOPPY

The computer contains two disk drives in its front. The one on the right is a "HARD" or "FIXED" disk that you will never have to handle. The one on the left is a floppy disc drive into which that program and data disks can be put. The hard disk can contain much more information than the floppy, and therefore our system is "hard disk based". All programs and data are installed on the hard disk. It can run without the floppy disk drive.

The only thing that the floppy disk drive is normally used for is to store copies of the half hour average data that is collected in case the hard disk fails and loses its data. The floppy disk should be changed every month.

THE PRINTER

The printer must be turned on and be on line to work. Both the power and the ready light should be on. To advance the paper hit the "On Line", then "Form Feed", then "On Line" button. If the paper does not stop accurately with the rollers on the perforation between pages, manually roll it to where it belongs. The printer can be confused by power spikes or programs that are aborted in mid-print. Turning the power switch off, adjusting the paper, and turning the power back on will fix any such "strange" problems.

RE-BOOTING

The computer can be restarted from scratch ("pulled up by its bootstraps") to recover from any type of error. However, DON'T DO THIS UNLESS ABSOLUTELY NECESSARY because it will lose at least one half hour's data. The procedure is:

1. Open the door to the floppy disk drive and simultaneously hold down keys "Ctrl", "Alt" and "Del". If that does not work, turn off the computer power (switch on right side rear of computer), wait 5 seconds, and turn it back on. The computer will do about 2 minutes of system checks and load programs from the hard disk.

2. Strike the "Caps Lock" key and type "MIDAS" to start MIDAS.

3. Bring up the "Log Display" by typing 3, (return), 1 (return), 1 (return), 1 (return).

4. Hold "Ctrl" and strike the "2" on the right hand numeric keypad (not the upper number keys) to switch to window 2.

5. Type "BEGIN" to begin the "SCHED" program.

6. Close the door to the floppy disk drive.

ERRORS: If this procedure does not work, there is a hardware problem with the computer, and maintenance should be called.

COPYING THIS DOCUMENTATION

The most recent version of this documentation is kept on the hard disk. To get a copy, switch to window 4 and type: "COPY MEGA.DOC PRN:".

Chapter 86

THE EFFECTS OF ENERGY PRICES ON ENERGY CONSERVATION INVESTMENTS

K. Graves, D. L. Turner

Energy conservation measures rapidly gained popularity during a period of steadily increasing energy prices, rapid inflation, and the availability of Federal and state tax credits for energy conservation investments. With the decline in oil prices, leveling of inflation, and expiration of relevant tax credits, however, investments in energy conservation must be considered more carefully.

A given energy conservation measure (ECM) can appear more or less attractive to potential purchasers under alternative scenarios of future energy prices and inflation; in the period of current uncertainty, a purchaser obviously wants a technology that will provide financial benefits under the widest possible extent of future energy and economic scenarios.

Given the high level of uncertainty in energy markets and for the economy, it is advantageous to be able to analyze the financial costs and benefits of investments in ECMS under numerous scenarios involving energy prices, general economic health, and specific financing arrangements.

This paper uses a microcomputer model, CONVEST II, initially developed for the U.S. Department of Energy, to provide just such analyses and to allow us to generalize about the impacts of future uncertainty on energy conservation investments. Two fictionalized ECMs, A and B, are examined in this paper under a series of alternative scenarios involving energy prices and general economic prosperity. Each scenario is evaluated using the following financial measures:

Cash Flow -- the after-tax influx of cash (on dollar savings) accruing, measured in real (i.e., base year) dollars.

Internal Rate of Return (IRR) -- a compound interest rate that would provide the investor with the same return over time as provided by the energy conservation investment.

Present Value (PV) -- the investment necessary to secure a promise of future payment.

Payback Period -- the number of years it takes for the project investment to pay for itself.

Benefit-Cost Ratio -- a ratio derived by dividing the dollar sum of all relevant benefits of the project by the dollar sum of all relevant costs of the project.

In our financial analysis there are three parties. Although our first party (the party having the ECM on its premises) is a for-profit entity, CONVEST II is also capable of examining financing plans for ECMs for nonprofit first parties. The second party is an energy service company (ESCo), which leverages an investment in energy conservation equipment to be installed in a building owned or operated by the first party. The ESCo undertakes the investment in return for periodic cash payments from the first party equal to a percentage of the energy savings flowing to the first party as a result of the conservation investment. A third party, such as a commercial lender, provides the bulk of the invested funds in return for fixed interest income paid by the second party. Although we use three parties, the analysis could as easily be done for one or two parties.

It should also be noted that the tax analysis portion of the program is based on the optimistic assumption that the investor's consolidated tax liability is large enough so that any tax credits may be fully claimed in the first year of project life. The program is pessimistic in that the full tax loss is incorporated as a negative component of cash flow in the year of occurrence. Depending on the actual tax situation of the investment entity, therefore, these assumptions may result in an understatement or an overstatement of a project's true IRR to a particular investor. The extent to which these under and overstatements offset each other will depend on the investor's consolidated tax liabilities and deferral policy regarding tax credits, and on the carry-back or carry-forward policy regarding operating losses.

BASE CASE SCENARIOS

Table 1 provides information on the monetary flows and parameters assumed for our two cases. In both cases, the economic and tax parameters are the same, as are base year energy expenditures. ECM A will save 40 percent of energy expenditures at a total cost of $372,000 (about 37 percent of one year's energy expenditures). Use of ECM B will save about 25 percent of energy expenditures at a total cost of $216,000 (about 22 percent of one year's energy expenditures). In both cases, the ESCo is assumed to finance about 90 percent of the total investment. It should be noted that straight line depreciation is assumed here, but a declining balance parameter would allow anything between straight line and double declining balance depreciation.

We compute the following measures of financial benefit: (1) benefit cost ratio --overall benefit-cost ratio not taking tax or financing arrangements into consideration; (2) PV of cash flow for first party; (3) ESCo IRR (total capital) -- the weighted average of IRR to debt and IRR to equity; (4) ESCo IRR (equity) -- return to ESCo on its equity, which is 20 percent of total investment in our analyses; and (5) lender IRR (debt) -- return to lender, which always equals the annual borrowing rate. The results of our analyses, shown in Table 2, indicate that ECM A would be preferred by the first party because it leads to a higher cash flow. ECM B, however, is preferred overall and by the ESCo, as indicated by its higher

PARTIES	ECM A	ECM B
First Party	for-profit entity	for-profit entity
Second Party	energy service company	energy service company
Third Party	commercial lender	commercial lender
ECONOMIC PARAMETERS		
Project Life	10 years	10 years
Annual Inflation Rate	3 percent	3 percent
Annual Borrowing Rate	10 percent	10 percent
ENERGY CONSERVATION AND SHARED-SAVINGS PARAMETERS		
Base Year Energy Expenditures	$1,000,000	$1,000,000
Pre-Investment Annual Energy Expenditure Escalation Factor	4 percent	4 percent
Avoided Annual Energy Expense due to Conservation Investment	40 percent	25 percent
Share of Avoided Energy Expense Paid to ESCo	50 percent	50 percent
INVESTMENT PARAMETERS		
Total Investment	$372,000	$216,000
ESCo Equity Contribution	$37,000	$22,000
Contribution Financed by 3rd Party at 10%/year	$335,000	$194,000
BASE CASE TAX PARAMETERS		
Tax Life	5 years	5 years
Property Ownership for Tax Purposes	ESCo	ESCo
Marginal Tax Rate	46 percent	46 percent

TABLE 1. BASE CASE SCENARIO PARAMETERS.

benefit-cost ratio and higher IRRs to ESCo equity and to total capital. Both ECM A and ECM B offer sufficiently high IRRs to the ESCo's equity contribution (exceeding 40 percent) to ensure ESCo interest in participating in the transaction.

ENERGY PRICE SCENARIOS

Although a base case of a 4 percent annual increase in energy expenditures is reasonable historically, the recent declines in oil prices have led to speculation

OVERALL	ECM A	ECM B
Benefit-Cost Ratio	6.9:1	7.4:1
FIRST PARTY		
PV of Cash Flow	$695,000	$434,000
SECOND PARTY		
ESCo IRR (Total Capital)	39.5%	42.0%
ESCo IRR (Equity)	42.8%	45.6%
THIRD PARTY		
Lender IRR (Debt)	10.0%	10.0%

Note: All values are real, after-tax yields; present value calculations are discounted to the present at the annual borrowing rate.

TABLE 2. DETAILED RESULTS FOR BASE CASE SCENARIOS.

about the role of energy prices in energy conservation investments. Two scenarios are examined here: one in which energy prices are assumed to remain constant over the lifetime of the investment, and one in which energy prices are assumed to decline at 4 percent annually. All other parameters are assumed to remain constant for this analysis, the results of which are shown in Table 3.

As a general result, the lower the energy price increase (or the greater the decrease), the less financially attractive is the installation of the ECM. In all scenarios, the first party prefers ECM A, through which a greater proportion of energy expenses are avoided. The ESCo, on the other hand, continues to prefer ECM B to ECM A. In all scenarios, however, even the one in which pre-ECM energy expenditures are declining, both ECM A and ECM B provide returns of more than 30 percent on the ESCo equity contribution; IRRs of greater than 30 percent are expected to be favorably considered by ESCos.

Figures 1 and 2 compare the cash flow stemming from the two ECMs being examined here for the first party and the second party, respectively. (Recall that the return to the third party consists of interest payments on a loan, and is constant across all scenarios examined thus far.) For both ECM A and ECM B, the real, after-tax cash flow increases because of the increasing energy expenditures that would exist without the ECM. With flat or decreasing energy expenditures, however, cash flow decreases over time for both the first and second parties.

It should be noted that the jump in the cashflow to the second party stems from the loss of depreciation expensing after the fifth year of the analysis. Recall that the ECM is assumed to be of the five-year type for depreciation, and that straight-line depreciation is used.

ECONOMIC SCENARIOS

In addition to uncertainty about energy prices, recent economic conditions, specifically interest rates and inflation rates, have also been subject to uncertainty. In the base case, the cost of capital (the prevailing interest rate) was assumed to be 10 percent and inflation was assumed to be 4 percent. In this section, we examine two alternative economic scenarios, one of which depicts a more inflationary cycle and one of which depicts a more deflationary cycle. The results of this analysis are shown in Table 4.

From Table 4 it is apparent that both ECMs examined here are robust in terms of their attractiveness to potential investors under alternative economic scenarios. Although perhaps somewhat counterintuitive, the inflationary cycle is less attractive to investors than the base case or deflationary cycle. The reason for this is largely that future dollars are worth less then current dollars, particularly in an inflationary time. For the first party, then, the factor of 50 percent of energy savings has not changed, but the present value of the payback from that savings has changed because of the higher inflation rate. Similarly, the second party also receives less valuable dollars under the inflationary cycle. For the third party, the important factor is not the interest rate received, but the difference between the nominal interest rate (12 percent for the inflationary cycle) and the inflation rate (7 percent), or 5 percent; this is less

	FLAT ENERGY PRICES		DECLINING ENERGY PRICES	
PARAMETER OF INTEREST	ECM A	ECM B	ECM A	ECM B
Pre-Investment Annual Energy Expenditure Escalation Factor	0%	0%	-4%	-4%
OVERALL				
Benefit-Cost Ratio	5.8:1	6.2:1	4.8:1	5.2:1
FIRST PARTY				
PV of Cash Flow	$579,000	$362,000	$485,000	$303,000
SECOND PARTY				
ESCo IRR (Total Capital)	35.4%	37.8%	31.4%	33.7%
ESCo IRR (Equity)	38.2%	41.0%	33.8%	36.4%
THIRD PARTY				
Lender IRR (Debt)	10.0%	10.0%	10.0%	10.0%

Note: All values are real, after-tax yields; present value calculations are discounted to the present at the annual borrowing rate.

TABLE 3. DETAILED RESULTS FOR ENERGY PRICE SCENARIOS.

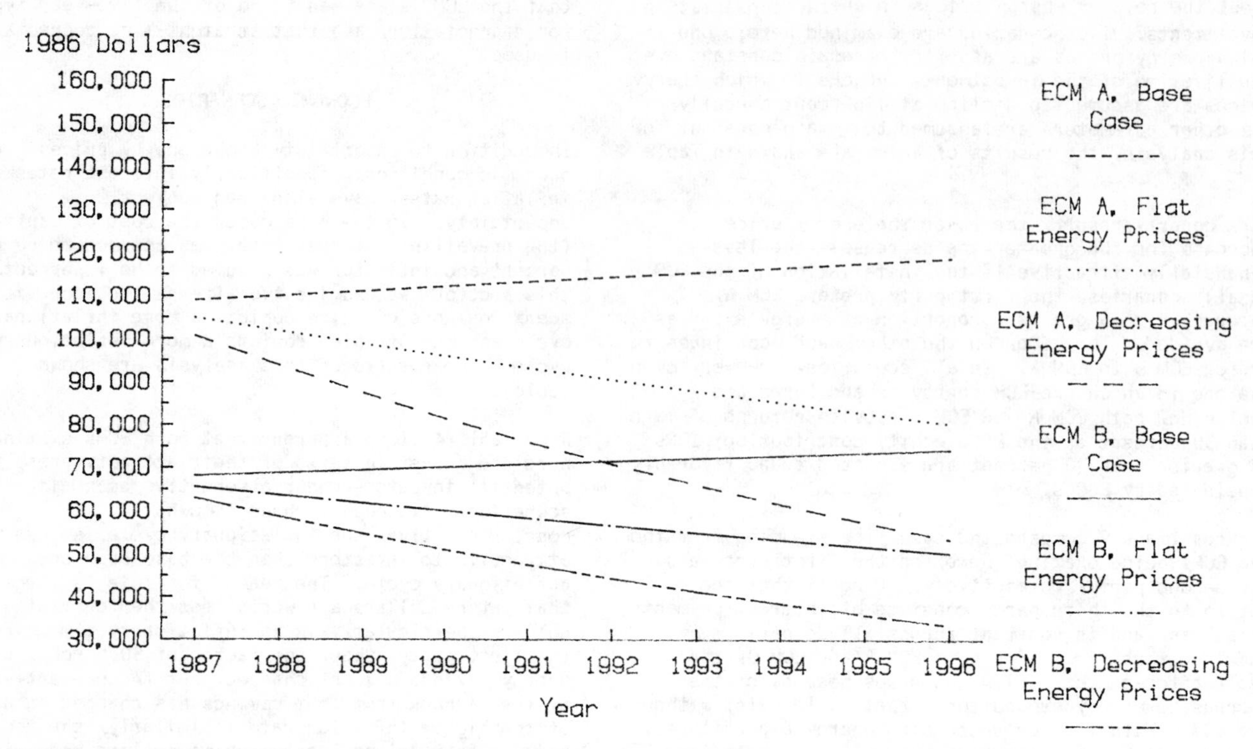

FIGURE 1. FIRST PARTY CASH FLOW FOR ENERGY PRICE SCENARIOS.

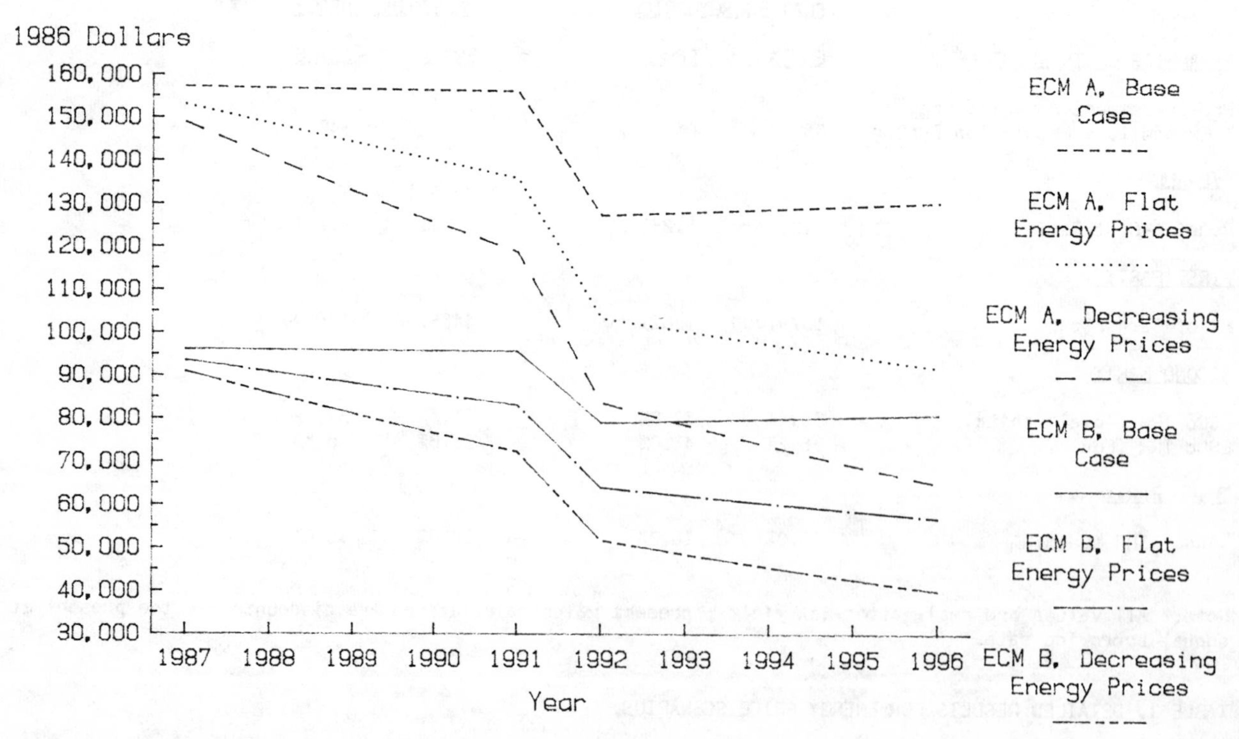

FIGURE 2. SECOND PARTY CASH FLOW FOR ENERGY PRICE SCENARIOS.

than the 7 percent difference between the inflation rate and nominal interest rate in the base case.

Figures 3, 4, and 5 show the real cash flow stemming from the installation of ECM A and ECM B for the first, second, and third party, respectively. Each party has a distinctive cash flow pattern, based on its share in the financial transactions. The increases or decreases in cash flow are strictly due to the changes in the inflation and interest rates.

The preferences for ECM A versus ECM B are similar in this case to those resulting from the energy price scenarios. Overall, ECM B is preferable to ECM A because of the higher benefit-cost ratio. The first party prefers ECM A under the inflationary and deflationary cycle. The second party continues to prefer ECM B because of the higher returns to equity investment.

COMBINED SCENARIOS

Although energy prices and the general economy may move independently of each other, it is more likely that they will move in tandem. In fact, the recent decline in energy prices led to corresponding decreases in the consumer price index, often used as a measure of inflation. Our analysis so far has indicated that declining energy prices will reduce the return from an energy conservation investment, as will an inflationary cycle. The combination of these two events, however, is unlikely to be maintained because of their interdependence. It is conceivable, however, to have flat (rather than rising) energy prices in conjunction with an inflationary cycle. Therefore, our "worst case" combined scenario consists of flat energy prices combined with an inflationary cycle. Our "best case" combined scenario joins a deflationary cycle with slowly rising energy prices (i.e., the 4 percent annually increasing energy expenditures used in the base case); this is exactly the same case examined in our economic scenario, deflationary cycle.

Table 5 presents detailed results from the best and worst combined scenarios. Even in the worst conceivable case, both ECM A and ECM B are attractive to potential investors. For the first party, the expected cash flow could be, for ECM A, anywhere from about $450,000 to more than twice that amount. For the ESCo, there is a tremendous range in the IRR to equity, from about 30 percent to about 50 percent.

Figures 6, 7, and 8 present the cash flow stemming from the best and worst case scenarios for the first party, second party, and third party, respectively. The differences in cash flow patterns again reflect the values of the relevant parameters of the analysis.

SUMMARY

Although, for the ECMs analyzed here, the returns to all investors are always favorable, the wide variation in the returns to these investors emphasizes the importance of conducting careful analyses of the energy prices, economic activity, and other factors underlying energy conservation investments; other proposed ECMs may not be as robust as those examined here in terms of their return to investors.

In addition, the analyses conducted here assumed that the energy savings brought about through installation of the ECM was known (to be 40 percent) with certainty. In reality, this factor is also subject to uncertainty and the effects of its possible variation should be analyzed.

	INFLATIONARY CYCLE		DEFLATIONARY CYCLE	
PARAMETERS OF INTEREST	ECM A	ECM B	ECM A	ECM B
Annual Inflation Rate	7%	7%	-3%	-3%
Annual Borrowing Rate	12%	12%	8%	8%
OVERALL				
Benefit-Cost Ratio	5.3:1	5.8:1	10.3:1	11.1:1
FIRST PARTY				
PV of Cash Flow	$537,000	$336,000	$1,038,000	$649,000
SECOND PARTY				
ESCo IRR (Total Capital)	35.1%	37.5%	47.2%	49.9%
ESCo IRR (Equity)	37.7%	40.4%	51.5%	54.7%
THIRD PARTY				
Lender IRR (Debt)	12.0%	12.0%	8.0%	8.0%

Note: All values are real, after-tax yields; present value calculations are discounted to the present at the annual borrowing rate.

TABLE 4. DETAILED RESULTS FOR ECONOMIC SCENARIOS.

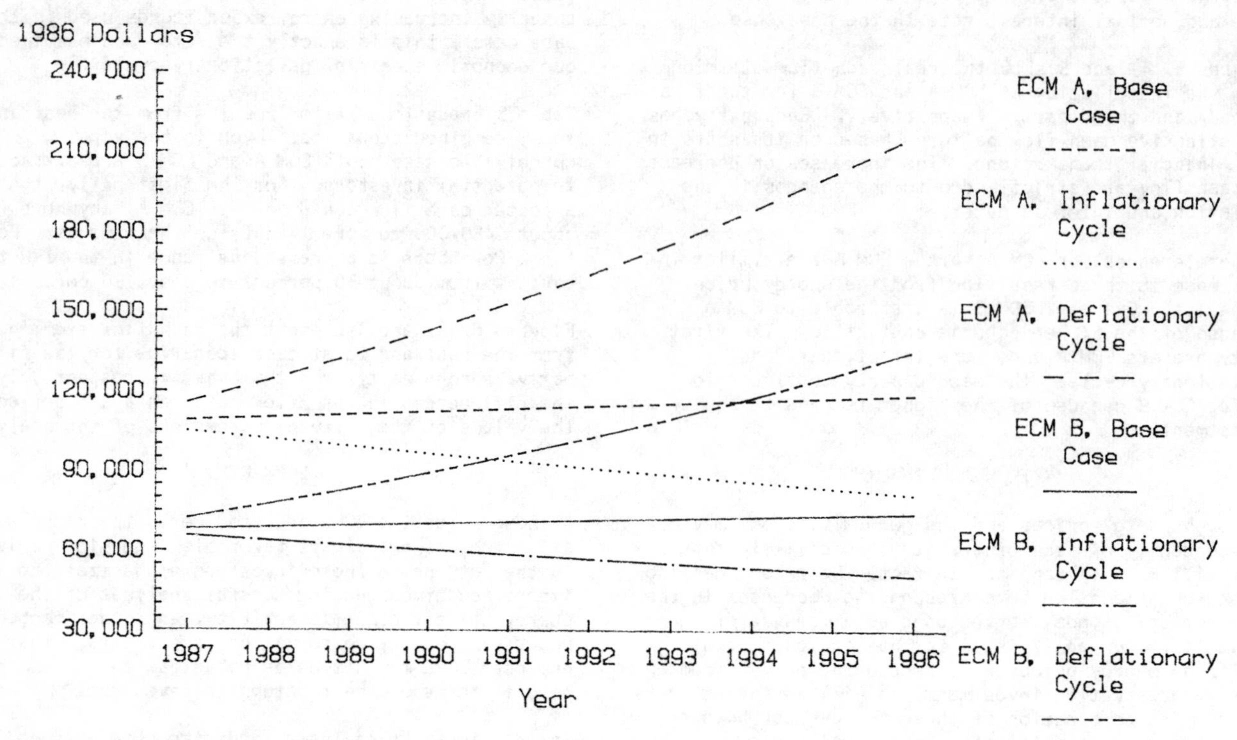

FIGURE 3. FIRST PARTY CASH FLOW FOR ECONOMIC SCENARIOS.

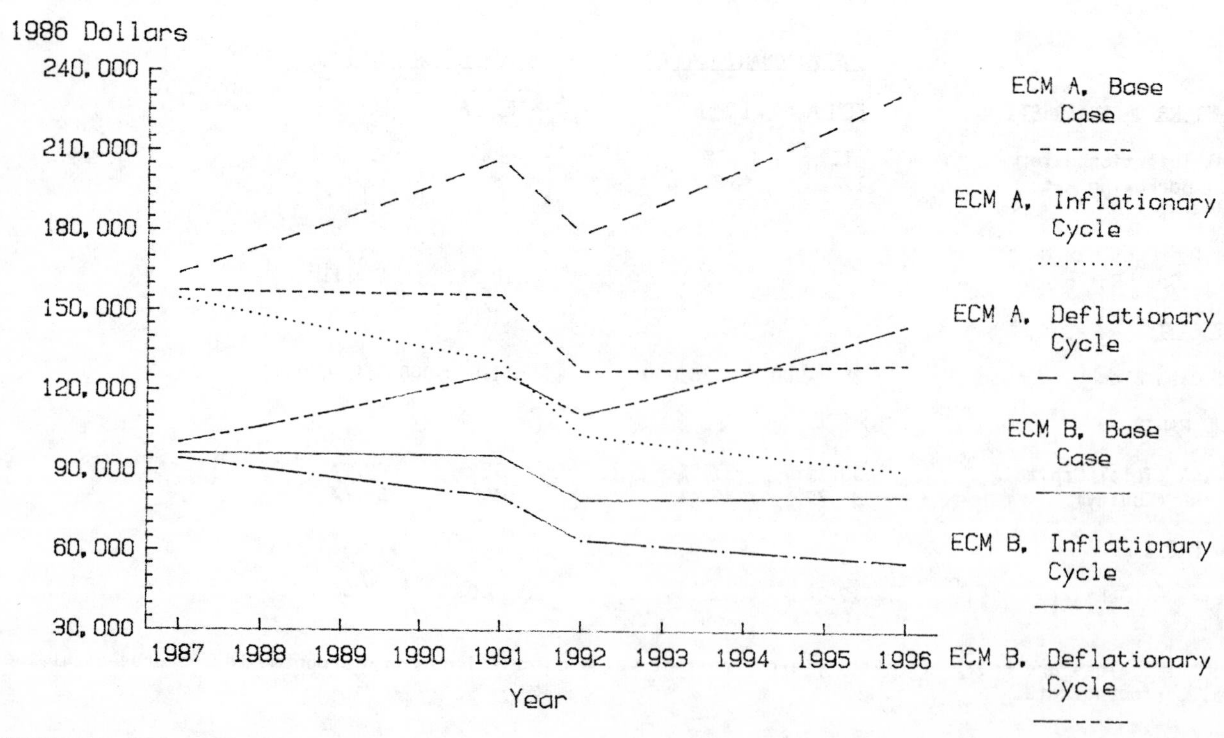

FIGURE 4. SECOND PARTY CASH FLOW FOR ECONOMIC SCENARIOS.

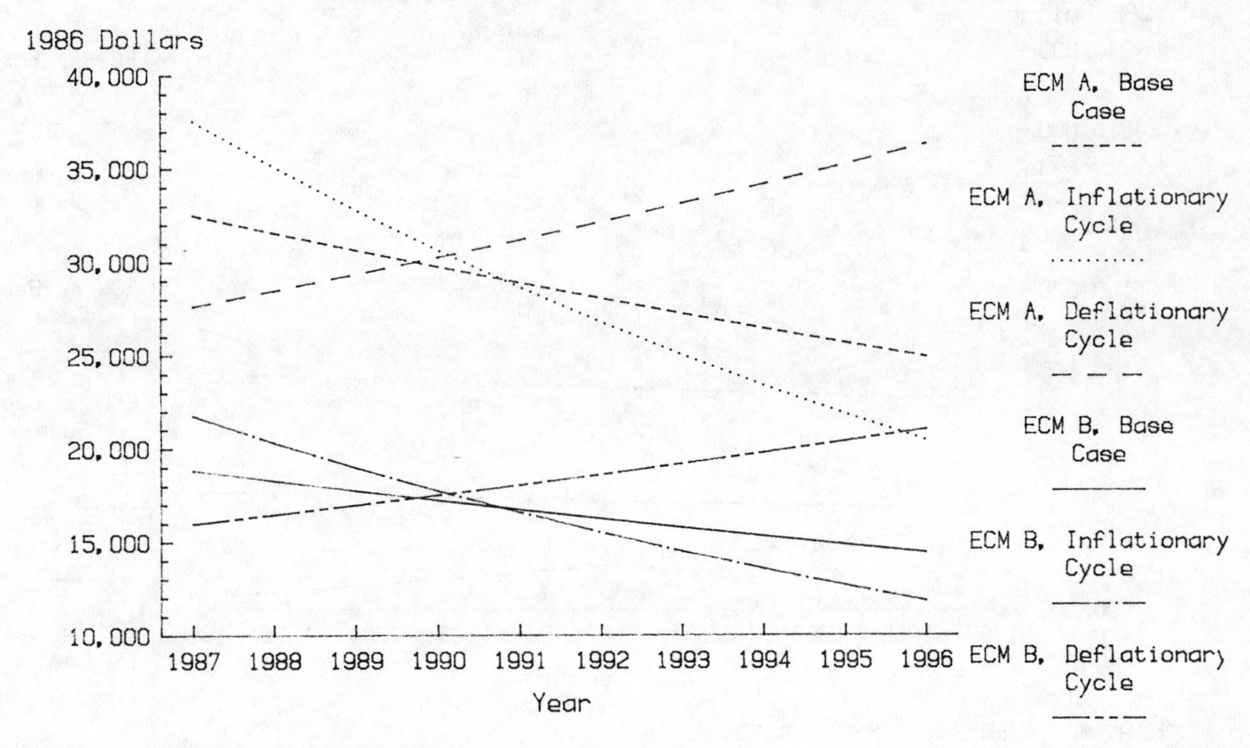

FIGURE 5. THIRD PARTY INTEREST FOR ECONOMIC SCENARIOS.

	WORST CASE		BEST CASE	
PARAMETERS OF INTEREST	ECM A	ECM B	ECM A	ECM B
Pre-Investment Annual Energy Expenditure Escalation Factor	0%	0%	4%	4%
Annual Inflation Rate	7%	7%	-3%	-3%
Annual Borrowing Rate	12%	12%	8%	8%
OVERALL				
Benefit-Cost Ratio	4.5:1	4.9:1	10.3:1	11.1:1
FIRST PARTY				
PV of Cash Flow	$455,000	$285,000	$1,038,000	$649,000
SECOND PARTY				
ESCo IRR (Total Capital)	31.2%	33.5%	47.2%	49.9%
ESCo IRR (Equity)	33.3%	35.9%	51.5%	54.7%
THIRD PARTY				
Lender IRR (Debt)	12.0%	12.0%	8.0%	8.0%

Note: All values are real, after-tax yields; present value calculations are discounted to the present at the annual borrowing rate.

TABLE 5. DETAILED RESULTS FOR COMBINED SCENARIOS.

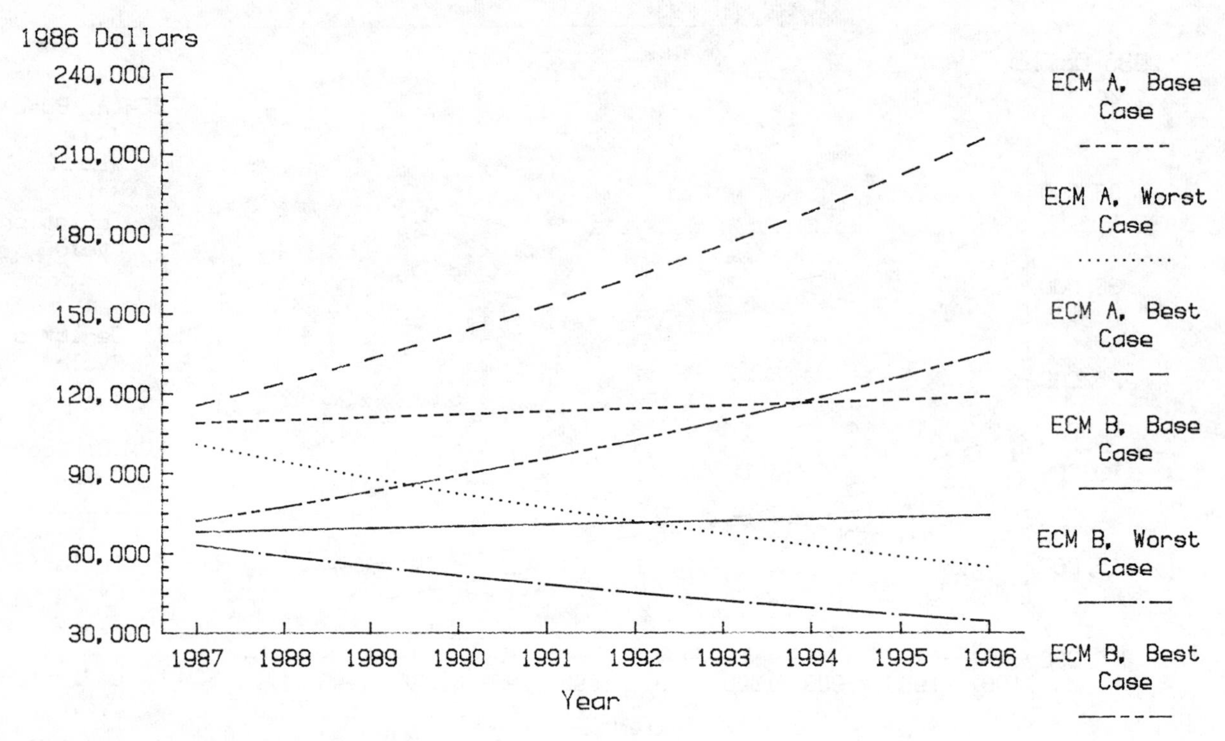

FIGURE 6. FIRST PARTY CASH FLOW FOR COMBINED SCENARIOS.

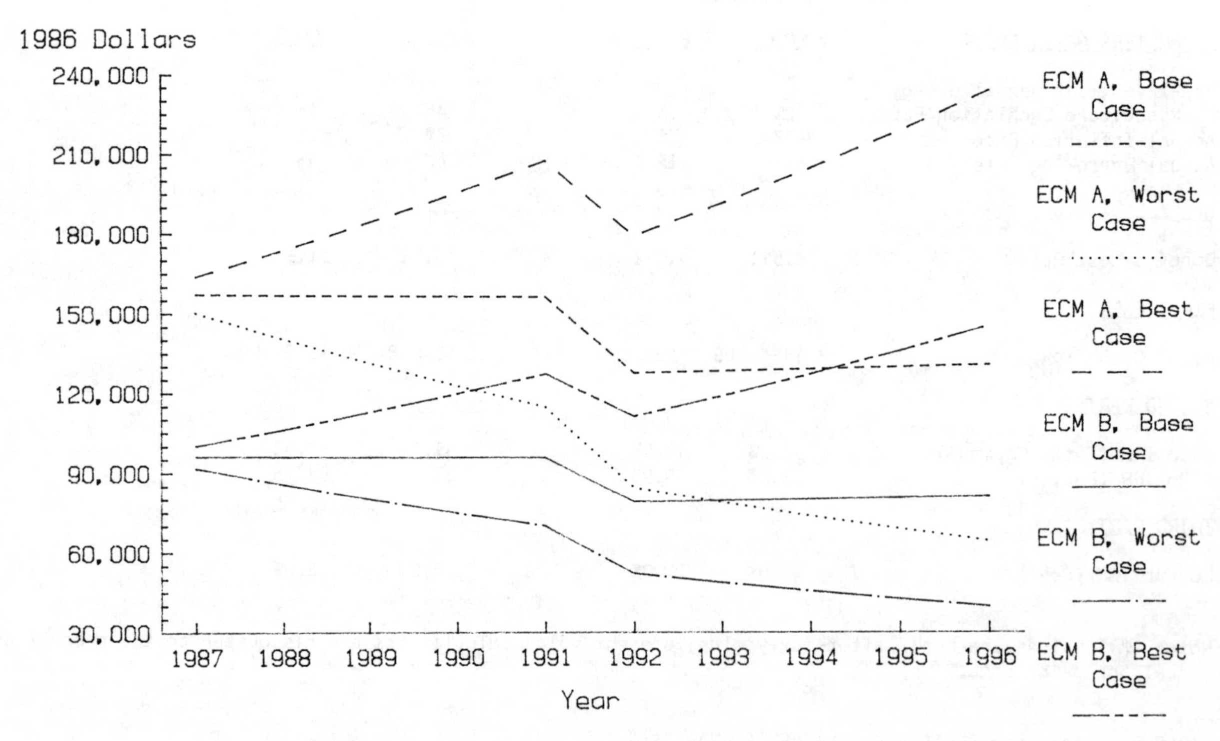

FIGURE 7. SECOND PARTY CASH FLOW FOR COMBINED SCENARIOS.

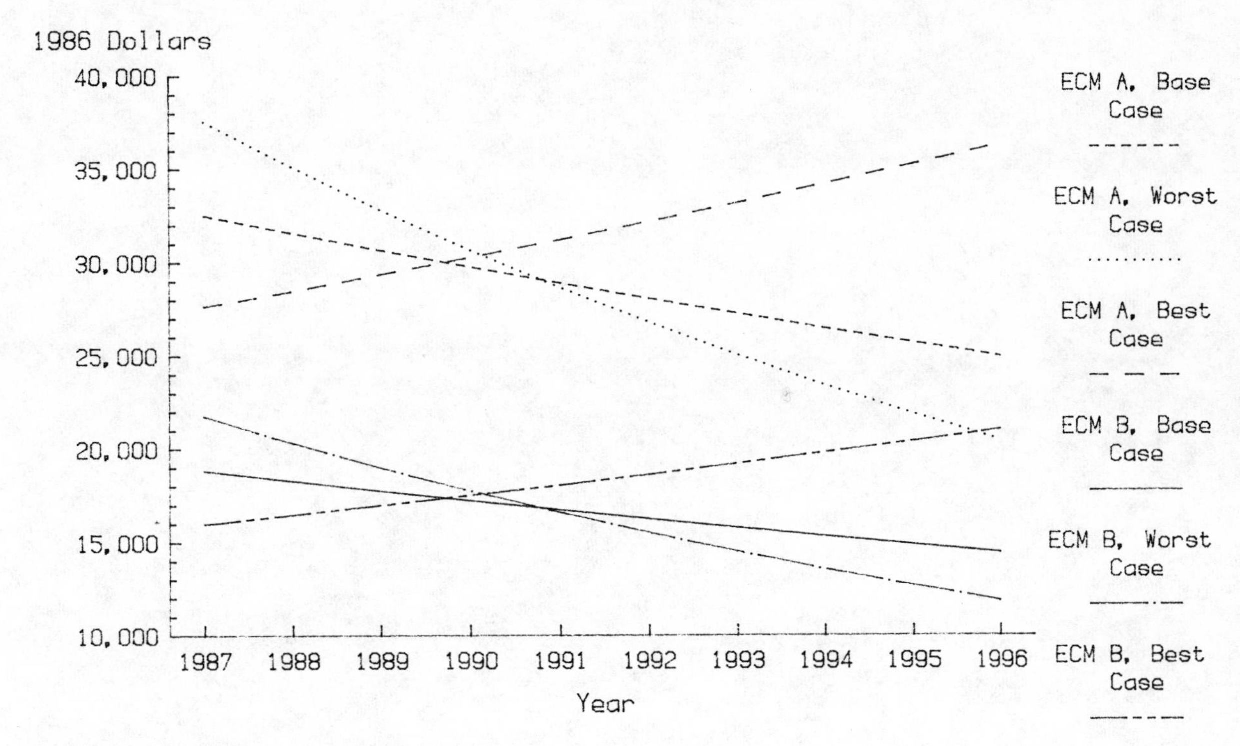

FIGURE 8. THIRD PARTY INTEREST FOR COMBINED SCENARIOS.

Chapter 87

USING SPREADSHEETS TO ANALYZE ENERGY RATES, PROJECTS AND RESULTS IN MANUFACTURING PLANTS

D. Pudell

INTRODUCTION

The purpose of this paper is to show how we at Sheller-Globe use spreadsheet programs on a personal computer to:

1) Analyze and compare the various utility rates available at our manufacturing plants. This allows us to determine if we are in fact on the best rate and what energy conservation opportunities should be pursued to maximize utility savings.

2) Analyze survey data collected in the field, highlighting possible projects and to assemble this data into meaningful reports.

3) Compute project savings and payback.

4) Monitor and follow-up projects from the idea stage through completion.

5) Audit the energy management program results and use this information to highlight areas for further cost reduction.

RATE ANALYSIS

In order to determine the best strategy to save energy dollars, one first has to understand how the utility company is charging for the energy used. Each utility has its own method of computing rates, and in many cases more than one rate may apply for a particular facility. A copy of all applicable rates should be obtained from the utility representative in charge of industrial or commercial accounts. This person can also help with an explanation of the various terms used in the rate such as demand charge, ratchet clause, fuel cost adjustment, power factor penalty, time of day, seasonal variations, etc.

Once you feel comfortable with the structure and terminology of the current rate you are using, try putting it into a spreadsheet program. The best way to start this process is to take a current bill and duplicate the calculations in the spreadsheet. Do not try to get too fancy at this point by trying to combine steps. In fact, it is better to have each calculation broken down as simply as possible. This allows for better understanding and future analysis.

After setting up the spreadsheet, test it by substituting another month's meter readings to see if it will in fact duplicate that bill. Variations can occur from numerous causes. The utility might have changed the fuel adjustment cost, there might be taxes included that are not broken out, or it may be in how they round the various numbers in intermediate calculations. The spreadsheet should be able to duplicate the calculations for any of the previous bills that were under that particular rate. If it does not work out, find why and make the necessary corrections. This spreadsheet model will be the basis for future decisions, and you want to be sure that it is right.

After you have a good working model of your current rate, you should model the other rates available to determine if there is any advantage to changing. In order to do a through analysis, you should calculate the past twelve month's usage using both the current and alternate rates to compare total annual costs. This is especially important if the utility has summer and winter charges. If you determine that another rate would be more favorable, contact the utility company and discuss a change.

Upon completion of the rate analysis, you will have a spreadsheet model that can be used to determine the cost effectiveness of projects, the impact of utility rate increases, and the accuracy of future billings.

IDENTIFYING COST SAVING OPPORTUNITIES

The next step is to do a "sensitivity analysis" on your rate model. This simply means to change some of the input numbers like KWH (kilowatt hours) KW (kilowatt) demand or power factor and see what overall result this has on the monthly and/or annual bill. This information will highlight the areas that should be investigated to achieve cost savings. For example, if large savings result from small charges in demand usage, you would of course audit your facility for demand limiting opportunities.

A common error is made in determining savings when the demand and KWH usage are reduced or the power factor is improved. Most of the time an average is used. For example, consider we have a medium size plant that is lit with mercury lights and we believe there would be a savings large enough to justify the expense of installing high pressure sodium vapor lights based on the guidelines of our particular organization. We are told by the HPS representative that his lights will consume one half the electricity while giving us the same amount of light. We have 100 twin 400 watt mercury fixtures, or a total connected load of 80 KW. If we replace these fixtures with HPS, the total connected load would be 40 KW. (For this example, ballast losses are not being taken into account.) Next, assume that the lights will operate 24 hours per day, 22 days per month. The KWH consumption would then be:

$$\text{MERCURY LIGHTS: } 80\text{ KW} \times 24\ \frac{\text{HRS}}{\text{DAY}} \times 22\ \frac{\text{DAY}}{\text{MO.}} = 42{,}240\ \frac{\text{KWH}}{\text{MO.}}$$

$$\text{HPS LIGHTS: } 40\text{ KW} \times 24\ \frac{\text{HRS}}{\text{DAY}} \times 22\ \frac{\text{DAY}}{\text{MO.}} = 21{,}120\ \frac{\text{KWH}}{\text{MO.}}$$

At this point it is still pretty simple. The KW demand and the KWH consumption are both one half for

CURRENT ELECTRIC RATE

Plant: ABC

Service Month: August 1985

	CALCULATIONS	MERCURY CHARGES	CALCULATIONS	HPS CHARGES
Input Data:				
Metered KWH	1,312,800		1,291,680	
Metered RKVAH	760,800		748,800	
Metered Demand	3,784.8		3,744.8	
Power Factor	86.5		86.5	
Fuel Adj. Cost ($/KWH)	$0.000909000		$0.000909000	
Demand Cost ($/KVA)	$13.686		$13.686	
Energy Cost ($/KWH)	$0.01273		$0.01273	
Monthly Service Charge		$400.35		$400.35
RKVAH	760,800		748,800	
Metered Demand	3,784.8		3,744.8	
Power Factor	86.5		86.5	
Billing Demand	3,785.0	$51,801.51	$3,745.0	$51,254.07
Metered KWH	1,312,800		1,291,680	
Power Factor Constant	0.9938		0.9938	
Adjusted KWH	1,304,661		1,283,672	
Billing KWH	1,304,661	$17,794.27	1,283,672	$17,508.00
TOTAL COST		$69,996.13		$69,162.42

FIGURE 1

the HPS lighting system of that used by the mercury system. This does not answer our question as to what the savings would be if we switched systems.

For the financial analysis, first assume that the only information we have obtained is the monthly bill which shows a KWH consumption of 1,312,800, a KW demand of 3,785 and a total cost of $69,996. In many cases, the individual would take the total cost and divide by the KWH to arrive at an average dollar per KWH.

$$\frac{\$69{,}996}{1{,}312{,}800\ \text{KWH}} = \frac{\$.0533}{\text{KWH}}$$

Applying this KWH cost to both lighting systems, the result is:

MERCURY LIGHTS: 42,240 $\frac{\text{KWH}}{\text{MO.}}$ x $.0533 = $2,251.39

HPS LIGHTS: 21,120 $\frac{\text{KWH}}{\text{MO.}}$ x $.0533 = $1,125.70

SAVINGS = $1,125.69

Listed in Figure 1 is a printout of a month's electrical billing calculated with mercury lights and HPS. Note that the metered KWH for the HPS is 21,120 KWH lower and the KW demand is reduced by 40 KW, reflecting actual conditions. The difference in total cost or the savings by going to HPS lights turns out to be:

SAVINGS = $69,996.13 - $69,162.42 = $833.71

This is 26 percent less savings than was calculated by the average dollars per KWH method.

ANALYZING SURVEY DATA

In any energy conservation project, whether large or small, there will be considerable data that must be gathered in order to reach a decision. The quicker the data can be collected and analyzed, the sooner a good project can be implemented to start saving money. Spreadsheet templates can be set up to handle any energy project or family of projects. The spreadsheet acts as a prompt asking for the data needed to complete the analysis. I have found it very beneficial to take a paper copy of a spreadsheet template into the field so that all the needed data is collected to complete the calculations once I am back at the office.

Figure 2 contains a spreadsheet entitled "Building Heat Loss Calculations". Although it is a simple spreadsheet to construct, it can be used to determine insulation savings, unoccupied temperature set back, improved heating source efficiency, changes in temperature during occupied hours, and the effects of fuel cost changes.

Figure 2 is set up to show the savings that can be expected from installing an energy management system to set back the building temperature during unoccupied hours. The input variables are listed under data. After all of the existing conditions are entered, accuracy of assumptions can be checked by comparing the total Btu's and cost in the existing column to what was actually consumed over the past year.

Once you are satisfied that the existing conditions, closely model what is going on at the facility under consideration. Move to the proposed data and determine savings by varying input data, in this case

BUILDING HEAT LOSS CALCULATIONS

Plant: ABC

Calculations for: Energy Management System

Data:	Existing	Proposed
"R" Factor	3.66	3.66
"U" Factor	0.273	0.273
Sq. Ft.	173,091	173,091
Inside Temp. Occupied	72	72
Inside Temp. Unoccupied	72	55
Average Outside Temp.	32.1	32.1
Hours per Week Occupied	50	50
Hours per Week Unoccupied	118	118
Heating Months per Year	6.5	6.5
Energy Cost/Million Btu's	$5.50	$5.50
Efficiency	70%	70%
Results:		
During Occupied Hours		
Btu's Lost (Millions)	2,639	2,639
Cost	$20,734	$20,734
During Unoccupied Hours		
Btu's Lost (Millions)	6,228	3,574
Cost	$48,932	$28,084
Total:		
Btu's	8,867	6,213
Cost	$69,666	$48,818
Total Annual Savings:		
Btu's (Millions)		2,653
Dollars		$20,848

FIGURE 2

inside temperature during unoccupied hours. In the example, we can see that at this particular location, which is occupied 10 hours per day, 5 days per week, a reduction of 17 degrees would save over $20,000 per year. You could determine the confidence level of your projected savings by playing "what if" with the spreadsheet. By making changes that could reasonably be expected to occur in variables such as occupied and unoccupied temperature, setback hours, fuel cost, etc., the impact on savings would be readily seen.

In Figure 3 we have a portion of an electric audit performed at a manufacturing plant. A recording electric meter was used to collect data on individual pieces of equipment. From the meter tapes, the information was entered into a spreadsheet where the various costs were calculated by using the information from the electrical rate spreadsheet for this plant. Once the data has been entered, it can be sorted to produce various reports such as the maximum or minimum demand cost or KWH cost, which machine has a low power factor and how much capacitance is needed to correct it, and what is the total cost per month to operate a machine.

PROJECT SAVINGS AND PAYBACK

To this point, we have seen some examples of how to determine project savings and how these savings might vary if future conditions change. With this information and the cost of the project, the simple payback can be easily calculated. Most of you need to go further than simple payback in order to get a project approved. Life cycle cost analysis is a method by which project costs are looked at over the entire life of the proposed machine or system. It takes into account the owning and operating costs associated with the project. The scope of this paper does not allow room to go into great detail on this subject as it can become quite involved.

In most cases, your accountants have a method in place that is understood and used throughout your

ELECTRIC AUDIT FOR ABC PLANT — DATE: 3/22/86

EQUIPMENT NAME	KWH	PEAK KWH	AVG. KWH	AVG. P.F.	KVAR	DEMAND COST	KWH COST /HOUR	P.F. COST	OPERATING HRS/MO.	TOTAL COST /MONTH
150 HP AIR COMPRESSOR	36.64	118.00	109.8	0.84	70.9	$1,290.92	$3.11	$19.92	520	$2,930
50 HP AIR COMPRESSOR	237.20	35.83	33.4	0.79	25.9	$391.98	$0.95	$7.29	347	$728
LIGHTING PANEL REGULATOR DEPT.	8.84	36.00	35.3	0.96	10.3	$393.84	$1.00	$2.89	217	$614
VARNISH OVEN	3.15	13.16	12.6	0.45	25.0	$143.97	$0.36	$7.02	572	$355
HOUSING DIE CAST MACHINE	11.91	20.76	20.4	0.71	20.2	$227.11	$0.58	$5.68	173	$333
OFFICE	16.18	10.78	10.8	1.00	0.0	$117.93	$0.31	$0.00	217	$184
PARTS WASHER	1.57	5.92	5.9	0.49	10.5	$64.76	$0.17	$2.94	217	$104
AUTOMATIC WELDER	1.42	5.08	4.5	0.13	34.1	$55.58	$0.13	$9.59	208	$92

FIGURE 3

organization. I would recommend contacting them for a copy and making up a spreadsheet to calculate the return on investment. In many cases you will find, as I did, that the accountants have already put this information into a spreadsheet. You will find that projects take less time to get approval when they are submitted on a form familar to the financial people at your location.

MONITORING PROJECT PROGRESS

Many times good project ideas never make it through to completion. It is not always due to lack of financial or technical feasibility. It is usually because the project gets put on the backburner and forgotten due to other day-to-day items that need attention. If no records are kept on project progress or what is to be done next, valuable time can be lost in getting the project installed.

The spreadsheet program that I am currently using also has a data base. This is used to track projects from the idea stage, through the under study phase, financial request and approval, and finally to completion. If at any point the project is found to be either technically or economically unfeasible, this can be noted for future reference. If the conditions change, the project can then be continued.

Each project record in the data base contains the following data fields: plant location, type of project, annual savings in Btu's and dollars, total cost, start and completion dates, status, last date reviewed, follow-up date and a brief description. Various sorting configurations can be set up to group and print out project information in any form desired. For instance, with just a few keystrokes, the total year-to-date savings for completed projects can be reported. A search can be performed to locate similar projects and information passed along to an individual looking at that type of project to save reinventing the wheel. Once a month, a printout can be made to list those projects that need follow-up. In all, it is an extremely helpful tool to monitor an energy conservation program's progress.

MONITORING PROGRAM RESULTS

In order to determine the success of any program, especially an energy management program, some kind of scorecard must be kept. Without a method to measure results, there is no way to determine if the goals of the program are being met. In addition, a good monitoring report will highlight areas where further program refinement is needed. It should, if designed properly, indicate where new energy cost reductions might be implemented.

SHELLER-GLOBE ENERGY CONSERVATION PROGRAM
MONTHLY REPORT

DIVISION ____________________

LOCATION ____________________

CURRENT MONTH Mar			YEAR 1986		PREVIOUS MONTH Mar		YEAR 1985		PERCENT CHANGE	COST/ MILLION BTU
	BTU (MILLION) CONSUMED	ENERGY COST			BTU (M) CONSUMED	ENERGY COST				
Electric	9,851	$125,901	DIR. LABOR STD. HOURS	94,682	9,175	$83,931	DIR. LABOR STD. HOURS	91,143	BTU PER STD. HR. ° DAY	CURRENT
Natural Gas	13,316	$74,757			22,581	$113,019				
Oil	6,876	$42,237	DEGREE DAYS	596	0	$0	DEGREE DAYS	586	-11.5%	$8.09
Propane	0	$0	BTU PER STD. HR. ° DAY	0.223	0	$0	BTU PER STD. HR. ° DAY	0.252	COST/ STD. HR. ° DAY	PREVIOUS
Coal	0	$0			0	$0				
Other	0	$0	COST PER STD. HR. ° DAY	$1.80	0	$0	COST PER STD. HR. ° DAY	$1.56	15.3%	$6.20
Total	30,042	$242,895			31,756	$196,950				

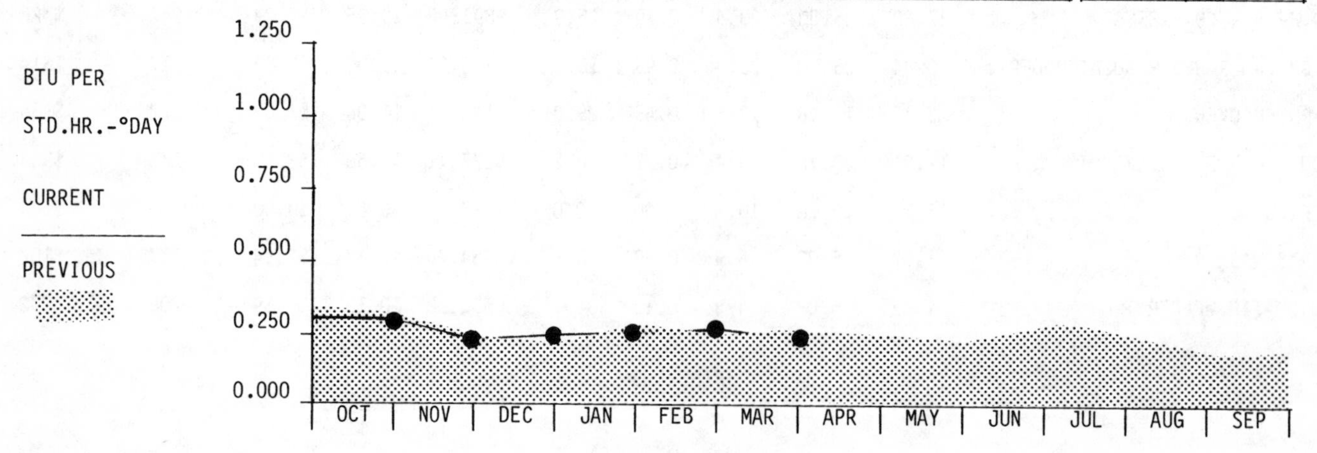

FIGURE 4

Figure 4 is an example of the format we use at Sheller-Globe to compare current energy consumption to the previous year. Each plant reports their monthly Btu consumption and cost for each fuel that is used. The direct labor standard hours earned are a measure of plant output. The degree days are reported so that an adjustment for weather can be made. When this report was developed, it was felt and later substantiated with multiple regression analysis, that the variations in energy consumption at a given location were dependent on the amount of production and the weather.

Each month the energy index expressed in Btu's per standard hour, degree day, is calculated and the current year-to-date is graphed with the previous year to show trends. This information is used to show the overall picture as to how a particular plant is performing energy wise. If a significant variation, either plus or minus, is observed, an attempt is made to determine cause. Action is then taken to continue an improvement trend. Likewise, if there is a problem the cause is sought and action is taken to correct it as soon as possible.

We have used a variation of this report to track a particular project. For instance, at one plant a number of steam traps were replaced. To determine if we had in fact accomplished our goal to reduce consumption, we looked at the major relevant factors. They were gas used in the boilers, production hours of only the departments using process steam, and degree days. After the calculations had been run, it was found that we had reduced gas consumption by 30 percent, approximately what had been predicted at the start of the project.

SUMMARY

In any energy management program, following a logical sequence of steps from beginning to end will help insure success. First, a plan should be developed. Spending time at this point will make the next step, implementation, go more smoothly. Results should be checked with some kind of accurate scoring system. Finally, the results of the entire program should be analyzed and a new plan developed, continuing the circle of events and improving the program with each cycle. Using a spreadsheet program on a personal computer makes the above process easier to manage. It will not do the thinking for you, but it will help you through the thinking process.

I hope we have given you food for thought in this area and possibly opened up a new dimension that will make you more effective in your current position.

Chapter 88

FINDING THE BOTTOM LINE IN BOILER AND COOLING SYSTEMS

L. G. Armwood

The phrase "bottom line" has developed from a business expression into an everyday idiom. Although in different contexts, bottom line has different meanings, the phrase has come to mean the final result. Even in business, non-managerial personnel may have functions that measure a bottom line in non-monetary terms.

In any organization, an important aspect of getting to the bottom line is the reduction of its so called fixed operating costs or overhead. While overhead costs are part of the requirements of doing business, they are not necessarily fixed costs. In particular, the utility costs for boiler and cooling systems can often be reduced by proper analysis of the systems.

Microcomputers have become an effective tool in providing accurate calculations in all areas of business. Key to the success of the microcomputer has been the development of software to meet special needs of a wide variety of users. To address the needs of management and engineers to control utility costs, software for microcomputers has been developed to model the operation of boiler and cooling systems in order to establish the bottom line for both management and engineer.

The need to control the cost of utilities is common to all organizations whether in business or in a non-profit institution. Within a particular organization, there may be different needs for each individual depending on their responsibilities. One group involved with the cost of utilities is the management of the organization. The other major group involved with the cost of utilities is the engineering department responsible for operating the utility system.

MANAGEMENT'S BOTTOM LINE

In the commercial field, building owners and property management companies are concerned with cost of utilities. This group must compete with other building owners and property management companies to provide a building with the lowest possible utility costs. If a building owner cannot control the cost of utilities, he will lose money and may lose tenants. If a property management company cannot control utility costs, they will be replaced by a company that can.

In institutions, the administrators are responsible for the utility costs. Even though an institution is not required to make a profit, they must compete directly with other institutions or for limited tax dollars. If an institution cannot control utility costs, cuts may have to be made in other areas limiting essential services.

In the manufacturing industry, plant and utility managers are responsible for utility costs. If the utility costs are not controlled, then the profit per unit is reduced. In very serious cases, the company could actually lose market share due to high overhead costs.

In each of the cases discussed above, management was responsible for the cost of the utilities. Management uses the cost data to budget current expenses and in marketing and budgeting forecasts. The individuals in these groups may or may not have technical training. And in only the small organizations would plant management be responsible for the actual operation of the boiler and cooling system.

ENGINEERING'S BOTTOM LINE

In all of the organizations discussed above, the actual operation of the boiler and cooling systems is the responsibility of the engineering department. It is the engineering department that is charged with operating the existing system as efficiently as possible and recommending steps to be taken to improve the operation of the system.

Operating the system as efficiently as possible will reduce the cost of utilities but cost is not the key factor to the engineer. A decrease in energy cost has no effect on the engineer; he must still operate the existing system as efficiently as possible. An increase in energy costs only means that there may be new energy conservation modifications that have become economical because of the increase in energy losses.

Because of the different functions of the managers and engineers, the managers and engineers have different goals, different bottom lines. To the manager, the bottom line is the cost of the utilities and how does the utility cost affect the final cost of the product or service.

To the engineer, the bottom line is how efficiently is the system operating, what can be done to maintain the efficiency, and if possible, what can be done to improve the efficiency?

Because of the availability of low cost computers, many boiler and cooling systems have been connected to energy management systems, EMS, and process control systems. Energy management systems are designed to optimize the use of energy and tend to ignore the 'source' of the energy, the boiler or cooling system. Process control systems are designed to optimize the production of energy but generally by controlling only one parameter of the system such as excess air in a boiler.

Neither the energy management systems nor process control systems are normally used to model the effect of changes to the system and to predict the effect of the changes on the utility costs. These systems also cost more than many organizations are willing to pay.

To meet the needs of both management and engineering, software packages have been developed for off-line use on microcomputers to allow management and engineers to find and improve their respective bottom lines. The Boiler Energy Analysis computer program has been designed to model boiler systems. The Cooling Energy Analysis computer program has been designed to model vapor compression cooling systems such as chillers.

For managers, the energy analysis computer programs can be used to measure current utility costs and as a planning tool to calculate the effect on the utility costs of changes in the system. For the engineer, the Energy Analysis computer programs can be used as an analytical tool to monitor the boiler or cooling system to identify problem areas and to calculate the savings from projected changes to the system.

Because the Energy Analysis software is designed to operate on microcomputers costs are low when compared to time-sharing systems. Since this software is designed to operate on IBM compatible computers with 256k of memory, the software can be run on most computers currently being used by business.

BOILER ENERGY ANALYSIS SOFTWARE

Most boilers are designed to operate efficiently when they are first installed. From that time on, the operating conditions begin to change and the boiler condition begins to decline. Management must know how these changes will affect the steam cost. The engineer must identify the problems so that they can be corrected or reduced. The engineer is also usually responsible for providing the steam cost data to management.

Boiler problems can be divided into the fireside and the waterside of the boiler. The fireside problems generally center around high stack temperatures, high excess air and improper load distribution between boilers. Most water side problems result from low process condensate return, high blowdown flow and high blowdown temperature.

The engineer's first step in understanding the boiler is to collect data on the current conditions. Much, and in some cases all, of this data has always been recorded on log sheets by the boiler operators. As numbers are recorded on a log sheet, the operating data shown in Table I is difficult to use to analyze the boiler condition.

TABLE I
BOILER OPERATING DATA

Steam pressure temperature max. boiler capacity flash steam pressure	Fuel analysis cost firing time Air temperature
Make-up water temperature chlorides	Stack gas temperature analysis
Process condensate temp. Feedwater chlorides Boiler chlorides Blowdown temperature Deaerator pressure Flash tank pressure	Mass flow readings steam, fuel or water

The Boiler Energy Analysis software can take the operating data listed in Table I and generate a complete picture of the boiler operation based on the ASME Power Test Codes, and water and energy balances on the boiler system. Key outputs generated by the Boiler Energy Analysis computer program are shown in Table II.

TABLE II
BOILER ENERGY ANALYSIS
OUTPUT DATA

Steam cost
Fuel cost
Cost of major energy losses
Boiler system efficiency
Combustion efficiency
Fuel to steam ratio
All major water and steam flow rates
Energy inputs and outputs
Fuel firing rate
All input data

It can be seen from Table II that the needs of the manager for steam costs can be met even if only one mass flow rate is available. More importantly, the operating data has been organized to give the engineer a clear picture of the mass and energy flows in the boiler. The engineer needs this data to troubleshoot the system.

Modeling

In order to satisfy the other needs of management and engineering, the Boiler Energy Analysis computer program has the ability to model changes in the boiler system and create an entirely new data set based on the new conditions. Because a new case has been generated, a series of changes can be combined to demonstrate the combined savings from a series of proposed changes.

A summary of modeling changes that can be made using the Boiler Energy Analysis computer program are shown in Table III.

TABLE III
BOILER ENERGY ANALYSIS
MODELING OPTIONS

Process condensate flow rate temperature Boiler cycles	Stack gas temperature excess air Inlet air temp.
Process steam flow rate pressure temperature	Fuel cost firing time
Waterside equipment deaerator flash tank heat exchanger	Fireside equipment economizer air preheater

Based on the cases generated in the modeling section, the engineer can determine what projects are feasible and rank them in order of their payback. Managers can use the data generated in the modeling section to plan capital expenditures for the boilerhouse and to forecast the impact of these changes on the cost of the product or service.

COOLING ENERGY ANALYSIS SOFTWARE

Unlike boilers, most operators of refrigeration systems do not monitor the load and cost of operating a cooling system unless the chiller is attached to an energy management system. This leaves management in the dark in terms of the actual operating costs of the cooling system. Managers who must estimate the costs of cooling in their plants do not know the true effect of cooling on their bottom line.

Periodic measurement of the operating condition of chillers is just as important for chillers as it is boilers because the chiller is more likely to slip from optimum conditions than a boiler since chillers are normally operated by part-time operators.

From the engineer's perspective, the efficiency of the cooling system, the coefficient of performance, is seldom calculated because the calculations require the use of pressure enthalpy diagrams. The engineer is then placed in the position of not being able to predict what improvements can be achieved in the system because he does not have a handle on what the current conditions are.

Operating problems for cooling systems are commonly the result of air in the refrigerant, high cooling water supply temperatures (leaving the cooling tower) and fouling of the condenser. All of these problems result in high condenser pressure and increased energy consumption by the compressor. Fouling can also reduce equipment life by causing under-deposit corrosion.

Air in the refrigerant can be detected and cured by purging the chiller when the condenser pressure, head pressure, reaches a predetermined point. If there is air in the refrigerant, the pressure will drop when the chiller is purged.

High cooling water supply temperatures can be monitored and controlled by plotting the approach of the cooling water supply temperature to the wet bulb temperature, cooling tower inspections and checking to ensure that the tower fan does not shut off at a needlessly high temperature.

Fouling of the condenser has proven to be a more difficult problem. Biological problems can cause serious fouling of a condenser in a matter of weeks. Deposits and scale, although they generally take longer to form, are more difficult to remove.

The traditional method of detecting fouling in a chiller's condenser has been to wait until the unit could be shutdown and visually inspect the tubes. Unfortunately, most units could not be inspected until the end of the cooling season. Even then, the extent of biofouling cannot be detected by visual inspection.

The Cooling Energy Analysis software was designed to meet the needs of management by calculating the cost of operating the cooling system and to meet the needs of the engineer by detecting and monitoring the most serious problem in cooling system operation, fouling of the condenser.

Using the input data shown in Table IV, the Cooling Energy Analysis computer program calculates the heat transfer coefficient for the condenser. Every heat exchanger has a heat transfer coefficient that relates the heat flux to the surface area and the average temperature difference across the exchanger.

TABLE IV
COOLING ENERGY ANALYSIS INPUT DATA

Condenser	Evaporator
pressure	pressure
temperatures	refrigerant type
tube length, dia. and count	
Compressor	
volts	
amps	
electrical costs	

Although only the chiller manufacturer knows the design heat transfer, it is possible to monitor the actual heat transfer coefficient to detect fouling in the condenser. A drop in the heat transfer coefficient means that the heat exchanger is fouling. If the actual heat transfer coefficient rises, then the heat exchanger is cleaner than in the base case.

In order to analyze the trend in heat transfer coefficient, the Cooling Energy Analysis provides the capability of printing the heat transfer coefficient in both side by side and graphical formats. This allows the engineer to develop a cost effective water treatment program to address fouling.

The chiller efficiency, the coefficient of performance is automatically calculated on the microcomputer using built in pressure enthalpy correlations for various refrigerants. Other data output by the Cooling Energy Analysis software is listed in Table V.

TABLE V
COOLING ENERGY ANALYSIS OUTPUT

Chiller	Compressor
load	efficiency
coefficient of performance	cost/day
load	horsepower
cost/ton of cooling	
Condenser	
load	
cw tube velocity	

Modeling

Because the problem areas of cooling systems are directly related to the condenser pressure, the modeling section of the Cooling Energy Analysis software is designed to calculate the savings from reducing the condenser to nominal values.

DISCUSSION

The introduction of microcomputers has brought a quick and inexpensive computing tool to management and engineer. Using software specially designed to solve problems related to boiler and cooling systems can result in more information with less effort and cost than could ever be achieved before.

This additional computing capacity has allowed managers and engineers to more easily calculate their specific objectives, their bottom line. Because the function of the manager and the engineer are different, each has different, but related bottom lines.

Chapter 89

PERSONAL COMPUTERS IN THE INTELLIGENT BUILDING

J. R. Neyer

INTRODUCTION

Due to the low cost of personal computer (PC) hardware and the abundance of PC-based software, many end-users of facilities automation equipment are already using PC's for a variety of data management applications. These applications include: spreadsheet generation, word processing, color graphics generation and display, maintenance management and work order generation and management. The same PC's can also be used to provide a low cost, high-level Man Machine Interface to either stand-alone or networked, distributed or centralized automation equipment. This yields a powerful centralized data acquisition system that can extend the capabilities of the above mentioned data management systems, as well as the control equipment, and greatly increases the performance and effectiveness of all levels of building operating personnel. It is the purpose of this paper to describe the trends in the PC-based data acquisition systems for the facilities automation industry.

In general, PC-based data acquisition system developers have designed their products with the following five criteria in mind:

1. Usability and Flexibility
2. Utilization of Existing Hardware
3. Compatiblity with Existing Software
4. Compatiblity with Existing Control Equipment
5. Access Security

These features are examined individually in the following sections.

USABILITY AND FLEXIBILITY

General

In order to be effective, PC-based data acquisition systems must be easy to use. Equally important however, is the requirement that it be easy for all levels of building personnel, from maintenance and security personnel to building managers and engineers, to learn how to use the systems. With this in mind, vendors are supplying systems that include extensive on-line help in the form of text screens and pop-up windows. This technique not only provides quickly accessed help references once the system is in use, but also shortens the operator and user's learning cycle. The ability to change and create the on-line help information adds flexibility and allows the end-user to tailor the system for specific application and /or personnel.

Also, there is a trend toward presenting information (in menus, real time data displays, and alarm displays) in English language format, rather than cryptic, encoded form that may be difficult for users to understand. For example, the menu text "Display the current status of the Air Handling Unit for the west wing" is much more descriptive and easy to understand for an electrician than a display image file name such as "AHU001".

Function Execution

The manner in which the system allows its functions to be executed by the operator contributes significantly to a system's usability. Most systems use a menu penetration technique, in which the operator is presented with a list of functions, each of which is initiated by a single (or in some cases, a sequence of) keystrokes. Once again, since the end-user's ability to modify the menus adds flexibility to the system, the system designers have built this menu editing feature into their systems. Normally menu entries allow the operator to display real-time data, display alarm and historical data, edit and create dynamic screen images of real-time data and execute support functions such as system-wide variable definition, security access information definition, on-demand data collection and off-the-shelf spreadsheet managers.

Allowing PC operating system (e.g.,DOS) command strings and batch files to be executed from the menus adds further flexiblity and usability to the system. For instance, a series of operating system commands that execute software programs to collect a snapshot of some real-time sensor data, transform it into a format understood by a spreadsheet manager and initiate the spreadsheet manager for observation and modification of the data can first be built into an operating system batch file by someone familiar with the PC's operating system. A menu entry can then be made which allows the entire batch command string to be executed by a single keystroke by someone not necessarily familiar with the operating system. Not only is this method easier to understand and faster to execute, but also it eliminates the possibility of error due to incorrect keyboard entries by the operator.

Data Presentation

Also contributing significantly to system usability, is the manner in which data (real-time, alarm and historical) is presented to the user. There are several forms and formats in which data is normally presented:

1. Individual or groups of real-time Numeric Point Data in list form.

2. Individual or groups of real-time Point Data embedded in a dynamic screen image.

3. Real-time and historical data in graphic plots.

4. Real-time and historical Alarm Data in list form.

The first form is sufficient for continuously monitoring individual sensors and groups of related items. It is relatively simple for the user to define (provided of course that he knows how to identify the control unit and point "name" of the sensor) and is updated quickly on the screen.

The second form is useful in making a more global or system-wide presentation of the data. Graphic symbols (i.e., valve symbols, motor symbols) can be intermixed with alphanumeric characters and real-time dynamic sensor and control data can be displayed in a variety of formats (i.e. not only numeric). Of course, this type of display is more time consuming for the user to define, in that he must build the entire screen image and define the dynamic points. To aid in this effort, vendors are providing sophisticated interactive editors to build the screen image and define the dynamic point data. Although this type of display normally contains more dynamic data than the numeric list type of display, its update response time is not necessarily slower. The reason for this will be explained when the third type of display is described.

Before describing the graphic plot type of display however, a few points should be made concerning trends in interactive screen editors. The key word here is interactive. Screen image builders that process (parse) a command string that defines the screen image text, attributes and dynamic fields and then "compile" the screen image are not only more difficult to use (the creator must be familiar with the "high-level" command language), but also require at least two operations to create and verify the screen image. That is, the creator must define the screen image definition command string and compile it, and then he must display the image to verify that it is correct, i.e. he has no instantaneous feedback as he creates the image. On the other hand, interactive editors provide the operator with continuous feedback as he creates the image. As mentioned previously, designers are building help images into their interactive editors and are using pop-up windows to simplify the editors' use.

The third type of dynamic display, graphic plots, is particularly useful in examining historical data. Data collected at the control equipment, where sampling the point is most accurate and where data trending functions are normally provided, is retrieved by the PC, scaled and then plotted in graphic form. Rescaling of the data, overlaying plots and evaluating individual point values on the curves add to the functionality of this type of data presentation. Of course it goes without saying that to provide this function, the display adapter used must be capable of operating in a graphic mode.

This brings us to the topic of screen update speed which was deferred in the earlier discussion. Normally, display adapters display graphic plotted data significantly slower than they display character data. The reason for this is two-fold. First, the direction and angle at which to draw a line connecting two points must be determined mathematically, and second, each individual dot on the screen, which makes up the line, must be displayed from the software program that is plotting the curve. On the other hand, displaying the individual dots that make up a character is normally handled by the display adapter hardware, which is designed to display them at high speed. With all this lead-in, designers are now selecting display adapters capable of operating in both character mode and graphic mode and switching between the two modes as needed. Thus when displaying data in the full screen image mode, the display adapter is operated in the higher speed character mode and only the dynamic fields that change value and/or status are refreshed.

The fourth type of display format, Alarm Data lists, is important for evaluating and logging abnormal occurrences in the control system. All control equipment has a means of reporting abnormal conditions, but may not necessarily have the memory or the functionality built-in to keep any kind of extensive alarm history. So in addition to logging alarms in real time, both on the PC's display screen and optionally its hard copy printer, vendors have built into their PC-based system historical alarm archiving and alarm management. As they are received, alarm messages are saved on the PC's hard (or floppy) disk for scrutiny at a later time. The historical alarm manager allows the user to sort the alarms according to date, time, control unit and/or message content for determining abnormal trends in the system.

Color Display Adapters and Monitors

With the current low cost of color adapters and monitors, the increased flexibility in the operation of the adapters, the increased recognition of data and the increased effectiveness of the operators, the trend is toward using color displays in PC-based data acquisition systems. The use of color adapters and displays increases the use of the PC-based data acquisition systems mainly because of the increase in the recognition of data when it is presented in color. Some studies indicate that this increase may be as high as 50-100% in recognition speed. Thus, alarm messages are being presented on color screens in high recognition colors (e.g., red) and dynamic data is displayed on screen images in colors that are suitable for the data type and "condition" of the control point. That is, designers have built into their interactive editors the ability to assign color attributes to dynamic point data according to the point's status. For example, the reading from a temperature sensor may be displayed in a dynamic screen image in the color white when it is sensing a temperature that's in its "normal" operating range, while the reading may be displayed in the color red when it exceeds its normal operating range. Or, the feedback from a switch may be displayed as the text "off" in the color yellow when its binary state is "0" and it may be displayed as the text "on" in the color green when its binary state is "1".

Another reason that color adapters and displays are being used to increase the effectiveness of the data acquisition systems is their ability to operate in the graphics mode for (color) curve plotting. Most color adapters can be operated in a graphic mode, while very few monochrome adapters can be. In addition, color plots are much easier to compare against each other when they are overlayed (oscilloscope style).

Dual Screens

There is a growing trend among vendors of PC-based data acquisition systems toward using two screens, one monochrome and one color, for the presentation of data. Dual screen operation is possible because of the aforementioned low cost of color adapters and monitors and the ability of the color adapter to co-exist in the same PC with a monochrome adapter. The increase in usability provided by two screens is basically two- fold: 1) when using interactive editors to create dynamic screen images and menu screen images, the screen not being used to edit the image can be used to simultaneously present help information and/or real-time alarm information, and 2) the second screen (normally the color screen) can be used to display real-time alarm information while the first is being used for PC operating system functions or other off-the-shelf data management functions, i.e., word processing and spreadsheet generation. The first feature has been discussed previously. The second simplifies background alarm processing, i.e., multitasking, and will be the topic of discussion in a later section.

USE OF EXISTING HARDWARE

General

There is a definite trend toward IBM PC-based systems among the manufacturers of PC-based data acquisition systems. There are many reasons for this trend, among which are the following: low cost, high availibility, a large number of compatibles, a large number of add-on hardware products and a large number of software products. In addition, the PC is quite suitable for this type of application and the functionality and flexibility it provides for its cost cannot be matched by many (if any) home-grown systems.

Color Graphics Hardware

Many vendors providing IBM PC based data acquisition systems are designing the systems around the IBM Enhanced Graphics Adapter (EGA) or compatible, and the IBM Enhanced Color Display (ECD) or compatible. This adapter/display provides high-resolution (640x350 pixels), 8 or 16 colors from a possible 64, both character and graphic modes and user definable special characters. Also, because there is a general trend toward standardization around the EGA/ECD by many vendors of other PC-based products, (e.g., business, graphic) it's certain that there will be many more EGA based general purpose products in the very near future. Besides, the cost of the EGA and ECD compatibles is continually dropping because of the growing number of hardware manufacturers producing these products. The EGA's ability to operate in the both the character and the graphic modes, its lower price, and its greater availability make it more suitable than the IBM Professional Graphics Adapter (PGA) and Display, which were designed mainly for Computer Aided Design (CAD) products. Its increased resolution, ability to co-exist with a monochrome adapter in the same PC and increased functionality make it more suitable then the previously highly popular IBM Color Graphics Adapter (CGA) and its clones.

Communications Hardware

This item is mentioned briefly here because of its importance in interfacing to the automation control equipment. Most designers of control equipment have provided an RS232C serial interface port through which their equipment can communicate to the outside world. It makes sense that the designers of the PC based data acquisition systems use a compatible interface in the PC. Since most multifunction cards available today (e.g., AST Six Pak, Sigma Designs Maximizer, etc.) come equipped with at least one RS232C serial port, designers are using this port to communicate with the control equipment at speeds ranging from 1200 baud to 9600 baud. The communication interface between the PC and the control equipment is the topic of discussion in a later section of this article.

COMPATIBILITY WITH EXISTING SOFTWARE

General

In spite of DOS's single task limitation and the disappointing performance of multitasking DOS products, most vendors are reluctant to write their own operating systems because of the large cost and time investments involved. DOS therefore remains the operating system of choice (CP/M-86 never gained wide acceptance, and UNIX although quite suitable for multiuser applications is generally not fast enough for real-time data collection). Some designers have managed to work around the DOS obstacles and have provided "background" alarm handling and rapid display screen updating functions. However, these functions had to be designed to co-exist in a relatively "well behaved" manner with DOS so that other software can be run simultaneously in the "foreground."

Background Alarm Handling

A powerful feature that has been added to many PC-based data acquisition systems is the background managing of abnormal (i.e., alarm) conditions. What this provides is a foreground/background environment in which the user can be performing a function, e.g. creating a spreadsheet, while the control equipment is simultaneously being polled for alarms. Then whenever an alarm message is received in the PC, the background alarm manager normally produces a hard copy on the printer, saves the message in a historical file and indicates to the operator that an alarm has been received. If the system has been designed around a dual screen concept (i.e. one color and one monochrome), then the alarm message can be directed to the screen not being used by the operator (normally the color screen) without interrupting his activity.

Data Collection for Existing Software Utilities

As mentioned at the start of this article, many facilities automation personnel are accustomed to off-the-shelf data management products, e.g., spreadsheet managers, maintenance managers, work order and inventory control managers. Vendors of PC-based data acquisition systems for the building automation industry have been sympathetic to users of these tools and have designed easy-to-define and easy-to-use data gathering mechanisms that not only collect data from the control equipment, but also translate it into a format that the spreadsheet manager, et al. can operate on. For example, the totalized run times of the fans in several air handling units, which are accumulated by the control equipment, can be fetched by the PC, where the data and its ID are translated and reformatted and passed along to a maintenance manager for use in the automatic generation of a Preventive Maintenance report.

COMPATIBILITY WITH EXISTING CONTROL EQUIPMENT

General

This feature is perhaps the single most difficult item for designers to deal with. The main reasons for this difficulty are:

1) there is currently no accepted communications protocol standard among manufacturers of automation control equipment and

2) in most cases the protocol used by the manufacturers is proprietary.

To further complicate the situation, some manufacturers have no standard among their own products. In the past year, however, a protocol standard has been proposed and is being well received by a growing number of facilities automation personnel. If accepted, this standard will not only facilitate communication with automation control equipment supplied by various manufacturers, but also will aid in the ability to communicate with a wide variety of equipment (e.g. from small specialized single device controllers to very large multipoint systems).

Signal Interface

As was mentioned previously, most control equipment manufacturers are now providing an RS232C communication port for interfacing to the outside world. Although standard off-the-shelf RS232C serial port cards are normally used in the PC's, some vendors of the PC-based data acquisition systems are designing their own cards with multiple connectors on a single serial card for the purpose of providing multitruck connections. In addition, many applications are using short-haul modems to convert RS232C to RS422A, and vice versa, for multidropping multiple pieces of control equipment, which may be scattered throughout a facility, to the same PC.

Dial-up

There is a trend among some vendors to provide the ability to communicate across telephone lines with control equipment installed in different locations and buildings in a building complex (e.g., a school campus, an office complex) or in different sites around a city or even in different cities (e.g., a fast food chain, a grocery store chain). The ability of the equipment in the remote location to dial into the centrally located PC and identify itself, coupled with the display of a user created centralized database record linked to the remote location in the PC and the ability of an operator to dial-up the equipment in the remote location and interrogate its status, adds another dimension of flexibility to the already powerful data acquisition systems. Of course, an interactive database editor is also present to create the remote site database information, which may include site name, address, phone number, emergency instructions (i.e., whom to call, what to do) and additional dynamic screens to be displayed.

ACCESS SECURITY

General

This feature is extremely important when providing PC systems to end-users with more than one operator. Basically, this feature means that each operator can be given a log on password and along with it a set of privilege levels that allow him to access the various features of the acquisition system . For example, one operator may be given a log on ID with privileges that allow him to look at dynamic screen images, but not permit him to create or edit the images, while another operator may be given a log on ID that permits him to look at dynamic screen images, but not permit him to modify setpoint values at the control equipment through the dynamic screen images.

SUMMARY

In summary, vendors are providing sophisticated centralized data gathering systems which are based in low cost, abundant personal computers. These systems provide the end-users with an array of easy-to-use, easy-to-learn and extremely flexible functions that extend the functionality of the facilities automation control equipment and simplify the jobs of all levels of operating personnel.

SECTION 30
NEW ENERGY TECHNOLOGIES

Chapter 90

DENSIFIED REFUSE-DERIVED FUEL – AN ALTERNATIVE ENERGY SOURCE

O. Ohlsson, K. E. Daugherty, B. J. Venables

ABSTRACT

The objective of this research effort is to produce an environmentally acceptable, chemically/biologically stable, and storable densified refuse derived fuel (dRDF) pellet. To accomplish this, a suitable binder(s) must be used. Over 150 binders were investigated by a laboratory screening procedure. Thirteen binder/binder combinations of the initial group of 150 binders were selected for further pilot plant studies. Approximately seven tons of RDF from Ames, Iowa and Refcom, Pompano Beach, Florida were pelletized in the summer-1985 in a series of experiments at the Jacksonville, Florida Naval Air Station using these binders. The pelletized dRDF was then subjected to a battery of chemical and physical tests. Results to date and work to be accomplished during the next fiscal year will be discussed.

INTRODUCTION

The U.S. currently discards about 425,000 tons per day of municipal solid waste (MSW), with the major portion discarded in sanitary landfills. In recent years, a number of energy-recovery facilities, predominantly mass burning facilities producing steam for local steam markets have been constructed to alleviate the problem of waste disposal and to recover energy from an underutilized resource. The total design capacity of these facilities currently amounts to about 8% of the waste generated per year.

Energy produced in the form of steam requires that steam markets be located close to the resource recovery facility and be capable of using the lower quality steam that is produced from the mass burning of waste. In addition, MSW is produced each day of the year and cannot be stored for appreciable periods of time. Therefore, the market being served must be capable of using the steam at least eight hours per day, five days per week. In a recent ANL study these factors have been shown to restrict the potential industrial steam market that can be served to about 23% of the available waste. The alternative to the use of steam for steam markets is the conversion of steam to electricity and its sale to the utilities under the Public Utility Regulatory Procurement Act (PURPA). However, the conversion of steam to electricity, which is the approach taken by most of the facilities now in operation or under construction, reduces the overall energy-recovery efficiency of the steam only facility by a factor of about four, which greatly affects the economics, and consequently, the breakeven tipping fee.

The limitations on the use of MSW as a feedstock indicates a need for seeking and developing alternative technologies to provide storable fuels, such as densified RDF (dRDF), that are transportable, economical, and environmentally acceptable.

Mechanical and, in some cases, chemical methods have traditionally been used for preprocessing MSW into a RDF fuel form. A typical processing line contains a shredder or multiple shredders to reduce raw MSW into particles of a manageable size, equipment for segregating magnetic ferrous materials, and air classifiers and screening devices for separating combustible and noncombustible materials. The combustible fraction is known as either coarse or fine RDF, depending upon the particle size. With additional processing, the RDF can be converted into densified RDF by pelletizing, extruding or briquetting. To improve the quality of the pellets, as well as their transportability and long-term stability under storage conditions, research was undertaken to investigate the effect of adding low-cost binders to the process.

Under contract to ANL, North Texas State University (NTSU) examined more than 150 possible binders and binder combinations in the laboratory. Various tests and evaluations were conducted on small pellets formed in the laboratory. Information from these laboratory-scale tests and the evaluation of cost data and environmental characteristics made possible the ranking of the binders and binder combinations. The thirteen (13) most promising candidates were selected for field testing at the Navy Civil Engineering Laboratory's (NCEL) pelletizing test facility, located at the Naval Air Station in Jacksonville, Florida. During these tests, fifty-four

(54) experiments were conducted using about seven tons of fluff RDF from two different facilities. Chemical and physical tests of the binder-enhanced densified RDF are currently underway. In conjunction with these tests, combustion emission characteristics and the ash heavy metal content also will be determined in laboratory tests.

LABORATORY STUDY

Approximately 150 different binder and binder combinations were preliminarily evaluated during the initial phase of the laboratory-scale study. Each was ranked by a series of criteria based on cost, environmental acceptability, and effectiveness as a binder. Many of these initial candidates were quickly eliminated by this preliminary screening. Sixty-seven (67) potential binders were identified from this initial group of 150. These binders included glues, oils, plastic cements, paint sludges, etc. These binders were subjected to a wide variety of environmental and laboratory study protocols. For example, the environmental protocols included toxicity properties, odor and potential emissions. Laboratory protocols included binder dispersability, binder Btu content, ability of the binder to wet the RDF substrate, binder ash content, pellet weatherability, pellet water sorbability, pellet caking, pellet ignition temperature, moisture content, durability, aerobic stability, and pellet fabrication costs. Where possible, ASTM and other standard procedures were used to conduct the laboratory testing.

Each of the various protocols was assigned a point value and the total number of points was summed up for each binder and binder combination. From the total number of points the binders shown in Table 1 emerged as being the most effective for the densification of RDF.

TABLE 1. HIGHEST RANKED BINDERS AND BINDER COMBINATIONS

Calcium oxide	Dolomite
Calcium hydroxide	Calcium lignosulfonate
Cement kiln dust	Calcium oxide/dolomite/Portland cement
Portland cement	Calcium hydroxide/dolomite
Bituminous flyash	Lignite flyash
Iowa coal fines	Calcium hydroxide/lignite flyash
Western coal fines	

Some observations that can be made concerning the most effective binders from the results of the laboratory study are:

- The best binders have large surface areas.
- The best binders are basic.
- The limited studies conducted during the laboratory study phase suggest that calcium hydroxide or combinations thereof will produce excellent quality dRDF pellets when commercially produced.

It is the opinion of the research team that the basic binders (those using calcium hydroxide or combinations thereof) perform best because of the following:

- The calcium binding agent breaks down the RDF substrate over a period of time producing by-products with acidic groups such as carboxylic acid groups.
- The calcium from the basic binders reacts in a complex or chelate formation mode with the acidic groups of the RDF. The calcium ties up the acidic groups and also reacts with the excess moisture in the RDF. The ligand-metal complexes are formed more quickly at higher temperatures.
- The calcium hydroxide produced by the basic groups reacting with moisture in the RDF, or present initially in the binder, gradually carbonates with the carbon dioxide which is present naturally in the air, to form calcium carbonate.
- The above processes form very strong and well-knit pellets that resist water penetration and can be stored for long periods of time with little biological and chemical degradation.
- Limited studies conducted to date suggest that the carbonated species will be calcined in the furnace during RDF combustion, and should allow the pellets to quickly break apart in the firing zone and be readily consumed as fuel.

JACKSONVILLE NAVAL AIR STATION TESTS

As a result of the above laboratory tests, we were able to gain the permission of the U.S. Department of Navy to use the Jacksonville Naval Air Station (JAX-NAS) facility in Florida for a series of large scale pilot plant tests. The facility consisted of conveying equipment, a surge bin, a vertical hammermill, a Sprout-Waldron pelletizer and a pelletizer-cooler.

In July of 1985, six and a half tons of minus 6 inch RDF was transported from Ames, Iowa to JAX-NAS. Another half ton of RDF was transported to JAX-NAS from the Refcom Pompano Beach Facility in Florida. This RDF was subjected to some additional separations in order to accommodate the equipment at JAX-NAS. Two concrete mixers were employed to mix the binder(s) and additional water on a pilot plant scale. Each concrete mixer held 35-40 pounds of RDF, moisture and binder. Approximately 150 pounds of material was necessary to make a pelletization run. During July and August, an average of two runs per day were conducted. These runs are listed in Table 2. In each run it was possible to accurately measure the binder percentage, the moisture content and produce a relatively homogeneous material.

TABLE 2 JACKSONVILLE NAVAL AIR STATION PELLET RUNS

Run #	Total # Pounds	% Binder	Binder Type	Init. Moist.	Final Moist.	RDF Type	Pellet Diam.	Spec. Grav.	% +3/8
1	200	0	None	12	14	Ames	1/2"	0.72	95.0
2	200	0	None	NA	19	Ames	1/2"	0.60	97.1
3	100	0	None	14	23	Ames	1/2"	0.59	98.2
4	100	0	None	12	28	Ames	1/2"	0.47	94.7
5	100	5	CH	10	31	Ames	1/2"	0.64	96.9
6	150	5	KD	11	30	Ames	1/2"	0.56	96.7
7	150	5	CH	11	25	Ames	1/2"	0.65	98.0
8	150	5	PC	12	29	Ames	1/2"	0.61	97.2
9	150	2	PC	10	20	Ames	1/2"	0.71	97.9
10	150	5	BFA	14	28	Ames	1/2"	0.56	96.3
11	150	5	BFA	9	23	Ames	1/2"	0.59	97.6
12	150	5	Iowa Coal	10	33	Ames	1/2"	0.53	95.6
13	150	5	Western Coal	9	23	Ames	1/2"	0.65	96.8
14	150	5	1-CH/4-FA	13	30	Ames	1/2"	0.61	96.6
15	150	5	1-CH/4-FA	9	21	Ames	1/2"	0.67	97.9
16	150	5	1-CH/4-KD	9	30	Ames	1/2"	0.52	96.7
17	150	5	1-CH/4-KD	11	22	Ames	1/2"	0.70	99.0
18	150	1	CH	9	31	Ames	1/2"	0.54	96.9
19	150	1	CH	10	21	Ames	1/2"	0.68	98.1
20	150	5	CH	9	19	Ames	1/2"	0.74	97.8
21	150	2	CH	9	17	Ames	1/2"	0.76	99.0
22	150	10	CH	36	36	Ref	1/2"	0.62	97.0
23	150	10	5-CH/5-PC	35	35	Ref	1/2"	0.64	96.4
24	150	2	CH	12	22	Ames	1/2"	0.71	98.2
25	150	2	CH	RP	13	Ames	1/2"	0.72	95.3
26	150	2	CH	RP	11	Ames	1/2"	0.79	97.1
27	150	5	D	13	19	Ames	1/2"	0.71	98.2
28	150	5	2.5-CH/2.5-D	12	19	Ames	1/2"	0.78	99.2
29	150	5	2.5-CH/2.5-D	28	28	Ref	1/2"	0.66	94.8
30	150	2	CH	11	11	Ames	1/2"	0.85	99.0
31	150	2	CH	11	11	Ames	3/4"	0.81	98.5
32	150	2	CH	10	19	Ames	3/4"	0.71	98.6
33	150	5	CH	9	22	Ames	3/4"	0.75	99.3
34	225	5	CH	9	30	Ames	3/4"	0.67	97.8
35	150	5	CH	RP	21	Ames	3/4"	0.80	96.9
36	150	0	None	11	20	Ames	3/4"	0.67	98.4
37	150	0	None	9	9	Ames	3/4"	0.73	97.9
38	150	0	None	10	29	Ames	3/4"	0.51	96.7
39	150	2	CL	10	22	Ames	3/4"	0.68	98.5
40	150	3.5	1.75-CH/1.75-D	10	21	Ames	3/4"	0.72	99.0
41	150	5	CH	19	19	Ref	3/4"	0.84	98.5
42	150	0	None	21	21	Ref	3/4"	0.76	98.2
43	150	0	None	10	10	Ames	3/4"	0.71	98.0
44	150	0	None	8	18	Ames	3/4"	0.61	98.9
45	150	1	CH	8	20	Ames	3/4"	0.66	99.0
46	150	2	CH	9	20	Ames	3/4"	0.69	99.3
47	150	4	CH	8	19	Ames	3/4"	0.71	99.2
48	150	8	CH	8	19	Ames	3/4"	0.80	98.0
49	150	0	None	8	27	Ames	3/4"	0.54	98.0
50	150	8	CH	8	28	Ames	3/4"	0.63	98.0
51	150	8	CH	9	8	Ames	3/4"	0.83	98.8
52	150	4.5	CH/PC/D	6.5	6.5	Ames	3/4"	0.77	98.3
53	4000	4.5	CH/PC/D	6.5	6.5	Ames	3/4"	0.77	98.3
54	100	4.5	CH/PC/D	NA	NA	Ames	3/4"	H#53	NA

LEGEND
F=Front end of pellet run
B=Back end of pellet run
PC=Portland Cement
KD=Cement Kiln Dust
% +3/8=inches
FA=Lignite Fly Ash
CH=Calcium Hydroxide
FA=Fly Ash
BFA=Bituminous Fly Ash
D=Dolomite
All runs conducted from 22 July-29 August, 1985
CL=Calcium Lignosulfonate
RP=Repelletized
Ref=Refcom, Pompano Beach
H=Hammermilled
NA=Not Available

The binders were added to the concrete mixers by means of a paint sprayer using compressed air. The binders were accurately weighed into the paint sprayer using a top-loading balance. Table 2 lists the pounds produced during a run, the percent binder as a function of the weight of RDF and the type of binder used. Each batch in the concrete mixer was tumbled for 60 minutes. The moisture content was measured to within plus or minus 1 percent with a microwave moisture analyzer. The moisture content was checked on the RDF initially, after adding water, after adding binder and after pelletization. The initial moisture content of the RDF and the final moisture content of the RDF after removal from the concrete mixer is shown in Table 2. The type of RDF employed, whether from Ames, Iowa or Refcom is also shown in Table 2.

The materials from the mixers were transferred to buggies and tipped into the surge bin which preceded the pelletizer. The pelletizer was a cylindrical die approximately 20 inches in diameter, with holes in the circumference to permit the extrusion of the pellets. The pellets, having temperatures of 160-180 deg. Fahrenheit when extruding from the die, were sliced into lengths of one to three inches and conveyed into the cooler. Two dies were available, producing either one-half inch diameter or three-quarter inch diameter pellets. The pellet diameters are listed in Table 2. The pellets remained in the cooler for approximately ten minutes. The pellets were collected from the cooler in buckets and transported to the front section of the plant for preliminary tests and packaging. Some of the preliminary tests which were run on the pellets included the specific gravity (bulk) shown in Table 2 and also the plus 3/8 inch size fraction shown in Table 2. A total of fifty-four runs were made. These runs included using the top binders found in the laboratory study, differing moisture contents, different RDF types and different pellet diameters.

It was important in these studies to develop a binder which was effective in densifying RDF, which was environmentally sound, which was of relatively low cost and which would produce a pellet which could be transported with little chemical and biological degradation. The moisture content in RDF can range upwards of thirty percent. Our research group, however, has seen Madison, Wisconsin RDF go as high as fifty percent in moisture content. It was desired to attempt to find a binder which was capable of pelletizing RDF which had moisture contents over thirty percent.

CONCLUSIONS

The following observations were made as a result of the Jacksonville Naval Air Station tests:

Figure 1 is a plot of the percent moisture in the RDF prior to pelletization vs the bulk specific gravity of the pellets. The zero binder curve indicates the location of the pellet runs outlined in dark circles which contained zero binder. As can be noted, the zero binder curve generally indicates pellet runs which had the lowest bulk specific gravity. The bulk specific gravity appears to be a reasonably good measure for assessing the durability of a pellet. The best binders in Figure 1 include runs #30, #28, #29, #23 and #22. The binder in each of these runs is, or includes, calcium hydroxide. All of the pellet runs in Figure 1 are for one-half inch sized pellets.

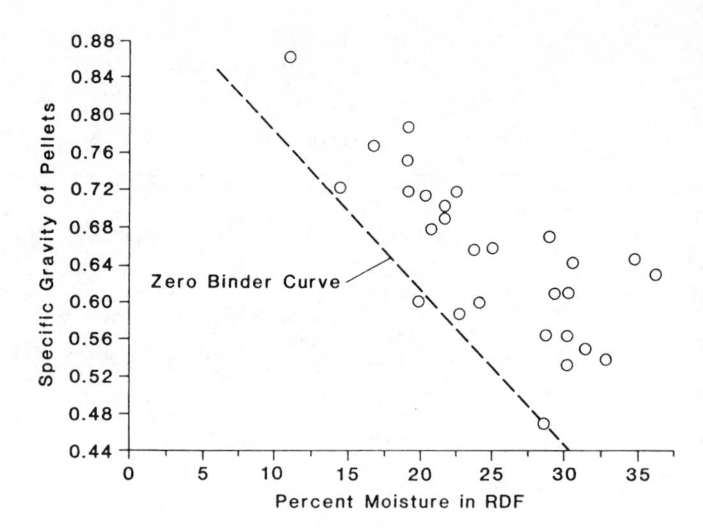

FIGURE 1. MOISTURE CONTENT VS SPECIFIC GRAVITY FOR 1/2 INCH PELLET RUNS

Figure 2 is a plot of the percent moisture in the RDF prior to pelletization vs the bulk specific gravity of three-quarter inch sized pellets. The zero binder curve indicates the location of the pellet runs outlined in dark circles which contained zero binder. As can be noted, the zero binder curve in Figure 2, as in Figure 1, generally indicates pellet runs which had the lowest specific gravity in bulk. The best binders in Figure 2 include runs #51, #41, #48 and #34. The binder in each of these runs, as in the case of the one-half inch sized pellets, is, or includes calcium hydroxide.

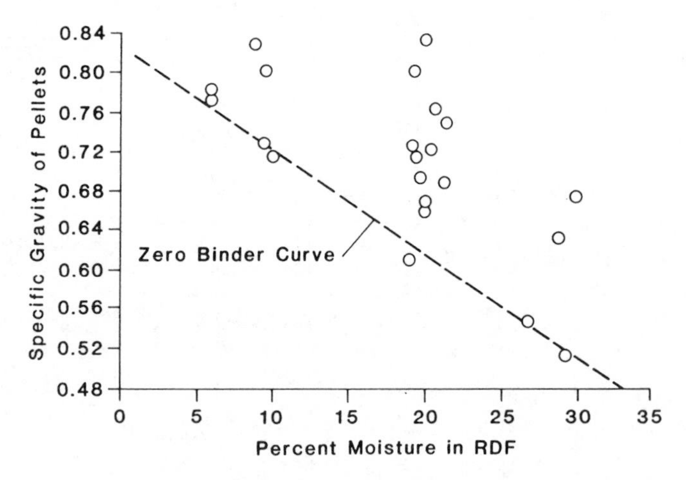

FIGURE 2. MOISTURE CONTENT VS SPECIFIC GRAVITY FOR 3/4 INCH PELLET RUNS

Some conclusions which can be drawn from the results of the Jacksonville Naval Air Station tests are:

- The binders increase the bulk specific gravity of the pellets substantially. The binders increase the percentage of the plus three-eighths inch size fraction of the pellets.

- The pellets become harder with time and even more so with appropriate binders.

- The optimum moisture content of the pelletization process is about fifteen percent. With one-half inch pellets it was not possible to produce a pellet with greater than 28 percent moisture. With three-quarter inch pellets it was not possible to produce a pellet with greater than 29 percent moisture. With both one-half and three-quarter inch pellets with a calcium hydroxide binder, it was possible to produce pellets with up to 36 percent moisture.

- Binders were capable of increasing the bulk specific gravity of a pellet at the same specific moisture content without a binder. The best binder appears to be calcium oxide or calcium hydroxide, or combinations of binders containing either calcium oxide or hydroxide.

- If the binder is purified calcium oxide or hydroxide, the cost in bulk is approximately three cents per pound. Lignite fly ash can contain upwards of twenty percent calcium oxide and is available at less than one-quarter cent per pound. Cement kiln dust can also contain upwards of twenty percent calcium oxide and is available from some cement plants at no cost.

- An increasing moisture content in the RDF requires a higher binder percentage. For example, using calcium hydroxide as the binder, a moisture content of the RDF in the 10-20 percent range would require approximately one percent binder, a moisture content in the 20-30 percent range would require approximately 1-3 percent binder, and a moisture content in the 30-40 percent range would require 3-6 percent binder.

- The high end of the range for the binder percentage is about ten percent. Above this binder content, the bulk specific gravity of the pellets decreases. The bulk specific gravity of the pellets is affected by both the binder percentage and the moisture content of the RDF. One example of the relationship between the bulk specific gravity of the pellets is shown in Figure 1. This figure illustrates that as the moisture content of the RDF is increased, the bulk specific gravity of the pellets is decreased. Figure 2 also illustrates similar behavior.

All of the pellets produced at JAX-NAS were placed in plastic containers and burlap bags and transported to the chemistry labs at North Texas State University. The pellets from the different runs are being subjected to the protocols established in the laboratory phase of the binder studies.

FUTURE WORK

We are presently conducting an extensive series of ASTM approved chemical and physical tests to determine optimum binder and moisture contents. During this year we expect to complete these tests and begin to study the combustion properties of the binder-densified RDF pellets. We are also preparing for combustion tests at several sites across the United States.

Some preliminary work indicates that the basic binders which have been shown to be effective for producing high quality pellets, may also reduce potential emissions from the pellet combustion. These may include potential emissions such as polyaromatic hydrocarbons, polychlorinated biphenyls, furans and dioxins. We are in the process of studying this aspect of the work using Fourier Transform Infrared Spectroscopy and Inductively Coupled Plasma as analytical tools. If work continues to demonstrate the effectiveness of these binders for the reduction of potential combustion emissions, then important implications are evident for co-firing fuels.

ACKNOWLEDGMENTS

We would like to thank Mr. Don Walter, Director of the Energy from Municipal Waste Program at the U.S. Department of Energy, who is providing the funding and vigorous support for this program. We would also like to thank Mr. Mike Roberts of the U.S. Department of Navy, who provided the facilities at JAX-NAS for pellet fabrication. Mr. Rob Chapman of Ames, Iowa and Mr. Peter Mooij from Refcom were extremely helpful in providing RDF for the project.

Chapter 91

SIMPLIFIED RETROFIT OF A LARGE CHILLED WATER SYSTEM

R. J. Pearson

ABSTRACT

A large medical center chilled water system was converted from a form of primary-secondary, constant volume pumping to only primary, variable volume pumping. Implementation consisted of:

1. Conversion of three-way valves to two-way valves.

2. Wholesale readjustment of controls.

3. Stopping of all secondary pumps.

The result was a significant improvement in cooling performance of air-handling equipment, postponement of a plan to purchase an additional 1000 ton chiller, and substantial energy savings. Total implementation cost, including fees, was $32,000. First-year pumping energy savings were $45,000.

SYSTEM DESCRIPTION

Five chillers with a nominal tonnage of 8000 tons provide cooling for a 420,000 sq. ft. Hospital, a 1,200,000 sq. ft. Medical Science Building (MSB), and several smaller miscellaneous loads. Refer to Figure 1 for a schematic diagram of the system. Valves V-1A through V-5A are automatic flow control valves which serve as maximum flow limiters through each chiller. Valves V-1B through V-5B are automatic shut-off valves which only allow flow through each chiller if it is operating. Pumps P-1 through P-5 are 125 horsepower primary pumps, which are manually energized as needed to maintain adequate flow through the system. In practice, a pump is energized with each chiller, then pressure differential between the main supply and return headers is observed as a double-check to ensure adequate flow in the system.

Pumps P-6, P-7 and P-8 are each 75 horsepower secondary pumps serving the Hospital through three-way mixing valve V-6. In the original mode of operation, two of these pumps ran continuously. The Hospital system consists of six large built-up air handling units of the dual duct and multizone type.

Pumps P-9, P-10 and P-11 are each 200 horsepower pumps serving MSB. One of these pumps is a variable speed. In the original mode of system operation, the variable speed pump ran continuously to maintain a minimum pressure differential between the MSB supply and return headers, and a second pump was occasionally energized. The MSB system consists of 27 built-up air handling units of the single zone, reheat type.

CHILLER OPERATION

The chilled water system is off below 50 degrees outside air temperature. As the outside air temperature increases, and the cooling load increases, chillers are manually energized, one at a time, to maintain a leaving chilled water temperature of 42 degrees. The chillers are generally energized in the following sequence:

Chiller No.	Type	Actual Tons
1	Electric Centrifugal	2000
2	Electric Centrifugal	2000
4	Absorption	700
5	Absorption	900
3	Turbine Centrifugal	1100
	Total Capacity	6700

Note that the automatic valves only permit water through energized chillers. Furthermore, the two electric centrifugals are in parallel with each other, and are in parallel with the absorption/turbine combination. The absorption/turbine combination utilizes chiller water in series <u>and</u> steam in series, with steam entering the turbine at 325 psi and exiting at 15 psi, at which pressure it is utilized by the absorption machines. Of course, this system only operates at optimum design conditions if all three chillers are energized at fairly heavy loads. As can be seen from Figure 1, chilled water flows in series through one or both of the absorption machines and then through the turbine chiller. When first one, and then the other, absorption chiller is energized, prior to energizing the turbine chiller, chilled water bypasses the turbine chiller through valve V-3C. Since the chillers are designed to operate in series, the evaporators are single pass, and the flow rate precludes delivery of 42 degree water unless all three chillers are operating. Therefore, at intermediate loads, with only one or both of the absorption chillers operating, but the turbine chiller off, the absorption chillers deliver a leaving water temperature of approximately 47 to 49 degrees. This water is then mixed with the 42 degree water leaving the electric centrifugal chillers, and the plant then delivers chilled water to the various buildings at a temperature higher than the desired 42 degrees, generally in the range of 44 degrees. The only way

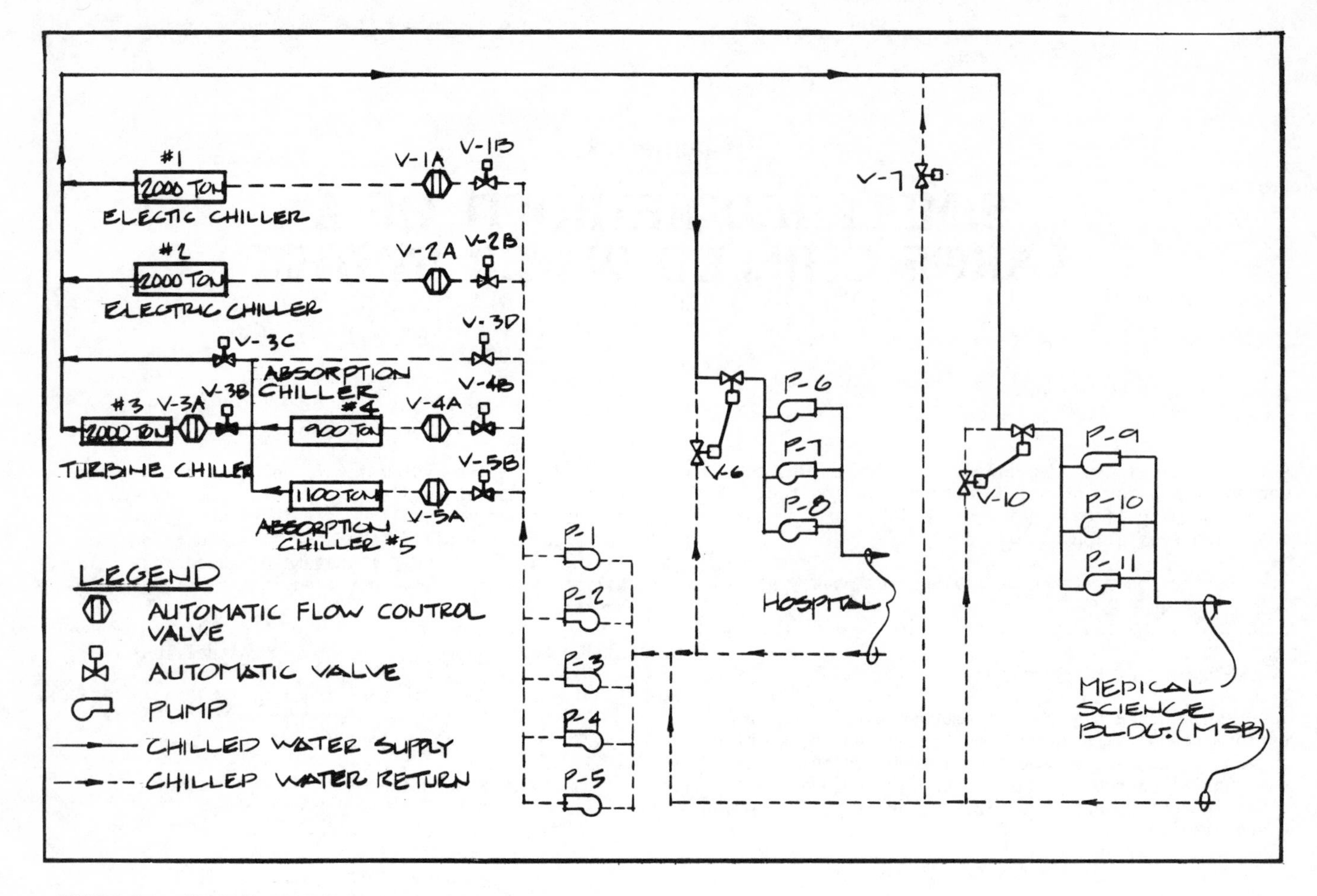

FIGURE 1. MEDICAL CENTER CHILLED WATER SYSTEM

to avoid this condition would be to energize both absorption chillers and the turbine chiller simultaneously, as soon as the load exceeds the 4000 ton capacity of the electric centrifugal chillers. This would theoretically make best use of steam, since it is only when all three of these chillers are energized that steam is used "twice". However, energizing both absorption chillers and the turbine chiller for light loads requires each machine to operate at an impractical light load. Therefore, the design efficiency of the turbine/absorption combination is only realized for a very small percentage of the cooling season. Furthermore, for a large number of hours in the "middle" of the cooling season, the chiller plant delivers chilled water at a temperature slightly warmer then the designed temperature.

CONTROLS

The chilled water controls pertinent to this discussion are illustrated in Figures 2 and 3. As shown in Figure 2, large built-up air handling units, serving the Hospital, each control the leaving air temperature through a receiver controller operating a three-way chilled water mixing valve. The original installation included a balancing valve in the bypass line at three of the five air handling units. The blank-off shown at this port of the three-way mixing valve in Figure 2 was not included in the original installation, and is discussed in a subsequent paragraph of this paper. Note that each of the Hospital air handling units is a multizone or dual duct type. It is Hospital practice to de-energize the hot decks of these systems in the summer. Thus, the hot decks become bypass decks, and the quantity of air bypassed is a function of both the cold deck air temperature and the system load.

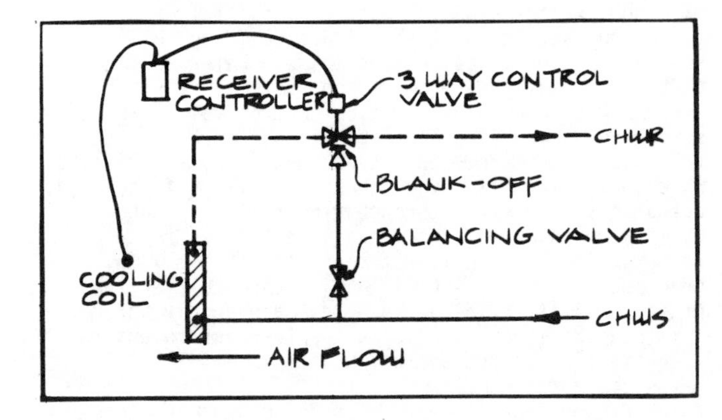

FIGURE 2. HOSPITAL AIR HANDLING UNIT CONTROL

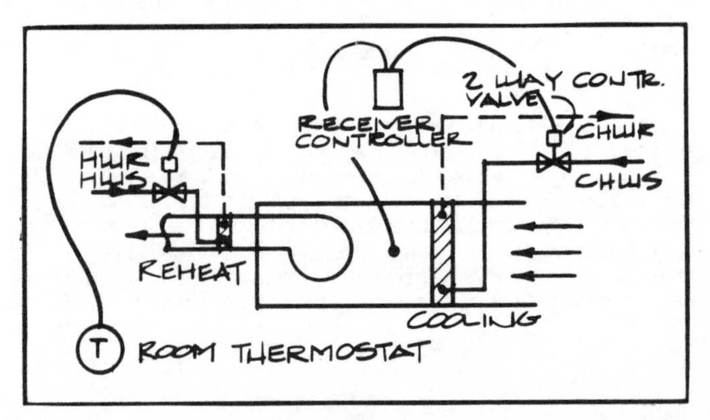

FIGURE 3. MSB AIR HANDLING UNIT CONTROL

As illustrated in Figure 3, the 27 air handling units serving MSB each utilize a receiver controller operating a two-way chilled water valve to maintain a given discharge air temperature. Space temperature in MSB is then determined by room thermostats controlling numerous reheat coils. Thus, if the leaving air temperature at the cooling coil is colder than necessary, the result is increased use of reheat energy, but the spaces served by such a unit are not over-cooled.

STATEMENT OF THE PROBLEM

When this engineering analysis was begun, the Medical Center's perception of the problem was as follows:

1. In warm weather, many portions of MSB and the Hospital were too warm.

2. This is true even though the chilled water temperature leaving the chiller plant only strays one or two degrees above the design goal of 42 degrees, and-

3. The chillers are not fully loaded.

4. Regardless of the fact that the chillers are seldom, if ever, fully loaded, it is assumed that they would be overloaded if all spaces in the facility were properly cooled. Therefore, it is desired to add at least an additional 1000 tons of cooling capacity.

5. System operation should be studied, and modified to include a new chiller which will satisfy all space temperatures during peak cooling loads.

ANALYSIS

System operation was observed under various load conditions from light spring and fall loads to heavy summer loads. Both chiller plant and air handling unit operation was observed, with entering and leaving temperatures of air and water, as well as space temperatures, being careully recorded. As indicated above, the chilled water plant was found to be capable of delivering 42 degrees under light load and heavy load; and capable of delivering 44 degree leaving water under moderate load conditions. It was also observed that the chilled plant was seldom, if ever, fully loaded. It was found that the air temperature leaving the cooling coils of all air handling units varied from 48 to 50 degrees (under light load conditions), to 62 to 65 degrees (under heavy load conditions). Further observation indicated that space temperatures remained satisfactory until air temperatures leaving the cooling coils exceeded 57 to 59 degrees, depending on the air handling system in question. Attention was also given to control and operation of the three-way valve V-6 serving the Hospital, and V-8 serving MSB. The original design statement indicated two reasons for the inclusion and use of these valves in the system:

1. To accommodate larger design flows in the terminal units than exist in the primary chiller system.

2. Through recirculation, to provide warm return water to the chiller plant, thus causing chillers to be fully loaded, and to operate more efficiently. In actual practice, it was found that as the load increased significantly on the chiller plant, the operator of the chiller plant would suggest new valve settings for valves V-6 and V-8 to the operators of the Hospital and MSB systems. These new valve settings would cause more water to be recirculated within each of the buildings, thus drawing less primary cold water from the primary system and delivering ever warmer chilled water to the air handling units. Thus, even though the chiller plant would always deliver chilled water between the temperatures of 42 and 44 degrees, heavy system loads would result in the chilled water temperature being delivered to specific air handling units at temperatures as high as 55 degrees. It appeared that a simple repositioning of valves V-6 and V-8 to eliminate recirculation would solve a majority of the cooling problems. However, the plant operators maintained that the larger flow rates required by the Hospital and MSB would cause improper plant operation. It was further maintained that the direct delivery of 42 degree water to the MSB units would create a load on the chiller plant far in excess of its capacity.

MODIFICATIONS

The need for and operation of mixing valves V-6 and V-8 was not clearly understood, and as stated above, the chillers did not operate full load, even during heavy system loads when various portions of the buildings would overheat. Therefore, prior to embarking upon a design to add equipment to the system, it was decided to undergo a series of system adjustments, to accomplish the following goals:

1. Lower the chilled water temperature delivered to air handling units during times of heavy load.

2. Make best use of the existing chiller plant, i.e., cause the chillers to operate at full load when necessary.

In order to deliver 42 degree chilled water to air handling units, it was desired to match primary and secondary flows, by positioning valves V-6 and V-8 to eliminate recirculation. Since the primary system flow varies depending upon the number of chillers energized, it was then necessary to develop flow rates in the secondary systems which would also vary with load.

This work was begun with the Hospital system. Under this program, as shown in Figure 2, those units with a balancing valve in the bypass line had this valve closed. Those units without a balancing valve in the bypass line had a blank-off plate installed at the bypass flange of the three-way valve. Thus, the three-way valves in the Hospital "became" two-way, throttling valves, and the flow rate of the Hospital system became proportional to load. Following this, valve V-6 was positioned for no recirculation and mixing of return water with supply water. Then, in a trial and error procedure, first one, and then both secondary pumps serving the Hospital were de-energized. It was found that the primary system produced sufficient pressure differential to provide adequate flow through the Hospital system, even with the water passing through the non-functioning secondary pumps!

Prior to repositioning of valve V-8 for MSB, it was recognized that delivery of 42 degree water to the air handling units in MSB would cause the majority of these units to deliver excessively cold air (approximately 48 to 50 degrees), thus using excessive chiller energy, and excessive reheat energy. This appeared to be due to the fact that over a period of time, many units had been re-adjusted from their original set points to deliver maximum cooling. Excessive cooling would not cause discomfort, or even be recognized by the occupants, since the reheat system would accommodate for it. Therefore, it was decided to recalibrate the receiver controller at each of the 27 air handling units to optimize the use of chilled water at each unit. This was accomplished by calibrating the receiver controllers under conditions of moderate to heavy load, when the leaving cooling coil air temperature was approximately 57 to 59 degrees, but prior to the inception of occupant complaints. The calibration procedure consisted of gradually raising the leaving air set point until the valve began to move from its fully open position, and began to control. This was done so that delivery of colder chilled water to each air handling unit would cause the chilled water valve to begin to throttle, in lieu of causing the unit to deliver even colder air. Having accomplished recalibration of the air handling units, valve V-8 was repositioned for no recirculation and mixing of return water with supply water, and pumps P-9, P-10 and P-11 were de-energized. The findings were similar to those for the Hospital, i.e., the primary pumps provided adequate flow for the entire system, and cooling performance of air handling units improved.

FINDINGS

Following the above modifications, the system was observed in operation under numerous load conditions, including several days of the heaviest possible load, when outdoor dry bulb and wet bulb significantly exceeded design conditions. Under full load conditions, all chillers were required to operate at their maximum capacity (approximately 6700 tons), but the chilled water temperature did not exceed 42 degrees, and all areas of both facilities maintained proper temperatures. It was clear from the marginal capability of the plant under these conditions that the recalibration of controls on the 27 air handling units in MSB was necessary to avoid overloading the chiller plant (and wasting enormous quantities of reheat energy).

From the above observations, it also became clear that a new chiller was not required to satisfy the cooling load. However, considering the inefficient operation of portions of the chiller plant, and the fact that no standby cooling exists, the Medical Center commissioned an additional study to establish a replacement schedule for the least efficient chillers, with the long-term goal being to improve plant efficiency and provide standby cooling.

Further observation showed that the system functioned well under all load conditions, including light and medium loads. Thus, a reasonable match of the chillers, pumps, and air handling units exists at all conditions of load. (Note that a number of small air handling units contain no chilled water valves. Thus, minimum flow through one chiller under light load conditions is not a problem.)

With secondary pumps de-energized, the following cost-saving calculations apply:

P-6 & 7:	2 x 60 KW x 3600 hrs. =	432,000 KWH
P-9 :	150 KW x 3600 hrs. =	540,000 KWH
		972,000 KWH
		x $.0285
	KWH Savings =	$27,702 per year

270 KWD x 5.77 $/KWD x 5 months =	$ 7,790
270 KWD x 5.77 $/KWD x .85 x 7 months =	9,270
Total Demand Savings	$17,060
Total Electric Savings	$44,762

The total cost of blank-offs, other minor piping modifications, and fees was $32,000. Therefore, the simple payback of the work accomplished was eight months.

CONCLUSIONS

The absorption/turbine combination of chillers in this plant is an example of the fallacy of designing systems and equipment with little or no consideration for the realities of light and moderate load operation. While the theoretical efficiency of these three chillers, when operating in unison at or near full load may be acceptable, there is little or no time during the entire cooling season when these three machines operate in this manner.

A considerable void may sometimes develop between design theory and practical system operation. Once a system is in operation, there is no substitute for "living" with it under various conditions. Frequently, careful adjustment of components, as well as trial and error operation of various portions of the system, will improve operation. When problems exist, such efforts should always be pursued prior to burdening the system with additional design theory.

REFERENCE

Heapy Engineering: "Chilled Water System Study for Cincinnati General Hospital", September 15, 1981

SECTION 31
PRODUCT INFORMATION

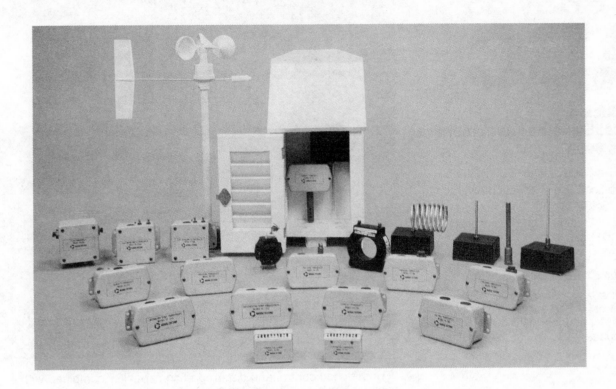

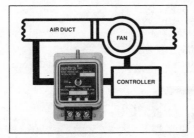

RECENT APPLICATIONS

Cogeneration & Power

AED Cogeneration Plant
Chester, ME

Alberta Power Ltd
H. R. Milner Generating Sta
Grande Cache, Alberta

Brown University
Cogeneration Plant
Providence, RI

Central Plant Inc
Sub. Pacific Lighting Corp
Santa Fe Springs, CA

Cental Power Plant I.M.H.
State of Rhode Island
Cranston, RI

Crisp County Power Commission
Cordele, GA

City of Commerce
Refuse to Energy Facility
Commerce, CA

General Motors
Truck & Bus Operations
Fort Wayne, IN

Lihue Power Plant
Foster Wheeler Kauai Inc
Lihue, Kauai, HI

Marion County
Solids Waste to Energy Facility
Brooks, OR

Mesquite Lake Energy Recovery
Imperial Valley, CA
(Lurgi Corp)

Metro Key West Inc
Resource Recovery
Key West, FL

Modesto Energy Recovery
Modesto, CA
(General Electric)

Penobscot Resource Recovery
Penobscot, ME
(General Electric)

Puente Hills
Energy Recovery from Gas Project
Whittier, CA

Cogeneration Plant
Signal Capital Corp
Sherman Station, ME

Simpson Paper Co
Gas Turbine Cogeneration Plant
San Gabriel Mill
Pomona, CA

Timber Energy Resources Cogeneration
Telogia, FL

15 MW Wastewood Fired
Generating Station
Greenville, ME

Westwood Energy Properties
Joliet, PA

York County Waste to Energy Facility
Biddeford, ME
(General Electric)

Other Applications

Boise Cascade Corp
International Falls, MN

Boise Cascade Corp
Rumford, ME

Boise Cascade Canada Ltd
Ft. Francis, Ontario

Champion International Corp
Hoerner-Waldorf Div
Missoula, MT

Champion International Corp
Houston, TX

Champion International Corp
Lufkin, TX

Champion International Corp
Quinnesec, MI

Hammermill Paper Co
Riverdale Pulp Mill
Selma, AL

Hammermill Papers Group
Sub Hammermill Paper Co
Selma, AL

MacMillan Bloedel Ltd
Aspenite Div
Hudson Bay, Saskatchewan

MacMillan Bloedel Ltd
Harmac Pulp Div
Nanaimo, B.C.

MacMillan Bloedel Ltd
Powell River Div
Powell River, B.C.

Union Camp Corp
Montgomery, AL

Union Camp Corp
Eastover, SC

Weyerhaeuser Co
Columbus, MS

Weyerhaeuser Co
Kamloops Pulp & Paper Div
Kamloops, B.C.

Weyerhaeuser Co
Plymouth, NC

LUMENITE TIMING AND ENERGY MANAGEMENT CONTROLS

"If elephants ate μPlums they'd never forget!"

Packed with features and juicy to look at!

A Bushel of μPlum Features:

- User program modules provide an unlimited number of distinct programs for holiday schedules, batching, or processing.
- Totally self prompting 32 character LCD display.
- Program resolution to the second. Loads can be turned on or off in one second increments.
- 8 tactile type keys accomplish all programming.
- Manual override of outputs through the keyboard, dip switches, or remote disconnect feature.
- Electronic locking feature prevents spurious signals from reaching the clock.
- 50 line program capacity expandable to 200 lines, 1600 set points.
- 8 isolated SPDT 5 amp output relays or channels.
- 10 year lithium battery back up for the clock and user programs.
- User dip switches provide various options such as inverse relay operation, relay disconnect, and self testing procedures.
- LED lamps for on/off load indication.
- Output relay disconnect terminal block allows remote on/off control of the output relays.
- 115VAC/230VAC 50/60 HZ operation.
- Optional analog boards may be inserted for demand limiting, optimum start/stop, remote communication, power line carrier control, printer interface, speech synthesis, and temperature sensor input.

Engineers Designers Manufacturers
2333 North 17th Avenue, Franklin Park, IL 60131
Call Toll Free 1-800-323-8510
In Illinois Call 312-455-1450

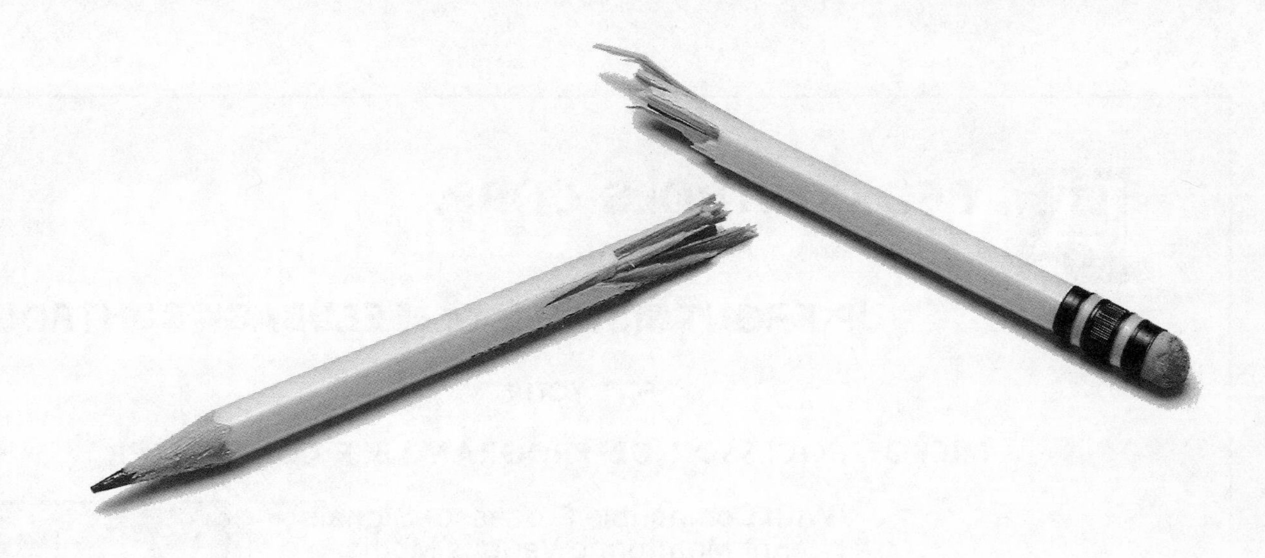

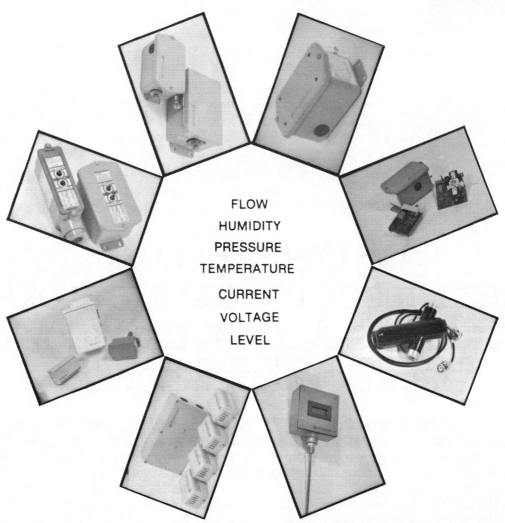

Expanding pillows for through-penetration fire stops

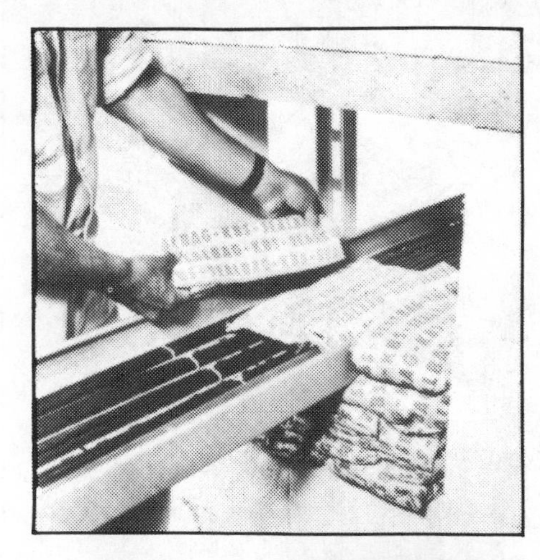

- expand and solidify under fire exposure into a heat-and smoke-tight seal
- rated up to 4 hours
- installed in minutes
- only fire stop system approved for use with aluminum tray
- ideal where frequent cable changes are expected (telephone exchanges)
- ideal for segregating computer cables in double floors
- easily removed and replaced without loss of effectiveness
- pays for itself in retrofitting alone

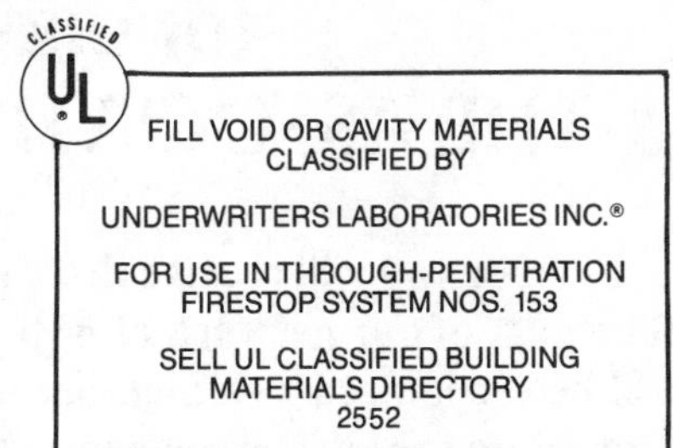

International Protective Coatings Corp.
725 Carol Ave., Ocean Twp., NJ 07712
201-531-3666 — Telex: 136267

PAT PEND P .3536625.7

Approved

Tested to ASTM 814, B.S. 476, ISO 834, UL 1479, NEN 3884, DIN 4102, SBN 1980
Rated by FIRTO, TNO, EMPA, UL, FM, SP 2, 3 and 4 Hrs.

Accepted by N.Y.C. M.E.A., Los Angeles, CA, Arizona, American Nuclear Insurers, etc.

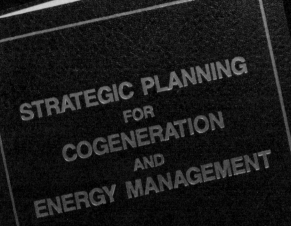

AET SYSTEMS

AET manufactures a line of microprocessor-based intelligent controllers. They are user programmable with full control strategies including DDC, PID, PWM, algebra, duty cycling, set-back, enthalpy, load shedding, and other building automation functions. They can be installed stand-alone or multiplexed with full telephone diagnostics and auto/dial alarming features.

AMERICAN AUTO-MATRIX, INC.

American Auto-Matrix will demonstrate the *AI2100/MAX* and *AI2100/STAR* systems at the 1986 WEEC. These general-purpose, microprocessor-based facility automation systems are capable of monitoring and control functions including direct digital control, energy management, fire and security management, life safety, and process control. IBM PC-compatible *AI2100/SPECTRA* software offers color graphics, data capture, maintenance management and more. Systems and software are used in commercial and institutional installations.

AMF CONTROL SYSTEMS, INC.

The *Model 6120 Snap* energy management systems is a 48-64 pts, stand alone system which is IBM PC compatible and offers networking capability. The system features time based, demand, temperature, variable voltage lighting with resettable set points, and refrigeration controls. It provides temperature compensated duty cycling, night setup/setback, password protection, hi/lo analog, security alarm, point checking, historical trending, externally requested software override timers, energy use summaries, and auto dial alarm function.

ANDERSON POWER PRODUCTS

The new *LUMAFLES*™ lighting control system is readily combined with EMS control or digital time schedulers, offering dynamic control of standard fluorescent lamps and ballasts over areas and time. 100, 60 and 20 ampere models

each contain 20 ampere modules to provide individual circuit control of area light levels with remote photo-cell, low level and off options. Scheduling, lumem depreciation, tuning, daylighting, and peak load shedding lighting management strategies can be selected.

BALTIMORE AIRCOIL COMPANY

Baltimore Aircoil will exhibit a working model of its *ICE CHILLER*™ thermal storage unit, which is designed to provide low first cost, reduced energy costs and space savings in air conditioning applications. B.A.C. will also have graphic displays of its full line of heat transfer products, including cooling towers, fluid coolers, heat exchangers, evaporative condensers and filters.

BEC CONTROLS CORPORATION

Up-front signal or feed-back control transducers sensing pressure, humidity, temperature, current, etc. for building energy microprocessors constitute the standard product line of Bec Controls. All provide standard current/voltage analog outputs with choices of inputs. Analog

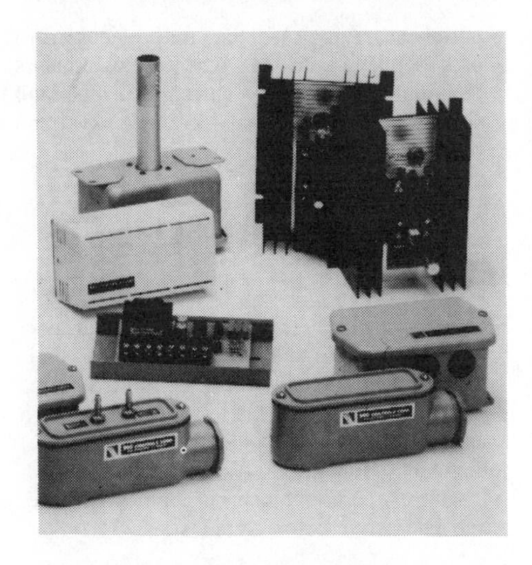

command signal power controllers for 10 and 30 loads compliment the transmitters and numerous sensors which are also available.

BEKAERT INTERNATIONAL TRADE-AMERICA, INC.

This exhibit will feature Vyncke solid fuel boilers, including wood-fired boilers from 12 BHP to 1440 BHP and plant waste systems from 100 BHP to 1300 BHP. Waste systems can automatically feed bulky waste which is now carried off or fed to a hog. Vyncke systems can produce hot water, steam and thermal oil.

BUILDING INSULATION SERVICES, INC.

Building Insulation Services fabricates, supplies and installs a wide variety of insulation systems used in existing buildings. These systems provide increased energy efficiency, improved lighting and better acoustics, and also eliminate condensation problems. Products offered include Owens Corning's *Energy Miser* system and Manville's *Thermoliner* system.

CELESCO TRANSDUCER PRODUCTS, INC.

Celesco Transducer Products, Inc. will introduce a broadened line of differential pressure and air flow transmitters for VAV applications. Available in OEM or packaged models, outputs of 0-5 vdc, 4-20 mA, and square-rooter conversion to flow are offered. Also displayed will be pressure sensors and transmitters suited for chiller, refrigerant and hydraulic pressure measurements and control.

CENTIN CORPORATION

A national open shop insulation contractor, Centin Corporation specializes in the internal insulation lining of gas turbine exhaust ducts. Service includes on site or remote site

installation. Also offered are *Duro-Flex*™ removable/reuseable insulation covers, both thermal and acoustic, using a variety of materials.

COMPUTER SCIENCES CORPORATION

Computer Sciences Corporation will be demonstrating its general purpose, large scale SCADA system, *INFO-SCAN.* The system is designed for large scale applications, and features stand-alone field panels, direct digital control, digitally directed analog, single or dual central station, and color graphic monitors using light pen technology. The system supports energy monitoring and control (EMS), security, electrical SCADA, and discrete process control.

CONTROL PAK CORPORATION

The *EM Series 96* building management system and ManagePak host software will be on display at Control Pak Corporation's booth at the 1986 WEEC. Designed to run on an IBM PC, *ManagePak* has color graphics for real-time

monitoring, plus generates management reports. *An Engineering Workstation* provides control strategy assistance, on and off line editing, and equipment survey.

CUMMINS ENGINE COMPANY, INC.

Cummins Engine Company will display diesel-powered generator sets with emphasis on peak shaving applications. Literature will be available on diesel generator sets, cogeneration and peak shaving.

DRANETZ TECHNOLOGIES, INC.

Dranetz will introduce a new auto-polling software package, *Power-Star,* for multiple remote site power monitoring with the company's *Series 800* electric power and demand analyzer and the IBM PC. *Power-Star* provides auto-dial, auto-answer as well as manual override for monitor-

ing and report generation with both spread sheet and graphics capabilities. The *Series 800* instruments with *Power-Star* are ideal for load management, demand monitoring, submetering, and curtailment contracts.

ESTERLINE ANGUS INSTRUMENT CORPORATION

The new *PMT-AC Motor/Load Surveyor* from Esterline Angus is designed to examine single and polyphase electrical loads, and to locate and diagnose those areas that will produce the greatest electrical energy savings. Housed in a

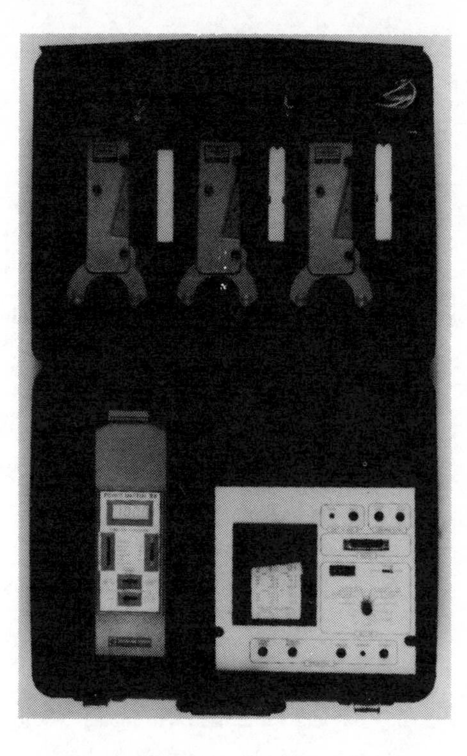

portable carrying case, the unit provides printouts identifying critical AC motor parameters including inrush motor current, currents and voltages, kWh and demand,kW, kVA, kvar and power factor.

ELECTRONIC SYSTEMS USA, INC.

Owners of older Honeywell systems can now avoid system obsolescence and make their systems user friendly with Electronic Systems USA's IBM PC and Intel compatible system upgrades. The *Building Control Console (BCC)* upgrades Honeywell systems with English language operation, energy control software, and interactive color graphics.

E-MON CORPORATION

The *E-Mon Demon* is a solid state digital kilowatt-hour meter which is unique in installation, application and physical size from conventional metering. The *E-Mon Demon* allows metering to be considered which was previously impractical due to prohibitive costs or space requirements. The unit may be installed without interruption of power.

ENERGY USER NEWS

Energy User News provides hard, time-sensitive, investigative news and in-depth features designed to aid the energy-related decisions of executives at industrial, commercial or institutional facilities whose responsibilities are conserving, controlling or purchasing energy.

ENGINEERING MEASUREMENTS COMPANY

The *Vortex AT*™ flowmeter combines the vortex characteristics with signal amplification to provide high noise immunity, improved accuracy, low flow measurement, bi-directional and high temperature (750°F) compatibility. The *Vortex AT*™ can measure any clear or dirty liquid as well as steam and gases. To insure

product reliability, all welded parts are 316 SS. and no elastromers or plastic parts are used.

FLUIDMASTER, INC.

Pro-Temp, by Fluidmaster, is a computerized water heater controller that improves performance and efficiency of hot water recirculating systems in multi-occupant facilities. *Models 8000* and *8000A,* featured at this year's WEEC,

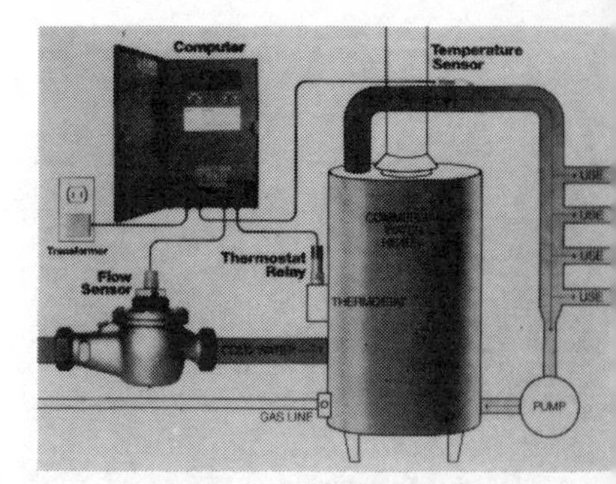

are engineered to deliver energy savings in applications such as hotels and motels, apartments, health clubs, hospitals, dormitories, and military barracks.

GENERAL EASTERN INSTRUMENTS CORPORATION

The *Model 850* transmitter from General Eastern can be utilized for the continuous monitoring of relative humidity and temperature for environmental and industrial control, energy management, clean rooms, computer rooms and environmental chambers. The transmitter is

compact (2½″x4¼″) and can be used with a built-in or remote bulk-resistant RH sensor which is impervious to most contaminants. It is fully temperature compensated and provides accurate readings throughout the operating range (0% to 99% RH and 32° to 122°F).

GEORGIA ENGINE SALES & SERVICE COMPANY

This exhibit will feature Waukesha engines and generator sets including diesel, propane and natural gas-fueled models for peak shaving, cogeneration, and standby service. These units are available with full service contracts, and can be custom-engineered to meet specific requirements, with or without waste heat recovery capability.

GEORGIA POWER COMPANY

Georgia Power Company sponsors many programs to promote user energy conservation. The 1986 Georgia Energy Design Award is cosponsored by the Georgia Association of the American Institute of Architects and Georgia Power Company. All building types are eligible. Entries must be works of architecture built in Georgia and submitted by the architect, who must be licensed to practice in Georgia.

HY-CAL ENGINEERING

The *Ultra-7™ Hybrid Temperature Sensor/ Transmitter, Model CT-877* is designed to provide maintenance-free room temperature monitoring for OEM's. The unit consists of a thin film PT RTD on a hybrid transmitter circuit, and is calibrated and laser trimmed during the automated manufacturing process. Due to hybridization of the circuit and elimination of the zero and span pots, the system requires neither recalibration nor maintenance. It is also designed to compensate for electronics heating effect.

ICSI

The *Ultralight* and *Sonilight* offered by ICSI are presence-sensing light controllers which operate on motion-sensing principles. The *Ultralight* directly replaces the light switch to control lighting up to 250 square feet in such areas as offices, supply closets, restrooms, etc. The *Sonilight* is designed for larger coverage areas of up to 3,600 square feet. Typical applications are classrooms, large partitioned office areas and conference rooms.

INTERNATIONAL POWER TECHNOLOGY

International Power Technology offers complete cogeneration systems which use proprietary Cheng Cycle gas turbine steam injection technology. The Cheng Cycle allows the system to follow fluctuating steam loads economically and generate additional electricity on demand. The company also offers a wide range of financing options and provides operations and maintenance services.

INTERNATIONAL PROTECTIVE COATINGS

International Protective Coatings provides expanding pillows which can be used to fill voids where cables, pipes and telephone lines penetrate walls or floors. Fire rated to 4 hour plus, these bags expand when exposed to heat and solidify when exposed to fire, providing smoke, water and air-tight fire seal. Available in three sizes, the bags can be removed and replaced without intermittent loss of protection.

THE JOHNSON CORPORATION

The Johnson Corporation will be exhibiting the *Liqui-Mover* line of energy-saving condensate handling systems, which handle condensate at any temperature with no pumps and minimal moving parts. The just-released smaller size *Self-Actuated Liqui-Mover (LMSA)* model will be featured. Johnson Energy Technologies, Inc., a new Johnson subsidiary, will display their energy conserving, easily removable, reuseable pipe, valve and fitting jackets for steam traps, pumps, heat exchangers and other equipment.

KSB, INC.

Extreme high pressure pumps, including radial split types, barrel types and can types are offered by KSB for applications including boiler feed, condensate and boiler circulators. State-of-the-art design and computer-aided selection are available for specific performance criteria. The pumps offer low first cost with high efficiency, reliability and economy. Modular design allows uprating and derating. Designed to satisfy API 610.

LUMENITE ELECTRONIC COMPANY

Lumenite will display a complete line of energy management products including 24-hour and 7-day timing controls, as well as the *μPlum*

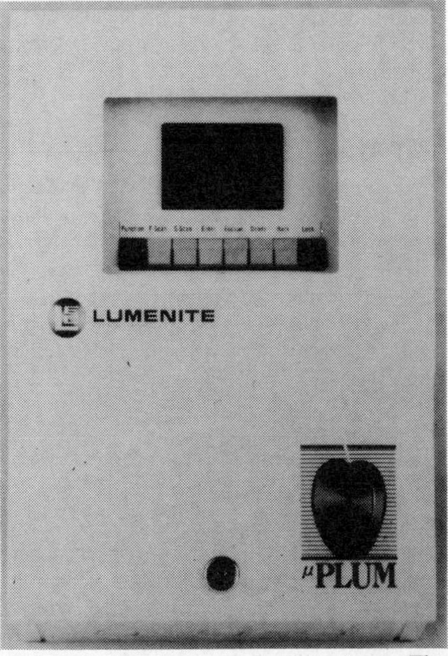

series of energy management systems. The *μPlum* line includes controllers, demand limiting controllers, analog input/output boards, optimum start/stop thermostats, and power line carrier options.

LUNSFORD SYSTEMS GROUP KOLLMORGEN CORPORATION

This exhibit will feature the new, state-of-the-art *Automatic Power Factor Correction System,* which uses a microprocessor-based control to

monitor the plant power line and automatically switch capacitors "on" and "off" line to maintain any preselected power factor desired. The unique control system and solid state switches allow zero crossover switching of capacitors. Hence, no transients are created to cause problems with processing computers, numerical controls, programmable controls, or other sensitive electronic systems.

MAMAC SYSTEMS

A complete line of DDC sensors and transducers will be displayed by Mamac, including temperature, pressure, flow, light, current, voltage, pneumatic interface, water alert, wind speed/direction, outside weather station, LED indicators and other peripherals compatible with all EMS/BAS/FMS and HVAC automation systems.

MICROCONTROL SYSTEMS, INC.

The MCS family of products, which include the *Microl, Temp-Miser I* and *Temp-Miser II* energy management systems, address a broad span of applications ranging from large industrial facilities to small convenience stores. Control strategies include state-of-the-art demand control, chiller and boiler reset as well as adaptive duty cycling, temperature control and load scheduling.

NATIONAL TECHNICAL SYSTEMS PRODUCTS GROUP

The *Sensonic* line of acoustic occupancy sensors for lighting control offered by NTS are all self-contained and are designed to replace existing wall switches. The *Sensonic* has fully adjustable time, light and sound sensitivity controls, and also provides a manual override switch to allow maximum flexibility for the user.

NORTH AMERICAN PHILIPS LIGHTING CORPORATION

North American Philips manufacturers a full line of incandescent, fluorescent, HID and photo/projection lamps (light bulbs) under the *Philips* and *Westinghouse by Philips* names. These lines feature energy-saving and reduced maintenance lighting, including SL and PL compact fluorescents, high color rendering, ultralume fluorescents and industrial/commercial energy efficient fixtures.

NUTEMP, INC.

New and quality used Carrier, Trane and York chillers will be offered by NuTemp, ranging from 5 to 2000 tons, and suitable for use in industrial and commercial cooling applications. The equipment can be delivered from stock within 72 hours.

PARAGON ELECTRIC COMPANY

Paragon offers the *EC128* energy management system, an economical small system for buildings of from 5–10,000 square feet. The unit has 12 outputs and 8 analog or digital inputs,

plus one demand input. It performs time-of-day scheduling, time-based and adaptive duty cycling, demand control, remote communications, temperature control including setback/setup, optimized start/stop, and reset control.

PARKER PNEUTRONICS

Parker manufactures modular pneumatic systems consisting of interchangeable modules and rack systems to provide fast, simple plug-in compatibility with most microprocessor controls. Both pneumatic valves and their support electronics are included on the same printed circuit board to reduce system design time. The recently introduced *E to P* proportional control module provides multi-channel control at reduced cost to HVAC system designers.

PEERLESS DIVISION LSI

The product line featured at this exhibit will include all types of refuse and wood residue handling equipment, storage bins, live floor trailers, chip trailers, log trailers, hydraulic loaders, cranes, and truck/trailer dumpers.

PROTEXULATE, INC.

Protexulate is a fine, white mineral powder treated by a unique process to repel water. In its modified state, this hydrophobic powder insulates and protects underground pipes and tanks. It is ideally suited for making repairs to pipe-in-pipe conduit systems, pre-insulated piping systems, and many other types of existing systems.

ROTRONIC INSTRUMENT CORPORATION

Rotronic offers a complete line of both fixed and portable HVAC humidity control transmitters for control/measurement of RH. The unique, solid-state sensor requires no calibration

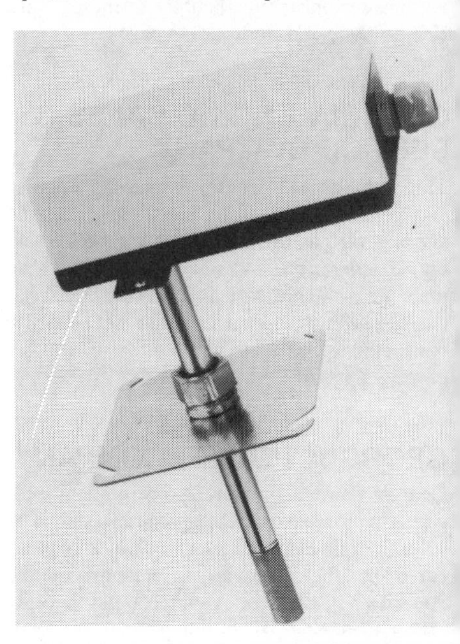

for 12 months or more when installed in normal HVAC environments. Outdoor units improve data from 0-100% RH. The transmitters operate with a variety of power supplies, and ouput signals are compatible with most energy management systems.

ROY F. WESTON, INC.

Roy F. Weston, Inc., provides complete energy management services for industry and government in five basic areas: energy conservation, including energy audits and facility design; resource recovery, including feasibility studies and construction management; cogeneration, including feasibility studies and design assistance; evaluation of alternative energy sources; and coal conversion.

SETRA SYSTEMS, INC.

Setra manufacturers high accuracy capacitive-type pressure transducers. A working display will show how the *261-1 Series* of transducers is used in direct digital control systems. The

units measure pressure from 0.1″WC FS to 25″WC FS and provide 0-5 VDC or 4-20 mA output with 1% accuracy.

SOLAR TURBINES, INC.

This display will focus on cogeneration products and services. Featured this year will be Solar's innovative *Contract Cogeneration* program, which enables energy users to get the energy they need with no capital investment at

a guaranteed rate based on their individual energy sales agreement. The exhibit will display a variety of industrial applications of Solar's products spanning three generations of cogeneration experience.

SOLIDYNE CORPORATION

Third generation energy controllers offered by Solidyne feature time-of-day and demand control, analog control, adaptive duty cycling, optimum start/stop, chiller/boiler optimization, enthalpy control, power line carrier, and two-way phone communication.

SOURCE COGENERATION COMPANY

Source provides a full range of cogeneration services, including preliminary analysis, feasibility study, engineering design, and facility ownership and operation. Expertise can also be offered in the negotiation, purchase and transportation of fuel supply for cogen projects.

SYLVANIA LIGHTING

Sylvania's booth at the 1986 WEEC will feature *Capsylite* halogen lamps, *Supersaver* fluorescent, *Metalarc* and *Lumalux* lamps.

SYNERGISTIC CONTROL SYSTEMS, INC.

Synergistic offers submetering products for electrical, thermal and other energy types. Products include the *C200* electric submetering unit, the *C300* pulse totalizing unit, the *C400* thermal metering unit (BTU calculator), and *EASYBILL* software package for the IBM PC. All meters have multifunction display, serial port for computerized remote reading, and optional pulse output.

THERMO ELECTRON ENERGY SYSTEMS

The Energy Systems Division of Thermo Electron serves as a contractor, developer and supplier of energy systems. Systems include cogeneration, wood-fueled and resource recovery power and/or process steam generating systems. Thermo Electron can provide financing, engineering, construction and operation of alternative energy plants at little or no capital outlay by the energy user.

TORK

Tork will display their *K Series* digital time switches for automatic on/off control of lighting, HVAC, and other electrical equipment. The switches offer full 365-day scheduling, and display in English language for ease in setting schedules.

TSI, INC.

The variable volume fume hood control system to be exhibited by TSI is used for reducing hood operating expenses. TSI will also show its *Model 1660* room pressure control system, which is used to maintain a negative pressure in a laboratory room or a postive pressure in a clean room. In addition, the display will include a complete line of portable air velocity meters.

TURBO REFRIGERATING COMPANY

Turbo offers state-of-the-art ice storage equipment for HVAC, industrial and process cooling. *Dynamic Ice Harvesting* provides a high efficiency single package ice thermal storage system. It is available in single packages 7.5 through 300 tons service; 75 through 7,000 ton/hours. *Hi-TD* chillers provide 33° chilled water for chilled water storage systems.

ULTRASONICS OF FLORIDA

The *UF 60* ultrasonic metered detector kit will be demonstrated at Ultrasonics' booth at the 9th WEEC. Enabling the user to detect sounds beyond the range of the human ear, the unit can be used to diagnose such problems as pressure or vacuum leaks, bad bearings, or steam trap by-passes. It comes equipped with interchangeable modules.

ULTRASYSTEMS, INC.

Ultrasystems provides a wide range of engineering and construction services to industry and government, with projects including alternative energy facilities and the design and construction of cogeneration, industrial power and food processing plants, as well as chemical and wastewater treatment facilities. Services include feasibility studies, design, engineering, financing, construction, and operations on projects ranging in size from micro cogen applications to small power production.

UNENCO, INC.

Unenco, Inc. will be displaying a full line of lighting control products, including dimming, occupancy sensors, and fluorescent power reducers. The Unenco-switch is designed for direct replacement of a standard light switch, and has manual override available in 120V and 277V. Occupancy sensors range in models that will cover from 200 to 1,000 square feet.

VAISALA, INC.

Vaisala's new *Models HMD 20U* and *HMW 20U* are relative humidity sensors/transmitters designed to solve the cost and maintenance

problems associated with measuring and controlling humidity in museums, archival storage areas, EMCS, HVAC systems, computer rooms, clean rooms, and other areas where accurate, reliable humidity measurement is important. The units feature low cost and zero downtime for recalibration.

WESTINGHOUSE ELECTRIC CORPORATION

Combustion Control Division

The Westinghouse *DCS-2400* digital control system, can function as a single-user graphics system, or can be expanded into a true multi-user, multi-tasking process interface network with a unique touch-screen recall option available. The *IMS-2100* works in conjunction with the Westinghouse general purpose con-

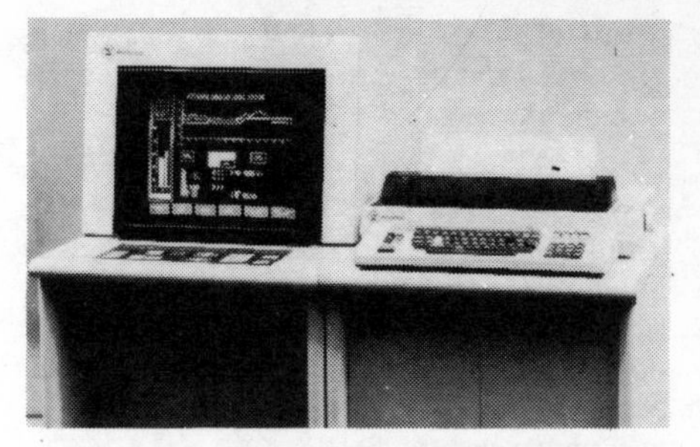

troller to provide low-cost reporting and information management of a boiler house operation.

XO INDUSTRIES, INC.

The *Model 440* electronic tuning ballast from XO Industries is designed to cut the cost of power for commercial and industrial lighting by as much as 35% without reducing the actual output of light. *Profit Line* tuning controls can

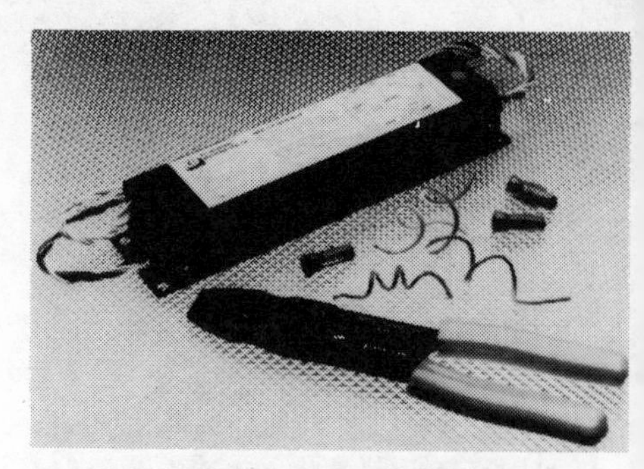

extend the Ballast's energy savings potential by another 25% to 30%.

YORK INTERNATIONAL CORPORATION

York's exhibit will feature a variety of York energy-saving HVAC products and services for both retrofit and new construction applications.

TJ 163.5 .B84 S864 1987

Strategies for energy
efficient plants and